D1507607

HOUGHTON MIFFLIN COMPANY EDITORIAL ADVISER IN EDUCATION • **HEROLD C. HUNT** • CHARLES WILLIAM ELIOT PROFESSOR OF EDUCATION • HARVARD UNIVERSITY

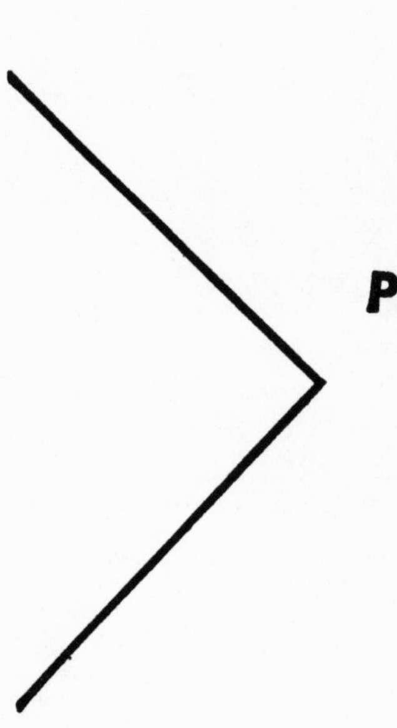

PERSPECTIVES ON

Readings in School

THE ECONOMICS OF EDUCATION

Finance and Business Management

CHARLES S. BENSON · *Harvard University*

Houghton Mifflin Company · *Boston*

 HOUGHTON MIFFLIN COMPANY • BOSTON

PRINTED IN THE U.S.A.

Preface

A book of readings in the literature of the economics of education may properly serve several purposes. First, the selections included in such a book can demonstrate the range of subject matter that bears upon the fiscal aspects of the work of the professional school administrator, a range which covers material from economics, school finance, and business administration. Second, the book can serve to display points of controversy in the field, display them, that is, in the language of the original contributors to the discussion. Third, the selections can offer coverage of topics so current that they fail of adequate treatment in standard texts. I have tried to make choices of readings that go some way toward meeting each of these functions. I do not mean to imply, however, that this book relieves the student of the need to consult the original sources in their full length, insofar as he has the time and the library facilities to do so.

This book is addressed more clearly to the school administrator than to the economist. Accordingly, considerable attention is directed to the conventional topics of taxation and grants-in-aid. But analysis of procedures for financing education under its existing structure does not exhaust the field. Indeed, it is with regard to the investigation of the economic returns from schooling that some of the most exciting work is now being done, and it is being carried on in Europe as well as in the United States. Similarly, some fundamental questions have been raised by economists and school finance authorities about the economic structure of public education and about the effective use of resources in the educational establishment. All of these matters are dealt with in greater or less detail in the pages that follow.

In making the selections, I have fortunately had a great deal of help. In particular, I would like to acknowledge gratefully the thoughtful suggestions I received from the following persons: R. D. Baldwin, W. Monfort Barr, Howard S. Bretsch, Jesse Burkhead, William L. Carter, William B. Castetter, Charles F. Faber, Walter G. Hack, Stanley E. Hecker, Clifford P. Hooker, H. Thomas James, O. D. Johns, Richard R. Jungers, William P. McLure, Allan Morehead, Edgar L. Morphet, Joseph M. Nygaard, Carl H. Porter-Shirley, J. W. Remaley, William H. Roe, R. M. Roelfs, Miles C. Romney, Everett B. Sackett, Doyne M. Smith, Robert C. Stewart, Merle T. Strom and Morris S. Wallace. The final responsibility for the choices is mine, and I must confess that a number of excellent pieces had to be left out for lack of space. In some cases it was necessary to make abridgments in the selections, but a strong attempt was made to keep such changes to a minimum.

It is my hope that the school administrator who reads these pages will come to look at his work in a new and interesting light and that he may possibly be stimulated further to make his own contributions to the growing body of literature in the field.

CHARLES S. BENSON

London, England

Contents

PART ONE

The Returns to Education

PART TWO

The Economic Structure of Education

PART THREE

Taxation for Schools

PART FOUR
Grants-in-Aid

PART FIVE

The Problem of Productivity in Education

PERSPECTIVES ON THE ECONOMICS OF EDUCATION

Readings in School Finance and Business Management

PART ONE

The Returns to Education

The strength of nations is measured to a significant degree by their rates of economic growth. Governments take action consciously and deliberately to raise the growth rates of their economies to higher levels. Business and labor groups, similarly, garner prestige when they are able to claim that they have made a contribution to an advance in productivity. Yet growth is a complex phenomenon, and our knowledge about the economy is limited. We cannot be sure just what combination of public and private policies is optimal to provide a high and sustained rate of progress.

Nonetheless, it has come to be recognized that there is a relation between education in a society and the material progress of that society. Policy makers of public and private agencies are now likely to consider education (or "training," as it is sometimes called) a strategic variable in planning for economic improvement.

Though it lay dormant for a century and a half, the notion that education and material progress are related is not a new one. Adam Smith, that eighteenth-century giant in the history of economic thought, held, first, that growth is primarily an effect of the division of labor, second, that dissimilar talents of individuals are acquired rather than natural (for the most part), and third, that the means through which people develop skills are "habit, custom, and education."[1] *These views were stated in 1776, but the economic significance of education was largely ignored until quite recently. Some of the reasons why the concept of "investment in man" was neglected are mentioned in the selections that follow.*

[1] Adam Smith, *The Wealth of Nations,* New York, Modern Library Edition, 1937, p. 15.

The contribution of education to economic growth may take various forms. (The particular contributions may change, moreover, as a nation passes through different stages of development.) There is, first, the matter of the quantity of education provided to members of the work force. Where the schooling made available to some groups falls below conventional standards, there are likely to be economic gains in closing the gap. For example, increased expenditures of resources on elementary education in some parts of the South would probably offer very high returns.

Next, education is basic to the advance of knowledge, and scientific knowledge is itself the basis of improvements in techniques of production in many industries today.

Lastly, a sharp rise in the quality of education offered by the schools over the whole country should produce economic returns, but it is not possible to specify what skills and attributes would be created or precisely how they would be used.

It has long been recognized that the pursuit of the goal of economic growth requires sacrifices in the immediate time period. We all know that investment in the capacity of the country to produce more goods in the future reduces the volume of consumer goods that can be had today. A note of caution: there are other costs. The rapid introduction of automated techniques may leave a wake of unemployable persons. The schools may be called upon to help relieve the social and economic needs of these persons. If the schools had abundant resources at their command, the aid could be provided without reducing the quality of education offered to our children, but the volume of resources that is now available in school districts can hardly be described as abundant. High growth appears to be associated with urbanization of the population. The migration of families from the low-income areas of the country to our great cities has placed heavy burdens on the school systems of those cities, burdens that sometimes appear to be beyond their capacity to cope with. The demands that the pursuit of economic growth places upon all our educational programs, urban, suburban, and rural, may call for changes in the political structure of the schools, not all of which changes will be to the liking of professional educators.

Perhaps most important, the recognition of the economic significance of education may cause an undue diversion of resources toward instruction in the scientific and technical fields. Should the result be that instruction in the humane disciplines suffers deprivation of support, the cost of promoting economic growth through the conscious manipulation of educational policy could be high indeed.

The student of school finance is necessarily a student of economics. The topics of taxation and grants-in-aid fall within the bounds of that field, however narrowly defined it is. Until lately, the economist has given no special attention to education; that is, he has not singled it out from the range of governmental services for particular consideration. This is no longer true, as the following selections will indicate. When the economist and the school finance authority join forces to study such topics as the relation between education and economic growth, it is hoped that a new field, the "economics of education," will take its place as a useful academic discipline.

PART ONE · THE RETURNS TO EDUCATION

Section A

THE GENERAL STATEMENT

In this section there are four discussions in general terms of the connection between education and economic growth. From material prepared for the Committee on Educational Finance, National Education Association, Harold M. Groves, an authority in the field of public finance, deals with the question of why economic growth is important. He also identifies certain major factors, including education, that play a part in advances in productivity.

The academic economist most clearly responsible for the revival of the concept of "investment in man" is Theodore W. Schultz. Selection 2 includes material from his presidential address to the American Economic Association, 1960, in which he shows how the concept casts light on some previously unanswered questions in the field and, further, how the concept has important policy implications. Though this paper is descriptive in nature, it should be noted that Schultz has published elsewhere the results of several investigations in the quantitative contribution of schooling to growth.

The next two selections (3 and 4) were written by men whose primary allegiance is to the profession of education: R. D. Baldwin and Harold F. Clark. Whereas the academic economist has stressed the role of education in raising the productive capacity of the individual, Baldwin makes the interesting point that a wide distribution of educational opportunities also serves to strengthen the demand for goods and services through its effect in reducing the inequality of the distribution of income in the society. Clark discusses three types of education from which the economy appears to have reaped especially high rewards, namely, that in the fields of agriculture, engineering, and medicine.

1

Education and Economic Growth

Harold M. Groves

Dr. Groves, Professor of Economics, University of Wisconsin, has made notable contributions to his academic field and to the public service. This statement is remarkable for the clarity and conciseness with which a complex topic is explored.

It has been said that while the decades from 1930 to 1950 were primarily concerned with economic instability and in considerable degree saw this problem brought under control, the 1960's will be mainly concerned with economic growth. Historically, the view has prevailed for many years that growth is primarily a matter of amassing more tangible capital. Especially since World War II, economists are discovering that growth may be mainly a matter of developing human talent and that it can be deliberately fostered by judicious but generous allocation of resources for this purpose. Some critics consider this discovery of major, perhaps revolutionary, importance. Obviously, it could have profound implications for education. From being a fairly respectable member of the family of items called consumption goods on which the nation spends its income, education is elevated in the eyes of many economists to the even more respectable capital-goods category on which the nation's future depends. All this is superimposed upon some continuing concern that we not only grow quantitatively but improve the utilization of our resources qualitatively. It is the purpose of this monograph to review the literature in, and contribute further analysis of, this area of thought and development.

Some attention has been focused recently on the especially remarkable progress in the field of agriculture and to a lesser extent in the field of medicine. There may be more than one explanation of these stellar performances, but it is noteworthy that each of these areas has been heavily saturated with research effort, and the first also has a unique record in the dissemination of knowledge. Here for about a century there has been a steady

Adapted from *Education and Economic Growth,* Washington, National Education Association, 1961, pp. 7–23. Reproduced with permission.

and accelerating advance in knowledge having application in agricultural production. New capital goods have been created based upon such knowledge, and these have reduced the need for labor possessing a low order of knowledge and skills. This in turn has had wide implications for the whole economy. . . .

Why Economic Growth

Growth is important to relieve much still prevailing and widespread substandard living even in the United States in 1960. One need only to glance at the statistics on inadequate housing to appreciate how much still remains to be accomplished in mitigating poverty. We should then remind ourselves that it is the growth of production rather than the redistribution of the product that has principally aided the common man.

Growth is important to extend greater economic assistance abroad. The future would look brighter for our international relations if we were assured that our decisions in this area were not to be sharply confined by budgetary pressures. The same is true of our defense budget.

Growth is important to facilitate improvement in public services, which in many areas leave much to be desired. All the projections of future governmental expenditures, especially those of state and local units, assume a substantial growth factor to relieve the taxpayer's load in the present decade. Some of them look gloomy enough even with this assumption. There are many other reasons why economic growth is important to all American citizens.

When this has been said, it is still in order to enter the reservation that how to use wealth wisely is at least as much of a problem as how to step up the growth rate. If the upper middle-class American has not found the good life by now, the augmenting of his private consumption through doubling the gross national product is not likely to achieve it for him.

. . . .

Concepts

Economic growth may be conceived in terms of the total increase in the output of goods and services in an area over a period — *the gross national product.* It may be conceived in terms of *productivity* or efficiency, the increased output per unit of input (of labor and capital) over a period. Among other things this latter approach takes account of the intangible factor of leisure ignored in gross national product. Moreover it focuses on the causes of increased output. Next there is the concept of *economic welfare,* which has thus far largely defied measurement. It is an objective concept, but it includes such matters as the greater or lesser consumption expenses associated with differing modes of production; for example, the time and expense of commuting to work. A few critics have always contended that mass production and great specialization have been overrated because they involve many social overheads associated with urban living. Finally there is *general welfare,* involving a large element of the qualitative and subjective. Education, unlike many economic goods and factors, plays a top role in all of these gauges of progress.

. . . .

Factors in Economic Growth

Looking next at the factors which might play a part in economic growth, we are confronted with a broad array of conditions that we can only mention and not discuss: inflation or no inflation; high or low interest rates; favorable tax policy; adequate financial institutions; much competition; a large free market; suitable social capital; optimum population increase; industrial organization (large-scale plants and firms); proper attitudes toward work, change, and enterprise. Some of these items have received particular attention with regard to growth in underdeveloped economies.

Capital and Labor Inputs

Growth can occur either by larger inputs of capital and labor or by their more efficient use. Abundance of tangible capital was the factor stressed by the classical economists. There is still persistent testimony to support the view that a high rate of growth and a high rate of capital formation are practically synonymous except that the former follows the latter as effect and cause. There can be no doubt that a fast-growing economy requires large amounts of new tangible capital and rapid replacement of obsolescent equipment. But it is one thing to hold that the expansion of capital must attend economic growth, and another to contend that expansion follows the growth, and still another to contend that the needed capital is not likely to be forthcoming in an economy as rich as ours. At least the existence of substantial overcapacity and unemployment leads one to doubt that a shortage of capital is currently limiting output. More savings could be induced by more restrictions on consumer credit, by some checks or controls on advertising outlay, and by reversing the propaganda which has told people for years that the way to help the economy and serve national objectives (except in wartime) is to spend freely.

As to labor input, some measures could perhaps be adopted to increase the portion of the population that is working. The most important objective here is to reduce unemployment. Not only is this important for its own sake but because unemployment is the "scare-word" which induces unions to bargain for leisure. The latest fear on this score is so-called automation. It is said that from April to September 1958, factory production rose (due to improved technology) 9 percent while the employment of production workers rose only 2 percent. Labor's remedy for this is the 30-hour week, not as a matter of preferring leisure to goods but as one of sharing short opportunity. A longer rather than a shorter work week is the most direct road to economic growth. But it can have no appeal at all as long as there is excessive unemployment.

The labor force has been sustained, despite a declining work week and a shorter working life, by a steady increase in the work participation of females. The evidence indicates that the decision of women to work outside the home is influenced by the amount which wives can add to the family income. This in turn depends a great deal on women's education.

Using the Available Capital and Labor

Full utilization of available capital and labor is partly a matter of reducing the frequency, duration, and degree of business recessions. During the six years ending in 1959 we encountered two recessions, and over one-third of the quarter-years were subnormal. But beyond this, economists since Keynes have come to appreciate the necessity of balance in the growth factors. Mention has been made of the present slack in the use of resources. Augmented saving (and even investment), ahead of growth and an adequate market for consumers' goods, will produce not growth but unemployment. Producers neither will nor should provide goods that cannot be sold or develop the capacity to produce goods for which no use can be foreseen. Moreover, full utilization of available labor is partly a matter of adaptation of skills to a changing market for them. Persistent shortages of workers in certain fields have existed along with unemployment. Educational programs of various sorts play an important role here.

Adequacy of Resources

Evidence indicates that in the future, the United States will be obliged to seek a rising proportion of its raw materials from abroad. But no matter what its population trend, the optimists see at least no important limitation on the economic growth of the United States arising from inadequacy of resources and energy. They argue simply that the greatest gift of nature to man is man himself and his ability to discover and utilize materials that previous generations did not appreciate. . . .

Improvements in Efficiency

Improvements in efficiency include a large category of potentialities variously described as technology, innovation, research, improvement in the quality of the labor force, and education. There is support for the view that the most fundamental of these is education and that it in fact underlies all the other items. The Staff Report to the Joint Economic Committee regarded more adequate support for education, meaning federal support, as its "single most important recommendation for strengthening our economic growth."

. . . .

Research

It has long been recognized that education as an economic factor functions in two capacities: the transmission and wide dissemination of knowledge and skills, and the development of new knowledge. In the latter capacity it functions both directly and in the development of personnel employed by industry and government for research.

. . . .

Future expansion of this activity seems assured by the high estimated returns for investment in it. But the outlay among industries is sporadic and of course provides little for basic research upon which applied research depends. If basic research is somewhat neglected, as alleged, this is not surprising; the benefits of basic research are often diffused among the whole human species. Basic research is confined mainly to the large universities, which, however, get substantial financial assistance from the federal government. The latter also does some research on its own, but most of this has a military orientation.

. . . .

Disseminating Knowledge

The great bulk of outlay for education in the United States is spent not on developing new knowledge but on transmitting what we already know. This is particularly true of the education of the rank and file as distinguished from the elite 5 or 10 percent from which researchers and executives are principally recruited. The American educational system surpasses all others in the breadth of its coverage at the middle and advanced levels. The British system operates on the assumption that about 11 years of education is all that most people can absorb. The American system is much more ambitious in this respect. Its objectives cover both quality and quantity. The combination is expensive. Moreover there are charges that it has resulted in inadequate attention for superior students. Education for superior students can be enhanced without doing less for the rank and file, but probably only at greater total expense. However, it should be added that much is currently being done for superior students.

From the economic point of view, the critics who suggest limiting the duration of universal education may have a point. But . . . we have not begun to measure the direct and indirect economic effects of broad education.

Education is of enormous importance both in creating skills and in guiding people, whatever their talents, into their most productive roles. In a democracy, enough people must understand enough about governmental economic programs so that the latter may facilitate rather than harass the economy. General education is important for the success of the direct tax system. It may well be that raising the general level of "intelligence" is quite as important economically as developing a few top performers.

Of course, it is on the consumption and the political sides that widespread dissemination of knowledge is most important, but there is an economic-growth aspect to all of this. Although such problems as disarmament, desegregation, economic instability, mental illness, juvenile delinquency, obsolete metropolitan government, ugly cities, and a hundred others may not be solved completely by education, in a democracy we can hardly hope to solve them without high levels of general enlightenment. The decision to educate everybody at public expense with no other limitation than the participant's willingness may seem generous, but the American propensity in this direction may not be so wild economically as the critics would have us believe.

2

Investment in Human Capital

Theodore W. Schultz

A society can make investments in the productive capacity of men as well as of machines. On the surface, this is a simple notion, but one that most economists have chosen to disregard. Professor Schultz of the University of Chicago portrays the important consequences of its acceptance for economic theory and for policy making.

Although it is obvious that people acquire useful skills and knowledge, it is not obvious that these skills and knowledge are a form of capital, that this capital is in substantial part a product of deliberate investment, that it has

Adapted from "Investment in Human Capital," *American Economic Review,* Volume LI, No. 1 (March, 1961), pp. 1–16. Reproduced with permission.

grown in Western societies at a much faster rate than conventional (nonhuman) capital, and that its growth may well be the most distinctive feature of the economic system. It has been widely observed that increases in national output have been large compared with the increases of land, man-hours, and physical reproducible capital. Investment in human capital is probably the major explanation for this difference.

Much of what we call consumption constitutes investment in human capital. Direct expenditures on education, health, and internal migration to take advantage of better job opportunities are clear examples. Earnings foregone by mature students attending school and by workers acquiring on-the-job training are equally clear examples. Yet nowhere do these enter into our national accounts. The use of leisure time to improve skills and knowledge is widespread and it too is unrecorded. In these and similar ways the *quality* of human effort can be greatly improved and its productivity enhanced. I shall contend that such investment in human capital accounts for most of the impressive rise in the real earnings per worker.

. . . .

Shying Away from Investment in Man

Economists have long known that people are an important part of the wealth of nations. Measured by what labor contributes to output, the productive capacity of human beings is now vastly larger than all other forms of wealth taken together. What economists have not stressed is the simple truth that people invest in themselves and that these investments are very large. Although economists are seldom timid in entering on abstract analysis and are often proud of being impractical, they have not been bold in coming to grips with this form of investment. Whenever they come even close, they proceed gingerly as if they were stepping into deep water. No doubt there are reasons for being wary. Deep-seated moral and philosophical issues are ever present. Free men are first and foremost the end to be served by economic endeavor; they are not property or marketable assets. And not least, it has been all too convenient in marginal productivity analysis to treat labor as if it were a unique bundle of innate abilities that are wholly free of capital.

The mere thought of investment in human beings is offensive to some among us. Our values and beliefs inhibit us from looking upon human beings as capital goods, except in slavery, and this we abhor. We are not unaffected by the long struggle to rid society of indentured service and to evolve political and legal institutions to keep men free from bondage. These are achievements that we prize highly. Hence, to treat human beings as wealth that can be augmented by investment runs counter to deeply held values. It seems to reduce man once again to a mere material component, to something akin to property. And for man to look upon himself as a capital good, even if it did not impair his freedom, may seem to debase him. No less a person than J. S. Mill at one time insisted that the people of a country should not be looked upon as wealth because wealth existed only for the sake of people. But surely Mill was wrong; there is nothing in the concept of human wealth contrary to his idea that it exists only for the advantage of people. By investing in themselves, people can enlarge the range of choice available to them. It is one way free men can enhance their welfare.

. . . .

The failure to treat human resources explicitly as a form of capital, as a produced means of production, as the product of investment, has fostered the retention of the classical notion of labor as a capacity to do manual work requiring little knowledge and skill, a capacity with which, according to this notion, laborers are endowed about equally. This notion of labor was wrong in the classical period and it is patently wrong now. Counting individuals who can and want to work and treating such a count as a measure of the quantity of an economic factor is no more meaningful than it would be to count the number of all manner of machines to determine their economic importance either as a stock of capital or as a flow of productive services.

Laborers have become capitalists not from a diffusion of the ownership of corporation stocks, as folklore would have it, but from the acquisition of knowledge and skill that have economic value. This knowledge and skill are in great part the product of investment and, combined with other human investment, predominantly account for the productive superiority of the technically advanced countries. To omit them in studying economic growth is like trying to explain Soviet ideology without Marx.

ECONOMIC GROWTH FROM HUMAN CAPITAL

Many paradoxes and puzzles about our dynamic, growing economy can be resolved once human investment is taken into account. Let me begin by sketching some that are minor though not trivial.

When farm people take nonfarm jobs they earn substantially less than industrial workers of the same race, age, and sex. Similarly nonwhite urban males earn much less than white males even after allowance is made for the effects of differences in unemployment, age, city size, and region. Because these differentials in earnings correspond closely to corresponding differentials in education, they strongly suggest that the one is a consequence of the other. Negroes who operate farms, whether as tenants or as owners, earn much less than whites on comparable farms. Fortunately, crops and livestock are not vulnerable to the blight of discrimination. The large differences in earnings seem rather to reflect mainly the differences in health and education. Workers in the South on the average earn appreciably less than in the North or West and they also have on the average less education. Most migratory farm workers earn very little indeed by comparison with other workers. Many of them have virtually no schooling, are in poor health, are unskilled, and have little ability to do useful work. To urge that the differences in the amount of human investment may explain these differences in earnings seems elementary. Of more recent vintage are observations showing younger workers at a competitive advantage; for example, young men entering the labor force are said to have an advantage over unemployed older workers in obtaining satisfactory jobs. Most of these young people possess twelve years of school, most of the older workers six years or less. The observed advantage of these younger workers may therefore result not from inflexibilities in social security or in retirement programs, or from sociological preference of employers, but from real differences in productivity connected with one form of human investment, i.e., education. And yet another example, the curve relating income to age tends to be steeper for skilled than for unskilled persons. Investment in on-the-job training seems a likely explanation.

Economic growth requires much internal migration of workers to adjust to changing job opportunities. Young men and women move more readily than older workers. Surely this makes economic sense when one recognizes that the costs of such migration are a form of human investment. Young people have more years ahead of them than older workers during which they can realize on such an investment. Hence it takes less of a wage differential to make it economically advantageous for them to move, or, to put it differently, young people can expect a higher return on their investment in migration than older people. This differential may explain selective migration without requiring an appeal to sociological differences between young and old people.

. . . .

Let me now pass on to three major perplexing questions closely connected with the riddle of economic growth. First, consider the long-period behavior of the capital-income ratio. We were taught that a country which amassed more reproducible capital relative to its land and labor would employ such capital in greater "depth" because of its growing abundance and cheapness. But apparently this is not what happens. On the contrary, the estimates now available show that less of such capital tends to be employed relative to income as economic growth proceeds. Are we to infer that the ratio of capital to income has no relevance in explaining either poverty or opulence? Or that a rise of this ratio is not a prerequisite to economic growth? These questions raise fundamental issues bearing on motives and preferences for holding wealth as well as on the motives for particular investments and the stock of capital thereby accumulated. For my purpose all that needs to be said is that these estimates of capital-income ratios refer to only a part of all capital. They exclude in particular, and most unfortunately, any human capital. Yet human capital has surely been increasing at a rate substantially greater than reproducible (nonhuman) capital. We cannot, therefore, infer from these estimates that the stock of *all* capital has been decreasing relative to income. On the contrary, if we accept the not implausible assumption that the motives and preferences of people, the technical opportunities open to them, and the uncertainty associated with economic growth during particular periods were leading people to maintain roughly a constant ratio between *all* capital and income, the decline in the estimated capital-income ratio is simply a signal that human capital has been increasing relatively not only to conventional capital but also to income.

The bumper crop of estimates that show national income increasing faster than national resources raises a second and not unrelated puzzle. The income of the United States has been increasing at a much higher rate than the combined amount of land, man-hours worked, and the stock of reproducible capital used to produce the income. Moreover, the discrepancy between the two rates has become larger from one business cycle to the next during recent decades. To call this discrepancy a measure of "resource productivity" gives a name to our ignorance but does not dispel it. If we accept these estimates, the connections between national resources and national income have become loose and tenuous over time. Unless this discrepancy can be resolved, received theory of production applied to inputs and outputs as currently measured is a toy and not a tool for studying economic growth.

Two sets of forces probably account for the discrepancy. . . . One is returns to scale; the second, the large improvements in the quality of inputs that have occurred but have been omitted from the input estimates. Our economy has undoubtedly been experiencing increasing returns to scale at some points offset by decreasing returns at others. If we can succeed in identifying and measuring the net gains, they may turn out to have been substantial. The improvements in the quality of inputs that have not been adequately allowed for are no doubt partly in material (nonhuman) capital. My own conception, however, is that both this defect and the omission of economies of scale are minor sources of discrepancy between the rates of growth of inputs and outputs compared to the improvements in human capacity that have been omitted.

A small step takes us from these two puzzles raised by existing estimates to a third which brings us to the heart of the matter, namely, the essentially unexplained large increase in real earnings of workers. Can this be a windfall? Or a quasirent pending the adjustment in the supply of labor? Or a pure rent reflecting the fixed amount of labor? It seems far more reasonable that it represents rather a return to the investment that has been made in human beings. The observed growth in productivity per unit of labor is simply a consequence of holding the unit of labor constant over time although in fact this unit of labor has been increasing as a result of a steadily growing amount of human capital per worker. As I read our record, the human capital component has become very large as a consequence of human investment.

Another aspect of the same basic question, which admits of the same resolution, is the rapid postwar recovery of countries that had suffered severe destruction of plant and equipment during the war. The toll from bombing was all too visible in the factories laid flat, the railroad yards, bridges, and harbors wrecked, and the cities in ruin. Structures, equipment and inventories were all heaps of rubble. Not so visible, yet large, was the toll from the wartime depletion of the physical plant that escaped destruction by bombs. Economists were called upon to assess the implications of these wartime losses for recovery. In retrospect, it is clear that they overestimated the prospective retarding effects of these losses. Having had a small hand in this effort, I have had a special reason for looking back and wondering why the judgments that we formed soon after the war proved to be so far from the mark. The explanation that now is clear is that we gave altogether too much weight to nonhuman capital in making these assessments. We fell into this error, I am convinced, because we did not have a concept of *all* capital and, therefore, failed to take account of human capital and the important part that it plays in production in a modern economy.

• • • •

A Note on Policy

One proceeds at his own peril in discussing social implications and policy. The conventional hedge is to camouflage one's values and to wear the mantle of academic innocence. Let me proceed unprotected!

1. Our tax laws everywhere discriminate against human capital. Although the stock of such capital has become large and even though it is obvious that human capital, like other forms of reproducible capital, depreciates, becomes obsolete, and entails maintenance, our tax laws are all but blind on these matters.

2. Human capital deteriorates when it is idle because unemployment impairs the skills that workers have acquired. Losses in earnings can be cushioned by appropriate payments but these do not keep idleness from taking its toll from human capital.

3. There are many hindrances to the free choice of professions. Racial discrimination and religious discrimination are still widespread. Professional associations and governmental bodies also hinder entry; for example, into medicine. Such purposeful interference keeps the investment in this form of human capital substantially below its optimum.

4. It is indeed elementary to stress the greater imperfections of the capital market in providing funds for investment in human beings than for investment in physical goods. Much could be done to reduce these imperfections by reforms in tax and banking laws and by changes in banking practices. Long-term private and public loans to students are warranted.

5. Internal migration, notably the movement of farm people into industry, made necessary by the dynamics of our economic progress, requires substantial investments. In general, families in which the husbands and wives

are already in the late thirties cannot afford to make these investments because the remaining payoff period for them is too short. Yet society would gain if more of them would pull stakes and move because, in addition to the increase in productivity currently, the children of these families would be better located for employment when they were ready to enter the labor market. The case for making some of these investments on public account is by no means weak. Our farm programs have failed miserably these many years in not coming to grips with the costs and returns from off-farm migration.

6. The low earnings of particular people have long been a matter of public concern. Policy all too frequently concentrates only on the effects, ignoring the causes. No small part of the low earnings of many Negroes, Puerto Ricans, Mexican nationals, indigenous migratory farm workers, poor farm people, and some of our older workers reflects the failure to have invested in their health and education. Past mistakes are, of course, bygones, but for the sake of the next generation we can ill afford to continue making the same mistakes over again.

7. Is there a substantial underinvestment in human beings other than in these depressed groups? This is an important question for economists. The evidence at hand is fragmentary. Nor will the answer be easily won. There undoubtedly have been overinvestments in some skills, for example, too many locomotive firemen and engineers, too many people trained to be farmers, and too many agricultural economists! Our schools are not free of loafers and some students lack the necessary talents. Nevertheless, underinvestment in knowledge and skill, relative to the amounts invested in nonhuman capital, would appear to be the rule and not the exception for a number of reasons. The strong and increasing demands for this knowledge and skill in laborers are of fairly recent origin and it takes time to respond to them. In responding to these demands, we are heavily dependent upon cultural and political processes, and these are slow and the lags are long compared to the behavior of markets serving the formation of nonhuman capital. Where the capital market does serve human investments, it is subject to more imperfections than in financing physical capital. I have already stressed the fact that our tax laws discriminate in favor of nonhuman capital. Then, too, many individuals face serious uncertainty in assessing their innate talents when it comes to investing in themselves, especially through higher education. Nor is it easy either for public decisions or private behavior to untangle and properly assess the consumption and the investment components. The fact that the return to high school and to higher education has been about as large as the return to conventional forms of capital when all of the costs of such education including income foregone by students are allocated to the investment component, creates a strong presumption that there has been underinvestment since, surely, much education is cultural and in that sense it is consumption. It is no wonder, in view of these cir-

cumstances, that there should be substantial underinvestment in human beings, even though we take pride, and properly so, in the support that we have given to education and to other activities that contribute to such investments.

8. Should the returns from public investment in human capital accrue to the individuals in whom it is made? The policy issues implicit in this question run deep and they are full of perplexities pertaining both to resource allocation and to welfare. Physical capital that is formed by public investment is not transferred as a rule to particular individuals as a gift. It would greatly simplify the allocative process if public investment in human capital were placed on the same footing. What then is the logical basis for treating public investment in human capital differently? Presumably it turns on ideas about welfare. A strong welfare goal of our community is to reduce the unequal distribution of personal income among individuals and families. Our community has relied heavily on progressive income and inheritance taxation. Given public revenue from these sources, it may well be true that public investment in human capital, notably that entering into general education, is an effective and efficient set of expenditures for attaining this goal. Let me stress, however, that the state of knowledge about these issues is woefully meager.

9. My last policy comment is on assistance to underdeveloped countries to help them achieve economic growth. Here, even more than in domestic affairs, investment in human beings is likely to be underrated and neglected. It is inherent in the intellectual climate in which leaders and spokesmen of many of these countries find themselves. Our export of growth doctrines has contributed. These typically assign the stellar role to the formation of nonhuman capital, and take as an obvious fact the superabundance of human resources. Steel mills are the real symbol of industrialization. After all, the early industrialization of England did not depend on investments in the labor force. New funds and agencies are being authorized to transfer capital for physical goods to these countries. The World Bank and our Export-Import Bank have already had much experience. Then, too, measures have been taken to pave the way for the investment of more private (nonhuman) capital abroad. This one-sided effort is under way in spite of the fact that the knowledge and skills required to take on and use efficiently the superior techniques of production, the most valuable resource that we could make available to them, is in very short supply in these underdeveloped countries. Some growth of course can be had from the increase in more conventional capital even though the labor that is available is lacking both in skill and knowledge. But the rate of growth will be seriously limited. It simply is not possible to have the fruits of a modern agriculture and the abundance of modern industry without making large investments in human beings.

Truly, the most distinctive feature of our economic system is the growth in human capital. Without it there would be only hard, manual work and poverty except for those who have income from property. There is an early morning scene in Faulkner's *Intruder in the Dust*, of a poor, solitary cultivator at work in a field. Let me paraphrase that line, "The man without skills and knowledge leaning terrifically against nothing."

3

America's "A No. 1" Economic Institution

R. D. Baldwin

Professor Baldwin of the University of West Virginia discusses the effects of education on the character of consumer demand. He also stresses the role that mass education has in maintaining consumer demand at a high level.

General Economic Conditions Underlying Prosperity

In an economy such as ours, what conditions underlie prosperity?

1. Perhaps most important — free, stable, democratic government. No modern economy can flourish on the shifting sands of political institutions which bind the many to the wishes of the few.

2. Abundant natural resources in both materials and men. Prosperity is unthinkable unless material and human resources are available.

3. Some systematic, dependable means of fusing material and human resources, under stabilized democratic auspices, into the dynamics of high-energy civilization.

Let's take the first condition — free, stable, democratic government. This nation is simply the collective thinking and will of its individual citizens. Through their elected representatives they determine and from time to time change the structure and form of their government, enact and enforce its laws, frame its policies, and maintain and operate its necessary services. In

Adapted from "America's 'A No. 1' Economic Institution: A Tip to Dun and Bradstreet," *The Educational Forum*, Volume VIII, No. 2, Part 1 (January, 1944), pp. 143–148. Reproduced with permission.

a very real sense, in such a land as ours, the citizen, in his collective capacity at least, is sovereign, with sovereign powers and sovereign responsibilities. And the sovereign must be not only intelligent, but informed.

. . . .

With regard to the second condition, unless oil, coal, gas, soil fertility, climatic factors, and natively intelligent men and women are available, schools cannot create them, nor out of them prosperity. Natural resources are potentials only, which acquire meaning as they are utilized to gain those worth-while human objectives which we call "the good life." Is it not arresting to note that, without schools, men and materials interact haltingly to produce relatively meagre standards of living; whereas, when schools are developed, like catalyzing agents, they speed up the action of man's mind upon material to create relatively prosperous societies?

. . . .

Thus, while schools cannot create them, they do supply the spark to fuse these human and material natural resources, making man the partner of the Creator in supplying the wealth of goods and services of assignable economic value which contribute so much to the material prosperity and spiritual progress of mankind.

Specific Economic Requisites of Prosperity

We have pointed out the part played by the school in promoting general conditions which underlie prosperity — the creative impact of human intelligence, under free, stable, democratic government, on the country's material resources. Let us turn now to a more particularized analysis of the economic foundations which undergird the structure of prosperity in our current American capitalistic economy. There seem to be three fundamental requisites, set down in plain-layman rather than traditional-economics terms:

1. A steadily increasing demand for goods and services.
2. Productive capacity of (1) machinery, (2) men, and (3) management adequate to supply this demand.
3. Income sufficient to enable consumers to purchase products and personal services available at prices which will keep the wheels of industry and commerce smoothly and steadily turning.

Fail to achieve any one of these, and prosperity under the high-energy civilization that has evolved here in the United States eludes our grasp. How do public schools contribute to the achievement of these specific requisites of prosperity, American style?

As to the steadily increasing demand for better goods and services, the late Edward A. Filene, far-seeing merchant of Boston, is pointed authority for the statement to his fellow merchants, and industrialists as well, that sound public education is the most effective builder of improved-quality consumer demand in modern society, bar none!

. . . .

Indeed a bit of not overly exhaustive but careful observation by the ordinary layman will disclose that areas generating the greatest urge of consumers for better goods and services are precisely those where education is most widespread and has been for the longest time available. The farther up the educational ladder public schools are available, in general the more refined, the more intelligent, the more urgent, and the more steady the consumer demand, and the higher the standard of living. A clear case in point is the standard of living of the Southern states, generally, compared with that of the states of the Pacific Coast.

. . . .

Let us now turn to the part played by schools in the country's productive capacity. In most discussions of the components of modern, high-energy civilization, machinery assumes a place of prime importance. Now schools do not create machines directly, as anyone knows. They are the products of inventive genius and manual skill, with chief emphasis on the former. Sociologists tell us that these are both products of a relatively rich cultural accumulation or heritage. They also point out that the richer this cultural heritage, the more essential it is that it (1) be made widely available for a longer period in the life of youth, and (2) be transmitted by society's specialized educational agency, the school. The American public school meets these specifications, thus contributing to mechanical productive capacity, in line with social theory. Practically, even the layman's lazy eye beholds patents steadily on the increase in countries which provide ready access for all to educational opportunity, and thus, by a process of untrammeled selection, open the way to and encourage inventive talent to perfect its techniques and expand its scope through research. It would appear to be no mere happy accident that mechanical genius is not only more frequently found but also more fruitfully focused in societies which maintain the more accessible and extended school systems.

But machines, remarkable as they are, and seemingly possessed of almost self-initiating intelligence, actually are not so self-sufficient. They depend for operation on human beings. The more remarkable and precise the machine, the more understanding must be the worker who tends it. And it is the American public school which raises the general level of understanding of all citizens. In the United States, where educational opportunity is more available than elsewhere, it is again no accident that the work done per man hour exceeds that done anywhere else in the world, outstripping its nearest competitor by a comfortable margin. In this connection it is relevant to point out that usually it is workers who have come to their assigned tasks with relatively generous educational equipment who invent improved machinery and perfect industrial processes.

But machinery of the most approved type and operators capable of becoming the world's best might still fail to produce the goods and services adequate to meet society's requirements were it not for efficient management. This skill in organizing machinery and manpower in such a way that waste in materials, motion, and mechanical and human energy is eliminated and industrial and distributive operations flow smoothly and serially from step to step — from the capture of the raw material to its completion in the fabricated product, thence through channels of trade to its destination in service to the consumer — is probably the distinctive contribution of the United States to material progress. This, coupled with the informed intelligence and developed initiative of American workers, makes American production and distribution still the envy and standard of efficiency of the world. And it is free education which is basically responsible. For is it not the public school which opens its doors to all alike, which discovers and enhances initiative by placing virtually unlimited opportunity before talent wherever found, whether in the child from t'other side of the tracks or the scion of wealth and privilege? Where else is this true? And how shall we measure the vastness of the school's contribution in this realm of management and efficiency engineering alone?

But there is still one further requirement to round out the economic circle of prosperity American style. It is not enough that there be a steadily growing demand for goods and services, and productive capacity in machinery, men, and management to meet this demand. These are essential; but the picture is incomplete until and unless demand is made effective through income widely enough diffused among the people to enable them to take away the products of the machine and their own labor at a price which will encourage the continuance and gradual expansion of production.

. . . .

Let's look at the record. And by way of helping to keep the record clear, suppose we begin by suggesting that (1) the American worker receives the world's highest wages, (2) he has experienced steadier employment at these higher wages than the worker in any other country operating under the capitalistic plan of industrial and commercial organization.

To account for these two conditions it is the considered judgment of the overwhelming majority of economists that the genius of American management and the greater skill and superior initiative of American workers result in higher production per man hour, and thus not only justify higher wages but also create the fortunes of American enterprisers. And we have already indicated that it is the school chiefly which accounts for these factors which promote superior productive capacity.

4

The Return on Educational Investment

Harold F. Clark

In fields as different as agriculture and medicine, it is possible to relate improvements in methods or practices to investments in education. Professor Clark of Teachers College, Columbia University, considers these kinds of returns in the following selection. Professor Clark is a pioneer in the measurement of lifetime earnings in various occupations.

For the past hundred and fifty years most economists have accepted as a matter of faith the position that the economic return on educational investment was high. Adam Smith made the statement some hundred and seventy-five years ago. Little effort has been made to develop proof of the argument. Anything approaching case-studies was nonexistent. The statement has been made over and over again in the intervening years. The economists have repeated the statement and then passed on to other items of more immediate concern to them.

. . . .

There are several reasons why the economists have not systematically studied the return on the educational investment. In the first place it is extraordinarily difficult to get the evidence. The factors that bring about economic advance are many and varied. One author who is particularly interested in studying the effect of capital on economic growth will assign a great role to capital. Another author, who is impressed with the *entrepreneur*, will assign to him the major role in economic advance. Another author will be impressed with scientific development. Some of the older authors were impressed very greatly by the natural fertility of the land. Many economists have been greatly impressed by the total range of natural resources.

In addition, education was being provided for many reasons, and many

Adapted from "The Return on Educational Investment," R. K. Hall and J. A. Lauwerys, eds., in *Education and Economics: The Year Book of Education*, 1956, London, Evans Brothers Limited, 1956, pp. 495–506. Reproduced with permission.

kinds of education were being provided. Many varieties of it obviously could not and were not expected to make any economic return. Consequently, the economists could not discuss education as a whole except as a general average. This necessarily blurred the issue and made the analysis more difficult.

. . . .

Many Kinds of Education

The problem is further complicated by the fact that much education is clearly provided for non-economic reasons. Some part of the educational programme is expected to raise the economic welfare either specifically or in general. On the other hand, in every country in the world a very large part of the educational programme is designed for other purposes. One or two illustrations may make the problem clearer.

A study of any of the great classical religions of the world is clearly important, and should be pursued somewhere within the educational structure. It is probably equally clear that, except by the most indirect and roundabout ways, such a study could not reasonably be expected to have any immediate effect, one way or the other, on the economic welfare of a country. The same would probably be true of opera, though doubtlessly, a very strong case can be made for some people knowing and appreciating opera.

There are literally hundreds of reasons for providing various parts of the educational programme. Improving the level of economic welfare is only one reason. One part of the educational system designed for some entirely different purpose might or might not have an important economic effect. There would be no reason to assume that it does until some evidence is available. If the economic level in a country is to be raised by education, it would seem as though the part of the education expected to be particularly useful would have to be designed, at least to some extent, to accomplish this purpose.

Education in General Has a Good Economic Effect

The above arguments do not mean that education generally does not have desirable results. It undoubtedly does. The economic consequences are much less direct than could be obtained if one cared to pay the price. It is undoubtedly safe to say on the average the total educational programme in any western country in the world to-day has a beneficial effect upon the economy as a whole. Much of this benefit, however, probably stems from a part of the programme.

A similar case can be made for education generally as it exists around the world. Probably a much stronger case can be made for the position that an educational programme can be designed to have an even more powerful effect on the level of economic welfare of any country. It is probably true that such a programme could rapidly change the economic status of any undeveloped country in the world. This assumes, of course, that the people would be interested in making the change.

The evidence is also very strong that at least in the technical fields a highly developed educational system pays enormous economic returns in the developed industrial countries of the world. There are good reasons to believe that education can have even a greater economic effect in the high-income countries than it has ever had up to the present time. The question seems to be almost entirely one of how much of the educational effort will be devoted to types of programmes that might reasonably be expected to improve the economic status of the country.

. . . .

THE DEVELOPMENT IN THE UNITED STATES

The development in the United States is a very interesting case-study of the place of education in increasing economic welfare. The United States was relatively fortunate in having large physical resources. It also was fortunate from the economic standpoint in obtaining a large number of settlers who were industrious and believed in saving and hard work. The combination of these with other factors was such that income would probably have been reasonably high with a relatively poor school system.

On the other hand, there are many reasons to assume that the development of a widespread school system has been a major factor in pushing the income of the United States to a far higher level than it would have otherwise been. An analysis of three specific areas of education may help to illustrate this.

There are some kinds of economic activity that are extraordinarily difficult to carry on unless the population has a high degree of literacy. Most of the people must be able to read and write. One economic development that seems to depend upon this is a widespread mass consumption market. Unquestionably, a mass market has been an important factor in making possible mass production. Mass production made possible far lower factory cost and consequently higher consumption, higher wages, and a higher standard of living. The high incomes, in turn, have made possible even larger mass production and mass consumption.

Clearly literacy is not an adequate cause of these complicated phenomena. Many other countries in the world have a very high degree of literacy and have not developed a mass market as is in the United States. Literacy is not an adequate cause, but at least in the past it has probably been a necessary requirement of certain kinds of mass markets. Here we have a case where at least a minimum amount of education was probably a necessary factor in a major American economic advance.

. . . .

Schools and Agricultural Development

The United States is burdened with agricultural surpluses of almost all kinds. This seems to be a curious problem and one that quite obviously seems puzzling to most of the world. A recent United Nations report estimated that probably half the people of the world are hungry a large part of their lives. It might appear as though any country should have the necessary skill to deal with too much food. Nuisance though an agricultural surplus may be to the United States, basically it is a great tribute to part of the educational system.

It is an entirely reasonable assumption to make that if our elaborate programme of agricultural education had not been developed, we in the United States would not be bothered with agricultural surpluses. In fact, we might very well have been greatly bothered, as so much of the world is, by not having enough food.

For a hundred years the United States has been developing a remarkable system of agricultural schools. These schools have been devoted overwhelmingly to increasing production on the farm and they have succeeded almost beyond belief. They probably will shift some of their analysis to dealing with agricultural over-production, and over a period of time they will solve that problem also.

The development of the agricultural educational system is a remarkable illustration of what can be done to deal with a fairly complicated part of an economic order. About a hundred and fifty years ago, most American farmers worked as their ancestors before them; a son learned his farming from his father, who had learned it from his father. Some changes went on slowly but perhaps took generations to develop and spread. A century and a half ago the American farmer was still planting wheat in the way it was planted in Biblical times. The farmer carried on his shoulder a bag of grain, broadcast it, then he covered it up and hoped for the best. The wheat was cut by hand and thrashed by a flail; processes that had been used for thousands of years in the Middle East.

Changes of many kinds started in many places other than the school system. But about a century ago, the schools began to play a very active and important part in increasing agricultural output. Agricultural colleges were started in each state of the Union. These colleges began to accumulate all kinds of technical information. They developed better types of wheat and corn; they improved all kinds of agricultural implements; and they expanded the technical knowledge of better breeds of cattle.

Very soon after the establishment of the agricultural colleges, agricultural secondary schools were set up. In the past three-quarters of a century approximately ten thousand agricultural high schools have been built. This means that almost any boy or girl in a rural area of America has access to technically accurate and reasonably up-to-date agricultural information. The agricultural teacher has probably attended the agriculture college. He keeps up with the new technical material and passes it on down to the boys and girls in his classes.

Throughout this same century agricultural experimental stations were also established in every state in the Union. These experimental stations became highly specialized centres searching for better methods of carrying on practically every phase of farming. They tested out a hundred different methods of growing a crop. Testing plots by the thousands became a customary part of landscape around all these institutions. There is scarcely any important aspect of American farm life that has not felt the impact of the scientific research of the agriculture experiment station.

During this period, a whole educational system of extension workers has been set up by the agricultural colleges. In other words, the agricultural colleges made a determined and systematic effort to carry their knowledge back to every farming community in the state. Then a system of county agricultural agents was established. These agents were trained, agricultural experts. There is one in almost every agricultural county in the country; altogether there are about three thousand of them. Finally, many rural elementary schools began to deal with some important agriculture problems. Now we have a comprehensive programme of education reaching a very large proportion of the total agricultural population.

Here is a brief outline of the total system: A universal system of elementary education producing literacy for almost everyone and also some acquaintance with agriculture procedures. A system of agricultural high schools extending into practically every important agricultural community in the country, training hundreds of thousands of boys and girls to be experts in all phases of agricultural life. A system of agricultural colleges covering the entire country and providing for agricultural leadership and producing highly trained personnel. A system of agricultural experimental and research stations covering every section of the country, and dealing at a very high, advanced technical level with all kinds of problems facing the farmer. Finally, a system of adult and extension education reaching back into the local communities, taking the technical information back to the farmer and his wife. Here is a system of education designed to try to improve agriculture. The only comment that can be made on it is that it has been amazingly successful.

. . . .

THE FIELD OF ENGINEERING

Engineering is another field of American economic life where the return on educational investment has probably been very large. Somewhat over a hundred years ago the first of the modern schools of engineering was established in the United States. Since then, several hundred engineering schools and departments of engineering have been opened. In most colleges and universities strong departments of science have been developed. Without them it is almost inconceivable that American economic life could have advanced as it has. The return on the money spent on engineering and technical education in the United States has been very high.

A century ago most industries in the United States changed fairly slowly. An improvement in a water-power flour mill or cotton mill was largely the accidental result of some ingenious worker or owner. The rewards were high for successful changes and many improvements took place in this way. However, the rise of the engineering schools changed the total picture. Technically trained men became available in substantial numbers in industry. They began to see the need and importance of systematically developed research. During the course of the past half-century industry itself has set up thousands of research and developmental laboratories. Now nearly two hundred thousand technical people are employed in these centres and some hundreds of thousands as assistants.

The more advanced industries all over the country are rapidly expanding their own, and encouraging the expansion of other, training facilities of all kinds. There is no end in sight to the process. The more technically trained people we have, seemingly, the more rapid the advance and the greater the need for trained people. It seems as though the educational return on the engineering, technical, and scientific training has been extremely large. Everything indicates that the larger these expenditures become, the more profitable they are, and the more the reason to expand them even further.

Many of the more technical industries in America are making large expenditures for scientific research development and training. The chemical and oil industries are outstanding illustrations. The automobile industry, the steel industry, and many other basic industries are expanding their training facilities. In some of the newer fields, e.g., electronics and aviation, industries are dependent almost entirely upon their developmental and research programmes.

The general picture, then, seems to be fairly clear. The engineering and technical schools have expanded greatly. The scientific departments of colleges and universities have provided basic training that has been invaluable to economic life. Industry itself has entered the picture on a major scale and is making a very large investment in the expansion of research and training. It has further moved into the systematic training of its own labour force. All the available evidence indicates that there is no end in sight to this process. The returns seemingly have been high and from all indications will remain high far into the future.

Medical Schools

A fairly strong and similar case can be made for the schools which are trying to improve the health of the United States. There seems little doubt that the medical schools plus the other allied agencies have been major instruments in expanding the average life-span there. Of course, many other countries have similarly increased the length of life; some of them have highly developed health educational programmes and some have not.

But it seems reasonable to assume that the return on the money spent on health education has been fairly substantial. Undoubtedly, the general rise in economic conditions, which has brought about better working conditions, better diet, and better housing, has also been a major factor in contributing to the rise in life-expectancy. However, when all these factors are taken care of, it is still probable that the return on education for health has been great.

A Possible Programme

It must be repeated again that there are many reasons for providing an educational programme. As a country becomes richer, it can provide all kinds of education simply as consumer items. This means it provides certain types of education for the same reason that it provides experiences in art, music, and in many other fields. The society can afford them and wants them. Now this non-economic education will undoubtedly expand greatly as societies become richer and can afford it.

However, it is also important for any country, including the United States, to have some general idea of the type of educational expansion that will bring a relatively high economic return. Clearly, we do not know the answer to this question in any final terms. However, there are strong reasons for believing that certain kinds of education in certain amounts will return a very high dividend to society.

In general, an educational programme that gives promise of bringing a high economic return to the United States will look about like this. Widespread and almost universal elementary education seemingly will more than pay for itself. Presumably, this programme would provide the minimum skills for literacy, for use of the native language, and for basic arithmetical competency. If there is a small part of the population that cannot absorb all this, it can probably profit from a certain amount of training to increase manual skills in certain limited fields.

Elementary schooling also provides a very wide basis for very large numbers to move into secondary school. As far as the United States is concerned, the number graduated from high school probably should be increased very substantially above the present level. About 60 per cent graduate from high school; the percentage probably should rise to about 80. This is an effort to make the decision on economic grounds. Whether the last 10 or 20 per cent of the population should be graduated from the high school on other than economic grounds becomes a question of social policy.

It is undoubtedly important to keep a widespread general education available for most of these high school students. But probably very substantial numbers are going to have to be given somewhat technical education for a variety of reasons. Certainly in the rural areas the agricultural high schools should remain. If the time ever comes when virtually everyone is graduated from high school and most people go to a technical institution, then the question can be raised whether most of the technical agricultural education should be moved above the secondary level.

Much the same attitude exists regarding the great cosmopolitan high school and also the technical high school within the cities. The programme should be kept as general as possible; but, on the other hand, for a large number of students it must provide the basis for an occupation. This applies to some extent to the commercial high school as well. Again, if the time ever comes when these communities are sending almost all their students through the secondary school and on through two years of technical training, they then might consider moving the technical work above the high school level. But economically, the far safer situation would seem to be a widespread provision at the high school level of technical education of many kinds, and at the same time encouraging as many people as possible to take more general courses.

Seemingly, some further substantial expansion of the college population is economically advantageous. Clearly, there can be an enormous expansion of college enrolment beyond the point that would pay an economic return. There are somewhat over 2½ million college students now and the estimates are that the number will almost double within the next generation. This will probably be a desirable move economically. The real answer will depend, of course, upon the distribution of these students within the various fields of higher education. There can be no question that a further great expansion in the engineering, technical, and scientific fields will bring a very great economic return. Probably a substantial expansion in the health field will pay economically. Some substantial increase both in numbers and in quality of the agricultural education will undoubtedly pay.

A fair case can probably be made that an increase in quality in college education generally will probably pay. At this point, however, we quickly run into the problem of adequate personnel. In the future it is not going to be possible to staff all the institutions that need high-grade ability with as many people as they want. Some better method will have to be found to see that able people are reasonably well distributed in the light of what they would like to do and of the needs of the society. An educational system that could do this would bring a favourable economic return to any society. The educational system in some countries is so narrow that it leads the able students into a few fields, and these are usually ones that the society does not need very much.

There are other important aspects of the American educational system that could undoubtedly be expanded with great economic advantage. It must also be kept in mind that many parts of the educational system should be expanded that would not normally be expected to provide an economic return.

Section B

THE QUANTITATIVE VIEW

Though there are several specific techniques for measuring the contribution of education to economic growth, the major ones now in use rely upon the assessment of the income differences that are associated with different amounts of schooling. That is, one compares the median income, say, of college graduates with that of secondary school graduates. Selection 5 by Edward F. Denison is a clear statement of one application of the general procedure. In reading the selection, it is helpful to note two points. (1) *The measure of economic growth itself is taken to be the average annual increase in gross national product in constant dollars* (*i.e., the effects of changes in the price level are ruled out*) *for the period 1929–1957. The actual figure is 2.93 per cent. One of the problems Denison considers is what part of the annual percentage gain in GNP can be accounted for by the increases over time in the quantity of education per member of the work force.* (2) *Denison assumes that the United States economy operates* (*approximately*) *under "constant returns to scale." E.g., if all factors of production were increased in quantity by one per cent, GNP would rise by one per cent. The share of labor contribution in the national output for the period 1929–1957 he estimates to be 73 per cent. Accordingly, a one per cent increase in labor input* (*such a gain being an effect, say, of more education for members of the work force*) *would raise GNP by 0.73 per cent.*

5

Education and Growth

Edward F. Denison

The major study of United States economic growth, by Dr. Denison of the Brookings Institution, formerly a staff member of the Committee for Economic Development, attracted wide attention in both lay and academic circles when it was published in 1962. This selection is an excerpt from that study, and it is directed at the particular contribution of the schools to economic progress.

This material considers the contribution that increased education of the labor force has made to past growth and is likely to make to future growth, together with the possibilities for altering future growth through the education route. It can deal only with changes in the *amount of formal* education received by members of the labor force. It cannot take into account changes (presumably improvements) in the quality of a day's schooling.

The fact that human knowledge has increased, providing more or better information to be imparted in school, is viewed as part of the effect of the "advance of knowledge" on growth rather than of increased education. Conversely, the beneficial effect of a better-educated population on the rate at which knowledge advances will be classified as a contribution of the "advance of knowledge" rather than allocated back to education.

The Effect of Additional Education on the Quality of the Labor Force

It is evident that additional education increases an individual's ability to contribute to production and his earnings. We need first to quantify this relationship. Data on the 1949 money income of males 25 years of age or more, classified by their age and number of years of school completed, can be obtained from the 1950 Census of Population. Typical differentials by level

Adapted from *The Sources of Economic Growth in the United States and the Alternatives Before Us,* New York, Committee for Economic Development, 1962, pp. 67–77. Reproduced with permission.

of education for males of the same age are about as shown in the first column of Table 1, although there are considerable differences among different age groups. These differentials represent the combined effect of additional education and the fact that, at the same age, individuals with more education have less work experience; they reflect the net benefit to earnings of additional education over the additional experience foregone for additional schooling.

Reliance, for broad groups, on the marginal productivity explanation of the distribution of income permits us to treat differentials in average earnings among these groups as a measure of differentials in the average contribution to production made by the individuals comprising them. However, the difference in education received and the associated loss of experience are not the

Table 1

Years of School Completed	(1) Mean Income as % of Mean Income of Eighth Grade Graduates	(2) Mean Income Differentials Used to Represent Effect of Education (% of Income of Eighth Grade Graduates)
None	50	70
Elementary School:		
1 to 4 years	65	79
5 to 7 years	80	88
8 years	100	100
High School:		
1 to 3 years	115	109
4 years	140	124
College:		
1 to 3 years	165	139
4 years or more	235	181

only characteristics that distinguish the groups, so that the differences in average earnings cannot be used without adjustment to measure earnings differences that are *due to* differences in education and associated loss of experience — the information that our investigation requires.

Clearly, the reported income differentials overstate these differences. Individuals of greater ability are more likely to continue their education. Wolfle states that most of those who do not enter high school come from the lower half of the ability distribution. The average score on the Army General Classification Test of those who enter high school is 105, of those who graduate from high school 110, of those who enter college 115, of those who graduate from college 121, and of those who receive the Ph.D. degree 130; however, there is a wide dispersion at each level.[1] Among individuals with

[1] Scores on the Army General Classification Test (AGCT) are approximately equivalent to the more familiar "IQ." The average score of the whole population is 100. About 34

similar AGCT scores, those with better school grades are more likely to continue their schooling. Insofar as this may reflect greater energy, application, or motivation that carries over into later life, the income differentials shown reflect these attributes as well as differences in length of education as such.

Too much should not be made of these points, however. Even if the association between natural ability or energy and amount of education were very close, the earnings differentials would have to be ascribed in large part to the acquisition of education. In fact, the association is far from complete. Wolfle notes that intelligence seems to be less important than other factors in determining which high school graduates do and which do not go on to college. Even among recent students, education of parents and family income, as distinguished from attributes of the student, are major determinants of the amount of education received. Parents' occupation, age at marriage, and many other influences are also at work. The association between ability and education must have been much smaller for the 1950 labor force, upon which Table 1 is based, than for recent students, who are usually expected to complete high school, or at least to continue school until age 16, if of average ability or better. Every group in the 1950 labor force, classified by years of school completed, included individuals with a wide range of natural ability and school grades. The number who attended college was much too small to include most of those with exceptional ability. Most had not completed high school.

It is likely that the larger portion of reported income differentials for the 1950 labor force in fact reflects the effect of additional education. I shall make the explicit assumption that, on the scale used in Table 1, three-fifths of the reported income differentials represent differences in incomes from work *due to* differences in education as distinguished from associated characteristics; these adjusted differentials are shown in column 2 of Table 1.[2] This three-fifths assumption is one of the major assumptions in this study that importantly affect the results at which I shall ultimately arrive for the sources of past growth, and that do not flow arithmetically from any data

---

per cent make scores between 80 and 100 and another 34 per cent between 100 and 120. Nearly everyone scores between 40 and 160. Dael Wolfle, *America's Resources of Specialized Talent*, the Report of the Commission on Human Resources and Advanced Training, Harper and Brothers, 1954, pp. 143, 145, 146, 182.

[2] The need for *some* downward adjustment of the reported income differentials in the use to which I shall put them may be clearer if it is approached from a different standpoint. As the general educational level moves up, the fraction of the population that has received any given amount of education (say, 12 years) presumably is drawn on the average from a lower segment of the ability distribution of the population; the average high school graduate today presumably has less "natural" ability than the average high school graduate a generation ago. Reducing the reported income differentials adjusts for this, although how accurately is, of course, uncertain. It may be observed, however, that Wolfle denies that (as of 1954) past increases in college enrollments resulted in any lowering of the average quality of college students. He also cites a study by Frank H. Finch indicating no decline in test scores on a standardized intelligence test by students in certain high schools over a 15-year period — a result ascribed to improved instruction in the lower grades. (Wolfle, *op. cit.*, pp. 173–4.)

that can be adduced. . . . I claim no more than that this is a plausible assumption. . . .

This assumption makes possible a calculation of the effects of increased education on past growth. For each year for which I could derive a distribution of individuals by number of years of school completed, I have calculated what the average earnings of males over 25 would have been if the earnings at each educational level were a constant fraction (that given in the second column of Table 1) of *actual* 1949 earnings of eighth grade graduates. The differences from period to period in average earnings so computed can be used to isolate the effect of changes in the length of schooling, measured in years, on average income. An adjustment is then possible to take account of changes in the number of days of school attendance during the year.

Distributions of males 25 and over by years of school completed are provided for 1940 and 1950 by the Census of Population. The Census Bureau has projected the distribution forward to 1960, 1970, and 1980 by the "cohort" method. This assumes, for example, that the 1950 distribution for those 25 to 29 years of age will be applicable to those 35 to 39 in 1960, those 45 to 49 in 1970, and those 55 to 59 in 1980. Distributions for the younger age groups are estimated by extrapolating recent trends. By a similar technique, I have constructed rough distributions for 1910, 1920, and 1930 by working backward from 1940.

Although these distributions require estimates for the older age groups in the years prior to 1940 and the younger age groups in future years, as well as some obvious assumptions about the distribution of deaths, any resulting errors are unlikely to impair our results much if the Census data for 1940 and 1950 are themselves accurate. However, there are indications that these data are biased. Although reporting by the youngest age class appears approximately correct, for older age groups there is evidently overstatement of educational achievement and this overstatement increases with age. The effect on projections made by the cohort method, if no adjustment were made, would be to understate the improvement in educational attainment over time, and hence the contribution of education to growth.

Use of distributions taken directly from the 1940 and 1950 Censuses, in implementation of the technique described above, indicates that the upward movement in the distribution of males by years of school completed would have raised average earnings by 4.44 per cent over that ten-year period. A similar computation that uses a 1940 distribution derived by working backward from the 1950 Census (a procedure comparable to that followed in other periods) yields only 3.63 per cent. The difference, 0.81 percentage points in a decade, is taken as a measure of the bias in the projection procedure, and calculated increases in every other decade have been adjusted by that amount. The results are shown in column 1 of Table 2. Column 2 of the same table shows percentage changes in the average (arithmetic mean) number of years of school completed by males over 25.

Not only the number of years of education but the number of days spent in school per year have greatly increased. By estimating for each Census year (from Office of Education data) the number of days per year spent in school at the time each age group was attending school, I compute the average number of school days represented by each year of school attended. The percentage increases calculated from these estimates are shown in column 3 of Table 2. The increases in days per year are of roughly the same magnitude as those in years of school completed.

Table 2

CALCULATION OF THE EFFECT OF LONGER EDUCATION ON LABOR EARNINGS PER MAN[1]

	Per Cent Change					Annual Rate of Change (per cent)
	(1)	(2)	(3)	(4)	(5)	(6)
Period	Labor Output per Man Considering Only Years of Education	Average Number of Years of School Completed	Average Number of Days of School Attended per Year of School Completed	Average Total Number of Days of School Attended	Labor Output per Man Based on Total Days of Education	Labor Output per Man Based on Total Days of Education
1910 to 1920	2.7	9.0	6.7	16.3	4.9	0.48
1920 to 1930	3.3	8.9	8.8	18.4	6.9	0.67
1930 to 1940	4.1	10.2	10.8	22.0	8.8	0.85
1940 to 1950	4.4	10.4	10.9	22.4	10.4	1.00
1950 to 1960	5.1	9.8	9.3	20.0	10.3	0.99
1960 to 1970	4.7	8.8	8.1	17.6	9.4	0.90
1970 to 1980	4.8	8.2	7.0	15.7	9.1	0.88
1910 to 1930	6.1	18.6	16.1	37.8	12.1	0.57
1930 to 1960	14.2	33.6	34.2	79.3	32.6	0.94
1960 to 1980	9.7	17.6	15.6	36.0	19.4	0.89
1910 to 1960	21.2	58.5	55.8	147.0	48.6	0.79
1910 to 1980	32.9	86.5	80.1	236.0	77.4	0.82

[1] Based on males 25 years of age or older.

The product of indexes of the average number of years of school completed and of the average number of days attended per year provides an index of the average total number of days of school attended by males over 25. Percentage changes based on such indexes are shown in column 4.

It is reasonable to suppose that increasing the number of days spent in school per year raises a man's contribution to production just as much as will an equal percentage increase in the number of years spent in school. In each decade, therefore, I multiply the percentage increase in labor earnings per man ascribed to increases in the number of years spent in school (column 1 of Table 1) by the ratio of the percentage increase in the average total number of days spent in school (column 4) to that in the average number of years spent in school (column 2) to obtain the full contribution of the increase in the amount of education to labor output per worker. The results are shown in column 5.

The meaning of the numbers given in this column, for example the 10.3 per cent increase shown from 1950 to 1960, is this. Provided males over 25 are typical, I estimate that, all other things being equal, if the labor force in 1950 had been as well educated as that of 1960, it would have contributed 10.3 per cent more to production than it actually did. Since labor represented about 75 per cent of the national income at that time, the national income would have been larger by 7.7 per cent. (Or, alternatively, if the 1960 labor force had been only as well educated as the 1950 labor force, it would have contributed 9.9 per cent[3] less to production than it did, and so on.)

. . . .

The computations made, it will be noted, refer to males 25 and over, but in appraising the contribution of education to growth I shall use them as if they referred to the entire labor force. This is unlikely to introduce any appreciable error. Further refinement would require data (particularly income differentials) that are largely unavailable.

THE CONTRIBUTION OF INCREASED EDUCATION TO PAST GROWTH

The education that the United States labor force has received has increased at a rate that can only be described as phenomenal. Its average member in 1960 had spent four-fifths again as many years in school as his counterpart in 1930, and two and one-half times as many as his 1910 counterpart.

With such enormous advances, it is not surprising to find that improved education has made a major contribution to economic growth. By my calculations, from 1929 to 1957 it raised the average quality of labor by 29.6 per cent, or at an average annual rate of 0.93 per cent. (This is practically the same rate as that given in Table 2 for the 1930–60 period.) The contribution was equivalent to an increase of the same amount in the quantity of work done, and the procedure used in that connection may be followed to estimate its contribution to the growth of national product. Multiplication of .93 by 73 per cent, the average share of labor in the national income over this period, yields .68 percentage points, or 23 per cent, of the 2.93 percentage point growth rate of national product as the direct contribution of more

[3] Computed as $100 - 100 \frac{(100.0)}{(110.3)}$.

education. (After further adjustments, my final estimate remains 23 per cent.)

. . . .

The main specific assumption underlying these results is that differentials in labor earnings *due to* differences in education equal three-fifths of observed differentials in money income among adult males of the same age classified by years of education. The effect of alternative assumptions can be easily approximated by multiplying my results by the ratio of the desired percentage to 60 per cent.

For example, if a figure of 50 per cent were substituted for 60, we would credit five-sixths of 23 per cent, or 19 per cent, of the growth of total product to education. Substitution of 67 per cent would ascribe to education 26 per cent of total growth.

My calculation of the contribution of more education to past growth does not take account of the fact that, had schooling not been extended, many of the children who would not have been in school would have been working so that the labor force would have increased more rapidly. However, the labor of a child worker should be counted as much less than that of an adult male. The effect of this loss of labor on the 1929–57 growth rate is estimated at less than 0.1 percentage points.

. . . .

Stimulating the Contribution of Education to Growth

Increased education is not only one of the largest sources of past and prospective economic growth. It also is among the elements most subject to conscious social decision. The laws governing school attendance and child labor have a pervasive effect, and schools are largely publicly operated and financed.

However, the influence of education on output is dispersed over a very long period. The changes in the educational background of the labor force measured in Table 2 reflect mainly improvements in schooling that were achieved many years earlier.

The median age of all persons in the labor force is 40 years. Only improvements in education achieved by about 1925 affected as many as half of the members of the 1960 labor force throughout their schooling. The education provided before World War I was still of importance. Even radical extensions of schooling for children now in school would change the average educational background of the labor force only moderately from that already in sight in the next decade or two.

This observation is in no sense intended to discount the importance to growth of decisions affecting education. We should take the long view. But it is only realistic to stress that for the near-term the educational background of the labor force has already been largely determined.

The following crude calculations illustrate the point. Suppose that, starting with those who would otherwise complete school in 1962 and continuing indefinitely, some action were taken that resulted in everyone remaining in school one year longer than he otherwise would. Suppose further, as would be in rough accord at prospective educational levels with the differentials given in Table 1, that the additional year raised the ability of these individuals to contribute to production by 7.5 per cent.

By 1970 only about 15 per cent of the labor force would have benefited by extra education, and the average quality of the entire labor force would therefore be raised by 1.1 per cent. But loss of those in school instead of at work in 1970 would cost us about 2.6 per cent of the labor force. If these young workers are counted as of half the quality of the *average* worker, this would mean an offsetting loss of 1.3 per cent of labor input. On balance, total labor input, adjusted for quality, would be reduced 0.2 per cent.

By 1980 we would be ahead. Almost 40 per cent of the labor force would have received the extra education, so average quality would be 3.0 per cent higher than otherwise. The cost would still be 1.3 per cent, so that the total labor input, adjusted for quality, would be increased 1.7 per cent and national product 1.4 per cent. This would raise the growth rate of the national product, computed from 1960 to 1980, by 0.07 percentage points.

Ultimately, sometime around the year 2010, the quality of the entire labor force would be raised by 7.5 per cent, while the cost in labor lost that year would still be around 1.3 per cent. Labor input would be larger by 6.2 per cent and national product by 5.2 per cent. Over the entire 50-year period from 1960 to 2010 we should have raised the average annual growth rate of national product by 0.10 percentage points.

Provision of an additional year's education would require the continuing use of 0.3 or 0.4 per cent of the national product, leaving that much less for other uses. So far as output available for noneducational purposes is concerned, this would deduct the equivalent of .02 percentage points from the growth rate over a 20-year period but less than .01 over 50 years.

Aside from its noneconomic benefits, the net effect of the additional year's education would thus be to add 0.09 percentage points to the growth rate of output available for uses other than education over the next 50 years.

To add a full year's schooling, over and above the considerable increase in education already in prospect, would be a large step, and the addition of .1 percentage points to the growth rate for 50 years would be a large result. However, it may surprise the reader that the effect would not be even larger in view of the importance of education to past growth. The reconciliation lies in the huge amount by which education has been extended in the past.

To consider growth over the long-run future, we must ask what changes in education are likely or possible. In practice, the amount of education received by young people cannot increase in the future at the rate that it has in the past.

The past great increase in schooling has been stimulated by the geographic expansion of 12-year public school facilities to cover the nation, the prohibition of child labor, and compulsory school attendance laws, as well as the decline in agriculture and such continuing influences as rising income. Though still exerting a strong delayed impact upon the educational level of the labor force, the effect of these great reforms on school attendance is running out. The remaining possibilities for increasing education through the high school years, though important in absolute terms and especially so in the South, are slight compared with past achievements. The average number of *days* a year that students spend in elementary and secondary schools is twice that of 1870. But in recent years it has been almost stationary. Indeed, except for some possible further reduction in absenteeism, to double it again would require the schools to remain open for all students 365 days a year. There is discussion of lengthening the school day, but little agreement as to the benefits this may be expected to bring.

A large further expansion in the proportion of young people attending college may be confidently anticipated. Moreover, if the income differentials shown in Table 1 are near the truth, an additional year of education at the upper grades (and especially if college is completed) adds more to earnings than an additional year in the lower grades.

But what is required to maintain the contribution of more education to the growth *rate* is maintenance of the *percentage* increase in the amount of education received, adjusted for the greater importance of the upper grades. For the long pull, this seems simply unattainable.

This prospect makes it all the more important to seek improvement in the quality of education, so as to offset the slackening of the increase in its quantity. But we should not be overly sanguine about this. Such objective evidence as is available suggests that the quality of a day's schooling has been improving for many years, even though my estimates cannot measure it. What is needed to prevent the contribution of education to growth from falling very sharply before the end of this century is a great *acceleration* in the rate of increase in quality.

This material has focused on education of the young, which comprises the great bulk of all formal education. Adult education, formal or informal, also affects the quality of the labor force, and more quickly. Its expansion could also help to maintain the contribution of education to growth.

The calculations in this discussion do not cover on-the-job training (unless provided by schools and colleges). This is undoubtedly a very important form of training but I do not know whether or not it has increased or decreased in amount per worker. Its omission involves the implicit assumption, so far as the past is concerned, that it has not changed in importance. In considering possibilities of stimulating future growth, more or better on-the-job training, as well as other forms of adult education, should not be overlooked.

Section C

EDUCATION AND THE WORK FORCE

The first two selections in this section deal with the matter of raising educational standards in places where these standards are judged to be relatively low. In Selection 6, Rufus B. Hughes, Jr. presents the thesis that income differentials between the North and the South are likely to be self-perpetuating unless, for example, better schooling in the South allows the regional pattern of resource allocation to be broken. (The reader may wish to compare the Hughes article with the somewhat contrary position on educational policy taken by A. D. Scott, Selection 35 below). Three perspectives on the problem of improving school opportunities for the residents of the slum areas of our great cities are included in Selection 7.

Two selections on future training requirements for manpower in the United States conclude this section. Seymour Wolfbein (Selection 8) offers a projection of the size and character of the labor force in 1970; he also discusses the educational and training problems that the changing nature of employment will cause us to face in the decade of the sixties. James R. Bright (Selection 9) treats the meaning of automation in some detail. The reader will see that Bright challenges the notion that automation results in an "across-the-board" rise in the level of skill requirements of the work force.

6

Interregional Income Differences: Self-Perpetuation

Rufus B. Hughes, Jr.

In general, the gap between per capita income in the South and in the rest of the country appears to have held fairly constant over time. Professor Hughes of Colorado State University argues that such a gap is likely to persist, once it comes into being. For the South to move ahead relative to the other states, a radical improvement in the quality of its education is called for.

The intent of this paper is to consider the manner in which our historic and current system of social and economic organization perpetuates interregional growth and income differentials once they come into existence. The rather general failure of American leaders to understand certain basic causes for such differentials, even as they persist in this country, leads to confusion in the formulation of domestic public policy and in international relations.

Here, it will be argued that a free market system of organization, by nature, causes advanced regions (whatever the original cause for advance) to grow, at least in part, at the expense of other regions. Consequently, once income differences emerge they tend to become self-perpetuating, unless some exogenous influence, e.g., government or chance, acts to offset market forces. These results flow from a process of circular causation — income differences causing differentials in savings and investments, human capacities and ambitions, etc., and these, in turn, causing differentials in income. With appropriate alterations, a similar argument might be made regarding international income differences.

Indications of Equilibrium Theory

To set the stage, consider a free-market economy initially in equilibrium and without interregional differences in socio-economic attributes. Now suppose the following:

Adapted from "Interregional Income Differences: Self-Perpetuation," *The Southern Economic Journal,* Volume XXVIII, No. 1 (July, 1961), pp. 41–45. Reproduced with permission.

(1) Development of a new production process which would convert a very common and widely distributed material into some widely demanded product.

(2) With this process, per unit cost of the product would be much below the cost associated with alternative processes.

(3) The new process is subject to economics of scale so that the output from one technically efficient plant would substantially saturate the market for the product, given a price that would permit continued operation of the plant.

(4) A decision is made to locate a plant using the new process in some particular region.

In terms of static (traditional) equilibrium theory the initial situation would be disturbed, thus loosing a series of resource adjustments which would continue until marginal returns in all uses and regions were equal again. The interregional consequences would be as follows:

(1) A geographic rearrangement of existing labor and capital resources. The concentration of resources would (a) increase in the region acquiring the new plant, (b) become less dense in neighboring regions, and (perhaps) (c) remain unchanged in very remote regions.

(2) An increase in the aggregate real income and, thus, in the aggregate value of the economy's resources. These gains would tend to be heaped most generously upon (a) resources initially located in the region selected for the new plant or subject to being moved at low costs and (b) resources initially suited (physically or otherwise) for use in exploiting the new process or subject to low cost conversion.

(3) Emergence of interregional growth and income differentials. Incomes would probably be higher in the region acquiring the new plant and diminish (though not uniformly) with distance from that region.

Since the traditional analytical framework concerns the reestablishment of equilibrium and ends at this point, one might expect the above situation to be stable until disturbed by another exogenous (chance) happening. Should chance events occur with geographic randomness, interregional income differences would (probably) prove temporary. A random distribution, however, seems unlikely. For various reasons, the higher income areas would continue to be favored.

. . . .

Differential Savings and Investments

. . . To begin with, interregional income differentials would be associated with savings differentials and, thus, with differentials in the availability of funds for investment. Even for ordinary business purposes investment opportunities in the higher income areas would have first choice on the use of such funds. This would include opportunities in agriculture as well as in other sectors. The tendency for investment funds to be more available in the region selected for the new plant, henceforth to be called the "developing region," and in nearby areas would be increased if, as seems probable, the central offices of financial institutions were located in growth centers rather than in other areas. Interregional availability of funds for developing human capacities and ambitions would be even more unequal; about which more will be said later.

Internal and External Economics

In discussing interregional growth differentials Professor Myrdal suggests that for regions which begin first the process of development there are ". . . ever-increasing internal and external economies — interpreted in the widest sense of the word, for instance, a working population trained in various crafts, easy communications, the feeling of growth and elbow room, and the spirit of new enterprise . . ." which would fortify and sustain the continuous growth of the developing region at the expense of others.

As evidence, one might examine the historic decline of the Indian textile industry in the face of enforced competition with imported textiles or the current difficulty of developing an Indian automobile industry. Under such conditions entrepreneurs in the retarded regions would encounter real cost disadvantages in most lines of production. As a result, with free trade, there might be a continuing net flow of investment funds away from the retarded regions (in spite of the low level of local savings) — forcing upon the local labor force (1) unemployment, (2) underemployment in agriculture, or (3) at best, employment in relatively low wage, capital extensive industry.

Migration Differentials

With a secular tendency for investment to be concentrated in a particular region, growth in the demand for labor would be concentrated in the same region, and population would not tend to a geographic equilibrium. Instead, the influx of people to the developing region would continue.

If, as is suggested by nearly all relevant migration studies, migration took a disproportionately large share of young adults, the burden upon development in outlying areas would be obvious. Residual populations of such regions would be left with inordinately large numbers of dependent old folks and children. On this score, regions with net migration losses would face a dilemma. Without increased local investment rates, the situation would not be improved by measures to inhibit migration.

The above does not reveal the full extent of the burden. At least fragmentary evidence supports two additional hypotheses:

(1) Except where movement occurs over short distances or where the channels are well established by previous migrants from the same parent

group, migration is selective, also, of the better qualified youth—judging qualifications in terms of initiative and education (and possibly native ability).

(2) Distance (or inaccessibility for any reason) discourages the amount of migration that occurs in response to any given differential in employment opportunities.

A part of this evidence will be cited here.

In studying migration of high school graduates from rural Minnesota, Floyd M. Martinson found that restless graduates with superior academic records were inclined to leave the rural community; while complacent students with poorer academic records were inclined to remain.

Two studies of emigration from rural Tennessee are, also, consistent with the hypothesis. One study concerns movement from an area of Weakley County where, due to the area's convenient location relative to public transportation facilities (among other things), most families have well established personal contacts with previous emigrants now living in industrial areas of the North Central Region. The other study concerns movement from an area of Lincoln County which is less conveniently located and in which personal contacts with earlier emigrants are less general.

In recent years migration from the more conveniently located county has been non-selective relative to education, thus taking proportionately more of the farm renter and laborer classes and leaving those who, by the right of inheriting farm property, have better income opportunities in the local area. In earlier times, before contacts with the outside were so well developed, migration from the area selected a larger share of the better educated.

In contrast, migration from the less conveniently located county has continued to select proportionately more of the better educated from all economic classes, leaving local problems of development to be solved by the relatively uneducated. Though family incomes were somewhat lower in the less accessible county (a larger share of the labor force being superfluous) the emigration rate was also lower. Such emigration differentials must, in large measure, explain the differences in economic levels between midwestern or northeastern rural communities and rural communities of the South—those in the South being less conveniently located relative to the major industrial centers.

If, as these studies suggest, emigration from isolated regions takes a proportionately larger share of the restless, intelligent, and educated young adults, regions that are remote from developing industrial centers would bear additional burdens of (1) losing a disproportionately large share of the most productive youth from each generation, as well as (2) not being so adequately relieved of superfluous population. The significance of such migration differentials in aggravating interregional income differentials may best be appreciated in the light of Professor Schultz's contention that the major share of recent economic growth can only be understood in terms of improved human capacities, i.e., investments in education, health, etc.

Differential Investment in Human Capacities

At this point it is relevant to consider the issue of interregional differentials in investment funds available for other than ordinary business purposes, i.e., for education, health, roads, etc. Only a small share of these investments are undertaken with expectations of business profits. Instead they are made by individuals (for the direct benefit of the individual or a relative) or by the public — not by business firms. It is convenient to consider here only expenditures for education and health, two of the main determinants of human capacities and motivations. In so doing there is no desire to down-grade the importance of other non-business investments.

The common practice is to treat investments in human productive capacities as consumption expenditures, thus ignoring that such investments are the *sine qua non* of progress.

In regions with below average incomes, as in the southern United States, many young people receive inferior education, both in regard to quality and quantity. The same is true regarding medical care. As a result, at maturity they are less capable of recognizing and exploiting the opportunities that exist. As indicated previously, the better qualified are likely to be enticed away by superior opportunities in more advanced regions.

Differentials in Economic Motivations

Accomplishing interregional equality would be difficult enough if the residual populations of the less developed regions were only less capable than the populations of other regions. Evidence suggests that consequent to their history of low incomes, lack of education, and the selectivity of outmigration (all of these being causally related) they are also less motivated to economic accomplishment.

In general, aspirations for income are limited by the experiences to which aspirants are exposed. . . . Persons reared with low incomes and living in communities where most people are poor tend to accept low incomes as normal, especially if their educational experiences have been so slight as to leave them substantially unaware of living conditions in other regions. Standards for economic status and accomplishment and, thus, socio-economic behavior tend to be adjusted in accordance with the concept of normality. Behavior in regard to migration, use of investment funds, education of children, birth rates, etc., are all affected.

Because their economic standards are low, populations of the less advanced regions fail to take full advantage of their economic potentials, i.e., in terms of income possibilities they utilize resources inefficiently. Suggestive evidence of the ineffective use of resources is contained in two analyses of income variations among families living in isolated, low-income rural communities.[1] In

[1] Rufus B. Hughes, Jr., "Demonstration Effects on Production," *Journal of Farm Economics*, Aug., 1960; "Marginal Returns on Agricultural Resources in a Southern Mountain Valley," *Journal of Farm Economics*, May, 1954.

these studies little net association between variations in family incomes and family resources was observed. Efficiency in resource use seemed to be adjusted (upward or downward) to the level required for maintenance of a very low income standard.

Consequent to low economic standards they continue, also, to have high human fertility rates though they have little chance for providing the great bulk of their youth more than meager expenditures for health and education or other than low wage employment or (perhaps) unemployment. The influence of childhood economic circumstances upon human fertility is indicated by analyses of three sets of data from Tennessee. All else the same, i.e., education, current income, etc., fertility rates were significantly lower among those reared under favorable economic conditions than among those reared under unfavorable conditions. This tendency was reinforced by an intercorrelation between childhood economic levels and educational attainments.

CONCLUSIONS

The process of human resource development and allocation, which leaves underdeveloped regions with a disproportionate share of inept people, would continue to be repeated (unless halted by chance events — as, for instance, the event that disturbed the initial equilibrium) until government or governments intervened to: (1) ensure a more equal geographic distribution of investment, (2) restrict interregional trade, (3) ensure the educational and vocational preparation of youth in underdeveloped regions, and/or (4) ensure mobility patterns that would relieve underdeveloped regions of superfluous people, but leave them a greater share of the types of people who would be essential for local development.

In a very real sense certain costs of greater equality would be negative. Because of the inherent inadequacy of free markets in regard to the development and geographic allocation of human resources, investments for developing the productive abilities of people do not approach the level at which marginal "social gains" would equal marginal "social costs." Conservative estimates place the rate of return on educational investments well above the returns on non-human capital forms. More "adequate" development and use of human resources would involve public action and reshuffling of economic positions. But as we have seen, the current distribution is as much the result of chance as of merit.

Contrary to orthodox opinion, free trade is not an unmixed blessing for all parties involved. Consequent to the cost advantages discussed under the section entitled *Internal and External Economies*, competition from unrestricted interregional trade may stifle nearly all lines of lucrative development in the more retarded regions. In order to reach this conclusion one need not argue that free trade fails to maximize aggregate income, though in certain respects this may be the case. He need only argue that the lion's share of such gains is captured by the developed regions. As a matter of justice, the less developed regions might reasonably claim the right to (1) selective regulation of trade and/or (2) income transfers from developed areas.

As yet no reference has been made to what Professor Myrdal has termed "spread effects." With sufficiently rapid technological progress, high rates of savings and investments, etc., real incomes in all areas might rise so rapidly and high as to cause interregional per capita income differentials to become insignificant. However, the fact that even in the United States such differentials are still relatively large does not argue well for leaving the problem of equality to be solved by "spread effects."

7

Education in Urban Centers

A Combined Selection

One of the distressing features of American education is the slum school. In this combined selection, Dr. James B. Conant of the Carnegie Corporation discusses the special educational needs of the children who live in the depressed areas of our large cities; Patricia C. Sexton, an authority in urban sociology, states the case for developing new programs for students from poor homes; and Harvey E. Brazer of the National Bureau of Economic Research offers observations on the difficult fiscal position of the urban centers.

a. Schools and Jobs in the Big Cities

James B. Conant

In preparation for a Conference on Unemployed, Out-of-School Youth in Urban Areas held in May, 1961, a few special studies were conducted in slum areas of large cities to find out what the facts really were with respect to the unemployment of youth in slum neighborhoods. In a slum section composed almost entirely of Negroes in one of our largest cities the following situation was found: A total of 59 per cent of the male youth between the ages of

Adapted from *Slums and Suburbs,* New York, McGraw-Hill Book Company, 1961, pp. 33–38. Reproduced with permission.

sixteen and twenty-one were out of school and unemployed. They were roaming the streets. Of the boys who graduated from high school 48 per cent were unemployed in contrast to 63 per cent of the boys who had dropped out of school. In short, two thirds of the male dropouts did not have jobs and about half of the high school graduates did not have jobs. In such a situation, the pupil may ask, "Why bother to stay in school when graduation for half the boys opens onto a dead-end street?"

An even worse state of affairs was found in another special study in a different city. In a slum area of 125,000 people, mostly Negro, a sampling of the youth population showed that roughly 70 per cent of the boys and girls ages sixteen to twenty-one were out of school and unemployed. When one considers that the total population in this district is equal to that of a good-sized independent city, the magnitude of the problem is appalling and the challenge to our society is clear.

I do not have to remind the reader that the fate of freedom in the world hangs very much in balance. Our success against the spread of communism in no small measure depends upon the successful operation of our own free society. To my mind, there is no question that a healthy society requires a sound economy and high employment. Communism feeds upon discontented, frustrated, unemployed people. As I write in June, 1961, the unemployment rate nationwide is something over 7 per cent for all age brackets, but unemployment among youth under twenty-one years of age is about 17 per cent, or more than twice the nationwide rate for all workers. These young people are my chief concern, especially when they are pocketed together in large numbers within the confines of the big city slums. What can words like "freedom," "liberty," and "equality of opportunity" mean to these young people? With what kind of zeal and dedication can we expect them to withstand the relentless pressures of communism? How well prepared are they to face the struggle that shows no signs of abating? I am deeply disturbed by the implications that widespread unemployment among the youth of our big cities has for the future of our society.

Although the causes of juvenile delinquency are complex and there is no one solution, employment opportunities are clearly important. A youth who has dropped out of school and never has had a full-time job is not likely to become a constructive citizen of his community. Quite the contrary. As a frustrated individual he is likely to be antisocial and rebellious, and may well become a juvenile delinquent. The adverse influence of the street is largely a consequence of gangs of such youths, out of school and unemployed. I doubt if anyone familiar with slums would deny that, if all the male youth by some miracle were to find employment, the social climate would change dramatically for the better. Some juvenile delinquents would remain, gangs might not wholly disappear, but the attitude of the neighborhood would alter in such a way as to make more effective the teacher in every classroom.

Unemployment is bad anywhere. Adult unemployment, especially in rural areas, towns, and small cities, is grievous because it usually involves the loss of support for an entire family. In such cases, one might say that solving the unemployment of adults has the top priority. But in the slums of the largest cities, the reverse is true. The great need is for reduction of unemployment of male youth under twenty-one.

Consider for a moment the long-run consequence of persistent failure of underprivileged youth to find work. Leaving aside the human tragedies involved in each individual instance and looking at the matter solely in terms of the welfare of our free society, one sees the special position of the large city slums. The boys brought up in slum neighborhoods, even if they come to the big city from the country as children, are conditioned to street life with all that this life implies. Out of work and out of school once they turn sixteen, these youth behave in ways that may have serious political consequences; similar behavior of youth in smaller cities would be far less serious. It is a matter of geography in the last analysis. Three factors are significant: first, group size (the larger the group, the more dangerous); second, the density of the population (the number of frustrated youth per block); third, the isolation of the inhabitants from other kinds of people and other sorts of streets and houses.

If one compares the slum areas in the largest cities with similar districts in small cities, the difference with respect to these three factors is evident. The youth in the big city slums dwell in a mammoth social complex. The surrounding city extends for many blocks. The business and industrial areas hem in the impoverished youth. In the case of the Negro, added to all the negative influences of a slum is the absence of any evidence that there is a pathway out. In spite of the high mobility of the family unit, or perhaps because of it, a tone is set by constant talk and the prevailing attitude of the older people. The tone is not one to encourage education or stimulate ambition. One often finds a vicious circle of lack of jobs and lack of ambition; one leads to the other. It is my contention that the circle must be broken both by upgrading the educational and vocational aspirations of slum youth and, even more important, by finding employment opportunity for them, particularly for high school graduates. It does no good whatever to prepare boys and girls for nonexistent jobs.

The difference between the Negro slum of today and the slums of the Northern seaport cities of sixty years ago is a difference that deserves attention. The worries I have expressed about the continuation of present conditions may appear to be neutralized by contemplating the record of the past. Big cities have always had slums. In the United States in the past it was possible for people to raise themselves by their own bootstraps in the course of a generation. Why be alarmed about the present situation? Such a complacent projection of the past into the obscure future is fallacious for several reasons. First and foremost is the fact that in the past most of the inhabitants of slums were recently arrived white foreign immigrants. They knew that their predecessors for generations had worked their way out of poverty in the cities. They were convinced that they could do likewise. The almost complete lack of such conviction — a consequence of the tragic story of the Negro in the United States — is the outstanding characteristic of youth in the Negro slum. Secondly, a foreign immigrant came from an impoverished but stable society, for the most part a peasant society with its own ancient mores. The pride of family and often strong church connections were social cement that kept the slums from being complete social jungles in spite of the fact that the dwelling conditions were often as bad as they are today. Lastly, for most of the period of our history labor shortages rather than labor surpluses were characteristic of our economy. Particularly, unskilled laborers were in demand. When this was not so, namely, in the depression years, organized society had to step in on a large scale to bolster the tottering social structure. Today automation has affected the employment scene; there is much less demand for unskilled labor. Racial discrimination makes unemployment chronic for the Negro male, North and South. In short, neither in terms of the kinds of people involved nor in terms of the economic and social setting is there much resemblance between the poor city districts of 1900 and those which are the sore spots of our modern cities.

What was especially disturbing to me in my visits to the largest cities was the discovery that the employment of youth is literally nobody's affair. To be sure, there are groups concerned with various aspects of the problem, but no single agency in any of the cities has the data as to the unemployment picture in that city. There is little up-to-date information about youth unemployment even city-wide and only the estimate of school people about the slum neighborhoods. Seldom are figures available to distinguish between the unemployed who are high school graduates and those who have dropped out of school before completing the twelfth grade. Most important, it is not possible to say with any accuracy how the unemployed youth are distributed among various neighborhoods. At the beginning of this chapter I cited special studies that were undertaken to ascertain the extent of unemployment among out-of-school youth in slum neighborhoods. These studies corroborated my guess that the situation was bad. There is a great need for reliable information of this sort. Until public opinion demands that the employment of youth be looked at with a microscope, so to speak, neighborhood by neighborhood, we are unlikely to rectify what may be a great hidden danger.

b. Toward Financial Equality for Schools of Rich and Poor Pupils

Patricia C. Sexton

A great deal more money is now being spent by the schools of Big City in upper-income areas. Certainly an argument can be made that in a democratic

From *Education and Income* by Patricia Cayo Sexton, pp. 253–256, 283–286.

society the reverse of this should be true, since need is greater in lower-income areas. Present inequalities in school expenditures are:

Drop-Outs: In one low-income high school alone, $192,000 was saved in one year on drop-outs. Education for lower-income students is therefore costing much less than the education of upper-income students, who rarely drop out of school before graduation.

Buildings and facilities: It is obvious from our data that a great deal more money has been spent for school buildings and facilities in upper-income areas.

Teachers: Considerably more money is being spent on teachers' salaries in upper-income schools, since . . . inexperienced teachers, who are heavily concentrated in low-income areas, are paid less in wages and fringe benefits than regular experienced teachers.

Club Activities: Indications are that most of the advantages of club activities go to upper-income students. These activities take up a great deal of teacher time and are therefore costly.

"Gifted"-Child Programs: These costly programs service upper-income students almost exclusively.

Evening School, Summer School, Parent Groups, Adult Activities: Since these services are provided disproportionately to upper-income groups, whatever costs are involved, in either teacher time or more direct expenditures, are being unequally distributed.

Another Related Cost Item: Each year about $3.6 billion is spent on higher education at the college and university level; this amounts to about one dollar for every four and a half spent on public-school education. Most of this money comes from public subsidies, though seldom from local board-of-education funds. *Most of this $3.6 billion is being spent on upper-income students, who make up the bulk of the college population.*

Possible reverse inequalities are:

Attendance Officers: Because Attendance Department areas did not coincide in any manageable way with our area divisions, the distribution of these services could not be determined. The main function of the Attendance Department, however, is law enforcement, a police rather than a social-service function.

Visiting Teachers: Since the department in charge of the Visiting Teacher program would not release any information, nothing could be determined about the distribution of these services.

Detention School: Detention School and Ungraded classrooms cost more to operate than regular classrooms, and lower-income children receive more "services" from these programs than upper-income children. However, if other educational costs were equitably distributed and counseling, Visiting Teacher, and other services were apportioned according to need, perhaps Detention School services, as well as Attendance Department services, would correspondingly decrease. It could also be expected that, with adequate educational and guidance services for low-income groups, the public costs of crime, prisons, mental institutions, and public-assistance programs would perhaps also tend to diminish.

We suggest, therefore, as a first step in providing equal educational opportunity to all children, that school expenditures be equalized, at the very least, among the various income groups. It may not be possible, or even desirable, to attempt an exact equalization of *facilities*, but it should be possible, as it would be highly desirable, to equalize *expenditures*.

Federal aid to education and other school-finance proposals are not at issue here. High-quality education, however, for whatever income group, costs money, more of it than we do or can raise by present school taxes.

Federal assistance is an obvious and pressing educational need — not so much in Big City as in areas where high-quality schools cannot be supported locally. Yet Big City is directly concerned with schools in other areas, for their products often end up in Big City schools.

In these stateside-underdeveloped areas the children most likely to be shortchanged are lower-income children, the same ones who seem to pull the short straw everywhere in the country. In this case, however, the deprivation is acute and desperate.

Big City schools too need more money to operate on, much more. Major reforms can hardly be undertaken without money and lots of it. Those concerned about our national destiny should be willing to pay. Nowhere is money more securely invested than in our schools, and nowhere are the returns greater, to upper-, lower-, and middle-income groups alike.

Those concerned about the education of the "gifted" should be aware that switching funds to their education will create shortages elsewhere, and they should be at least prepared to make up the difference with tax increases.

. . . .

There perhaps would be some differences of opinion about what specific goals a program of education for underprivileged children should pursue. It would seem likely, however, that there would be general agreement about these two broad objectives: education for lower-income children that would provide such skills and understandings as would enable them to compete as far as possible on the same levels with upper-income children for the rewards of school and of later life; education that would equip them to function as useful citizens in a democracy and to lead richer, fuller lives.

If experimental programs aimed at these objectives are to achieve maximum success, it will require that they be bold and imaginative and that they incorporate all reasonable ideas from the widest possible variety of sources and points of view. The invitation to new ideas (from whatever source) would mean that all presently fixed ideas about what education should be might better be converted into tentative ideas, to be tested alongside a great variety of conflicting ideas. It is very possible that the most effective program of education for underprivileged children has not yet been tried out or even suggested, and so it would seem advisable in an experimental program to welcome all ideas, old or new, from sources inside and outside the schools, and to exhaust all possibilities in an effort to provide the best possible education for lower-income children, and indeed for all children.

The evidence seems to indicate that such experimental programs should provide a style of education that is packed with present and future meaning for the average student.

It should be a style that appeals to the very practical, though inquiring and searching, mind of the typical American student, a style that meets him where he is, with his heritage of tastes and interests, and leads him to a richer range of interests.

Certainly it should not be a style of education that says: "We have all the answers; we have the perfectly refined tastes; we will tell you what to do, what to like, and you must either accept it or give up your dream of being 'educated.'"

Students know much more than we think they know — even those from the lowest status levels in our society. Their tastes, their interests are often more alive and more vibrant than their teachers' and more in keeping with the times. The older generation cannot impose its exact image on the younger generations, any more than "elite" groups can impose their ways on the "masses." Nor would such an imposition necessarily be desirable, even if it were possible. History shows that many of the great innovations in culture and the arts had their origin in mass tastes, so the elite cannot be too smug about its record.

Certainly there should be more exchange, more give and take between the teacher and the learner. We must listen to the younger generations and make a serious effort to understand what they are saying. We should find out what their needs are and what they would like to learn. If they want to learn about jet planes, we should not insist upon Latin grammar.

Unlike the "gifted" child, who will more often do what he is told to do, learn what he is told to learn, the "average" child demands education that is challenging and packed with meaning, and he will not participate in the educational process unless he gets it.

Progress in education seems to move very slowly. Perhaps this can be attributed to the fact that educators are often uncertain about what to do or how to do it. But, in addition, there seems to be a strong tendency among many educators to resist changes in the old ways of doing things, while clinging uncertainly to the educational status quo. Like most people, they tend to feel more comfortable with things as they are, fearing that changes might impose additional burdens on them or threaten their job security. Of course some of these fears are justified by the actual results of some experimental programs. But very often these fears, especially when they arise before programs are even tried out, are more in the nature of reflex actions than reasonable apprehensions. When such irrational fears have been in control of large blocks of opinion, they have often seriously impeded educational progress, obstructing all but the most minor changes in school organization. As a result, the reputation of educators has been injured, and the educational enrichment and stimulation such programs could provide have been denied to both teachers and students.

Some of this opposition to innovation is directed against changes in "what a teacher does in the classroom," some of it against basic revisions in school organization, and some of it against the introduction of new tools and techniques of teaching. In fact it seems that — from one source or another — there is rather serious opposition to almost all suggested changes in what the schools are doing. And every educational point of view seems to have some area of irrational opposition to innovation.

If education is to take new and better directions, then some way must be found of either allaying such irrational fears or pushing on in spite of them. It should also be added that, if these new directions are to be pursued, school leaders and administrators will need to call upon all available sources of courage and imagination within themselves and within others. Perhaps an insufficiency of these qualities has been as responsible as anything else for the lag in educational progress.

c. Some Fiscal Problems of Major Metropolitan Centers

Harvey E. Brazer

The economic and demographic changes taking place in and around the major metropolitan centers of the nation are bound to have important fiscal repercussions. In per capita terms, expenditure requirements seem certain to increase, both absolutely and relative to those in smaller cities and in the satellite communities. On the other hand, the property tax base, per capita, will be likely to decline, while state aid distributed on the basis of population will increasingly fail to reflect relative needs and obligations.

The per capita expenditures of the major metropolitan center may be expected to increase as a consequence of the fact that the generation of demand for public services in such centers is, in important degree, a function of the number of persons living in the surrounding metropolitan area. While it is hazardous to venture prognoses on the basis of cross-section analysis for any

Adapted from "The Role of Major Metropolitan Centers in State and Local Finance," *American Economic Review*, Volume XLVIII, No. 2 (May, 1958), pp. 306–309, 315–316. Reproduced with permission.

one year, my own statistical analysis and that conducted earlier by Professor Hawley confirm the hypothesis that the per capital outlays of the central city are associated with the size of the population resident in the metropolitan area outside of the central city. Persons living in suburban communities who work, play, or shop in the central city add to the need for street and parking facilities and traffic control and add as well to the demands upon the city's facilities in such areas as police and fire protection, recreation, and sanitation. Population size of the central city itself, on the other hand, does not appear to influence the level of per capita expenditures. Given the certainty, therefore, in the absence of substantial annexations, that the ratios of metropolitan area population to core city population will continue to increase rapidly, it follows that the expenditure requirements of the core cities or major metropolitan centers will increase substantially more rapidly than would be indicated by increases in their own populations and rising levels or standards of public service.

If the function of the central city is changing and is to continue to change in the directions suggested by economic and social developments, its expenditure levels and patterns will change as well if the role of the municipality in the provision of public services is to conform with and facilitate the achievement of its economic role. This must mean greater emphasis upon facilities designed to ease the problem of transporting persons and goods. Major efforts must be made to improve traffic arteries designed to move traffic from the center to the peripheries and from one area in the city to another. For the purposes of the city itself, the comparatively neglected problem of inter-area arterial streets or expressways is probably the more important one. Expensive terminal facilities are undoubtedly indispensable complementary requirements — in the form of truck and bus terminals and parking facilities. Whenever possible, efforts should be devoted to encouraging the use of mass transit facilities, if only because of their far greater efficiency and lower private and public costs than those involved in the use of private automobiles. Each of these kinds of activities, however, suggests a transfer in resource use from the private to the public sector of the economy, and, hence, higher relative levels of public expenditure. Such increases in expenditures, however, may well be so closely tied to the city's abilities to perform its functions that the alternative to their assumption may be only chaos and economic strangulation through traffic congestion. Moreover, if the national total of the costs of urban traffic congestion are anywhere near the 5 billion dollars per year suggested by some observers and, since the bulk of such costs is incurred in the major metropolitan centers, it is quite conceivable that adding an amount equal to as little as half of this sum annually to large-city expenditures designed to improve transportation facilities would represent true social economy.

If, as seems likely, the population of the central cities should be composed increasingly of lower income families, welfare and some other expenditure categories may become more heavily burdened. However, the net result of changes in the composition of the population is difficult to foresee. The need for expenditures of a kind that supplement private income through transfer payments may increase, but some that are complementary in demand with private goods may decline. Furthermore, to the extent that the center of the metropolitan area is vacated by growing families whose places are taken by older couples and single individuals, the demand for such services as education and recreation may fall. Obviously, the net budgetary effect will differ from one city to another, depending upon the municipality's functional responsibility for education and welfare and upon the precise nature of the population shift. For New York City, for example, it is easy to foresee substantial increases in expenditure requirements. But for cities such as Milwaukee and Minneapolis, where the nonwhite population is now and may continue to be comparatively small and large-scale inmigration is not being experienced and where both education and welfare are not primary responsibilities of the city government, the prospects are quite different, in scale at least, if not in direction.

If existing revenue structures could be expected to supply an expanding flow of dollars which, in per capita terms, would be likely to match the increased need for funds, the fiscal outlook might well be a happy one. But the propect is, rather, that the very development that we expect to bring an increase in expenditures will be likely to bring as well reductions in or only slowly rising tax bases and revenues.

The property tax accounts for some 60 per cent of the total tax revenues of the seventeen major metropolitan centers and 46 per cent of their total general revenues, the latter ratio ranging from under 30 per cent for New Orleans to about 95 per cent for Houston. Under present and foreseeable circumstances, however, the per capita property tax base of our central cities in real terms is likely to decline. This suggestion follows, first, from the fact that a great deal of property is being and will continue to be removed from the tax rolls as space is taken for the provision of transportation facilities in the form of limited access and widened arterial highways and streets, public parking sites, and terminals.

A second factor that is suggestive of a decline in the property tax base is the less intensive use of urban land; that is, the reduction in the ratio of brick and mortar to land area. Contributing to this decline are the increasing need for private parking facilities closely adjacent to factories, office buildings, theaters, shops, churches, and so forth; plants designed so that they can be readily engineered for the horizontal movement of goods; and the increasing insistence on the part of architects and city planners upon the desirability of providing for "green spaces" if redeveloped areas are not to revert rapidly to slum and blight.

In addition, because major metropolitan centers may expect to lose substantial portions of their manufacturing activity while gaining in service employment, defined in the broadest sense, this must mean a continuing shift from the location in the cities of the more capital-intensive to more labor-intensive activities. This, then, provides a third major reason for expecting that the property tax base per person served, if not per person resident in the city, will decline.

Finally, if income levels of central city residents decline through population shifts, we may expect as well that the value of residential property occupied per person will fall.

In some degree the improvement of transportation facilities or the easing of traffic congestion and easier entry to and egress from the central city may add to property values. But I should guess that suburban property values will be the principal beneficiaries of such improvements, and that the central cities will do well if they can manage by such means to prevent traffic congestion and other related difficulties and costs from bringing about rapid deterioration in land values.

. . . .

If our major metropolitan centers are to assume a rational role in state and local finance, the principal changes suggested are these: (1) state legislatures should broaden the cities' taxing powers to permit the exercise of the powers inherent in their size and economic structures; (2) reliance on the property tax should be diminished substantially over time, with land values assuming an increasingly important part of the total bill; (3) sales and income taxes and service charges should become the predominant sources of central city revenue; and (4) state aid to cities should recognize that demands for services are a function not alone of resident population but also of population density and the number of nonresidents served.

For the central cities it is important that some contribution to the financing of city services be forthcoming from the "contact" population. Thus full or partial priority should be afforded them in taxing the incomes of nonresidents earned in the city. However, to the extent that state aid may be based on the ratio of metropolitan area to city population, the case for this priority diminishes.

Extension to the major cities of limitations on borrowing powers that may be appropriate for local units generally is no more defensible than is the extension to them of narrow limits on their taxing powers. Certainly, if such limitations are continued, it becomes increasingly absurd to base them on assessed values of property as, even under present circumstances, the property tax becomes a decreasingly important measure of the city's ability to service debt.

Both the effectiveness and propriety of the kind of fiscal program I have outlined depend upon the assumption that the national government will succeed in achieving economic stability and at least minimal objectives in income distribution. Obviously in the face of substantial fluctuations in economic activity and price levels and the existence of large numbers of families in receipt of less-than-subsistence incomes, rational financing of our major metropolitan centers becomes impossible to achieve.

8

Social and Economic Implications of Our Rapidly Changing Population

Seymour L. Wolfbein

Dr. Wolfbein, at present Assistant Secretary of Labor, is recognized as an authority on labor force participation and training. In concise terms, this selection identifies the major problems we will face with respect to education of the work force in the decade ahead.

From a social and economic point of view, population change has three major dimensions which present us in large part with some of the overridingly important issues of today and the immediate future: These are changes in sheer size, changes in composition, and changes in geographic distribution. These changes and these issues can be seen best through the people themselves — how they perform now, what their prognosis is for the future.

Five major population groups stand out as the main protagonists in this arena. How they fare in the current decade will be the prime determinant of social and economic progress in the United States. It is possible to gauge their performance from many points of view; but none is more critical than the relationship between education and employment for each one of these groups: the youth; the unskilled; the older worker; the Negro; and persons residing in depressed areas.

Net Increase in Labor Force

Everything remaining equal, an increasing population brings an increasing labor force or working population, and the 1960's are no exception. It is expected that the net increase in the labor force of the United States will be 13.5 million — the biggest upturn in the economically active sector of the population in this country's history.

Behind this large net increase stands an even bigger grand total of gross

Adapted from "Social and Economic Implications of Our Rapidly Changing Population," in Committee on Educational Finance, *Financing Education for Our Changing Population*, Washington, National Education Association, 1961, pp. 20–23. Reproduced with permission.

change which gives us a much clearer perception of the problems posed during the current decade. Here is the balance sheet for the 1960's:

		(Millions)
Number of workers in 1960		73.6
Subtract:		
Withdrawals from the labor force because of death, retirement, marriage, childbearing, etc.	–15.5	
1960 workers still in labor force in 1970		58.1
Add:		
Young workers coming into the labor force during the 1960's	26.0	
Women returning to the labor force during the 1960's	3.0	
Number of workers in 1970		87.1

This balance sheet speaks for itself, but one statistic deserves special emphasis: There will be 26 million new young workers entering the job market during this decade, as the record postwar baby crop becomes of labor market age. This is a figure unparalleled in our history, 40 percent above the 1950's.

Internal Composition of Changes: Age and Sex

Numbers related to sheer size tell only part of the story. Just as important is the internal composition of these expected labor force changes. Here are our expectations for the current decade:

Expected Labor Force Changes, by Age and Sex, 1960–70

	In the Labor Force		Change: 1960–70	
	In 1960 (in millions)	In 1970 (in millions)	Number (in millions)	Per Cent
All persons 14 years and older	73,550	87,092	13,542	18.4
Males	49,971	57,443	7,472	15.0
14–24	8,963	13,121	4,158	46.4
25–34	10,913	12,173	1,260	11.5
35–44	11,367	10,999	–368	–3.2
45–54	9,681	10,725	1,044	10.8
55–64	6,484	7,721	1,237	19.1
65 and over	2,563	2,704	141	5.5
Females	23,579	26,649	6,070	25.7
14–24	4,822	7,046	2,224	46.1
25–34	4,364	4,905	541	12.4
35–44	5,268	5,470	202	3.8
45–54	5,141	6,555	1,414	27.5
55–64	3,031	4,313	1,282	42.3
65 and over	953	1,360	407	42.7

We will be using this table also as a reference point for our later discussion, but three major facets can be referred to at this point very briefly, which the table emphasizes again: the strategic role to be played by youth; the continued entry of women into the labor force; and the actual *decrease* among men in the critically important working age group 35–44 years of age. The juxtaposition of a tidal wave of new young workers and an actual diminution of workers in one of the prime age groups underscores the almost unique manpower posture we are facing into during the 1960's.

INTERNAL COMPOSITION: DEPLOYMENT OF WORKERS

How our working population deploys itself occupationally and industrially is also, of course, basic to the social and economic issues we will want to assess. Here it is important to know that, under the impact of tremendous increases in productivity and technological change, we are a country which actually has more persons employed in industries which produce services than in industries which produce the tangible goods we all need. Here is the latest industrial scorecard for the wage and salary workers in the United States (March 1961):

Goods-Producing Industries
(in millions)

Manufacturing	15.5
Construction	2.5
Mining	.6
Agriculture	5.0
	23.6

Service-Producing Industries
(in millions)

Transportation and public utilities	3.8
Trade	11.4
Finance, insurance	2.5
Service	6.6
Government	8.8
	33.1

By the same token, we now have more white-collar workers than blue-collar workers, and there is nothing in the offing which will change this major contour of our work force, as the following tabulation shows:

	1910	1959	1970
All workers	100%	100%	100%
White-collar	22	42	45
Professional and technical	5	11	13
Proprietary and managerial	7	11	11
Clerical and sales	10	20	21
Blue-collar	37	37	36
Skilled	12	13	13
Semiskilled	14	18	18
Unskilled	11	6	5
Service	10	12	13
Farm	31	9	6

Five Population Groups

We have attempted to present a few of the major relevant trends in the first three sections; we now move on from this vantage point to the five population groups we mentioned at the start. Each presents a major social and economic issue today; each apparently will continue to do so in the years immediately ahead.

Youth. We have just completed the thirteenth consecutive quarter during which at least one out of every eight teen-age boys has been unemployed. The record for the teen-age girls is just about the same; their unemployment rates are at least double the national average. Somewhat higher unemployment among youth may be expected since they do move more extensively from one job to another and are at the beginning of their career development. But among them are the school drop-outs, whose unemployment experiences are very severe. All of this is made all the more serious, since we have already seen that this decade will bring an unparalleled 26 million new young workers into the job market — and if current levels prevail, 7.5 million of them will be drop-outs, without a high-school diploma and very ill-fitted for the job world ahead.

The problem of the drop-out is critical. The job structure, already oriented toward the professional, technical, and skilled trades, leaves a narrower band of employment opportunities for the youngster without adequate preparation. His unemployment rate is triple the national average; when he is employed, it is at the most menial and low-paying jobs.

Unskilled. For a long time now, the differential unemployment experience among the different skill groups in our working population has been very marked. Most severely affected have been the unskilled manual workers — not only under the impact of recessions, but also in terms of the long-range substantial and significant decline in the number of unskilled jobs. Today, one in every five of our unskilled workers is unemployed — a rate which is two-thirds higher than that for semiskilled workers, 100 percent higher than that for the skilled craftsmen. There is nothing in the offing which can serve to alter these differentials, again especially in the light of our current and expected industrial and occupational structure.

Negroes. Negroes tend to have the least amount of educational attainment, are highly concentrated in the unskilled trades, and still, of course, experience a substantial amount of discrimination in employment. As a result, their unemployment rate is double that of their white colleagues; they account for about one out of every 10 workers, but two out of every 10 unemployed.

Older Workers. Unemployment rates among persons 45 years of age and over have compared very favorably with those of other age groups during the postwar period, especially under the protection of seniority systems which prevail in a significant number of industrial sectors. However, the older worker is at a significant disadvantage when he loses his job; he has a much more difficult time getting re-employed. Right now 40 percent of men 45–64 years of age who are unemployed have been out of work continuously for 16 weeks or longer.

Depressed Areas. Cutting across these groups is the changing geography of American industry which is leaving in its wake areas of substantial unemployment. Our most recent data (for March 1961) show that fully 101 out of the 150 major labor areas in the U.S. are now classified as "areas of substantial labor surplus." Another 184 smaller areas are in this category, too. Experiencing an unemployment rate of at least 6 percent, all of these depressed areas now account for more than 3 million, or about 55 percent of all the unemployed in the country.

PATHWAYS TO SOLUTIONS

These five groups represent some of the more intractable social and economic problems of today and the decade ahead. Leaders in education, as elsewhere, will find, more and more, *four major pathways* in the forefront of discussion as possible routes to be taken to arrive at solutions.

Education, Training, Skill Development. My definition of education contains this dimension: "To help the person withstand the inevitable changes between what he learns and what will be expected of him throughout his life." This argues for viewing education and training as a development process which continues throughout the lifetime of an individual. It calls for the development of guidance and counseling at the elementary-school level; for more creative and meaningful curricula — especially for the manually talented — at the secondary-school level in order to increase the holding power of the schools; for the broadest kind of training to increase the flexibility, the adaptability of persons vis-a-vis the changing job world; for an organized, systematic program of supported retraining and re-skilling of unemployed workers to fit them for new, different employment opportunities. A good beginning toward this last point is contained in the Area Redevelopment Act now before the Congress.

End of Discrimination. Vigorous action, on all fronts, is needed to end discriminatory education and employment practices against Negroes, older workers, and other sectors of our population. Given the challenge ahead of us, discriminatory practices add a dangerous dimension to our already grave domestic situation as well as to our posture in the international field. The current efforts in the field of government-related employment are indicative.

Mobility. As the 1960 Decennial Census returns come in, we are once again reminded of the substantial migration and mobility of our population. Just as much attention should be paid to the changing geography of industrial and business employment opportunities. The geography of our nation's employment has also changed. And mobility, in fact, is the traditional manner in which we have matched the changing location of our population and the changing location of our economic opportunity. Support will be asked to change the institutional forces which hinder mobility and on the positive side to take concrete steps toward increasing mobility wherever necessary—from steps toward vesting pension rights to the possibility of help in relocating unemployed persons to areas of economic opportunity.

Automation and Technological Development. Cutting across many, if not most, of our current and expected employment and unemployment problems is the factor of productivity. It is fundamental to our aspirations for higher economic growth. Yet increased productivity can and does have important effects on the displacement of workers. Not only government, but labor and management as well, have shown increasing concern with this problem. Studies made in the Department of Labor show that action has been taken in a number of instances which mitigated and even prevented the displacement effects of technological improvements. We need to focus, coordinate, and broaden our efforts in this field, as well as in the areas of education, full opportunity for all, and mobility. These are some of the major social and economic issues emerging from our rapid population changes in the 1960's.

9

Does Automation Raise Skill Requirements?

James R. Bright

Professor Bright of the Harvard Graduate School of Business Administration has made intensive studies of the process of automation. This selection is a careful, balanced assessment of the actual effects of automation on skill requirements.

Does the complexity of automatic machinery require extensive retraining of the labor force?

Will the average unskilled worker become unemployable?

Will maintenance needs and technical difficulties cause a radical change in the composition of the labor force?

On what basis should the productivity gains of automation be distributed?

How will the changes in job content caused by automation affect our present wage policies and job evaluations?

Much of the furor over automation has been concerned with its impact on the work force, and hence on society. The above questions represent the key areas of controversy raised by the central assumption that automation increases skill requirements.

It seems immediately obvious and apparently logical that automatic machinery does result in higher work-force skills, but is this really correct? I hold that it is not — and that, despite a number of exceptions here and there, the opposite is a truer picture of reality. It follows that a good many managements stand to make some serious errors in wage policy, employment standards, personnel recruitment, labor contract negotiations, union relationships, and training-program planning because of misunderstanding the impact of automation in this regard. It is even possible that faulty social legislation may be enacted because of lack of critical consideration of the true facts.

. . . .

Adapted from "Does Automation Raise Skill Requirements?" *Harvard Business Review,* Volume XXXVI, No. 7 (July–August, 1958), pp. 85–97. Reproduced with permission.

TRUTH & CONSEQUENCES

The popular train of thought is so persuasive and simple that almost all of us tend to accept, or at least not to challenge strongly, the upgrading-through-automation conclusions. They are found again and again in the testimony before the Congressional hearings on automation, in many union publications, in popular writings and speeches, and in numerous professional statements by managers, engineers, economists, social scientists, and students of management. While there are many shades of opinion in this school of thought, one will search far and wide in current automation literature to find any dissenting views. In simplest terms, the reasoning runs like this:

> Automation results in machinery of a more automatic nature, directed by highly automatic controls. Both the machinery and the control devices are more complex and sophisticated in their action, and must be carefully integrated to achieve performance requirements.
>
> Therefore, the employees manning, servicing, and directing this equipment need a higher degree of understanding. They will require additional training, higher types of skills, and even new levels of education. Thus the job content of individual factory tasks generally will require more skill.
>
> The factory payroll will therefore have to include more skilled and fewer unskilled persons. Furthermore, the effect of automatic machinery will be to eliminate many workers and to put relatively highly skilled operators in their places. Meanwhile, the maintenance force will have to be expanded, at least as a proportion of the work force. Obviously, the factory work force will be upgraded by these effects. A more highly skilled work force is inevitable and essential.

What Effect on Labor? From this conclusion two general points of view have evolved. Many managers, manufacturers of machinery, engineers, and automation enthusiasts have held that upgrading is a blessing of automation. It will relieve labor of drudgery and of monotonous, repetitive work. The superior levels of education and training required to man the automated plant deserve and will command higher prestige and pay for the worker. Automation should be welcomed because it will upgrade labor into higher caliber, more dignified, satisfying, and valuable social and economic positions.

The other point of view — so vehemently expressed by many labor leaders, but also supported by some social scientists, popular writers, and even a few politicians — originates from the same premises and concludes: "Exactly so!" Spokesmen then proceed to a logical and alarming end: not only will the average worker be displaced by the higher productivity of automatic equipment; he will be barred from the plant because he lacks the education, training, and skill necessary to hold one of the automated jobs. The automated plant thus becomes a technological lockout for the common man. Extensive retraining efforts and legislation to soften the blow to labor are, therefore, an urgent social necessity.

Are such sweeping generalizations on firm ground? On what basic premises do they rest? There are several underlying assumptions that seem to be interwoven:

(1) Automatic machinery demands higher degrees of skill and/or training on the part of the worker than the old equipment did.

(2) Automatic machinery requires more maintenance attention and/or higher types of maintenance skills than the old machinery did.

(3) More engineers and technicians are required to design, build, install, and operate highly automatic production machinery.

(4) These changes are occurring in significant percentages and over short intervals.

(5) The present work force cannot meet the new demands, at least without elaborate retraining.

(6) Conditions in the company are such that a net displacement of unskilled workers in favor of skilled workers will occur at the time the automation is installed.

Popular Claims Disputed. During the several years which I spent in field research on managerial problems in so-called automated plants and in exploring automation with industrialists, government personnel, social scientists, and other researchers, I did not find that the upgrading effect had occurred to anywhere near the extent that is often assumed.[1]

On the contrary, there was more evidence that automation had *reduced* the skill requirements of the operating work force, and occasionally of the entire factory force including the maintenance organization.

I found frequent instances in which management's stated belief that automation had required a higher caliber of work-force skill was refuted when the facts were explored. Other managers admitted, and on several occasions emphasized, that they had made substantial errors in assigning high wage rates to some automated jobs. These wage rates not only proved to be out of line with the difficulty of the task but were unfair in contrast to the wages of employees working with conventional machinery. As will be cited later, the training time for some key jobs was reduced to a mere fraction of the former figure.

Here, then, was a series of results which directly opposed common automation claims. They certainly challenged the truth, or at least the universal applicability, of the assumption that the automated factory requires a more highly skilled work force than the conventional one. This is not to deny that

[1] For the results of this research, see James R. Bright, *Automation and Management* (Boston, Division of Research, Harvard Business School, 1958).

there were examples of skill increases required by automation. But it did seem that their importance was exaggerated.

A significant conclusion which developed out of this study is that automaticity (or automation) does not inevitably mean lack of opportunity for the unskilled worker. On the contrary, automated machinery tends to require less operator skill *after certain levels of mechanization are achieved*. It seems that the average worker will master different jobs more quickly and easily in the use of highly automatic machinery. Many so-called key skilled jobs, currently requiring long experience and training, will be reduced to easily learned, machine-tending jobs. To understand how this can be, let us examine the demands automatic machinery truly makes on the skill and training of the worker.

The "Skilled Worker"

Perhaps the best way to start is by asking: What kinds of contributions does the worker make to production tasks? Or, better still, for what contributions is he paid? As a general list of things for which he receives compensation we might include:

1. *Physical effort* — the expenditure of energy through bodily movement, either to manipulate materials and tools or to control the environment.
2. *Mental effort* — the use of mental powers to sense and analyze job requirements, and to direct action accordingly. This also implies attention and concentration.
3. *Manipulative skill* — the employment of a specialized physical dexterity.
4. *General skill* — understanding and ability in a task not too susceptible to learning through mechanical rote or formal analysis. This is similar to competence in an art.
5. *Education* — the knowledge of and competence in the use of a formally organized body of theory and fact apparently required by the task.
6. *Experience* — the ability, comprehension, and judgment that have grown out of practice at the task.
7. *Exposure to hazards* — the extraordinary conditions in which the operator's own safety is jeopardized to some degree.
8. *Undesirable job conditions* — the unpleasant environment conditions or work arrangements that require special consideration.
9. *Responsibility* — the extent to which the worker controls the safety, quality, or productivity of the activity with respect to persons, equipment, and/or materials.
10. *Decision making* — the extent to which the worker must or can make judgments that have a significant effect on successful performance.
11. *Influence on productivity* — the extent to which the worker increases productivity above an expected norm by the contribution of unusual effort, skill, knowledge, or ability.

12. *Seniority* — the mechanistic measurement of service that presumably reflects greater contribution by the worker through some of the factors above, and perhaps also a reward for loyalty.

While this list might be challenged in detail, its concept seems valid: that is, that there are different physical and mental activities which the worker may contribute to a production task. That there is room for disagreement on these activities or my suggested definitions also shows that the phrase, "skilled worker," has a highly subjective connotation. Certainly these words are not used consistently by many of us, or uniformly by industry.

It is immediately apparent that not all of these demands or contributions are equally important in a given task, nor are they of a constant relative importance from one production task to another. In even a simple activity the worker's contribution can vary depending on the equipment used. Consider, for instance, the physical effort of a construction worker using wheelbarrow and shovel versus the skill, mental effort, and experience required to use a bulldozer on the same job. Therefore, to understand how automation affects the work-force skills we must consider how each of the demands in any given job is affected by increasing degrees of mechanization and automatic control. How is job content altered by the increasing sophistication of a mechanism's performance?

QUALITIES OF MECHANIZATION

Mechanization is not an equivalent thing in every production system. One production line is "more mechanized" than another. Wherein lies the difference? Part of the explanation is that mechanization has at least three fundamental qualities or dimensions:

Span — the extent to which mechanization spreads across a sequence of production events.

Level — the degree of mechanical accomplishment by which a given production action is performed (thus reflecting, in part, the fact that automatic control leads to increasing sophistication in the response of the machinery to environmental conditions).

Penetration — the extent to which secondary and tertiary production tasks, such as lubrication, adjustment, and repair, are mechanized.

Levels of Accomplishment. The concept of level, which is the aspect that has the most impact on the operator, is based on the assumption that there are different degrees of mechanical accomplishment in machinery. We can sense this by asking ourselves a question: In what way does machinery supplement man's muscles, his mental processes, his judgment, and his degree of control?

We can examine the characteristics of mechanical performance by analyzing how tools refine and supplement man's abilities. This analysis can be arranged and related in a chart, as in Exhibit 1, which on careful study begins to clarify the relationship of contributions by the worker and by the machine as automaticity increases. A distinct evolution is apparent in these levels:

> First, there is the substitution of mechanical power for manual effort, which takes some burden from the worker (after Level 2).
>
> Then, as increasing degrees of fixed control yield the desired machine action, the worker does less and less guidance of the tool (Levels 5–8).
>
> As the ability to measure is added to the machine, a portion of the control decision information is mechanically obtained for the operator (after Level 8).
>
> As the machine is given still higher degrees of automaticity, more and more of the decision making and appropriate follow-up action is performed mechanically (i.e., by the mechanisms). For instance, as the selection of necessary machine speeds, feeds, temperature control, and so on is mechanized, further "decision-making," "judgment," "experience," and even "alertness" demands are lifted from the worker (Levels 12–14).
>
> Finally, the machine is given the power of "self-correction" to a minor, and then to a greater degree (Levels 15–17), until the need to adjust the machine has been completely removed from the worker.

One need not accept my particular classification of "levels" to confirm the fundamental point. Machinery performance can be classified in other ways and still will confirm, on careful inspection, that successive advances generally reduce operator tasks. In other words, it would seem from this that the more automatic the machine, the less the operator of the machine has to do.

But earlier we recognized that the worker's contribution on the job embraces more than a few items such as "skill" or "effort." The question therefore is: How are each of the 12 possible work contributions we saw affected by increasing levels of mechanization? It seems clear that some job demands will decrease with increasing automaticity, but perhaps there are others that will increase.

It does not seem possible to make accurate quantitative measurements, at least at this stage of our understanding, but it is worthwhile to examine several types of work contributions and hypothesize as to how they will be affected by increases in level of mechanization.

. . . .

Training & Education. Is it not true that as a more complex tool is provided, the worker needs increased training in order to understand the operation of the machine, its adjustment, and its application to the task? After all, he must learn how the machine works, and he must know how to apply it to a variety of operations. For example, training a journeyman machinist takes up to four years.

Exhibit 1

LEVELS OF MECHANIZATION AND THEIR RELATIONSHIP TO POWER AND CONTROL SOURCES

INITIATING CONTROL SOURCE	TYPE OF MACHINE RESPONSE		POWER SOURCE	LEVEL NUMBER	LEVEL OF MECHANIZATION
FROM A VARIABLE IN THE ENVIRONMENT	RESPONDS WITH ACTION	MODIFIES OWN ACTION OVER A WIDE RANGE OF VARIATION	MECHANICAL (NONMANUAL)	17	ANTICIPATES ACTION REQUIRED AND ADJUSTS TO PROVIDE IT.
				16	CORRECTS PERFORMANCE WHILE OPERATING.
				15	CORRECTS PERFORMANCE AFTER OPERATING.
		SELECTS FROM A LIMITED RANGE OF POSSIBLE PRE-FIXED ACTIONS		14	IDENTIFIES AND SELECTS APPROPRIATE SET OF ACTIONS.
				13	SEGREGATES OR REJECTS ACCORDING TO MEASUREMENT.
				12	CHANGES SPEED, POSITION, DIRECTION ACCORDING TO MEASUREMENT SIGNAL.
	RESPONDS WITH SIGNAL			11	RECORDS PERFORMANCE.
				10	SIGNALS PRESELECTED VALUES OF MEASUREMENT (INCLUDES ERROR DETECTION).
				9	MEASURES CHARACTERISTIC OF WORK.
FROM A CONTROL MECHANISM THAT DIRECTS A PREDETERMINED PATTERN OF ACTION	FIXED WITHIN THE MACHINE			8	ACTUATED BY INTRODUCTION OF WORK PIECE OR MATERIAL.
				7	POWER TOOL SYSTEM, REMOTE CONTROLLED.
				6	POWER TOOL, PROGRAM CONTROL (SEQUENCE OF FIXED FUNCTIONS).
				5	POWER TOOL, FIXED CYCLE (SINGLE FUNCTION).
FROM MAN	VARIABLE			4	POWER TOOL, HAND CONTROL.
				3	POWERED HAND TOOL.
			MANUAL	2	HAND TOOL.
				1	HAND.

NOTE: The concept of levels of mechanization (and the idea of a mechanization profile to measure mechanization throughout a manufacturing sequence) was first presented in my article, "How to Evaluate Automation," HBR July–August 1955, p. 101. This analysis has since been refined and is presented in detail with explanations of each level in *Automation and Management,* op. cit., pp. 39–56.

At the lower levels of mechanization it is quite clear that the worker must have additional education as the machinery becomes more complex. When power is applied to the tool, and as adjusting and regulatory devices requiring careful adjustment to obtain proper application are provided, the worker obviously has to learn more about the machinery — perhaps much more, if the equipment is complex. He also may need more training to understand the principles underlying the machine's operation and adjustment. Accordingly, the need for education and training definitely increases.

But does it continue to increase as automaticity approaches the *higher* levels? Apparently not. In the metal-working field and in many other equipments, the effect of automatic cycling (Level 6) is to substitute workers of lesser training ("machine operators") for machinists. The reason is almost self-evident: when a pattern of predetermined actions can be mechanically achieved, there is no particular need for the understanding, the training, and the education on the part of the operator that existed when adjustment and control lay in his hands.

Therefore, at some point after Level 4, the education required by the worker no longer increases. After the mechanization levels introducing measurement (in effect, stages in which the machine signals the need for human judgment), the critical judgment required of the operator actually becomes less. Again, the degree and point of change will vary with equipment, but the common effect seems to be a rising-then-falling curve, as hypothesized in Exhibit 2. In many instances, the need for education and understanding of principles may continue well into the higher levels. However, these eventually become unnecessary contributions as reliability increases.

Mental Effort. One of the major conclusions in the case study presented by Charles R. Walker in *Toward the Automatic Factory*[2] is a claim that mental effort is substantially increased by automaticity. A number of statements in union literature and speeches also insist that the "mental strain" on the worker is the most formidable demand imposed by automatic machinery. What *does* happen when we relate mental effort to levels of mechanization?

Obviously, when he works with hand tools (Levels 2 and 3) and with hand-controlled equipment (Level 4), the worker must concentrate in order to avoid misdirecting the tooling, to "control" the activity, and to detect conditions that might disrupt successful functioning. As the machine is given the capacity for automatic cycling through the desired sequence of events (Levels 5 and 6), the need for concentration on the actual direction of the machinery is reduced; at the same time, however, it is entirely possible that alertness to malfunctioning, to the quality of the output, and so on is a far more worrisome mental task, at least in some instances, because of faster cycling. So, on these levels increased mental strain *might* be a very real thing.

[2] New Haven, Yale University Press, 1957; see also Charles R. Walker, "Life in the Automatic Factory," HBR January–February 1958, p. 111.

Consider next what happens as the machine is given the facility for measurement on higher levels of mechanization. In a primitive way, the machine begins to detect and to report the character of some operating conditions. Therefore, the operator no longer needs to be quite as alert (depending on just what characteristics are measured and signaled). In some instances, as with safety valves, for example, the operator may be quite at ease until the warning signal is given to him. A number of workers on highly automatic machining lines, in which automatic gauging and signaling of performance were employed, acknowledged this effect of automaticity. These men and

Exhibit 2

HOW EDUCATION REQUIRED OF OPERATORS MAY VARY WITH THE LEVELS OF MECHANIZATION

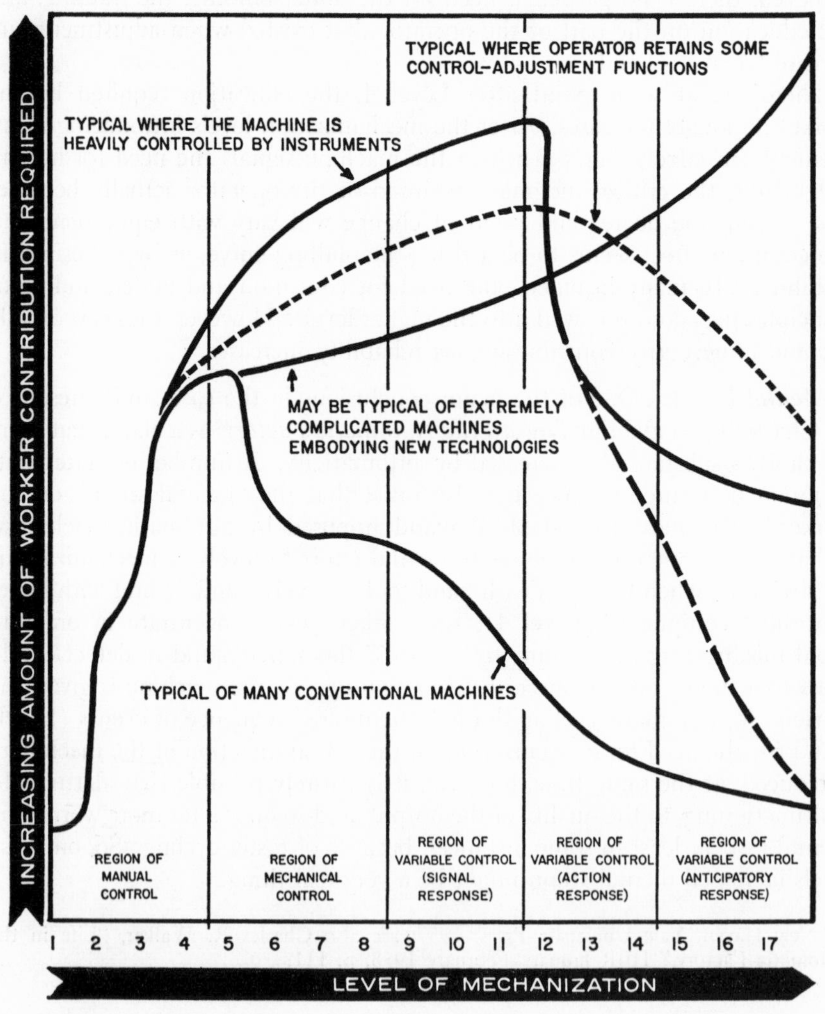

women stated in many ways that they found the jobs more interesting and less tedious because they were able to relax more than under former conditions. Attention, concentration, and mental effort were required only at the moment faulty performance was signaled.

The mental effort requirements would seem to be reduced further as still higher levels of mechanization are employed. Here the machine not only detects the need for a modification in its performance, but it begins to make such a modification without human attention. We might say that on Levels 9–11 the machine calls for human help. On Levels 12–17 the machinery adjusts itself as necessary, in an increasingly sophisticated manner. By definition, the more automatic machines employ control devices that regulate their performance to achieve the desired end *without human attention.* Therefore, mental strain as a result of mental effort is ultimately reduced.

How, then, can it be said that mental strain will continue to grow with increasing automaticity? Take Charles Walker's findings. On closer examination they are not contradictory at all. For, as Walker's description indicates, the steel mill he studied was not a Level 17, or even a Level 12, operation. The span of mechanization was broken at several points, much of the machinery operated at Levels 5 and 6, and only in a few instances throughout the manufacturing sequence was Level 12 reached or exceeded. Increased mental strain had resulted — not because the equipment was more automatic, but because it was not automatic enough! It was more integrated, faster, bigger, but many "control" problems, now more critical than ever because of the potential for more serious error through increased speed and power, were still left to the workers. Even so, after the men once learned to live with the equipment, there was (I infer from their reported reactions) considerably less mental strain.

. . . .

Counteracting Trends

It would be a mistake, of course, to assume that the reduction of job content is the only effect of automaticity. Three other trends should be noted that may counteract, in some cases, the gradual reduction of the human contribution:

1. *Responsibility for a Larger Span of the Line.* Because less attention is required on a given machine, the operator may be given more machines to tend. He becomes responsible for the manning of a physically larger portion of the production sequence or a larger number of identical activities. This may require a knowledge of additional machines, and hence additional technical skills on the part of the worker; it may also require more effort on his part and more attention. The net result may be a significant increase in responsibility because of the possibility and/or probability of more costly damage if the system under his control malfunctions.

Therefore, as the worker becomes responsible for more machines, two types of effect are possible:

(a) He may be required to learn an additional technical art roughly on the same skill level as that which he previously possessed. For example, a milling-machine operator might be required to master a broaching machine and a drilling-tapping machine if they are integrated by automation in his work station. While these skills might not be more difficult or higher in degree, they definitely are additional requirements. They may or may not call for additional training.

(b) He may be required to learn an operation which involves a much higher degree of skill. I did not encounter many instances of this in my study. One example was that of a master control board operator in a fertilizer plant: semiautomatic control of the mixing activity definitely involved more understanding, attention, and responsibility on the part of the individual.

2. *Responsibility for Higher Caliber Duties.* In some automated jobs, the demands on the operator for conventional duties are practically eliminated, but his *new* duties may embrace a portion of the setup work or the inspection job. In other automated lines, there may be no operator in the conventional sense. The individual responsible for this area of the production line may be a setup man or an inspector.

To illustrate, I encountered an instance in which a maintenance man was "manning" an automatic line. On another line where pistons were milled to weight automatically, the "operator" combined the remaining conventional operator duties with those of a setup man. He put the system into operation, verified performance, and made adjustments. He had to have a knowledge of machinery distinctly above that of a machine operator (although not necessarily above that of a journeyman machinist or a versatile job setter). Clearly, an upgrading of the job has resulted.

The line between "set up" and "operate" is a narrow one. In many industries an individual may perform the same setup function as described above without requiring distinctly superior knowledge and training. Operators on some kinds of textile machinery are a good example. Therefore, this source of job content increase may not be common or serious.

3. *Addition of New "Specialists'" Jobs.* One upgrading effect of automation is to create new kinds of skilled jobs. These may require distinctly superior education, or demand significantly higher levels of comprehension and responsibility.

For instance, in an attempt at automatic coal mining the operator was expected to direct a continuous miner operating 1,000 feet underground by remote control based on observation of the performance on an industrial TV screen. Again, in some highly conveyerized factories, such as assembly plants and breweries, and in those process industries where a plant is substantially directed from a central control panel, it is evident that automation has indeed created a new order of skill, education, and responsibility requirements on the part of the worker manning the control system.

Realistic Evaluation

... The fact is that the jobs just described do not exist in any great number in industry — even in plants with a high over-all level of mechanization. Take the third category, for instance — specialized jobs in the remote control of operations. Often a highly mechanized factory will have only one control board job of the type described, and at the most only a handful of such positions. Accordingly, the net effect of automation in almost every plant I studied was still to reduce — or at least not to increase — the demand for skills and abilities on the part of the direct labor force.

As in the factory, so in our everyday life. Is today's car with automatic choke, automatic transmission, power brakes, and power steering harder or easier to drive than a Model T Ford? Who needs the greater skill and experience for successful performance: the housewife who bakes in an automatic oven or her grandmother who had to learn the art of baking in her coal stove through lengthy experience and who had to apply continuous, critical attention for successful results?

Failure to appreciate that growing automaticity commonly tends to simplify operator duties is bound to lead to serious management errors. Unsound policies may be written into union contracts. Excessively strict hiring standards may be established. These will be unfair to many employable people. They will also raise labor force costs unnecessarily. In addition, inappropriate and unfair wage rates will be established if the character of skill required by automation advances is not properly understood.

Indirect Labor

So much for direct labor. What about the effect on skills of shifting direct labor personnel to indirect labor jobs?

As automation displaces the machine operator, the line between direct and indirect labor becomes hard to distinguish. Has the operator become a setup man or the setup man an operator? Regardless of one's answer, an important skill change is evident in the setup activity. Machine preparation and adjustment frequently are more complex, more difficult, and require a wider range of technical knowledge and competence. This is due not only to the complexity of the equipment, but even more to the intermingling of the five types of control systems — hydraulic, pneumatic, electrical, electronic, and mechanical. Also, work-feeding devices must be synchronized and otherwise regulated, and new degrees of precision must be obtained by careful adjustment.

The increased demands imposed on the setup man are quite noticeable when a plant moves, say, from Level 4 of mechanization to Level 12 or higher.

On the other hand, if the old equipment already required a high degree of setup skill (as on a conventional engine-block line), then the move to automation probably does *not* increase the setup man's skill and training requirement's significantly. In the case of a recently automated engine plant, for example, all job setters and their supervisors were given three hours of training in addition to the basic familiarization course given to the operators. Does this mean that there has been a distinct increase in the demand on job setters' knowledge? Hardly.

Where indirect labor mans nonproduction-line machinery, such as power plants and material-handling devices which are in themselves automated, the result is comparable to that for production-line machinery. The demand on the worker increases up to some point; then the spreading automaticity of the machinery generally begins to reduce his contribution in almost every respect.

To be sure, some new kinds of indirect labor jobs requiring a high degree of technical education may be created. An outstanding example is the introduction of numerically controlled machine tools. The programing of tapes requires, at present, considerable technical education. These duties might be regarded as setup jobs of a very high caliber. It may be that engineering or mathematical training will become the bare minimum education for the translation of desired results into programing instructions, or at least for the design of the procedures. Although present evidence indicates that only a few such people are required in each plant (not one for each tape-controlled machine tool), the jobs may become key ones.

In those plants that build their own automatic machinery, there is a greater requirement for the peculiar talents needed for machinery development. Such cases are the main source of complaints about the shortage of adequately skilled people. Not only is technical training needed, but also some kind of skill in visualization, imagination, and mechanical creativity. The latter was by no means obtainable simply by hiring more engineers, several experienced managers told me. They went on to point out that the real production bottleneck in their factories was in the area of conceiving, designing, and building new machinery.

Significantly, those firms that did not build their own equipment — and they were in the clear majority — had no complaints of this sort.

Maintenance Force. What about the maintenance force? As I mentioned earlier in this article, it is popularly assumed that maintenance will increase absolutely, or at least proportionally, under automation. And is it not obvious that the maintenance force will require a new order of skill?

That last question cannot be answered with a simple "yes" or "no" because the maintenance force comprises a number of kinds of skill, and these are not all equally affected by moves toward automation. For instance, I found *no* evidence that tinsmiths, pipe fitters, welders, and carpenters require increased skill, *some* evidence that hydraulic and pneumatic repairmen need better training because of the increased complexity of the control circuitry; and *much* evidence that a substantial proportion of electricians need rather complete retraining.

The average plant electrician is no more prepared to cope with electronic circuitry than the average household electrician is able to repair a TV set. It is a whole new technical world, and it most definitely requires specialized training in theory and practice. One major engine plant has studied this problem and concluded that almost 2,000 hours would be needed in class and shop work to provide adequate electronic training, in addition to the firm's existing journeyman electrical training program of three years.

All of the plants I studied employing even small amounts of electronically controlled machinery offered this same complaint about maintenance skills. Frequently, the shortage was so critical that it distorted attitudes toward the entire maintenance problem. This is where the trouble lies. For instance:

> Lack of electronic maintenance skills was stated to be a critical problem in one plant, and indeed was so. On closer examination, however, it was found that not every electrician needed to have electronic training. Of 700 men on maintenance, approximately 80 were electricians, and the plant engineer estimated that he needed just 3 to 4 competent electronic repairmen per shift. In other words, only about 10% of his electricians needed the specialized skill — and these amounted to only 1% of his total maintenance force!

Such percentages do not make the shortage less critical, but they suggest quite a different scale of difficulty and a much smaller retraining problem.

Automation also suggests the need for a new type of repairman: one competent in the five kinds of control circuitry we noted are involved. The reason for this new demand is that it is too costly to send out a whole crew of repairmen or to send a series of individual specialists — each getting a little bit further with the malfunctioning machine and finding that his skill is not enough. The downtime implications of this procedure are more than disturbing as the span of mechanization grows. Obtaining this kind of maintenance ability involves a training problem and a union relations problem which very few managers have tackled, and fewer still have solved.

. . . .

Engineers & Technicians. Are more engineers and technicians required to design, build, install, and operate highly automatic production machinery? If the plant builds its own automatic machinery, it is likely that more designers and builders will be needed — but not a great many more. For instance, the automation program of one 10,000-man plant resulted in the addition of a 63-man machine-building force. This small proportion was typical of the few firms I observed that did not buy from outside builders. The numbers of technicians required, of course, varied with the amount of machine-building activity. This activity theoretically might have been great but usually was limited by budget and personnel available.

Those firms that do not build their own automatic machinery obviously will not hire designers and builders, but will they need more technical support for operations? In a few instances, I found upgrading of foremen had taken place. Here and there engineering graduates were being hired as line supervisors and maintenance supervisors. While the number of such instances was small, it was noticeable that the lack of adequately trained supervisors was one of management's principal complaints. The missing ingredients, it was claimed, were alertness, perception, and judgment with respect to equipment operation and the implications of downtime. "The ability to see ahead — to plan instead of to live from hour to hour — is what the old line foreman doesn't have."

In spite of this feeling, it was significant that almost all of the firms were getting along with their old foremen. In short, it does not appear that the firm adopting automation today must anticipate hiring many — if any — engineers, unless it intends to develop or build its own automation equipment.

Total Effect. In sum, I see little justification for the popular belief that present labor is employable in automated plants only with extensive retraining or that there is a major shortage of new skills in the automated factory. The 13 plants I studied employed almost 50,000 people. Their automated production systems involved about 5,000 persons and were serviced by 2,000 to 3,000 "maintenance" men ("housekeeping" functions confused precise identification). Less than a dozen instances were encountered where an operation required new calibers of direct or indirect labor skills.

At the outside, perhaps 50 instances of severe shortages of maintenance skills resulted. These largely reflected lack of electronics training.

In total, then, these limited observations and the theory offered here both suggest that automaticity does not necessarily result in a net upgrading of work-force skill requirements to a major extent. In fact, automation often tends to reduce the skill and training required of the work force. (Note, however, that I have not attempted to deal with the increased demand for engineers and other technologists required to support the machine and control-building industries as the demand for automaticity grows. There may be serious skill shortages here, but they are hardly a part of the automation user's problem.)

Section D

THE ADVANCE OF KNOWLEDGE AND CULTURE

Man's material progress is strongly related to the discovery of new techniques for use in productive processes. An earlier, popular view held that discovery was fortuitous, the act, probably, of some erratic genius who appeared from nowhere and quietly performed his feat of magic. Alfred Marshall, an outstanding figure among English economists at the turn of the century, stated, however, that invention was not so fortuitous an activity that it could not be fostered by a mass education. Selection 10, a brief excerpt from his writings, is a classic on the significance of schooling.

In modern times invention has come to be a process deliberately nurtured in both private and public agencies. As Sumner Slichter points out in Selection 11, there has arisen an "industry of discovery," represented by the independent research and development companies and by the R & D departments of other private firms and governments. The flow of new ideas continues apace: the institutionalization of invention has not stilled the creative spark. Given the complexity of modern technology, the schools have a major responsibility to provide adequate training for future scientists and also to serve a screening function, this latter to the end that there be no undue wastage of talent.

Creative activity, moreover, is not confined to the technical sphere of man's life. Innovation occurs in the arts as well. August Heckscher draws attention in Selection 12 to the role of the schools in maintaining the cultural excellence of our society.

10

Education and Invention

Alfred Marshall

Professor Marshall had a long and illustrious career at the University of Cambridge, England. In simple and elegant style, he discusses the contribution of primary schooling to invention.

It is true that there are many kinds of work which can be done as efficiently by an uneducated as by an educated workman: and that the higher branches of education are of little direct use except to employers and foremen and a comparatively small number of artisans. But a good education confers great indirect benefits even on the ordinary workman. It stimulates his mental activity; it fosters in him a habit of wise inquisitiveness; it makes him more intelligent, more ready, more trustworthy in his ordinary work; it raises the tone of his life in working hours and out of working hours; it is thus an important means towards the production of material wealth; at the same time that, regarded as an end in itself, it is inferior to none of those which the production of material wealth can be made to subserve.

We must however look in another direction for a part, perhaps the greater part, of the immediate economic gain which the nation may derive from an improvement in the general and technical education of the mass of the people. We must look not so much at those who stay in the rank and file of the working classes, as at those who rise from a humble birth to join the higher ranks of skilled artisans, to become foremen or employers, to advance the boundaries of science, or possibly to add to the national wealth in art and literature.

The laws which govern the birth of genius are inscrutable. It is probable that the percentage of children of the working classes who are endowed with natural abilities of the highest order is not so great as that of the children of people who have attained or have inherited a higher position in society. But since the manual labour classes are four or five times as numerous as all other classes put together, it is not unlikely that more than half the best natural genius that is born into the country belongs to them; and of this a great part is fruitless for want of opportunity. There is no extravagance more prejudicial to the growth of national wealth than that wasteful negligence which allows genius that happens to be born of lowly parentage to expend itself in lowly work. No change would conduce so much to a rapid increase of material wealth as an improvement in our schools, and especially those of the middle grades, provided it be combined with an extensive system of scholarships, which will enable the clever son of a working man to rise gradually from school to school till he has the best theoretical and practical education which the age can give.

. . . .

We may then conclude that the wisdom of expending public and private funds on education is not to be measured by its direct fruits alone. It will be profitable as a mere investment, to give the masses of the people much greater opportunities than they can generally avail themselves of. For by this means many, who would have died unknown, are enabled to get the start needed for bringing out their latent abilities. And the economic value of one great industrial genius is sufficient to cover the expenses of the education of a whole town; for one new idea, such as Bessemer's chief invention, adds as much to England's productive power as the labour of a hundred thousand men. Less direct, but not less in importance, is the aid given to production by medical discoveries such as those of Jenner or Pasteur, which increase our health and working power; and again by scientific work such as that of mathematics or biology, even though many generations may pass away before it bears visible fruit in greater material wellbeing. All that is spent during many years in opening the means of higher education to the masses would be well paid for if it called out one more Newton or Darwin, Shakespeare or Beethoven.

11

The Industry of Discovery

Sumner Slichter

The late Professor Slichter of Harvard University was a respected observer of the American business scene. Known for his optimism about the industrial prospects of our society, he describes here the exciting ramifications of the way in which inventive activity is now encouraged and supported.

A fallacy widely held among economists has been the view that the supply of investment opportunities has a tendency to run out, so that after some discoveries have been made additional discoveries become more difficult to make. . . .

As a matter of fact, a large proportion of technological discoveries aid in the making of additional technological progress and, thus, the creation of additional investment opportunities. They place at the disposal of engineers and others new techniques that can be employed in developing new kinds of apparatus, new processes, new products. Of basic importance has been the gradual mastery of the art of machining metals to close tolerances, of various sources of power and various ways of delivering power to a given point, and of various forms of electric and electronic controls. The process by which the making of technological discoveries enlarges the capacity of the economy to make additional discoveries will go on indefinitely and will steadily raise the ability of the economy to create investment opportunities.

The growing capacity of the economy to make technological discoveries has within the last several decades given rise to the industry of discovery. The rise of this new industry has been far more important than any one of the great inventions that collectively make up the "industrial revolution." What has happened is that it has become possible to set up a growing number of problems (most of them of an engineering nature but of great practical importance) that can probably be solved by the expenditure of an estimated amount of time and effort. The essential point is that the cost, the chance of success, and the value of the results can be estimated with sufficient accuracy

Adapted from *Economic Growth in the United States*, Baton Rouge, Lousiana State University Press, 1961, pp. 101–106. Reproduced with permission.

so that it can be decided in a more or less intelligent fashion (1) how much money an enterprise may advantageously put into its research department or (2) whether contracts for research may be made with outside agencies with a reasonable chance that the money will have been well spent. In short, it has become possible to apply a rough sort of economic calculus to expenditures on research. The calculus that is used is different from the one that is employed when proven techniques are being used. Those who decide what problems should be studied and how much should be spent on studying them may not be able to explain how they reach their judgments. But proof that some sort of an economic calculation is being applied is found in the enormous growth of expenditures on research in American industry. Enterprises are not throwing their money away; they are spending it because they have good reason to think that the expenditures will prove profitable.

In earlier days the chances of success were so uncertain that attempts to make important technological discoveries were largely made by men who were impelled by far stronger motives than the desire for pecuniary gain. Only such powerful drives as love of one's fellow men or the thirst for fame or glory or insatiable curiosity can explain the willingness to risk life or limb to make a desired discovery or to demonstrate that an invention would work. The history of medicine and aviation is full of such heroic efforts to make discoveries. The community was fortunate to have dedicated men striving to make discoveries, but there was a great drawback to this state of affairs. Since the chance was remote that the would-be inventors would achieve success, business concerns were unwilling to put resources at the disposal of researchers, and only a few more or less fanatical spirits were willing to devote their lives to technological research.

All of this has gradually been changed by the progress of science and technology — by the accumulation of a wider and wider variety of technical skills and larger and larger funds of knowledge available for use in applied research and by the improvement of instruments and methods of investigation. This accumulation of knowledge and improvement in methods of investigation has eventually made it possible to apply the economic calculus to research and to establish the new industry of discovery.

The rise of the industry of discovery has revolutionary consequences for the economy and requires a drastic restatement of the general theory of demand. In the first place, the rise of the industry of discovery means that men and enterprises have a vested interest in discovery. Men make a living and business concerns make sales by disturbing our lives — by introducing innovations that enterprises are compelled to use in order to survive or that consumers cannot resist buying. No longer is research confined to the relatively few men who do not need an economic motive to do it. It becomes a way of making a living for many tens of thousands of able men. And even the few men who do not require an economic motive to do research are far better able to get much-needed economic support for their efforts. Thus, for the first time in human history the making of discoveries has been able to compete with other industries for men and materials by offering a good living to men and a good return to capital. In the second place, the rise of the industry of discovery gives business a far greater command of the demand for goods than it has ever enjoyed before. Enterprises need not sit back and wait for demand to grow. They have it within their power to create huge demand for goods by creating obsolescence. This new capacity to foster a large and growing demand for goods that the economy has acquired makes existing theories of demand quite inadequate and in some respects erroneous.

At present the size of the industry of discovery is limited, not by the number of problems on which it is worth doing research, but by the number of properly trained researchers. Eventually the growth of the industry will be limited by the number of problems that are worth studying. This number will tend to grow because it will be increased by improvements in methods of investigation and by the growth in the stock of accumulated knowledge available for the study of problems.

The immediate effect of discoveries is to increase the supply of investment opportunities, since capital is ordinarily required to put most discoveries into effect. In the long run the effect of discoveries upon the supply of investment opportunities depends upon whether the discoveries tend to increase or decrease the capital that can advantageously be used with each worker. Both kinds of inventions (labor-saving, which increase the use of capital relative to labor, and capital-saving, which reduce the use of capital relative to labor) are being made, but the labor-saving type of invention has predominated. This is indicated by the long-term growth in the amount of capital per worker. The prospect that labor-saving inventions will continue to predominate means that the growth in the industry of discovery will steadily raise the capacity of the economy to create investment opportunities and to raise the demand for investment-seeking funds.

Since it is only rather recently that it has been feasible to apply the economic calculus in a broad way to discovery, the industry of discovery will probably grow at an abnormally rapid rate for the next several decades. It could advantageously use far more well-trained technical people than it is able to hire. While the industry is building up its labor force to the needed size, the impact of its growth upon accelerating the rate of discovery will be unusually great. Eventually the economy will have a considerably higher rate of discovery than the present rate, but one that is increasing less rapidly. A high but steady rate of discovery will be less disturbing than a lower but rapidly accelerating rate.

There is a tendency for discoveries to increase the need for additional discoveries — or to make the development of additional improvements in technology more profitable. This effect of technological discoveries is not to be confused with the technical assistance in making new discoveries that is derived from the use of previously developed techniques. But the existence of any technique or kind of apparatus (the steam engine, the electric motor, the internal combustion engine) creates the opportunity to develop a multitude of investment opportunities that are based upon applications of this technique. For example, the possibility of bringing electricity to farms or of using internal combustion engines on farms created the opportunity to develop all kinds of farm equipment to use the new sources of power. Examples of technological discoveries making the development of additional discoveries advantageous can be multiplied indefinitely.

12

Excellence in the Quality of American Culture

August Heckscher

Writing for the President's Commission on National Goals, Dr. Heckscher pleads the case for attention to the cultural accomplishments of our society. This selection should serve to remind us that the significance of education is not measured solely by the degree to which it fosters economic growth — nor even by the degree to which it increases our understanding of the arts. The important thing, according to Heckscher, is the quality of the new art, music, and literature that are produced in our society.

The Nature of Goals

This chapter does not want to be a catalogue of the deficiencies — any more than a hymn to the virtues — of the American cultural scene. That there are lacks and deficiencies has been sufficiently indicated. The problem is what we can do about them — what reasonable objectives and goals we can set for the decade ahead. But a word, first, about the nature of the goals one can define realistically in this area of the national life.

The arts have sometimes been seen as an adornment, something added to society after science and economics have done their work. Such a view can

From the Report of the President's Commission on National Goals, *Goals for Americans*, © 1960 by The American Assembly, Columbia University, N.Y. Reprinted by permission of the publisher, Prentice-Hall, Inc., Englewood Cliffs, N.J.

scarcely be related to the concept of democracy, and it is definitely not the point of view of this chapter.

Democracy conceives of the whole pattern of existence as being unfolded from within. To the extent that the democratic process is not distorted by plebiscites or the manipulation of public opinion, it finds the people not merely consenting to legislative enactments but generating the forces and impulses from which legislation — and indeed every common purpose and aspiration — is born. The image of such a society is not laid up in heaven. It is being made and constantly remade by the myriad choices and decisions of the citizenry.

If this is true of the laws, it is certainly true of the arts in a democracy. The cultural life of a free people must be sought out. It cannot be decreed. It can be encouraged, guided, sustained. It cannot be imposed from above nor created by will or rational desire. For this reason goals in the cultural field must have a different scope from those that can be set elsewhere. In part the goals must consist of a sensitive appreciation of what is going on in the depth of society, a capacity for awareness, a gift for distinguishing between true and spurious forms of art. At their most ambitious these goals must consist of efforts to encourage and bring to fulfillment the best of what already exists in embryo.

To take this point of view is not to maintain that government at various levels has no role in the development of a democracy's cultural life. A people that truly values the arts will scarcely want to leave unused on their behalf the major instrument of common action. But the very nature of the arts, as here defined, sets bounds to what government can do. Its role must be limited and the expectations it creates must be modest.

. . . .

The Fine Arts and the Creative Few

Related to popular art but not synonymous with it is the realm of the fine arts — the creations of the few, directed to the comparatively small and specialized audience. It is this level of art which gives ultimate distinction to a civilization, being not only in itself the expression of human achievement at its highest but acting as a fertilizing and purifying influence throughout the domain of the popular arts.

The United States today has its own schools of painters, sculptors, composers and architects. It is producing significant results in the performing arts. No one in this generation is likely to ask, Who reads an American book? or, Who looks at an American painting? Critics in this country and abroad acknowledge a high degree of creative genius. Its museums and private collections show the foremost art of all centuries, and this is the object of wide public interest and appreciation. The great books are sold in inexpensive editions to very large numbers. In music, the classic compositions have an immense and continuous hearing; and the most famous works of the drama (particularly Shakespeare's) are kept alive for a broad audience.

Fine art is thus being created and enjoyed, both in the form of new works and of the classics. To keep the creative sources in our society open and productive must be a prime objective. In a world where ideology and the interests of the state seek in so many cases to control art and bend it to particular ends, the freedom of the American artist is noteworthy. At the same time we need to be constantly on guard against those who seek to judge or limit this freedom either because of ideological significance or the political affiliations of the artist.

In a more positive way, the artist must be encouraged and his work supported. It is being gradually recognized in this country that the teacher is entitled to a wage proportionate to the importance and dignity of the work he performs. The same fact must come to be recognized in regard to the artist. At bottom the problem is one of a changed attitude — a change which must begin with a different evaluation of the artist himself. Americans have been accused of being "anti-intellectual." In regard to art the charge could be even more grave: that they are not so much against it as indifferent to it. The artist has been allowed to make his way in a kind of freedom which has too often been bare and unprofitable because it was not part of an atmosphere of understanding. The place the artist has held in societies of the past, and holds in many countries of the present-day world, should by itself be enough to give Americans pause.

Disinterested and considerate help for the artist is particularly necessary because of the mass nature of our society. The innovator too far in advance of his times or too independent of current trends and fashions is likely to find the great audience unwilling to listen. The performer who does get the ear of this audience, moreover, is subject to subtle temptations and pressures to compromise the quality of his work. The existence of the popular arts in their present pervasive and insatiable forms provides, indeed, one of the obstacles to the highest development of the fine arts. The need is to make possible fruitful interaction between the artist and the mass audience, but at the same time to give the artist the means of keeping a life somewhat apart, under conditions allowing him to develop in his own way and at his own pace.

The relation between high art and popular art is subtle and complex. As we have said, the artist must be permitted by society a refuge and a sense of privacy; yet in the larger perspective it is his influence alone which saves the popular arts of industrialism and the mass media from becoming dehumanized and vulgar. How, precisely, is this influence to be exerted? If the artist's work is merely imitated and broadly reproduced, there occurs both a loss of quality in the original and a blunting in the perception of the great audience. The work of art is the expression of a unique vision, to be accepted as such, understood on its own terms and within its limited and necessarily rarefied sphere. Yet without that vision all areas of life and art decline.

THE MAINTENANCE OF EXCELLENCE

It is not necessary here to try to trace out all the interactions between the high arts and the popular arts; the points at which they are linked or separated need not, for our purposes, be made precise. But it is necessary that our society be clear in regard to certain principles which can alone assure the maintenance of excellence and the concentration of an intense and undefiled artistic life.

These principles are not readily acceded to by the typical American. As a people we retain a lively, changeable culture, colorful and varied as befits a society constantly on the move and blessed with a bewildering variety of choice. We have fantastic devices for spreading this culture and a vast hunger to enjoy it. It is not easy, therefore, to maintain standards of excellence, to pursue without compromise the highest forms of art, to admit that not everything is simple or to be apprehended at a first glance. Yet it is essential that there be stated and kept in mind the hard, even bitter truths about the nature of art.

We list the following points, not as inclusive, but as some of the basic presuppositions which a people must come to accept and respect if its culture is not to fall into mediocrity.

1. Art is a matter for professionals. Its practice requires training, discipline and the most unflagging dedication. Nothing is more appealing in the United States today than the enthusiasm with which do-it-yourself culture is followed by the people. The activities of Sunday painters, amateur actors, weavers, wood-workers, musicians, etc. — all have their value. They are part of that constructive use of leisure of which we spoke earlier. But they do not attain, except in the most exceptional cases, the level of true art. The line between the professional and the amateur, between the artist and the audience, is one which any first-rate culture must maintain.

2. Art is not self-evident nor of necessity immediately enjoyable. It requires in the spectator an effort of the spirit and of the mind, sufficient to put himself in harmony with a vision other than his own. Americans have grown accustomed to say that they know what they like. We have had dinned into us that the customer is always right. These attitudes may be adequate for the consumer of mass-produced merchandise; they have very little to do with the person capable of appreciating art in any of its subtle forms.

3. Art is not a matter of numbers. The museums in our contemporary society may find it necessary for economic reasons to cater to a wide public. They may find it tempting and attractive to engage in various educational activities. Insofar as they do these things they may be community centers or educational institutions, both of which we would be poorer without. But to the degree that they perform such services they are not concerned with art in the sense in which we have been speaking of it. Numbers and popularity are not related to this kind of art; indeed the preservation of excellence and

the setting of ultimate standards may be incompatible with efforts to broaden public appreciation.

4. Art is not self-expression. Just as art cannot be understood without effort, so it cannot be created without travail. It lives by laws of its own, laws not always easy to communicate or to understand. But the true artist in any field is bound by these laws and is responsible for keeping them by a strict inner discipline. This is as true of the most abstract or experimental art as of objective and traditional art. Above all, art is its own end, and has nothing to do with therapy or emotional release.

Having stated these broad principles, it remains to add that the life of art requires a vigorous and independent critical spirit, embodied in a small group of men and women no less dedicated than the artists themselves. The critic, in a viable culture, is as sharply separated from the creator of art as the professional is from the amateur. For him to play his true role — understanding art not in terms of public preferences but in terms of its own nature and end — he must have objectivity and the chance to practice it consistently. A recognition by both the artists and the public of the critic's function is a sign of a viable culture. The United States has not been distinguished by the number of its critical journals of a high order nor in all cases by the capacity of its critics to withstand the commercial and popular pressures.

Toward a Positive Attitude

The most significant goal in the field of the arts is that their enhancement and development should be considered a goal — that the American people should recognize the objectives in this area of their common life to be on an equal plane with those to which in the past they have given their best efforts. It has been all too natural, during epochs when a continent was being subdued or amid the fresh responsibilities of world power, to think of the arts as something pleasant but peripheral. The time has now come when we must acknowledge them to be central and conceive their fullest development as essential to the nation's moral well-being.

This country is being watched by peoples — many of them as new to nationhood as they are old in cultural achievements — who ask whether under such a system as ours the highest values can be maintained. It is being watched — and judged. Among our own people, meanwhile, there is a deep and persistent questioning about the significance of our material advance. The ultimate dedication to our way of life will be won not on the basis of economic satisfactions alone, but on the basis of an inward quality and an ideal. Among much that on the surface appears to be complacency or materialism, the Americans — the younger generation especially — are looking for something at once more demanding and more genuinely satisfying than what passes for happiness by current standards. To minimize or frustrate this quest is to risk weakening the fabric of our whole society.

PART TWO

The Economic Structure of Education

In considering the structure of our school system, it is helpful at the outset to note a few features of educational outputs. Education has characteristics of both a "producer's good" and a "consumer's good." Insofar as education raises the capacity of an individual to do work, it is a producer's good, yielding a monetary return similar to that obtained when an individual buys himself a mechanical tool. But education is desired in and of itself, since it enables a person to lead a richer and more interesting life, at whatever economic station he holds. Thus, schooling can be described as a consumer's good, too. Under both forms of return, the yield is obtained (normally) during quite a long period of time.

The complexity of educational products goes much deeper than this, however. Schooling at all levels is obtainable through private purchase. For education to exist as a service performed in the private sector, at least two conditions must be met: (1) that there is an individual demand for the service and (2) that the "exclusion principle" can be applied. (The exclusion principle refers to the power of a buyer to "exclude" non-buyers from consumption of the particular goods or services he himself has purchased.) Yet education also yields "social benefits," i.e., services which are consumed in approximately equal amounts by all. For example, we have seen that education contributes to the economic strength of the country, which is to say that it contributes to the survival of our democratic institutions; this is a benefit that is shared in approximately equal measure by all citizens. Education, thus, has elements of both a private want and a public want. Even if there were no social benefits from education though, schooling would still be subject to support from taxation, because the provision of education is judged to be "meritorious."

With respect to merit wants, alas, there is likely to be sharp controversy about the appropriate level of service that is to be provided for the more indigent members of the society. These are points about the nature of the educational product that are discussed in the selection by Musgrave (13).

Granted that there are complexities inherent in the nature of educational products, it is not surprising to find that the structure under which these products are provided is itself complex. Decisions on the allocation of educational resources are affected by the actions of private bodies and by public agencies at each level of government. This is ably depicted by McLure (14).

It remains true, nonetheless, that the most concentrated measure of power over the allocation of resources in elementary and secondary schools is held by local public boards — in most states, at least. There are arguments to be made for and against local control of education. Tiebout (15) indicates that localism provides a measure of consumer choice in the public sector. By choosing his locality of residence, for example, a person is able to select how much educational service he will buy. (The choice is constrained, however, by such practices as residential zoning, which are themselves related to the extreme reliance of local governments on property taxation.) The 1937 statement of the Educational Policies Commission (written with the assistance of Charles A. Beard) holds that local control is a bulwark against indoctrination of the people (16).

On the other hand, Morrison (17) would have the state governments exercise strong direction of their school systems. He was particularly concerned about the unequal distribution of educational resources among the districts, a condition still apparent in our country 40 years after Morrison stated his position.

One of the most startling suggestions for reordering the administration of our schools (and one that has received substantial support from some members of the academic community) was advanced in recent years by Friedman (18). He would find it desirable to shift much more of the operation, as distinct from the financing, of education into the private sector. He argues that there would be advantages both in terms of increasing the choices for type of schooling that could be exercised by parents and in terms of raising the efficieny of educational enterprises. Vaizey (19) takes issue with Friedman's position; the question is clearly drawn in these two papers.

The economic and cultural significance of education is widely recognized. It might have been expected that as our society became richer — and as we came to feel less pressure on our household budgets simply to meet the stark necessities of life — we would devote a larger share of our resources to schooling. Hirsch (20) indicates that this has not happened. The "income elasticity" of education is of a value roughly equal to 1, which is to say that national income and educational expenditures have increased in almost exactly the same proportion.

Ideally, the economic structure of education would serve several ends: that the total level of educational spending be made adequate for our country's needs; that the distribution of educational resources among individual school units provide a reasonable approximation to equality of opportunity; and that the efficiency of school operations be increased. The reader would do well to keep these criteria in mind when he reads the following selections.

13

The Classification of Public Goods

Richard A. Musgrave

Professor Musgrave of the Department of Economics, Princeton University, recently published an outstanding volume in his field, entitled The Theory of Public Finance. *The following excerpt considers the conditions under which it is appropriate to include a service within the public sector.*

The pricing mechanism of the market secures an optimal allocation of resources, provided that certain conditions are met. These conditions are met reasonably well over wide areas of economic activity, so that the bulk of the allocating function may be left to the forces of the market. In these areas, public policy need not concern itself with matters of allocation. Yet conditions arise in many connections where the forces of the market cannot secure optimal results. Here we are faced with the problem of how public policy can intervene to secure a more efficient resource allocation. In some cases, the required adjustment is made best through budget policy, while in others, different techniques are more suitable. Let us note briefly the major situations where problems of allocation policy must be faced.

To begin with, an occasion for adjustment arises where, for institutional reasons, the organization of industry precludes free entry, so that allocation diverges from that obtained under purely competitive conditions. This is the general case of monopoly control. The existence of market imperfections must be allowed for in the determination of efficient budget policy, and budget policies may be used to remove them. However, the regulation of competition is not primarily a problem of budget policy. More commonly, it is dealt with by legislation to control industrial organization or to regulate the price and output policies of firms. Since our study is concerned with budget policy, this aspect of allocation control enters our discussion only in a collateral way.

A second and more difficult problem of adjustment arises in the case of lumpiness of productive factors and of production processes that involve decreasing cost. These conditions may not only lead to monopoly, but they make it futile to demand that the monopolist behave like a competitor. Optimal determination of output requires an equating of average revenue with marginal cost. Under conditions of decreasing cost, the firm cannot be expected to follow such a policy, since it involves a loss. A tax-subsidy process — and, hence, budget policy — is required to secure an optimal output.

Next, we have situations where external economies or diseconomies are generated by the operation of particular individuals or firms. Establishment of an expensive store may increase real estate values in the neighborhood, even though the store cannot collect for the services thus rendered. A railroad into new territory may lead to gains in economic development that greatly exceed the profits to the particular railroad. Since the market permits a price to be charged for only a part of the services rendered, the development may be unprofitable from the private, but profitable from the public, point of view. Similarly, private operations may involve social costs that are not reflected in private cost calculations and, hence, are not accounted for by the market. A factory may pollute the air and damage an adjoining resort. The smoke nuisance is a cost to the particular community, yet it is not a private cost to the firm. The resort owners cannot collect from the firm since they cannot prevent its use of the common air. Thus, what is profitable to the private firm may be unprofitable from a social point of view.

Other discrepancies may arise from differences between public and private risk, and again others from differences between public and private time preferences. Indeed, if we assume that any one person's welfare depends on that of all others — a case of keeping up with the Joneses — we must conclude that the satisfaction of all private wants involves gains and losses that are not accounted for in the market.

We thus find a wide array of situations where the market mechanism involves varying degrees of inefficiency in resource allocation — inefficiencies that arise collateral to the satisfaction of private wants. Nevertheless, the satisfaction of such wants in most cases is best left to the market. Depending upon the nature and severity of the inefficiencies, corrective action may be desirable and feasible; but such action as is taken remains more or less marginal.

Let us now turn to situations where the market mechanism fails altogether and where the divergence between the social and private product becomes all-inclusive. This is the case of *social wants* proper, the first type of public wants to be considered. Social wants are those wants satisfied by services that must be consumed in equal amounts by all. People who do not pay for the services cannot be excluded from the benefits that result; and since they cannot be excluded from the benefits, they will not engage in voluntary payments. Hence, the market cannot satisfy such wants. Budgetary provision is needed if they are to be satisfied at all. Determination of the required budget plan is complicated by two factors, both of which arise because the same amount of services must be consumed by all.

A primary difficulty arises because true preferences are unknown. Since, as we have noted, no one can be excluded from the benefits that result, consumers will not readily reveal their true preferences. Yet the government must determine these preferences before it can decide how to satisfy them efficiently. A way must therefore be found by which to induce people to reveal their preferences.

A second difficulty arises even if we assume that the true preferences of all individuals are known. The difficulty arises because there is no single most efficient solution to the satisfaction of social wants or to the problem of supplying services that are consumed in equal amounts by all. This difficulty exists, at least, if we apply the criterion of efficiency as understood in the determination of market price. Therefore, a more specific welfare function is needed to secure an optimal solution. . . .

The suggested distinction between private and social wants is not of an absolute sort. Inefficiencies arise in the satisfaction of private wants through the market process, and wherever such is the case, one could say that an element of social want is involved. The difference is essentially one of degree, but the same may be said for most categories in economics, e.g., consumption and capital formation. The distinction remains of fundamental importance. In the case of private wants, the divergence between private and social product is a more or less marginal matter; in the case of social wants, the divergence becomes of the essence. Private wants are provided for adequately by the market. Social wants must be satisfied through the budget if they are to be satisfied at all. For purposes of public policy, the difference in degree thus becomes an important difference in substance.

So far, we have considered situations where corrective policy is required in order to secure an allocation of resources that is in line with consumer preferences. A different type of intervention occurs where public policy aims at an allocation of resources which deviates from that reflected by consumer sovereignty. In other words, wants are satisfied that could be serviced through the market but are not, since consumers choose to spend their money on other things. The reason for budgetary action in this case is *not* to be found in the technical difficulties that arise because certain services are consumed in equal amounts by all. Separate amounts of individual consumption are possible. The reason, then, for budgetary action is to correct individual choice. Wants satisfied under these conditions constitute a second type of public wants, and will be referred to as *merit wants*. The problem they pose must be distinguished clearly from that posed by social wants.

SOCIAL WANTS

Let us now take a closer look at the nature of social wants. Such wants cannot be satisfied through the mechanism of the market because their enjoyment cannot be made subject to price payments.

Exchange in the market depends on the existence of property titles to the things that are to be exchanged. If a consumer wishes to satisfy his desire for any particular commodity, he must meet the terms of exchange set by those who happen to possess this particular commodity, and vice versa. That is to say, he is excluded from the enjoyment of any particular commodity or service unless he is willing to pay the stipulated price to the owner. This may be referred to as the *exclusion principle.* Where it applies, the consumer must bid for the commodities he wants. His offer reveals the value he assigns to them and tells the entrepreneur what to produce under given cost conditions.

This mechanism breaks down with social wants, where the satisfaction derived by any individual consumer is independent of his own contribution. Such, at least, is the case where the individual consumer is but one among many, and any contribution he may render covers only a small part of the total cost. Consider, for instance, such items as a flood-control project, the more general benefits of which accrue to an entire region; a sanitary campaign that raises the general level of health throughout an area; expenditures for the judiciary system that secure internal safety and enforce contractual obligations; or protection against foreign aggression. All these contribute to the welfare of the whole community. The benefits resulting from such services will accrue to all who live in the particular place or society where the services are rendered.[1] Some may benefit more than others, but everyone knows that his benefit will be independent of his particular contribution. Hence, as we have said, he cannot be relied upon to make a voluntary contribution. The government must step in, and compulsion is called for.

The difficulty thus created would be slight if the problem were merely one of collecting tax bills. Unfortunately, this is not the case. The tax collector, while important, does not solve the problem of the economist. The latter must determine what expenditures should be made and what taxes should be collected. To do this, a way must be found to determine people's true preferences in social wants, i.e., the preference pattern by which they rate the satisfaction of their total wants, private and social. The difficulty arises because the market mechanism fails as a device for registering consumer preferences. Since the services that satisfy social wants can be had without payment, the individual consumer need not reveal his evaluation thereof (and invite corresponding tax assessments!) through market bids. Because of this, signals are lacking and true preference scales for social wants are unknown. Such, at

[1] It is evident that the case of social wants must involve joint consumption; but joint consumption, as usually defined, does not necessarily involve social wants. A circus performance involves joint consumption on the part of those who attend. Yet entrance fees can be charged, different amounts can be consumed by various people, and the service can be provided through the market. Demand schedules can be added horizontally. For a social want to arise, the condition of equal consumption must apply to all, whether they pay or not. In other words, we must combine the condition of joint consumption with that of inapplicability of the exclusion principle. Only then will demand schedules be added vertically.

least, is the case with central finance. In the case of local finance, some registration of preferences may occur by moving from less to more congenial fiscal communities, a factor that will be disregarded for the time being.

Since the market mechanism fails to reveal consumer preferences in social wants, it may be asked what mechanism there is by which the government can determine the extent to which resources should be released for the satisfaction of such wants; the extent to which particular social wants should be satisfied; and the way in which the cost should be spread among the group. In a democratic society, the decision to satisfy one or another social want cannot be imposed in dictatorial form. It must be derived, somehow, from the effective preferences of the individual member of the group, as determined by his tastes and his "proper" share in full-employment income. A political process must be substituted for the market mechanism, and individuals must be made to adhere to the group decision. The problem is to determine the kind of voting process or group decision that offers the best approximation to the solution (or one of the solutions) that would be chosen if true preferences were known.

The preceding argument is based on the premise that individuals *can* evaluate social wants, that is, that such wants form part of individual preference scales along with private wants. Without this, no determination of public preferences can be made that meets the requirements of a democratic society as we understand it. This approach differs from an alternative view, according to which social wants are collective in nature and are experienced by the group as a whole or its leaders, as distinct from its members. It is futile to debate which of these is the correct interpretation. Let us look upon our preference for the individualistic over the organic view as a matter of value judgment and be content to show that our formulation makes empirical sense. I see no reason why individuals should not be able to evaluate the benefits they derive from the satisfaction of social wants, along with the benefits they derive from the satisfaction of private wants. To be sure, it may be simpler to assess the advantages of installing a lock in one's own house than to appraise the precise benefits one derives from military protection against foreign invasion; or one may find it simpler to measure the advantages of improving one's own yard than to evaluate one's gain from the installation of public parks. Such differences in degree may exist, but they are not inherently a matter of public versus private wants. Similar distinctions arise between various types of private wants, some of which are more immediate (such as medical consultation in the case of illness) and some of which are more remote (such as preventive medical care). Considerations of this sort, therefore, do not contradict our basic proposition that social wants are an integral part of the individual's preference pattern.

Individuals, at the same time, are social beings, dependent in their preferences and actions on their social environments, and their relations to others. While all wants are evaluated in terms of individual preference patterns, these patterns are not determined in a Robinson Crusoe setting. All sorts of social motivations enter, be it with regard to private or to public wants. While social preference must be anchored in individual valuation, it does not follow that people are selfish monsters. Altruistic or social motivation may be imbedded in the structure of individual-preference patterns. A person may favor expenditures for courts or for education, not only because they will improve his safety, increase his learning, give the pleasure of dealing with more educated neighbors, or because he expects them to think well of him if he appears socially minded; he may favor them simply because he feels that he should contribute to the good life of others.

Such considerations will be present in varying degrees; but they will not be so strong or universal as to justify the assumption that people will reveal their true preferences in social wants on a voluntary basis, independent of any assurance that the same will be done by others. With all due allowance for social interdependence and altruistic motivation, such an assumption would be unrealistic and inconsistent with the premises of all other phases of economic analysis. The first difficulty . . ., therefore, is how to induce people to reveal their individual preferences in social wants.

Suppose, now, that this part of the task has been accomplished in some fashion. We may expect to find that individual preferences differ with regard to social as well as to private wants. In the case of private wants, such differences are reflected in the purchase of varying amounts of goods and services at a common price. This solution is inapplicable to social wants, since the same amount of goods and services must be consumed by all. If costs are to be allocated in response to individual preferences, different prices must be charged to various consumers, or different tax assessments must be placed on various voters. This suggests that a solution may be obtained which is analogous to that of efficient pricing in the market. Unfortunately, this is not the case. The condition of equal consumption by all does not permit a single most efficient solution; or, to put it more precisely, it permits such a solution only on the basis of a social preference function that goes much beyond the conditions of efficiency required to evaluate the allocation of resources in the satisfaction of private wants. This is the second basic difficulty in the provision for social wants, a problem that remains even if individual preferences can be determined.

Taxes . . . are designed to cover the cost of public services. Will the distribution of these tax payments be regressive, proportional, or progressive? Since they are to express the individual's valuation of social wants as based on the proper distribution of income, the answer depends on the income elasticity of social wants. If this elasticity in the typical case tends to be unity, tax contributions will be proportional; if it is above unity, they will be progressive; and if it is below unity, they will be regressive. In any case, note that the considerations behind the question of progression are quite different in this context from considerations arising in connection with distributional adjustments.

MERIT WANTS

The . . . public wants dealt with under social wants are wants whose satisfaction should be subject to the principle of consumer sovereignty. The basic rule is that resources should be allocated in response to the effective demand of consumers, determined by individual preferences and the prevailing state of distribution. Indeed, social wants are quite similar in this fundamental respect to private wants.

We now turn to our second category of public wants. Such wants are met by services subject to the exclusion principle and are satisfied by the market within the limits of effective demand. They become public wants if considered so meritorious that their satisfaction is provided for through the public budget, over and above what is provided for through the market and paid for by private buyers. This second type of public wants will be referred to as *merit wants*. Public services aimed at the satisfaction of merit wants include such items as publicly furnished school luncheons, subsidized low-cost housing, and free education. Alternatively, certain wants may be stamped as undesirable and their satisfaction may be discouraged through penalty taxation, as in the case of liquor.

The satisfaction of merit wants cannot be explained in the same terms as the satisfaction of social wants. While both are public wants in that they are provided for through the public budget, different principles apply. Social wants constitute a special problem because the same amount must be consumed by all, with all the difficulties to which this gives rise. Otherwise, the satisfaction of social wants falls within the realm of consumer sovereignty, as does the satisfaction of private wants. The satisfaction of merit wants, by its very nature, involves interference with consumer preferences.

In view of this, does the satisfaction of merit wants have a place in a normative theory of public economy, based upon the premise of individual preference in a democratic society? A position of extreme individualism could demand that all merit wants be disallowed, but this is not a sensible view. To begin with, situations arise that seem to involve merit wants but on closer inspection involve social wants. Certain public wants may fall on the border line between private and social wants, where the exclusion principle can be applied to part of the benefits gained but not to all. Budgetary provision for free educational services or for free health measures are cases in point. Such measures are of immediate benefit to the particular pupil or patient, but apart from this, everyone stands to gain from living in a more educated or healthier community. Wants that appear to be merit wants may involve substantial elements of social wants.

Moreover, a case for the satisfaction of merit wants and for interference with consumer sovereignty, narrowly defined, may derive from the role of leadership in a democratic society. While consumer sovereignty is the general rule, situations may arise, within the context of a democratic community, where an informed group is justified in imposing its decision upon others.

Few will deny that there is a case for regulating the sale of drugs or for providing certain health facilities. The advantages of education are more evident to the informed than the uninformed, thus justifying compulsion in the allocation of resources to education; interference in the preference patterns of families may be directed at protecting the interest of minors; the freedom to belong may override the freedom to exclude, and so forth. These are matters of learning and leadership which are an essential part of democracy reasonably defined and which justify the satisfaction of certain merit wants within a normative model.

The basic doctrine of consumer sovereignty, finally, rests on the assumption of complete market knowledge and rational appraisal. In the modern economy, the consumer is subject to advertising, screaming at him through the media of mass communication and designed to sway his choice rather than to give complete information. Thus, there may arise a distortion in the preference structure that needs to be counteracted. The ideal of consumer sovereignty and the reality of consumer choice in high-pressure markets may be quite different things. At the same time, the satisfaction of merit wants remains a precarious task. Interferences with consumer choice may occur simply because a ruling group considers its particular set of mores superior and wishes to impose it on others. Such determination of wants rests on an authoritarian basis, not permissible in our normative model based upon a democratic society.

To the extent that merit wants are admitted, the provision for such wants differs basically from the provision for social wants. In the case of the latter, the problem is one of giving effect to individual evaluations. Even though policy will not be determined by unanimous vote, the task remains one of fitting the result as closely as possible to individual tastes and effective demands. Majority rule is a necessary evil to approximate the desired result, not a principle desired as such. In the case of merit wants, however, the very purpose may be one of interference by some, presumably the majority, into the want pattern of others. The solution to the determination of social wants, based on the true preferences of all individuals alike, does not apply in this case.

Providing for the Satisfaction of Public Wants

Suppose, now, that it has been decided which public wants, social or merit, shall be provided for through the public budget. What, precisely, do we mean by saying that the government must "provide" for the satisfaction of such wants?

We mean, simply, that the goods and services needed to satisfy public wants must be paid for out of general revenue. The goods and services must be supplied free of direct charge to the user; at the same time, they need *not* be produced under the direct management or supervision of the government. This is an important distinction to be made in order to avoid confusion.

Consider, for instance, the case of military protection. Provision for protection means that resources must be diverted to the construction of guns or of naval vessels. It does *not* mean, necessarily, that the guns or ships should be constructed by a public enterprise — or, necessarily, by private firms. One may consider also the matter of public playgrounds. The problem here is to determine the amount and type of playground facilities to be provided; but the decision to *provide* for such facilities does not tell us whether they should be supplied by public enterprises or through contract by private construction companies.

To bring out this distinction, we may visualize two economies, one in which all goods are produced by the government and sold on the market, and another in which all goods are produced privately but purchased by the government and distributed free of direct charge. In the former case, there is no provision for public wants, while all production is under public management. In the latter case, there is no public production, but all resources are devoted to provision for public wants. Provision for public wants, therefore, does not require public production management, just as public production management does not require provision for public wants. Quite different criteria apply in determining the proper scope of each.

14

Structures of Educational Government

William P. McLure

This selection describes the multifarious groups that have a hand in making educational policy. Professor McLure is Director of the Bureau of Educational Research, University of Illinois.

If the primary question before this generation concerns the goals of education, a close second must consider the means of attainment or government. What is the form of this institution for the provision of such an important function in society? Where are the difficulties that impede progress, the

Adapted from "Structures of Educational Government: As Viewed by the Educator," in William P. McLure and Van Miller, eds., *Government of Public Education for Adequate Policy Making*, Urbana, University of Illinois Press, 1960, pp. 22–26, 28–33, 38–41. Reproduced with permission.

strengths that facilitate purposes? If the citizens can see its structure, will they understand better the operation of its parts, diagnose its strengths and weaknesses, and determine measures for improvement?

The people of this country face a never-ending task of keeping informed about needed change in both the aims of education and the means of government. Their decisions on these matters are fateful policies and thus demand the highest degree of enlightenment. In the past few years mounting numbers of policies have been proposed for public education in an atmosphere of apparent uncertainty and confusion. A situation of better clarity and firmness with respect to the choices that confront the American public is to be desired.

The system in which policies are made is itself part of the government of education. Citizens must not only comprehend what policies are needed but they must understand the structure of the system, the places where policies are made, and the nature of governmental machinery most likely to accomplish the intended purposes. Structure implies organization, division of work and responsibility, interdependence, and exchange of activities. The American system is a complex form of government in which lurks danger of serious malaise in operation on the one hand and unlimited potential of strength on the other. The deliberations in this conference are motivated by the concern that some crucial needs of education in America too often become obscured because of deficiencies in the structure and operation of educational government.

The most dramatic issues included today in public debate about education do not explicitly relate the central problems associated with aims and purposes to government, or if they do, the treatment of the latter factor is extremely limited. Nevertheless, the existence of a relationship is very real and indigenous to the creation of sound policy, for policy is made and implemented in the governmental process.

. . . .

Description of Educational Government

A large number of groups and individuals with varying responsibility and influence shape the policies that determine the course of public education in this country. Some are legal entities, clothed with either implied or specific powers or both. Others are extralegal or informal in nature, deriving their status from the value and customs of self-government.

For purposes of this discussion a general classification of the types of agents or "pieces of government" has been prepared. These classes group the various agents conveniently for analysis. The formal (legal) and the informal (extralegal) are suitable concepts for dividing all agents into two genotypical categories. Further classification lists them as educational and general[1] agents at

[1] The term "general" is used rather than "political" because some of these agents are not derivatives of the informal partisan political structures.

four levels: the local community, regions, state central units, and the federal government. In some cases the names of particular organizations are used as illustrations. The list follows:

AGENCIES PARTICIPATING IN THE GOVERNMENT OF EDUCATION

Legal Structure	*Extralegal Structure*
I. LOCAL COMMUNITY UNITS	
A. Educational Agents	
1. Public school systems (districts)	1. Professional groups, e.g., teachers' associations
2. Township school trustees (custodians of school funds, property)	2. Parent–teacher associations
	3. Citizens' education advisory committees
B. General Governmental Agents	
1. Municipalities	1. Community planning groups
2. Township officials	2. Civic clubs
3. Local courts	3. Religious groups
4. Law enforcement agents	4. Labor unions
	5. Philanthropic organizations
	6. Political groups
	7. Business groups
II. REGIONAL UNITS	
Intrastate: intermediate between local and state central agents	
A. Educational Agents	
1. County superintendent of schools (26 states)	1. Professional and lay advisory groups
2. District school superintendents (7 states)	
3. Boards of cooperative educational services	
4. Junior college districts	
5. Institutes and technical colleges	
B. General Governmental Agents	
1. County boards of supervisors (26 states)	1. Associations of governmental officials
2. Boards for library services	2. Political groups
3. Agricultural extension service	3. Civic groups
	4. Farm organizations

Interstate: coordinate between states or intermediate between state and federal units

Legal Structure	*Extralegal Structure*
A. Educational Agents	
1. Southern Regional Education Board	1. Associations of public school systems and institutions of higher education for accreditation and other purposes
2. Midwest Inter-Library Center	2. Athletic associations
	3. Councils for research and educational development
B. General Governmental Agents	
1. Public health programs of the federal government	
2. Social security programs of the federal government	

III. STATE CENTRAL UNITS

A. Educational Agents	
1. State department of education (administrative agents)	1. Associations of teachers, and other professional groups
2. State boards of education for vocational education, elementary and secondary education, all public education, all higher education, groups of higher educational institutions, single institutions of higher education, teachers' certification, teachers' retirement system, museums, public libraries	2. Parent–teacher associations
3. Educational commissions for general school problems, scholarships, higher education, educational surveys	3. Associations of school boards
4. School building authorities	4. Citizens' education advisory committees
5. Special institutions for schools for handicapped persons, corrective institutions, vocational and technical schools	
6. Colleges and universities	
B. General Governmental Agents	
1. Legislatures	1. Taxpayers' associations
2. Executive departments for revenue, health, highways	2. Labor unions

3. Courts
4. Commissions for children and youth, athletics, handicapped children

3. Chambers of Commerce
4. Agricultural associations
5. Manufacturers' associations

IV. THE FEDERAL UNIT

A. Educational Agents

1. Department of Health, Education, and Welfare, U.S. Office of Education
2. National Science Foundation

1. National Education Association and affiliates
2. Council of Chief State School Officers
3. American Council on Education
4. Foundations

B. General Governmental Agents

1. Eight departments of cabinet rank
2. Twenty-seven commissions, bureaus, boards, and other agencies

1. White House Conference on Education
2. President's Commission on Education Beyond High School

This list gives some indication of the highly diffused nature of the government of public education in this country. Each of the four levels of government has several agencies with some kind of responsibility for education. In addition numerous informal groups participate actively in educational affairs. An examination of the functions and relationships of these parts will reveal the dominant problems and issues of our time. The points at which policies are needed to solve problems and issues are the places to examine the crucial nature of the governmental structure.

. . . .

STRUCTURE OF BASIC LOCAL DISTRICTS

The structure of local school districts has been caught between two demands. One is a claim of intrinsic needs for organizing students, staffs, and facilities to accomplish educational purposes. The other is to satisfy sociological and political doctrines which place emphasis on the community and its dynamics of operation. Two acute circumstances have existed for some time — the rural, sparsely settled areas and the big metropolitan centers. Today over three-fourths of the youth are in urban centers. Nearly two-thirds are in some nearly 200 metropolitan areas. These centers have special problems of defining the basic administrative unit and in turn arranging the internal structure in relation to effective community organization. The areas of great population sparsity likewise face the difficulty of organizing districts for adequate internal organization of schools with sufficient size to meet educational standards without breaking ties with the community.

All but fourteen states which undertook reorganization of their local school districts consistently have set minimum enrollments too small for these units in sparsely settled areas. Small districts have been combined into larger units but, in the majority of cases, the new ones have fallen so short of what was needed educationally as to lag a quarter of a century or more out of date.

Two good examples are the states of New York and Illinois. A third of a century has passed since New York State embarked on a program of consolidating small rural and village school districts into what were originally called "large" Central Rural (twelve-grade) Districts. That early objective is today almost completed. But within the past decade a second round of reorganization has been under way for these districts which have fewer than 600 pupils in twelve grades. Most of the ones now slated for further reorganization were formed in the early years of this program. Students of administrative organization regard this minimum as far too low for adequate educational purposes. Why, may we ask, do we base such programs of change on concepts of minima that are so soon out of date?

In Illinois, where a reorganization movement started fifteen years ago, about one-third of the geography of the state remains unchanged. In the areas that have been reorganized, 60 per cent of the new districts have fewer than 600 pupils and 90 per cent have fewer than 1,000 pupils. Already, responsible students are saying that these districts are out of date, especially for organizing high schools and post-high school programs. Evidence of this fact is found in action of the Seventy-ninth (1959) General Assembly of Illinois, H.B. 892, permitting consolidation of two or more of the recently reorganized community unit school districts. Will Illinois follow a quarter of a century behind New York in the process and pattern of reconstructing the local district? Will other states like Nebraska, South Dakota, Kansas, and Wisconsin in turn lag behind Illinois? Or will they profit from experience in other states and move directly to more adequate patterns?

The general lag in the reorganization of local school districts may be shown by a few statistics. The U.S. Office of Education reports 127,422 local school districts in 1931–32, 70,993 in 1951–52, and 54,773 in 1955–56. In 1957 the U.S. Bureau of the Census reports 50,446 local districts. Of this number, 7,031 are found in metropolitan areas which have nearly 60 per cent of the total population in the nation. By definition these areas contain some rural territory where the small school problem is fully as acute as it is in the non-metropolitan areas. One-half of all pupils enrolled in public elementary and high schools in this nation are in 2,028 local school districts within metropolitan areas which have more than 1,200 pupils. The number of districts with more than 12,000 pupils in twelve grades is about 281. In short only about 10 per cent of the local school districts in the United States have more than 1,000 pupils. About 60 per cent have fewer than 100 pupils. About half of the student population is in districts with fewer than 3,000 pupils.

The problems associated with reorganization of the local administrative unit of school government are most difficult in the rural and metropolitan areas. In some respects the latter may be attracting more attention at present than the former due to the rapid rate of population growth. The metropolitan community is, as Anderson[2] aptly describes it, "politically amorphous, without structure or unity . . . a community that is not fully a community." At the present time the population growth in the nation is occurring almost entirely in metropolitan areas.

The implications of this trend are tremendous in terms of economic, social, political, educational, and other conditions. In a recent report,[3] the Council of State Governments describes the problem of government in metropolitan areas as "a series of problems." According to this study, the heart of the dilemma is "the absence of general local governmental organizations broad enough to cope with metropolitan matters." They further point out the absence of "area-wide governmental jurisdictions that can effectively provide and finance services, that can plan and regulate and that are constructed to facilitate adequate accountability to the metropolitan public for their actions." They listed four major problems in the series as (1) inadequate structure of local governments, (2) deficiency of services and controls, (3) financial inequalities and weaknesses, and (4) inadequate and ineffective popular control by citizens.

Nearly half of all governmental units in metropolitan areas are for education. Some observers have expressed the opinion that structure of school government in these areas may not be improved until some headway is made toward reducing the large number of overlapping jurisdictions of other governments.

In areas of sparse population the improvement of education depends to a significant degree upon creation of local districts of adequate size along with other factors as good will and interest, financial resources, and adequate personnel. Lack of adequate size of student population is one of the largest structural defects of local district government in these areas. Although many studies on cost-quality relationships have shown finance to be ranked highest as a conditioner, size of student population is a close second to finance.

. . . .

The factor of over-all size of student population is most significant as a condition which affects the capacity of the administrative unit to carry out the educational purposes and to work effectively with the community in

[2] William Anderson, "Political Influences of the Metropolis," *The Metropolis in Modern Life*, ed. Robert Moore Fisher (Garden City, N.Y.: Doubleday and Company, Inc., 1955), pp. 57–8.

[3] Council of State Governments, John C. Bollens, Director, *The States and the Metropolitan Problem* (Chicago: The Council, 1956), p. 17.

meeting the needs of all youth. To apply principles of organization to local districts judged most nearly ideal in relation to size would provide a practical standard for public consideration in examining this whole question. A standard derived in this manner would reveal that most local districts are understaffed both in terms of numbers of personnel and in the pattern of arrangements or division of work. A modern school requires more than a principal and a coterie of teachers with full-time classroom instruction, augmented by a complement of custodians, cooks, and bus drivers. An adequately organized school system requires more than a school or a mere aggregation of schools. It requires additional staff who supplement and integrate the leadership of the schools into a system which can utilize professional skill and the potential of the community most effectively.

One of the myths in organization of local districts is the notion of comparability of schools. Under the restrictions of the autonomous small district structure, schools have been organized on the premise that all things can be done for all students, regardless of the numbers. Such a viewpoint is no longer tenable. The large cities with great masses of population are the only local units which have been able to give much attention to the strategical problem of concentrating programs, services, and schools with varying patterns of curricula to meet the different needs of individuals. This does not mean that the big cities are models. They too have special problems in taking full advantage of the factor of size.

The growth of urbanization does suggest a fundamental need in organization, namely, the creation of regional structures to serve population masses which local units do not reach adequately. This means that big cities need some decentralizing into effective subcommunity structures and the small suburban districts need more centralization. In the sparse areas of the little village and open country, some kind of superstructure or regional unit is needed to centralize certain special programs and services.

. . . .

Structure of State Central Agents for Public Education

At the state level the types of formal and informal agents for governing education are about as numerous as they are at local and regional levels. These agents, together with local and regional units, complete the system known as the state school system. The concept of state responsibility for public education in the United States embraces all of these agents operating within the framework of a total system which is ultimately subject to popular control.

One of the chief difficulties in dealing with the crucial policy issues in education today is the conflict between a literary theory of local self-government and a legal theory of state responsibility. A unitary concept of structural and functional relationships between local, regional, and central units is not easy to comprehend. Relationships among the units are becoming increasingly complex, and as a consequence strong tendencies seem to be shifting the center of control toward state and federal levels of government.

Members of the education profession have generally adhered to the proposition of a large measure of localism in educational government with freedom from strong centralized power at state and federal levels and undue influences from pressure groups in the informal structure. It is impossible here to do more than merely allude to the uneasy balance of these forces in educational government.

A few contemporary developments may illustrate the urgency of a comprehensive re-examination of the whole system of controls on education. Consider, for example, two educational agents: (1) state departments of education commonly assigned regulatory powers over elementary and secondary education, and (2) agents assigned responsibility for operating institutions of higher learning.

What is an effective organization of these agents to cope with the increasing complexity in government? How does practice square with theory? Note the status of these structures as reported recently by the U.S. Office of Education. Each state has a central office or state department of education for general responsibility over elementary and secondary schools. Forty-four of these departments operate under a policy-making board of education. In four states — Florida, Idaho, Montana, and New York — a single board of education has general supervision and control over education at all levels. Eighteen states have two agents, one for public schools and one for higher education. Twenty-six states have three or more state agents.

In Hawaii and Alaska the traditional structures for education have been changed in the transition from territories to statehood. Hawaii's territorial board of education and commissioner of education were both appointed by the governor. The governor still appoints the board, but the board now appoints the commissioner. Alaska did the reverse; although her territorial board of education, which was appointed by the governor, had the authority to appoint the commissioner — and the new state constitution grants the legislature permission to continue this — the legislature of 1959 established an advisory rather than a regulatory state board, with the commissioner as well as the members of the board appointed by the governor. Why the legislature took this action in the light of recent trends in other states to strengthen state school government is difficult to understand.

Some problems are becoming more acute because of the proliferation of state agents of control. A good example is found in the organization of post-high school education at both junior and senior college levels. Some states have assigned junior college programs to the public school system rather than reconstructing the system of higher education for this purpose. In other instances there is an expansion of senior institutions to accommodate increasing enrollments in the professions. In some instances, former teachers colleges have expanded into state universities, often with separate governing boards, thus placing directly in the hands of legislatures decisions at the operational level which could be delegated better to an educational agent for coordination. The issue of a single board for higher education versus independent boards of operating units is still a moot question. Proponents of both systems invoke principles of organization theory with appropriate emphasis to suit their preference. Citizens too become divided according to special identities and loyalties. Thus a rationale for the solution of some major problems tends to become obscured.

State departments of education continue to increase the size of their staffs to discharge the growing volume of responsibility assigned to them by law. The internal structures of these offices reflect the tendency to fragmentize operational units and programs. Some of this practice results from action of special interest groups within the state. Some is induced through action of the federal government in stimulating new programs. As a consequence of these tendencies, there is a need for building new structures both within and among agents to work for coordination and unity of purpose and operation.

Expansion of state departments in recent decades has been done largely to meet the responsibilities for regulatory control and administration of special programs and services. The areas of research and technical consultative services have not expanded sufficiently. States are allowing the initiative for research and experimentation to shift to the federal level. Of course, it is the policy of the U.S. Office of Education to promote and to stimulate more of these activities at the state level in the interest of strengthening leadership there. On the other hand there is reason for concern if external stimulation is not accompanied by internal motivation of great vitality and strength.

The big issues concerning the contribution of the state department of education to the government of education are found by looking first at the nature of changes in functions and processes and second at the needs for revising structure. The state department derives its powers from the same source as does the local district or the regional unit, namely the body of law composed of the statutes and the constitution. The central agent cannot overstep its bounds in relation to the subordinate units. If it does, its actions can be questioned and taken to the courts for adjudication. The processes of government take shape as all legal agents interpret their responsibilities under the law or have them interpreted for them and then act to discharge them.

The design of educational government in both its structure and processes of operation is laid in the body of state law, modified by federal law and interpretations of the courts. In recent years school legislation has reached a state of affairs which is little short of utter confusion and chaos. How can a legislative body deliberate on hundreds of educational bills? It is not uncommon nowadays for most legislatures in regular session to consider from 300 to 500 bills dealing with education. Many of them are designed to correct the squeaks in existing laws. Many are restrictive and inconsistent with fundamental principles of human behavior and of efficiency of operation.

Laws are becoming so complicated as to hamper accomplishment of the ends which they are intended to serve. A study is needed of the extent to which law is encroaching upon judgment and discretion in administration of education. For example, the facts on the extent to which all agents of educational government depend on legal advisers to interpret the law might be shocking. There are few major decisions that a superintendent or a board of education can make confidently without first securing the opinion of a counselor. What is more important is the tendency among local agents to rely heavily on the legal advisers in the state central office because of the sheer mass, conflicts, and ambiguities of the law. And many times the law, as it affects the pupil or the school, is what the adviser says is the law. His interpretation may go unchallenged because of the expense and difficulties involved in following the chain of recourse to the attorney general and then into the courts for final decision. The result is an expenditure of an inordinate amount of human energy finding out what the law says can be done and what cannot be done.

Many thoughtful educators and laymen are fearful that in the mounting volume and complexity of legal machinery sight is being lost of the basic problem of creating arrangements for exercise of more effective public responsibility in making policy with respect to goals and their execution.

Now, to examine the other side of the coin, what are the forces which are creating this apparent swamp of administrative law? Legislatures cannot be charged with insincerity or lack of effort. The major weakness has been the shortage of basic knowledge available to legislatures for designing more effective structures and processes of educational government.

A role of greater dynamic leadership seems to be the trend for the state departments of education. Some developments are occurring in these offices which, if broadened, can have far-reaching effects on improving education in many respects. Of special significance is the current expansion in research and statistical services which is being stimulated partially by federal funds under the National Defense Education Act of 1958. For many years research has been listed by authorities as a prime responsibility of state departments of education, and yet only recently have most states come, by force of circumstance, to understand the implications of this function. Legislatures throughout the country are beginning to grant additional financial support to state departments for development of this function. Although only a few departments have thus far given more than lip service to research, it is possible that bold and imaginative strides will be taken in the future.

There is widespread enthusiasm for establishing high-speed computer systems in state education offices for data processing. Given proper methods and assistance in local and regional units for collection of original data in good form, the possibilities of opening up new knowledge about education are unlimited. To do so, however, will require organization for research beyond the stage of processing descriptive statistics or even conducting studies in these offices. State departments have a unique position in the total educational structure to develop a role of leadership in securing cooperative assistance from colleges and universities, state educational associations, and other groups in pursuing systematic study of many problems.

The current developments in research and data processing in state departments of education may portend a significant change in the role of this office. The power that lies in top-level command of knowledge is demonstrated vividly in business and national defense. Is it too unrealistic to expect the state department of education to serve a unique role in the marshaling of knowledge about education and the means of maintaining a dynamic system of educational government?

15

A Pure Theory of Local Expenditures

Charles M. Tiebout

This penetrating piece of analysis by Professor Tiebout emphasizes the important distinction between services provided by central governments and those supplied by localities. For local services, an element of consumer choice exists, similar in nature to that which is characteristic of private markets.

Local Expenditures

Musgrave . . . implicitly assume[s] that expenditures are handled at the central government level. However, the provision of such governmental services as police and fire protection, education, hospitals, and courts does not necessarily involve federal activity.[1] Many of these goods are provided by local governments. It is worthwhile to look briefly at the magnitude of these expenditures.

Historically, local expenditures have exceeded those of the federal government. The thirties were the first peacetime years in which federal expenditures began to pull away from local expenditures. Even during the fiscal year

Reprinted from "A Pure Theory of Local Expenditures," *Journal of Political Economy*, Volume LXIV, No. 5 (October, 1956), pp. 418–424, by permission of The University of Chicago Press.

[1] The discussion that follows applies to local governments. It will be apparent as the argument proceeds that it also applies, with less force, to state governments.

1954, federal expenditures on *goods and services exclusive of defense* amounted only to some 15 billions of dollars, while local expenditures during this same period amounted to some 17 billions of dollars. There is no need to quibble over which comparisons are relevant. The important point is that the often-neglected local expenditures are significant and, when viewed in terms of expenditures on goods and services only, take on even more significance. Hence an important question arises whether at this level of government any mechanism operates to insure that expenditures on these public goods approximate the proper level.

Consider for a moment the case of the city resident about to move to the suburbs. What variables will influence his choice of a municipality? If he has children, a high level of expenditures on schools may be important. Another person may prefer a community with a municipal golf course. The availability and quality of such facilities and services as beaches, parks, police protection, roads, and parking facilities will enter into the decision-making process. Of course, non-economic variables will also be considered, but this is of no concern at this point.

The consumer-voter may be viewed as picking that community which best satisfies his preference pattern for public goods. This is a major difference between central and local provision of public goods. At the central level the preferences of the consumer-voter are given, and the government tries to adjust to the pattern of these preferences, whereas at the local level various governments have their revenue and expenditure patterns more or less set. Given these revenue and expenditure patterns, the consumer-voter moves to that community whose local government best satisfies his set of preferences. The greater the number of communities and the greater the variance among them, the closer the consumer will come to fully realizing his preference position.

A Local Government Model

The implications of the preceding argument may be shown by postulating an extreme model. Here the following assumptions are made:

1. Consumer-voters are fully mobile and will move to that community where their preference patterns, which are set, are best satisfied.
2. Consumer-voters are assumed to have full knowledge of differences among revenue and expenditure patterns and to react to these differences.
3. There are a large number of communities in which the consumer-voters may choose to live.
4. Restrictions due to employment opportunities are not considered. It may be assumed that all persons are living on dividend income.
5. The public services supplied exhibit no external economies or diseconomies between communities.

Assumptions 6 and 7 to follow are less familiar and require brief explanations:

6. For every pattern of community services set by, say, a city manager who follows the preferences of the older residents of the community, there is an optimal community size. This optimum is defined in terms of the number of residents for which this bundle of services can be produced at the lowest average cost. This, of course, is closely analogous to the low point of a firm's average cost curve. Such a cost function implies that some factor or resource is fixed. If this were not so, there would be no logical reason to limit community size, given the preference patterns. In the same sense that the average cost curve has a minimum for one firm but can be reproduced by another there is seemingly no reason why a duplicate community cannot exist. The assumption that some factor is fixed explains why it is not possible for the community in question to double its size by growth. The factor may be the limited land area of a suburban community, combined with a set of zoning laws against apartment buildings. It may be the local beach, whose capacity is limited. Anything of this nature will provide a restraint.

In order to see how this restraint works, let us consider the beach problem. Suppose the preference patterns of the community are such that the optimum size population is 13,000. Within this set of preferences there is a certain demand per family for beach space. This demand is such that at 13,000 population a 500-yard beach is required. If the actual length of the beach is, say, 600 yards, then it is not possible to realize this preference pattern with twice the optimum population, since there would be too little beach space by 400 yards.

The assumption of a fixed factor is necessary, as will be shown later, in order to get a determinate number of communities. It also has the advantage of introducing a realistic restraint into the model.

7. The last assumption is that communities below the optimum size seek to attract new residents to lower average costs. Those above optimum size do just the opposite. Those at an optimum try to keep their populations constant.

This assumption needs to be amplified. Clearly, communities below the optimum size, through chambers of commerce or other agencies, seek to attract new residents. This is best exemplified by the housing developments in some suburban areas, such as Park Forest in the Chicago area and Levittown in the New York area, which need to reach an optimum size. The same is true of communities that try to attract manufacturing industries by setting up certain facilities and getting an optimum number of firms to move into the industrially zoned area.

The case of the city that is too large and tries to get rid of residents is more difficult to imagine. No alderman in his right political mind would ever admit that the city is too big. Nevertheless, economic forces are at work to push people out of it. Every resident who moves to the suburbs to find better schools, more parks, and so forth, is reacting, in part, against the pattern the city has to offer.

The case of the community which is at the optimum size and tries to remain so is not hard to visualize. Again proper zoning laws, implicit agreements among realtors, and the like are sufficient to keep the population stable.

Except when this system is in equilibrium, there will be a subset of consumer-voters who are discontented with the patterns of their community. Another set will be satisfied. Given the assumption about mobility and the other assumptions listed previously, movement will take place out of the communities of greater than optimal size into the communities of less than optimal size. The consumer-voter moves to the community that satisfies his preference pattern.

The act of moving or failing to move is crucial. Moving or failing to move replaces the usual market test of willingness to buy a good and reveals the consumer-voter's demand for public goods. Thus each locality has a revenue and expenditure pattern that reflects the desires of its residents. The next step is to see what this implies for the allocation of public goods at the local level.

Each city manager now has a certain demand for n local public goods. In supplying these goods, he and $m - 1$ other city managers may be considered as going to a national market and bidding for the appropriate units of service of each kind: so many units of police for the ith community; twice that number for the jth community; and so on. The demand on the public goods market for each of the n commodities will be the sum of the demands of the m communities. In the limit, as shown in a less realistic model to be developed later, this total demand will approximate the demand that represents the true preferences of the consumer-voters — that is, the demand they would reveal, if they were forced, somehow, to state their true preferences. In this model there is no attempt on the part of local governments to "adapt to" the preferences of consumer-voters. Instead, those local governments that attract the optimum number of residents may be viewed as being "adopted by" the economic system.

A Comparison Model

It is interesting to contrast the results of the preceding model with those of an even more severe model in order to see how these results differ from the normal market result. It is convenient to look at this severe model by developing its private-market counterpart. First assume that there are no public goods, only private ones. The preferences for these goods can be expressed as one of n patterns. Let a law be passed that all persons living in any one of the communities shall spend their money in the particular pattern described for that community by law. Given our earlier assumptions 1 through 5, it follows that, if the consumers move to the community whose law happens to fit their preference pattern, they will be at their optimum. The n communities, in turn, will then send their buyers to market to purchase the goods for the consumer-voters in their community. Since this is simply a lumping together of all similar tastes for the purpose of making joint purchases, the allocation of resources will be the same as it would be if normal market forces operated. This conceptual experiment is the equivalent of substituting the city manager for the broker or middleman.

Now turn the argument around and consider only public goods. Assume that the costs of additional services are constant. Further, assume that a doubling of the population means doubling the amount of services required. Let the number of communities be infinite and let each announce a different pattern of expenditures on public goods. Define an empty community as one that fails to satisfy anybody's preference pattern. Given these assumptions, including the earlier assumptions 1 through 5, the consumer-voters will move to that community which *exactly* satisfies their preferences. This must be true, since a one-person community is allowed. The sum of the demands of the n communities reflects the demand for local public services. In this model the demand is exactly the same as it would be if it were determined by normal market forces.

However, this severe model does not make much sense. The number of communities is indeterminate. There is no reason why the number of communities will not be equal to the population, since each voter can find the one that exactly fits his preferences. Unless some sociological variable is introduced, this may reduce the solution of the problem of allocating public goods to the trite one of making each person his own municipal government. Hence this model is not even a first approximation of reality. It is presented to show the assumptions needed in a model of local government expenditures, which yields the same optimal allocation that a private market would.

The Local Government Model Re-examined

The first model, described by the first five assumptions together with assumptions 6 and 7, falls short of this optimum. An example will serve to show why this is the case.

Let us return to the community with the 500-yard beach. By assumption, its optimum population was set at 13,000, given its preference patterns. Suppose that some people in addition to the optimal 13,000 would choose this community if it were available. Since they cannot move into this area, they must accept the next best substitute. If a perfect substitute is found, no problem exists. If one is not found, then the failure to reach the optimal preference position and the substitution of a lower position becomes a matter of degree. In so far as there are a number of communities with similar revenue and expenditure patterns, the solution will approximate the ideal "market" solution.

Two related points need to be mentioned to show the allocative results of this model: (1) changes in the costs of one of the public services will cause changes in the quantity produced; (2) the costs of moving from community to community should be recognized. Both points can be illustrated in one example.

Suppose lifeguards throughout the country organize and succeed in raising their wages. Total taxes in communities with beaches will rise. Now residents who are largely indifferent to beaches will be forced to make a decision. Is the saving of this added tax worth the cost of moving to a community with little or no beach? Obviously, this decision depends on many factors, among which the availability of and proximity to a suitable substitute community is important. If enough people leave communities with beaches and move to communities without beaches, the total amount of lifeguard services used will fall. These models then, unlike their private-market counterpart, have mobility as a cost of registering demand. The higher this cost, *ceteris paribus*, the less optimal the allocation of resources.

This distinction should not be blown out of proportion. Actually, the cost of registering demand comes through the introduction of space into the economy. Yet space affects the allocation not only of resources supplied by local governments but of those supplied by the private market as well. Every time available resources or production techniques change, a new location becomes optimal for the firm. Indeed, the very concept of the shopping trip shows that the consumer does pay a cost to register his demand for private goods. . . .

Thus the problems stated by this model are not unique; they have their counterpart in the private market. We are maximizing within the framework of the resources available. If production functions show constant returns to scale with generally diminishing factor returns, and if indifference curves are regularly convex, an optimal solution is possible. On the production side it is assumed that communities are forced to keep production costs at a minimum either through the efficiency of city managers or through competition from other communities. . . . Just as the consumer may be visualized as walking to a private market place to buy his goods, the prices of which are set, we place him in the position of walking to a community where the prices (taxes) of community services are set. Both trips take the consumer to market. There is no way in which the consumer can avoid revealing his preferences in a spatial economy. Spatial mobility provides the local public-goods counterpart to the private market's shopping trip.

External Economies and Mobility

Relaxing assumption 5 has some interesting implications. There are obvious external economies and diseconomies between communities. My community is better off if its neighbor sprays trees to prevent Dutch elm disease. On the other hand, my community is worse off if the neighboring community has inadequate law enforcement.

In cases in which the external economies and diseconomies are of sufficient importance, some form of integration may be indicated. Not all aspects of law enforcement are adequately handled at the local level. The function of the sheriff, state police, and the FBI — as contrasted with the local police — may be cited as resulting from a need for integration. In real life the diseconomies are minimized in so far as communities reflecting the same socioeconomic preferences are contiguous. Suburban agglomerations such as Westchester, the North Shore, and the Main Line are, in part, evidence of these external economies and diseconomies.

Assumptions 1 and 2 should be checked against reality. Consumer-voters do not have perfect knowledge and set preferences, nor are they perfectly mobile. The question is how do people actually react in choosing a community. There has been very little empirical study of the motivations of people in choosing a community. Such studies as have been undertaken seem to indicate a surprising awareness of differing revenue and expenditure patterns. The general disdain with which proposals to integrate municipalities are met seems to reflect, in part, the fear that local revenue-expenditure patterns will be lost as communities are merged into a metropolitan area.

Policy Implications

The preceding analysis has policy implications for municipal integration, provision for mobility, and set local revenue and expenditure patterns. These implications are worth brief consideration.

On the usual economic welfare grounds, municipal integration is justified only if more of any service is forthcoming at the same total cost and without reduction of any other service. A general reduction of costs along with a reduction in one or more of the services provided cannot be justified on economic grounds unless the social welfare function is known. For example, those who argue for a metropolitan police force instead of local police cannot prove their case on purely economic grounds. If one of the communities were to receive less police protection after integration than it received before, integration could be objected to as a violation of consumers' choice.

Policies that promote residential mobility and increase the knowledge of the consumer-voter will improve the allocation of government expenditures in the same sense that mobility among jobs and knowledge relevant to the location of industry and labor improve the allocation of private resources.

Finally, we may raise the normative question whether local governments *should*, to the extent possible, have a fixed revenue-expenditure pattern. In a large, dynamic metropolis this may be impossible. Perhaps it could more appropriately be considered by rural and suburban communities.

16

Educational Independence and Human Values

Educational Policies Commission

Not all the arguments for local control can be cast in economic terms. This selection touches on a most fundamental point, however, namely, the role that local control plays in preserving freedom of thought.

The pressure of the public services upon the community for revenues has been largely responsible for the rise and growth of a movement for budget reform and for the consolidation of all administrative agencies in a centralized system. Leaders in this movement call attention to the increase in expenditures rendered necessary by the expansion of public services. They point out that as the services have multiplied and outlays have strained the resources available, budget-making and the unification of agencies have become imperative. They insist that since resources are limited and curtailments in expenditures are demanded, all the services seeking places in the budget must be appraised as parts of a common program. Extremists among them propose to make educational administration a mere branch of the general administration, headed by a single political officer, and to treat the school budget as a mere division of the general budget. Besides urging these alterations in the position of the schools, they advocate a thoroughgoing centralization of accounting, purchasing, plant construction, and personnel administration.

Any Adaptations to Schemes of Centralization Are to be Made Within the Limits of Educational Objectives

Educational administrators recognize the exigencies out of which the demand for efficiency and economy has sprung, and the community interests which they are designed to serve. Where it can be demonstrated that there are net advantages in the consolidation or coordination of administrative

Adapted from *The Unique Function of Education in American Democracy*, Washington, National Education Association, 1937, pp. 104–106, 113–119. Reproduced with permission.

operations, it should be effected, insofar as the unique services of education are not thereby impaired. At all times there should be a free exchange of technical experiences and opinions in respect of common administrative processes throughout the entire government; and this exchange will be facilitated as the standards of competence and public responsibility are raised in all branches of government. But in these consultations and efforts in cooperation, school and college authorities are compelled by the obligations of their trusts to safeguard the fundamental nature of the educational function, and to point out with unceasing reiteration its primary and basic character, its intellectual and moral contributions to the maintenance of the society upon which all services depend for their existence and support. Whether it is a question of budget-making, the keeping of accounts, the selection of personnel, the purchase of supplies, or the design and construction of school buildings, the indubitable requirements of education call for fiscal and administrative distinctions fully adapted to the care and training of youth.

This does not mean that educational authorities are or should be indifferent to the demand that school budgets be made and school administration conducted with reference to the total financial situation of the community or of the larger areas to which they may be related. In the best of jurisdictions school budgets are prepared with a view to the requirements of the other services and the financial resources available to all. In these jurisdictions school authorities are well informed respecting the state of general revenues and expenditures and do give to appropriate budget-making officers, as well as to the public, complete information relative to school receipts and outlays. They also seek information on the general situation from fiscal officers and invite from other specially qualified persons and the public a consideration of the tentative educational budget before reaching final determinations. This best practice should be more widely extended. By such processes of developing information and suggestions, the advantages of economy and efficiency may be obtained without surrendering that degree of autonomy necessary to the discharge of educational obligations. Understandings of this character are the more readily effected where school superintendents are well prepared by training and experience for taking leadership in community affairs and for presenting to the public and its official representatives the school budget in terms of the human values covered by its items; and like demands may properly be made upon other administrative officials in their special fields. Herein seems to lie the hope for meeting the legitimate demands for efficiency and economy in general administration while safeguarding the fiduciary trust vested in educational authorities by the American system of government.

. . . .

THERE ARE SPECIAL GROUNDS FOR VIGOROUSLY SUPPORTING EDUCATIONAL INDEPENDENCE

But general principles are not enough. In view of the pressures brought upon the schools by organized minorities, in view of recent legislation questioning the integrity and loyalty of teachers, in view of recent political interference with professional appointments and dismissals, in view of the demand that education be placed immediately under the financial control of executive and legislative authorities, it is necessary to go into details. Why does public policy assign a high degree of independence to education?

SCIENTIFIC INSTRUCTION IS INDEPENDENT OF POLITICS

With respect to technical and scientific subjects of instruction in the schools, especially those related to the practical arts, education is in fact independent of political turnovers at the polls. The rule applies to mathematics, the natural sciences, and many elements of studies less exact in nature. The swings of popular majorities do not affect the validity of the multiplication table. The law of gravitation operates under Democratic as well as Republican or Socialist administrations. The conjugation of English and Spanish verbs is not ousted by an incoming party fresh from victory. If in a moment of excitement a legislature should order the schools to teach that the world is flat, educational administration cannot obey, if it is to be loyal to knowledge and truth. Where it is necessary to formulate a curriculum adapted to the demands of the practical arts or community needs of any kind, the selections to be made, the methods to be adopted, and the organization to be effected must be entrusted to those having technical competence, if the very ends of instruction are not to be defeated. However able political executives and legislatures may be, they can do no more than lay down general principles of educational policy and must entrust specifications to educational authorities.

THE HUMANITIES HAVE THEIR INDEPENDENT IMPERATIVES

In the domain of the humanities — literature, the fine arts, economics, political science, and sociology, for example — the prescriptions of the subject matter are less exact than in languages and the natural sciences; but even in this domain there are immense bodies of authentic and exact knowledge which competence and loyalty to truth must take into the reckoning. Even to enumerate them requires an encyclopedia; for instance, the *Encyclopedia of the Social Sciences*. But illustration may be given. The prices of commodities, the wages of labor, and the costs of industrial insurance are not accidents, wholly subject to legislative fiat, irrespective of prevailing conditions. If they were, the Congress of the United States, or at all events a sovereign constitutional body could, by mere resolution, make everybody rich.

In human affairs, no less than in the astro-physical universe, there are some necessities by which even sovereign political force is limited. Although these necessities are not as clear and positive as in the physical world, political policy must take account of them and accept their requirements, at least in the long run. Competence has not yet reduced them to an exact science, but competence alone is fitted to explore and set forth their boundaries. Hence it must be said in the broad field of the humanities, where differences of opinion do appear, there are many findings sustained by the general consensus of competence. These findings do not dictate policy to political authorities, but they do set limits to the operations, methods, and results of policy. For this reason even partisanship must allow a high degree of liberty to inquiry and teaching in the humanities, unless it is totally indifferent to the outcomes of its own determinations. Although it is difficult to make this as clear to the heedless as the exigencies of the multiplication table, intelligence is fully aware of it, at least in sober moments.

The Teaching of Controversial Questions Calls for Judicial Prerogatives

Into cultural subjects, such as history and economics, new ideas, or ideas foreign to the accepted thought and practice of the community, inevitably come, unless the subjects are deliberately distorted. For example, it is impossible to teach European history as truth without considering the diverse types of political, social, and economic theory and practice which have appeared in that history as fact. To state and describe those theories and practices with exactness and balance requires expertness of a high order and a scientific spirit foreign to the passionate disputes of partisan debate. Not even the ablest student of the subject will claim infallibility or the possession of "the whole truth." But certainly the informed and disciplined mind can come nearer to the ideal type of fair and balanced instruction in such difficult subjects than the uninformed mind inflamed by partisan or sectarian passions.

. . . .

Preparation for Citizenship Transcends All Partisan Limits

There are wider and more secure reasons for a high degree of educational autonomy than the exigencies of mere competent instruction in the natural sciences and the social studies. They lie in the process of democratic government itself. These processes, as already indicated, involve freedom of citizens to propose measures of government, liberty of discussion, unawed and unbought decisions on policies and measures, and continuous reexamination and appraisal of their results. These processes call for knowledge and an attitude of mind which are indispensable to the endurance of democracy. To acquire, preserve, and disseminate such knowledge is a primary function of education.

It is likewise the bounden duty of education to give that mental training which prepares the people for discussion in an informed and equitable spirit, and for the acceptance of popular decisions without resort to force, "the parent of despotism."

In the higher ranges of public education, issues of current society must come into instruction unless it is to be sterile and false to life. Here under the direction of trained and competent teachers pupils may be taught to look all around modern problems, to examine the points of view from which discussion proceeds, to acquire knowledge, to learn the assumptions on which decisions depend, and to develop that even temper so necessary to the preservation of democratic institutions. When the processes and ends of our democratic society are placed above the exigencies of partisan politics and the immediate advantages of power, then it becomes evident that education as a safeguard and preparation for democratic living must not be subjected every hour and in every way to the unrestrained control of men and women lifted into political office for a brief term by the fortunes of campaigns and elections.

To Education Are Entrusted Enduring Interests and Values

Beyond this argument it seems impossible to go. Yet one more step seems necessary. Owing to the nature of popular usage, there is danger that the term *democratic society* be taken too narrowly, in a mere political sense. Society is more than politics. It embraces all culture. And democracy implies the widest possible diffusion of culture and all the means essential to the good life. Committed by its historical and immediate obligations to cherishing and advancing the funded wisdom, knowledge, and aspirations of the race, education carries responsibilities which outrun the fortunes of annual, biennial, or quadrennial elections, the ups and downs of parties, the twists and turns of public opinion. In a literal sense, education is rooted in eternity, despite its proper affiliation with temporal events. It is concerned with all the humane interests which shape society, government, and public policies, and give richness to individual life. The very nature of such obligations and undertakings accords to education in the United States a special position among the administrative services of government.

17

State Control of Education

Henry C. Morrison

It is rare that a professional educator takes an unequivocal position in favor of centralization of school administration. This the late Professor Morrison of the University of Chicago did. It cannot be denied that his arguments are strong ones.

It has been suggested that the political concept behind the local control of schools is perhaps more important than the visible school district itself. It is part and parcel of our devotion to Local Government. It is well to be clear about that concept itself, to see what it is and what it is not.

In practice we are likely to confuse Local Government with two other concepts which in reality have nothing to do with it. These are Municipal Self-government and State Sovereignty. All three are commonly lumped together as being the same thing by journalists and candidates for office. Let us take the last first and work backward.

State Sovereignty is a fundamental fact and principle in our Federal Republic. It means that certain sovereign powers are specifically committed to the Federal Government and others reserved to the several States. We thus have Federal Government and Government in forty-eight States in a dual sovereignty, but some of our lives and activities are regulated by one of the sovereigns and the rest by the other. That is all the Government we have. Town, city, and county governments are creatures of the States. State Government is not a form of local government; it is Commonwealth Government.

Local self-government, on the other hand, refers to the principle that matters which concern a given local community, and in their nature do not concern any other community, are left to the incorporated municipality to provide for and administer. That is Municipal Government proper, and it is the same thing when it is carried out by a township, an incorporated village, or a county, as it is when it is operated by a chartered city. Illustrations of

Reprinted by permission of The University of Chicago Press, from *American Schools*, by Henry C. Morrison; Chicago, University of Chicago Press, 1943, pp. 260–266, 282–283, 304–305.

Municipal Government are found in the maintenance of fire departments, streets and sewers, public parks, and enactment of ordinances to govern existence within the municipality as such. Traffic regulations and sanitary ordinances are good illustrations.

Local Government, however, as we are accustomed to the term, means the commitment of affairs which are admittedly Civil in their nature and not Municipal, that is to say, which are of the State and affect everybody in the State and often in other States as well, to the several counties and municipalities. We say that they are State affairs locally administered by *locally-chosen* officers. Instances in most States are the prevention and punishment of crime as distinguished from misdemeanors, the care of the public health, the maintenance of courts for the trial of both civil and criminal cases, the registering of deeds, the probating of wills, and especially the maintenance of Public Instruction. The tendency, no doubt, is to transfer these Civil functions to the State Government where they belong, but the process lingers unduly.

All the foregoing Local Government, not local self-government but Government locally conducted, has been part of our theory of Government itself. In point of fact, it is tradition handed down from other days, other conditions, and another kind of society. Some of it comes down to us from Medieval England and indeed from Anglo-Saxon England. In our country the tradition goes back to frontier days, isolated communities, and poor transportation, and then there was reason for it. There could be no central State administration of Civil affairs, when communication was so slow that even in the smaller States not even a message could be got through to the seat of Government and an answer received under several days at the best. Constabulary had to be local if criminals were to be apprehended at all. Courts had to be locally provided for, since it would be intolerable for litigants to be obliged to travel to a remote city in quest of justice.

These were all reasonable grounds for Local Government; but it is more than likely that other grounds were the main motive, or at least would have been motive if there had been no good geographical reasons. Here, again, is particularism in all public affairs as well as in those of the schools, and out of particularist interests and attitudes came intense suspicion of any kind of central Government. But keeping Government "in the hands of the people" meant not Commonwealth democracy but rather keeping it in their own hands and those of their neighbors. There may be something admirable in that, for it at least meant a willingness to assume the responsibilities of Government. That is the generous way to look at it all. More cynically, one may suspect that it arose out of an overweening love of having one's fingers in every pie. So long as conditions persisted in which tradition originated, and so long as the population was mainly British in origin, it worked fairly well, or at least not ill, and more than one chapter might be written showing how it did contribute to the secure foundations of the Republic.

. . . .

The school district is simply an extreme and special case of Local Government, and the subtownship district an ultra-extreme case.

Dillon in *Municipal Corporations* has this to say about school districts large and small:

> An incorporated city or town sometimes embraces by legislative provision two *distinct corporations*, as, for example, the municipal and the school corporations existing within the same territory. It is in such cases a distinct corporation for school purposes. . . . More generally, however, *school districts* are organized under the general law of the State, and fall within the class of corporations known as *quasi*-corporations. . . . It [the school district] is but an instrumentality of the State, and the State incorporates it that it may the more effectively discharge its appointed duties.

This corporate character has important consequences in the whole popular conception of the School and in the manner in which schools are carried on.

In the first place, let the legal theory be what it may, the corporate character of the school district makes the School as enterprise conform to the ideology of a communally-supported undertaking maintained for the benefit of citizens who have children of pupillary age, and the School as an instrumentality of the Commonwealth falls into the background and is forgotten. It becomes hard for people to understand the School as an institution or to see it as anything else than a public enterprise set up for their special benefit, conducted according to their ideas and desires in curriculum, methods of teaching, and extra-curricular activities. Hence it is notoriously easy for ill-considered and even nonsensical instruction to invade the schools and divert them entirely not only from their general social function but from their civil purpose as well, under the eloquent leadership of an army of quacks who no doubt make the most enthusiastic gland doctor green with envy.

Second, while the indubitable civil function of the schools is analogous to those of the courts, the civil service, and the Army and Navy, that is to say, the function of an instrument of democratic Government, the corporate character puts teachers and school officers in the status of labor under contract. We do not contract with the servants of the State and Federal Governments: we elect them or appoint them or enlist them. A formidable body of law has grown up around the contractual relations of teachers.

One of the most unfortunate consequences is the universal tendency of the best teachers to drift into the wealthier districts and into those in which the teaching is easiest. The effect is that the districts which have but slender fiscal resources, and those in which teaching is most difficult — and which by consequence need good teaching most — have to put up with relatively inferior and frequently incompetent teaching. We do not allow the wealthier and more comfortable sections to monopolize the best judges, nor do we reserve the most desirable Army and Navy service to the best soldiers and seamen.

. . . .

INEQUALITY IN RESOURCES

The absurdity of the school-district form of managing and supporting schools has chiefly appeared in works which exhibit and analyze gross inequalities in the money resources of the several districts in all the States which still have the system. That attack runs back fifty years and longer. It is perhaps the most critical problem of all, or at least the most immediate.

Most of the States have essayed the task of correcting the evils by the apportionment of State school aid according to some mathematical formula. I have shown that any such policy involves a mathematical absurdity.[1] The only way in which inequalities in support, and other inequalities as well, can be eliminated is through consolidation of management and support in the State Government itself, even as the cities have similarly abolished their own internal inequalities.

But even if we could find a formula which would accomplish all our mathematical aspirations, so that the resources per child to be schooled would be on a parity throughout the State, and so that money could be thrown into each district according to the varying *instructional* requirements of children, and so that the tax burdens in all of several thousand school districts would also be on a parity, it does not follow that *educational* opportunities would be made equal. That depends upon the quality of the supervisory and teaching personnel that can be secured, and the latter in turn upon the qualities of the school-board members who are available in the several districts. Moreover, mere equalization of educational opportunity gets us nowhere. The education may be meager, misdirected, quite without validity. . . .

The sum of the whole matter seems plainly to be that the school-district system itself is so obsolete, so far removed from the society in which it was once valid, that it has become an incurable malady in our commonwealths.

. . . .

THE STATE UNIT

The national problem in Public Instruction in the second quarter of the twentieth century, or any other century, is in fundamentals no different from what it was in the second quarter of the seventeenth in Colonial Massachusetts. It is the transmission of Civilization to the whole generation of children and young people who are presently to be part of our body politic.

The problem does not countenance a solution which merely provides for schools which may follow any courses which the vagaries, or the fads, or the ignorance, or the poverty of each of a hundred and fifty thousand different school boards and teaching bodies may dictate. The solution is positive and definitive, not opinionative and wilful and indeterminate. The task is not

[1] See *School Revenue*, chap. viii and esp. Sec. V.

one of making it legally and fiscally possible for each of a multitude of local communities "to give *an* education suited to their needs" — or what they think are their needs and what is suited — but rather to guarantee that, so far as is humanly possible and in so far as circumstances do not prohibit, all children shall be put in possession of full General Education.

. . . .

If there were no body of accumulated experience, as there is, it would still be inferable from the premises themselves that the task of guaranteeing General Education to all implies a unit for the government, administration, and support of schools which is coextensive with the sovereignty which undertakes the guaranty — a unit which is headed by an executive and administrative authority which is supreme in its functions throughout the area and in control of a fiscal system which is capable of directly reaching every school. In our Federal Republic the smallest unit which is capable of being used for the purpose is each one of our sovereign States.

Such an authority is, in our present use of terms, a State Board of Education.

. . . .

It has hitherto several times been noted that one of the troublesome anomalies which the obsolete district system has carried with it is the contractual status of teachers, principals, and other school officers. Contract for personal services in the schools goes back to a time when the maintenance of schools was felt to be parallel to the conduct of any private enterprise. Teachers were "hired to teach" the coming term very much as hands were hired on the farm or a ship's company signed on for a voyage. The churches under which the regime grew up similarly hired their clergy, although a parish might in time go through the process of "settling the minister." Even so the minister seldom had any protection against a domineering deacon or bossy woman in the congregation.

All that has long been forgotten, especially in the cities; nevertheless, status remains. Once more the form abides, although substance has for the most part been lost.

It is pretty hard to get that wholly desirable *esprit de corps* called "devotion to the service" unless the service be on a State or Federal basis. In a local contract for teaching there is simply a job to the fore, and if a job, then a better job soon. Where the teaching position is subject to annual contract, or annual appointment, and all the neighborhood is engaged in expressing opinion about the teacher's methods and personal character, there will not likely ever be good methods or really self-respecting teachers.

Assuming, on the other hand, that the State School Unit were in operation, administered by a State Board of Education having also control of the instrumentalities for training teachers, the whole picture changes.

The State Unit implies a State Teaching Force, the pay of which is not a matter of contract but rather depends upon a regular salary schedule for all teachers in a class wherever they teach, with such local adjustments, also part of the schedule, as the Board may find expedient. It implies that school people shall receive their checks directly from the treasurer of the Board, who may also be the State Treasurer, and not be subject to the financial naïveté of city officials who periodically set up the institution of payless paydays, sometimes to the unconcern of a State court which has to be engaged in the administration of a school system by litigation.

18

The Role of Government in Education

Milton Friedman

Professor Friedman of the Department of Economics, University of Chicago, is known as a supporter of the position that the influence of the market economy should be extended whenever possible. Here he applies his tools of analysis to the case of elementary and secondary education.

The role assigned to government in any particular field depends, of course, on the principles accepted for the organization of society in general. In what follows, I shall assume a society that takes freedom of the individual, or more realistically the family, as its ultimate objective, and seeks to further this objective by relying primarily on voluntary exchange among individuals for the organization of economic activity. In such a free private enterprise exchange economy, government's primary role is to preserve the rules of the game by enforcing contracts, preventing coercion, and keeping markets free. Beyond this, there are only three major grounds on which government intervention is to be justified. One is "natural monopoly" or similar market imperfection which makes effective competition (and therefore thoroughly vol-

Adapted from "The Role of Government in Education," in Robert A. Solo, ed., *Economics and the Public Interest*, New Brunswick, N.J., Rutgers University Press, 1955, pp. 123–142.

untary exchange) impossible. A second is the existence of substantial "neighborhood effects," i.e., the action of one individual imposes significant costs on other individuals for which it is not feasible to make him compensate them or yields significant gains to them for which it is not feasible to make them compensate him — circumstances that again make voluntary exchange impossible. The third derives from an ambiguity in the ultimate objective rather than from the difficulty of achieving it by voluntary exchange, namely, paternalistic concern for children and other irresponsible individuals. The belief in freedom is for "responsible" units, among whom we include neither children nor insane people. In general, this problem is avoided by regarding the family as the basic unit and therefore parents as responsible for their children; in considerable measure, however, such a procedure rests on expediency rather than principle. The problem of drawing a reasonable line between action justified on these paternalistic grounds and action that conflicts with the freedom of responsible individuals is clearly one to which no satisfactory answer can be given.

In applying these general principles to education, we shall find it helpful to deal separately with (1) general education for citizenship, and (2) specialized vocational education, although it may be difficult to draw a sharp line between them in practice. The grounds for government intervention are widely different in these two areas and justify very different types of action.

General Education for Citizenship

A stable and democratic society is impossible without widespread acceptance of some common set of values and without a minimum degree of literacy and knowledge on the part of most citizens. Education contributes to both. In consequence, the gain from the education of a child accrues not only to the child or to his parents but to other members of the society; the education of my child contributes to other people's welfare by promoting a stable and democratic society. Yet it is not feasible to identify the particular individuals (or families) benefited or the money value of the benefit and so to charge for the services rendered. There is therefore a significant "neighborhood effect."

What kind of governmental action is justified by this particular neighborhood effect? The most obvious is to require that each child receive a minimum amount of education of a specified kind. Such a requirement could be imposed upon the parents without further government action, just as owners of buildings, and frequently of automobiles, are required to adhere to specified standards to protect the safety of others. There is, however, a difference between the two cases. In the latter, individuals who cannot pay the costs of meeting the required standards can generally divest themselves of the property in question by selling it to others who can, so the requirement can readily be enforced without government subsidy — though even here, if the cost of making the property safe exceeds its market value, and the owner is without resources, the government may be driven to paying for the demolition of a dangerous building or the disposal of an abandoned automobile. The separation of a child from a parent who cannot pay for the minimum required education is clearly inconsistent with our reliance on the family as the basic social unit and our belief in the freedom of the individual.

. . . .

Government subsidy of only certain kinds of education can be justified on these grounds. To anticipate, they do not justify subsidizing purely vocational education which increases the economic productivity of the student but does not train him for either citizenship or leadership. It is clearly extremely difficult to draw a sharp line between these two types of education. Most general education adds to the economic value of the student — indeed it is only in modern times and in a few countries that literacy has ceased to have a marketable value. And much vocational education broadens the student's outlook. Yet it is equally clear that the distinction is a meaningful one. For example, subsidizing the training of veterinarians, beauticians, dentists, and a host of other specialized skills — as is widely done in the United States in governmentally supported educational institutions — cannot be justified on the same grounds as subsidizing elementary education or, at a higher level, liberal education. Whether it can be justified on quite different grounds is a question that will be discussed later in this paper.

The qualitative argument from the "neighborhood effect" does not, of course, determine the specific kinds of education that should be subsidized or by how much they should be subsidized. The social gain from education is presumably greatest for the very lowest levels of education, where there is the nearest approach to unanimity about the content of the education, and declines continuously as the level of education rises. But even this statement cannot be taken completely for granted — many governments subsidized universities long before they subsidized lower education. What forms of education have the greatest social advantage and how much of the community's limited resources should be spent on them are questions to be decided by the judgment of the community expressed through its accepted political channels. The role of an economist is not to decide these questions for the community but rather to clarify the issues to be judged by the community in making a choice, in particular, whether the choice is one that it is appropriate or necessary to make on a communal rather than individual basis.

We have seen that both the imposition of a minimum required level of education and the financing of education by the state can be justified by the "neighborhood effects" of education. It is more difficult to justify in these terms a third step that has generally been taken, namely, the actual administration of educational institutions by the government, the "nationalization," as it were, of the bulk of the "education industry." The desirability of such nationalization has seldom been faced explicitly because governments have in the main financed education by paying directly the costs of running educational institutions, so that this step has seemed required by the decision to subsidize education. Yet the two steps could readily be separated. Governments could require a minimum level of education which they could finance by giving parents vouchers redeemable for a specified maximum sum per child per year if spent on "approved" educational services. Parents would then be free to spend this sum and any additional sum on purchasing educational services from an "approved" institution of their own choice. The educational services could be rendered by private enterprises operated for profit, or by non-profit institutions of various kinds. The role of the government would be limited to assuring that the schools met certain minimum standards such as the inclusion of a minimum common content in their programs, much as it now inspects restaurants to assure that they maintain minimum sanitary standards. An excellent example of a program of this sort is the United States educational program for veterans after World War II. Each veteran who qualified was given a maximum sum per year that could be spent at any institution of his choice, provided it met certain minimum standards. A more limited example is the provision in Britain whereby local authorities pay the fees of some students attending non-state schools (the so-called "public schools"). Another is the arrangement in France whereby the state pays part of the costs for students attending non-state schools.

One argument from the "neighborhood effect" for nationalizing education is that it might otherwise be impossible to provide the common core of values deemed requisite for social stability. The imposition of minimum standards on privately conducted schools, as suggested above, might not be enough to achieve this result. The issue can be illustrated concretely in terms of schools run by religious groups. Schools run by different religious groups will, it can be argued, instill sets of values that are inconsistent with one another and with those instilled in other schools; in this way they convert education into a divisive rather than a unifying force.

Carried to its extreme, this argument would call not only for governmentally administered schools, but also for compulsory attendance at such schools. Existing arrangements in the United States and most other Western countries are a halfway house. Governmentally administered schools are available but not required. However, the link between the financing of education and its administration places other schools at a disadvantage: they get the benefit of little or none of the governmental funds spent on education — a situation that has been the source of much political dispute, particularly, of course, in France. The elimination of this disadvantage might, it is feared, greatly strengthen the parochial schools and so render the problem of achieving a common core of values even more difficult.

This argument has considerable force. But it is by no means clear either that it is valid or that the denationalizing of education would have the effects suggested. On grounds of principle, it conflicts with the preservation of freedom itself; indeed, this conflict was a major factor retarding the development of state education in England. How draw a line between providing for the common social values required for a stable society on the one hand, and indoctrination inhibiting freedom of thought and belief on the other? Here is another of those vague boundaries that it is easier to mention than to define.

In terms of effects, the denationalization of education would widen the range of choice available to parents. Given, as at present, that parents can send their children to government schools without special payment, very few can or will send them to other schools unless they too are subsidized. Parochial schools are at a disadvantage in not getting any of the public funds devoted to education; but they have the compensating advantage of being run by institutions that are willing to subsidize them and can raise funds to do so, whereas there are few other sources of subsidies for schools. Let the subsidy be made available to parents regardless where they send their children — provided only that it be to schools that satisfy specified minimum standards — and a wide variety of schools will spring up to meet the demand. Parents could express their views about schools directly, by withdrawing their children from one school and sending them to another, to a much greater extent than is now possible. In general, they can now take this step only by simultaneously changing their place of residence. For the rest, they can express their views only through cumbrous political channels. Perhaps a somewhat greater degree of freedom to choose schools could be made available also in a governmentally administered system, but it is hard to see how it could be carried very far in view of the obligation to provide every child with a place. Here, as in other fields, competitive private enterprise is likely to be far more efficient in meeting consumer demands than either nationalized enterprises or enterprises run to serve other purposes. The final result may therefore well be less rather than more parochial education.

Another special case of the argument that governmentally conducted schools are necessary to keep education a unifying force is that private schools would tend to exacerbate class distinctions. Given greater freedom about where to send their children, parents of a kind would flock together and so prevent a healthy intermingling of children from decidedly different backgrounds. Again, whether or not this argument is valid in principle, it is not at all clear that the stated results would follow. Under present arrangements, particular schools tend to be peopled by children with similar backgrounds, thanks to the stratification of residential areas. In addition, parents are not now prevented from sending their children to private schools. Only a highly limited class can or does do so, parochial schools aside, in the process producing further stratification. The widening of the range of choice under a private system would operate to reduce both kinds of stratification.

Another argument for nationalizing education is "natural monopoly." In small communities and rural areas, the number of children may be too small to justify more than one school of reasonable size, so that competition cannot be relied on to protect the interests of parents and children. As in other cases of natural monopoly, the alternatives are unrestricted private monopoly, state-controlled private monopoly, and public operation — a choice among evils. This argument is clearly valid and significant, although its force has been greatly weakened in recent decades by improvements in transportation and increasing concentration of the population in urban communities.

The arrangement that perhaps comes closest to being justified by these considerations — at least for primary and secondary education — is a mixed one under which governments would continue to administer some schools but parents who chose to send their children to other schools would be paid a sum equal to the estimated cost of educating a child in a government school, provided that at least this sum was spent on education in an approved school. This arrangement would meet the valid features of the "natural monopoly" argument, while at the same time it would permit competition to develop where it could. It would meet the just complaints of parents that if they send their children to private nonsubsidized schools they are required to pay twice for education — once in the form of general taxes and once directly — and in this way stimulate the development and improvement of such schools. The interjection of competition would do much to promote a healthy variety of schools. It would do much, also, to introduce flexibility into school systems. Not least of its benefits would be to make the salaries of school teachers responsive to market forces. It would thereby give governmental educational authorities an independent standard against which to judge salary scales and promote a more rapid adjustment to changes in conditions of demand or supply.[1]

• • • •

[1] Essentially this proposal — public financing but private operation of education — has recently been suggested in several southern states as a means of evading the Supreme Court ruling against segregation. This fact came to my attention after this paper was essentially in its present form. My initial reaction — and, I venture to predict, that of most readers — was that this possible use of the proposal was a count against it, that it was a particularly striking case of the possible defect — the exacerbating of class distinctions — referred to in the second paragraph preceding the one to which this note is attached.

Further thought has led me to reverse my initial reaction. Principles can be tested most clearly by extreme cases. Willingness to permit free speech to people with whom one agrees is hardly evidence of devotion to the principle of free speech; the relevant test is willingness to permit free speech to people with whom one thoroughly disagrees. Similarly, the relevant test of the belief in individual freedom is the willingness to oppose state intervention even when it is designed to prevent individual activity of a kind one thoroughly dislikes. I deplore segregation and racial prejudice; pursuant to the principles set forth at the outset of the paper, it is clearly an appropriate function of the state to prevent the use of violence and physical coercion by one group on another; equally clearly, it is not an appropriate function of the state to try to force individuals to act in accordance with my — or anyone else's — views, whether about racial prejudice or the party to vote for, so long as the action of any one individual affects mostly himself. These are the grounds on which I oppose the proposed Fair Employment Practices Commissions; and they lead me equally to oppose forced nonsegregation. However, the same grounds also lead me to oppose

Many detailed administrative problems would arise in changing over from the present to the proposed system and in administering the proposed system. But these seem neither insoluble nor unique. As in the denationalization of other activities, existing premises and equipment could be sold to private enterprises that wanted to enter the field, so there would be no waste of capital in the transition. The fact that governmental units, at least in some areas, were going to continue to administer schools would permit a gradual and easy transition. The localized administration of education in the United States and some other countries would similarly facilitate the transition, since it would encourage experimentation on a small scale and with alternative methods of handling both these and other problems. Difficulties would doubtless arise in determining eligibility for grants from a particular governmental unit, but this is identical with the existing problem of determining which unit is obligated to provide educational facilities for a particular child. Differences in size of grants would make one area more attractive than another just as differences in the quality of education now have the same effect. The only additional complication is a possibly greater opportunity for abuse because of the greater freedom to decide where to educate children. Supposed difficulty of administration is a standard defense of the *status quo* against any proposed changes; in this particular case, it is an even weaker defense than usual because existing arrangements must master not only the major problems raised by the proposed arrangements but also the additional problems raised by the administration of the schools as a governmental function.

. . . .

---

forced segregation. Yet, so long as the schools are publicly operated, the only choice is between forced nonsegregation and forced segregation; and if I must choose between these evils, I would choose the former as the lesser. The fact that I must make this choice is a reflection of the basic weakness of a publicly operated school system. Privately conducted schools can resolve the dilemma. They make unnecessary either choice. Under such a system, there can develop exclusively white schools, exclusively colored schools, and mixed schools. Parents can choose which to send their children to. The appropriate activity for those who oppose segregation and racial prejudice is to try to persuade others of their views; if and as they succeed, the mixed schools will grow at the expense of the nonmixed, and a gradual transition will take place. So long as the school system is publicly operated, only drastic change is possible; one must go from one extreme to the other; it is a great virtue of the private arrangement that it permits a gradual transition.

An example that comes to mind as illustrating the preceding argument is summer camps for children. Is there any objection to the simultaneous existence of some camps that are wholly Jewish, some wholly non-Jewish, and some mixed? One can — though many who would react quite differently to Negro-white segregation would not — deplore the existence of attitudes that lead to the three types; one can seek to propagate views that would tend to the growth of the mixed school at the expense of the extremes; but is it an appropriate function of the state to prohibit the unmixed camps?

The establishment of private schools does not of itself guarantee the desirable freedom of choice on the part of parents. The public funds could be made available subject to the condition that parents use them solely in segregated schools; and it may be that some such condition is contained in the proposals now under consideration by southern states. Similarly, the public funds could be made available for use solely in nonsegregated schools. The proposed plan is not therefore inconsistent with either forced segregation or forced nonsegregation. The point is that it makes available a third alternative.

The adoption of such arrangements would make for more effective competition among various types of schools and for a more efficient utilization of their resources. It would eliminate the pressure for direct government assistance to private colleges and universities and thus preserve their full independence and diversity at the same time that it enabled them to grow relatively to State institutions. It might also have the ancillary advantage of causing a closer scrutiny of the purposes for which subsidies are granted. The subsidization of institutions rather than of people has led to an indiscriminate subsidization of whatever activities it is appropriate for such institutions to undertake, rather than of the activities it is appropriate for the state to subsidize. Even cursory examination suggests that while the two classes of activities overlap, they are far from identical.

Vocational or Professional Education

As noted above, vocational or professional education has no neighborhood effects of the kind attributed above to general education. It is a form of investment in human capital precisely analogous to investment in machinery, buildings, or other forms of non-human capital. Its function is to raise the economic productivity of the human being. If it does so, the individual is rewarded in a free enterprise society by receiving a higher return for his services than he would otherwise be able to command.[2] This difference is the economic incentive to acquire the specialized training, just as the extra return that can be obtained with an extra machine is the economic incentive to invest capital in the machine. In both cases, extra returns must be balanced against the costs of acquiring them. For vocational education, the major costs are the income foregone during the period of training, interest lost by postponing the beginning of the earning period, and special expenses of acquiring the training such as tuition fees and expenditures on books and equipment. For physical capital, the major costs are the expenses of constructing the capital equipment and the interest during construction. In both cases, an individual presumably regards the investment as desirable if the extra returns, as he views them, exceed the extra costs, as he views them. In both cases, if the individual undertakes the investment and if the state neither subsidizes the investment nor taxes the return, the individual (or his parent, sponsor, or benefactor) in general bears all the extra cost and receives all the extra returns: there are no obvious unborne costs or unappropriable returns that tend to make private incentives diverge systematically from those that are socially appropriate.

If capital were as readily available for investment in human beings as for investment in physical assets, whether through the market or through direct

[2] The increased return may be only partly in a monetary form; it may also consist of non-pecuniary advantages attached to the occupation for which the vocational training fits the individual. Similarly, the occupation may have non-pecuniary disadvantages, which would have to be reckoned among the costs of the investment.

investment by the individuals concerned or their parents or benefactors, the rate of return on capital would tend to be roughly equal in the two fields: if it were higher on non-human capital, parents would have an incentive to buy such capital for their children instead of investing a corresponding sum in vocational training, and conversely. In fact, however, there is considerable empirical evidence that the rate of return on investment in training is very much higher than the rate of return on investment in physical capital. According to estimates that Simon Kuznets and I have made elsewhere, professionally trained workers in the United States would have had to earn during the 1930's at most 70 per cent more than other workers to cover the extra costs of their training, including interest at roughly the market rate on non-human capital. In fact, they earned on the average between two and three times as much. Some part of this difference may well be attributable to greater natural ability on the part of those who entered the professions: it may be that they would have earned more than the average non-professional worker if they had not gone into the professions. Kuznets and I concluded, however, that such differences in ability could not explain anything like the whole of the extra return of the professional workers. Apparently, there was sizable underinvestment in human beings. The postwar period has doubtless brought changes in the relative earnings in different occupations. It seems extremely doubtful, however, that they have been sufficiently great to reverse this conclusion.

It is not certain at what level this underinvestment sets in. It clearly applies to professions requiring a long period of training, such as medicine, law, dentistry, and the like, and probably to all occupations requiring a college training. At one time, it almost certainly extended to many occupations requiring much less training but probably no longer does, although the opposite has sometimes been maintained.

This underinvestment in human capital presumably reflects an imperfection in the capital market: investment in human beings cannot be financed on the same terms or with the same ease as investment in physical capital. It is easy to see why there would be such a difference. If a fixed money loan is made to finance investment in physical capital, the lender can get some security for his loan in the form of a mortgage or residual claim to the physical asset itself, and he can count on realizing at least part of his investment in case of necessity by selling the physical asset. If he makes a comparable loan to increase the earning power of a human being, he clearly cannot get any comparable security; in a non-slave state, the individual embodying the investment cannot be bought and sold. But even if he could, the security would not be comparable. The productivity of the physical capital does not — or at least generally does not — depend on the co-operativeness of the original borrower. The productivity of the human capital quite obviously does — which is, of course, why, all ethical considerations aside, slavery is economically inefficient. A loan to finance the training of an individual who has no security to offer other than his future earnings is therefore a much less attractive proposition than a loan to finance, say, the erection of a building: the security is less, and the cost of subsequent collection of interest and principal is very much greater.

. . . .

What form should government intervention take? One obvious form, and the only form that it has so far taken, is outright government subsidy of vocational or professional education financed out of general revenues. Yet this form seems clearly inappropriate. Investment should be carried to the point at which the extra return repays the investment and yields the market rate of interest on it. If the investment is in a human being, the extra return takes the form of a higher payment for the individual's services than he could otherwise command. In a private market economy, the individual would get this return as his personal income, yet if the investment were subsidized, he would have borne none of the costs. In consequence, if subsidies were given to all who wished to get the training, and could meet minimum quality standards, there would tend to be overinvestment in human beings, for individuals would have an incentive to get the training so long as it yielded any extra return over private costs, even if the return were insufficient to repay the capital invested, let alone yield any interest on it. To avoid such overinvestment, government would have to restrict the subsidies. Even apart from the difficulty of calculating the "correct" amount of investment, this would involve rationing in some essentially arbitrary way the limited amount of investment among more claimants than could be financed, and would mean that those fortunate enough to get their training subsidized would receive all the returns from the investment whereas the costs would be borne by the taxpayers in general. This seems an entirely arbitrary, if not perverse, redistribution of income.

The desideratum is not to redistribute income but to make capital available for investment in human beings on terms comparable to those on which it is available for physical investment. Individuals should bear the costs of investment in themselves and receive the rewards, and they should not be prevented by market imperfections from making the investment when they are willing to bear the costs. One way to do this is to have government engage in equity investment in human beings of the kind described above. A governmental body could offer to finance or help finance the training of any individual who could meet minimum quality standards by making available not more than a limited sum per year for not more than a specified number of years, provided it was spent on securing training at a recognized institution. The individual would agree in return to pay to the government in each future year x per cent of his earnings in excess of y dollars for each $1,000 that he gets in this way. This payment could easily be combined with payment of income tax and so involve a minimum of additional administrative expense. The base sum, $y, should be set equal to estimated average — or perhaps modal — earnings without the specialized training; the fraction of earnings paid, x, should be calculated so as to make the whole project self-financing. In this way the individuals who received the training would in effect bear the whole cost. The amount invested could then be left to be determined by individual choice. Provided this was the only way in which government financed vocational or professional training, and provided the calculated earnings reflected all relevant returns and costs, the free choice of individuals would tend to produce the optimum amount of investment.

. . . .

Insofar as administrative expense is the obstacle to the development of such arrangements on a private basis, the appropriate unit of government to make funds available is the Federal government in the United States rather than smaller units. Any one State would have the same costs as an insurance company, say, in keeping track of the people whom it had financed. These would be minimized for the Federal government. Even so, they would not be completely eliminated. An individual who migrated to another country, for example, might still be legally or morally obligated to pay the agreed-on share of his earnings, yet it might be difficult and expensive to enforce the obligation. Highly successful people might therefore have an incentive to migrate. A similar problem arises, of course, also under the income tax, and to a very much greater extent. This and other administrative problems of conducting the scheme on a Federal level, while doubtless troublesome in detail, do not seem serious. The really serious problem is the political one already mentioned: how to prevent the scheme from becoming a political football and in the process being converted from a self-financing project to a means of subsidizing vocational education.

19

Education as a Public or Private Good?

John Vaizey

In this selection the Friedman position is challenged by John Vaizey of Worcester College, Oxford. Mr. Vaizey is a prolific writer on the economics of education.

The extreme *laissez-faire* view of the finance of education has been presented by Milton Friedman. The basic philosophical position is that in a free society, "with the freedom of the individual, or more realistically the family, as its ultimate objective," the government's "primary role is to preserve the rules of the game by enforcing contracts, preventing coercion, and keeping markets free." There follow three, and only three reasons for government intervention: one, where natural monopoly or market imperfection makes effective competition impossible; the second, where the external effects (or as Friedman calls them "the neighbourhood effects") are important so that individual cost and returns do not coincide with true costs and returns, and compensations cannot be paid to or by either parties to an exchange for the indirect losses or benefits they incur; and, thirdly, where the parties to transactions (children or the mentally ill) are not "responsible" units and action has to be taken on their behalf. . . .

In analysing the results of these philosophical presuppositions Friedman divides education into general and vocational education.

Now, already, before proceeding to a discussion of his analysis, it will be seen that the assumptions from which he chooses to argue are not widely acceptable; indeed, many would regard them as so eccentric as not to merit serious discussion. Nevertheless, since they lie at the basis of much pseudo-economic debate, it is worth-while to spell out some of the objections to the assumptions, before presenting objections to the analysis itself.

Educationally he is not likely to be widely followed in his division of education. "General" and "vocational" education cannot be divided in any meaningful sense. And his reliance on the "family" as the basic unit of society is

Reprinted with permission of The Free Press from *The Economics of Education*, by John Vaizey, London, Faber and Faber, Ltd., 1962, pp. 28–36.

not one that would readily stand up to sociological analysis; society often has a duty to encourage children to defy the family. Education, indeed, can in a substantial degree be regarded as an intervention to save the individual from the family. By his vagueness about the unit of welfare Friedman has fatally undermined his position.

But what of the economics? In the first place, "freedom" interpreted as "market freedom" is not necessarily an over-riding objective even of societies of which one approves; national survival, the preservation of a culture, the development of a just society may all over-ride this "freedom." The ballot-box is held by many to make the workings of representative democracy far more subtle in its defence of the individual than the market, especially when (as is always the case under capitalism) money incomes — which are "votes" in the market — are distributed most unequally. Further, education and civilization are good in themselves; without them a society is only free to be ignorant.

It consequently follows (as Mill and others have always argued) that government's positive role is greater than that of "keeping the ring"; whether the positive role be to link the past and the future, as Burke would hold, or to create a good and a just society as Tawney and Laski, for example, taught. Friedman, in fact, represents one limb of an argument which is not in the central economic tradition.

The classical economists took a more sophisticated view of mankind than is now generally allowed, as Lord Robbins has shown; looking back, of course, it can be seen that their view was *simpliste* and shot through with emotion and value-judgment. They are seen as apologists or detractors of emergent capitalism. But their view was an arguable one, and carried with it moral and social consequences that were not unworthy.

The reasonable, educated man, they argued, eschewed pain and sought pleasure; he knew his own mind and his own interest; and the pursuit of his own interest inevitably led him to a summit of personal fulfilment in economic as well as domestic life. A man who sought to do otherwise was harming himself, and this was *ex hypothesi* impossible unless he was either ill-informed or sick. Remove ignorance and ignore the mad, and men knew their own concerns best. This seems to me a reasonable view, though it may exaggerate self-knowledge and the degree of serious-mindedness of the average sensual man; but it is an error in the right direction so far as personal freedom and happiness go. Thus far I agree with Friedman.

The social corollary of this doctrine had a positive and a negative side. Positively, they argued, the sum of men's individual actions added up to the sum of the general good. Partly this was through the operation of the "hidden hand"; the free market adjusted men's needs and desires to their possibilities of fulfilment. In a way this was true. It was because eighteenth-century government was so inefficient and corrupt that they conceived of all markets as being better than all governments, except in the limited spheres of public order and education, together with a limited amount of support for the poor. This was their positive doctrine. It had its limitations, but in essence they were historically right; it is improbable that unreformed governments could have carried the exploding population of the time through the industrial revolution to an age that could afford Victorian social reform.

The negative side of the doctrine was to decry the mystical doctrine of the state, whether in the form held by Burke, or in Hegel. It was to assess the organs of the state as pragmatically as possible that the great utilitarian economists conceived their social purpose.

Their argument ran that man as a responsible being is acting adequately if he pursues his own interests; these interests to some extent are tautologically defined as interests which are identical with the general good — so that he won't do what is "bad" — but nevertheless the limit of public action is firmly set by the fact that man as a political animal is morally and intellectually inferior to man as an individual or family unit.

Now, it is clear to us where their doctrine failed. Some people do not know their own interests at all; none of us know all of our own interests all of the time; we have to delegate our choices and our responsibilities to doctors, teachers, soldiers, sewermen, and so on. Moreover, our interests conflict. My coal fire gives you bronchitis. Above all, suppose all things were bought and sold; our incomes are unequal so some have more votes than others in the election of goods and services; and not many of us would care that at all times the distribution of incomes was absolutely "fair," or corresponded to "need."

For we believe that the use of the word "fair" is a valid use of the word in relation to income even if the free market is working perfectly. Professors of medicine *may* be scarcer than professors of education, but it is "unfair" that one should be paid more than another; women teachers are less scarce than men teachers, but equal pay is "fair" — and so on. And we believe that people have "needs" even if they have not the money to turn them into market demands.

The rise of the bourgeois state has fundamentally changed the situation. The Factory Acts, the Education Acts, the Public Health Acts were passed by combinations of social and political forces, and when passed, the Acts were effective because of the development of new administrative techniques. Thus a responsible citizen could act publicly as well as privately in the public interest; he could, for instance, sit . . . on an education committee. The question became: how to administer the state to create positive good.

Economics took note of this situation. It developed two doctrines. One was of the need to control the economy as a whole; unemployment, for example, was beyond an individual's power to avert. Keynes showed convincingly that the sum of individual responses to a depression was perverse; far from averting it, they intensified it. Only the government could act; a responsible man could only achieve his own ends by acting publicly. Similarly only some third body could reconcile directly conflicting interests. We all want pleasant views from our windows; we can only have them if there are Town and Country Planning Acts to stop us from putting our houses on the top of Box Hill, or Acts to control the location of industry despite our wish to work where we like. Thus there has to be an economic doctrine to advise on the acts of the state which is a positive doctrine, implying that the acts are both possible and desirable.

Thus we *have* to reconcile a man's private ends with his public ends, and the private ends of men with each other — all problems specifically thrown out by Friedman, except in the inadequate admission of "neighbourhood effects." The problems arise because of the possibility of exercising control over public events through public bodies, and because of a more complex view of self-interest.

Thus the basic tenets put forward by Friedman are unacceptable to those who accept the central tradition of economics.

Having thus argued about the basis of the thesis, it is necessary to deal in detail with the analysis erected by Friedman as a superstructure.

He acknowledges the need for a society to have a basis of education, whose benefits do not necessarily accrue directly to the individual, but which create a "stable and democratic" society. This means that a society can require children to be educated; it does not follow that the state should provide the education in whole or in part. Extreme cases need special care, but the rest of education could be provided as the private schools are now, by private *entrepreneurs* for private fees. This would both make the size of families more responsive to economic pressures and incentives (shades of Malthus!), and enable parental choice of school to be fully exercised. The government could give a subsidy to encourage this expenditure; but that should be the limit of its commitment. The government could also impose minimum standards "much as it now inspects restaurants to assure that they maintain sanitary standards."

It is important to realize that the argument assumes that parental choices are valid. This is not so: many studies have shown that parents make choices which are ill-informed and not in the children's own interests. It further assumes that there is no valid educational end in itself which is achievable only at levels above the minimum whether parents want it or not for their children. This is most questionable. Parental choice ranks lower for many than giving children access to the cultural heritage which is theirs. In a given context, truth, beauty, and goodness are not necessarily matters of choice.

Friedman counters this argument by saying that there is division of opinion about cultural values (especially religion). This is undoubtedly so; it qualifies, indeed, as an understatement; about the quality of many cultural values, however, the consensus of cultivated responsible opinion in the United Kingdom is in agreement, and it is not dictatorial to say that access to this heritage is a "democratic right." Further, many people would feel that this problem is best settled by the process of public discussion and debate in a responsible representative democracy, than by the free play of the market.

Friedman considers the exacerbation of class differences in education arising from the payment of fees, and points out that social segregation exists in state schools because of the geographical background of the pupils; this is certainly a valid point. He points out, too, that in isolated rural areas there is a "natural monopoly" of school provision which makes it uneconomic to provide a variety of schools.

All in all, Friedman comes down for a mixed system of state and independent schools, in which the state schools would give government a "standard against which to judge salary scales and promote a more rapid adjustment to changes in conditions of demand or supply."

For higher education Friedman is in favour of more complete *laissez-faire,* in which government-operated institutions cover their costs by fees. He also advocates that the costs of vocational education should be covered by the beneficiaries, on the grounds that the returns on investment in human capital are high. The finance of education, he suggests, should be by loans which give "a share in an individual's earning prospects" to the lender; the lender would advance to the student "the funds needed to finance his training on condition that he agreed to pay the lender a specified fraction of his future earnings!"

It will be clear that the argument as developed by Friedman depends entirely on his initial premise, and also on the validity of his distinction between general and higher or vocational education. Many would reject both.

Nevertheless, in certain circumstances there may be a case for charging fees in education. I have argued that if the right to pay for education is to be maintained, and social policy welcomes the integration of the private and the publicly-maintained schools, and there is also a shortage of public finance for education, there may be a case for charging fees.

Education has been supplied free not only because education is necessary, but as part of the policy that families shall be no worse off because they have children, than childless couples or bachelors and spinsters. It has also been supplied free because families with clever or peculiar children would be unduly penalized by paying for more expensive education than families with ordinary children.

It is by no means self-evident that a family which chooses to have children is thereby lowering its standard of living, unless children are regarded as an unmitigated curse. In one sense a family is changing its pattern of expenditure by having children. Nor is investment in children a dead loss to the parents and a gain to the state. Studies show how dependent old people may be on their children for support and help. A large family is sometimes the best insurance policy.

It seems that the question of whether to charge fees or not, for what parts of the education services, to whom, and how much, are not questions to which "economic science" gives unequivocal answers. They are, rather, purely pragmatic questions which arise in a desire to get more finance for education than can be provided by rates and taxes. Of course, if fees are charged for compulsory education, then these charges are a tax on parents — a payment they cannot escape and which is enforced by law. But, in general, fees are a price like any other price; and it is a matter of political convenience to decide whether a price-tag shall be attached to any part of the public education system.[1]

I have shown that economic reasoning would suggest that publicly-financed education is a legitimate end of public activity, even to extreme exponents of "classical" economic doctrine. Similarly, there is no economic reasoning which would suggest whether or not a private sector of education should or should not exist alongside a publicly-maintained sector; the choice is a complex of political, social, and economic considerations. But the question of whether fees should be charged in the public sector, or subsidies should be given to the private sector is an entirely pragmatic matter for an economist.

In the long-run, from the point of view of the economy, the important question is how much education is given in real terms. The question of who pays for it is more a question of the distribution of the burden; although, of course, it also affects the distribution of the benefits.

It seems that in the Western world the national income per head is likely to rise over the foreseeable future. This will make it easier to levy taxes to support education; it will also make it easier for parents to pay fees. In the short-run — perhaps the next ten years — it seems, however, that outlays on education will rise faster, perhaps substantially faster, than the yield of taxes. Consequently there is a considerable fiscal problem arising from the expansion of education; and it is in this context that proposals for changing fees have been revived.

What considerations should we bear in mind?

The size of family, it seems, is tending to rise quite fast. A more realistic notion of the cost of having children might not be a bad thing for many parents, therefore, over the next ten years. This would substantially ease the problem of providing teachers for a rising number of children of primary age. Before the war, when the fear was that the race might die out, the problem was exactly the opposite: how to encourage people to have children. It can be seen, then, that circumstances alter cases; fees might be wrong then but right now.

It is also true, as I have shown, that the consequences of education yield considerable sums in cash to those who are successful, and whose education costs most. It would not be unreasonable to expect them to pay for their education, either as a family, or as a person (by means, for example, of repay-

[1] I have dealt with the theoretical and practical questions of charging fees in *The Costs of Education*; *The Establishment* (edited Hugh Thomas, London 1959); and in *The Times*, 5th July 1960. This point is Mills's.

able loans as in Holland). The problem with this approach to education is that it immediately leads to sex-discrimination — girls earn less, and get married. Consequently, unless higher education is to be almost exclusively male, girls would still have to be subsidized. Some students, too, take up unremunerative careers. It is difficult to penalize them without discouraging just the people whom society on very reasonable grounds should encourage; priests, writers, teachers, and social workers are among them. It is true, however, that the greater benefits by far in education go to the higher socio-economic groups; so it would not be unreasonable to charge them more for their benefits. Progressive taxation could be seen, in this sense, not as redistributive but as charging for benefits received.

Charging fees also raises the major problem that it will discourage some people from making use of the education system. Their views are short-sighted, as Marshall argued; the children are not able to force their parents to educate them and there is a limit to what the state can do to impose burdens on parents; poverty is associated with big families, and parents in low socio-economic groups and with low intelligence tend to have big families. Thus any proposal to charge fees in education will be riddled with exceptions for the clever, the handicapped, the poor, and the stupid; and it will give rise to a new cause of discrimination within education which will arouse profound hostility.

Another method of raising money by fees is to break education down into its components. Pupils could be charged for transport, meals, milk, medical attendance, books, and boarding maintenance, for example. But once again, the exceptions will be numerous, and you run the risk of breaking up an efficient system by discouraging the use of part of it.

20

The Costs of Public Education

Werner Z. Hirsch

The following selection treats the matter of the relation between income and educational expenditures. Professor Hirsch is a member of the Department of Economics, Washington University. He has made several impressive studies of the determinants of educational expenditures and of economies of scale in school districts.

This study is designed to shed light on the cost and expenditure level changes of the public primary and secondary education sector of our economy — a sector employing more than 2 million men and women, who serve almost 35 million pupils. This sector in 1958 spent more than 30 percent of all the money spent by State and local governments, an amount representing about 3.3 percent of national income and 3 percent of gross national product. In order to trace and understand changes in the cost of education and relate them to the rest of the State and local government sector, the latter sector is examined first in some detail. This sector, for example, accounts for about 12.3 percent of gross national product, and perhaps 3 to 3½ percent of the Consumer Price Index of the U.S. Department of Labor. There are indications that since 1952 the cost of State and local government services increased up to three times more rapidly than did the other items included in the index.

To shed light on the cost behavior of this sector, a functional service breakdown is attempted, and the question is raised: "Which State and local government services provided the major monetary push?"

State and Local Government Sector

In terms of general expenditures, education, highways, public welfare, and health and hospitals have been the four most important State and local government services since the turn of the century. Education expenditures have

Adapted from *Analysis of the Rising Costs of Public Education,* Study Paper No. 4, Materials Prepared in Connection with the Study of Employment, Growth, and Price Levels for consideration by the Joint Economic Committee, Congress of the United States, Washington, Government Printing Office, 1959, pp. 2–3, 32–38.

accounted for an increasingly large share of all expenditures. They increased from about 25 per cent in 1902 to about 35 percent in 1958. General expenditures for public primary and secondary education advanced at a somewhat slower pace than did those for higher education.

The relative importance of highway expenditures showed great fluctuations. During the first quarter of this century a steady advance from 17 to 25 percent was registered. From then on until the end of World War II a steady decline set in, which has been reversed only in recent years. Public welfare expenditures, at least in relative terms, grew more rapidly than any of the other main services. Most of their advance took place during the first half of the 1930's. Finally, the relative share of health and hospital expenditures has shown a very steady, though not rapid, increase. Many other services have lost in importance.

. . . .

What is the picture of State and local government expenditures if they are adjusted for price level changes; i.e., in constant dollars? The U.S. Department of Commerce has prepared a series of implicit deflators applicable to State and local government purchases of goods and services which goes back to 1929. This series does not make allowance for quality changes. While State and local government expenditures — measured in current dollars — increased from 1929 to 1957 by almost 370 percent, expressed in 1954 constant dollars these expenditures have not even quite doubled. Between 1929 and 1945 the constant dollar expenditures moved relatively little and without definite direction. Since then a pronounced and steady rise has started. The average annual increase of the last 10 years — measured in constant dollars — was about 8 percent.

Costs of Public Education

What about cost changes in the single most important State and local government sector, i.e., public primary and secondary education? More specifically, what forces have decisively contributed to cost increases in this sector?

A large number of factors can be identified as possibly affecting current expenditures, plus debt service, for public primary and secondary education. Some of them have assumed greatly different values since the turn of the century. Thus, for example, the number of pupils in average daily attendance — ADA — increased almost three times since 1900, high school enrollment relative to total public school enrollment increased about six times, and the percent of pupils living in urban as against rural America has increased about 40 percent.

Turning to some economic factors, it is noteworthy that the average salary of a teacher advanced about 14 times, while per capita personal income increased about 9 times.

An examination of some characteristics of public education itself reveals that while in 1900 virtually no appreciable auxiliary services were rendered, in 1958 pupils were fed in school cafeterias, attended by school health services, and brought to school in school buses, etc. In 1958, almost 14 percent of current school expenditures, plus debt service, were applied to auxiliary services. In addition, the school term was lengthened an average of 60 percent and the number of principals, superintendents, and consultants per pupil almost doubled.

. . . .

EDUCATION COST IN CONSTANT TERMS

A truly serious shortcoming of the deflating efforts of the U.S. Department of Commerce is its admitted inability to adjust for anything but price level changes. It expresses State and local government purchases in constant dollar terms, but neglects changes in the variety, scope, and quality of services.

Thus, an effort will be made to develop first a series which in concept resembles that of the U.S. Department of Commerce, i.e., cost of public primary and secondary education in constant dollars. Thereafter, more terms than merely price level will be held constant, leading to an education cost index in real terms.

By deflating the actual expenditure series by an average annual salary index — with, for instance, 1954 = 100 — a new series results which testifies to the

Table 1

TOTAL CURRENT EXPENDITURES PLUS DEBT SERVICE FOR PUBLIC PRIMARY AND SECONDARY EDUCATION, SELECTED YEARS, 1900–1958
(In thousands of dollars)

Year	Unadjusted (1)	Adjusted for Pupils in ADA (1954 = 100) (2)	Adjusted for Salary Level (1954 = 100) (3)	Year	Unadjusted (1)	Adjusted for Pupils in ADA (1954 = 100) (2)	Adjusted for Salary Level (1954 = 100) (3)
1900	193.9	467.2	2,281.2	1942	2,378.6	2,900.7	6,037.1
1902	214.2	497.0	2,353.8	1946	2,995.1	3,869.6	5,737.7
1910	384.8	769.6	3,029.9	1948	4,092.4	5,021.3	5,931.0
1913	473.0	890.8	3,529.9	1950	5,090.7	5,858.1	6,468.5
1920	938.5	1,489.7	4,116.2	1952	6,219.8	6,857.6	6,895.6
1922	1,332.0	1,852.6	4,367.2	1954	7,458.3	7,458.3	7,458.3
1930	2,095.0	2,527.1	5,646.9	1956	9,054.6	8,368.4	8.368.4
1932	2,147.9	2,477.4	5,805.1	1958	[1]11,020.0	[1]9,467.4	[1]8,973.9
1940	2,192.0	2,548.8	5,814.3				

[1] Estimate.

Sources: Worksheets made available by the U.S. Department of Health, Education, and Welfare.

expenditures that would have been incurred if 1954 salary conditions had prevailed throughout the period.

Such a deflated series is presented in column 3 of Table 1 and can be compared with the actual expenditure series in column 1. While between 1900 and 1958 actual expenditures had increased 56-fold, the increase of the salary adjusted series extends merely from about $2.3 billion to $9 billion — less than threefold — and only 5 percent of that actually incurred.

The U.S. Department of Commerce's constant dollar series of State and local government purchases extends back to 1929. During 1930–57 it advanced by 88 percent, while during the same period the education cost series in constant dollars advanced distinctly less, i.e., 56 percent.

By the way, in the same manner adjustments have been made for the number of pupils in average daily attendance. (See col. 2 of Table 1.) In terms of 1954 average daily attendance, expenditure increases from 1900 to 1958 would have been twentyfold, i.e., slightly more than one-third of the actual increase.

What can be said about expenditures for public primary and secondary education in constant terms? To answer this question an attempt will be made to measure the cost of an education unit, so standardized that its variety and scope are held reasonably constant, and expressed in per pupil in average daily attendance terms.

. . . .

Since the turn of the century an increasingly large number of auxiliary services — school bus transportation, cafeteria, health services, etc. — have been introduced. Their cost has progressed from near zero in 1900 to almost $1.5 billion in 1958. But these auxiliary services have not necessarily improved the quality of education itself.

If expenditures for auxiliary services are subtracted from the other current expenditures plus debt service, the 1900–1958 increase is only 48-fold (col. 1 of Table 2). By adjusting this series for changes in salary level, the increase is further reduced to less than 2½-fold (col. 2 of Table 2).

In addition to excluding auxiliary services, it appears proper to use an education unit which is neither affected by the number of pupils in average daily attendance nor the length of the school term. Thus, the education unit which will be used is daily public primary and secondary education per pupil in average daily attendance, leaving aside auxiliary services. In column 3 of Table 2, per-pupil annual expenditures are given, and in column 4 they are reduced to a daily basis. Finally, in column 5, daily per-pupil expenditures (minus auxiliary services) in 1954 dollars are given. This series might be quite appropriate to indicate the cost of a given bundle of public primary and secondary education in constant terms. This series together with the current and constant dollar series is presented in Chart 1.

Costs in real terms exhibit amazing stability during 1900–1958. For the years for which data are available, 1922 was the low year with $1.37 daily ex-

Table 2

TOTAL CURRENT EXPENDITURES PLUS DEBT SERVICE FOR PUBLIC PRIMARY AND SECONDARY EDUCATION MINUS AUXILIARY SERVICES, SELECTED YEARS, 1900–1958

Year	Unadjusted Annual, Thousands of Dollars (1)	Adjusted for Salary Level (1954=100), Thousands of Dollars (2)	Per Pupil Expenditures, Dollars (3)	Daily per Pupil Expenditures, Dollars (4)	Daily per Pupil Expenditures in 1954 Dollars (5)
1900	193.9	2,281.2	18.233	0.126	1.482
1902	214.2	2,353.8	19.357	.134	1.473
1910	379.8	2,990.6	29.607	.188	1.480
1913	463.0	3,455.2	34.007	.215	1.604
1920	892.8	3,915.8	55.281	.341	1.496
1922	1,262.7	4,140.0	68.506	.418	1.370
1930	1,942.8	5,236.6	91.359	.529	1.426
1932	2,003.6	5,415.1	90.069	.526	1.422
1940	2,012.7	5,338.7	91.311	.522	1.385
1942	2,158.9	5,479.4	102.655	.588	1.492
1946	2,646.0	5,069.0	133.308	.754	1.444
1948	3,565.4	5,167.2	170.511	.960	1.391
1950	4,377.5	5,562.3	196.443	1.104	1.403
1952	5,302.4	5,878.5	227.991	1.279	1.418
1954	6,438.2	6,438.2	251.062	1.406	1.406
1956	7,750.3	7,162.9	279.392	1.570	1.451
1958	[1]9,530.0	7,760.6	319.167	1.786	1.454

[1] Estimate.

penditure per pupil, and 1913 was the high year with $1.60. Over the 58 years, an overall decline of about 3 percent was registered. To the extent that the standardization of the educational unit has been successful and appropriate data in general were used, the analysis can reflect on the productivity variable as a residual. Apparently, productivity in the public schools has changed very little, if at all. . . .

For policy as well as projective purposes, there is much interest in measuring the income elasticity of public primary and secondary education, a concept which was briefly discussed above. Measuring income elasticity requires that a net regression coefficient relating expenditures to personal income be computed and then multiplied by the mean personal income of the period divided by the corresponding mean expenditures figure. It assumes that expenditures are representatives of the "amount" of education. . . .

With these considerations in mind, the following hypothesis was enunciated and tested:

X_1 — daily total current expenditures plus debt service for public primary and secondary education per pupil in average daily attendance is a function of,

X_2 — percent of public high school enrollment relative to total public school enrollment,

X_3 — percent of pupils (5 to 19 years old) in average daily attendance living in urban areas, and

X_4 — per capita personal income.

Chart 1

INCOME ELASTICITY OF PUBLIC EDUCATION

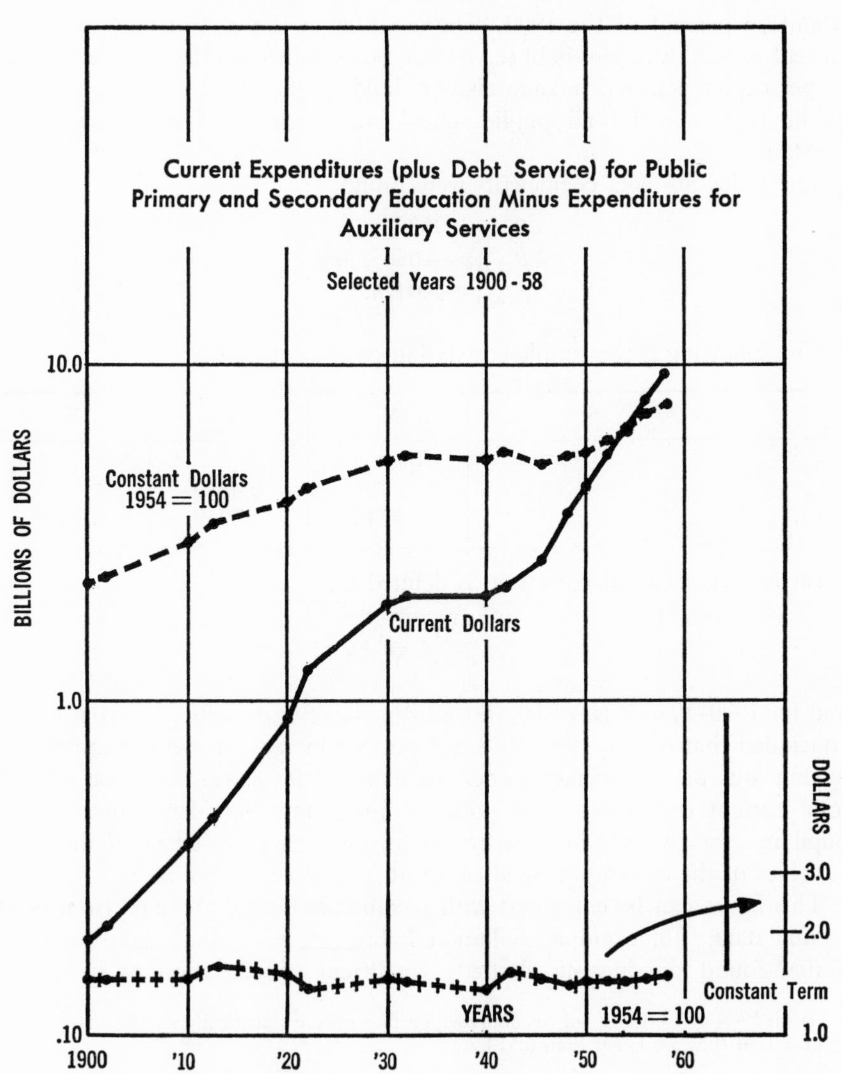

In brief,

$$X_{1a} = f(X_2, X_3, X_4).$$

The multiple regression equation was found to have the following values for selected years during 1900–1958:

$$X'_{1a} = .112568 + \frac{0.004274}{(.0024)} X_2 - \frac{0.005200}{(.0022)} X_3 + \frac{0.000924}{(.8715)} X_4.$$

The statistically significant coefficient is $\beta_{14.23}$.[1]
The coefficient of multiple determination adjusted for degrees of freedom lost — $R^{*2}_{1.234}$ — is 0.969. It is statistically highly significant at an $\propto$ of 0.05. About 76 percent of the 1900–1958 variation in the cost of daily per pupil current expenditure plus debt service can be explained on the average in terms of per capita personal income change, holding the effect of changes in the public high school — all public school enrollment ratio and urbanization constant.

The following beta coefficients were found:

$$\beta_{14.23} = .9625,$$
$$\beta_{13.24} = —.0565, \text{ and}$$
$$\beta_{12.34} = —.0474.$$

The following is the simple correlation coefficient matrix:

	X_1	X_2	X_3
X_2	0.6892		
X_3	.5707	0.9659	
X_4	.9746	.7049	0.5854

Income elasticity of education is defined as,

$$\frac{\partial X_1}{\partial X_4} \cdot \frac{\overline{X}_4}{\overline{X}_1},$$

and for 1900–1958 it is +1.09, just a little above unit elastic. Thus, it can be concluded that during 1900–1958, a 1 percent increase in per capita personal income was on the average associated with a 1.09 percent increase in daily total current expenditures for public primary and secondary education per pupil in average daily attendance. It assumes that the effect of the other variables of the equation is held constant.

This figure can be compared with income elasticities obtained from cross-section data. For example, Solomon Fabricant, using 1942 data of the 48 States, found the income elasticity coefficient of education to be +0.78.

[1]With 17–4 or 13 degrees of freedom lost, coefficients are statistically significant at an $\propto$ of 0.05 if they are larger than 0.514.

Fabricant's analysis included two additional independent variables — urbanization and density. Income elasticity of all State and local government services were +0.90; but if education was excluded, it was somewhat higher, i.e., +0.96. Such services as come under the heading of general control, health and hospital, highways and police, were income elastic, while in addition to education, fire, public welfare, and sanitation were income inelastic.

Harvey E. Brazer estimated the income elasticity of education for 40 large cities using 1949 median family income and 1953 per capita operating expenditure data. He computed the income elasticity to be +0.73. Other variables included in the analysis were:

Ratio of city population to metropolitan areas' population in 1950.
Students in average daily attendance per 1,000 of 1950 population, and intergovernmental revenue per capita, for education, 1953.

The present author used 1951–52 and 1954–55 cross-section data to estimate income elasticity of education for the St. Louis City-County area. It was found to be +0.58. In the analysis the following additional variables had been included —

Pupils in average daily attendance,
High school pupils in average daily attendance as percent of all pupils in average daily attendance,
Pupils in average daily attendance per square mile, and
Percent increase in pupils in average daily attendance, 1951–56.

The coefficient of +0.58 is distinctly below the +10.1 for fire protection and +0.98 for police protection found in the St. Louis study. This study also estimated the elasticity with respect to per capita income of major education expenditure categories, which are also reproduced in Table 3. It is interesting to note that, with but one exception, the income elasticity for instruction is lowest. Fixed charges are the exception, where a low income elasticity is not surprising. By definition these charges vary little with income. The fact that the income elasticity of instruction is so low gives cause for concern, as long as the quality of instruction requires great improvement.

As was to be expected, income elasticities computed with the aid of cross-section data are lower than those based on time series data. Actually, depending on the type of data used, the coefficient answered slightly different questions. Income elasticities of education based on cross-section data reflect the average percentage change in per pupil education expenditures that is brought about as average per capita personal income changes from one school district to the next by 1 per cent within a given year or sets of years. If based on time series data, the coefficient testifies to the average percentage change in per pupil education expenditures that results as average per capita personal income changes over time by 1 per cent. The first provides a static picture, while the second reflects dynamic changes in our society.

But no matter which of the two concepts is used, there can be little doubt

Table 3

INCOME[1] ELASTICITIES OF SELECT LOCAL PUBLIC SERVICES, ST. LOUIS CITY-COUNTY AREA, 1951–52 AND 1954–55

Services	Income Elasticity
Education:	
Total current plus debt service	+0.56
Total current without debt service	+.52
General control	+.50
Instruction	+.42
Auxiliary services	+1.15
Plant operation and maintenance	+.55
Fixed charges	+.29
Fire protection	+10.1
Police protection	+.98

[1] Since assessed valuation of real property is highly correlated with income and information about it is much more readily available, the former is used for measurement. The rank correlation coefficient, relating 1949 median income with 1954–55 per pupil assessed valuation of 10 of the districts about coterminous with municipal or census tract boundaries, is +0.905, which is highly significant at an x of 0.05.

that the income elasticity of public education is quite low. (Especially low appears to be the income elasticity of instruction.) It is low in comparison to income elasticities of other public services and in particular such consumer amenities as air conditioning, automobiles, golf, speedboats, etc. It is also low compared to what it must be if public education in the United States is to be improved. No doubt, people's attitudes toward education and the existing tax system, which relies so heavily on proportional property and sales taxes, are mainly responsible for the low income elasticity of education.

The United States can readily afford the expenditures needed to raise the level of education as required by our status as a leading world power; but the necessary funds will only become available if an increasing portion of people's income is channeled into public education. This will require the combined leadership of all branches of government and educators. Further shifts will be needed in the responsibility of financing education from local to State and possibly Federal Government. Matching Federal funds combined with specific performance criteria for eligibility for aid appear to offer a useful approach.

Among the States' performance criteria two will be mentioned — tax effort and partial statewide equalization of educational opportunity. Only States that raise a given per cent of personal income for education should be eligible. In addition, a certain minimum education budget needs to be underwritten by the State for each and every child in the State.

PART THREE

Taxation for Schools

Though the larger share of power in the administration of elementary and secondary schools rests in the hands of local public bodies, the financing of education in the United States is affected by tax policies of the state and federal governments, as well, of course, as the local. It is known that approximately 40 per cent of school revenues are provided through grants-in-aid from the states. Views on the revenue potential of state taxes play an important role in determining the volume of these grants. The connection between federal tax policy and school support is less obvious, because central government grants account for a relatively small share of educational revenues at the elementary and secondary levels and, further, because education is a minor item in any functional classification of the federal budget. Yet the relation is significant. There has been a tremendous growth in the volume of federal levies; accordingly, it is probable that the attitude of the householder toward all taxes, including his local ones, is shaped to some degree by his feelings, positive or negative, toward the processes of central government finance. Next, the fact that state and local levies can be listed as deductions under the federal income tax means that the distribution of tax burden by income class in financing the operations of state and local governments is markedly different from what unadjusted figures (i.e., estimates of state-local tax burden unadjusted for the deductions allowed under the federal levy) would show. Lastly, the sheer magnitude of the central government means that the tax structure it employs, in and of itself, can hardly be neutral with respect to the rate of economic growth. Thus, federal tax policy affects the size of the economic base on which state and local governments place their levies.

There are three main bases for the levy of taxes: income, consumption, and wealth. The federal government relies most heavily on the income base, though it does tax consumption (e.g., gasoline and liquor excises) and wealth (gift and estate levies) to a minor extent. State governments place levies on both income and consumption; with respect to the latter, they make heavy use of general sales taxes, so far eschewed by the central authorities. The states now rely very little on taxes on wealth. Local governments, by and large, are restricted to levies on wealth under one main instrument, the property tax. A kind of specialization in use of tax instrument by level of government prevails, though it is not clean-cut because some state governments have rather catholic tastes in obtaining their funds.

By definition, a tax is a compulsory levy. The extraction of funds from households under threat of legal sanction can possibly be made palatable but never pleasant. During any period of relative stability in a society, certain "normal" levels of taxation come to be generally accepted and, once accepted, are extremely difficult to breach. Such conventional levels of taxation should never be confused with absolute limits. For any major tax instrument an absolute limit to yield does not in the practical sense exist. In a major social upheaval, such as a war, the conventional limits of taxation are likely to be discarded. After the period of upheaval has passed, the volume of non-emergency public services is more likely to expand and absorb the revenue than are tax rates to fall to their former levels. Unfortunately for locally administered services, it is central government levies that are likely to respond in this fashion to emergencies. This allows central government services to rise to a higher plateau. Activities, like schools, that derive the largest part of their revenues from state and local taxes cannot expect to receive such windfall gains in receipts.[1]

Under this argument states and localities will probably face continual pressures for revenues, since the undeniable public demands for more and better services come into inevitable conflict with the conventional norms of tax effort. However, all is not hopeless. We do enjoy increases in income, and tax revenues, even under fixed rates, respond more or less automatically to the increase in economic well-being.

Although an absolute limit to taxation can be said not to exist, it is true that increases in tax rates have effects on the economy. Thus, taxes may affect (1) the incentive to work, (2) the capacity of individuals to make investments in the future productivity of our system, and (3) the inclination of consumers to purchase particular types of goods and services. With respect to point (3) any distortion engendered by a tax affects, ultimately, the occupational

[1] Jack Wiseman, "The Evaluation of Local Government in the National Financial Structure," *Institute of Municipal Treasurers and Accountants,* Lecture No. 11, Session 1958–59, p. 193.

structure of the country. Some of the effects of particular tax instruments may be judged to be harmful. Such harmful effects may possibly be reduced by a change in the tax structure. Some may have to be accepted as a cost of financing services.

Section A

GENERAL CONSIDERATIONS OF TAX POLICY

According to Due (Selection 21), the desirable characteristics of a tax are economic neutrality, equity, and low costs of collection and compliance. To assess wherein a particular kind of tax departs from economic neutrality is an extraordinarily complex undertaking in analysis. To judge which taxes are more equitable than others is difficult, too, but here the question turns on whether a satisfactory measure of consensus can be found on what constitutes fairness in taxation. And it may turn out that "equitable" taxes carry high costs of collection or compliance. In short, the defense of one's favorite levy is an uneasy art.

Nonetheless, to consider the neutrality and equity aspects of taxation in anything more than highly abstract terms, it is helpful to have information on what the distribution of the tax burden among households actually is. Selection 22 by Musgrave presents estimates of that distribution. The reader may wish to compare Musgrave's estimates with what he had intuitively felt the relation between tax liability and income to be.

21

The Principles of Taxation

John F. Due

Professor Due, a member of the Department of Economics, University of Illinois, is an internationally recognized authority in the field of taxation. Here he explores some of the assumptions that underlie current thinking about tax policy.

Most governmental activities, by virtue of their community benefits, must be financed by taxation rather than by sale to the users. Since these governmental services convey their benefits to the community as a whole, there is no possible way in which they can be divided into segments and sold. It is this characteristic of certain activities which initially led governments to undertake them. In other cases the sale of the services, while technically possible, would be regarded as inequitable. When a government enters the welfare field, "sale" is meaningless, since no service is being rendered which could be sold.

Taxation, by definition, involves compulsion; the taxpayers are required to make certain payments, regardless of their individual dispositions in the matter. In a democracy at least, the taxes will not be imposed unless they meet with the approval of a majority of the representatives of the people. But, once they are levied, no individual has the choice of paying or not paying. Because of this compulsory aspect, the collection of taxes may have very significant effects upon the behavior of individuals and the functioning of the economy, which must be taken into consideration in the selection of taxes if the tax structure is not to interfere with the attainment of the economic goals of society. Furthermore, if the goals of society are to be realized, the burden of the taxes must be distributed among various persons in a manner consistent with these goals.

. . . .

Adapted from *Government Finance*, revised edition, Homewood, Ill., Richard D. Irwin, Inc., 1959, pp. 102–120. Reproduced with permission.

NATURE OF THE PRINCIPLES OF TAXATION

The principles of taxation can be selected only in terms of the goals which are accepted as the appropriate objectives of the economic system. The consensus of opinion in present-day society is considered to regard three goals as of paramount importance for optimum economic welfare: (1) maximum freedom of choice, consistent with the welfare of others; (2) optimum standards of living, in terms of available resources and techniques and in the light of consumer and factor-owner preferences; and (3) a distribution of income in conformity with the standards of equity currently accepted by society.

In terms of these goals, three major principles or desirable characteristics of the tax system have been developed:

1. Economic neutrality. The tax structure must be established in such a way as to avoid interference with the attainment of the optimum allocation and use of resources and, where possible, to assist in the attainment of the optimum.

2. Equity. The distribution of burden of the tax must conform with the pattern of income distribution regarded as the optimum by the consensus of opinion in contemporary society.

3. Minimum costs of collection and compliance, consistent with effective enforcement. This rule requires that taxes be established in such a manner as to minimize the real costs of collection, in terms of resources required to collect the taxes and to comply with the tax laws on the part of the taxpayers, as well as in terms of the direct inconvenience caused the taxpayers in the payment of the tax.

. . . .

THE PRINCIPLE OF ECONOMIC NEUTRALITY

If taxation is not to interfere with the attainment of optimum standards of living, the taxes must not alter the choices or courses of action on the part of members of society, except in those cases in which interference will allow closer attainment of the goal. Taxes must, of course, reduce total spending; this is their basic economic function, since inflation will result if private spending is not reduced by an amount equivalent to government spending (in periods of full employment). But, so long as the unregulated functioning of the economy will allow the attainment of optimum output, relative to consumer and factor-owner preferences, in the private sector of the economy, taxes must not alter relative consumer or factor-owner choices, or they will reduce levels of living below the optimum.

On the other hand, when automatic attainment of the optimum adjustment is not realized, appropriate selection of taxes may allow closer attainment of this adjustment. Thus, for example, if the consumption of liquor becomes excessive, relative to the optimum, because real costs to society due to drunkenness are not borne by producers of the products and thus do not appear in the prices, a special tax on this product, designed to reduce consumption and production to optimum levels, is justifiable in terms of the goal of optimum adjustment of production. On the whole, since the free-market system, despite its limitations, is regarded as the preferred form of economic organization, it can be presumed that any change in behavior produced by taxes is undesirable in terms of optimum living standards, unless it can be demonstrated in each particular case that the changed behavior due to the tax actually allows closer attainment of the accepted goals.

Unneutral Effects of Taxes. There are several ways in which taxes may alter human behavior. In the first place, they may affect consumer choice. If, for example, a tax is levied on the sale of one commodity but not on that of another, the relative prices of the two are altered, and a readjustment in relative consumer purchases will result. A given dollar expenditure by the consumer will no longer acquire the same quantities of particular factor units regardless of the good purchased, and thus optimum allocation of factors in terms of consumer wants cannot be attained, if the adjustment was the optimum one in the absence of the tax. . . .

Taxation may also result in an alteration of the decisions of factor owners with respect to the quantity of factor units which they make available to producers. So far as workers are concerned, taxes may alter the relative desirability of work and leisure. A tax which applies to the return from work but does not affect leisure increases the advantage of the latter as compared to the former. But for those persons who have a relatively inelastic demand for goods and an elastic demand for leisure, the tax will actually result in their working more instead of less. If persons work less, national income is reduced; if they work more, it is increased. But in any event the disturbing of the previous relationship may be charged with loss in economic welfare, under the assumption that the original balance struck between work and leisure was the optimum one. Likewise, various forms of taxes may alter the relative choices of occupations and affect the allocation of labor and other resources among occupations. . . .

On the other hand, if factor-owner decisions are considered to be contrary to the best interests of society, taxes may be justifiably used as an instrument to bring them into conformity with the accepted standards. If, for example, society wishes to encourage persons to enter the labor market when they would prefer to remain idle, appropriate adjustments in taxes may produce this result.

Finally, taxes may alter the choice of methods of production. For example, taxation may affect the relative advantages of various techniques and cause a shifting away from those which would allow maximum efficiency in the use of resources. Taxation may affect the relative output of consumption goods and capital goods; if the previous rate of capital formation was that regarded by society as the optimum, a loss in economic welfare results. Taxes may lessen the incentives to maintain maximum efficiency, a charge frequently made against excess profits taxation. On the other hand, if optimum efficiency is not being attained, it is possible that taxes may result in increased effort to gain efficiency.

. . . .

EQUITY IN THE DISTRIBUTION OF BURDEN

The second requirement is a distribution of tax burden among various persons which conforms with accepted standards of equity. Determination of equity in taxation must rest upon value judgments relating to the over-all pattern of income distribution which is regarded as desirable; the most equitable tax system is that which is most closely in conformity with the standards of equity in the distribution of real income which are accepted as most desirable by the consensus of opinion in society. Further discussion of the question of equity in taxation must therefore involve largely an exploration of general social attitudes toward the nature of an equitable distribution.

The Two Aspects of the Problems of Equity. The problem of equity has two major aspects. The first is that of proper treatment of persons in like circumstances, while the second is the desirable relative treatment of persons in unlike circumstances. For the first problem the rule of "equal treatment of equals," that persons in the same circumstances should be taxed to the same extent, is almost universally accepted, although the question of defining "like circumstances" remains. The answer to the second aspect of the problem is much more complex. The rule that persons who are in some sense "better off" than others should pay more taxes is likewise generally accepted. But the determination of what constitutes "better off" and of the appropriate relative burdens on persons in different circumstances is one upon which the consensus of opinion is much less clear. These questions require careful exploration.

There are two general approaches to the problem of equity in taxation which have dominated thinking and policy determination in the field; these are essentially alternative routes to the definition of "like circumstances" and to the establishment of suitable bases for measuring differences in circumstances and determination of appropriate relative treatment of persons in varying circumstances. The first principle is that of benefit, under which equity is interpreted to require equal treatment of persons who receive equal benefits from government activities and adjustment of taxes on persons who receive different benefits in proportion to the amounts of benefits received. The second is the ability approach, which requires equal treatment of persons regarded as possessing the same taxpaying ability and relative adjustment of taxes on persons in unlike circumstances on the basis of the degree of taxpaying ability possessed.

The Benefit Basis. The benefit principle involves the application to the entire governmental sector of the private sector, or *commercial,* rule that goods be paid for by the users. Not only would services sold to the users be paid for by them, but the entire tax structure would be erected upon this principle as well, all taxes being adjusted in terms of benefits received.

Perhaps the most basic argument for the benefit principle of distribution of tax burden is simply one of analogy. Since persons pay for the output of the private sector on the basis of the amount of the product which they receive, it is argued that they should do likewise in the governmental sector. To those who accept this point of view, equity requires that persons pay for all goods and services which they receive, whether produced in the private or governmental sector, and thus that it is inherently "unfair" to make some persons pay for what others get. In addition, the benefit principle is defended on the basis of incentives, by the argument that any tax structure built upon the ability principle inevitably penalizes success and discourages initiative. The person who has little income or wealth pays little, while the person of ability and initiative who earns a high income and accumulates wealth is penalized heavily by the tax burden imposed upon him. Such a premium on failure, it is argued, curbs incentive and willingness to work and therefore retards the development of the economy.

. . . .

Objections to the Benefit Basis. The argument that governments should follow the rules of the private sector of the economy is itself of little merit. Reasoning by analogy from the private to the governmental sector is rarely useful, since governments for the most part perform those functions which private enterprise cannot undertake, largely because the output cannot be sold to the individual users. For the same basic reason — the fact that the benefits accrue to the community as a whole rather than separately to individuals — governments cannot sell these services, nor can they measure the benefits received as a basis for taxes. For the bulk of governmental activities the benefit principle encounters a fundamental contradiction. The government produces the services because the benefits do not accrue separately to individuals; it therefore cannot collect charges for them on a benefit basis, because the benefits cannot be identified with individuals. The only way in which the benefit rule could be followed would be through the establishment of arbitrary criteria of benefit; but such a procedure would not involve the taxing of persons on the basis of actual benefit but according to some indicator of it, such as wealth or income, with incentive effects little different from those of the ability principle.

With other governmental services, some direct benefits are conveyed, as is true, for example, of education. But frequently some of the benefits are social in character. But, more significantly, with many of these activities, even though benefits can be identified with individuals, the pattern of distribution of burden that would result is obviously contrary to that regarded by the consensus of opinion in society as equitable. The principle would mean, for many services, the same per capita burden for the poor as for the rich, although the latter have far greater means with which to make tax payments. The lower-income groups would give up goods essential to a minimum living standard, while the wealthy would give up only a portion of their savings, or marginal luxury spending, a result not in conformity with accepted principles of equity in distribution of burden. In some instances, such as education and recreation, the poor make greater use of the services than the wealthy. Thus the wealthy would pay less for these services than the poor. The benefit principle is contrary to the whole philosophy of governmental welfare activities, designed to increase the economic well-being of the lower-income groups. As pointed out many years ago by Wagner, the German public finance authority of the last century, the entry of governments into the welfare field rendered impossible any general use of the benefit principle.

. . . .

Equity: The Ability Principle. The principle of distribution of tax burden which is in conformity with the generally accepted standards of equity is that of ability to pay. By "ability," in present-day usage, is meant simply economic well-being or the over-all level of living enjoyed by the taxpayer. The principle that accepted standards of equity require that persons who have the same ability to pay should pay equal amounts of taxes and that the persons who have greater ability should pay more to the government than those who are less well off is today almost universally accepted.

On the basis of earlier theories of economic welfare, attempts were made to justify the ability approach on the grounds of sacrifice. It was argued that the payment of a large tax by a person who was well off involved no more sacrifice or disutility than the payment of a small tax by a person who was less well off. But this argument was based upon the assumption that satisfactions of different persons can be compared; modern welfare theory points out that such comparisons are not possible. The present-day justification for the ability principle is simply the fact that, from all indications, it is in accord with consensus of attitudes toward equity in the distribution of real income and of tax burden. Equity questions always involve value judgments, and tax structures can be evaluated, from an equity standpoint, only in terms of their relative conformity with the consensus of thought in the particular society.

In addition, the ability principle does have the advantage of being workable. Various measures of ability or economic well-being can be developed, and since these are also to a large extent the means with which taxes are paid, the tax obligations can be met.

It must be granted, however, that the ability-to-pay principle may have some adverse incentive effects and thus may violate the neutrality rule. Taxes imposed on the basis of various measures of economic well-being penalize success and work and reward idleness and failure and may weaken the incentives of some persons. . . .

The Measures of Economic Well-Being. If the ability principle, as outlined, is to provide workable criteria for establishment and evaluation of tax structures, suitable measures of ability or economic well-being must be developed. Three primary ones have been utilized: income (usually adjusted for various circumstances affecting expenditures necessary for a given standard of living), personal wealth, and amounts spent, either for certain categories of goods or in total.

Income as a Criterion of Economic Well-Being. A family's economic well-being depends primarily upon the income of the family during the period. . . . The quantity of goods persons are able to acquire during the period (including the use value of durable consumer goods owned) and the net increase in savings are the best measure of how well the family lives, or, in other words, its level of living during the period. Accordingly, income is today generally regarded as the best single criterion of economic well-being and thus of ability to pay taxes.

However, the actual level of living which can be attained with a given money income depends in part on certain circumstances affecting the amounts that must be spent in order to attain a given level of living. The most obvious is the number of persons in the family; the more children a family has, the lower is the level of living possible with a given money income. Amounts that must be paid for medical expenses provide another example. Accordingly, the most satisfactory criterion of ability is not the figure of income alone, but the income figure adjusted in terms of these circumstances. . . .

The Significance of Wealth. Apart from these circumstances the economic well-being of the family is influenced not only by the income received during the period but also by the amount of accumulated wealth possessed as well. To the extent that this wealth is invested in income-yielding outlets, the wealth is in part reflected in income. But, nevertheless, if two persons have the same income and are in otherwise similar circumstances but have different amounts of wealth, they are not equally well off. The person with wealth is not under the same compulsion to save as is the person without. The person who has little wealth must save in order to attain the same degree of security against risk as the other person and therefore cannot enjoy the same current level of consumption. Furthermore, the person with wealth may, if he chooses, spend a portion of this wealth each year to maintain a higher level of living than that which the person without the wealth can attain.

The problem is much the same if the person with wealth has invested it in durable consumption goods, particularly a home. While logically the rental value of the home should be included in taxable income, in practice it is not. Accordingly, if income alone is used as the measure of ability, the person who has such wealth essentially enjoys some tax-free income, since he avoids the heavy rental payments of the person who has not yet acquired his home, and he likewise is not under the same obligation to accumulate a reserve.

In general, therefore, both wealth and income are measures of economic well-being. Of the two, income is the better measure, since it, to a greater extent than wealth, determines the level of living. Many persons have high incomes and enjoy high levels of living and yet have little accumulated wealth. Other persons, especially older persons owning their homes, have considerable amounts of wealth but little current income. Thus primary reliance upon wealth would result in a serious departure from the rule of taxing persons in relation to their economic well-being. But some use of the wealth criterion, along with primary use of the income basis, will adjust the tax structure more closely in terms of over-all economic well-being.

Consumption Expenditures as a Measure of Economic Well-Being. It has been argued by various persons over the years that the appropriate measure of ability is not total income but the amount of income spent. It is claimed that economic well-being depends upon consumption purchases alone, that wealth accumulated yields no satisfaction until it is used for consumption purposes. This argument goes back to the statement by the philosopher Hobbes, that equity requires the taxation of persons on the basis of what they take out of the product of the economy, not on the basis of what they add to it. The expenditure basis is also defended on the grounds of simplicity and of the avoidance of double taxation of income saved.

On the other hand, the expenditure approach is condemned on the grounds that it would favor the miser, the person spending a small percentage of his income, and is difficult to make progressive, or even keep from being regressive, with the use of traditional expenditure-based taxes, such as sales taxes. . . .

Equity: The Relationship Between the Tax and the Size of the Base. Regardless of the measures of economic well-being selected, the question of the appropriate relationship between the amount of tax and the amount of the measure, that is, of the tax base, possessed by the taxpayer must be answered. One aspect of the problem can be solved easily: the equal-treatment-of-equals rule requires that persons who are considered to have the same taxpaying ability — the same amount of the base selected as the measure of ability — should pay the same amount of taxes. Thus on the basis of the income measure, two persons having the same income and being in the same circumstances in other defined respects (number of dependents, etc.) must be charged the same amount of tax.

However, the other aspect of the problem — that of the relative burdens on persons having different amounts of the base — is more difficult to resolve. In terms of the primary measure, income, there are three alternative possibilities:

1. A progressive relationship, the percentage of income paid in taxes increasing with increases in income.

2. A proportional relationship, the ratio of tax to income being the same throughout, regardless of the size of the income.
3. A regressive relationship, the ratio of the tax to income being lower with large incomes than with small.

If the tax is levied directly upon income, the nature of the rate itself (progressive, proportional, regressive, relative to the amount of the measure of the tax possessed by the taxpayer) will be the same as the behavior of the tax paid relative to income. But if the tax is not levied on income itself, there may be a difference between the rate structure and the relationship of tax to income. A sales tax has a proportional rate, but the amount of tax paid, relative to income, is likely to be regressive. The Alaska business receipts tax is one of the few levies to have regressive rates.

The "Sacrifice" Approach to the Problem. From the middle of the nineteenth century until recent years, a series of attempts has been made to interpret ability in terms of individual sacrifice and to determine the answer to the question of the desirable type of rate structure on the basis of considerations relating to the behavior of utility or sacrifice.

There were at least three distinct approaches to ability in terms of sacrifice. The first idea was that of *equal sacrifice:* that equity required adjustment of tax rates in such a manner that the sacrifice created for all persons should be the same. Others argued that sacrifice should be *proportional* to income rather than equal at all income levels. The rationale of the proportional-sacrifice doctrine was the argument that persons with greater incomes received much more benefit from society and thus should bear more tax sacrifice rather than the same amount as persons with smaller incomes. Thus, for example, under the equal-sacrifice doctrine, a person with $10,000 income would be taxed so as to bear the same real burden as a person with $5,000 income; with the proportional-sacrifice doctrine, the former would be made to bear twice the sacrifice. The proportional-sacrifice principle would essentially seek to leave utility from national private product distributed in the same manner as before the tax.

The third version was the *minimum-aggregate sacrifice* or equimarginal-sacrifice doctrine, the principle that persons should be taxed in such a manner that the total sacrifice for society would be kept to the minimum possible figure. This, in turn, required that the adjustment of taxes insure that the marginal sacrifice — the disutility arising from the payment of the last dollar of tax — would be the same for all persons. If this point were not attained, the shifting of tax burden from some persons to others would reduce the sacrifice of some persons more than it increased the sacrifice of others, and thus lessen aggregate sacrifice.

All these doctrines were based upon two assumptions: (1) that the law of diminishing marginal utility operates in relation to income, that is, that the marginal utility gained from successive dollars of income declines as income rises, and (2) that all persons have equal capacity for enjoyment of income. The second assumption involves interpersonal utility comparisons, the comparing of relative satisfactions received by different persons.

The earlier exponents of the various sacrifice doctrines maintained that each of the doctrines required progression in taxation. Eventually, however, it was recognized that, even in terms of the assumptions above, this did not follow in all cases. Under the first two doctrines, diminishing marginal utility of income (assuming, of course, equal capacities for enjoyment of income) required merely that a larger absolute sum be taken from the rich than from the poor rather than a greater percentage. The proportional-sacrifice doctrine would require progression if marginal utility of income fell with a sufficient degree of rapidity, but not otherwise. On the other hand, the minimum-aggregate-sacrifice theory, under the assumptions, would require not merely progression but the eventual taking of all incomes in excess of a certain figure, and none from persons with incomes below this figure. This policy is obviously inconsistent with the maintenance of high levels of output and with generally accepted principles of equity in the distribution of income.

Inadequacies of the Sacrifice Approach. In recent decades increasing doubt has been raised about the usefulness of any of these sacrifice doctrines. Both the basic assumptions have been questioned.

1. It is widely argued that the principle of diminishing marginal utility does not necessarily apply to income as a whole, even with respect to one individual. As persons' incomes rise, their wants may increase in intensity. As persons become accustomed to higher levels of living, their desire to maintain them and increase them further may be just as intense as the previous desires were for the lower levels. The prestige value of progressively higher income levels serves to hinder the operation of the principle. As a consequence, it is difficult to argue conclusively that additional increments of income yield persons less satisfaction than earlier increments. A man may feel the loss of 1 per cent of his income as keenly if he receives $10,000 as if he earned $4,000.

2. As indicated previously, modern welfare theory denies the possibility of comparing the utility or disutility of different persons, and the assumption of equal capacities for enjoyment of income is not a realistic one. Even if it be assumed that one person receives greater satisfaction from the first thousand of income than from the tenth thousand, it does not necessarily follow that one individual receiving $1,000 gets greater satisfaction from it than another person gets from an additional $1,000 when he is already receiving $10,000. It cannot even be argued that two persons with the same income and other circumstances receive the same total or marginal utility. It is generally conceded today that, with the present state of knowledge, interpersonal utility comparisons are impossible. Sacrifice or disutility from the payment of tax is not only unmeasurable (though it may be compared

with sacrifice from payments of other amounts) for one individual, but it is completely noncomparable among individuals. Any attempt to build a basis for the tax structure upon disutility or sacrifice is therefore futile, and equity must be established on a basis which does not depend upon comparisons of utilities among individuals.

The Minimum-Living-Standard Approach. One justification for progression is based upon the relationship between total income and the amount regarded as essential for a minimum living standard. It can be argued that a person has no taxpaying ability until he obtains sufficient income to allow him to live and therefore that he should not be taxed upon this minimum. If this argument is accepted, ability would be measured by the portion of income over and above the minimum, and, since this excess constitutes a higher percentage of high incomes than of low, a tax structure progressive according to income is justified. In other words, progression is required because persons with relatively low incomes require all or most of the income for a bare minimum standard of living, and, the higher the income is over this minimum, the greater is the surplus and thus the greater the percentage of income that can equitably be taken by taxation. Acceptance of this principle, however, does not justify progressive *rates* but merely the degree of progression that arises when a certain sum is deductible from the incomes of all persons.

Progressive Rates and Accepted Standards of Equity in the Distribution of Income. The significant justification for progressive rates, as distinguished from the progression created by the exemption of a certain amount of income, is based on accepted standards of optimum patterns of income distribution. The strongest argument for progression is the fact that the consensus of opinion in society today regards progression as necessary for equity. This general acceptance of the desirability of progression is, in turn, based upon the point of view that the pattern of income distribution, before taxes, involves excessive inequality from the standpoint of the best interests of society. This conclusion is, of course, a value judgment, based upon accepted attitudes toward an optimum distribution of income. It does not necessarily rest upon an assumption of interpersonal utility comparisons; excessive inequality can be condemned on the basis of inherent unfairness in terms of the standards accepted by society, upon the inequality of opportunity which results, and upon the effects of inequality in creating social and political instability.

But, as a matter of fact, this principle is accepted in large measure upon an implicit comparison of relative satisfactions gained from incomes in various income groups. Most persons would agree, for example, with the statement that a marginal 1 per cent of income is "worth less" or is "of less importance" or a source of less satisfaction to a millionaire than an additional

1 per cent of income is to a person with a $1,500 income. The fact that there can be no "proof" of this or, in fact, any really significant meaning to the statement does not alter the influence which such beliefs have upon popular attitudes and thus on the development of the generally accepted principle that equity in taxation requires progressive rates.

The Degree of Progression. Since the justification for progression rests upon community consensus about standards of equity in the distribution of income, the desired degree of progression must rest upon the same basis. Thus there are no objective criteria for the establishment of the scale of progression, which must be determined on the basis of the interpretation of the exact degree of income inequality which is regarded as most acceptable by a consensus of thinking in society. At one extreme, the taking of all income earned beyond any particular figure is almost universally regarded as inequitable; at the other, most persons accept the principle that considerable lessening of inequality is desirable. Within these limits, it is impossible to make any categorical statements about the exact degree generally desired. Most of the discussion of the problem is in terms of relatively minor changes in existing schedules; popular thinking is undoubtedly greatly influenced by the degree of progression which has been in use over recent years.

To some critics of progression the lack of any objective standard for determining the degree of progression is a decisive argument against any deviation from proportional taxation. However, if the principle is accepted that some progression is definitely more equitable than none at all, the lack of an objective standard of progression is no conclusive argument against its use. But determination must rest upon the personal opinions of those responsible for the framing of the tax laws in regard to the consensus of opinion about desired patterns of income distribution, as well as a consideration of the possible incentive effects of the various degrees of progression.

The Possible Conflict of Equity and Neutrality Considerations. It has been widely argued by persons opposed to progression or to a high degree of progression that progressive tax rates, by interfering with incentives, curtail economic development and lower national income below potential levels. That some conflict between equity considerations and those of avoidance of adverse effects on the economy is possible cannot be denied. From the standpoint of economic neutrality (assuming optimum economic welfare in the absence of the tax), the most desirable form of tax is one which is completely independent of the economic activities which a person undertakes. In this sense a poll tax is the ideal of all levies. But such taxes are obviously inequitable under usually accepted standards. There is little evidence that highly progressive rate structures are having disastrous effects on the economy; so long as such evidence is lacking, the case against progression is weak. But the possibility of adverse incentive effects must not be ignored.

Minimum Costs of Tax Collection and Payment

A final principle of taxation is that of minimizing the costs and difficulties of collection of the taxes. Effective and inexpensive administration is important if the use of resources to effect the transfer is to be minimized, since, to the extent that resources are used for this purpose, the output of goods and services in the economy is curtailed. Likewise, effective administration is essential for maintenance of equity. No matter how equitable a particular tax structure appears to be in theory, it will not conform in fact with accepted standards of equity if substantial numbers of persons are able to evade or avoid the tax.

The Factors Affecting Administrative Efficiency. Effective administration can be obtained only if the tax base is clearly defined and the tax liability ascertainable with reasonable ease by both the taxpayer and the tax-collecting agency. Ambiguities in the definition of the base make application of the tax difficult for the taxpayer and greatly complicate the task of the government in checking upon the correctness of tax payments made. Ambiguities, as a rule, center around the problem of drawing the line between the taxable base and closely related items which are excluded.

The ability to check upon tax liability depends in large measure upon the general nature of the tax base. The larger the number of taxpayers, obviously, the harder is the task. Whenever the base of the tax consists of a large number of small transactions or when the transactions do not have clearly ascertainable values, the problems of administration are increased. Almost all broad-based taxes encounter these difficulties to a greater or lesser degree. They must be recognized, however, as inevitable problems with such levies as the income and property taxes, and administrative procedures must be developed to meet them.

Effective enforcement likewise necessitates the establishment of the tax base in such a fashion that persons are unable to escape from the tax by readjusting the manner in which they conduct their activities. It is essential that tax structures be framed to insure completeness of intended coverage; there have long been many loopholes, for example, for avoiding federal income taxes. Elimination of these loopholes is not always easy, since drastic measures to close them may create new inequities. But every effort must be made to insure that avenues of escape are minimized so far as possible.

Costs to the Taxpayer. Effective collection, from the standpoint of the economy as a whole, requires minimum cost not only to the governmental units but to the taxpayers as well. Simplicity in tax legislation and provision of adequate, clearly worded information are of the greatest importance. Likewise, convenience of payment is greatly increased if the tax is payable in small amounts during the year, so that persons will not have to accumulate large sums for payment at infrequent intervals.

The Administrative Staff. Effective collection obviously requires an efficient administrative organization; the tasks in the establishment of such an organization are comparable to those involved in the development of any governmental agency. The exact level to which the staff of the tax-collection agency should be extended is not always easily determined. It is obvious that the aim is not the minimum possible staff; if the force is too small, the government will lose directly in revenue more than it saves in collection costs, through outright evasion. The rule is generally accepted that the administrative force should be extended at least to the point at which an additional dollar spent on administration is equal to the additional revenue received, because if the government stops short of this point, it is suffering a direct and immediate financial loss.

Actually, however, there may be substantial justification for extending the administrative organization beyond this point. Improved enforcement not only brings in more revenue directly from the persons checked but likewise insures more complete payment from other persons who realize that they are likely to be caught if they seek to evade the tax. At some point, of course, the gains, both direct and indirect, will no longer exceed the additional cost, and further expansion would be undesirable. This point represents the goal, but determination of it may be difficult.

THE BURDEN OF TAXATION

Under conditions of full employment, when governments divert resources from the private sector of the economy in order to carry on their activities, private-sector output is reduced below the levels otherwise attainable. This reduction is the burden or real cost of the governmental activities; from the standpoint of society, it is, of course, offset, and presumably more than offset, by the benefits from the governmental services. This private-sector burden exists whether or not taxes are imposed to finance the government expenditures. When taxes are used, as they normally are, the type of tax will control the pattern of distribution of the burden among various persons in society. This pattern is frequently called the *incidence* of the tax. In nonfull-employment periods no reduction in private-sector output is necessary to free resources for governmental use; but if taxes are collected to finance the governmental activities, private-sector output will be reduced below levels otherwise attainable, and thus, again, a real burden exists, the nature of the distribution of which depends upon the type of tax employed.

In some instances the tax may be borne directly by the persons who pay it to the government; the dollar disposable income of these persons falls by the amount of the tax, and if no changes in prices of commodities or factor services occur, the real burden rests entirely upon the initial taxpayers, in proportion to the amount of tax which they pay. In other cases, however, as for example with an excise tax, or an income tax which affects the supply of labor, changes in relative prices will occur, and essentially shift some of the burden of the tax on to other persons. Thus if the seller of a commodity subject to an excise tax is able to raise the price of his product, he may be able to maintain his own real income more or less unchanged, while the purchasers of the product will find their real incomes reduced, since they cannot buy as many goods with their given dollar income as before. While some persons prefer to ignore factor-price changes in the discussion of burden, a much more meaningful concept of incidence is one which takes them into consideration.

22

Who Pays the Taxes?

Richard A. Musgrave

The person who writes a check to meet a tax bill is not necessarily the person on whose income the levy actually falls. This makes the analysis of the distribution of the tax burden complex. In this selection Professor Musgrave presents his estimates of taxes borne by different income classes.

I begin with my first topic, who pays the taxes. We have prepared in this connection a revision of our earlier estimates of tax burden distribution for the year 1948. While there have been no drastic changes in tax structure, the great increase in income since that time has rendered the earlier figures of little use for present purposes. The methods followed are more or less similar to those of the earlier study. While the calculations were made in less detail, some of the criticisms of the earlier study were taken into account.[1]

Adapted from "The Incidence of the Tax Structure and Its Effects on Consumption," in Joint Committee on the Economic Report, *Federal Tax Policy for Economic Growth and Stability*, Washington, Government Printing Office, 1955, pp. 97–102.

[1] See R. A. Musgrave, J. J. Carroll, L. D. Cook, and L. Frane, "Distribution of Tax Payments by Income Groups: A Case Study for 1948", *National Tax Journal*, March 1951: and R. A. Musgrave and L. Frane, "Rejoinder to Dr. Tucker", *National Tax Journal*, March 1952.

Table 1

ESTIMATED DISTRIBUTION OF TAX PAYMENTS FOR 1954
(Per cent of total yield contributed by income brackets)

	Spending Unit Income Brackets (thousands of dollars)							
	0– $2,000	$2,000– $3,000	$3,000– $4,000	$4,000– $5,000	$5,000– $7,500	$7,500– $10,000	Over $10,000	Total
Federal Taxes								
(1) Personal income tax	1.6	3.7	8.0	10.2	28.3	13.9	34.3	100
(2) Estate and gift taxes	...	...	...	...	...	...	100.0	100
(3) Corporate profits tax	3.3	4.5	6.3	6.8	15.0	6.9	57.1	100
(4) Excises	8.2	9.8	14.4	14.8	28.2	10.3	14.3	100
(5) Customs	8.2	9.8	14.4	14.8	28.2	10.3	14.3	100
(6) Social-insurance contribution	6.8	10.3	17.9	18.5	28.6	8.6	9.1	100
(7) Total	3.7	5.6	9.7	10.9	24.4	10.7	35.0	100
(8) Without social-insurance contribution	3.2	4.9	8.5	9.8	23.9	11.0	38.7	100
State and Local Taxes								
(9) Personal income tax	.2	2.3	6.0	7.2	22.0	12.7	49.5	100
(10) Inheritance and gift taxes	...	...	...	...	...	...	100.0	100
(11) Corporate profits tax	3.3	4.6	6.4	6.8	15.0	6.9	56.9	100
(12) Excise and sales taxes	8.2	9.8	14.4	14.8	28.2	10.3	14.3	100
(13) Property	7.0	8.4	13.0	13.9	25.7	10.0	22.1	100
(14) Social-insurance contribution	4.7	8.8	13.2	18.8	30.8	11.5	12.1	100
(15) Total	6.9	8.5	13.0	13.9	26.3	10.1	21.3	100
(16) Without social-insurance contribution	7.0	8.5	12.9	13.6	26.0	10.0	21.9	100
All Levels of Government								
(17) Total	4.6	6.4	10.6	11.8	25.0	10.5	31.2	100
(18) Without social-insurance contribution	4.3	6.0	9.8	10.9	24.5	10.7	33.8	100

Table 2

ESTIMATED EFFECTIVE RATES OF TAX FOR 1954

(Tax as per cent of income)

	Spending Unit Income Brackets (thousands of dollars)							
	0– $2,000	$2,000– $3,000	$3,000– $4,000	$4,000– $5,000	$5,000– $7,500	$7,500– $10,000	Over $10,000	Total
Federal Taxes								
(1) Personal income tax	3.1	5.3	7.1	8.4	11.5	14.2	14.6	10.7
(2) Estate and gift taxes	. . .	. . .	. . .	. . .	. . .	. . .	1.4	.3
(3) Corporate profits tax	3.7	3.8	3.3	3.2	3.6	4.1	14.1	6.2
(4) Excises	5.0	4.5	4.1	3.9	3.6	3.3	1.9	3.4
(5) Customs	2.3	.3	.2	.2	.2	.2	.1	.2
(6) Social-insurance contribution	3.6	4.1	4.4	4.2	3.2	2.4	1.1	3.0
(7) Total	15.7	17.9	19.1	20.0	22.2	24.2	33.2	23.8
(8) Without social-insurance contribution	12.1	13.8	14.7	15.8	19.0	21.8	32.1	20.9
State and Local Taxes								
(9) Personal income tax	.01	.1	.2	.2	.4	.5	.8	.4
(10) Inheritance and gift taxes	. . .	. . .	. . .	. . .	. . .	. . .	.4	.1
(11) Corporate profits tax	.2	.2	.1	.1	.2	.2	.6	.3
(12) Excise and sales taxes	5.7	5.1	4.6	4.4	4.2	3.8	2.2	3.9
(13) Property	4.8	4.3	4.1	4.1	3.8	3.6	3.4	3.8
(14) Social-insurance contribution	.5	.7	.7	.9	.7	.6	.3	5.9
(15) Total	11.2	10.4	9.8	9.8	9.1	8.8	7.7	9.1
(16) Without social-insurance contribution	10.7	9.7	9.1	8.9	8.4	8.1	7.4	8.5
All Levels of Government								
(17) Total	26.9	28.3	28.9	29.8	31.3	33.0	40.9	32.9
(18) Without social-insurance contribution	22.8	23.5	23.8	24.7	27.4	29.9	39.5	29.4

Table 3

EFFECTIVE RATES USING BROADER INCOME CONCEPT
(Tax as per cent of income)

	Spending Unit Income Brackets (thousands of dollars)							
	0–$2,000	$2,000–$3,000	$3,000–$4,000	$4,000–$5,000	$5,000–$7,500	$7,500–$10,000	Over $10,000	Total
Federal Taxes								
(1) Personal income tax	2.7	4.7	6.4	7.6	10.6	13.2	14.0	9.9
(2) Estate and gift taxes	. . .	. . .	. . .	. . .	. . .	. . .	1.3	.3
(3) Corporation profits tax	3.2	3.4	3.0	2.9	3.3	3.8	13.5	5.7
(4) Excises	4.4	4.0	3.7	3.5	3.4	3.1	1.9	3.1
(5) Customs	.3	.3	.2	.2	.2	.2	.1	.2
(6) Social-insurance contribution	3.1	3.7	4.0	3.8	3.0	2.3	1.0	2.7
(7) Total	13.7	16.1	17.3	18.0	20.5	22.6	31.8	22.0
(8) Without social-insurance contribution	10.5	12.4	13.3	14.2	17.5	20.3	30.8	19.3
State and Local Taxes								
(9) Personal income tax	.01	.1	.2	.2	.3	.5	.8	.4
(10) Inheritance and gift taxes	. . .	. . .	. . .	. . .	. . .	. . .	.4	.1
(11) Corporation profits tax	.1	.2	.1	.1	.1	.2	.6	.3
(12) Excise and sales taxes	5.0	4.6	4.2	4.0	3.9	3.5	2.1	3.6
(13) Property	4.2	3.9	3.8	3.7	3.5	3.4	3.2	3.5
(14) Social-insurance contribution	.4	.6	.6	.8	.6	.6	.3	.5
(15) Total	9.8	9.4	8.9	8.8	8.4	8.2	7.4	8.4
(16) Without social-insurance contribution	9.3	8.7	8.3	8.0	7.8	7.6	7.1	7.9
All Levels of Government								
(17) Total	23.4	25.5	26.2	26.8	28.9	30.8	39.2	30.4
(18) Without social-insurance contribution	19.9	21.1	21.6	22.2	25.3	27.9	37.9	27.1

Results of Study

1. *Over-all Picture.* . . . The results are summarized in Table 1 which shows the percentage distribution of taxpayments by spending unit income brackets. The data are for 1954 and both the Federal and the State and local tax structures are covered. In Table 2 we show the so-called effective rates of tax, that is, the ratio of taxpayments to income received for the various income brackets. It is this ratio which we look upon to determine whether the tax structure is regressive or progressive, and by how much.

The estimated incidence of the total tax structure, including all levels of government and all taxes, is shown in line (17). We find that the incidence is progressive throughout the scale, although the degree of progression appears to be quite moderate over the lower and middle income ranges. The picture for the Federal tax structure alone is more distinctly progressive as shown in line (7). That for State and local taxes is regressive as shown in line (15).

The general picture may be qualified in two ways. For one thing some people feel that social insurance contributions (all or in part) ought not to be counted since they go to purchase special benefits which are not included in the picture. While I don't quite subscribe to this view, those who do will find the over-all picture excluding social-security taxes in lines (8), (16), and (18). As shown in line (8) this makes for a more progressive picture, especially at the lower end of the scale.

A second qualification arises from the definition of income. It will be noted that the distribution of taxpayments shown in Table 1 is essentially independent of the income concept used. But the pattern of effective rates shown in Table 2 reflects both the distribution of taxpayments and the distribution of income; and the distribution of income in turn depends on the particular income concept that is used. The pattern of effective rates shown in Table 2 is based on a concept of adjusted money income, including outright money incomes as defined by the Survey Research Center[2] plus imputations for (a) capital gains and fiduciary incomes, and (b) retained earnings of corporations and the unshifted part of the corporation tax. The items under (b) must be included in the concept of income in order to permit a fair computation of effective rates because the entire unshifted part of the corporation tax is imputed to the shareholder. Now it might be argued that this is too narrow a concept, that allowances should be made also for other items of imputed income such as rental value of residences, food consumed on farms, employer contributions to pension funds, and so forth. In Table 3 we repeat the results of Table 2, using such a broader income concept. Since the imputed income thus added is distributed more equally than money income, a somewhat larger fraction of total income comes to be allocated to the lower

[2] Survey Research Center of the University of Michigan, the data of which provide the primary basis for this study.

groups. Since the distribution of taxpayments remains the same, the pattern of effective rates becomes slightly more progressive for the case of the Federal and slightly less regressive for the case of the State and local tax system.

In appraising the total picture, we are thus left with four patterns, shown in lines (17) and (18) of Tables 2 and 3. Which of these is the most meaningful pattern is essentially a matter of judgment. While I see good reasons for thinking in terms of lines (17) and (18) of Table 2, some readers may wish to operate with the broader income concept; and others may wish to use an even broader base including, say, an imputed income for the services performed by housewives.

2. *Particular Taxes.* We now turn to the role of particular taxes in bringing about this over-all pattern of incidence.

Personal income tax. Turning again to Table 2, we find that the Federal personal income tax is the most distinctly progressive element in the tax structure. As shown in line (1), this feature does not only apply to the middle and higher income ranges but also at the lower end of the scale. This, I think, is a factor of paramount importance for Federal tax policy and a strong reason for placing primary emphasis on the personal income tax. The progressivity of State income taxes is more moderate, as shown in line (9). In estimating the incidence of these taxes, we assume in both cases that income-tax payments stay put with the taxpayer.

Estate and gift tax. The estate and gift tax is a highly progressive part of the tax structure. If we assume that the tax falls on the donor, we will not be far off if we allocate the total amount to the top income bracket. If we assume it to fall on the recipient, some of the burden might accrue to the lower brackets, but the amount will be small. While the estate and gift tax is a highly progressive element in the tax structure, its weight in the total picture is very slight.

Corporation income tax. The estimated incidence of the corporation income tax, as shown in lines (3) and (11), follows a **U**-shaped pattern. It is more or less proportional or even regressive over the lower to middle range of the income scale and becomes progressive only in the higher brackets. This somewhat surprising result reflects two factors which enter the analysis. One factor is the assumption that two-thirds of the corporation tax is borne by the shareholder while one-third is passed on to the consumer. Thus one-third of the corporation tax is in fact treated as a sales tax, with a correspondingly heavier burden on the lower income groups. While I am not in a position to prove that this is the true ratio, I believe that theoretical reasoning as well as empirical observation renders this a much more defensible assumption than the standard textbook proposition that the corporation tax cannot be shifted except through its effects on capital formation. A second factor is that the ratio of dividend to other income is higher in the lower than in the middle income brackets, reflecting the importance of retirement income in the low brackets. To the extent that the corporation tax falls on the shareholder, the lower income brackets thus assume a proportionately larger burden than may be expected. . . .

These results as well as certain other considerations suggest that the corporation tax is not as progressive an element of the tax structure as some people believe it to be. Indeed, the popularity (insofar as taxes can be popular) of the corporation tax may well be due to the fact that its friends consider it to be highly progressive, while those who prefer it to the personal income tax suspect that in fact it is pretty much in the nature of a sales tax. Both can't be right at the same time. The incidence of the corporation tax, unnecessarily to say, is of crucial importance to tax policy. It has immediate bearing on the problem of integration and to me implies a strong argument in favor of the dividend credit (at the corporate level)approach. Also, it is of evident importance to the choice between taxes on consumption and taxes on investment.

Excises and customs. The estimated incidence of excise and custom duties, shown in lines (4), (5), and (12) of Table 2, is distinctly regressive throughout the income scale. This result is based on the assumption that such taxes are paid for by the consumer and reflects the familiar fact that consumption expenditures decline as a per cent of income when moving up the income scale. The assumption that such taxes are paid by the consumer is not beyond dispute, but I believe that it is a rather sensible one.

Property tax. The estimated incidence of the property tax, shown in line (13), is again regressive, though less so at the upper end of the scale than that of excise and sales taxes. The general principle, in estimating the incidence of this tax is that the part assessed on owner-occupied residences rests on the owner, the part assessed on the improvement component in business property (including rental housing) rests on the consumer, and the part assessed on the rent component of business property rests on the owner. Farm real estate is treated as business property. . . .

Social insurance contributions. The estimated incidence of social insurance contributions, shown in lines (6) and (14) is progressive up to the $4,000 income range and becomes regressive thereafter. In arriving at this result, it was assumed that the employee contribution and one-half of the employer contribution fall upon the employee; and that one-half of the employer contribution is passed on to the consumer.

Conclusions

It goes without saying that the above estimates of tax incidence must be used with reservation. They do not constitute the results of laboratory experiments which unfortunately are not at the economist's disposal. Nor do they involve as exhaustive a statistical analysis as might be undertaken. . . .

In spite of these reservations some such information is needed for intelligent policymaking, and the picture here presented should give a fair approximation to the distribution of taxpayments. The primary conclusion, as I read it, remains that the over-all tax structure in the United States is but moderately progressive over the crucial range of middle incomes, extending from, say, \$2,000 to \$10,000 and including nearly three-quarters of all spending units. Whether this is good or bad from the point of view of equity is not for the economist to say, but it is a factor to be kept in mind in future tax legislation. Secondly, let me draw your attention to the sharp distinction in the incidence of the Federal and the State-local tax package, and what this implies for future trends in our fiscal structure. Finally, there is the distinction in the incidence pattern of particular taxes, and the somewhat surprising role of the corporation tax.

Section B

INCOME AND SALES TAXATION

The first selection (23) in this section continues the discussion of the economic neutrality (or lack of it) of the income tax. Though the contributors are directing their comments specifically to income taxation by the federal government, the points apply in good measure to state income taxes as well, particularly in the cases of those states that use a progressive rate structure. It should be noted that the writers in this combined selection are forced to rely to a degree on their personal judgments, and the reader may wish to draw his own set of conclusions about the extent to which a levy on income departs from the criterion of economic neutrality.

Due (Selection 24) gives a balanced appraisal of the general sales tax. Further, he presents his view on what the "ideal" type of sales tax is.

The last two selections in this section deal with state taxation wholly. The material compiled by the National Education Association (Selection 25) describes how each state government raised its revenues in 1961. Finally, Galbraith (Selection 26) discusses the hard choice that legislators face in deciding between levies on income or consumption.

23

Economic Effects of Income Taxation

A Combined Selection

The question of the economic effects of income taxation is examined from three perspectives in this selection. Professor Butters is a member of the faculty of the Graduate School of Business Administration, Harvard University; Mr. Greenewalt is Chairman of the Board, E. I. du Pont de Nemours & Company; and Professor Break is in the Department of Economics, University of California, Berkeley.

a. Effects of Taxation on the Investment Capacities and Policies of Individuals

J. Keith Butters

This paper discusses the effects of taxation on the investment capacities and policies of individuals. This topic is important because of its relation to the formation and growth of business enterprises.

To put the problem into perspective, it should be noted that taxes may affect the formation and growth of business enterprises in two ways: First, they may dull the incentives needed to induce promoters and entrepreneurs to undertake new developments and the owners and managements of existing enterprises to adopt a vigorous policy of expansion; second, they may curtail the supply of capital required to finance the formation of new enterprises or the growth of existing enterprises.

This paper is concerned with one phase of the second of these areas of tax effects, namely, outside equity capital supplied to business by private investors. The reason for this emphasis is that individual investors supply a major part of the ownership funds available from sources other than retained

Adapted from "Effects of Taxation on the Investment Capacities and Policies of Individuals," in Joint Committee on the Economic Report, *Federal Tax Policy for Economic Growth and Stability,* Washington, Government Printing Office, 1955, pp. 126–133.

earnings to new and growing enterprises, particularly those of small to moderate size.

The effects of taxation on the investment capacity and policies of individuals can best be analyzed by breaking the subject into three main questions:

1. Whose investment decisions are important?
2. How have taxes affected the investment capacity of these groups of investors?
3. How have taxes affected the investment policies of these groups?

Whose Investment Decisions Are Important?

The first task is to ascertain which classes of the population are important, insofar as the effects of taxation on the flow of equity capital from private individuals to business are concerned. In particular, are most of such funds supplied by the large mass of the population with small- to medium-size incomes, or by the small proportion of individuals in the society who receive sizable incomes? When the sharply differing impact of the tax structure on people in different income classes is considered, it quickly becomes apparent that this is a key question for any inquiry into the effects of taxes on individual investors.

Broadly speaking, the evidence leads to an unambiguous answer to this question. *From the standpoint of the flow of equity capital from private investors to business, the investment decisions of individuals in the upper income and wealth classes are of overwhelming importance.* This conclusion is based on an analysis of (1) the groups in the population which have the capacity to invest in business equities in large amounts, and (2) the groups which are disposed to do so. It is supported by a study of the accumulations of new investable funds by different income groups, of the attitudes toward business equities by different income groups, and of the distribution of the ownership of common stock among different income and wealth groups. Because of space limitations, I shall cite in detail only our findings on the last of these points.

Our estimates on the concentration of stock holdings were originally made primarily on data for the year 1949, supplemented to some extent by data for other years. As of 1949 we estimate that approximately 65 to 70 per cent of all the marketable stock held by private individuals was owned by family spending units with a net worth in excess of a quarter of a million dollars. In view of the rise in stock prices and other asset values which has occurred between 1949 and 1955, it seems highly probable that an analysis of current data would show an increase, rather than a decline, in this percentage. Precise data on the fraction of family spending units with this amount of wealth are not available, but it is clear that only a relatively small fraction of 1 per cent of all spending units have a net worth as large as $250,000.

Classified by income groups our best estimate is:

1. About 35 per cent of all the marketable stock held by private individuals is owned by approximately the top one-tenth of 1 per cent of family spending units. As of 1949, this fraction represented family spending units with incomes of $50,000 and over.

2. About one-half of all such marketable stock is owned by the top one-half of 1 per cent of all family spending units. As of 1949, this fraction represented family spending units with incomes of $25,000 and over.

3. About 75 per cent of all marketable stock owned by private investors is held by approximately the top 1 per cent of the population. As of 1949, this fraction represented family spending units with incomes of $15,000 and over.

In percentage terms there seems little reason to believe that estimates based on current data would show any striking shift in the above figures; such limited current data as are available do not appear to indicate that any such shift has occurred. The absolute income levels representing the cutoff points for any specified fraction of the population have, of course, risen between 1949 and 1955 because of the general rise in income levels which has occurred during these years.

As already indicated, the above data constitute only one of several sources of evidence which point to the conclusion that business must look mainly to a very small percentage of the population for the outside equity capital which it hopes to obtain from private individuals. It would take a marked shift in investor habits to invalidate this conclusion.

Effect of Taxes on Investment Capacity of Upper-Income Individuals

The charge is frequently made that the severe rates of the personal income tax have, for all practical purposes, wiped out the capacity of individuals with large incomes to save. The reason for this widespread conviction is not hard to understand. The increases in personal income tax rates since the 1920's have been so great that on superficial examination they appear to establish a prima facie demonstration of this thesis. Moreover, it can be shown beyond any reasonable doubt that the tax increases of recent years have cut severely into the incomes of upper-bracket individuals and undoubtedly also into their capacity to accumulate new investable funds, provided that the incomes of these individuals bear the full brunt of the individual income tax.

This demonstration, however, falls far short of showing that taxes have wiped out, or anywhere nearly wiped out, the capacity of upper-bracket individuals to accumulate new investable funds. On the contrary, the evidence indicates that as a group individuals in the upper income percentiles are still accumulating large amounts of new investable funds despite existing tax rates.

Two reasons appear to explain the continued large accumulations of funds by individuals in the upper-income groups.

First, the habit of saving appears to be deeply ingrained in most individuals with moderate to large incomes. All the evidence indicates that the overwhelming majority of the individuals in the top 1 per cent of the population — ranked by size of income — are still accumulating positive savings, and that the savings of at least half of these individuals amount to a fairly sizable fraction of their incomes before taxes, say, to a fifth or more.

Within the group of persons receiving very large incomes, it is quite possible that those whose living standards were geared to high levels before the period of very high income taxes, and whose disposable incomes have been sharply reduced by the imposition of such taxes, may have ceased to save significantly or may even be living off their capital in many instances. This group, however, appears to be more than offset by individuals whose incomes (both before and after taxes) have risen along with or after the imposition of very high tax rates. The evidence appears to indicate that, as the income of such persons (say, young executive or professional persons) rises, the advance in their living standards is keyed to their disposable income rather than to their income before taxes, and that (by and large) they continue to save despite the high income taxes which they must pay.

A second major explanation of the continued capacity of upper-bracket individuals to accumulate substantial amounts of investable funds is that there are numerous ways in which many groups of upper-bracket individuals can accumulate investable funds without having them subjected to the full impact of the individual income tax. While the data for appraising the extent to which advantage is taken of the opportunities of avoiding the full impact of the individual income tax are not very satisfactory, it can safely be concluded that the use made of them contributes substantially to the surprisingly large accumulations of savings still being made by individuals with large incomes.

In general, then, our conclusion is that the changes in the tax structure over the past 15 to 20 years have substantially reduced the capacity of upper-bracket individuals to accumulate new investable funds as compared with what they would have been able to accumulate under a less progressive tax structure, but that, for the reasons indicated, their remaining capacity is still very large — much larger than is popularly supposed.

Effect of Taxes on Investment Policies of Upper-Income Individuals. Besides curtailing the investment capacity of individuals, taxes could restrict the supply of funds which individual investors are able and willing to invest in business equities by reducing the incentive for individuals to risk their funds in such investments. The fact that individuals with large incomes are still able to accumulate large amounts of investable funds under existing tax rates makes it all the more important to determine the effect of taxes on the investment policies of these individuals. If there is real substance to the allegation that taxes have dried up or seriously impeded the flow of equity capital to business, they must have greatly reduced the willingness of individuals to put their funds to venturesome uses; the restrictive effects of taxes on the investment capacity of individuals, though real, have not been sufficiently powerful by themselves to substantiate this allegation.

The first point to be made in discussing the effects of taxes on the investment policies of individuals is that patterns of investor thinking and reactions are extremely complicated and diverse. For this reason any summary statement on this point must necessarily be oversimplified. I shall deal only with the effects of taxes on the willingness of investors to incur differing degrees of investment risks, that is, to follow venturesome or conservative investment policies; other types of tax effects, such as those on the timing of investment transactions or on the use of such means as gifts and trusts to reduce income and death tax liabilities, will not be considered.

At a general level, one fact stands out very clearly. The ways in which taxes affect the investment policies of individuals can be meaningfully discussed only in the light of the investment objectives of groups of investors. Two individuals, similarly situated as to age, family responsibilities, and income and wealth status, may react to the tax structure in very different ways if they have different investment objectives. Before reporting our conclusions on tax effects, therefore, it will be helpful to describe the range of investment objectives which characterize individual investors. Broadly speaking, these investors can be classified into the following categories:

1. Investors who take the extreme position of conservatism and who strive simply (or mainly) to preserve their capital. Most individuals with capital preservation as their main investment objective seem to have in mind the dollar value of their wealth rather than its real value in terms of purchasing power.

2. Investors who have both capital preservation (or security) and a moderate income yield as investment objectives, but who are very reluctant to make investments which involve an appreciable degree of risk of capital loss.

3. Investors who place a major emphasis on an "adequate income yield" or a "good return" from their investments and who are willing to assume somewhat greater risks of capital loss provided that the prospective income yield is great enough to warrant the assumption of these risks.

4. Investors who stress both an adequate income yield and an opportunity for capital appreciation as investment objectives and who are willing to assume still greater risks of capital loss provided that the prospects for capital appreciation are good.

5. Investors who are interested almost exclusively in capital appreciation and who have relatively little interest in income yield. This type of investor typically expects to assume high risks of capital loss provided that the compensating opportunities for large capital gains are sufficiently attractive.

From the standpoint of tax effects, the most significant breakdown of investors by categories of investment objectives is between those investors who have capital appreciation as a main or important investment objective and those who do not. Individuals with capital appreciation as a major investment objective typically react very differently to the tax structure than do those whose major emphasis is on income yield or on security. To the extent that taxes influence investment decisions at all, they drive the great majority of investors with the latter objectives into more conservative investments, whereas they typically induce investors interested mainly in capital appreciation to make even more venturesome investments than they otherwise would.

A much larger proportion of investors in the upper-income groups than in the lower-income groups has capital appreciation as a main or important investment objective. For example, only about one-fourth of the individuals whom we interviewed with incomes of less than $7,500 expressed a strong interest in capital appreciation as an investment objective as compared with well over half those with incomes of $25,000 and over.

Because of the sharp differences in the reaction to the tax structure of income-minded and security-minded investors, as compared with appreciation-minded investors, the general nature of the tax effects on individuals can best be described by discussing these two groups separately.

Income-Minded and Security-Minded Investors. Income-minded and security-minded investors, in making investment decisions, tend to balance the current income yield of their investments against the risk of capital loss, and to give very little weight in their investment decisions to the possibility of capital gains usually present in investments which also present high risks of capital loss. The high rates of the individual income tax exert by far the most important tax influence on the investment decisions of these groups of individuals, and their predominant effect is to drive these individuals into lower-yield, less risky investments than they would otherwise make. The intensity of this tax effect is, of course, closely related to the tax brackets of the investors concerned.

For these groups of investors, the high income-tax rates on upper-bracket individuals exert their main effects by greatly reducing both the absolute yield and the relative yield on investments with a high yield (such as common stock) as compared with low-yield investments (such as Government bonds). For individuals in very high-tax brackets, the after-tax yields on such investments as common stocks may even be reduced below those available from some types of low-risk investments such as tax-exempt securities and certain life-insurance policies. This reduction (or even reversal) in after-tax yield differentials causes many investors with income or capital preservation as an investment objective to shift part of their funds out of, say, common stocks and into lower-yield investments because they do not regard the income yield remaining after taxes from high-yield securities as adequate compensation for the risks of capital loss inherent in their ownership.

Theoretically, the fact that in computing taxable income capital losses may be deducted, at least in part, constitutes a partial offset to the foregoing repressive effects. To the extent that capital losses can be offset against otherwise taxable income or capital gains, the net amount at risk by the taxpayer is less than the total amount involved. In other words, the maximum net loss which can be suffered by the taxpayer is the total amount of his investment less any compensating tax savings in the event that the investment turns out to be a total loss. Much has been made of this point in theoretical analyses of tax effects.

Practically speaking, however, these offsetting considerations to the repressive effects of high income-tax rates are of very limited importance for the categories of investors now being discussed. For one reason, the severe restrictions placed on the deductibility of capital losses by the tax law greatly reduce the potency of loss deductions as a factor influencing the investment decisions of individuals. Subject to minor qualifications, the maximum tax benefit which can be derived from the deductibility of capital losses on assets held for more than 6 months is 25 cents for each dollar of realized loss, and even this tax benefit is dependent on the availability of capital gains against which the loss can be offset.

A second reason of major importance in reducing the practical importance of loss offsets for these groups of investors is that these offsets are not usually in the forefront of investor consciousness. As a general statement, investments are made because the investor expects them to be successful, not because he anticipates that they will be a failure. Given this expectation, it is only natural that greater attention is given by investors to the impact of taxes in reducing the return available in the event of success than to the cushioning effect of loss offsets in the event of failure. Consequently, for investors who are motivated by the prospective income yield of their investments rather than by a desire for capital gains, the existence of high surtax rates typically constitutes an investment deterrent and would, we believe, continue to do so even if substantially more generous loss offsets were permitted than are now allowed.

As already noted, the income-tax effects just described account for the large majority of tax-motivated shifts in a conservative direction by the groups of investors under discussion. The only other tax effect causing any considerable number of security-minded and income-minded individuals to shift to more conservative investment positions is the desire for liquidity stimulated by the estate tax. The estate-tax structure creates a definite incentive for many individuals, especially those in the top wealth classes, to increase their holdings of liquid assets and of life insurance in order to provide a ready means of payment of their estate taxes on their death. Generally speaking, however, shifts in this direction appear to be moderate in degree. Only a minority, even of the wealthiest individuals, appear to increase their holdings of these assets substantially for estate-tax reasons.

In contrast, only rarely are income-minded and security-minded investors stimulated by tax considerations to take greater rather than smaller investment risks. Individuals who do react in this way generally are persons under such pressure to maintain a given level of income that they are prompted to shift to more venturesome forms of investment as high taxes (and other factors such as increases in the general cost of living, the loss of earned income on retirement, and declining interest rates) place increasing pressure on their standard of living. Such individuals usually do not have large incomes.

Tax Effects on Appreciation-Minded Investors. The tax effects on investors interested mainly in capital appreciation are quite different from those just summarized for the income-minded and security-minded investors. Our evidence points overwhelmingly to the conclusion that, for appreciation-minded investors, *the single most important feature of the tax structure is the differentially low rate at which long-term capital gains are taxed in comparison with the much higher rates on ordinary income, especially for individuals in the upper income-tax brackets.* This differential has stimulated inherently venturesome individuals to seek out investments which offered prospects of capital gains rather than the receipt of ordinary income. As a consequence, it has caused this group of investors to shift funds out of relatively conservative investments, offering little or no opportunity for capital appreciation and into more venturesome types of investments such as relatively speculative marketable common stocks, closely held companies, new ventures, real estate, and oil properties. The incentive to invest in real estate and oil properties, it should be noted, is further stimulated by the opportunity of obtaining what many investors regarded as important tax advantages in the form of percentage depletion and current deductibility of intangible drilling costs on oil properties and depreciation deductions on real estate.

The power of these inducements is reflected in the fact that, of the appreciation-minded individuals who respond at all to tax effects, the overwhelming majority move into more venturesome investment positions because of taxes.

Our evidence indicates that many more investors are attracted by the favorable rate differential accorded capital gains than are repelled by the existing restrictions on the deductibility of capital losses. The differential between the tax rates on capital gains and on ordinary income was mentioned very frequently, especially by investors with large incomes, as a motivating factor in investment decisions. In contrast, only a handful of instances were encountered in which the existing limitations on the deductibility of capital losses were cited as deterrents to venturesome investments. Similarly, the absolute level of the capital gains rate and the length of the 6-month holding period were cited as investment deterrents only in a very small number of instances.

No single motivation was responsible for the limited number of instances in which appreciation-minded individuals were driven by the tax structure into less venturesome investment positions. The desire for liquidity to meet eventual estate-tax liabilities was occasionally mentioned as a reason for increased holdings of liquid assets and insurance. Other investors indicated that they were reluctant to invest in new ventures or closely held companies because the high rates of the corporation income tax limited the potential growth of these companies. Finally, in a very few cases, the level of the capital gains tax was cited by appreciation-minded investors as an explanation of a decreased willingness to make venturesome investments. But, as we have already indicated, for appreciation-minded investors as a group all these factors combined were far outweighed by the positive inducement to venturesome investments offered by the differentially low rate at which long-term capital gains are taxed in comparison with ordinary income.

Over-all Appraisal. With all the foregoing factors taken into account, the following is the best one-paragraph summary of our findings which I can give: The tax structure in recent years has cut substantially into the investment capacity of the upper income and wealth classes — the strategic source of venture capital for investment in business — and, on balance, it also decreased the willingness of these investors in the aggregate to make equity-type investments. In other words, for equity-type investments considered as a whole the investors who were induced by taxes to shift to less risky investment positions appear to have overbalanced the opposite reaction of appreciation-minded investors. The latter group, however, may have been so stimulated by the tax structure to seek out investments offering unusually large capital gains potentialities as actually to increase the flow of capital to such situations. However this may be, it is clear that the combined impact of these effects fell far short of drying up the supply of equity capital which private investors were willing and able to make available to business. The evidence indicates that the accumulation of investable funds by the upper-income classes has been consistently large during postwar years, despite the existing tax structure, and that individuals with large incomes and substantial wealth continue as a group to hold and invest a large proportion of their funds in equity-type investments.

b. The Effect of High Tax Rates on Executive Incentive

Crawford H. Greenewalt

I was glad to accept the invitation of your committee to present my views as to the probable impact of high personal taxation on the future of business enterprise. It is encouraging to me to see a committee of the Congress in-

Adapted from "The Effect of High Tax Rates on Executive Incentive," in Joint Committee on the Economic Report, *Federal Tax Policy for Economic Growth and Stability*, Washington, Government Printing Office, 1955, pp. 185–191.

quiring into this subject, for I am convinced that it is an area of extraordinary importance to national growth and prosperity.

Inasmuch as my views are not wholly based on demonstrable evidence, and must rest to some extent on opinion, I should first define the bounds of my competence. I am not an authority on taxation, and I have no technical qualifications either for defending or for deprecating any particular method of tax assessment.

Neither am I an expert on budgetary matters, and so I cannot suggest how much it is wise, or desirable, or necessary, for our Government to spend. The views I shall express are those of an executive who must face the very practical problems involved in the operation of a large corporation. These, of course, embrace the present, and the usual problems of customer, employee, and stockholder relations. In a much more important sense, however, they are problems of the future and comprise, insofar as possible, the development of policies and practices which will insure continuing effective performance well beyond present horizons.

One of our difficulties arises out of the realization that governmental expenditures will remain very high for a considerable period, even with maximum emphasis on economy, and that the tax burden on our people will be correspondingly large by previous standards. If this were not the case, the question of executive incentives would hardly be an issue of importance.

As our country has developed and matured, we have become increasingly dependent on an active and dynamic industry for our economic growth and prosperity. Without minimizing in the slightest the important contributions to our national economy made by the farmers, the professions, the service trades, the fact is that our standard of living is firmly anchored to our industrial development.

Since this is so, it follows that how business and industry fare must be a matter of great importance to all Americans. Their standard of living, their future well-being, are vitally dependent upon an American industry that continues to be dynamic, resourceful, and progressive. This desirable state of affairs can continue only so long as industry can compete successfully for the limited supply of talented people. For an industrial corporation is not a machine that can be run by automation. It is a team of human beings that must have first-class direction by intelligent and able management. And if we have learned one fundamental truth in industry, it is that first-class performance can never come from second-class performers.

It is not an exaggeration to say that the success of any business enterprise will depend very substantially upon the caliber and character of its management group. I have thought a good bit about the personal characteristics that lead to managerial competence, for selection of outstanding people is my most important single responsibility. The best I can do is to define an executive as one with the ability to blend men with a great variety of essential technical talents into a harmonious and well-knit ensemble. The analogy with the conductor of a great orchestra might be used, but the executive has a tougher job, since we have no Beethovens or Mozarts in the business world to provide us with a score that we can follow.

But whatever definition or analogy one wishes to use, I am quite sure that the competent executive is a rare bird — and is found only by combing through large numbers of eager candidates.

His job also becomes more and more difficult as time passes and our industrial technology becomes still more complex. The executive of the next generation must inevitably be a better man than his predecessor, just as managerial competence has grown from its position a generation ago.

The point I make is that industry, if it is to keep abreast of its responsibilities to the Nation, must have a great number of first-class minds at its disposal. It must compete for them with all other phases of our society, for there are never enough to go around. The fields of government, education, the military, the arts, the professions, all are seeking to persuade able young men to cast their lot with them. Each has its own type of incentive to offer, and the demand for talent always exceeds the supply.

THE ESSENTIAL QUESTION OF INCENTIVE

The question of incentive is essential, whether we are speaking of business getting its share of the talent crop or of encouraging the exercise of that talent once it is enlisted. It is perhaps unfortunate that human beings should require lures of any kind as the price of initiative, but I am afraid we have not yet reached that state of grace in which people will surely do their best without external motivation. People being people, they will for the most part respond with their highest abilities only when there is some stimulus or some satisfaction associated with success.

Adequate incentives, of course, differ with different people. Some are attracted most strongly by the promise of prestige. Some are more interested in leisure time, to follow scholarly pursuits or perhaps simply to meditate upon the ills of the world. To some people, public notice or outward signs of rank and importance are alluring goals. Some seek power. For most, however, the strongest and probably the most desirable incentive is financial reward. Furthermore, financial reward is not only an incentive in itself; it is the only fluid medium that can be used to balance the attractions of the more intangible compensations, such as prestige, power, or public notice.

There is another aspect of the monetary incentive that seems to me worthy of comment. It is the only reward that can be cut down on a basis of fixed percentages. We do not, for example, withhold 91 percent of an Oscar going to the best moving-picture actress of the year. The winner of a Nobel prize does not have to give the Government a certain percentage of the prestige accruing to him. A brilliant violinist does not have to share his applause with the collector of internal revenue. These illustrations may seem facetious, yet they are based on a serious foundation, for we do in fact make the recipient of monetary rewards, and him alone, give up significant percentages in taxes. We are, that is, penalizing only one manifestation of success, and this seems to me, frankly, not only unfair but, for the future, a dangerous practice.

I do not propose to debate the relative nobility of these various carrots that are held out before us human donkeys, for that seems to me to make little difference so long as there is one toward which we will stretch. I see no reason, however, to believe that financial gain is any less worthy than prestige or recognition, and it is certainly less stultifying than the lust for power or mere social preening. It is, also, the incentive that American industry has historically used.

This is largely because it is the type of inducement most consistent with the business environment. In other fields, tangible and intangible incentives have been developed over the years, each more or less characteristic of its own activity. In the academic world, for example, professional prestige and personal recognition have a certain magnetism that attracts gifted minds even though the financial remuneration is unjustifiably low.

The world of politics affords an opportunity for public service and public attention which, to some people, is highly attractive. In the arts and the theater, one has the goal of fame and the limelight. In pure science there is the distinction that goes with the highest awards such as the Nobel prize. In the Army, Navy, and Air Force, incentive to move up through the various echelons of command is based on rank and perquisites; even the church has its hierarchies and various symbolic tokens of achievement.

Business, for the most part, is in a poor position to compete in these intangible areas. With few exceptions executives of great ability remain relatively unknown. A player of even minor roles in the films, a leader of a jazz orchestra, or a writer of only average accomplishment may be far better known than many leaders of industry. For businessmen there are few medals, prizes, degrees, uniforms, patriotic citations, or grandiose honorifics. There are few featured players on the industrial stage.

There is, of course, the satisfaction that comes from work well done. But this is peculiar to no special section of our society; it is common to all. For the purposes of this discussion, it simply cancels out.

And so industry must rely most importantly on financial compensation. As it becomes increasingly less able to do so, it will lose its capacity to induce qualified people to make their careers in industry, or to seek to advance to their maximum capacity.

The Erosion of the Money Incentive

It is here, as I see it, that our danger lies. I am certain that the effectiveness of the money incentive is being eroded by the tax rates that prevail in the upper brackets today. While many companies are experimenting with nonmonetary incentives, basically industry must rely upon the coin of compensation most suitable to its character. I am afraid the raw truth is that, in the long run, we shall begin to lose out and our proportion of the available candidates will fall unless some relief can be obtained.

I am necessarily talking in the future tense, because it is quite clear that the point of concern is not the executive of today, or even of the immediate future. I think, if we are to focus the picture, we must rule out consideration of the present management group. I doubt that high personal taxation has had substantial effect upon the performance of present-day management people, even though they may not be happy over the realization that at top levels each additional dollar of gross income nets its earner about 9 cents. I confess to some pain in this respect myself, but I cannot say that I am inclined as a result to work less diligently or to take my responsibilities less seriously.

Today's executives are, I think, reasonably immune. By the time a man has reached a position of eminence within his organization, he is influenced importantly by his sense of loyalty, his sense of obligation, a preoccupying interest in the work, or, as has been unkindly suggested, by conditioned reflex.

The same applies, I would guess, to those who may be regarded as the immediate successors, for they too have reached a point where the challenge and associations of the work present an incentive that will probably override reduced financial motivations. At this point one might ask: If we are not talking about present management, who is it that concerns us?

There are two major areas of concern. There is, first, the effect of high income-tax rates on long-range monetary incentives, which promises to make it more difficult than heretofore to persuade young men with real ability to enter the ranks of business. Let me make it clear that I am not asking for an improvement in industry's competitive position opposite the other fields of endeavor. I merely want to maintain it.

There is, second, increased difficulty, also tracing to high tax rates, in persuading men of ability who have risen to the point where they are in sight of reaching their top capacity to keep on going rather than to rest on their oars.

I want to comment on each of these, for they are the heart of industry's problem.

It has been noted by many sociologists that for young men of ability the lure of security at a modest level has gained greatly in recent years as against the desire to venture and work to reach the top. I suspect that one of the basic reasons for this is that the financial rewards offered today just don't seem worth the struggle. Why, a young man could well be thinking, should he enter the industrial arena when he knows that the higher he gets on the ladder, the more of his time will be spent working for the Government and the less working for himself? And this is a critical question, for in most cases the choice of a career made by a man when he leaves college governs his activities for the rest of his working life. If he enters law, medicine, the church, politics, the armed services, Government, the arts, teaching, research, business, the chances are strong that he will not leave that field, but will perhaps through inertia make it his career.

Beyond this, I am sure that with few exceptions, the young man with the ability to do well in one of these fields could do well in many of them. There is, save in cases of unusual physical coordination such as marks an Artur Rubinstein, or a Caruso, or even a Babe Ruth, no particular identifiable set of abilities impelling one to choose any of these fields. Enrico Fermi, for example, was an outstanding scientist. From my knowledge of him, I feel sure he would, had he so elected on leaving college, have made an outstanding business executive, a splendid lawyer, or doctor, or writer, or what you will.

What I am saying is that each of these fields must appeal to the same group of talented young men, and trust that the incentives it has to offer will attract sufficient numbers of them to carry on its work. And since the chief incentive industry has to offer is financial, it follows that any erosion of that incentive makes it more difficult for industry to get its share of the supply, with inevitable serious consequences for the future.

Of those who enter the business field, a certain number will be equipped potentially to handle the executive functions at various levels. It is to the advantage of the individual company, and ultimately to the advancement of the American economy, that those advancing into the upper levels of management be selected from as large and as eager a group as possible.

I think it is plain that the selection of 1 man from a list of 50 promising candidates offers more qualitywise than the selection of 1 man from a field of 20, or 15, or 5. The principle is the same in business as it is in the military, say, or in Government. As citizens, we are uneasy when we note a reluctance on the part of individuals to seek public office. As a business executive, I feel uneasy if there are not more than a few talented candidates for advancement. And this leads me to the second major area of difficulty.

Is Promotion Less Attractive?

In business, as elsewhere, it is important for us to induce as many of our younger men as possible to set their sights on the job ahead and to broaden their shoulders for responsibilities to come. If we are to do so, the game must be worth the candle. And some of my associates have already noted that there are signs among the younger men that promotion is a little less attractive than it used to be. How this trend may be expected to show up, in specific terms, is hard to say; my own guess is that it will take the form of slow attrition, beginning with borderline cases. Where we now have 10 who want to try for the jobs of major importance, we may have 9 tomorrow — 1 candidate deciding that since it is worth considerably less after taxes, it isn't worth the extra effort. So we have 9, and the next year we may have 8, and management will be the poorer for the loss. For it is that extra effort that wins, that has made American industry what it is today. The progress we have made has not been achieved by perfunctory or routine performance; it has come about because people have been inspired or induced to give everything they had to the task at hand, and not to take it easy. The industrial miracle of America has come because our people have shown a capacity for accomplishment well beyond their rated potential. It must follow that anything that weakens that capacity will weaken our industrial potential, and with it, the Nation.

In the Du Pont Co. we recognize 16 levels of employment, each successive one embracing more authority and more responsibility than the one below. In order to make it attractive for a man at one level to strive to advance to the next, there must be sufficient incentive to make the increased effort seem worthwhile. And this increase must be net, after taxes, for actual spendable money is what counts. The large gross figure, impressive though it may appear, gives one no advantage opposite the landlord or the butcher, or the increased financial demands that go with increased responsibility and higher standing in the community.

However, in order to provide significant net increases for the levels down the line, the gross salaries in the top levels must be very high indeed. Suppose we assume that the net increase between levels which will provide incentive to advance is about 25 percent, and then work out the progression for 16 levels. One arrives at figures at the top which are in the realm of pure fantasy which perhaps explains why my predecessor 30 years ago received a compensation after taxes twice as great as mine today with no adjustment for the purchasing power of the dollar. Being an honest man I think I should say that when I pointed the discrepancy out to him he replied merely that he was easily twice as good as I and hence deserved it.

. . . .

WHO WILL BE THE LOSER?

This brings us up against the hard fact that if, through declining incentives, business cannot attract the great numbers of capable management personnel it must have to move ahead, the chief losers are not the individuals concerned. If the caliber of management available to American business declines, the results will be reflected inevitably upon everyone, in business or not. The economy we have created in this country is closely intertwined; the effect of one activity upon another is intimate and continuous.

Management ineptitude would assess its penalties in terms of higher costs, diminished opportunity, and a slowing down of the kind of bold venture that is necessary to growth. It would be demonstrated, I think, in declining stability, for often the failure of one firm engulfs others. In so highly integrated an economy as ours, shock waves are transmitted with great speed and ruinous force. We cannot sustain many such shocks without impairing our strength and security as a nation.

And so every citizen has a stake. He wants lower prices, expanded employment, a degree of job security, good prospects for advancement. He wants better schools, better medical facilities, better care for the aged, more cultural facilities. He can have them in an era of rapidly expanding population only if industry grows more dynamic rather than less, better managed rather than worse.

This is why all of us must take with great seriousness any threat to the future successful operation of industry, for it is clear that industry is the keystone of our economic arch. The real wealth it produces makes possible progress in all our other fields of endeavor, educational, cultural, charitable, governmental, and so forth. Conversely, any act that cripples our industry, cripples the Nation and the free world along with it. In proof one need only look at Communist efforts to foment discord in American industry.

It is essential that our friends as well as our enemies realize the disastrous consequences of any such development, for economic laws take no account of motives. Violate them and the penalty is assessed even though the violation might have been committed for the most worthy and helpful motives.

I see in the present high tax levels such a threat to American industry. Let me emphasize again that my concern is not with the present crop of executives nor with their immediate successors. It is with the future. It is somewhat nebulous and hard to grasp because it is not an immediate and finite problem. But its importance is no less great because of that, and statesmanship implies concern for what lies ahead as well as for what presently confronts us.

How the problem is to be met is a question to which I do not have the answer. I am hopeful that the deliberations of your committee may produce helpful data and valuable conclusions. But of this I am sure: the dollars involved in the high-tax brackets constitute but a very small percentage of the return to the Government from personal-income taxes. I am not necessarily arguing for a limitation, but for the sake of illustration it can be pointed out that personal-income taxes in excess of 50 per cent paid in the calendar year 1954 amounted to $1,075,000,000. This is 3.8 per cent of total personal-income-tax collections for that year. It is, incidentally, 1⅔ per cent of Federal expenditures for 1954, and would have run the Government for 6 days.

The exactness of these figures is not important, however. What is important is that it would be a tragic thing, indeed, if, for such a relatively small amount, we should jeopardize the future successful operation of our industry. If it should not hold its own in the years to come — indeed, if it should not do much better than hold its own — all of us will face a bleak and static future.

c. The Effects of Taxation on Work Incentives

George F. Break

The point of view that high income-tax rates such as have prevailed in this country since World War II seriously sap the work incentives of the American people and thereby deter economic growth has been presented with great vigor and persistence. Typically the conclusion is treated as self-evident or as so reasonable, given a little thought, as to eliminate the need for direct empirical evidence. One may admire the strategy of this line of attack, but further investigation shows the forces involved in it to be largely illusory.

The first three sections of this paper are concerned with the economic factors which determine the influence on work incentives of the taxation of earned income. It will be seen that there are at least as good reasons for believing that such taxation will have a net incentive effect as there are for believing it will have a disincentive effect. In the next two sections a similar analysis is applied to income taxes on property incomes and to excise and sales taxes. Finally, the findings of a number of recent empirical studies of worker behavior are examined briefly. The results are likely to surprise those who have accepted the disincentive argument as conclusive. High income taxes, it would appear, have as yet not had any serious disincentive effects. It is true that some workers have been led to contract their efforts, but at the same time others have been induced to work both harder and longer. Whatever the merits of fiscal policies aimed at lowering income-tax rates may be, the encouragement of greater productive activity on the part of workers does not appear to be one of them.

Incentive and Disincentive Effects of Income Taxation

To many taxpayers the disincentive proposition given at the beginning of this paper probably appears realistic enough. They may reason that "with tax rate as high as they are now it is not worth my while to do any extra work because the income from it after taxes is inadequate." The implication, of course, is that at lower tax rates the additional work would be undertaken. In reaching this conclusion, however, the taxpayer is likely to be thinking in terms of a given base income to which a larger reward from a given amount of extra work is added when tax rates are lowered. This argument overlooks an important fact — that lower tax rates would increase the taxpayer's base income — and at higher income levels, as empirical studies have shown, people typically want to take more leisure time rather than less. A lowering of

Adapted from "The Effects of Taxation on Work Incentives," in Joint Committee on the Economic Report, *Federal Tax Policy for Economic Growth and Stability*, Washington, Government Printing Office, 1955, pp. 192–197.

income-tax rates, in short, exerts two opposing influences on work incentives: a stimulating one because after-tax rates of pay are higher, and a discouraging one because for a given amount of work taxpayers have more money. Conversely, an increase in tax rates, by lowering wage rates, tends on the one hand to induce greater effort because taxpayers find themselves with less money to spend, but, on the other, makes added effort less attractive by reducing the reward.

Some workers may react to higher taxes by simply tightening their belts, preferring to economize on consumer goods and services and on saving rather than on leisure time. Others may work more, thereby economizing on leisure as well as on other things. Still others may work less, illustrating the disincentive effects of tax increases. These people, it may be noted, show a marked lack of attachment to the rewards from productive activity, since they are led by a fall in earned income as a result of taxation to cut their incomes still further by reducing their efforts. Such a reaction is, of course, possible. To elevate possibilities of this sort to the rank of inevitabilities, as some of the more ardent critics of income taxation are prone to do, seems, however, more than a little extreme.

Another way of describing the effects of income taxes on work incentives is in terms of the value to the worker of the disposable income obtainable from the last unit of work he does. "Value" in this case does not refer simply to the number of dollars earned but more fundamentally to the usefulness of those dollars to the worker and his family. When tax rates rise the value received from a unit of effort is reduced since fewer dollars are brought home to the family coffers, but the usefulness of each dollar is increased since the family has fewer total dollars to spend. If, on balance, the value of the income earned by the last unit of effort decreases, the worker will tend to work less as a result of the increased tax rates; if, on the other hand, the value increases he will continue to work as much as before and may well wish to expand his supply of labor. Opposite results occur when tax rates are lowered. Again we note the existence of opposing lines of influence and the indeterminacy of the final outcome at this level of analysis.

High income taxes, then, do not necessarily have important disincentive effects. Some workers, it is true, may work less hard because of the influence of high tax rates. Others, however, may be led to increase their efforts, and a good many people may be virtually unaffected. Additional evidence is needed before any useful conclusions can be drawn. Fortunately, both theory and observation can help provide that evidence.

The Effects of Inflexible Monetary Commitments

Most of us have more than a nodding acquaintance with relatively fixed monetary commitments of one kind or another. Monthly payments on a home mortgage or rental to a landlord, life-insurance premiums, contributions to pension and annuity funds or to prepaid medical plans, union or professional dues, and other fixed costs of earning income, periodic payments incurred when consumer durables are bought on time, the obligation to support and educate children or to care for elderly relatives — all fall in this category. Possession of such commitments tends to make the taxpayer react to an increase in income taxes by increasing his efforts to earn income. The disincentive effect of lower take-home rates of pay is more than offset by the incentive push of a lower level of income when living expenses are not easily contracted.

High income taxes, therefore, are likely to have incentive effects on workers with large families, on young people who are setting up homes and acquiring their stock of consumer durables, and upon all who, for whatever reason, have become heavily indebted to others. A period following a rapid rise in consumer and mortgage debt, when higher taxes may well be called for because of strengthening inflationary pressures, is relatively favorable to the imposition of higher income taxes since their incentive effects will be intensified and their disincentive effects lessened by the previous growth in fixed-debt obligations. For similar reasons, a high and rising birthrate is favorable to high income taxes. On the other hand, Government policies which reduce the pressure of fixed monetary commitments on the worker, such as baby bonuses, provision for old age and retirement, for temporary periods of unemployment, or for sickness and injury tend, by themselves, to strengthen the disincentive effects of income taxation. These adverse tendencies, however, will be offset to the extent that Government benefits of this sort are closely matched by contributions on the part of the beneficiary.

A worker is also effectively committed to the maintenance of a given level of living in the face of an increase in income taxes if that level of living represents the minimum necessary for continued physical existence in his society. On the lowest income groups, therefore, income taxes may be expected to have incentive effects. At higher income levels the purely physical pressure of minimum subsistence is absent, but it may be replaced by equally effective social pressures — well-defined modes and standards of living which the workers feel they must maintain.

Fixed monetary commitments of various kinds, therefore, exist at all income levels. Together they provide an important set of factors which strengthen the incentive effects of high income taxes at the expense of the disincentive effects.

The Effects of Changes in Personal Exemption Allowances

A raising or lowering of personal exemption allowances has a powerful effect upon income-tax revenues because of the large proportion of income taxed at the lowest bracket rates. Such changes are also likely to affect work incentives. Unfortunately we can specify the result definitely only for those who remain in the same tax bracket both before and after personal exemptions are altered. For them the marginal rate of tax, and hence take-home rates of pay on the last units of work done as well as on any additional units that might be done, remains constant, while disposable incomes rise or fall as exemption allowances rise or fall. The sole effect on incentives, therefore, comes from the changes in disposable income, larger exemptions tending to reduce effort and smaller exemptions to increase it.

A large number of taxpayers, however, will be shifted into a different tax bracket when personal exemptions are changed. For them both marginal and average tax rates — i.e., take-home rates of pay and disposable incomes — change, and opposing influences on work incentives are again set in motion. Increased exemptions, for example, stimulate desires for more leisure time as a result of increased disposable incomes, but increased rates of pay at the margin make work more attractive. The strength of the latter effect will differ at different points on the income scale since rate changes from one tax bracket to the next are not uniform. By far the largest change, of course, occurs at the bottom of the tax scale where the rate plummets from 20 per cent to zero for the income receiver who moves down out of the first bracket.

The net incentive or disincentive effect of a given change in personal exemptions, therefore, will depend upon the extent to which taxpayers are concentrated at the boundaries of the various tax brackets rather than at the centers. For those at the boundaries the effect may go either way, but those at the centers will be induced to work harder by reduced exemption allowances and to work less by greater exemptions. A relatively even distribution of taxpayers over the various tax brackets, therefore, would create the presumption that lower exemptions are favorable to work incentives and higher exemptions unfavorable. On the other hand, a significant concentration at the bracket boundaries, especially at the bottom of the lowest bracket, could easily produce exactly the opposite result.

The Tax Treatment of Property Incomes

Another relevant issue to be taken into consideration in studying the incentive effects of any income tax is the treatment of incomes which are more or less independent of any labor services rendered by the income receiver. At given levels of yield — and this is the only important comparison to make — a general income tax which treats all types of income equally will be more favorable to work incentives than one which exempts some property incomes entirely and taxes others only partially.

As compared to the selective tax, the general one taxes certain kinds of property income more heavily but all other types of income less heavily. Since the two taxes are equally productive, taxpayers as a group have the same total disposable income in each case, but under the general tax they realize higher rates of take-home pay from the rendering of labor services.

This acts as an incentive to still greater effort. The fact that this kind of tax treats some kinds of property income more severely has little or no effect on work incentives since little or no labor is involved in the creation of these incomes. On the average, therefore, the general tax is more favorable to productive activity. It has the further virtue, of course, of being more equitable since it treats all types of income the same way.

For these reasons policymakers should scrutinize closely proposals which would have the effect of narrowing the base of the individual income tax. If the incomes involved are largely of the property type, the influence of the income tax at given yields is shifted in the disincentive direction. Present provisions concerning capital gains and losses, tax-exempt bond interest, percentage depletion, certain allowable deductions (such as those for meals and the like, which to a large extent are personal consumption on the part of the taxpayer rather than costs of earning income) all tend to make the individual income tax less favorable to work incentives than it would otherwise be.

THE INCENTIVE ASPECTS OF EXCISE AND SALES TAXES

One of the traditional tenets with reference to the relative merits of different kinds of taxes is that excise and sales taxes are more favorable to work incentives than are income taxes. Let us examine this assumption for a moment.

Consider first the probable effects on work incentives of the price changes induced by sales and excise taxes. A general increase in consumer good prices, for example, makes consumers with relatively fixed money incomes worse off and thereby tends to induce more effort.

The rewards from that effort, however, have undergone a reduction in their buying power and so the effort itself is less attractive than it once was. When considering the extra work the worker finds himself both pushed toward it (by his lower real income) and repelled (by the lower real rates of pay) at the same time, and he may in the final analysis expand his labor supply, contract it, or leave it unchanged.

It is true that many consumers may fail to perceive the price changes induced by changes in excise taxes, but they are likely to be much more aware of what it costs them to maintain their accustomed standard of living and what happens to the level of their cash balances in the process. Some evidence of the effects of high prices on worker behavior is provided by a recent British investigation which found that approximately 40 per cent of the workers interviewed regarded high prices as a factor which deterred their productive efforts and some 70 per cent thought they were also a factor making for greater incentive.

Taxpayers may, of course, do more work not in order to buy additional things but primarily to raise their level of saving. Even in this case, however, the tax-induced price increases are by no means irrelevant. The saving may be specifically earmarked for a future purchase of a taxed good or service. Unless the tax is believed to be temporary, the incentive effect is likely to be the same here as in the case of a person who works in order to consume. Even the person who saves in order to accumulate a certain amount of capital may adjust his goals upward when prices rise.

Finally, excise and sales taxation will affect work incentives in still another way. Such taxes reduce the money incomes of certain income receivers below the levels which would otherwise prevail. An excise tax on watches and clocks, for example, will lower the earning power of workers who are highly skilled in watchmaking, and these effects are likely to spread to all who do the same type of high-precision, fine-scale work. As we have already seen the incentive effects on these people may go either way. Lower income levels induce more effort, but reduced rates of pay have the reverse effect. Until we know more about the types of workers whose incomes are reduced by different kinds of sales and excise taxes and the extent to which these reductions take place — and this whole area of analysis is currently undergoing extensive examination — we cannot formulate a complete picture of the incentive-disincentive effects of sales and excise taxation.

The Effects of Labor Market Rigidities

So far we have not concerned ourselves with the extent to which the worker is free to satisfy his own preferences with regard to the amount of labor services he supplies to the market. The great majority of workers, of course, must either have a full-time job or none at all. We cannot, however, count on this fact to neutralize, for such workers, the potential incentive or disincentive effects of income taxation. For one thing, their preferences may be only temporarily frustrated. Future bargaining with employers may restore the balance. In addition, workers typically have ways of changing their labor supply other than by altering the number of hours worked a week or the number of weeks worked a year. Overtime opportunities may be available and be refused or exploited more fully, other members of the family may enter or leave the labor force, proposed ages of retirement may be altered, or absenteeism on a day-to-day basis may change. These possibilities must be kept in mind in evaluating the results of empirical studies. Inflexible behavior in one area or disincentive effects in another do not necessarily imply either insensitivity or reduced incentives as far as the labor supply as a whole is concerned.

24

The Rationale of Sales Taxation

John F. Due

Under what conditions is the use of a sales tax most defensible? Professor Due examines this topic in the light of his pertinent analysis of the nature of the levy.

Perhaps more than any other tax, the sales tax has been introduced as a measure designed to raise large sums of money quickly, under the pressure of financial emergency. The extremely broad base possible with such a tax allows the attainment of a very substantial yield, even at relatively low rates. This high yield capacity has not only provided a strong incentive for the adoption of the tax, but has proven to be a substantial obstacle in the way of removal of it. While revenue considerations almost solely accounted for the establishment of the taxes, arguments in justification of their use have been developed in terms of accepted standards of tax policy. In some cases, and particularly in the United States at the Federal level, various groups have supported establishment of sales taxes on the basis of tax policy alone, rather than need for additional revenue. It is desirable to examine the sales tax in terms of the general philosophy underlying it, and usually accepted standards of taxation.

The sales tax is basically regarded as a form of consumption taxation, that is, as a levy whose burden is distributed in proportion to consumption expenditures. This philosophy is fully realized only if the exact amount of the tax is shifted forward to consumers, and factor incomes remain unchanged. While in a general way this result is likely to be attained, there are certain to be many exceptions to it, and if wage levels respond very closely to changes in the cost of living index, the final pattern of burden distribution may be substantially different from the expected one. But primary evaluation of the tax can be made in terms of the assumption that the tax is fully shifted to the consumers, with no additional shifting, and thus is borne in proportion to consumer expenditures.

• • • •

From *Sales Taxation*, by John F. Due, Urbana, The University of Illinois Press, 1957, pp. 30–42. By permission of Routledge & Kegan Paul, Ltd., London.

The Justification for the Use of Sales Taxation

The basic arguments for the use of a sales tax center around three primary points: (1) the superiority of the expenditure basis of taxation to the income basis, from the standpoint of incentive effects, economic growth, and inflation-control, (2) the superiority of the sales tax from an administrative standpoint, compared to both the income tax and the spendings tax, the alternative form of expenditure-based taxation, and (3) the need for autonomous revenue sources on the part of the states in a Federal system. Each aspect will be discussed.

Incentive Effects and the Expenditure Basis of Taxation. A primary argument for the use of the consumption–expenditure basis of taxation, that is, the establishment of a tax structure in which tax liability depends upon consumption rather than income, is the claim that the expenditure basis avoids the adverse effects on economic incentives which an income tax, particularly a highly progressive one, creates. The complaints against the income tax on the basis of incentive effects are well known, and need not be repeated in detail. The income tax, by taking a portion of all earnings from investment, may restrict the development of new businesses and the expansion of old, in part by lessening the supply of money capital available, in part by lessening the incentives to expand. Incentive to avoid risky investment is particularly strong if capital gains are taxable as income. On the other hand, the sales tax does not affect the earnings from new capital equipment directly (assuming that the total demand for goods produced with the equipment is unaffected by the tax) and does not even do so indirectly so long as the earnings are not used for the purchase of taxable goods.

Furthermore, the income tax, by taking a portion of all earnings from work, may alter the incentives to undertake work, particularly marginal activity, such as overtime work or that of additional members of the family. The effect may be in the direction of increasing the amount of work, if the family strives to maintain its old level of living despite the tax; it may reduce it if the elasticity of demand for income in terms of work is high. In either case the tax can be charged with distorting work–leisure patterns. On the other hand, the sales tax will have no such effect, so long as additional income is desired for purposes free of sales tax, particularly saving. However, to the extent that additional income is sought for the purpose of acquiring additional goods subject to tax, the effects of the two taxes will be more nearly the same. Even in this case, however, there is apparently a tendency for workers to react more strongly to reductions in take-home monetary incomes than to reductions in the real value of their incomes through price increases. This phenomenon is illustrated by the much greater tendency of unions to strike against a reduction in real income arising out of a cut in money income than they are to strike against an equal reduction arising out of a rise in the price level.

Some advantages could be claimed for the sales tax with respect to incentive effects even if the income tax regarded as the alternative had proportional rates. But in practise most income taxes are progressive, and the sales tax may be regarded as a substitute for higher marginal rates of the tax. If the problem is posed in this form the relative advantages of the sales tax in avoiding adverse incentive effects are greater; high marginal rates of the income tax are particularly likely to restrict both investment and marginal labor activity of various forms. But this additional superiority of the sales tax can scarcely be attributed to the expenditure basis of the tax, but to the lack of progression; the extreme incentive effects of the income tax could be eliminated in such a case by alterations in the income tax, as well as by shift to the expenditure form. But in practice such a revision of the income tax might prove to be politically unpalatable, and thus establishment of a sales tax might be the only way to avoid the adverse effects of the high progression. Once a certain degree of progression is established, it is commonly regarded as political suicide to espouse the cause of lower progression, even though the existing degree may have been established with little rhyme or reason.

Long-Range Capital Formation and Economic Development. A closely related advantage claimed for the sales tax because of its expenditure basis is the argument that such a tax restricts the long-range rate of capital formation and economic development less than income taxes. The sales tax does not lessen the *incentive* to save as does the income tax, and its burden is concentrated more heavily upon those persons who will be compelled to reduce consumption rather than savings. Thus, for a given sum of tax revenue, a greater portion of the sales tax will be absorbed from sums which would otherwise be spent on consumption than in the case of the income tax; thus the overall ratio of savings to national income will remain higher, and the rate of capital formation which is possible without inflation will be greater. This effect is distinct from any effect which the income tax may have upon the incentives to undertake business expansion.

This argument, of course, is valid only if the total level of consumption, after taxes, is high enough to insure that investment does not lag behind savings at full employment levels. If investment is inadequate, all potential savings will not be utilized, and the actual rate of capital formation will lag behind the potential rate. The significance of the argument, even if investment is adequate, depends, of course, upon the actual extent to which the income tax reduces the overall ratio of savings to national income, and this cannot be determined at all precisely.

The argument, to the extent to which it is valid, has greatest significance in undeveloped countries, ones having obviously inadequate capital equipment relative to manpower. In such cases an increase in the rate of capital formation may allow a very sharp rise in the overall standard of living. In more highly developed countries, an increased rate of capital formation is not necessarily advantageous; the optimum rate of capital formation in such circumstances is difficult to define.

Equity Considerations. Despite the widespread acceptance of the principle that the income basis of taxation conforms most closely with accepted standards of equity, arguments are advanced that at least supplementary use of the sales tax can increase the overall equity of the tax structure. In most extreme form, this argument maintains that expenditures, not income, appropriately measure economic well-being and thus taxpaying ability, and that inclusion of the portion of income saved within the measure of the tax is basically inequitable. Closely related is the argument that inclusion results in discriminatory double taxation, since both the original income and the earnings on it are taxed. The taxation of the original income reduces the amount which can be saved and thus the amount of return on the savings, while the return itself is again subject to tax. This argument is open to serious question; the opposite point of view, that additions to savings constitute, in themselves, elements in the measure of economic well being, and that taxation of both saved income and the earnings from them does not constitute discriminatory double taxation in any meaningful sense are much more widely accepted.

In more moderate form, the sales tax is defined on an equity basis on the grounds that the income basis tends to discriminate against persons who have not yet accumulated wealth compared to those who have, and places an inadequate burden on persons making large current consumption purchases out of previously accumulated wealth. The sales tax permits those persons who have not yet accumulated to do so without suffering tax burden on the portion of income used for this purpose, and it reaches effectively those persons spending from accumulated wealth. Also, the sales tax insures some payment from persons who, legally, or illegally, are able to escape adequate payment under the income tax.

Furthermore, the income tax does not differentiate between various forms of income on the basis of differences in spending power, in any satisfactory way. The greater the accumulated wealth which a person already has, the greater is the spending power of additional income, since he is under no compulsion to save for purposes of emergency. Furthermore, the greater the assurance of continuation of the income, the greater is the spending power involved. The sales tax provides the differentiation because it applies only to the actual amounts spent.

Ease of Administration. One of the primary arguments for the use of the sales tax in preference to both income taxes and spendings taxes is the greater ease of administration. In the first place, the sales tax is collected from a relatively small number of business firms, instead of from large numbers of individuals, and thus control is easier and less expensive. Secondly, the tax is collected on the basis of figures of total sales, which are much easier to ascertain and subject to less interpretative questions than net earnings, which must be calculated for the portion of the income tax applying to any type of business activity. Thirdly, it avoids the fundamental problems of delimiting income in the case of capital gains in a period of changing prices.

This argument is of particular significance with respect to the lower income groups, for which income tax administration may become expensive, relative to revenue. In a country with large numbers of persons in the lower income groups, an income tax with reasonable exemptions is likely to reach only a small proportion of the population; if the remainder are to make some contribution to tax revenue, the sales tax may be the only feasible basis.

Administrative considerations also serve as an argument in favor of the sales-tax type of expenditure tax relative to the spendings tax, which would be based upon consumer expenditures, but would be collected directly from individuals by means of returns.

The argument of administrative effectiveness has played a particularly important role in the development of sales taxation in countries in which standards of tax administration, tax compliance, and literacy are relatively low. In such countries effective collection of income taxes is almost impossible, and reliance upon sales taxation becomes imperative. This is a partial explanation of the dominance of commodity taxation in many countries two and three centuries ago, and of its continued importance in some countries down to the present time.

The Sales Tax in Federal Government Structures. A further argument has relevance only to countries with Federal or semi-Federal governmental structures.

In such countries, there is a tendency for the Federal governments to dominate the income tax field; with high Federal rates it becomes difficult, as a practical, political matter, for the states to rely heavily upon this source of revenue. As a consequence, particularly if they receive only limited financial support from the Federal government, there is a tendency for them to turn to sales taxes in order to obtain a significant autonomous source of tax revenue. The importance of state sales taxation in the United States can be attributed in part to this situation.

The Merits of Sales Taxes Compared to Excise Taxes. The preceding discussion has centered around the relative merits of the sales tax relative to income taxes. But the tax may also be compared with its cousin, a system of excise or special sales taxes. As compared to this type of tax, the sales tax has three major advantages. In the first place, because of its greater coverage, a lower rate is possible for the raising of a given sum. The lower the rate, the less is the incentive given to evasion and the less serious are the objectionable results of the tax, other features being the same. But more significantly, the sales tax avoids the inevitable discrimination created by the excise taxes against those persons who have relatively high preferences for the taxed articles. This discrimination may in some instances be justified on the basis of deliberate social policy, as in the case of the tax on liquor. Or it may be regarded as justifiable because of special benefits received by the persons paying the tax, as in the case of the gasoline tax. But with most commodities, the consequent discrimination is contrary to usually accepted standards of equity. A sales tax, if properly designed, is uniform on all consumption expenditures.

Finally, the excise taxes will lead to reallocation of consumer demand and thus a reallocation of resources. If it is assumed that the allocation of resources is at the optimum, in terms of consumer demand, before the tax is introduced, the reallocation may reduce economic welfare. If a tax on theatre tickets causes persons to take walks for amusement when they would prefer to go to the theatre, the persons lose satisfaction (find themselves on lower indifference curves), yet the government gets no revenue. If, of course, the optimum was not previously attained, the tax could conceivably result in a more optimum resource allocation. But it is almost inconceivable that a widespread excise tax system could do this by accident on any scale, and review of excise tax systems, such as that of the United States, suggests on the basis of common-sense observations that the opposite is much more likely to be true. A uniform sales tax will cause no reallocation of resources, except as noted in the previous chapter.

The Objections to Sales Taxation

The primary objections to the use of sales taxation are likewise so well known that detailed analysis is unnecessary, but a review of them is desirable.

Equity Arguments. The basic and most widely accepted objection centers around the distribution of the burden of the tax by income group, under the assumption that the tax is shifted forward to the final consumers of the products. The tax tends to place a relatively heavy burden on all persons whose expenditures on taxable goods constitute relatively high percentages of their incomes. Such a distribution pattern is not necessarily inherently objectionable. A defense could be made for placing a heavier tax on a person who spends substantial amounts in excess of his income for consumption purchases than that on a person with the same income who spends less on consumption and uses the balance for business expansion. But it is argued that the relatively heavier burden is in many cases inflicted on persons ill able to pay it, with consequent inequity. In the first place, persons in the lower income groups tend to spend higher percentages of their incomes and save lower percentages than those in the higher income groups; as a consequence, if the sales tax applies to all consumption expenditures, the tax will tend to be regressive relative to income. . . . With food taxable, the burden is highly regressive. These results must be interpreted with some care; in any particular period, the lower income groups will include some persons who are in these income levels only temporarily, and whose consumption patterns are largely conditioned by past and expected future income. But nevertheless, the results have some significance.

In many cases, governments have sought to reduce the degree of regressiveness by the exemption of food. Food exemption materially reduces not only the relative regressiveness of the tax, but also the absolute burden on the lowest income groups. In other cases, governments have sought to introduce some degree of progression by applying higher rates to a number of commodities regarded as "luxuries." This policy is typical of the British purchase tax, and is also found in substantial measure in the Netherlands tax and other sales taxes. But this policy results in some discrimination among consumers on the basis of taste, as does food exemption to a somewhat lesser extent.

The general regressiveness of the tax is not so much an argument against use of the sales tax, but against excessive reliance upon it as an element in the overall tax structure. So long as the sales tax remains a minor segment of the total, any regressiveness which it may have is more than offset by the progressiveness of the income tax, at least for those income groups affected by the income tax. Unfortunately the income taxes of some countries, of which the United States is an outstanding example, are not significantly progressive for the great majority of taxpayers which fall into the first income tax bracket and are all taxed at the same rate.

Apart from the overall tendency to place a relatively heavy burden on persons in the lower income groups, the tax tends to penalize any groups whose circumstances compel them to spend higher percentages of their incomes to attain a given standard of living. Thus the tax tends to burden large families more heavily than smaller families with the same income, since the former must spend a higher percentage of income to attain a given living standard. Essentially the large family has less taxpaying ability than the smaller, yet the sales tax burden upon it will be greater. Newly married couples spending high percentages of income for consumer durables, persons losing property by casualty and forced to replace it, persons who are ill and required to buy expensive medicines are all subjected to relatively heavy burden, compared to that on others with comparable incomes. At the very best, the sales tax is a relatively crude method of distributing burden among various people — although admittedly it does a more satisfactory burden than the income tax on persons spending large amounts for accumulated wealth and on those able to escape the income tax.

These criticisms can be advanced against a sales tax even if it is levied in the most satisfactory form, is shifted in its entirety, is uniform relative to consumer expenditures on all items (except those deliberately treated in different fashion), and does not result in factor price changes. But in practice sales taxes rarely attain these requirements. The significance of deviations from them can be summarized briefly:

1. The taxes are rarely universal; to the extent that various types of expenditure are not included, persons are given an artificial incentive to increase the consumption of these goods, and discrimination results in favor of persons having relatively high preference for the untaxed goods. In many instances, most or all services are not taxed, for example.

2. The shifting is not likely to be complete or exact. To the extent that the tax does not shift fully, it rests as an unequal burden upon the owners of the businesses. To the extent that it pyramids through application of percentage markups by merchants, consumers are burdened by an amount in excess of the tax, and either excess profits are created or excess capacity is perpetuated, at least for a time.

3. Even with complete shifting, the tax may not comprise a uniform percentage of the retail prices of various goods. If the tax is imposed prior to the retail level, as may be necessary or desirable for administrative reasons, the tax will not comprise a uniform percentage of the consumption expenditures on various goods since the margins between the stage at which the tax is applied and the final retail sale may differ widely. Furthermore, if any producers' goods are subject to tax, as is common, the overall final burden will be greater on some goods than on others, because of variations in the capital equipment costs relative to retail selling prices in the production of various goods. If the sales tax takes the multiple-stage turnover-tax form, the variations in final tax burden by commodity will be tremendous, because of the wide variation in the average number of transactions through which various goods pass on the way from initial production of materials to final consumption.

4. The sales taxes may result in wage increases, because of the importance of the cost of living level as a factor in wage negotiations. These increases are likely to be greater in some fields than in others; some groups of workers, therefore, may be able to shift a portion of the tax burden on their consumption purchases onto other persons, particularly persons purchasing goods produced by their labor. As a consequence, a haphazard pattern of overall burden distribution results.

On the other hand, in some instances the tax may result in declines in the prices of certain factors. If, for example, a particular type of factor has higher productivity in one industry than in any other, and the output of this industry falls sharply as a result of price increases consequent to the tax, or producers curtail output because of inability to shift the tax, the prices of these factors will fall. Thus the tax shifts backwards, and the final distribution of burden will be contrary to accepted standards of equity. If all factor prices fell by the same proportion and commodity prices did not increase, the pattern of burden distribution would be the same as that of a proportional income tax, and more acceptable, in terms of usual standards, than that of a fully shifted sales tax. But, it is obvious that any such uniform backward shifting of the tax is impossible.

Deflationary Effects. The argument that a sales tax is superior to an income tax as an instrument of inflation control suggests a relative disadvantage of the sales tax, compared to the usual type of income tax, in any period in which there is a tendency toward unemployment. The sales tax not only impinges more heavily on the lower income groups, which spend, on the average, higher percentages of their incomes, but likewise gives at least a limited incentive to spend less and save more. Not only is the direct restrictive effect upon consumption greater, per dollar of tax revenue, than that of the income tax, but as a consequence of the decline in consumption, the restrictive effect upon investment may also be greater. The direct and immediate restrictive effect of an income tax upon the incentive to undertake investment may be greater than that of a sales tax, as outlined above, but investment depends in large measure upon the volume of consumption sales. Thus to the extent to which the sales tax curtails the latter to a greater extent than an income tax, the net final deflationary effect may be greater.

Effects upon Allocation of Resources and Methods of Production. A universal sales tax, completely shifted to the final consumer, and applying only to final consumption goods, should be completely neutral with respect to allocation of consumer income among commodities — and thus resource allocation — and with respect to choice of methods of production. But sales taxes are typically not of this character. Any exemption from the tax will tend to increase relative consumption of the commodities affected; if this cannot be defended on the basis of general economic or social policy, it must be regarded as contrary to optimum economic welfare. Any incomplete shifting or price increases in excess of the amount of the tax will have the same effect. Likewise, as explained subsequently, it is very difficult to confine sales taxes entirely to final consumption goods; to the extent to which any producers' goods are subject to tax, some methods of production are made more expensive relative to others, and thus attainment of optimum efficiency in production is checked.

Sales vs. Spending Taxes. A sales tax shares with the spendings tax the advantages (and disadvantages) of the use of the consumption expenditure basis of taxation. But the sales tax is much inferior to the spendings tax, except in the field of administration. A spendings tax can avoid the regressiveness and the burden on the lower income groups arising from the sales tax, and can be made progressive in rate. Thus the tendency for the propensity to consume to fall as income rises can be more than offset by the progressivity of the rates. The spendings tax can be adjusted in terms of family size and other determinants of tax capacity at a given level of income in a manner impossible with the sales tax.

General Evaluation

In terms of usual standards of equity, a sales tax, no matter how carefully established, is inferior to the income tax. It tends to penalize persons whose circumstances compel them to spend relatively high percentages of their incomes to attain given standards of living, and it cannot be adjusted satisfactorily in terms of various considerations which affect taxpaying ability at given income levels, such as numbers of dependents and medical expenses. It frequently operates in perverse fashion, striking more heavily the persons least able to pay. Certain modifications, such as the exemption of food, may alleviate the basic objection of the heavy burden placed on the poor, but cannot solve all inequities and often create new ones. The basic case for permanent use of a sales tax must rest upon three primary arguments:

1. The danger that the raising of income taxes beyond certain levels will seriously impair economic incentives, and thus reduce the level of national income and the rate of economic growth.

2. The need for autonomous revenue sources for states and Federal governments in a Federal system.

3. The difficulties of administering a broad-coverage income tax in countries with relatively low standards of tax administration and compliance, and the difficulties of administering a spendings tax. This tax offers the same advantages as the sales tax with respect to incentives and capital formation, but is perhaps even more difficult to administer than the income tax.

Thus the case for use of sales taxation is strongest under the following circumstances:

1. When the overall level of governmental expenditures is so high that the income tax, together with other suitable taxes, cannot yield adequate revenues without serious incentive effects. The case for the sales tax, of course, increases as these incentive effects become more clearly demonstrated; in many countries, such as the United States, there is actually little evidence of them at the present time.

2. When a rapid rate of economic growth is imperative if standards of living are to be improved, and it is obvious that high income taxes will lessen the potential rate of capital formation by reducing significantly the overall propensity to save. A sales tax compels a temporary reduction in consumption and insures that the savings of the higher income groups will be available for capital formation. This argument is, of course, of primary importance in undeveloped countries.

3. In countries in which administrative standards and taxpayer attitudes do not permit effective enforcement of income taxes applying to a high percentage of the population. If income levels are such that very large numbers of persons would be paying only small amounts of income tax, the problems with income tax enforcement are multiplied.

4. In countries with Federal governmental structures, to insure autonomous revenue for one of the levels of government, particularly the state level. Unfortunately in some Federal countries the Federal governments have preempted both the income and sales tax fields.

5. In countries in which there is relatively little inequality in income distribution, and thus the significance of the regressiveness of the pattern of burden distribution is minimized.

On the whole, the sales tax must be regarded as a second-best tax — one to be employed only if various circumstances make complete reliance on income and other more suitable taxes undesirable. A carefully designed sales tax is not perhaps as objectionable as it was once regarded; it offers definite advantages over widespread excise tax systems, with their inevitable discrimination among various consumers and business firms and their tendency to distort consumption patterns; and it is definitely superior to high rate "business" taxes with uncertain incidence and possible serious economic effects. But it must be regarded as secondary to income taxation, in terms of usually accepted standards of taxation.

REQUIREMENTS FOR AN OPTIMUM SALES TAX STRUCTURE

The extent to which a sales tax most fully attains the usually accepted standards of taxation — or deviates from them the least — depends to a major extent upon the exact structure of the tax. Some of the major complaints which are advanced against present sales tax structures actually arise from specific features of the existing taxes, rather than from the fundamental character of sales taxation itself. Three major requirements for an acceptable sales tax structure are outlined in the following paragraphs. . . .

1. Uniformity of burden distribution by commodity. If a sales tax is to avoid the discrimination against individuals on the basis of relative preferences for various goods and possible unjustifiable distortion of resource allocation, the tax burden must constitute a uniform percentage of consumer expenditures for all purposes, except in those cases in which deviation from this rule is deliberately made in conformity with general social or economic policy.

Such uniformity requires that the tax be imposed in such a manner that the amount of the tax constitutes a uniform percentage of the selling price to the final consumer, that the tax is shifted forward to the final consumer in exact amount, and that factor prices are not affected by the tax.

2. Neutrality with respect to production and distribution. Under the assumption that business firms will seek to use the most efficient methods of physical production and channels of distribution in the absence of the tax, it is necessary that the sales tax be established in such a manner that it is neutral with respect to production and distribution techniques, if loss in efficiency of production is to be avoided. Two requirements are necessary for the attainment of this goal. In the first place, the amount of the tax on each commodity must be the same regardless of the production and distribution channels employed. If the tax is greater for example, if the commodity is sold directly by producer to retailer than if it is sold through wholesale distributors, firms will be discouraged from making such direct sales; if it is less, vertical integration will be artificially and uneconomically encouraged.

In the second place, the tax itself must apply only to final consumption goods; if any producers' goods are included within the scope of the tax, the costs of some methods of production will be raised compared to those of others, and the choice of production techniques will be altered. Taxation of such items as capital equipment is particularly objectionable because of its restrictive effect upon investment; this result is most objectionable in periods of deflation, in undeveloped countries, and in others in which modernization of industry is of particular importance.

3. East of administration. Thirdly, the tax must be established in such a manner that administration can be made effective at reasonable cost, and compliance difficulties and costs for the taxpaying firms minimized. Evasion of the tax results, of course, in inequity as well as in loss of revenue. Additional costs for the taxpaying firms arising from the operation of the tax are real costs to the economy, and result in an ultimate burden on the consumers in excess of the tax revenue received by the government.

25

State Taxes in 1961

Committee on Educational Finance

This material, prepared by the Committee on Educational Finance, National Education Association, shows in concise terms the structure of our state tax system. There is also given a brief discussion of recent changes in state income and sales taxes. Of particular interest are the differences in the degree to which particular states rely on the various types of levies.

Trends in State Tax Collections

During the 1951–61 period, the amount of taxes collected by all state governments has increased from $8,933 million to $19,002 million. On a per-capita basis, collections increased from $58.55 to $106.03. Over the period, total state tax revenue for all states has increased each year, although in some years some states experienced lower collections.

Table 1 shows the trend of state tax collections from 1951 through 1961. A careful examination of the table suggests that sharp year-to-year changes in amounts of state tax collections have generally paralleled changes in nationwide economic conditions. Effects of the three economic recessions that have occurred since 1951 are clearly reflected in 1954, 1958, and 1961. As is

Adapted from "Nine State Taxes, 1961," *CEF Report*, Number 5 (February, 1962), pp. 1–5, 9. Reproduced with permission.

Table 1

STATE TAX REVENUE: 1951–61

Fiscal Year	Total State Tax Revenue (in millions)	Amount of Increase over Previous Year (in millions)	Per-Capita State Tax Revenue
1	2	3	4
1951	$ 8,933	. . .	$ 58.55
1952	9,857	$ 924	63.62
1953	10,557	695	67.01
1954	11,089	537	69.16
1955	11,597	508	70.95
1956	13,375	1,778	80.37
1957	14,531	1,156	85.74
1958	14,919	383	86.53
1959[a]	15,848	929	90.29
1960[b]	18,036	2,188	100.64
1961[b]	19,002	966	106.03[c]

Sources: 1951–56: U.S. Department of Commerce, Bureau of the Census. *Statistical Abstract of the United States, 1958*. Washington, D.C.: Government Printing Office, 1958. p. 405.

1957–60: U.S. Department of Commerce, Bureau of the Census. *Compendium of State Government Finances in 1960*. Washington, D.C.: Government Printing Office, 1961. p. 8.

1961: U.S. Department of Commerce, Bureau of the Census. *State Tax Collections in 1961*. Series G-SF61, No. 3. Washington, D.C.: the Bureau, August 24, 1961. p. 3.

[a] Amounts shown are 49-state totals, excluding Hawaii.
[b] Amounts for 1960 and 1961 are 50-state totals.
[c] Based on provisional estimates of population as of July 1, 1960.

evident from the table, the 1957–58 recession caused a more noticeable leveling off in the amount of state tax collections than did the others, that year showing the lowest annual increase ($383 million) recorded for the period. Amounts of increase per year in both 1954 and 1961 also showed a considerable decline from the year preceding. However, part of the upward movement reflects state legislative actions affecting the base and rate structure.

The average increase per year from 1951 to 1961 has been $1,006 million. The largest annual increase, $2,188 million, occurred in 1960, following a period of rapid recovery in the economy in the early part of 1959. Extensive tax law changes adopted by many states in 1959 also contributed to the growth of state tax revenue in 1960.

Per-capita state tax revenue for all states in 1961 was $106.03, up $5.39 from the previous year. It ranged from $205.92 in Hawaii to $63.23 in New Jersey. Some of the differences among the states are accounted for by differences in responsibility between state and local governments, by the level of services, and by economic conditions.

. . . .

General Sales Taxes

State legislatures in 1961 made further efforts to strengthen the general sales tax. The most outstanding events were enactments of new sales tax laws by Texas and Wisconsin. Thus, the number of states using a general sales tax rose to 37. The levy in Texas on sales and use is at the rate of 2 per cent of each retail sale of tangible personal property, and it became effective September 1, 1961. Exemptions from the new tax include, among other items, food for human consumption and prescription medicines. Beginning February 1, 1962, retailers in Wisconsin became subject to a 3 per cent sales and use tax on the gross receipts from the sale of tangible personal property. This new tax measure in Wisconsin, which excludes basic necessities of family food, medicine, and clothing, applies to items specified rather than to all sales.

In 1961, general sales tax rates were raised by four states. Three states increased their rates by ½ per cent; Connecticut, 3 to 3.5 per cent; Illinois, 3 to 3.5 per cent; and Utah, 2 to 2.5 per cent. West Virginia raised its rate from 2 to 3 per cent, to be effective through June 30, 1962. In Washington, a 4 per cent tax rate which has been in effect on a temporary basis since 1959 became permanent. Also made permanent was a 76 per cent surtax on the business and occupation tax which had been scheduled to revert to 60 per cent level on July 1, 1961.

Other changes made in 1961 include the provisions for broadening the tax base in a number of states. Florida expanded its sales tax base, effective June 22, 1961, to include all purchases made by state and federal banks and meals served in institutions of higher education. Illinois, in addition to increasing the tax rate, broadened the tax base to include building materials used in construction and the transfer of property in the sales of services. The 2.5 per cent Kansas tax now applies to sale of beer and cigarettes. In Maine, the sales tax base has been extended to take-out food products from restaurants. Effective June 1, 1961, Maryland lowered the point at which collection of its 3 per cent sales tax starts from 51 cents to 25 cents, and restaurant meals costing over $1 have been made subject to the tax. North Carolina revised its tax law extensively by repealing most of the exemptions, including sales of food and nonprescription drugs and medicines. On the other hand, North Carolina repealed 1/20 of 1 per cent tax on the gross sales of wholesale merchants. Wyoming broadened the base of the sales tax to include sales of house trailers.

At the end of 1961, 16 states had a sales tax rate of 3 per cent; 12 states, 2 per cent; 3 states, 4 per cent; 3 states, 3.5 per cent; 2 states, 2.5 per cent; and 1 state, 3/8 of 1 per cent.

The sales tax still remains the most important source of tax revenues of the states. In 1961, the general sales tax ranked first as a producer of state tax revenues in 31 states. The importance of this tax as a source of state tax revenue in the various states is evident from Table 2. For the country as a whole, receipts from the sales tax accounted for almost one-fourth (23.7 per cent) of all state tax collections in 1961.

. . . .

INDIVIDUAL INCOME TAXES

The major development in the field of individual income taxes in 1961 was the enactment of new tax laws in West Virginia and New Jersey. In addition, five other states raised their tax rates in 1961.

The new individual income tax law in West Virginia, effective with the 1961 tax year, provides for the levy of a tax at the rate of 6 per cent of the federal income tax. Withholding and declarations of estimated income are also required. New Jersey enacted a limited individual income tax characterized as a commuter net income tax applicable only to income derived from New Jersey sources by New York residents and from New York sources by New Jersey residents. The tax is levied on net income at rates graduated from 2 to 10 per cent, the same as in New York. Withholding by New Jersey employers from wages of New York residents employed in New Jersey became effective July 1, 1961.

Higher rates on existing individual income taxes were voted in five states. Alaska raised its rate by 2 percentage points to 16 per cent of the total federal income tax, effective January 1, 1961. The withholding tax has also been increased from 14 to 16 per cent of the federal tax withheld. Delaware raised its tax by establishing new brackets and rates ranging from 9 per cent on net income over $30,000 and up to $50,000 to 11 per cent in excess of $100,000. Previously all net income in excess of $8,000 was taxed at the rate of 8 per cent. Minnesota increased the primary tax rate on individuals by 5 per cent. An additional tax of 1 per cent of the first $1,000 of adjusted gross income is imposed upon individuals whose net income tax liabilities do not exceed $10, and a temporary 15 per cent surtax is to be in effect through December 21, 1962. One other aspect of the change is an increase from $14 to $15 in the credit allowed for dependents. New Mexico raised its individual income tax rates from a range of 1 to 4 per cent to a range of 1.5 to 6 per cent, effective April 1, 1961, through December 31, 1963. It also adopted the federal income tax base as its base.

The Wisconsin personal income tax rates have been increased 1 per cent in each tax bracket beginning with the calendar year 1962 and corresponding fiscal years, and tax years thereafter. The new income tax rates range from 2 per cent on the first $1,000 of taxable income to 10 per cent on that over $15,000. Personal exemptions have been raised to $10 for the taxpayer and each dependent, and $15 for persons over 65 years of age.

New York reduced its tax a flat 10 per cent for the tax year 1960. The maximum tax rate in Mississippi decreased to 5 per cent for 1962, by a law enacted in 1960 which reduces the maximum rate from 6 per cent to 3 per cent over a six-year period. Massachusetts extended through June 1963 the surtaxes on various types of income which had been scheduled to expire in 1961.

In addition to West Virginia, which enacted a new income tax law with withholding provisions, five more states (Minnesota, Missouri, New Mexico, Oklahoma, and Wisconsin) have adopted the withholding feature as a means of providing additional revenue. This makes a total of 25 states now using the general withholding system. In addition to these 25, California and Iowa require withholding from the wages of nonresidents. As mentioned above, New Jersey's limited commuter income tax is also collected through withholding.

Table 2 MAJOR STATE TAX COLLECTIONS IN 1961
(As per cent of total tax revenue)

State	Sales and Gross Receipts							Income		Licenses		Property	Others
	Total	General Sales or Gross Receipts	Motor Fuels	Tobacco Products	Alcoholic Beverages	Insurance	Others	Individual Income	Corporation Net Income	Motor Vehicles and Operators	Others		
1	2	3	4	5	6	7	8	9	10	11	12	13	14
Alabama	72.5%	32.9%	25.7%	6.6%	2.7%	3.0%	1.6%	9.8%	3.2%	2.1%	5.9%	5.1%	1.4%
Alaska	31.2	. . .	16.2	4.4	7.5	3.1	. . .	32.8	4.6	7.0	13.6[a]	.7[b]	10.0[c]
Arizona	65.0	40.4	15.0	2.1	2.2	1.8	3.4	8.5	3.5	6.1	2.1	14.3	.6
Arkansas	70.4	33.5	24.0	5.7	3.5	2.5	1.2	6.3	6.6	9.4	3.8	.2	3.4
California	58.3	31.9	15.6	2.9	2.3	3.0	2.6	12.0	12.2	6.3	2.0	5.8	3.5
Colorado	47.8	23.7	17.4	. . .	2.8	2.7	1.1	23.7	8.4	8.2	4.2	4.3	3.5
Connecticut	68.6	31.7	18.7	4.8	2.9	6.0	4.5	. . .	12.3	9.1	3.0	.0	7.0
Delaware	24.9	. . .	12.0	2.9	2.2	2.2	5.7	35.4	8.7	5.8	19.8[d]	3.6	1.7
Florida	75.9	32.2	23.9	1.9	8.9	2.3	6.6	. . .	. . .	10.9	5.0	4.0	4.3
Georgia	73.0	37.6	21.9	5.3	5.3	2.8	.0	13.4	6.2	4.9	1.9	.3	.3
Hawaii	69.1	51.4	8.5[e]	1.7	2.7	1.7	3.1	24.3	4.4	. . .	1.4	. . .	.8
Idaho	34.1	. . .	20.8	4.7	2.6	3.8	2.3	27.2	7.9	16.7	7.7	5.2	1.2
Illinois	81.3	43.9	16.7	4.9	4.7	3.3	7.8	. . .	. . .	12.4	2.3	.1	3.8
Indiana	83.6	47.9	25.4	4.3	3.5	2.5	.0	. . .	. . .	9.6	3.0	1.8	2.1
Iowa	61.2	31.0	21.5	4.4	1.2	3.0	.1	14.0	1.7	17.1	1.7	1.5	2.8
Kansas	64.3	35.4	18.9	4.3	2.6	3.0	.1	11.2	4.0	11.2	3.2	4.1	2.0
Kentucky	61.7	26.4	21.4	2.9	5.5	2.2	3.4	16.0	7.5	4.2	3.0	5.3	2.2
Louisiana	48.3	18.6	13.8	6.0	4.4	2.2	3.3	3.0	3.8	2.9	5.5	3.2	33.3[f]
Maine	76.8	31.6	26.3	7.6	2.5	2.8	6.0	. . .	. . .	11.1	6.3	1.9	4.0
Maryland	54.1	21.4	16.0	3.0	2.6	2.5	8.7	25.2	5.7	7.7	1.7	3.8	1.7
Massachusetts	34.8	. . .	15.1	7.8	5.1	2.4	4.4	29.7	6.6	5.1	18.6[g]	.0	5.1
Michigan	68.0	40.3	15.3	6.6	2.8	2.2	.8	. . .	. . .	7.9	9.4	5.7	9.1
Minnesota	34.6	. . .	15.1	6.0	5.0	2.7	5.9	25.4	9.7	11.6	2.8	6.4	9.4
Mississippi	73.0	36.6	23.9	5.8	2.4	2.9	1.4	4.0	6.4	4.2	4.4	2.0	6.0

Missouri	59.9	36.6	13.8	3.9	1.6	4.0	.1	13.8	3.5	12.4	4.4	4.4	1.6
Montana	44.8	. . .	25.3	8.9	5.7	3.2	1.8	19.8	6.8	6.3	6.6	8.5	7.1
Nebraska	55.8	. . .	40.8	6.8	3.4	4.1	.7	. . .	. . .	6.6	4.9	30.8	1.8
Nevada	74.9	29.8	18.0	3.2	2.8	2.1	19.0[h]	. . .	. . .	12.9	7.4	4.3	.5
New Hampshire	61.9	. . .	31.5	10.1	2.6	4.7	13.0	3.8	. . .	16.4	5.8	4.3	7.8
New Jersey	55.7	. . .	26.0	12.4	5.7	5.1	6.6	. . .	6.8	19.3	11.1[i]	.7	6.4
New Mexico	56.8	28.9	20.0	3.8	1.7	2.0	.4	6.0[j]	. . .	9.9	3.1	6.5	17.7[k]
New York	30.9	. . .	10.6	6.1	2.8	3.3	8.0	38.5	13.4	6.9	2.9	.2	7.3
North Carolina	52.5	18.7	21.7	. . .	3.7	2.9	5.5	19.6	11.4	6.8	5.7	2.4	1.6
North Dakota	60.5	25.2	21.2	5.9	4.9	2.8	.5	7.6	2.4	15.7	4.3	4.0	5.5
Ohio	74.6	29.2	24.6	7.1	4.1	3.5	6.2	. . .	. . .	11.2	8.0	4.7	1.4
Oklahoma	57.1	20.5	21.1	5.2	4.0	3.5	2.7	6.3	5.2	13.9	3.0	. . .	14.5[l]
Oregon	23.5	. . .	19.1	. . .	.7	2.9	.7	42.2	10.5	15.3	5.1	.0	3.4
Pennsylvania	62.9	33.3	14.2	5.7	4.2	4.0	1.5	. . .	13.3	9.0	9.6	.1	5.1
Rhode Island	72.3	25.9	17.9	7.4	3.4	2.9	14.8	. . .	9.3	10.0	2.9	. . .	5.5
South Carolina	69.5	28.7	21.6	5.0	7.1	2.5	4.5	11.7	8.9	4.3	3.7	.5	1.4
South Dakota	78.3	29.8	27.8	6.2	4.8	3.8	5.9	. . .	.8	12.7	5.3	.0	2.9
Tennessee	72.1	34.3	25.0	6.0	2.8	3.3	.7	1.9	6.8	8.3	8.3	.0[b]	2.7
Texas	50.5	. . .	23.3	11.3	4.4	4.1	7.4	. . .	. . .	11.4	8.7	4.9	24.5[m]
Utah	55.8	28.8	20.4	2.4	.9	2.4	.9	15.1	6.2	6.8	3.6	7.7	4.8
Vermont	44.7	. . .	18.8	7.9	9.1	2.7	6.2	25.9	4.9	16.2	3.5	.6	4.1
Virginia	45.2	. . .	26.3	4.1	5.7	3.6	5.5	23.8	8.3	7.0	6.0	6.7	3.0
Washington	82.3	56.3	13.3	4.0	2.8	1.7	4.2	. . .	. . .	5.1	3.1	7.1	2.3
West Virginia	80.5	46.2	17.9	5.1	1.7	3.4	6.1	.5	. . .	13.5	3.1	.2	2.3
Wisconsin	30.4	. . .	17.1	5.0	3.4	2.2	2.7	32.7	12.9	10.1	2.5	7.6	3.8
Wyoming	59.2	28.7	22.1	4.2	1.5	2.8	.0	. . .	. . .	15.4	6.8	17.5	1.0
50 states	57.8%	23.7%	18.1%	5.2%	3.6%	3.1%	4.2%	12.3%	6.7%	8.6%	5.3%	3.3%	6.0%

Source: U.S. Department of Commerce, Bureau of the Census. *State Collections in 1961*. Series G-SF61, No. 3. Washington, D.C.: the Bureau, August 24, 1961. p. 5–7.

[a] Includes license tax on occupations and businesses, accounts for 7.8 per cent.

[b] Back taxes only; not included with number of states using tax.

[c] Includes severance tax, accounts for 7.0 per cent.

[d] Includes license tax on corporations, 16.3 per cent.

[e] Does not include state collections of county-levied taxes, amounting to $5,225 million in fiscal 1961.

[f] Includes severance tax, accounts for 32.2 per cent.

[g] Includes license tax on corporations, 14.0 per cent.

[h] Percentage shown is for amusements tax.

[i] Includes license tax on corporations, 8.9 per cent.

[j] Includes corporation income tax.

[k] Includes severance tax, accounts for 17.1 per cent.

[l] Includes severance tax, accounts for 12.0 per cent.

[m] Includes severance tax, accounts for 22.6 per cent.

26

Tax Policy to Achieve Social Balance

John Kenneth Galbraith

Professor Galbraith of Harvard University, at present Ambassador to India, attracted much attention in 1958 when he presented his thesis that the public sector of our economy stands in a socially disadvantageous position, compared with the private. Here he argues that the social balance can best be righted by greater use of sales taxation.

The solution is a system of taxation which automatically makes a pro rata share of increasing income available to public authority for public purposes. The task of public authority, like that of private individuals, will be to distribute this increase in accordance with relative need. Schools and roads will then no longer be at a disadvantage as compared with automobiles and television sets in having to prove absolute justification.

. . . .

However, even though the higher urgency of the services for social balance is conceded, there is still the problem of providing the revenue. And since it is income taxes that must be used, the question of social balance can easily be lost sight of in the reopened argument over equality. The truce will be broken and liberals and conservatives will join battle on this issue and forget about the poverty in the public services that awaits correction and, as we shall see presently, the poverty of people which can only be corrected at increased public cost. All this — schools, hospitals, even the scientific research on which increased production depends — must wait while we debate the ancient and unresolvable question of whether the rich are too rich.

The only hope — and in the nature of things it rests primarily with liberals — is to separate the issue of equality from that of social balance. The second is by far the more important question. The fact that a tacit truce exists on the issue of inequality is proof of its comparative lack of social urgency. In the past the liberal politician has countered the conservative proposal for

Adapted from *The Affluent Society*, Boston, Houghton Mifflin Company, 1958, pp. 311–317. Reproduced with permission.

reduction in top bracket income taxes with the proposal that relief be confined to the lower brackets. And he has insisted that any necessary tax increase be carried more than proportionately by the higher income brackets. The result has been to make him a co-conspirator with the conservative in reducing taxes, whatever the cost in social balance; and his insistence on making taxes an instrument of greater equality has made it difficult or impossible to increase them. Meanwhile, the individuals with whom he sympathizes and whom he seeks to favor are no longer the tax-ridden poor of Bengal or the first Empire but people who, by all historical standards, are themselves comparatively opulent citizens. In any case, they would be among the first beneficiaries of the better education, health, housing, and other services which would be the fruits of improved social balance, and they would be the long-run beneficiaries of more nearly adequate investment in people.

The rational liberal, in the future, will resist tax reduction, even that which ostensibly favors the poor, if it is at the price of social balance. And, for the same reason, he will not hesitate to accept increases that are neutral as regards the distribution of income. His classical commitment to greater equality can far better be kept by attacking as a separate issue the more egregious of the loopholes in the present tax laws. These loopholes — preferential treatment of capital gains and the special depletion allowances for mineral, including in particular oil, recovery — are strongly in conflict with traditional liberal attitudes, for this is inequality sanctioned by the state. There is work enough here for any egalitarian crusader.

While there is much that the federal government must do by way of redressing balance, it is in state and local services that the imbalance is most striking. Here, however, the solution — though it involves another wrench in liberal attitudes — is most clear. It involves much expanded use of the sales tax.

So long as social balance is imperfect there should be no hesitation in urging high rates. Coverage should be general on consumer products and services. In the affluent society no useful distinction can be made between luxuries and necessaries. Food and clothing are as difficult as ever to do without. But they can be and frequently are among the most opulent of expenditures.

The relation of the sales tax to the problem of social balance is admirably direct. The community is affluent in privately produced goods. It is poor in public services. The obvious solution is to tax the former to provide the latter — by making private goods more expensive, public goods are made more abundant. Motion pictures, electronic entertainment, and cigarettes are made more costly so that schools can be more handsomely supported. We pay more for soap, detergents, and vacuum cleaners in order that we may have cleaner cities and less occasion to use them. We have more expensive cars and gasoline so that we may have highways and streets on which to drive them. Food being comparatively cheap and abundant, we tax it in order to have better medical services and better health in which to enjoy it. This forthright solution has the further advantage that sales taxation can be employed with fair efficiency by states and even by cities. It is in the services rendered by these governments that the problem of social balance is especially severe. The yield of the sales tax increases with increasing production. As wants are contrived for private goods more revenues are provided for public use. The general property tax, the principal alternative to the sales tax, is rigid and inflexible. Since its rates must ordinarily be raised for additional services, including those that are associated with increasing incomes and product, the burden of proving need is especially heavy. This tax is a poor servant of social balance.

During the present century the use of sales taxation by states and cities has been growing. Liberals have ordinarily resisted its use. At a minimum they have viewed it with grave misgiving. This has again made the liberal the effective enemy of social balance. The reasons for this opposition provide an interesting example of how ideas, as they remain stereotyped in face of change, can force those who hold them into roles inconsistent with their own professions. The American liberal has been, all things considered, the opponent of better schools, better communities, better urban communications, and indeed even of greater economic stability.

The effect of a sales tax varies greatly as between a poor and an affluent country, and the difference is one not of degree but of kind. Under the *ancien régime* in France the tax on salt achieved an enduring reputation for its oppressiveness which it retains in parts of modern India to this day. In the United States a tax on salt, even one that doubled or trebled its price, would work no perceptible hardship. It is not that salt is more dispensable now than in the day of the *gabelle.* But where it was then a major object of expenditure it is now an insignificant one. And where the price of salt once affected visibly and directly what remained for other use, it is now too small to have a noticeable effect.

As with salt so with other things. In a family which can buy only bread and cloth, a tax on bread and clothing means that children will be hungrier and less well clad. In a family which can buy many things the adjustment comes at the margin in spending for gasoline, installment payments, the races, or the quality of the ceremonial steak.

Thus does affluence alter the case against sales taxation. It will be argued that some people are still very poor. The sales tax, unlike the income tax, weighs heavily on the small consumption of such individuals. But if the income tax is unavailable or in service of other ends, the only alternative is to sacrifice social balance. A poor society rightly adjusts its policy to the poor. An affluent society may properly inquire whether, instead, it shouldn't remove the poverty. Moreover, improved social balance is one of the first requisites for the elimination of poverty. The modern liberal rallies to protect the poor from the taxes which in the next generation, as the result of a higher investment in their children, would eliminate poverty.

Section C

PROPERTY TAXATION

For many years the property tax has been regarded as having a very stable yield. Evidence to support this point is given in the article (Selection 27) by Groves and Kahn. (In examining this statement, the reader should note that the income elasticity of a certain tax is not the same measure as income elasticity of, say, educational expenditures — see Selection 20 above). Surprisingly, the increase in the real property tax base has been quite large in the postwar years, and Netzer (Selection 28) suggests that the earlier views on the stability of yield of the instrument are erroneous.

Whatever its yield may be, the question remains as to whether the property tax has such serious drawbacks as to cause concern about its continued use. Selections 29 and 30 consider some of these deficiencies, as well as the question of whether there is any alternative levy that could be used by local governments, should the state legislatures allow them to make a change.

It is reasonable to expect that there will be no radical departure in local taxing practice in the near future. The most constructive action, then, is to seek improvement in the administration of the property tax. Bird discusses this matter in Selection 31. Improvement in assessment practice is doubly important, since improper methods produce inequities not only among the citizens of a given locality but also between those citizens and other taxpayers in the state. This is because property assessments are the chief measure of local resources ("ability") used in determining the distribution of state funds for schools.

27

The Stability of State and Local Tax Yields

Harold M. Groves and C. Harry Kahn

This pioneering article by two University of Wisconsin economists set the stage for much of the postwar discussion of property taxation in the United States. Of chief interest is the extreme inflexibility of yield ascribed to property levies, as compared with other important forms of taxation.

Public finance literature of recent years has given much attention to the question of built-in flexibility in the federal tax system in general, and the income elasticity of some of the taxes of which the system is composed in particular. On the state and local level, however, interest in relation to the ups and downs of the economy still centers on stability rather than flexibility. The continued emphasis on sales and excise taxes in most state tax systems is in part attributable to this trend.

Stability of revenue is, properly speaking, a special case of *adequacy.* Although adequacy is not included among Adam Smith's canons of taxation, it is frequently considered an important qualification of a good state and local revenue system. By adequacy is meant not only the capacity of a particular tax to produce a given initial amount of revenue but also its capacity to sustain this level in such a manner as to permit the maintenance of a given volume and quality of governmental services. A "fairly" stable tax system, and it should be remembered that state and local governments depend primarily on taxes to finance their services, is thus one which assures the treasury an approximately constant real income over a period of time. In a period of changing prices, assuming that money incomes change in proportion to the price level, tax yields would have to change in proportion to the change in income in order to maintain the level of government services. However, when total money income changes due to a change in real output with a constant price level, tax yields could remain constant and still sustain government services. But in most cases, except when the expansion of total

Adapted from "The Stability of State and Local Tax Yields," *American Economic Review,* Volume XLIII, No. 1 (March, 1952), pp. 87–94. Reproduced with permission.

money income has passed the point of full employment, changes in both price level and real income are involved. It follows that in general, from the point of view of maintaining a given level of tax-financed government services, tax yields may be allowed to vary in the same direction as total income, but the variation should be less than in proportion to the variation in total income.

Thus, in contrast to the federal government whose special and strategic position in the economy makes deficits and surpluses from fluctuating revenues a blessing and hence instability of taxes (built-in flexibility) a virtue, the states and their subdivisions are primarily interested in "built-in stability" and, therefore, in taxes whose income sensitivity is low. Like the individual firms under pure competition, whose wage-costs and prices are data to which they must adjust, these smaller units of government are also part of what is studied under the heading of "microeconomics." They have few if any of the unique powers that make fluctuating tax yields a matter of minor concern to the federal government. This study, accordingly, is devoted to the problems arising from the desire for revenue stability on the part of state and local authorities.

Classification of Taxes According to Their Stability Record

As has been pointed out above, the cost of government is likely to fluctuate less than income payments. Hence, if it is desired to maintain intact at all times the level of government services and to finance them from taxes primarily, the *total* of state and local tax revenues has to be of less than unit income elasticity. In order to judge the extent to which the tax yields of a given state fulfill the stability requirement, it is necessary to obtain elasticity coefficients for the various state and local taxes. The term income elasticity (e) with respect to a given tax may be defined as the ratio of the percentage change in tax yield (T) to a given percentage change in income payments (Y) and may be written as $e = \frac{\Delta Y}{T} / \frac{\Delta T}{Y}$.

According to their degree of revenue stability, taxes may be divided into three groups:

1. Taxes whose yield is very stable, that is, whose income elasticity is substantially less than unity. In the limiting case, elasticity of zero, tax base and tax rate would not change as total incomes change. Examples somewhat approaching this case are certain types of licenses, a rigidly administered property tax, and above all the poll tax. Taxes with an income elasticity of .80 and less may be said to fall into this group.

2. Taxes whose yield varies roughly in proportion to fluctuations in income payments. Examples of this type can be found in the general sales tax area. Here tax collections vary in proportion to the amount of dollar expenditures on the taxed goods. Their income elasticity is close to unity.

3. Taxes that have a high sensitivity to changes in income, that is, whose

yield varies considerably more than in proportion to changes in income. This is the case wherever (a) the tax base varies more than in proportion to income, and/or (b) the average rate of tax rises as income rises due to a graduated rate schedule. The group is best exemplified by the individual and corporate net income taxes. Their elasticity coefficient is generally above 1.5.

. . . .

Table 1 presents some of the taxes whose yields were related to state income payments in connection with a recent Wisconsin tax study. Tax yields were

Table 1

STATE TAXES CLASSIFIED BY SENSITIVITY TO CHANGES IN STATE INCOME PAYMENTS

Taxes	Period Covered	Index of Elasticity	Per Cent Change in Tax Yield with 25% Change in Income
I. *Taxes of Low Income Elasticity* (0–.80)			
Wisconsin utility property taxes	1930–50	.08	1.8
Wisconsin general property assessments	1929–48	.22	5.0
Wisconsin alcohol taxes	1935–49	.33	7.6
Wisconsin motor fuel tax	1934–49	.36	8.4
Wisconsin highway taxes (incl. motor fuel)	1932–49	.40	9.3
Wisconsin insurance taxes	1930–50	.49	11.6
Wisconsin privilege dividends tax	1937–50	.60	14.3
Wisconsin cigarette tax	1941–50	.63	15.1
Wisconsin telephone tax	1930–50	.72	17.4
Ohio cigarette tax	1940–48	.73	17.7
II. *Taxes of Medium Income Elasticity* (.81–1.20)			
Ohio sales tax	1937–48	.99	24.7
North Carolina sales tax	1940–49	1.00	25.0
Iowa sales tax	1935–49	1.02	25.6
Missouri sales tax	1938–49	1.03	25.8
Michigan sales tax	1934–49	1.09	27.5
Oklahoma sales tax	1937–39	1.11	28.1
California sales tax	1934–49	1.11	28.1
Illinois sales tax	1934–48	1.11	28.1
III. *Taxes of High Income Elasticity* (1.21 and over)			
Indiana gross income tax	1934–49	1.41	37.0
Maryland individual income tax	1942–49	1.54	41.0
Wisconsin taxes on income			
Total Normal	1935–49	1.64	44.2
Normal on individuals	1936–50	1.75	47.8
Normal on corporations	1936–50	1.50	39.8
North Carolina individual income tax	1938–49	1.81	49.8

taken on a fiscal year basis and matched with income data of the immediately preceding calendar years. This allows a six months' period for time lags between tax collections and income payments. The choice of taxes included in this analysis was somewhat arbitrary. It was determined largely by the availability to the authors of data for taxes whose yields remained relatively uninfluenced over a reasonable period of time by changes in the law concerning rates, definition of tax base, or administration.[1]

It will be observed that the periods covered in most cases include part of the 1930's and most of the 1940's. For purposes of illustration, each elasticity coefficient is accompanied by the percentage change in tax yield which would result from a 25 per cent change in income.

The first group of taxes presented in the table comprises taxes which fluctuate little in response to changes in income, that is, primarily the unit sales taxes and the general and special property taxes levied in Wisconsin. The unit sales taxes are based on the quantity consumed and will therefore, fluctuate in direct proportion to consumption of the taxed goods. The demand for goods which are selected for taxation, especially at the state level, is usually inelastic to income change, which is presumably one of the reasons for their being taxed. The low sensitivity of the Wisconsin privilege dividends tax, a 3 per cent tax on all dividends originating from business transacted in Wisconsin, stands in marked contrast to the high sensitivity of the tax on the total of corporate income (1.5). Since the Wisconsin corporation tax has only a negligible degree of progression, most of this difference in income-sensitivity should be ascribed to the efforts of corporations to maintain stable dividend payments. The inheritance and gift taxes were omitted from Group I since, due to lack of correlation between income payments and these taxes over the short run, no meaningful coefficient could be obtained.

The second group, taxes of medium income elasticity, consists entirely of the general sales tax family, and the coefficients for the states for which data were readily obtainable indicate that the revenue yields vary on the whole almost in proportion to variations in income payments. In contrast to the unit sales taxes of Group I, these taxes cover a wide range of consumer goods and their yield is a function of both quantity sold and price. The ratio of taxation to income under various conditions depends on the relation of consumption spending to money income. It is, of course, possible that the exemption from tax of certain categories of goods, whose prices may be more or less volatile than the general price level, may have its effects on the elasticity coefficient. However, the category most frequently exempted, food, appears

[1] A reasonably thorough check has been made to avoid situations involving major changes other than those in income. In some cases, such as rate changes, adjustments could be made without great difficulty. Minor changes in legislation or administration, of course, had to be disregarded. The frequent revision of statutes was a particular obstacle in estimating the stability of state income taxes by this method, and for that reason no indices other than for Maryland, North Carolina, and Wisconsin are presented here.

The stability of property tax collections as such could not be estimated, other than by way of correlating assessed valuations with income: property tax rates change too frequently.

to have little effect in this sense, for although the quantity of food consumed has been more stable than income, food prices have been less stable. The result of these offsetting movements is that food expenditures and income change at about the same rate.

The third group in the table consists of taxes whose income elasticity exceeds 1.2. The presence here of the gross income tax of Indiana is explained by condition (a) as stated in the definition of this group. The gross income tax is usually considered more akin to the general sales than to the income tax family. Its coefficient of 1.4 is primarily caused by the fact that, though without graduation of rates, the tax has income exemptions which have the effect of increasing (decreasing) the ratio of tax base to income whenever state income rises (falls). The Wisconsin corporation income tax is also of the (a) type. It has no graduation, but corporate income is more volatile than income payments in general.

Both conditions (a) and (b) are found in the graduated net income taxes: as incomes rise, more persons move from exempt status to taxable status, and simultaneously everybody's average rate of tax rises due to the graduated rate feature. Here an elasticity coefficient greater than 1 is built into the tax law itself although the value of the coefficient usually does not depend on the rate schedule alone but also on the prevailing distribution of income. . . .

THE STABILITY OF STATE TAX SYSTEMS AS A WHOLE

In the previous section we presented data on the income elasticity of various state and local taxes. The question now arises, what is the result when these taxes are combined in the state and local tax system? An over-all (state and local) elasticity coefficient for each of seven midwestern states was computed for this purpose (Table 2). It indicates that for the total of state and local taxes there may be no stability problem. If the coefficients are again interpreted on the basis of response to a 25 per cent change in income payments, the variations of the most stable system would be about 10 per cent and that of the least stable only 13 per cent over the period studied. The state-collected taxes, however, show less stability and vary from 15 to 22 per cent with a 25 per cent variation in income. Moreover, the states' executive budget tax revenues are frequently less stable than state-collected taxes as such since several of the latter, as, for instance, the very stable highway taxes, are usually earmarked for specific purposes, thus leaving the unstable taxes for purposes supported by less powerful interests. Wisconsin's executive budget taxes have an index of 1.04. It may be of interest to note that Musgrave and Miller found the income elasticity of the federal tax system for 1947 to be about 1.5.[2] The over-all index owes its low value to the heavy

[2] R. A. Musgrave and M. H. Miller, *Am. Econ. Rev.*, Vol. XXXVIII, No. 1 (Mar., 1948), p. 126. This elasticity coefficient may not be strictly comparable to the one presented in this paper since the former is based on the 1946–47 experience only while the latter summarizes the experience of several years (see Table 1).

Table 2

SEVEN STATE TAX SYSTEMS CLASSIFIED BY SENSITIVITY TO CHANGES IN INCOME PAYMENTS[a]

	Total State and Local Taxes	Total State-Collected Taxes
Illinois	.43	.74
Indiana	.52	.82
Iowa	.50	.83
Michigan	.53	.77
Minnesota	.49	.79
Ohio	.43	.63
Wisconsin	.56	.90

[a] The composition of each state tax system is that of 1948.

weight of the very stable property taxes. Some may object that the high delinquency rate of property taxes in the early 'thirties contradicts the low elasticity coefficient used in this study. But that would be putting the cart before the horse, for it was precisely because of the low income elasticity of the property tax and the heavy reliance upon it that these systems broke down.

28

The Elasticity of the Property Tax Reconsidered

Dick Netzer

In 1957 Dick Netzer took sharp exception to the Groves-Kahn estimates of property tax elasticity. The following excerpt is a restatement, buttressed with recent data, of his 1957 view that the elasticity of that levy is relatively high.

Probably no feature of the December 1957 paper received more abuse than the assumption of unit elasticity in projecting property tax revenues. The

Adapted from "Financial Needs and Resources Over the Next Decade: State and Local Governments," in National Bureau of Economic Research, *Public Finances: Needs, Sources, and Utilization*, Princeton, Princeton University Press, 1961, pp. 33–36. Reproduced with permission.

criticisms took two forms. First, it was asserted that whatever my estimates of the elasticity of the underlying base — the market value of taxable property — history has demonstrated that changes in assessments lag behind changes in value to a major extent and that therefore in an environment of growing output, income, and wealth, state and local agencies will find themselves relying on a revenue source which inadequately reflects growth. It was the use of assessments, not market values, that produced the 0.22 elasticity figure for the periods between 1929 and 1950 alluded to above.[1]

I reject this contention, for several reasons. First, there is no real evidence to indicate that assessments are in fact insensitive to secular changes in GNP, however sticky they are in the short run in the face of cyclical changes. The evidence that does exist is meager, but it suggests the contrary conclusion. It must be repeated that the present projections assume away cyclical movements which are large or prolonged.

Second, this criticism implies that with growth but no inflation, the ratio of assessed to market values of existing properties will continuously decline and/or new improvements and additions will be ignored in a wholesale scale by tax assessors. This seems wholly unreasonable. To be sure, reassessments are periodic rather than continual and increases in real value which are a consequence of growth in the economy rather than changes in the physical character of the property (e.g., the rising value of potential homesites now in farm use on the fringes of growing metropolitan areas) are apt to be inadequately reflected by assessors. However, for the economy as a whole in the environment postulated, it is inconceivable that such lags would lower the elasticity figure by more than, say, 0.15. And, as will be seen shortly, there is good reason to believe that the conservative elasticity figure used — 1.00 — is actually a good deal more than 0.15 below the true post-war experience. Moreover, there are offsets to these deficiencies in assessment practices. Assessment practices *are* improving, albeit more slowly than reasonable men can abide, in part through the adoption of just passably good practices by the more primitive jurisdictions and in part through continual improvements in all sorts of procedures, techniques, and assessment aids and equipment of a mundane sort, on the part of more advanced assessment offices and officers. In addition, if there is to be no more inflation, the lags occasioned by the recent inflation will be caught up with, as assessors begin to regard current market values as more "normal."

Third, even if there are moderate lags in assessments, the goal here is to appraise fiscal resources available to state-local governments, not, at least in the first instance, to gauge how heavily they will tap these resources. In the assumed economic environment, market values, not assessments (or putting it otherwise, a measure which holds effective, not nominal rates constant) seem very much the appropriate measure of available resources.

[1] See Harold M. Groves and C. Harry Kahn, "The Stability of State and Local Tax Yields," *American Economic Review*, March 1952, pp. 87–102.

The second major criticism, less frequently voiced, is much more to the point. This, simply, questions my estimates of changes in the underlying base, market values. Walter Heller, the formal discussant of the earlier paper, queried whether offsetting influences had been at work among the components of the property tax base in the post-war period and whether it is reasonable to assume their continuance.[2] The projections here are based on a new set of estimates of changes in the property tax base, not a repetition of the earlier computations, although the resulting elasticity figures are identical.

The method used was to prepare separate estimates of changes in current market values (or depreciated replacement cost) for the major classes of property ordinarily subject to levy, and to combine these series into an index, weighting the components on the basis of their share of total assessed value in 1956, as reported in the 1957 Census of Governments. The separate series were also expressed in 1946 dollars, and combined on the basis of these weights, into a 1946 dollar index. The four series used were: residential nonfarm real estate, which accounted for about 42 per cent of 1956 assessments; other nonfarm real estate, including here all state-assessed rail and public utility property, about 30 per cent of the 1956 tax base; farm real estate, about 10 per cent of the tax base; and tangible personal property-inventories, producer durables, and motor vehicles, about 17 per cent of the tax base. Intangibles, which amount to only about one-half of the 1 per cent of total assessed values, most of this concentrated in a single state, were ignored. The basic approach was to bring forward to the present, somewhat crudely, on the basis of available evidence various components of the national wealth estimates presented by Raymond Goldsmith in *A Study of Savings*. For residential nonfarm real estate, this method produces results for 1956 very close to the equalized value total based on the Census Bureau's assessment-ratio survey for six months in 1956. For nonresidential real estate, the results, while not as close to the Census data, are not unacceptably far off that benchmark. Department of Agriculture data were used for farm real estate, rather than the Goldsmith-based approach.

Table 1 indicates the results of these methods. The current value-current GNP elasticities are relatively low for farm real estate and relatively very high for inventories and durables, and in general the elasticity figures are higher for the first half of the period than for the second half, which is understandable in view of the rapid rises in the price level in the 1945–51 period. On a deflated basis, the elasticity figures for the earlier years are far lower than for the more recent years, especially for the nonfarm real estate categories which together comprise nearly three-fourths of the 1956 tax base.

There are two reasons why I suggested above that the use of unit elasticity in the projections in conservative. First, the deflators used are probably much too large. Essentially, they are based on the rise in the costs of producing

[2] A.E.A. *Papers and Proceedings*, May 1958, p. 332.

Table 1

ESTIMATED CHANGES IN VALUES OF TAXABLE CLASSES OF PROPERTY FOR TAXES PAYABLE IN FISCAL 1946–57[a]

	Residential Nonfarm Real Estate	Other Nonfarm Real Estate	Farm Real Estate	Inventories and Durables	Weighted Total[b]
Percentage increase in tax base, current market values:					
1945–56	149	135	105	238	151
1945–51	87	71	73	139	90
1951–56	33	37	19	41	32
GNP elasticities of revenues at: constant effective rates — current dollar GNP *vs.* current market values:					
1946–57	1.37	1.24	0.97	2.18	1.38
1946–52	1.34	1.09	1.12	2.14	1.38
1952–57	1.22	1.37	0.70	1.52	1.19
constant dollar GNP *vs.* deflated values:					
1946–57	1.02	0.68	0.30	2.18	1.00
1946–52	0.60	0.20	0.24	1.92	0.64
1952–57	1.67	1.54	0.47	2.20	1.54

[a] Tax base computations apply to values in calendar year preceding fiscal year in which taxes are payable; to give effect to lags in collections, GNP changes between tax payment years are used in computing elasticities.

[b] Weighted by proportion which each class is of total assessed value in 1956.

new properties (improvements to real estate and tangible personalty), and they imply an immediate and proportionate revaluation of existing properties. This is no doubt a considerable exaggeration of actual price effects. Second, I suspect that the 1952–57 period may be a better indicator for the future than the earlier period, because of the relative magnitudes of inflation in the two periods, as well as the relative volumes of investment activity. To give some weight to lags in the assessment process, a rather conservative elasticity figure has been employed in the projections. However, ignoring these lags, and throwing caution to the winds, an elasticity figure of 1.4–1.5 would seem to be indicated.

29

Some Unfortunate Features of the Property Tax

Procter Thomson

It is generally conceded that the property tax has certain markedly undesirable features. The following selection by Procter Thomson, an expert in local finance, is a brief catalogue of its deficiencies.

The property tax, the main source of local revenue, illustrates the ancient maxim "uneasy lies the head that wears a crown." The property tax is both defective in principle and deficient in practice. But according to some authorities, in addition to the virtue (if any) that age confers upon it, taxation of real property is the only source of revenue local units are competent to administer. If this contention is true, if other forms of taxation are too complex for cities and schools to handle or if the attempt to employ them would erode their economic base, then discussing the disabilities of property taxes is an invitation to despair. For nothing is either good or bad, to paraphrase the Bard slightly, save alternatives make it so. And if the property tax has no feasible alternatives — save loss of local initiative or wholesale reduction in local services — we must accept it as it is and pass on to more fruitful areas of inquiry.

But alternatives do exist. The principal sources of public revenue are wealth, income, and consumption. Of these three the taxation of wealth secures the minimum amount of revenue with the maximum amount of fiscal inequity, economic inefficiency, and administrative difficulty.

Inequity

Fundamentally, the property tax is unjust because it fails to treat equals equally. Income from property is only a fraction of income in general, somewhere between 1/4 and 1/3, in fact, for the U.S. economy as a whole, and dif-

Reprinted from *California Local Finance*, by John A. Vieg and Others, pp. 15–18, with the permission of the publishers, Stanford University Press, the Haynes Foundation and Claremont Social Research Center.

ferent families have widely different ratios of wealth to income. To the extent, therefore, that taxes on property are ultimately borne by owners of property and to the extent that personal income represents the most equitable measure of that illusive magnitude, "ability to pay," the property tax violates one of the basic criteria of taxation in a democratic society.

INEFFICIENCY: THE FLOW OF CAPITAL

The property tax distorts the pattern of investment between different communities. Communities with high tax rates have a lower volume of commercial and residential investment and those with low tax rates have a higher volume of investment. Differences in tax rates lead to improper allocation of resources.

Some of these effects, admittedly, take a very long time to work themselves out and all of them are mixed and interspersed with a number of other forces. A growing community with a high tax rate, for example, will not expand quite as rapidly as it otherwise would. But regardless of disturbing factors, the long-run return on capital in one area must be roughly equal to the return in any other area. As a result, buildings are relatively scarcer and their rents before taxes are relatively higher in high tax communities while the reverse is true in low tax communities so that net yields in both are approximately equal after taxes are paid.

How does this adjustment affect economic efficiency? It is bound to affect it adversely because the location of business, residential, and commercial activities no longer reflects the natural advantages of different communities. Differences in tax rates create artificial scarcity and artificial abundance. If X would have been a good place for a shopping center or an apartment house and Y a relatively poor site, the differences in taxes ought not to repeal the comparative advantage which nature establishes.

INFLEXIBILITY

As most California communities have discovered, the property tax is inflexible. It is inflexible in principle because the market values of assets, which are the capitalized net worth of income streams running into the distant future, do not always keep pace with year-to-year changes in community income. It is inflexible in practice because assessed values tend to lag behind market values.

These twin disabilities create, in California as elsewhere, the sorry spectacle of wealthy communities and impoverished governments during periods of economic growth and cumulative inflation. And state legislatures have enthusiastically compounded the natural disabilities of the tax by imposing legal barriers on both the operating margin and the borrowing margin of cities, schools, and other local agencies. Altogether, no more perfect formula for fiscal mismanagement could be devised than to place the governments of expanding metropolitan areas upon a narrow fiscal base and then deny them the power to use that base when they need it. Legal limits on local tax rates are, in one sense, however, a kind of left-handed recognition of the inherent inequities and diseconomies of the property tax *per se*. The remedy, we trust, is sufficiently obvious that he who runs may read: Retire the property tax from active duty as rapidly as possible.

Administration

A favorite indoor sport of writers on public finance is to complain about the assessment practices and administrative standards of the local property tax. The bill of particulars varies little from one community to another. In the first place, property is never assessed at its full value; for California as a whole the assessed values are about a quarter of the market values and the ratio has been falling intermittently throughout most of the postwar period. Second, different tax areas have widely differing ratios of assessed to market value; as far as can be determined, California counties in 1957 varied from 20 to 27%, i.e., the highest level is 35% greater than the lowest. Third, different kinds of property within the same tax jurisdiction are assessed at different ratios of market value. Fourth, in all jurisdictions some property escapes assessment altogether; this is particularly true of the personal property tax, which falls mainly "upon those unfortunate individuals who are burdened either with a vigorous conscience or a groundless fear of legal consequences."

The causes of these variations are not hard to isolate. Apart from the inherent difficulties of identifying and measuring millions of parcels of residential property according to a fair and equitable formula, the virtual impossibility of conducting search and seizure operations to catch hundreds of millions of pieces of personal property, and the unbelievable complexity of the recording and reporting arrangements required by this bootless enterprise, there are six causes susceptible of remedy this side of Utopia:

1. The elected, often technically untrained, assessor who is subject to political pressure both to reduce individual assessments and to lower the general level of assessments in the area under his jurisdiction,
2. State aid programs which, however desirable on other grounds, provide an incentive for competitive underassessment because state money is paid to schools in inverse proportion to the amount of assessed value per child,
3. The ancient tradition of underassessment and differential assessment in local units which perpetuates itself by its own inertia,
4. The preoccupation of professional assessors with a metaphysical magnitude called "true value" which renders them incapable of recognizing the impact of inflation on asset prices,

5. The political climate which converts a technical issue, the value of property, into a power struggle between the taxpayer, or taxpayers as a group, and the assessor,

6. Failure to coordinate and centralize the assessment of property in the hands of a unified agency with effective power to achieve equalization between different tax jurisdictions.

30

The Inevitability of Rates

John R. Hicks, Ursula K. Hicks, and C. E. V. Leser

A distinguished group of English economists make the case that the property tax has characteristics which render it uniquely suitable for use by local authorities. As an exercise the reader may wish to see if he can suggest another instrument that could meet the particular needs of local government.

English local authorities have always depended on rates as their main local source of revenue; but that is of course no reason why they should continue to do so in the future. The rating system is at present in a very sorry mess; and it is not going to be an easy matter to put it straight. Why then, some of our readers will probably object, must we bother to do so? Even at the best, rates are far from being an ideal tax; if they have now got into such confusion, surely we have an excellent opportunity for getting rid of them and substituting something better. There are many people who take this view; and we are well aware that we are going to provide them with ammunition for their attack on the rating system. Our own conclusion however is different; we believe that the rating system has to be preserved, and therefore ought to be reformed, however arduous a matter it may be to reform it. But since the arguments against rates are becoming familiar, and the arguments in favour of rates are much less familiar, it does not seem desirable to

From John R. Hicks, Ursula K. Hicks and C. E. V. Leser: *The Problem of Valuation for Rating*, Occasional Paper VII of the National Institute of Economic and Social Research, published by the Cambridge University Press, 1944, pp. 6–11.

set out the case here, even though the discussion must lead us a little away from the problem of valuation, which is our proper scope.

Quite apart from the objections to the present rating system which arise out of the difficulties of valuation, rates have been criticized on two main grounds of principle. On the one hand it is observed that they are a regressive tax (the poor man pays a larger percentage of his income in rates than the rich man does). There is no doubt that this is correct, though the extent of the regressiveness is often exaggerated. On the other hand, they are a tax on housing — a tax, that is, upon a form of expenditure which it is a matter of social policy to encourage, not to discourage like expenditure on alcohol or tobacco. In both these ways the imposition of rates seems to be contrary to the aims of a progressive social policy.

These are certainly very weighty objections; if rates were a national tax, paid to the central government, instead of a local tax, it is quite conceivable that they would be strong enough to tilt the balance of argument against the rating system. But even this is not certain; it does not follow, for instance, that a tax is a bad tax merely because it is regressive. With the expenses of government on their present scale, it is not possible for governments to raise the whole of their revenue from the wealthy and the middle-class; this is true even in peace time. There is not enough income in the upper brackets to meet the bill. The working-class has got to pay some taxes. Now it is very largely a matter of convenience whether this working-class share in taxation is paid in the same way as wealthier people pay the bulk of their taxes (by income tax) or whether it is paid in a different way. The test of equity in taxation is satisfied if poorer people pay a suitably lower proportion of their incomes in taxes than richer people do — but this test must be applied to all taxes taken together, not to any particular tax. It may well be more convenient for poorer people to pay the bulk of their taxes in a different form from that in which richer people pay the bulk of their taxes; if this is done, the poor persons' taxes, taken by themselves, will be regressive; but the demands of equity are still satisfied if the total burden of all taxation is properly progressive.

The argument against rates on the score of their being a tax on housing is very probably a stronger argument. But even here it should be noted that the repressive effect on house-building can be offset by housing subsidies. This may seem a cumbrous procedure, but it is not so very irrational. The housing subsidies are only paid to new houses, and new working-class houses; they therefore cost very much less than the rates on all houses bring in.

Thus neither of the arguments against rates is quite as strong as it looks at first sight; nevertheless it may be granted that if the *central* government had raised its revenue in this way, it is likely that rates would have disappeared long ago. The reason why they have not disappeared, and are unlikely to disappear, is that rates are a local tax, not a national tax. In order to be a suitable source of local finance, a tax has got to satisfy some very stringent requirements. There are in fact very few taxes which do satisfy these requirements. They are satisfied by rates, but they are not satisfied by most of the alternatives which have been suggested. It is very doubtful if there is any other possible tax which satisfies the requirements and which could be relied upon to produce a large amount of revenue.

The first requirement of a local tax is that it should be a very stable source of revenue. Very much the greater part of a local authority's expenditure takes the form of rather long-run commitments. Obviously it cannot suspend the service of its debts; but likewise it cannot easily reduce the number of its employees without the most disruptive effect on its whole organization, while the rates of wages and salaries which it pays are largely outside its control. It is therefore very difficult for it to contract its expenditure when its income falls off. If local revenues were subject to violent fluctuations, every downward fluctuation would produce a severe crisis. The central government, if it experiences a contraction in revenue, can run into debt; it is indeed to be hoped that the national governments will in the future be more willing than in the past to meet depressions in trade in this way. But this solution is not open to local authorities to any important extent — nor is it desirable that it should be. Local authorities are not sovereign bodies; they have to work under a fixed code of rules. One of the most important of these rules is that which establishes central control of local borrowing. This control could not be abandoned without running the gravest risk of abuses, and at the same time abandoning one of the most important of the economic controls at the disposal of the central government. Now if local authorities were frequently obliged to borrow, not for capital purposes, but in order to meet casual deficiencies in local revenue, either the central control of borrowing must be abandoned, or one of the most important forms of local autonomy must be abandoned. For the central control of borrowing, as it exists at present, is not only a safeguard against abuses (it would be far harder for a local authority to resist unjustifiable demands for increased expenditure, if it could not point to the extra revenue it would have to raise to match that expenditure); it is also a safeguard of local autonomy. The only autonomy which is possible for a subordinate authority is autonomy within a set of rules; as long as revenue is reasonably stable, the control of borrowing provides a very workable rule on the financial side. So long as the local authority does not run into debt, it can on the whole spend what it likes. But if it were liable to run into debt purely because of a depression in trade, every trade depression would result in a suspension of local autonomy. The local authority would be unable to spend anything without central sanction.

Rates are a very stable source of revenue. At least in peace-time, the land and buildings in an area can be relied upon to be there; they are unlikely to be much diminished in quantity, though they may be increased. So long as they are valued according to their normal value, temporary fluctuations being discarded, their rateable value is affected to a minimum extent by fluctuations in trade. It may indeed be argued that the practices we shall be analysing have made rateable values too stable — too conventional; but no reform of valuations ought to go so far as to remove this precious characteristic of general stability.

There are, of course, other taxes whose yield is fairly stable; but they are not the progressive taxes (income tax and death duties, for instance); for profits are exceedingly sensitive to fluctuations in trade, so that taxes which fall largely on profits are exceedingly liable to have a fluctuating yield. The other stable taxes are the consumption taxes; thus on this ground alone they would be suitable enough as sources of local finance, though less suitable than rates. The main objection to consumption taxes as sources of local finance is the ease of evading them by making one's purchases in a neighbouring district where rates of tax are lower. Even in the United States, where such evasion is more difficult because of the greater dispersion of population, petrol taxes have proved a rather unsatisfactory source of state revenue because it is so easy for the population living on the fringes of a highly taxed state to fill their tanks by preference on the other side of the border. It can hardly be doubted that in England the use of any consumption tax for local purposes would drive trade out of the large towns into the surrounding country — thus leaving the finances of those towns in an even more serious condition than they are often in at present. For while divergences in local rate poundages have something of the same tendency (people move out to escape the high rates), it would be far easier to buy one's petrol or cigarettes in the cheaper area, or even to do all one's shopping there, than it is at present to change one's residence.

The stability of rateable value as a source of revenue is probably the decisive argument in favour of rates; for it follows from this that the rating system cannot be abandoned without a radical change — for the worse — in the political character of English local government. But there is another argument which tells the same way, and which should not be overlooked.

The attempt which has been made in modern England to organize social services through the local authorities may be politically admirable, but it has led, in the economic sphere, to very paradoxical results. The purposes of the social services is to secure a minimum standard of amenities for all citizens; all those who cannot provide such amenities for themselves, out of their own incomes, should have them provided by the public authority. Now if the public authority in question is the local authority (as on political and administrative grounds there are strong reasons for concluding that it should be) then the greatest burden is laid upon those local authorities which have the largest proportion of poor people within their districts; and this must mean, whatever system of taxation is used, that the greatest burden falls upon the poorest authorities. The resulting inequity has been realized, and an attempt to meet it has been made by the giving of grants. But however generous the grants may be (there can be no doubt that in fact the grants received by many poor authorities are not nearly generous enough), it is impossible by grants to overcome the whole difficulty. If the grants given were sufficiently generous, they might enable the poor authority to reach an appropriate minimum level of expenditure without imposing unduly heavy taxation (we are far from reaching this point in practice). Yet even so, the poor authority would only be able to go beyond this level of expenditure (as it might have the best of reasons for desiring to do) if it imposed a higher rate of tax than a rich area would need to impose in order to finance a similar expansion. However generous grants become, they cannot give the poor authority the same liberty as the richer authority derives naturally from its greater wealth.

This inequality is bound to exist under any system of local taxation; whatever type of tax is employed, a poor town will have to pinch more than a rich town if it is to squeeze out an extra five shillings per head of its inhabitants. Nevertheless it is important to notice that some sorts of tax are much less hampering to the poor area than others are.

The least hampering type of tax is the rather regressive tax to which everyone contributes, the sort of tax which we have found to be desirable as a *local* tax on other grounds. The most hampering variety is a progressive tax, such as income tax, from which everyone whose income falls below a certain level is exempted, or largely exempted. The wealthy authority, which has plenty of freedom anyway, would find its resources improved by the introduction of a local income tax in place of rates; for the advantages which it would gain from the ability to make larger inroads into the incomes of its wealthier citizens would outweigh the loss from the exemption of the poorest. Thus when the matter is looked at from the point of view of a wealthy authority, the local income tax seems to be a most desirable reform; it would increase the resources at the disposal of the authority, and enable it to lighten the burden on its poorer citizens. But from the point of view of a poor authority, the position is very different. It would be easy to find local authorities in England and Wales whose wealthy citizens are a mere handful, and whose poor citizens, who do contribute to rates, but who would contribute very little to a local income tax, are the immense majority. Such an authority would lose enormously by the introduction of the more progressive tax; and although the direct loss might be made up by larger grants, the independence of the authority would be seriously undermined. At present, if its citizens decide that there is some amenity which they desire badly enough for them to be willing to meet its cost out of their limited incomes, then they can have it, each of them bearing his share in the cost. But with a local income tax, the greater part of the cost would have to be borne by the few large or moderately large incomes, and in a poor district these might not amount to enough in total for the requisite revenue to be obtainable from them. Even if the revenue was obtainable on paper, it would usually be obtainable only by imposing a high rate of tax — and a high rate of income tax would be vastly more effective than high rates in driving people out of the district. High rates rarely absorb more than a small fraction of the ratepayer's income; but a local authority which imposes a high rate of income tax would find that anyone with an income worth taxing would avoid it like the plague. With a local income tax, or any other sharply progressive local tax, poor areas would be simply unable to get any special amenity they might happen to want, unless they could persuade the central government to meet the bill, or unless they could finance it by cutting their expenditure on other services.

These are the essential arguments in favour of rates as a basis for local taxation; it will perhaps be granted that they are cogent arguments. To use local government — really independent local government — as a vehicle for the execution of a social policy that is national in scope, is an extraordinarily difficult thing to do; but it can be done, and it is certainly well worth doing. Yet it seems unlikely that there is any basis other than a tax for the type of rates on which it can be done.

Enough has perhaps been said to show why the total supersession of rates by some other form of tax is unlikely and certainly undesirable. And that is all that has to be shown for present purposes. If rates are to remain, they deserve to be reformed; it seems clear that they will remain important enough to deserve reform, however hard a matter it may be to reform them.

If indeed all that is proposed is a substitution of some other form of tax for a part of rate revenue, then the foregoing arguments are somewhat less conclusive. The argument about stability loses some, but certainly not all, its force; the argument about the poor authority is certainly less telling. Nevertheless, it should be realized that there are great advantages in raising local revenue from a single tax of determinable type, and these advantages should not be lightly abandoned. If, for example, a local authority had the choice whether to raise the bulk of its revenue from tax A, which fell mainly on the rich, or tax B, which fell mainly on the poor, a very disagreeable element of division would be introduced into local politics. One does not only think of the poor district, containing a few wealthy landowners, which might be tempted to indulge in a little social revolution of its own by taxing the landowners out of existence. One also thinks of the middle-class area, containing a small number of poor people, which is compelled by government regulation (of which its councillors disapprove) to do something for these people, and which may be tempted to express its disapproval by arranging that as much as possible of the cost is borne by the poor people themselves. The economic conflict between classes is bound to cause trouble in a society such as ours; but it will cause far less disunity if it is played out on the national stage, where it is less complicated by personalities than it tends to be in local politics.

It remains possible that some way could be found for enabling a local authority to raise some fixed part of its revenue from some other tax than rates; but it is hard to see that this arrangement would differ substantially from the system of grants which is at present in existence.

31

The Regulatory Role of the States in Property Tax Administration

Frederick L. Bird

Property tax administration is improving. The gains in this field yield significant benefits for public education. Dr. Bird has been responsible for advising numerous state commissions as these bodies have grappled with the complex kinds of problems reported on here.

For more than one hundred years state governments have been trying in one way or another to correct defects of local property assessment. In view of the considerably less than perfect results obtained, the conclusion must be either that their efforts have not been so skillful and zealous as they should have been or that the job is impossible of accomplishment. That good quality assessing exists in one-fifth of the 1,263 assessing areas covered by the special studies of the 1957 Census of Governments denies the second conclusion; but it raises a question of why the states have permitted continuance of mediocre to poor assessing in wide sections of the nation.

The efforts of the states have included provision for (1) review of original local assessments; (2) county and state supervision and equalization; (3) centralized state assessment of railroad and other public utility property; and (4) strengthening of local assessing organization and administration — all recognized means for obtaining high-standard assessment administration. But the adoption, promotion, and refinement of these devices and procedures have been slow and spasmodic over the years, as the following summary will show. The professional and financial resources devoted to these purposes, at best, have been less than needed; and more often than not, they have been conspicuously inadequate. A recent development that holds some hope for the future of the property tax, and of local self-government, however, is the accelerated and widened interest in the problems involved, and in the in-

Adapted from *The General Property Tax: Findings of the 1957 Census of Governments*, Chicago, Public Administration Service, 1960, pp. 66–77. Reproduced with permission.

tensive exploration of means by which the states may better meet their responsibilities in property tax administration.

. . . .

Areas of Recent Constructive Action

At the local level, many municipalities have in recent years made marked advances in their government organization and methods of management. In the modernization of their fiscal administration, assessment administration has not been neglected; the work has been made the responsibility of trained assessors, equipped with the necessary tools and techniques. This progress has represented local effort. Since it has been handicapped in some instances by state constitutional provisions requiring the election of local assessors or imposing obstacles to constructive legislative revision of the property tax, no uniformity of progress is to be expected if the matter is left solely to the efforts of local governments.

State advances during this period in organization for fiscal administration have contributed in a general way to the improvement of assessment administration by providing professional staffs at the state level for tax research and administration. As compared with a handful of state administrative tax commissions fifty years ago, all of the states now have such commissions or their equivalent. Whether these agencies are separate commissions, single commissioners, or divisions of unified finance departments, most of them have divisions or sections specializing in property assessment supervision, equalization, and some actual assessment. There is increasing recognition, however, that in the great majority of the states more power, organization, and money are needed to do the kind of a job that is called for.

The increasing professionalization of state and local tax administration and the development of tax study and research have made, and continue to make, valuable contributions to the advancement of assessment administration. The work of professionally trained assessors, tax and appraisal consultants, and tax economists in the state tax commissions, universities, and governmental research bureaus has not only produced better assessing and equalization in the specific areas of their operations but has had a much wider educational value. The two national organizations of tax administrators, the National Association of Assessing Officers and the National Association of Tax Administrators, exert a wide influence through their publications, conferences, and advisory services. In an increasing number of states the provision by state agencies of assessing manuals, sales ratio studies, and conferences and in-service training for assessors, as well as publication of the findings of tax study commissions, is contributing to general improvement of assessing standards.

The means for obtaining high-standard assessment administration are well known professionally. The first prerequisite clearly is to eliminate from the general property tax base both intangible personalty and those kinds of tangible personalty that are unduly difficult for the assessor to locate and appraise — to make the assessor's job one that is feasible to handle competently and in accordance with the tax law. The present situation is one of an infinite variety of policy among the states, ranging from a few states that have narrowed the general property tax base to real property, to a few others that maintain the legal fiction of taxing virtually all classes of property at the full ad valorem rate.

The other means relate primarily to administration. They call for local assessing areas large enough to support full-time assessing staffs; appointment of well-trained, professional assessors; state assessment of public utility and industrial property lying in more than one local jurisdiction or requiring specialized types of expert appraisal; improvement of provisions for administrative review of original assessments; regular and systematic state equalization of local assessments; and effective state supervision of local assessment work.

. . . .

STATE SUPERVISION

Review and equalization are necessary adjuncts of assessment administration as now conducted in the majority of local assessing areas; but, as one prominent group of assessing experts declared, they "are totally inadequate substitutes for good original assessment," and "it follows that state participation in the assessment process has greater potentialities for good when directed to improvement of original assessments than when directed to subsequent stages of the process."[1] Strengthening of state supervision has been urged again and again by tax specialists and tax study commissions — very recently, for example, by a Connecticut Tax Study Commission, as follows:

> The Commission recognizes that legislative adoption of its own recommendations concerning assessment standards and procedures can have little assurance of accomplishing their purpose without an adequate system of state guidance in their application and methods for measuring results obtained under them.

Most of the states provide by law for some supervision of the local assessment process by a state agency. The supervisory powers provided in the statutes range from very comprehensive and demanding provisions in a minority of states to relatively negligible provisions at the other extreme; but in the majority of states they are sufficient to permit a moderate to high degree of adequacy in supervision. There has been widespread failure, because of

[1] National Association of Assessing Officers, *Assessment Organization and Personnel*, p. 353.

inadequate organization, or appropriations, or both, to use these powers effectively; but this situation has an increasing number of exceptions. A few states are doing a reasonably good job of supervision, including one or two where talented and energetic administration is more than compensating for limited legal powers, and there has been encouraging recent progress in a number of states in strengthening the regulatory laws and stepping up supervisory activity.

State supervision of the local assessment process includes, in varying degree, advisory and educational functions and regulatory activities. The former cover such useful services as answering inquiries, explaining the tax laws, issuing informative pamphlets and manuals, visiting local offices, holding conferences, and providing in-service training courses. The latter have to do with issuance of rules and regulations, prescribing forms, requiring reports, assessing omitted property, making or ordering reassessments or reconvening local boards of review for this purpose, and enforcing compliance with the tax laws, including, in a few states, the power to remove an assessor from office for neglect of duty. If local assessing administration were everywhere as well organized and staffed as it is in a minority of local areas, state supervision could confine itself mainly to the cooperative development of technical refinements in assessing; but under the widely prevailing conditions, supervisory efforts have to concentrate on promoting the rudiments of acceptable assessment.

Highly centralized direction and supervision of local assessing apply in the state of Maryland, where the local assessing areas are countrywide (including the city of Baltimore, which is not located in a separate county). The State Tax Commission itself assesses, for local taxation, the tangible personal property of ordinary business corporations, the operating property, except land, of railroads and other public utilities and contract carriers, and also distilled spirits. Through its chief supervisor of assessments and local supervisors of assessments, the commission supervises the local assessment of property throughout the state. It appoints the local supervisor (chief assessor) for each county, designates the number of additional assessors to be employed, may remove an assessor for any cause at any time, sets up assessment standards, forms, and procedures, may order general and special reassessments, and carries on technical work of general utility. Its most recent major project has been the development of detailed tax maps for all areas not having them.

In both intra-area and interarea uniformity of assessment, Maryland ranks relatively high, according to the Census study. So great a degree of supervisory authority may not be necessary to achieve good-quality assessing on a statewide basis; but recent progress in other states appears to have been contingent largely on improvement of the regulatory laws, the availability of a competent, energetic state supervisory agency, and the willingness of the legislature to provide funds for an active program of more than temporary character. This conclusion may be illustrated by recent developments in Kentucky and Oregon.

Kentucky is a state of 120 counties, most of them small, rural and without highly professionalized administration. Assessing is done on a countywide basis under elected assessors (county tax commissioners). A program to improve local assessing in the state has been in progress since 1949, when a special session of the legislature, called partly to consider the problem of local assessment, corrected certain statutory hindrances to good assessing, gave county assessors a better status, authorized the State Department of Revenue to develop a program of assistance to assessors, and appropriated $300,000 for the first year's program.

The basis for the very considerable success of the program has been the competence of the department, its continuous effort, and its policy of seeking the cooperation of the assessors and the public. The program is carried on by a local valuation section of the department's valuation division, the section including a central technical staff and a field staff. The technical staff develops standard assessment procedures for the county assessors, assists them in assessing complex types of property, and supervises reassessment projects. The field staff operates on an area basis, each member being assigned to work with a dozen counties in installing and using modern assessing methods and equipment.

Supplementary legislation of a constructive nature has been enacted from time to time, such authorizations for the department to assist cities in conducting property reappraisal projects and for assessors to use excess fees of their offices to purchase equipment. Representative of the progress of the program have been the preparation and publication of the *Kentucky Property Assessment Administration Manual,* for which the department received the Achievement Award of the National Association of Assessing Officers; emphasis on installation of mechanical equipment in assessors' officers; and an orientation course, taught by members of the department and using the administration manual as a text, for the 32 newly elected county tax commissioners who took office December 2, 1957.

The Oregon program is a combination of technical assistance to county assessors, strengthening by the state legislature of assessment jurisdiction and supervision, and statewide property reappraisal under direction of the State Tax Commission. Action by the legislature, particularly in 1955, was forthright in seeking remedies for chronic assessment ills. Legislation was adopted that requires supervised, mandatory use of sales-ratio studies by county assessors, and provides for state assessment of large industries and all standing timber. Another law required that there be one certified appraiser in each county assessment office for every $30 million of true cash value of property assessed by the office, such certification being by the State Tax Commission on the basis of examination.

The methodical reassessment program and the State Tax Commission's efforts to make it the basis for permanently better assessment administration throughout the state are the main key to how successful the outcome of the over-all program will be. The reassessment program, initiated in 1951 and 39 per cent completed at the end of 1956, is scheduled for completion in 1961. As it has progressed it has disclosed gross inequities in assessment — producing orchards assessed at the value of bare land, homes that have never been on the tax roll, timber assessments ranging from 0.8 per cent to 1523.8 per cent of full value, and entire plants that have escaped their share of taxes; but as Tax Commissioner Stewart states, "there is much greater good that comes from the less sensational, but more significant, adjustments made in properties that have been on the roll, but whose value may be upped or lowered by smaller amounts." Also brought to light have been the very inadequate tools with which many assessors work. According to the Tax Commission, "nearly all counties have lacked adequate records and maps for the appraisers. The absence of reliable means to locate, identify, and record the property has plagued the reappraisal program since its beginning."

The commission's clear understanding that a thorough reappraisal is only a beginning of the job is encouraging for the future. "Soon after the advent of the reappraisal program," the commission has declared, "it became apparent that reappraisal alone was not a 'cure-all' for assessment ailments. Rather it was more analogous to emergency 'first-aid,' while a much broader and more intense equalization and maintenance program was needed to accomplish the desired results." The Valuation Division set out, therefore, "to eliminate many of the inequalities that were immune to the curative powers of reappraisal" by issuing rules and regulations "calculated to bring about a much greater degree of uniformity in assessment practices" and by seeking "a substantial improvement in the quality and quantity of appraisal personnel at the county level." That these efforts have been backed by strong legislation has already been noted.

. . . .

The property tax is far from being an ideal tax, and few tax theorists would claim that it is even a very good tax. It is not clearly a benefit tax, it is not based on ability to pay, and it tends to operate as a regressive tax. But it has behind it a tradition of great usefulness to local government, it has tremendous going-concern value, and it has qualities, not possessed by most other sources of revenue that are exceedingly important for the financial stability and autonomy of local government.

The property tax is sometimes called the most inefficiently administered tax in the United States. It would be more fair to say that it has the most uneven quality of administration — because it is handled reasonably well in some jurisdictions. Given competent administration, it could be made more productive, more reliable, and less distasteful to the taxpayer. In fact, the best means of saving the property tax would be to make it more respectable by good management.

PART FOUR

Grants-in-Aid

Grants-in-aid for education are intended to serve a number of ends. The objective of equity has long attracted the attention of school finance authorities. By means of grants, the distribution of educational services and the distribution of the school tax burden are to be brought more closely in alignment with some criterion of fairness. Next, the grants are expected to promote efficiency in expenditures, with regard both to the choices of types of educational outputs and to the choices of methods used in producing them. The most obvious case in point is the use of financial incentives by state governments to encourage consolidation of small school districts. The National Defense Education Act follows in this tradition of using money rewards to induce local districts to allocate their own funds in a more efficient manner. In these two examples, of course, the federal and state governments took it upon themselves to decide what "efficient manner" means.

A third objective in the use of educational grants is tax relief for the citizens of the receiving governments. This is clearly a much more valid aim of state grants to local districts than of federal grants to states, since tax relief is generally aimed at reducing the burden of some particular levy, such as the property tax. Fourth, it is sometimes intended that school grants stimulate spending on the part of the receiving governments. In recent years several states have begun to use general-purpose, percentage aids, and stimulation of local spending is a quite legitimate objective of such types of subventions. (Percentage grants, incidentally, were used extensively in England for a long period of years.) These appear to be certain major objectives of grants-in-aid.

These objectives are to be fulfilled, it is generally agreed, under the constraints (1) that a "proper" degree of state (or local, as the case may be) autonomy in the administration of schools is preserved and (2) that there is no serious distortion in the allocation of resources among the whole group of public services. People are likely to hold different views of how seriously these constraints are violated under any given scheme of grants.

The problems of designing educational grants are, indeed, quite basic ones. There is no assurance that citizens are in consensus on the ranking of the objectives of grants — or have the same intensity of feeling about the various objectives, whatever the ranking. Further, as soon as one admits the objective of equity (and it seems a remote possibility that one could fail to take it into account in some degree), he faces the problem of trying to measure the relative needs and resources of the receiving governments.

It might appear, for instance, that needs can be measured by school expenditures in a local district. This is the basic assumption of percentage grants. However, expenditures can fluctuate from one district to another on account of (1) variations in quantity and quality of services offered, (2) differences in necessary costs, i.e., differences in input prices or scale factors over which the district has no control, or (3) diverse conditions of efficiency of operation. The state might well wish to contribute a share of the costs of items (1) and (2) above, but it probably would not want to put itself in the position of subsidizing inefficiency. On the other hand, under the widely used Strayer-Haig type of grant, it is assumed that the state can estimate a dollar figure that represents what an adequate education costs in any of its districts. Now, it is reasonable to believe that some districts receive more education per dollar of expenditure than do others. For example, some districts are in a very favorable position to recruit highly skilled teachers because of such factors as location, reputation of the system, etc., factors that are not subject to change in the short run, if at all. At the same time, it is difficult to measure the quality of teachers except in highly subjective terms (see Selections 46 and 47 on the question of merit pay). Hence, it has not been possible to incorporate differences in degree of access to the market for teachers' services into a Strayer-Haig formula in any rigorous way.

With regard to the measurement of local resources, the situation is not wholly satisfactory, but the problems appear to be less complex. By and large, state governments use equalized property valuations per pupil as the index of local resources. Income per pupil might be a preferred measure, particularly under percentage grants, because the range in ability as described by income is much less than that shown by property valuations; thus, the extremely high shares of state support, in poor districts running possibly from 75 to 90 per cent, can be avoided. Inevitably, such rates of support raise questions of fiscal responsibility and establish pressure for state control of local expenditures. Nonetheless, it has seemed good to keep the measure of local ability closely related to the local tax base. Under this argument, income could not become the index of local resources until such time as the prevailing form of local taxation is a levy on income.

With respect to general-purpose grants from the federal government to the states, the task of measuring needs and resources also exists. Fortunately, there is fairly general satisfaction with the estimates of state personal income (computed by the Office of Business Economics, Department of Commerce) as the index of state resources. The matter of determining the real differences in costs of education among the states has hardly been started. It is distressing that attention has been distracted from this highly germane economic issue to the more politically sensitive questions of church-state relations and racial integration.

PART FOUR · GRANTS-IN-AID

Section A

THE QUESTION OF FEDERAL AID

Many authorities in the field of educational finance hold that the federal government should provide large-scale, general-purpose aid, with all states sharing in the bounty. A bill with this end in view, popularly known as the Murray-Metcalf bill, was under consideration in several recent sessions of Congress. In 1959 Walter W. Heller (Selection 32) presented a notable statement in support of the bill. His statement is an excellent review of the arguments for the assumption by the federal government of a major share of responsibility in financing elementary and secondary education.

Other persons feel that federal general-purpose aid is necessary for the welfare of the country but should be paid only to the poorer states. This was the view to which the late Senator Taft came in 1946, as revealed in his speech on the Senate floor on August 1 of that year. More recently, the Committee for Economic Development (Selection 33) has advanced a plan for federal support in strict equalizing form.

Discussions about the pros and cons of federal grants to the states sometimes overlook the wide range of responsibility the central government has already accepted in the field of education. Stiles (Selection 34) comments on the important contribution that the Cooperative Research Program is making in improving the techniques of instruction. Since neither state governments nor local districts receive funds under this program directly, the Cooperative Research Program can be regarded as a form of aid "in kind."

Many arguments against federal aid, such as the claim that it establishes central control of education, are quite familiar. In Selection 35, Scott makes a somewhat different kind of negative argument, namely, that grants impede the mobility of economic resources. Buchanan in the same selection rises to the defense of grant programs.

32

The Responsibility of the Federal Government in the Support of Schools

Walter W. Heller

Dr. Heller, now Chairman, Council of Economic Advisers, presents his important testimony on the need for general-purpose grants to the states. Formerly Dr. Heller was Chairman of the Department of Economics, University of Minnesota.

In appearing before you today on the role of the Federal Government in the support of public elementary and secondary education, I wish to speak primarily as an economist. Without in any sense neglecting education's abiding human and moral values, without slighting its critical importance as a basic ingredient of democracy, without ignoring the heated political controversies over Federal control and interference, one may still conclude that the key issues in the debate over Federal support for schools in the space age are increasingly economic in nature.

(a) Are we investing enough in public education in the light of—
   1. The rich rewards it offers in economic growth and military superiority?
   2. The existing deficiencies in teachers' salaries and school buildings?

(b) Can our economy afford the greatly expanded financial effort required to realize the full potential of public education as a contributor not only to human betterment but also to economic growth and military power?

(c) Once the dimensions of our total effort have been determined, how should the costs be shared? The answer to this question will depend—
   1. On the nature of the objectives being served; that is, to what extent is public education an instrument of national economic and defence policy in addition to its traditional functions?

Adapted from *Federal Grants to States for Elementary and Secondary Schools*, Hearings before the Subcommittee on Education of the Committee on Labor and Welfare, Senate, 86th Congress, 1st Session, Washington, Government Printing Office, 1959, pp. 81–102.

2. On the role of the Federal Government as a fiscal transfer agent for the States in an interdependent economy; that is, to what extent should educational support for poorer States be drawn from wealthier States?
3. On whether the State and local governments have the necessary taxable capacity to finance the required level and quality of education; that is, will our total investment in education be large enough without Federal support?

This statement will take up each of these issues in the order listed, and will conclude with a consideration of the fears of Federal control, Federal deficits, and inflation which seem to be playing so large a role in thwarting efforts to obtain Federal participation in public school financing.

OUR INVESTMENT IN EDUCATION

To determine whether we should allocate more of our national resources to public education requires a careful consideration of the returns that education offers on our investment. These returns fall into four general categories:

(a) Increased capacity to enjoy the fruits of our labors, to open the way to individual self-fulfillment and an improved quality of life.

(b) Creation, through human knowledge and understanding, of the informed and responsible citizenry which is the keystone of a free democratic society.

(c) Development of the human resources which lie at the base of an expanding economy and material abundance.

(d) Creation of the skills, technological competence, and comprehension which are the ultimate source of military security and world leadership in an age of missiles, satellites, and cold war.

. . . .

Russia's sensational advances in science, highlighted by its successes in space exploration, have brought education's contributions to economic and military strength to the forefront of our national thinking. But our national shortage of developed brainpower was only underscored, not created, by the need to match Soviet advances. This shortage is basically a product of our —

explosive rate of technological change and the increasing complexity of our social organization. Not only are the tasks that must be performed to keep our society functioning ever more intricate and demanding, they are constantly changing in character. As a result, we are experiencing a great variety of shortages of human resources in fields requiring high competence and extended training. We are having to become more and more concerned with seeking and cultivating talent. We have become more conscious of the strategic importance of education in our society.[1]

Professional and technical workers rose from 4.3 per cent of the labor force in 1900 to 8.6 per cent in 1950 and are projected to increase to 14 per cent in 1975. Corresponding reductions are taking place in the needs for less highly trained personnel. These figures dramatically illustrate the higher standards of adequacy that are constantly being required in American education.

The relationship between education and our military strength and national survival is even more direct. Higher and higher levels of education are required to supply a literate and well trained source of military manpower in an age of electronic and nuclear weapons. Far more crucial, the apparent lead of the Soviet Union in missiles and space exploration can be overcome only by accelerated research and technological advance. In this much broader sense, education is a powerful weapon of greater importance to our national defense than military hardware. It spells the difference between being the world's first rate and the world's second rate power, scientifically and militarily. Our successful measures to increase plant capacity through various forms of subsidies and incentives — like accelerated amortization, price guarantees, and loan programs — must now be supplemented, perhaps in part supplanted, by equally strong and determined measures to expand brain capacity.

The National Defense Education Act is making a valuable, though limited and highly specialized, advance on this front. It in no way conflicts with, nor removes the pressing need for, broad measures like the Murray-Metcalf bill. This broader program of Federal support will strengthen the foundations on which the required higher levels of human understanding, skill, and scientific achievement can be built.

What kind of financial commitment must we make to gear our educational system to the performance of these vital tasks? Again, the Rockefeller group speaks with great cogency on this problem:

> Perhaps the greatest problem facing American education is the widely held view that all we require are a few more teachers, a few more buildings, a little more money. Such an approach will be disastrous. We are moving into the most demanding era in our history. An educational system grudgingly and tardily patched to meet the needs of the moment will be perpetually out of date. We must build for the future in education as daringly and aggressively as we have built other aspects of our national life in the past. . . .
>
> Even allowing for considerably greater efficiency in the use of educational funds, it is likely that 10 years hence our schools and colleges will require at least double their present level of financial support to handle our growing student population. In other words, by 1967 the entire educational effort is

[1] Rockefeller Brothers' Fund. "The Pursuit of Excellence — Education and the Future of America," panel report V of the special studies project. Garden City, N.Y., Doubleday & Co., 1958, pp. 6–7.

likely to call for expenditures on the order of $30 billion, measured in today's prices.[2]

If the urgent recommendations of the Conant report, "The American High School Today," are to be carried out, the $30 billion projection may prove to be modest. Consider, for example, Dr. Conant's recommendations for counselors, individualized teaching programs, more rigorous required courses, ability grouping, developmental reading, and a host of other improvements. All of these will serve as steps to the higher quality required by the complexities and dangers of tomorrow's world, and all of them are expensive.

Even apart from these and other qualitative improvements, increases in numbers and changes in the age composition of school-age children will push school costs up steadily for years to come. Enrollments in public elementary and secondary schools stood at 34 million in the fall of 1958, will rise to 36 million in 1960–61, 40 million in 1963–64, and 42 million in 1966–67. Rising even faster than total enrollments are secondary school enrollments. Annual per pupil costs in high school are running about 1.4 times higher than elementary school costs for teachers, and 1.3 times higher for classroom construction.

The point here is not just that the numbers are increasing, but that the most expensive numbers are increasing, those in the secondary schools.

In considering future costs, one is also struck with the rapid rise in costs in the past 10 years. Taking only current expenses (capital outlays grew even faster) one finds that the cost of public elementary and secondary education rose from $4.2 billion in 1948–49 to $10.7 billion in 1958–59, an increase of 155 per cent.

OUR DEFICIENCIES IN SCHOOL BUILDINGS AND TEACHERS' SALARIES

As against the demonstrated need for a vast increase in our educational effort and in spite of the best efforts of State and local units to do the job, we find the American school system still suffering from classroom shortages and inadequate salary levels. If our goal is not merely maintenance of our educational effort, but its expansion and upgrading, the deficiencies are all the more glaring.

Although the U.S. Office of Education estimates that 71,600 classrooms were constructed in 1957–58, the resulting net reduction in the classroom shortage was a mere 1,800, from 142,300 in the fall of 1957 to 140,500 in the fall of 1958. At this annual rate of net gain over obsolescence and increased

[2] *Ibid.*, pp. 33–34. The Rockefeller Panel for Special Studies, project IV, projected public, not total, outlays for education at $30 billion in 1967, and this figure is utilized in the discussion below. Total public and private expenditures for education, all levels were about $18 billion in 1956–57. Estimates of public expenditures for education for the calendar year 1957 round to $15 billion.

enrollments, it will take decades to wipe out the backlog. If, in the course of urban redevelopment, we apply modern standards of school construction and safety to many of the older school buildings in the central cities of our metropolitan areas, the backlog of obsolescence is considerably greater. To eliminate many thousands of small high schools, as urged by Dr. Conant and others, an even greater building program is required.

Low salaries for teachers and chronic shortages of qualified teachers have ceased to be news. To some extent, standards for teachers have been held down to match the salary level. Young people with only 2 years of college education can still get elementary school teaching certificates in a fourth of the States.

Even with low standards of admission, some States have found it possible to staff their schools only by accepting teachers who have not obtained regular teaching certificates. This year, 7.4 per cent of our public schoolteachers are working on temporary or emergency certificates, a proportion of 1 in 13. And this is a continuing condition that has shown no improvement in the past 8 years. Although the great majority of teachers do have college degrees and many have advanced degrees, more than one-fourth of our elementary school teachers are not college graduates.

This condition is a tragic one for the schools and for the Nation. Many adults today feel a lack of the training needed for wise decisions and skillful action in meeting the problems of our complex society. But, whatever the demands upon our generation, we know that they will be far greater upon the children who constitute the coming generation of adults. Without gifted and dedicated teachers at every level of the school system, our children cannot be prepared for the challenges they must meet.

Yet, the economic regards for teaching are below the levels that would permit our schools to compete on even terms in the highly competitive market for the limited supply of human talent. In this school year of 1958, over 200,000 teachers are being paid annual teaching salaries of less than $3,500. The average salary this year of the instructional staff of the schools — classroom teachers, principals, supervisors — is only $4,935. For the past several years, the average annual salaries of teachers has been only a few percentage points higher than the average annual earnings of all wage and salary workers in the United States. Careful studies by the National Education Association conclude that to meet any reasonable estimate of a professional level of compensation, teachers' salaries would have to be at least 60 per cent above their present average level.

Not only are schools currently understaffed and teachers underpaid, but recommended provisions for better counseling and supervisory services, for small classes for the mentally talented as well as for the slow learners, and the like will involve a substantially enlarged school staff. To provide the numbers of qualified teachers needed and to raise their salaries to professional levels present major financial challenges.

UNDERLYING ECONOMIC CAPACITY TO SUPPORT EDUCATION

An appraisal of the Nation's economic capacity to finance the required quantity and quality of education calls for a comparison of educational expenditures with the gross national product (GNP), the Nation's total output of goods and services each year. An inspection of the 1948–57 record and the Rockefeller Fund projects for 1957–67 (revised for recent changes in GNP) makes it undeniably clear that the United States has ample economic resources to overcome past deficiencies and to meet the huge new demands in public education. The underlying capacity exists, provided the American people have the will to allot somewhat more of their growing income to educating their children and somewhat less to frivolities, indulgences, and luxuries.

I might note, by the way, that in 1958 the GNP dropped by $3 billion to $437 billion. The official estimates of the Treasury are for a GNP of $475 billion in 1959. If I may have the temerity to enter an estimate for next year, I think we will cross the $500 billion gross national product mark in 1960. This growth in GNP has implications for Federal revenues which I will come to later on in my statement.

If this projection is correct — that we will have a GNP of $475 billion this year and $500 billion next year — we are well on the way to the 4 per cent growth rate of the Rockefeller Brothers' Fund which would put our gross national product at $651 billion in 1967, with a $30 billion educational expenditure. That would mean that the portion of our gross national product that we devote to education would rise to 4.6 per cent.

Table 1

EDUCATION EXPENDITURES COMPARED TO GNP

Year and Growth Rate	Gross National Product in 1957 Dollars		Public Education Expenditures	
	Total (in billions)	Per Capita	Amount in 1957 Dollars (in billions)	Per cent of Gross National Product
1948	$316.6	$2,159	$ 7.0	2.2
1957	440.3	2,572	15.0	3.4
1967, 3 per cent growth rate[1]	591.7	2,916	30.0	5.1
1967, 4 per cent growth rate[1]	651.7	3,211	30.0	4.6
1967, 5 per cent growth rate[1]	717.2	3,533	30.0	4.2

[1] These growth rates are taken from The Rockefeller Report on the U.S. Economy: Rockefeller Brothers' Fund. The Challenge to America: Its Economic and Social Aspects. Special Studies Project IV, America at Mid-Century Series. Garden City, N.Y. Doubleday and Co., 1958. Rockefeller projections are revised for recent revisions in gross national product.

Several points about this brief compilation of key figures are worth noting. While our investment in education as a percentage of GNP has risen 55 per cent from 1948 to 1957 (from 2.2 to 3.4 per cent of our total output), the Rockefeller projections indicate a slower rate of increase in the coming decade if our rate of growth in GNP matches or exceeds its postwar pace. That is, although the 3 per cent projection represents the long term rate of growth of the economy in roughly the 20th century, the 4 per cent rate has characterized the economy since World War II and is, therefore, a more current and probably more reasonable basis for projection. The 5 per cent growth rate, which the Rockefeller group posts as a target, would enable us to increase public education expenditures to $30 billion by 1967 — 100 per cent in absolute terms, with an increase of only 24 per cent in such expenditures when they are taken as a proportion of the Nation's total output.

Or to put it another way, this doubling of public educational expenditures would absorb 10 per cent of the 10-year increase in GNP at a 3 per cent rate of growth, but only 5 per cent of the increase at a 5 per cent rate of growth.

These figures bear out the impression that the Nation has ample economic resources to support almost any educational effort it may wish to undertake. In fact, it is safe to say that the limits to our public support of education lie less in our pocketbooks than in our hearts and minds. This Nation has a full enough pocketbook to finance any educational program it sets its mind to and its heart on.

But the economist cannot stop here and consider his job finished. He also has a task of translating national economic capacity into specific terms of fiscal responsibility and fiscal capacity. This requires, first, consideration of the role education plays in carrying out the implicit and explicit responsibilities of the Federal Government and, second, an examination of the fiscal capacity that each level of government can draw on to finance its share of the educational function.

Federal Responsibility for Support of Public Elementary and Secondary Education

Given the compelling need for expansion of our educational efforts and the evident economic capacity to meet this need, what factors shape the role of the Federal Government as a participant in the financing of public schools?

First and foremost, education is an essential instrument for carrying out functions which are a direct Federal responsibility. Education is an investment in human resources from which we expect to reap positive gains in the form of higher productivity, more rapid advancement in technology, a better informed and better implemented foreign policy, and a stronger Military Establishment and greater military potential. Here, the benefits of education transcend all State and local lines. They involve our national economic strength, prestige, and security, even our national survival. For the Federal Government to assume part of the costs of public education to serve these ends is no act of largesse or charity to the State and local governments. It is simply the best available method of discharging certain national obligations. As in the case of aids for land grant colleges, no part of the educational function would be centralized, yet national objectives would be served by Federal contributions to the financing of local school systems.

It is worth noting that this point is quite independent of the adequacy or inadequacy of State-local fiscal capacity and taxing efforts to support education. This point says simply that there is a strong national interest in better schooling to serve objectives that the Federal Government has been charged with both by the Constitution and by legislation, such as the Employment Act of 1946. Perhaps some would argue that the Federal Government should step in only if the State and local governments do not have the necessary taxable capacity to do the job (a question which is examined below). But the answer to this is quite plain: State and local governments should not be forced to the limit of their fiscal capacities to carry out, without Federal support, functions in which there is a strong Federal interest. If they are forced to do so in the field of education, other State and local functions will be deprived of their rightful share of State-local revenues and resources.

Consider for a moment the relative Federal contributions to the support of highways, health, welfare, and other State-local functions as shown in Table 2.

Table 2

PER CENT OF SELECTED STATE-LOCAL EXPENDITURES FINANCED BY FEDERAL AID, STATE REVENUES, AND LOCAL REVENUES IN THE FISCAL YEAR 1957

Function	Source of Funds for State-Local Expenditure		
	Federal	State	Local
(1)	(2)	(3)	(4)
Education[1]	4	42	54
Highway[2]	12	64	24
Public welfare	46	35	19
Health and hospitals	4	55	41
Natural resources	12	67	21
Other[3]	5	24	71
Total	9	43	48

[1] The National Defense Education Act of 1958 may slightly increase the Federal share beginning with fiscal year 1959.

[2] 1957 figures do not show the full effect of the increased Federal support of highways.

[3] Includes such activities as police, local fire protection, sanitation, and local parks and recreation which are financed largely from local revenue sources, and all other activities.

Source: U.S. Department of Commerce, Bureau of the Census. "Summary of Government Finance 1957." Series G–GF–57, pp. 27–28.

Is there a difference in kind, or even in degree, between the Federal Government's responsibility in the area of education where it finances 4 per cent of total State-local costs, and its responsibility in such other areas as highways where it finances 12 per cent, and public welfare where it finances 46 per cent?

Second, the combination of great population mobility and sharply unequal educational opportunity creates a problem which no single State or region can solve by itself. Census data show that roughly 20 per cent of the U.S. population changes residence each year, including 3 per cent who move across State lines. In numbers, this means that each year nearly 3 million people change residence and over 5 million people cross State lines. In a decade, one can assume that one-fourth of the population has changed its State of residence. The cumulative result of this movement, combined with the marked disparities in educational opportunity inherent in the fact that our wealthiest States have three times the per capita income of our poorest States, is that no community is immune to the effects of substandard education.

There is no way in which any given State can insulate itself from low standards of education in the other States. Only the federation of States — operating through its agents, namely, the President and the Congress — can surmount this problem by furnishing the financial support needed to raise the national floor of education to at least a tolerable minimum.

A third reason for Federal support of education is the vastly superior taxing powers of the National Government. The whole is greater than the sum of its parts. Our single Federal Government, covering the entire United States, is not hobbled by 49 State boundaries and 100,000 local jurisdictions. Both as an economic and as an administrative matter, the Federal Government has greater freedom and greater power to tax. It is not haunted by the fear of interstate competition and interstate migration of upper-income individuals. This competitive process prevents the localities from levying property taxes as high and the States from levying income and consumption taxes as high as might be required to carry out the wishes of their voters. In contrast, the Federal tax system permits full expression of voters' wishes without the hobbling fear of interstate competition.

Also, the Federal Government has at its command vastly superior administrative resources, division of labor, and the like. No State can match the inherent and adduced resources of the Internal Revenue Service. In other words, Federal collection of taxes coupled with Federal aid to States is not a case of "paying the additional freight of a round trip to Washington." The "freight" of administrative costs is, in fact, far less for an integrated nationwide agency like the Internal Revenue Service than it is where the tax collection process is divided among over 100,000 State and local units. To be sure, citizens are willing to pay a considerable premium for independent taxation at the State and local levels as a cost of preserving local independence and vitality. But where this cost can be reduced without reducing the stature of the State and local government — and especially where the Federal

Government is getting the benefit of the existing State-local administrative mechanism in education to fulfill its own functions — the net public interest would seem to be richly served.

The Federal Government can more readily, more equitably, and more economically convert our vast national economic capacity into tax dollars than can the State and local governments. Couple this with its direct interest in elementary and secondary education as an instrument for carrying out assigned Federal functions, and the positive case for Federal financial support becomes inescapable.

THE FISCAL POSITION OF STATE AND LOCAL GOVERNMENTS

In spite of the foregoing arguments, it is often alleged that State and local governments are in a strong fiscal position to meet the rapidly expanding needs in the field of education. There was a statement yesterday by the U.S. Chamber of Commerce that the State and local units could do this job themselves. It is pointed out that very substantial advances have been made in the levels of teachers' salaries, in the building of schools, and in the aggregate provision for education, without the benefit of Federal aid. This assertion, though true, not only ignores the Federal Government's growing responsibility for supporting schools to achieve national ends, but also fails to take account of the hard fiscal facts of life with which State and local governments are confronted today.

. . . .

The explosive postwar resurgence of State-local government is primarily a response to the fourfold pressures of population, prosperity, public works backlogs, and price inflation.

First, the sheer force of numbers — the growth of total population by 40 per cent from 1946 to 1965 (projected) — has immensely increased the demand for local government services. Population imbalance intensifies the problem. The "expensive" age groups are expanding much faster than the productive age groups. From 1946 to 1965, school-age population (ages 5 to 17) is rising by 78 per cent, and the 65-and-over age group is rising by 63 per cent. But the most productive group in between is rising only by 21 per cent. In other words, the school-age population is increasing almost twice as fast as the total population and four times as fast as the 18–64 age group.

This means that the people who require State and local expenditures are increasing by leaps and bounds compared to the basic taxpaying group, the 18 to 64 age group.

Second, prosperity generates more demands for new and improved State-local services than revenues to pay for them. As the average family's disposable income (after taxes) rises from $5,300 in 1956 to $7,100 in 1975 (as estimated by the Committee for Economic Development), people are demanding new services and higher levels of existing services from government. In the 1930's and 1940's when we were fighting first for economic and then for military survival, only one government — the National Government — could cope with these national crises. But currently and in the foreseeable future, both the pressure of numbers and the pressure of quality will focus primarily on new and improved State and local services: schools, roads, health, parks, sewer systems, smoke abatement, urban redevelopment, and the like.

Third, these pressures are further compounded by the huge backlog of public construction born of depression and war, combined with vast new demands arising from the "flight to the suburbs" and deterioration of the core of our metropolitan centers. Various estimates have placed average annual State-local public construction outlays in the second postwar decade at a level nearly double that of the first.

. . . .

Fourth, inflation has hit State-local government disproportionately hard. Such governments are heavy buyers in markets for services and products whose prices have risen especially fast. The so-called price deflators — roughly equivalent to price indexes — for various segments of the economy reflect this pressure. Taking 1947 as 100, the preliminary 1958 deflator for gross national product as a whole was 133; for Federal purchases of goods and services, 146; for new construction, 150; and for State-local purchases, the highest figure of all, 162.

What does this mean? This means that State and local price levels have risen 62 per cent under the impact of inflation as against a national rise of GNP as a whole of 33 per cent, almost double that of the general price level increase. Even between 1954 and 1958, when the Consumer Price Index increased only 8 per cent, the price per unit of goods and services purchased by State-local governments rose 16 per cent.

Superimposed on rising prices for goods and personal services is the sharply rising cost of money. Interest rates on the huge volume of State and local bonds have risen not only absolutely, but relative to other interest rates. The yield on high-grade municipal bonds has risen from 2 per cent in 1951 to 3.84 per cent in December 1958. In other words, the cost of money that is borrowed to finance schools and local construction has almost doubled from 1951 to 1958. . . .

Even more revealing is the ratio of municipal to U.S. Government bond yields; in 1951 it was 78 per cent; by December 1958 it was 101 per cent. In spite of the exemption of State and local bond interest from Federal income taxes, State and local governments now have to pay higher rates on long-term money than the U.S. Treasury. In other words, the market for "municipals" has become so "heavy" that the tax exemption privilege has lost much of its effectiveness in holding down State-local interest rates. This implicit Federal subsidy is going more and more to the bondholder and less and less to the hard-pressed school districts and other State-local units.

The impact of these multiple pressures has been cushioned to a considerable extent, first by substantial balances built up in State and local treasuries during the war, and then by revenues flowing from rapid economic growth during the period 1948 to 1957. But the 1958 recession drove home how razor thin the State fiscal margin has been. State-local expenditures continued their uninterrupted rise from an annual rate of $38.6 billion in the first half of 1958 (as shown in the national income account), to $43.4 billion in the second half of 1958, a 12-per cent increase. But tax revenues rose much less rapidly from $33.4 billion to $36.3 billion, a rise of only 9 per cent.

The foregoing is not to say that State and local units should relax for a moment their efforts to adjust their administrative structures and revenue systems to provide more adequate support for governmental services. In fact, the problem cannot be solved by action at one level of government alone — it must be a concerted attack at all levels of government.

. . . .

THE ISSUE OF FEDERAL CONTROL

Advocates of Federal aid for public schools must overcome two major arguments: (a) that such aid will lead to Federal control and undermining of States rights; (b) that the Federal Government cannot afford such an additional financial burden in the face of its huge current deficit, its growing debt, and the danger of inflation.

When we separate the true issues from the false, the charge that Federal support means Federal control simply falls to the ground. Opponents of Federal school support have no monopoly on the conviction that strong responsible government at the State-local level is the broad base on which the Federal system of this country is built. Most advocates of Federal aid for schools would be the first to reject it if they felt it threatened to undermine this base. But viewed in the light of logic, Federal support for schools of the type embodied in the Murray-Metcalf bill will strengthen the financial base of the States and localities without in any way encroaching on their sphere of self-governing responsibility.

The vitality of State and local governments rests on (a) their capacity to provide the services legitimately demanded by their voters; (b) the efficiency and economy with which they conduct their affairs; (c) the right of self-determination, and its vigorous pursuit, without fear of Federal domination.

If State and local governments are to retain the confidence of their citizens, they must meet the basic test of ability to serve. But their fiscal ability will not be equal to their fiscal need in the absence of Federal support to undergird their efforts. To continue to force the States to rely entirely on their own tax resources for school financing under these circumstances is to invite local weakness and to court eventual direct Federal intervention. Seen in this light, Federal school aid becomes a positive and affirmative contribution to the strength and vitality of the local government. As the second section of the Murray-Metcalf bill incisively states, if local units have insufficient financial resources at their disposal, "the control of our Nation's schools is not directed by State and local school boards but is dictated by the harsh demands of privation. Without the means to pay for alternatives, school boards have no freedom of choice. In order to provide State and local school boards with actual, as well as nominal, control of schools, the Congress has the responsibility for appropriately sharing in their financial support." This statement puts Federal support in precisely its proper perspective as a source of strength, not a threat, to self-governing local units.

A second fear often expressed is that Federal aid will lead to loose and wasteful spending. But waste and inefficiency are generally associated with open-ended financial arrangements where the total funds exceed reasonable needs or where the spender knows that "there's always more where that came from." But the Murray-Metcalf bill provides funds that are limited in amount and modest relative to needs. This fact, plus the evidence available from other Federal aid programs, gives every confidence in the belief that State and local officials will spend these funds just as wisely, efficiently, and responsibly as they spend funds from their own sources.

At the same time, there would be no restriction of the sphere of local self-government and responsibility. State-local initiative in improving elementary and secondary schools and State-local determination of educational policies and standards would be explicitly protected within the type of Federal program projected in the Murray-Metcalf bill. This kind of support is designed to accomplish the national objective in education through the instruments of decentralized administrative responsibility and control at the State and local levels: If the Federal Government does its fair share of the financing job, one can rely on the State-local decision-making process to meet America's critical needs for a higher quality and greater quantity of public education.

The Murray-Metcalf bill is an expression of the genius of our federalism in its ability to achieve national objectives in a tightly interdependent economy through constructive cooperation among different levels of government. Under this approach, the Federal Government does what it can do best; namely, mobilize financial resources through taxation, and State and local governments do what they can do best; namely, make grassroots decisions and carry out functions under the direct control and close scrutiny of the local electorate.

. . . .

Inflation

Finally, one encounters the fear of inflation. For both the short run and the long run, this fear seems misplaced when dealing with proposals for stronger financial support for education. On one hand, our economy is still operating well below its full potential. Latest figures show seasonally adjusted unemployment still standing at 6.1 per cent of the labor force, over half again as high as the level which characterizes full employment. The average workweek, at 40.2 hours, is considerably below its recent peaks. Investment in plant and equipment is at the rate of $30 billion, against a peak rate of $38 billion last year. Most impressive of all, the Federal Reserve Board's unofficial indexes of capacity and output in 17 basic materials industries (including steel, copper, textiles, cement, and industrial chemicals), show output at a level of only 76.5 per cent of capacity. To deny ourselves additional classrooms and higher teachers' salaries in the face of these figures would be economically illogical.

For the longer run, education is indeed one of our best bulwarks against inflation. A rapid growth in productivity is our best ultimate safeguard against rising prices. Our goal should be to satisfy the rising income claims of the participants in the productive process by sharing an expanding product rather than by pushing up prices and eroding the value of the dollar.

Here education stands head and shoulders above most competing programs. As we have shown earlier in this statement, education as an investment in human beings pays rich dividends in greater productive capacity. It develops not only the skills and understanding needed on the production line, but also the brainpower needed to break through technological barriers and reach new heights of human accomplishment. Given the creativity of educated minds, the returns on our educational investments are more than worthwhile, they may be infinite. We can erect no better advance defense against creeping or grinding inflation than to expand, through education, the productive and creative power of our children.

33

The Role of the Federal Government

Committee for Economic Development

In a significant policy statement the Committee for Economic Development makes a case for a scheme of federal support under which only the poorer states would receive funds. The reader may wish to compare the arguments here with those given by Heller for a broader plan in the preceding selection.

The question of the role of the Federal government in school finance has been heatedly debated in the postwar years. Persons earnestly devoted to the improvement of education are to be found on each side of this issue.

The Federal government has participated in the support of public elementary and secondary schools since the land grants of 1785 and 1787. The largest Federal programs at present are those for school lunches and for construction and operation of schools in "Federally affected" districts. The latter provide payments, regarded as in lieu of taxes, to districts with large numbers of children whose parents are employed on tax-exempt Federal property.

Most other Federal programs are for the promotion of some specific educational purpose — such as vocational education, or the teaching of science, mathematics, and modern foreign languages for which support is provided by the National Defense Education Act of 1958.

The proposals for additional Federal support that are now being most discussed, however, are not intended to promote a particular type of education or educational program but to provide general support of education — although they may restrict the use of funds to some specific object of expenditure, such as construction or teachers' salaries. Proposed support may be in the form of grants or loans to the states or of tax rebates. The proposed allocation among the states may be proportional to school-age population, enrollment, Federal income tax collections, or some other standard. Some proposals would vary aid inversely with income levels; others would penalize states devoting a less-than-average proportion of personal income to education.

Adapted from *Paying for Better Public Schools*, New York, The Committee, 1959, pp. 31–34, 39–48. Reproduced with permission.

Table 1

SELECTED DATA RELATING TO THE PERSONAL INCOME AND SCHOOL EXPENDITURES OF THE STATES

	(1) Personal Income per Student in Average Daily Attendance as % of U.S.	(2) Personal Income per Capita (of the whole population) as % of U.S.	(3) Current Public School Expenditures per Student in Average Daily Attendance as % of U.S.	(4) Revenue Receipts from State and Local Sources as a % of Total Personal Income	(5) Rank in col. (4)	(6) Current Expenditures of Public Schools as a % of Total Personal Income	(7) Total Expenditures of Public Schools as a % of Total Personal Income
United States	**100**	**100**	**100**	**3.11**		**2.83**	**3.80**
District of Columbia	184	127	122	2.06	49	1.88	2.39
Delaware	167	139	128	2.43	45	2.16	3.80
Illinois	156	120	123	2.44	44	2.25	2.97
New York	154	124	153	3.26	27	2.80	4.20
New Jersey	146	123	133	2.91	34	2.57	3.24
Connecticut	143	139	113	2.18	48	2.23	2.91
Rhode Island	135	98	108	2.42	46	2.27	2.50
Massachusetts	128	115	106	2.32	47	2.36	3.03
Ohio	124	109	99	2.66	42	2.26	3.07
Pennsylvania	120	104	108	2.83	36	2.56	3.48
Nevada	117	122	116	3.09	29	2.80	4.04
Missouri	115	98	96	2.71	41	2.38	3.15
Maryland	113	107	103	2.72	40	2.58	3.72
Wisconsin	112	95	106	2.97	32	2.70	3.78
New Hampshire	106	91	96	3.01	30	2.55	3.26
Michigan	104	107	110	3.28	25	3.00	4.14
California	104	125	115	3.28	26	3.14	4.49
Indiana	100	99	96	2.99	31	2.70	3.54
Oregon	95	98	123	4.32	4	3.65	4.74
Colorado	95	98	108	3.51	15	3.23	4.14
Minnesota	92	91	103	4.08	7	3.16	4.70
Nebraska	90	88	89	2.78	38	2.77	3.34
Florida	90	90	90	3.60	13	2.82	3.79
Washington	89	105	111	3.85	10	3.52	4.43
Montana	89	94	112	4.78	2	3.54	4.25
Texas	87	88	94	3.32	24	3.05	3.81
Kansas	87	92	99	3.50	16	3.20	4.22
Iowa	84	88	102	3.48	17	3.41	4.32
Wyoming	82	100	127	4.31	5	4.09	5.73
Arizona	81	93	109	3.95	9	3.82	4.48
Maine	80	83	71	2.61	43	2.51	2.86
Vermont	79	84	86	3.35	21	3.10	4.68
Virginia	75	82	71	2.82	37	2.67	3.58
South Dakota	74	75	101	4.12	6	3.88	4.73
Louisiana	73	76	98	4.59	3	3.82	5.11
North Dakota	72	75	94	3.47	18	3.70	4.46
Idaho	69	82	80	3.36	20	3.32	4.15
Kentucky	67	68	61	2.93	33	2.57	3.29
Oklahoma	65	82	81	3.56	14	3.23	4.16
Utah	65	84	86	4.90	1	3.75	5.50
West Virginia	62	75	67	3.15	28	3.07	3.37
Tennessee	61	69	60	2.90	35	2.80	3.46
New Mexico	60	85	115	3.95	8	5.40	5.92
Alabama	54	65	52	2.76	39	2.71	3.14
North Carolina	54	67	63	3.80	11	3.26	4.05
Georgia	49	72	63	3.42	19	3.62	4.34
South Carolina	49	59	61	3.32	23	3.53	4.60
Arkansas	49	58	60	3.73	12	3.46	4.18
Mississippi	43	50	49	3.32	22	3.24	4.02
Alaska	NA	NA	154	NA	NA	NA	NA
Hawaii	79	90	82	NA	NA	2.93	3.48

NA — Not Available

Source: Computed from personal income data of the Department of Commerce, Office of Business Economics (*Survey of Current Business*, August 1959) and estimates of the Research Division of the National Education Association for school revenues, expenditures, and average daily attendance (from *Estimates of School Statistics, 1958–59*). Personal income is based on the average for calendar years 1956, 1957, and 1958. School statistics are for school year 1957–58.

All these proposals aim either at a higher level of school support, or at lower state and local taxes than would be forthcoming in their absence, or at some of each.

Proponents of general Federal assistance stress that we live in one society, not 50, and we have a national government created to preserve the unity of the society and serve the interests of all of its members. Educational opportunity for all children is essential to the purposes for which the national government exists. It is required for the national defense. The citizens and taxpayers of each state have a responsibility to share in the provision of education for the children of every state. The boundaries of a school district or state set essentially arbitrary limits to the responsibility of citizens to support the education of children within the society. The national interest in, and national responsibility for, schools means that the Federal government *should* share substantially in school support.

It is further maintained that the states and localities *cannot* finance the increase in school expenditures that the national interest and the welfare of the population require. This increase is claimed to be very large, sometimes estimated at 50 to 60 per cent of present expenditures aside from the cost of rising enrollments, mainly to increase teachers' salaries and to reduce the number of students per teacher. While the revenues of the Federal government rise with the growth of the economy, and at an even faster rate, the revenues of states and localities rise slower than the national income. Additional state and local revenues for schools must come largely from higher tax rates, at a time when other urgent state and local functions are also clamoring for more funds. Even though it is true that the entire national income lies within the borders of the several states, economic competition among the states keeps each from moving forward energetically to tax the income within its borders. None can get taxes too far out of line with its neighbors, for fear of retarding its own economic development, so all advance together at an inadequate rate.

Finally it is maintained that the states and localities *will not* improve education even as rapidly as they can. The present condition of our schools shows this. To awaken 50 state governments, to say nothing of 45,000 school districts to the need will take a long time — more time than we have. Moreover, in many cases the structure of state governments resting on outdated constitutions and controlled by legislatures that underrepresent urban areas, makes them unresponsive to the desires of their citizens for better schools.

Opponents of any additional Federal aid consider any further encroachment by the Federal government on the responsibilities of the states and localities undesirable. They believe that the recent record of the public schools in obtaining greatly increased financial support to hire teachers, raise salaries, and build schools during a difficult period of sharp expansion of enrollments, viewed against a long-term record of rising school support, speaks strongly in favor of continuing to rely on the traditional sources of school finance. Insofar as the deficiencies of public education stem from financial limitations, and many do not, the proper approach to improvement is greater citizen participation to obtain support for school programs, the reorganization of school districts into sound units accompanied by their release from undue restrictions on taxation and borrowing, and properly conceived state foundation programs. Progress in these directions is in fact being made, and it would not be accelerated by Federal grants. Teachers' salaries have already been greatly increased, and the full effects upon the teacher supply have not yet been felt. Insofar as further pay increases prove necessary, they can be financed from existing sources.

Opponents also suggest that with Federal tax rates now very high, the argument that Federal revenue sources are superior to those of state and local governments has lost its force. Any important relief from state anl local taxation involves large sums, and corresponding increases in Federal taxation. With Federal income taxes already high and sharply progressive, substantial additional Federal revenue could be obtained only from taxes with a broad base. Higher rates in the first bracket of the personal income tax (or lower exemptions) or else sales taxes would probably be required. But sales and income taxes are also the main revenue sources open to state governments, and the states may well shoulder most of the burden of increased tax requirements. There does not appear to be a great deal to choose between increased state taxes and increased Federal taxes.

Opponents of additional Federal aid also weigh more heavily than its supporters the prospect that general Federal financial support may mean Federal intervention in school affairs and the seriousness of this development if it should occur.

The majority of this Committee agrees that further extension of the scope of Federal government activities in the field of elementary and secondary education is undesirable. We find that in most of the country additional Federal school support is unnecessary. Hence we oppose Federal grants to support schools throughout the country. However, we also find that some parts of the nation cannot, with any probable allocation of their own resources, support their schools at a level that meets the nation's requirements. Although we are reluctant to see further expansion of the Federal role in education, we conclude that to secure adequate schools throughout the country it is necessary for the Federal government to supplement school finances in the states where incomes are lowest. The following section discusses the need for such support and describes a program to meet this need.

A Program for Federal Support in the Low-Income States

There is a strong national interest in the provision of good schools throughout the nation. Each of us, however, wherever he may live, and the nation as a whole, is vitally affected by the quality of education provided to all the children of the country. At the same time there is a strong national interest in a decentralized school system, implying decentralization of major financial responsibility. This decentralization is a guarantee against monolithic political influence over the schools and makes the school system resistant to demagoguery. Moreover it maintains a close connection between parents and the education of their children, and facilitates adaptation of school programs to local needs. On the whole, the decentralized system not only has been consistent with good schools but also has contributed greatly to the quality of public education.

The national interest in good schools everywhere and the national interest in a decentralized school system are not irreconcilable. The combination of these two interests calls for the assumption of an important but limited responsibility by the Federal government. This is a residual responsibility. It is to provide support to the extent necessary in situations where the decentralized system cannot provide good schools. And this support should be reserved for cases where the deficiency is clear.

The clear and present need is for Federal financial assistance to the states that have extremely low personal incomes relative to the number of schoolchildren.

The quality of school systems, as we have stressed, cannot be judged exclusively by the resources available to them. Nor is it possible to identify differences in the resources available to the schools precisely with differences in dollar expenditures, since there are also regional differences in the general level of prices and climatic conditions. But schools where expenditures are very low clearly are not, in general, providing an education comparable to that obtained elsewhere. Price differences appear to be fairly small and neither they nor climatic conditions explain much of the inter-state differences in school expenditures.[1]

Present expenditures in a number of states are so low as to demand improvement. Exactly how low is too low is a question not subject to clear-cut answer. But 80 per cent of the national average based on current expenditure per pupil in average daily attendance is, we suggest, a reasonable standard, below which school expenditures should be considered unacceptably low. We arrive at this figure after considering geographic differences in wages and living costs.

Eleven states fell below this 80 per cent floor in 1957–58 — most of them far below it. The facts are shown in Table 2.

These eleven states had 22 per cent of the nation's public school enrollment. The standards affecting more than one fifth of the nation's schoolchildren cannot be dismissed as unimportant.

[1] States with the lowest expenditures per pupil also have the lowest teachers' salaries. Teachers' salaries in these states are significantly farther below the national average than are earnings in other occupations and differentials in other occupations themselves reflect in part differences in ability. Low teachers' salaries do not permit these states to provide good education at low cost; on the contrary, low financial capacity forces these states to be content with the teachers they can hire at low salaries.

The size of the increase in present expenditures that would be required to reach the 80 per cent level (shown in the last column of the table) leads us to conclude that in most cases the sums required are not likely to be forthcoming from sources within these states.

Table 2

STATES FALLING BELOW 80 PER CENT OF NATIONAL AVERAGE IN EXPENDITURE PER PUPIL

State	Current Expense per Pupil in Average Daily Attendance as % of U.S. Average (1957–58)	Percentage Increase in Current Expenditures Required to Reach 80% of the National Average
Mississippi	49	63
Alabama	52	53
Arkansas	60	33
Tennessee	60	33
Kentucky	61	31
South Carolina	61	30
North Carolina	63	28
Georgia	63	26
West Virginia	67	19
Virginia	71	13
Maine	71	13

Mississippi, Arkansas, South Carolina, North Carolina, and Georgia already devote much higher proportions of their personal income to public schools than the country as a whole, despite their low incomes per capita, and would need to increase present expenditures by 26 to 63 per cent.

While the present effort of the other states is not so impressive, low school expenditures in Alabama, Tennessee, Kentucky, and West Virginia clearly are due mainly to low income rather than to a below-average ratio of school support to income.

These nine states, at least, have little prospesct of closing the gap by increased local support. The low position of their school expenditures is not likely to be corrected automatically in any reasonably short period of time by elimination of the factors primarily responsible for it — low per capita income and many children.

The goal of raising to acceptable levels the resources devoted to public education in states where expenditures now are markedly deficient can be largely achieved by a moderate annual expenditure of Federal funds — provided that the program is directed strictly to the equalization objective. We cannot propose that the Federal government simply provide each state with the amount, if any, required to raise existing expenditure levels to the desired minimum standard. This would penalize states now making the greatest financial effort to support schools and reward states making the least effort. It would eliminate the incentive to increase local support of schools.

We do propose a Federal program that avoids these defects. It is a program designed to aid education in states with personal income per student in average daily attendance in public schools that is below 80 per cent of the national average. For each student in average daily attendance this program would pay such states an amount equal to the product of (1) the amount by which its personal income per student in average daily attendance falls short of 80 per cent of the national average and (2) the national ratio of current school expenditures to personal income.

For example, personal income per student in average daily attendance in the nation as a whole was $11,446. Eighty per cent of this was $9,157. In Mississippi, personal income per student in average daily attendance was only $4,893. Subtracting $4,893 from $9,157 gives $4,264. In the nation as a whole, current school expenditures equalled 2.83 per cent of personal income. For each student in average daily attendance Mississippi would get 2.83 per cent of $4,264, or $121. With 444,200 students, Mississippi would thus receive a total grant of $54 million.

Such a program would permit any state to reach the 80 per cent level in current expenditures by devoting the same proportion of its residents' income to current school expenditure as the nation as a whole. And they could do better by providing more. The formula makes no allowance for the fact that even the same proportion of income devoted to education implies a greater effort by a poor than by a rich state.

The total cost of such a program, if it had been in effect in the 1957–58 school year and if all eligible states had satisfied the two conditions set forth below, would have been $544 million. This payment would have been divided among the 19 states in which income per schoolchild was less than 80 per cent of the national average (Table 3, column 2).

The nation has a right to assurance that recipient states make a reasonable financial effort to support schools from their own resources. Grants should be made only to states that provide current school revenues from state and local sources equal to at least the same proportion of their personal income as does the nation as a whole. In 1957–58, fifteen of the nineteen eligible states exceeded this requirement, all but one by a wide margin. The other four states would have needed to provide a total of $51 million more from their own resources to qualify. Since the national percentage of income devoted to school support may be expected to rise, the minimum effort required of recipient states by this provision will be an increasing one.

The program should also guarantee against the substitution of Federal for local funds in the support of education. The evidence presented earlier shows a strong popular urge to bring schools at least up to standards of adequacy typical of the country at large. For this reason, even without a special provision, it is unlikely that the benefits of Federal grants would be offset in any significant degree by a lessening of financial support from within the states.

However, as a further assurance against this possibility (in addition to the requirement as a condition of aid for continued matching of the national average effort), a provision should be included to eliminate grants to any state if its per-pupil current school revenues from state and local sources should fall below their level at the time the program is introduced.

Grants should be eliminated under these provisions only after a state is notified and given time to meet the conditions of the program. We do not anticipate that it would become necessary, in fact, to withhold funds for failure to meet the specified conditions.

Table 3

COST AND IMPLICATIONS[1] OF FEDERAL EQUALIZATION GRANTS
(based on 1956–58 income differentials and 1957–58 expenditures)

State[2]	Personal Income per Pupil as % of U.S. Average (1)	Grants ($ millions) (2)	Expenses per Pupil as % of U.S. Average	
			Actual (3)	With Support Programs (4)
Mississippi	43	54	49	86
Arkansas	49	37	60	91
South Carolina	49	50	61	92
Georgia	49	95	63	94
North Carolina	54	81	63	88
Alabama	54	55	52	84
New Mexico	60	13	115	134
Tennessee	61	43	60	84
West Virginia	62	24	67	85
Utah	65	10	86	101
Oklahoma	65	25	81	97
Kentucky	67	22	61	78
Idaho	69	5	80	92
North Dakota	72	3	94	102
Louisiana	73	13	98	105
South Dakota	74	2	101	107
Virginia	75	12	71	83
Hawaii	79	[3]	82	83
Vermont	79	[3]	86	87
Maine	80	none	71	71
Total		544		

[1] Assumes the provision of additional state and local funds, totaling $51 million, required to qualify for Federal grants in five states; that there would be no other change in school support from existing sources; and that the additional funds would be used entirely for current expenses.
[2] Table includes all states with either personal income per student in average daily attendance, or current school expenditures per student in average daily attendance, below 80 per cent of the corresponding national figure.
[3] Less than $500,000.

We may now illustrate the effects of such a program by calculating how school expenditures would have been changed had the program been in effect in 1957–58. We assume in this calculation that the only change in existing revenue sources would have been the provision of the $51 million required to qualify for the program in four states (Alabama, Virginia, Kentucky, and Tennessee). We also assume all the additional funds to be used for current expenses. Per-pupil current expenditures would then have been raised above 80 per cent of the national average in all states but Kentucky, which would have been at 78 per cent, and Maine, which would not have been eligible for grants in that year (Table 3, column 4). Maine had already raised its expenditures to 75 per cent of the national average in 1958–59, according to preliminary information. By comparison, the actual minimum was 49 per cent, with nine states below 70 per cent.

It will be noted that of the $544 million paid under this program, about $200 million would represent payments to states in excess of amounts required to bring them up to 80% of the national average per-pupil expenditures. All but $21 million, the part helping to raise states above, or further above, the 100% level, would contribute to equalization, however. Such payments — and the appearance in Table 3 of several states that do not appear in Table 2 — reflect the fact that most of the recipient states are already spending a higher proportion of income on current school expenditures than the country as a whole. We do not consider such payments an undesirable feature of the formula, and in any event they are essential to avoid unfair discrimination and penalization of local effort.

A distribution of the states, and the number of their pupils in average daily attendance, by the actual level of current expenditure per pupil in average daily attendance in 1957–58 is compared with the distribution that would have existed with the suggested Federal equalization program (making the same assumptions as before) in Table 4. The national average in 1957–58 was $324.

The improvement in the distribution of pupils that could have been brought about by the expenditure of $544 million in Federal grants is striking.

Several aspects of our proposal, and certain additional implications, may now be noted

1. There must not be, and the purposes of the proposal do not necessitate, any Federal controls or conditions over education whatsoever associated with the proposed grants. It is only necessary to require that funds received actually be spent for public education, and conformance with regulations to be established by the Office of Education for uniform reporting of average daily attendance and school finance. We stress in the strongest possible terms that the program should include no Federal requirement for "loyalty oaths," and no control of subject matter, teaching methods, teacher qualifications, or any other aspects of the educational process.

2. Our formula utilizes current expenditures rather than total expenditures

Table 4

ACTUAL DISTRIBUTION OF EXPENDITURE COMPARED WITH DISTRIBUTION UNDER PROPOSED PROGRAM

Current Expense per Pupil in Average Daily Attendance	Number of States[1]		Thousands of Pupils in Average Daily Attendance[1]	
	Actual	With Proposed Program	Actual	With Proposed Program
$460–500	2	2	2,335	2,335
420–459	1	2	840	1,044
380–419	6	6	2,264	2,264
340–379	12	13	8,961	9,449
300–399	12	13	7,366	8,342
260–299	7	13	2,022	6,126
220–259	2	2	912	712
180–219	7	0	4,459	0
140–179	2	0	1,113	0
Total	51	51	30,272	30,272

[1] Includes Alaska, Hawaii, and the District of Columbia.

in the calculation of the amounts to be paid under the proposed program. However, an effective school program requires a proper balance between capital plant and current expenditures. The most efficient use of funds requires that states be free to use Federal grants for either purpose. A requirement controlling use of Federal funds as between current and capital outlay would in any event be largely futile since a state could readily circumvent it by an offsetting shift in the allocation of its own funds.

3. The geographic distribution of low-income states is such that most of the payments under the proposed program would go to states that until recently maintained segregated school systems, and some of which still do so. The object of equalization grants is to improve the financial support of public schools where it is inadequate, not to affect state policy with respect to segregation or integration. If legislation is necessary or desirable to supplement enforcement of constitutional provisions by the courts, it should be considered separately on its own merits. Under the proposed program funds would be allocated only for pupils in attendance in public schools, and only for use in support of public education.

4. State and local financial planning requires that the approximate amount of Federal grants to a state be foreseeable and that the amount not fluctuate greatly from year to year. On the other hand, it is desirable that payments adjust to changing requirements without long delay. Any legislation adopted must be permanent. Allocations must be based on a formula that determines the dollar amount of payments. They cannot be based on some percentage

allocation of an annual appropriation that varies in amount from year to year for the convenience of the Federal budget or with the whim of legislators. It it desirable to base allocations on average personal income during the preceding two or three years in order to minimize any irregular fluctuations and make the amount of aid more foreseeable a year or two in advance. No similar averaging is necessary for average daily attendance, which is not much subject to irregular fluctuations. The formula proposed will automatically adjust allocations, with a short time lag, as the need for equalization aid changes with shifting patterns of per capita income or school attendance.

5. Of the nineteen states that would receive payments under our proposal, all but three are among the states that have already reorganized school districts by compulsory state law, or through compulsory joint state and county action under strong state authority. This is an assurance that there would be little waste of Federal funds resulting from over-decentralization of school districts. However, consideration might be given to some provision for a minimum Federal standard to encourage more efficient school districting, applicable after an appropriate period as a condition for Federal grants.

6. The national figure for current expenditure per pupil in average daily attendance that is used in the formula should be net of payments under this program. The formula leaves grants under other Federal programs undisturbed.

7. In states where per-pupil expenditure is below 80 per cent of the national average, the deficiency in available funds is invariably absorbed in part by classes of above-average size and in part by below-average teachers' salaries. In most of the states where teachers' salaries are very low, they are not so far below the national average as total expenditures per pupil. Given the existing relationships between teachers' salaries and per-pupil expenditures, it is likely that the result of the proposed program would be to raise the average teacher's salary in all states receiving grants to at least 80 per cent of the national average. We consider the raising of teachers' salaries where they are substandard to be an important objective of the proposed program. But it requires no special mention in the formula.

8. The costs of this program would tend to increase for some time as enrollments and per-pupil expenditures rise. However, the increase over the next decade or so is unlikely to be more than in proportion to national current school expenditures, and probably would be a little less, because income per pupil schoolchild in the low-income states may rise more than corresponding national figures. A check of past experiences shows that if such a program had been in effect from 1953–54 to 1957–58, aid payments would have increased by a slightly smaller percentage than total current expenses for public schools. We use $600 million as a round estimate of the annual cost of the program if it is introduced in the near future, somewhat above the $544 million calculated for 1957–58. Over the longer run, raising schools in the low-income states much closer to the standards prevailing elsewhere

should itself be a powerful force operating to narrow differentials in productivity and incomes. This would automatically reduce, and perhaps ultimately eliminate, Federal grants under the proposed formula.

These statements presuppose, of course, that there would be no change in the terms of the program. But the proposed program provides an adequate, perhaps even a generous, degree of equalization support. We do not think greater assistance can be justified on equalization grounds.

Our proposal is intended to enable reasonably adequate support for education, as measured against standards prevailing in the rest of the country, to be provided in those states that have relatively small economic ability to support schools. We propose this program in the interest of the entire nation and of the residents of all sections of the country, as well as for its benefit to the children directly concerned. The majority of this Committee believes that it merits support from the entire country on these grounds. We are convinced that the expenditure required will contribute more to the welfare of the country than many existing Federal expenditures, some of which, as we have pointed out elsewhere, could well be cut. But if the program implies higher taxes, these will be well justified by the anticipated benefits. This Committee is now reviewing the problem of Federal taxation and expects in a subsequent statement to present suggestions for financing essential Federal expenditures, including those we here recommend for education.

34

The Cooperative Research Program

Lindley J. Stiles

Dr. Stiles is Dean of the School of Education, University of Wisconsin. This statement was given in support of the Improvement of Educational Quality Bill of 1962, one of the provisions of which would have liberalized the way that Cooperative Research funds can be disbursed.

Research, both basic and applied, is the key to school improvement. Awareness of this fact led the 83rd Congress, in 1954, to pass Public Law 531 which authorized the Commissioner of Education "to enter into contracts and jointly financed cooperative arrangements with universities and colleges and State educational agencies for the conduct of research, surveys, and demonstrations in the field of education." The first appropriation, almost a million dollars, was made under this law for fiscal 1957. The following year the budget was increased to $2.3 million. For fiscal 1962, it was raised from $3.4 million to $5 million.

These appropriations for what has come to be called the cooperative research program of the Office of Education, small as they have been compared to the $160 million appropriated for research in agriculture and almost half a billion allocated for health research last year, have laid the foundation for a nationwide push toward quality in elementary and secondary schools. The cooperative research program has soundly demonstrated the value of basic research as the foundation of school improvement. It now stands ready to move ahead to accelerate basic research and to translate research discoveries into educational programs.

Contributions of Cooperative Research

The value of the basic research that has been conducted under the cooperative research program is illustrated by the following brief descriptions of sample investigations. Those presented were selected to illustrate the range

Adapted from *The Improvement of Educational Quality Act of 1962,* Hearings before the Select Subcommittee on Education of the Committee on Education and Labor, House, 87th Congress, 2nd Session, Washington, Government Printing Office, 1962, pp. 79–84.

of questions being studied, the kind of basic knowledge being discovered, the potential impact the results hold for improved quality of education, and the need to expand the cooperative research programs to provide for field testing, demonstration, and implementation in schools.

1. What is the nature of creative ability (the kind possessed by the "creative genius")? How may such talents be identified and developed through education? Cooperative research projects at the Universities of Chicago and Minnesota have documented the significant fact that creative ability and measured intelligence (IQ) are not identical. This discovery may well change educational procedures from kindergarten through graduate schools. In the past, and still in most situations, schools have operated on the assumption that the child with the high intelligence rating would also be the most creative. Some individuals do possess both kinds of abilities; some do not. The latter group may be ignored by teachers or excluded from educational opportunities that would ripen their creative powers into peak performances.

A second outcome of these investigations, equally important as the first, has been the development of substantial evidence that creative ability, unlike intelligence which remains relatively constant, can be developed, extended, and improved. The implications of this possibility for school programs are obvious.

The next steps for research on creative ability are to discover the kinds of factors that make for creativity in a person, in any field, and to design educational programs and procedures that produce maximum development. When such knowledge is available, schools and teachers can be geared to the discovery and development of creativity. Achievement of this objective is of paramount importance to the Nation as well as to the individuals whose potential creative talents are currently being ignored.

2. What is teaching competence? How do different types of teachers affect the learning of students? How may good teachers be developed? A number of the cooperative research projects have attacked the basic question: What is a good teacher? Essentially they have sought to test whether commonly held assumptions about teacher competence are valid. For example, two such beliefs are (a) that children in a given class will react to a particular teacher in much the same way, even though variations from child to child will exist; and (b) the competent teacher may be described by a fairly definite pattern of behaviors that are valid for most teaching situations. A cooperative research project at Brooklyn College proved that the impact of the teacher on students is determined by the teacher's approach and professional personality on the one hand and by the feelings and levels of intelligence of learners on the other. In short, all children do not react similarly to a particular teacher as had been assumed and the behavior that makes a teacher competent will vary with different types of students.

Of the three types of teacher behavior studied — classified as turbulent, self-controlled, and fearful — the self-controlled type of teacher achieved the most uniform learning gains with children of different personality types and levels of ability. Yet 46 per cent of the teachers in this experiment were classified as fearful which proved to be the least effective kind of teacher.

Next steps in this research relate to selection of persons to prepare for teaching, teacher education itself, and the possibility that teachers of the fearful type—of which there apparently are many now in teaching—can change their personality structure.

3. Can elementary school children learn elements of the basic structure of higher mathematics (algebra)? If so, will early emphasis on algebraic concepts improve the learning of mathematics? Traditionally schools have taught arithmetic to elementary school children with the study of concepts of higher mathematical structure being assigned to the high school curriculum. A recently completed cooperative research study at the University of California at Los Angeles demonstrated that young children (first graders) can double their rate of mastery of mathematics if it is taught in relation to basic algebraic structures. Next steps in this project involve the development of curricular materials for the first three elementary school grades that will teach children to view mathematics as a logical system of relationships rather than a series of unrelated concepts. These materials will then be introduced into a demonstration project, authorized under the cooperative research program, to help schools across the Nation learn how to use the new mathematics program.

It is believed that this type of instruction in mathematics will promote broad transfer of learning skills to other subjects of the school curriculum. Further research will test whether pupils who develop an understanding of mathematical structure demonstrate logical thinking in other types of learning.

4. What is the effect of size of school organization on student learning? Educators have long advocated the consolidation of small school districts into larger units of school organization. Most of the reasons given have dealt with such factors as school costs, school facilities, class size, quality of teachers, libraries, pupil activities, and supplementary services. The presumption underlying the arguments for larger school districts has been that they would increase student learning, but no proof was available.

A study at the University of Wisconsin, which in recent years has been supported by the cooperative research program, is comparing the effect of five nonreorganized and five reorganized school districts on student learning on such factors as (a) educational opportunities provided, (b) educational achievement of pupils, (c) educational costs, and (d) the effect on community social and economic processes. Measurements have been or will be taken of pupils in both the nonreorganized and reorganized schools at grades 1, 6, 9, and 12. Although the final phase of the study has yet to be completed, the following results of the first three measuring points, grades 1, 6, and 9, are available:

(a) The children in communities with reorganized schools have more educational opportunities. Examples of the opportunities that are available to a larger degree in the reorganized communities are (1) library facilities, (2) more general and special supervisors, (3) more help for exceptional children (bright as well as handicapped), (4) broader curriculum, (5) more curriculum materials, (6) fewer grades in each classroom, and (7) a more complete inservice training program for teachers.

(b) Despite the fact that children in both types of districts were comparable in achievement and intelligence at first grade, by sixth grade the children in the reorganized districts had significantly outperformed the children in the nonreorganized school districts on 21 of 22 measures of achievement in reading, arithmetic, geography, and science.

(c) Reorganized schools cost more because they provide more and better services. In terms of the achievement gain of pupils, a unit cost analysis would show the nonreorganized schools to be more expensive.

(d) Reorganized schools have little effect upon community social and economic processes.

Although this study has a number of years to run before final results will be available, it already has shown the positive impact of reorganized schools on student achievement at the elementary school level. A related experiment is now in progress to measure the effect of four different ways of reporting this study to citizens. One involves television reports, another films, the third printed material, and a fourth personal presentations. The purpose of this reporting project, which is also supported by the cooperative research program, is to discover the most effective and efficient ways of putting knowledge discovered through educational research to work to improve schools.

5. Which children are mentally retarded? How may they be identified? Can some children so classified be improved educationally to the point that they can lead normal lives? These and other questions have been the basis for cooperative research projects since the program was first initiated in 1957. Already significant knowledge breakthroughs are being made that will give many children, heretofore classified as mentally retarded, a better chance to lead normal lives, at substantial financial savings. For example, new evidence produced by cooperative research projects suggests that some of the children that have been labeled as "mentally retarded" may, in reality, merely be the products of retarded homes. Experiments have proved that some such children can often be taught to read at an early age. The apparent retardation results, preliminary studies indicate, from a family environment that provides no stimulation for young minds; where the home lacks books, magazines, and newspapers; where adult conversation is meager and devoid of substance and parental instruction minimum.

The next research steps on this problem involve the verification of which children are actually retarded and which merely are undernourished intellectually to a point that they appear retarded. Boston University is currently testing experimentally a large number of children to improve identification techniques.

Other research on mental retardation is concerned with programs of instruction that will raise certain mental retardates educationally to a point that they can benefit from programs of "special education" in school instead of having to be institutionalized. One study has already documented the fact that mentally retarded youngsters suffer parallel deficiencies in physical strength and agility. Another identified the disabilities mentally retarded children experience in such intellectual tasks as reasoning, insight, perception, as well as general mental responsiveness.

6. How may the rate of learning of the blind be increased? A cooperative research project at the University of Louisville has proved that the rate of learning of blind children can be increased fourfold (from 60 to 240 words per minute) by improving the listening comprehension of such students. Before this important discovery, the blind have been limited to receiving information at frustratingly slow rates of speed through braille and ordinary voice recordings. This research demonstrated that by the use of "compressed speech" recordings the rate of listening—and, consequently, of learning—could be dramatically increased. Further research, now under way, offers hope that soon the blind can be trained to digest material at rates comparable to those who see.

7. What are the causes of juvenile delinquency? How may they be corrected? Juvenile delinquency has typically been attributed to such general factors as slums, poverty, broken homes, and mental deficiency. Studies supported by the cooperative research program have produced evidence that specific types of delinquency, as is true of types of disease, each of which has a cause, are also attributable to specific causes. For example, a study of repeated acts of delinquency among low-ability boys, aged 14 and younger, conducted in Detroit, revealed that "indifference toward school and parents who excused such behavior" was the single factor that distinguished "repeater" delinquents from "nonrepeaters." "Slovenly personal habits and residence in rundown rooming houses or housing projects" proved to be a single cause of "repeater" delinquency in a group of above-average boys. The importance of such a discovery lies in the mandate their results provide for making systematic diagnoses and prescriptions for specific types of juvenile delinquency instead of blaming all types on general causes.

8. What is the impact of home and school environment upon adolescent motivation to learn? One cooperative research study, conducted in 10 rural and 10 urban high schools, in and near Chicago, identified the impact that adolescent climates, in school and community, have on motivation to learn. The results support the conclusion that academic achievement is often thwarted, in both boys and girls, by the requirements adolescents establish for acceptance in peer groups. Further research on this problem needs to be done to discover how to change adolescent social climates to make them support the achievement of educational excellence as a respected goal among youth.

9. What are reliable standards for the identification and development of academic abilities? To provide detailed and long-range standards for the identification and development of academic abilities and other talents in young people, the cooperative research program is sponsoring, with assistance from the National Institute of Mental Health and the Office of Naval Research, a nationwide study of the aptitudes and abilities of high school students. In this Project Talent, which was initiated in 1960, 450,000 high school students, from 1,000 high schools representative of all States and classified according to size of senior class and holding power of the schools, have been given comprehensive tests that measure all aspects of ability and achievement. Information about student interests, activities, and home backgrounds are also being obtained as well as characteristics of the schools they attend, including for the latter such factors as curriculum, size of classes, training of teachers, and counseling services.

Complete analyses of the data from Project Talent will provide new guides for the discovery and development of talent in high school youth. They will also establish new standards for measuring the achievement and progress of pupils. The data provided will make it possible for standardized tests to be developed that provide greater comparability of scores. Already the Armed Forces are keying some of their tests to the benchmarks this project is making available.

This study illustrates the type of data collecting that is necessary to provide a national comparison of school achievement. Without the resources of the cooperative research program such an up-to-date picture of the Nation's talent resources would not be possible to obtain.

10. How may results of educational research be evaluated and translated into the bloodstream of school programs? School improvement requires both basic research and programs of application to translate research results into schools. As research studies increase in number, the need to assemble, evaluate, and to make available established knowledge is increased. The cooperative research program and title VII of the National Defense Education Act have jointly supported two projects at the Center for Documentation and Communication Research at Western Reserve University. One has aimed at providing a detailed analysis of educational research results with selective distribution of pertinent discoveries. The objective is to develop a stockpiling system for basic educational research discoveries to make them readily available for application to specific educational problems. A second type of project is concerned more directly with evaluating the type of research results that should be stockpiled and with estimating the cost involved in maintaining such a system. Clearly what is being attempted here is exploratory. The aim is to demonstrate the most economical and efficient means of supplying up-to-date and valid research results to those engaged in improving the Nation's system of education.

These are brief descriptions of selected examples of the 445 cooperative research investigations that have been jointly sponsored with 110 colleges and universities, 17 State departments of public instruction in 40 States, Washington, D.C., Guam, and Puerto Rico, since the program started in 1957. The overall quality of the projects supported is partially indicated by the fact that the advisory committee, composed of outstanding experts on educational research who evaluate each proposal, recommended for contracting less than one-third of all proposals submitted. The most persuasive evidence, however, that these investments in educational research have been sound and productive is found in the breakthroughs that are being achieved in the discovery of new, pertinent knowledge about learning and school problems on which better quality programs of education can be developed. The rate of discovery of new knowledge through educational research, in relationship to the amount invested and number of research projects, is believed to run well ahead of new knowledge discovery rates in other fields.

Next Steps to Improve the Quality of Schools

Beginning in a small way as it did, in a field in which scientific research had been badly neglected, the cooperative research program is rapidly becoming a major force for educational excellence in the United States. Its projects are seeking answers to a wide range of critical questions that confront schools. They are being directed by competent researchers, including in increasing numbers investigators from such fields as sociology, anthropology, psychology, political science, economics, the arts, English, foreign languages, and the sciences as well as from education itself. Equally important to the enlistment of the efforts of established researchers is the role the cooperative research program is playing in recruiting and training young research workers, a function that needs to be expanded through a fellowship program.

Improvements in the quality of educational research are being made by the leadership provided by the cooperative research program. Staff members conduct and organize seminars, on both regional and national bases, to identify critical research problems and to refine research designs, procedures, and instrumentations. Consultation is being provided to individual researchers and to institutions to improve the quality of research proposals, designs, and procedures. Such assistance is particularly valuable to smaller institutions whose resources for educational research are yet to be tapped. Outstanding research scholars have been commissioned through cooperative research contracts to systematically analyze educational research procedures as applied to particular problem areas and to suggest improvements that have greater promise. Finally, results of research are being distributed widely through the publications of the Office of Education, in research papers presented at meetings of various educational organizations, and through the professional periodicals.

The value of the cooperative research program, to date, rests primarily in the support it has provided for basic research. With no stockpile of knowledge on which to draw, it is essential that this type of discovery be continued and expanded as rapidly as possible. Educational programs will be no better than the basic knowledge from which they are created. As discoveries are achieved through basic research, the next steps involve the organization of programs of field testing and development to translate knowledge into efficient and workable educational programs and practices. Project English, recently announced by Commissioner McMurrin, is a good example of a developmental project. As is the case in other fields, often basic and developmental research proceed hand in hand as a part of the same project since any type of application always raises new problems that must be solved to permit further progress.

The final phase of a comprehensive program of educational research, that Congress authorized under the cooperative research program, provides for the transfer of the refined results of developmental projects to all schools. This last effort involves the school by school reorganization of curriculums, the updating of the preparation of teachers, the tooling-up of instructional resources, and the development of systems of quality control to guarantee that outcomes sought will be achieved.

The cooperative research program has successfully inaugurated the first phase of its mission — that of stimulating sound basic research efforts. It is moving into field testing and demonstration operations out of which will come direct nationwide improvements in schools. Advancement of the programs through these successive stages will require substantially greater appropriations from the 87th Congress. For example, about $10.75 million ($20.47 million on a full-funding basis) will be needed in fiscal 1963 to finance approved basic research projects and to initiate a fellowship program for young researchers. The amount of $120 million will be required to establish a program of field testing and demonstration in all subject fields that are not now supported adequately by the National Science Foundation, to develop a quality program of teacher education for the Nation (including the inservice improvement of teachers), and to provide regional research centers that tap the resources of schools, State departments, and colleges and universities to study school problems peculiar to each section of the country.

The amount needed to finance a comprehensive program of research and development aimed at increasing the quality of schools is justified by the success of the first phase of the program. It must be provided if schools are to be improved. At present, expenditures for educational research, both basic and applied, from all sources including the contributions of philanthropic foundations, are less than one-half of 1 per cent of the annual operating budget for education in the United States. This level of investment must be compared with the 5 to 15 per cent of annual operating budgets that business and industry finds it necessary to invest in research to keep solvent and abreast of the times. For education to do the same, it must substantially increase its investments in educational research and development.

Not all the funds needed for educational research and development will come from the Federal Government. Local school systems, State governments, business and industry, and philanthropical foundations will bear their share of the research costs. Experience with the cooperative research program so far indicates that for every dollar of Federal money invested in research, $4 to $6 from local and other sources are being made available. The cooperative research program, being the partnership that it is with the State departments of public instruction, local schools, and institutions of higher learning, provides leadership and stimulation for greater investments in research by all other agencies.

The promise of excellence in education rests on the willingness of the Nation to support a comprehensive program of educational research and development to improve schools. Authority for such a program is already established in the original legislation that created the cooperative research program in the Office of Education. Although this basic legislation needs now to be amended to permit grants for research as well as contracts, a change being sought by the leaders in the program, it exists as the major vehicle through which the Federal Government, State agencies, local schools, colleges and universities may jointly achieve quality objectives for schools.

35

The Effects of Federal Grants on the Allocation of Resources

A Combined Selection

In these excerpts from articles by Mr. Scott, University of British Columbia, and by Professor Buchanan, Department of Economics, University of Virginia, the question of the effects of federal grants on the mobility of resources is debated. This is a kind of controversy with which economics journals abound.

a. A Note on Grants in Federal Countries

A. D. Scott

The field of government finance in federal countries poses many problems, and there has recently been a revival in the flow of literature on this subject. The recent contributions of Professor Maxwell[1] and Mr. Birch[2] have emphasised that there exists a financial dilemma which is common to all federal nations.

There is, however, a further problem which has not been fully perceived in the existing literature. This further problem is essentially long-run in its nature; probably that is why it has been overshadowed by the short-run political and administrative difficulties which so beset attempts to systematise federal finances.

The dilemma of the federal nation can be sketched in a few paragraphs. It will be better understood if the vocabulary is first explicitly set forth. "Provinces" and "states" are used interchangeably to mean political sub-

Adapted from "A Note on Grants in Federal Countries," *Economica*, New Series, Volume XVIII, No. 68 (November, 1950), pp. 416–422. Reproduced with permission.

[1] Maxwell, J. A.: *The Fiscal Impact of Federalism in the United States*, Cambridge, Mass., 1946, esp. Chapter 17.

[2] Birch, A. H.: "Federalism and Finance," *The Manchester School*, May 1949, pp. 163ff.

divisions of a federal "country" or "nation." A "unitary" country or nation is one that is not broken down into provinces or states. A collection of neighbouring unitary countries is said here to form a "Balkan" area; a Balkan area could be transformed into a federal country by political union. Thus nineteenth-century Australia, the thirteen American colonies, and seventeenth-century Australia, the thirteen American colonies, and seventeenth-century India were Balkan areas for the purposes of this paper.

In every federal country there are some geographical areas where the average *per capita* income is lower than that in the other areas. Many factors help to account for these differences. In the literature on the subject they are generally subsumed under the heading of differences in resources — in some areas there are more resources *per capita* than in others — and the term is usually meant to include the advantages of transportation, ports, climate, drainage, and soil, as well as of deposits of raw materials. It also seems to include the possession of a stock of capital goods, and the head offices of financial corporations. Let us call the provinces located in areas of few resources *per capita* "poor" provinces.

It is implicit in the concept of federal countries that certain functions must be administered by the local authorities rather than by the central bodies. Responsibilities may be assigned after consideration of the comparative efficiency of the two layers of government, or of the historical, traditional, ethnic, religious, legal, constitutional and personal factors which apply in the particular case. Each province, charged with dispensing services to its citizens, levies its own taxes and sets its own standards of services. By contrast, in a unitary country, all functions of the government are handled by one central body which taxes all its citizens on any equitable basis thought suitable and dispenses the services of government on a uniform basis throughout the nation.

In the "ideal" nation used as a model in the last chapter of Professor Maxwell's book, federalism poses no more problems than unitary concepts. In this ideal nation, the citizens, though heterogeneous, are so thoroughly mixed that each province is identical with its neighbours. In such a federal country it seems likely that each province would tend to levy the same burden of taxes and to provide the same bundle of government services *per capita*. However, when we turn to a situation closer to reality, we find that "poorer" provinces in our sense cannot levy the same tax *per capita* as the rich provinces; for the low personal incomes in the poor states are by assumption the sole source of provincial government finance. In these poor provinces, the bundle of services distributed to the citizens must be correspondingly small.

The bundle of services distributed by the states consists of such types of personal assistance as health and hospital facilities, unemployment payments, family allowances, retirement and pension funds and subsidised utility enterprises. Such services are particularly important to poor people, who would be unable to provide their equivalent themselves. Thus, while the quantity of these services distributed *per capita* is less in poor states than in rich states, the *total* of amenities received by people in poor states is much less than in rich states, for in the latter the citizens, being richer, can provide amenities privately for themselves. Such differences in the total bundle of amenities received (living standards) is commonplace among the units of a Balkan area, where each country is left to stew in its own juice. But under federalism the continued existence of considerable differences in the amenities received by different sets of citizens is considered incompatible with nationhood.

The literature of federal finance has undertaken to describe the difficulties which arise when a nation tries to augment the services received by the inhabitants of poor states. It has been shown that any method used violates one canon or another of desirable government conduct — for the central government must either relinquish completely the responsibility for the funds that it has collected, or else it must interfere to an excessive degree in the management of provincial affairs. The methods used involve the use of grants, either conditional or unconditional, of a compromise between them. In the final analysis they amount to a transfer of central government income collected in the richer states to recipients of government services in the poorer states.[3] Such transfers are typical of a large unitary nation, where little attention is paid to the geographical location of government collections and expenditures.

In addition to the difficulties of a theoretical and administrative nature which are present in every type of grant system, there is an objection frequently forwarded by politicians. In often well-founded exasperation, they complain that the richer states, in contributing to the welfare and service costs in the poorer states, are subsidising inefficiency there. In such cases, transfers are undesirable in the same sense that a subsidy to a firm which would otherwise be beyond the range of normal profitability is a disservice to the efficient allocation of resources. In the literature, such complaints are rightly discounted, for the financial shortcomings of poor states cannot be explained by the ineptness of administration in a few of them.

It is the purpose of this note to point out that there is a valid objection, on the grounds of inefficiency, to making such transfers. This objection is that such transfers provide amenities to poor people in resource-poor states, a situation which may be undesirable in the long run for the following reason: the maximum income for the whole country, and so the highest average personal income, are to be achieved only by maximising national production. This in turn can be achieved only when resources and labour are combined in such a way that the marginal product of similar units of labour is the same in all places. An increase will result when labour is transferred from places where its marginal product is low to places where it is high; or, to put it another way, the intensity of the application of labour to scarce resources should be the same everywhere, in order to maximise production.

[3] The question of tax-collecting efficiency will not be discussed here. This means that we neglect all problems arising from the transfer of funds collected by the central government in one area to the local government in the *same* area.

Such a labour transfer can come about in two ways. The first is by means of controlled labour allocation, either with or without the additional bribes of free transport to new places of work. The second results from the existence of real wage (amenity) differences between the two areas such that the worker can better his lot by moving to an area where the bundle of amenities received in return for his labour *plus* those received as a right of local citizenship is greater than the bundle in his former home. It is contended here that transfers of government income from place to place counteract this incentive to labour mobility and thus prevent the maximisation of national production.[4]

The reader may agree, yet suggest that a note on federal taxation is not the appropriate place to interject a plea to allow the natural law of classical economics to work itself out. The fact is that a federal nation is, in its simplest form, one of the best organisations for achieving labour mobility. In a unitary state it is very difficult to control the level of amenities provided to the people of specific areas. Thus, the government must provide to the farmers of the Outer Hebrides the same incentive payments to agriculture and the same mass of social benefits that it provides to the crowded midlands and the fertile rural areas. People in depressed areas are literally cared for in their homes. The real wage differential which might otherwise be an incentive to move to areas of relative labour shortage is weakened by the free provision of government services anywhere in the country.

Things are different in a Balkan area. When the small country is overpopulated relative to other countries, it cannot transfer income from richer citizens. Thus the bundle of amenities shrinks as the resources disappear, and shrinks still further if the population grows, till emigration becomes obvious and sensible. At least part of the emigration from Ireland and the Continent in the nineteenth century can be explained on this basis. If, in this Balkan area, a confederation takes place, the labour mobility situation is initially what

[4] This argument is correct only when stated in marginal terms, and in terms of similar units of labour. It is quite possible for the average product of labour in one province to be higher than in other areas, while the marginal product is lower. Such a situation occurs when the curve of average labour productivity falls very steeply as more men are hired — a curve which might describe a mining province of high average income for a certain number of men, yet of low marginal product when more men are present than can be used in the existing mines. The low marginal product, or unemployment, would drive them from the province of high average income to a poor province with a higher marginal product.

Again, it has been implicitly assumed here that all labour is of equal personal efficiency. If this assumption is relaxed, then labour of low productivity will tend to move to poor areas where the marginal product of labour is low, and find some sort of employment. The drift back to the farms during depressions is an illustration of this case, though it cannot be wholly explained by it.

In these two cases, the improved standard of life in poor provinces which results from federal grants will actually increase the national product by attracting labour from the richer provinces. There are, however, no general empirical reasons for believing that the demand for labour in rich states is so severely limited, or that the contribution of inefficient labour to the national product is actually being wasted by being applied in richer provinces.

I am indebted to Professor F. W. Paish for the points made in this footnote.

it was before the change, except that there are fewer physical and psychological barriers to migration to richer areas. But on the basis of history it can be predicted that an immediate arrangement will be made to grant transfer payments to the poorer states. According to Mr. Birch, the arrangement in Canada was on the principle of covering the provincial deficits of the poorer provinces — deficits which could otherwise have been covered only by raising the tariffs to very unpopular levels.[5] It should not be assumed that these deficits were the result of luxurious living or inefficiency. On the contrary they were to maintain services similar to those deemed normal in the rest of the new federation. Either higher taxation, or the lack of amenities privately provided will encourage labour migration. The tendency to transfer income to the weaker provinces has become stronger as the political power of the provinces has grown, and the tendency to move out of the deficit provinces seems to have become weaker. The more amenities that are provided in the poorer areas, the greater is the inducement to stay and multiply upon them. And the poorer the people (under our assumptions, the greater the overapplication of labour to resources), the higher the proportion government amenities are of total family income, and the less the attractiveness of higher real wages is elsewhere.

There is little more to be said on this subject. It may be objected that maximising national production by increased labour mobility is a long-run end, while the usual discussion of federal problems is concerned with other, short-run, difficulties. This is true, and it is also true that mobility can be achieved by methods such as allocation which are not incompatible with federal grants to states. However, the proposals discussed by Mr. Birch and Professor Maxwell for income transfers are not mere stopgaps, but are recommendations for permanent policy, and as such will involve the drawbacks suggested in this note, of impeding the automatic tendency for an economy to allocate labour where it is most productive. We see evidence of this whenever an exasperated nation evacuates persons from an unproductive area, refusing to aid them to scratch a living in a wilderness or in a desert. However, if these persons are living in an organised political subdivision of that country, they are no longer evacuated to better land (or even left to their own devices) but are now the recipients of federal aid to their province or state on the explicit grounds that they have the misfortune (not the foolishness) to live atop an area that lacks resources or natural advantages sufficient to give them a standard of living equal to that in other parts of the nation. The deficiency of resources is not apologised for — it is flaunted as a signal to commence a flow of relief and assistance. It may be pertinent to point out that a federation of Europe would face the same problems as any federation: the contributions of the central treasury to the exchequers of the various components would vary directly with the poorness of the recipients.

[5] Birch: *op. cit.*, pp. 163–165. See also Copland, D. B.: "Problems of Federal Finance and Federal Grants in Australia," *Quarterly Journal of Economics*, May 1937, p. 497, where the problem of covering the deficit in the poor Australian states is reviewed.

(Of course, a new or young province can and often does make a sort of infant-industry argument, in which the "investment" of federal funds is justified on the basis that when readjustment has taken place, the local productivity will be as high as or higher than that found elsewhere. Such an argument must be assessed on its own merits, and nothing in this note refers to such a situation.)

This note, then, differs from arguments for one or another type of grant chiefly in the end that it is desired to achieve: grants can be said to have various internal types of advantages such as efficiency, responsibility, directness, or cheapness. They also contribute to the short-run external advantages of freedom from want. But they achieve this freedom from want in such a way that the material end of a *federal* nation, which must surely be in these days the production of a higher income collectively than could be achieved on a fragmentary basis, is defeated. No country can make decisions about taxation and expenditure on purely economic grounds such as these. Still, it seems worth while to consider the long-run harm that may be done by fiscal devices selected for their administrative and political virtues.

b. Federal Grants and Resource Allocation

James M. Buchanan

The "resource-allocation," or "efficiency," argument is, to the economist, perhaps the most significant of the several objections which have been made to the transfer of income by the central government from the high-income areas to the low-income areas within a unified economy. This argument has been present in much of the literature on the fiscal problem of federal countries, and it has recently been advanced in cogent fashion by A. D. Scott. It can be summarized best in his words:

> There is a valid objection, on the grounds of inefficiency, to making such transfers. This objection is that such transfers provide amenities to poor people in resource-poor states, a situation which may be undesirable in the long run for the following reason: the maximum income for the whole country, and so the highest average personal income, are to be achieved only by maximising national production. This in turn can be achieved only when resources and labour are combined in such a way that the marginal product of similar units of labour is the same in all places. An increase will result when labour is transferred from places where its marginal product is low to places where it is high. . . .

Reprinted from James M. Buchanan, "Federal Grants and Resource Allocation," *Journal of Political Economy*, Volume LX, No. 3 (June, 1952), pp. 208–217, by permission of The University of Chicago Press.

> It is contended here that transfers of government income from place to place counteract this incentive to labour mobility and thus prevent the maximisation of national production.[1]

This paper will examine critically the validity of the above argument. It will be necessary to outline the conditions required to make the argument theoretically acceptable and to determine whether such conditions are approximated in the real world. Finally, the implications of the argument for other problems of social and economic policy will be considered. Although the analysis is intended to be of general applicability, factually it is based upon the conditions prevailing in the United States.

I

Two conditions must be present in order that the line of reasoning summarized in the above quotation from Scott be valid. First, income differentials among regional units must reflect resource disequilibria, if they are to be eliminated, or at least substantially reduced, by the shifting of resources. Second, the desirable shifting of resources must be reduced by the transfers of income from the high- to the low-income areas.

In order to examine the second condition, let the first be assumed present. Assume that income differences among states result primarily from incomplete adjustment of resources to market criteria. This implies differences among regions and states in resource or factor ratios. More precisely, the situation is one in which the low-income levels of the "poor" sections are largely attributable to the comparative abundance of unskilled labor in relation to capital, skilled labor, and entrepreneurship. Thus, the returns to capital and entrepreneurship tend to be higher, the returns to unskilled labor lower, than the corresponding rates of return in the richer sections.[2] Income differences among regions will tend to be reduced by an out-migration of the relatively abundant resources and an in-migration of the relatively scarce resources in all areas.

Will a transfer of income by the central government from the rich geographical areas to the poor areas tend to retard, to promote, or to have no effect upon these desired resource shifts? There are many ways in which real-income transfers among regions can be accomplished. Such a transfer occurs within the central government's fiscal system, if this system is at all redistributive. But this kind of transfer has no resource effects in the geographical sense. The central government's fiscal system "treats equals equally"

[1] A. D. Scott, "A Note on Grants in Federal Countries," *Economica*, XVII (November, 1950), 418 f.

[2] The areas with such relatively low rewards to the bulk of the labor force are classified as "poor" for three obvious reasons. First, the income of an area is generally calculated not in gross but in per-capita or median terms. Second, labor applied in an area tends to reside in the same area, whereas this need not be true of capital or entrepreneurship. Third, labor produces and receives a much larger share of the total social product than does capital.

in principle, and in practice the differences in treatment which are present are not geographical. For resource effects in the geographical sense to be present, i.e., for an income transfer to be "resource-distorting," like units of resource must be treated differently in different geographical areas as a result of the transfer. Therefore, the argument applies only to transfers among regions which involve differential fiscal treatment among individual "equals" or among "like resource units." The following discussion is limited to three methods of income transfer which do involve differential treatment: (1) differential income taxation by the central government, (2) unconditional equalizing grants, and (3) conditional equalizing grants-in-aid.

If central-government personal income tax rates are varied from area to area in some direct relation to relative income levels, while the same level and distribution of central-government expenditure are maintained, an income transfer is accomplished in a simple and practicable manner. These changes in tax burdens may or may not cause changes to be made in the rates of state-local taxation (expenditure) in either the "gainer" or the "loser" states, or both. Assume first that the changes in net tax burdens generate no offsetting reactions in state-local tax and expenditure structures. The newly established fiscal pattern will provide an incentive for some individuals (families) to migrate from the high-income to the low-income states in order to reduce their total tax burden. And, more important for this problem, some of the low-income states' residents who might otherwise have moved out in response to market-determined rewards will be induced by the reduced fiscal pressures to remain. This effect cannot be controverted. However, the conclusion that the transfer will tend to be "resource-distorting" rather than "resource-correcting" is valid only upon the acceptance of an extremely simple model in which all human resource units are homogeneous and all other resources are geographically immobile. Such a model clearly is not approximated in the real world. All types of labor are not abundant in the low-income regions; only the categories of the unskilled and the semiskilled are relatively overcrowded. Highly skilled labor and entrepreneurship are relatively scarce, along with capital. In so far as the income transfer tends to reduce the net out-migration of unskilled and semiskilled labor from the low-income states, it may be considered "resource-distorting." But, in so far as it tends to reduce the net out-migration (or increase net in-migration) in the ranks of the highly skilled technicians, professional people, and potential entrepreneurs, the transfer is "resource-correcting."[3] It seems probable that the latter groups are more "tax-conscious" than the former, although this

[3] The excessive out-migration from the South of its more productive, professional, and educated groups has long been decried by southern leaders, and there is widespread recognition that an insufficient supply of potential entrepreneurs is almost as important as insufficient capital in maintaining the region's economic backwardness. On these points see Calvin B. Hoover and B. U. Ratchford, *Economic Resources and Policies of the South* (New York: Macmillan Co., 1951), pp. 38 ff., and W. H. Baughn, "Capital Formation and Entrepreneurship in the South," *Southern Economic Journal*, XVI (1949), 147–60.

conclusion might be reversed if negative income taxes (subsidies) were introduced into the structure. The fiscal incentives provided *rentier* groups have no direct resource-allocative effects, since these groups, as human resources, are not currently productive. But, if the net in-migration of *rentiers* into the low-income state tends to be accompanied by a movement of capital, this effect of the income transfer is conducive to desired resource adjustment. Apart from this indirect effect, this type of income transfer should exert no influence upon the location of capital investment.

On balance, the resource effects of the transfer of income by geographically discriminatory personal income taxation cannot be determined a priori if there are no offsetting changes in state-local fiscal systems. Adverse effects will be present for some segments of the labor force, favorable effects for other segments. The net result cannot be determined without empirical investigations into actual situations.

This conclusion is reinforced if the case is considered in which the transfer policy does generate offsetting reactions in state-local fiscal systems. Here the analysis becomes equivalent, in all essential respects, to that of an unconditional grant and need not be considered separately.

Assume now that the central government transfers income among states by a series of equalizing unconditional grants. "Equalizing" means that more money is transferred per capita to the low-income states. An unconditional grant is defined as a grant of funds to a subordinate unit with no conditions attached concerning the manner or direction of expenditure. Upon the receipt of a grant the recipient (low-income) state faces a wide range of alternative changes which can be made within the state-local fiscal system. The same level of public services may be retained, allowing state-local taxes to be reduced by the amount of the grant. At the other extreme, the whole of the grant may be employed to expand the provision of services, with taxes unchanged. The normal situation would probably be some combination of tax reduction and expenditure expansion.

If the grant is applied solely to the financing of existing state-local expenditures, thus allowing state-local taxes to be reduced, no clearly discernible pattern of resource distortion or correction appears. Specific effects will, of course, depend directly upon the type of tax which is reduced and the amount of the reduction. Certain generalizations may be made, however, without an analysis of each particular tax. The major portion of state-local revenue is derived from indirect taxes (excises, specific, and/or general) and nonpersonal direct taxes (property taxes), with the former constituting the primary revenue source for state governments and the latter for local units. Relatively little revenue is produced at either level by direct personal taxes (income taxes). If the supposed reduction takes place at the state level in the form of the reduction or repeal of excises, the resource-allocative effects will be slight, if present at all. The permanency and continuing popularity of indirect taxes is perhaps primarily attributable to their "hidden" nature. They are not "felt" in such a way that they enter significantly into conscious individual choices among alternative occupational opportunities. But, even if this is not true and allocative effects are present, the analysis outlined above also applies here. The net effect would be "resource-distorting" for the less skilled segments of the labor force and "resource-correcting" for the remaining groups.

If state taxes are maintained at constant rates, the funds from the grant may be used to allow some reduction in taxes at the local-government level. This will mean reduction in property tax rates and assessments, or true rates. For the most part this affects real property to the exclusion of other forms. In this case it seems evident that the over-all results must be considered as promotive of desired resource adjustment. In the long run, the reduction in tax rates on real property will tend to decrease rents, thus exerting some resource effects on all occupational classes, some of which will be in the right direction, others of which will be adverse. But, in the short run, the lowering of tax rates does not reduce rents. Therefore, the out-migration of unskilled workers is not discouraged appreciably. Members of this group seldom own large amounts of taxable property and do not benefit much from the windfalls resulting from a rate reduction. There is some short-run effect on the persons who own real property; the latter tend to be, however, the skilled, the professional, the proprietary.

But the major resource effect of the reduction of true property tax rates will probably be on the movement of capital. Local property tax burdens must enter into the calculations of prospective industrial investors. If tax reductions are accompanied by corresponding reductions in the provision of local services or by a shifting of local taxes to other local groups, the net effects on industrial location may be negligible or even adverse. The unilateral reduction of local property taxes, however, cannot be overlooked as a locational factor of some import.

The assumption underlying the argument outlined by Scott and others seems to be that the grants are to be used primarily to extend and expand the provision of state-local public services. Here, as above, a detailed analysis would require a discussion of the effects of expanding each state-local public service. But limitation to a few general types is necessary and possible. An expansion of the so-called "general" functions of state-local government need not be considered. The expansion can be assumed to take place in one of the following four areas: highways, education, social services, and unemployment compensation or relief.

The analysis here is of the conditional grant-in-aid. Such a grant is defined as one from the central government to a state-local unit with conditions attached concerning the manner or direction of expenditure. The resource effects of a required expansion of state-local services will be no different from a similar expansion resulting from the choice of the state-local unit.

Central-government grants to states for the maintenance and the expansion of the highway system will be considered first. The provision of a relatively better highway system in the low-income states seems likely to exert negligible effects on the geographical mobility of human resources. Few individuals will remain in a low-income area because the road system is improved when, otherwise, they would have moved out. On the other hand, the improved highway system will have some effect on the geographical mobility of capital resources, and in the right direction. Highways constitute an integral part of the total transportation system and are becoming more and more important in industrial-location decisions. The provision of a relatively better highway system in a low-income state will tend to attract capital investment which perhaps could not otherwise be attracted, including investment in transportation itself. On balance, then, it must be concluded that equalizing highway grants tend to promote rather than to retard desired resource adjustment.

Next, the allocative effects of equalizing educational grants must be analyzed. Available data concerning internal migration within the United States indicate that the higher the school-leaving age the greater the proportion of the population which migrates. In addition, among those who do migrate, a greater proportion of the better-educated groups migrate longer distances. These facts may be explained by two basic reasons. First, the better-educated are more fully informed concerning the availability of alternative employment opportunities. Second, they are more fully cognizant of the advantages to be secured from the higher real income which migration to other areas may make possible. Equalizing educational grants would likely increase somewhat the average number of years of schooling completed in the low-income states, as well as the efficiency of the schooling at all levels. The resulting increased mobility of the labor force in these states need not be accompanied by decreased mobility in other areas; therefore, this effect must promote desired resource adjustment. Even if the education levels of the low-income states were to be improved at the expense of reducing the educational standards of the high-income states, the resource effect would still be beneficial, since a net out-migration from the low-income states is needed. This effect of equalizing grants on mobility of the labor force via increased school-leaving age will become fully operative only after a relatively long period. The inauguration of such a grant-in-aid program will affect potential migration of people currently of school age.

Short-run effects are derived from decisions made by families concerned with currently available educational facilities for their children. The relative inadequacy of educational programs in the low-income states causes some families to migrate from, or fail to migrate to, these states. But the unskilled and the semiskilled groups would not seem to be significantly affected by such considerations. The families who seriously consider educational facilities as important in the making of a locational choice tend to be the educated themselves: the technicians, the professionals, the managers, and the proprietors.

The improvement of educational facilities in the low-income states will also tend to be "resource-correcting" in its effect upon capital inflow. A better-educated labor force will prove more attractive to potential investors, other things remaining the same. Public education can do much toward providing the labor force with the minimum essentials of training, which have heretofore been missing in the school systems of the low-income states. Educational grants, if not bound up with arbitrary and restrictive conditions, can supply the low-income states with the financial means of shaping a program directly toward their primary need, industrialization. The "farm" boys can then be taught the rudiments of industrial techniques, not provided in the general environment of a predominantly agricultural society. Obviously, this beneficial effect will not be present if the grants are conditioned so as to prevent this type of program from being put into effect, for example, grants-in-aid to provide training in vocational agriculture.

If the grant-in-aid results in expanded expenditure in the field of the social services, the argument advanced by Scott and others is more applicable. But some breakdown among the different social services is necessary even here. First of all, grants making possible the relative improvement of public health facilities in the low-income states seem to be almost identical in effect with the educational grants discussed above. This improvement would not only make it possible for greater numbers to be physically able to migrate but would also provide an incentive for additional capital investment in a region endowed with a more robust labor force. Few, if any, families are influenced in their occupational and locational choices by the availability of better hospitals, and those who are so influenced are either the better educated or the unproductive.

More direct effects will, of course, be present when the grants are conditioned so as to require expenditure on the provision of social assistance to the relatively unproductive groups: the blind, the aged, the crippled, etc. These groups, for whom public assistance at the state-local-administered level provides an essential and important means of support, are influenced in their choice of residence by comparing the assistance payments made in the different states. Yet, since these groups are relatively unproductive, the resource-allocative effects will not loom large; in so far as they are unproductive they are not resources in an economic sense. Resource-allocative effects will be present if members of such groups are partially productive or are members of families in which there are productive workers. It is perhaps to the advantage of the lower-income states and of the nation to have as many such people move out as possible. Grants of an equalizing nature which allow these states to expand public assistance will reduce the net out-migration for these groups. In an argument just the reverse of the one examined here, Mr. Birch apparently justifies conditional grants of this nature in order to "protect" the "more progressive" states from such migrants.[4]

[4] "The problem of social legislation may be stated simply. If the policies adopted vary significantly from one state to the next, the chances are that the more progressive states will suffer. The unemployed and the unwell will be attracted to them, while industry will be repelled" (A. H. Birch, "Federalism and Finance," *Manchester School of Economic and Social Studies*, XVII [1949], 164).

Grants providing unemployment relief will likely be resource-distorting. This is evidently the case when unemployment is not general and grants are made to provide relief in areas where isolated blocs of surplus labor exist. Such grants clearly tend to preserve the structural dislocation indicated by the presence of the unemployment. But the areas receiving this type of grant do not necessarily coincide with those of permanent low incomes. The same is true for relief grants made in times of general unemployment. If, as is the case in the United States, the low-income states are predominantly agricultural, relatively less actual unemployment may appear in these states than elsewhere, although underemployment will be present to a greater degree.

The scope of this paper does not allow a detailed discussion of other and more specific grants-in-aid. The analysis given above is sufficient to indicate that no general pattern of resource distortion can be established. Without further qualification it cannot be stated that income transfers from the high-income to the low-income areas will tend to retard the movement of resources toward their most productive employments. In each case the results will depend upon the way in which the transfer is carried out and the relative importance of the offsetting effects on different resource categories. In most of the cases discussed above the transfers seem to have the effect of encouraging the flow of resources in the direction indicated to be desirable by market criteria. In some cases the effects will clearly be the opposite, but the exact results cannot be ascertained in any case without detailed empirical inquiry.

The argument that geographical income transfers of the sort discussed will, in general, tend to prevent desired resource shifts seems to rest on three errors in reasoning. First, attention has been concentrated on the mobility of only one of the two basic productive factors, labor. A relative surplus of labor implies a relative shortage of capital resources, and the movement of capital is as important as that of labor in attaining long-run resource equilibrium. The effects of grants on the inflow of capital to the poor areas has been almost completely overlooked. Second, homogeneity in the labor force itself has been assumed. This assumption is useful for many problems, but it leads to error here. Although the low-income areas are characterized by a relative abundance in the quantitatively important segments of the labor force, many selective types of labor are relatively scarce. Third, the specific way in which the transferred funds are expended has not been considered. The analysis assumes that grants are always used to provide "good things" for the people, but the precise nature of the "amenities" has rarely been spelled out. If it had been recognized that different means of expending the transferred funds exert different effects, this would itself have been sufficient to limit drastically the generality of the argument.

II

The generality of the initial argument may be reduced still further, however, if it can be shown that the existence of geographical income differentials is not due solely to resource disequilibria and that substantial interarea differences might well be present even with perfect resource adjustment. The assumption that income differences are almost wholly attributable to improper resource allocation lies behind much of the discussion. The following statement is representative: "If competition were perfect in the sense that there were no limitations on the divisibility and mobility of factors, little or no geographical differences in wealth or income could continue to exist."[5]

Income differences among geographical regions may be attributed in the main to resource maladjustment, and certainly most competent students of the problem of the low-income region of the United States, the South, agree that this is of primary importance. But to attribute differences wholly to this seems incorrect. Geographical differences in rewards to like units of resource will be completely eliminated by the free play of economic forces (i.e., no restrictions upon either migration or trade). Factor-price equalization, however, carries with it no full equalization of incomes, although it tends, of course, to reduce the differentials. It will eliminate income differences only on the acceptance of one of two highly unrealistic assumptions. First, if it is assumed that all units of the labor force are homogeneous and possess equal capacities to move into varying occupational categories, then regional disparities in income will tend in the long run to be removed by resource-shifting. No matter how the areas are delineated, per capita real incomes will tend to be equal in all areas.

If the assumption of homogeneity among human resource units is relaxed, then per capita real incomes in different regional areas of an economy will tend to be equalized only if all areas are completely identical in all the factors which make for distinct occupational characteristics. If men possess differing inherent or acquired capacities, something supplementary to equalizing income differences will arise among occupational groups Hence, for per capita incomes to be the same the occupational patterns within all areas must be substantially identical. This would require that there be no distinguishing differences in climate, topography, soil, mineral resources, proximity to sea, invested capital resources, etc. In one sense, all of these are productive "factors," but to speak of perfect divisibility and mobility of such geographically fixed characteristics as climate and mineral resources is nonsensical. Evidently this assumption of equivalent occupational characteristics cannot be accepted even as a first approximation to any real-world situation. The acceptance of this would deny the existence of many of the advantages of interregional or international trade.

Differences among states in average-real-income levels would likely be present therefore even should the marginal conditions of optimum resource adjustment be satisfied. It can be shown further that these marginal conditions can never be satisfied in such situations unless some interarea transfers of income are made. If income levels are different, then the fiscal "pressures"

[5] United States Congress, *Federal, State and Local Government Fiscal Relations* (Senate Doc. No. 69) (78th Cong., 1st sess. [1943]), p. 185.

upon like resource units will tend to be different. In the low-income states, taxes must be higher and/or benefits from combined state-local services lower than in the high-income states. Resource units in the low-income states will be subjected to a heavier fiscal "pressure" than like units in other states. Therefore, if market conditions alone should indicate identical real rewards for a resource unit in a high-income and in a low-income state, the owner of the unit would tend to be attracted to the high-income state by the more favorable fiscal position. Hence, the optimum allocation of economic resources defined by market criteria will not be the equilibrium allocation attained by individual choices. This distortion can only be removed by a system of equalizing interarea income transfers. Such a system would have as its objective the removal of fiscal differences among like resource units, the enforcement of "equal treatment for equals." In this case, the argument that equalizing grants tend to prevent desirable resource allocation is just the reverse of the truth. Income transfers are required before the optimum can be attained. It must be conceded, however, that the distortion considered here will not be present except in the neighborhood of the equilibrium position. Thus, while the conclusion of this section tends to lessen the generality of the Scott argument, it is not directly applicable to current situations in the real world where a significant portion of the areal inequalities in incomes could certainly be removed by resource shifts.

III

There remain to be examined briefly the over-all implications of the resource argument for public policy. The use of the fiscal system to promote a more desirable allocation of economic resources has often been proposed. The Marshall-Pigou proposals to tax increasing-cost industries in order to subsidize decreasing-cost industries are perhaps among the most familiar. However, none of these proposals has ever been made with the complete neglect of distributional considerations.[6] But the Scott objection to federal grants implies a negative utilization of the fiscal mechanism to secure optimum resource adjustment without any attention at all to the distributional effects of such action. And, in this case, these effects are clearly contrary to commonly accepted ethical standards. If a transfer of income from a high-income to a low-income state is justified on other grounds, then the failure to carry out the transfer on the basis of this efficiency argument obviously leaves the poor worse off, relative to the rich, than they would have been had the transfer been carried through as proposed.

It is evident that the positive-policy equivalent of this efficiency objection would not be generally acceptable in a liberal society. No one has come forward with a proposal to tax the low-income agricultural laborers of the cotton-growing South at a much heavier rate than their "equals" elsewhere

6 See A. C. Pigou, *A Study in Public Finance* (3d rev. ed.; London: Macmillan & Co., Ltd., 1949), p. 70.

in order to provide them with an added incentive to move off farms into industry. Nor has anyone suggested that the proper solution to the whole problem of distressed and blighted areas is the severe and discriminatory taxation of residents to force desired out-migration. Yet the support of such seemingly harsh and oppressive measures is similar to objecting to interarea income transfers solely on "allocative" grounds. Thus, even if the economic analysis behind the resource-allocation argument against central-government grants to low-income states were completely acceptable, which it has been shown not to be, the use of this objection in forming policy would carry with it many implications concerning the proper use of the "fisc" which cannot and should not be summarily passed over without thorough examination.

Equalizing transfers carried out by the central government designed to relieve the fiscal plight of the low-income states, whether in the form of differential tax rates or in that of equalizing grants, cannot be rejected for efficiency reasons. It has been shown that the allocative effects vary from instance to instance, allowing no universally applicable conclusions to be drawn. In specific cases resource effects should perhaps be taken into account, but primarily the transfer policy should be based on alternative objectives: equity, national interest, and the preservation of minimum standards of the public services.

c. Federal Grants and Resource Allocation

A. D. Scott

I

Professor J. M. Buchanan's recent article, "Federal Grants and Resource Allocation,"[1] provides a general analysis of arguments that federal income-equalizing policies lead to a misallocation of resources. Since he has done me the honor of selecting my own "Note on Grants in Federal Countries"[2] as a model of such arguments, I should like to make a few comments on the whole topic.

As Buchanan has suggested, the contention that federal grants distort the allocation of resources is based on the assumption that they are used primarily to extend and expand the provision of state and local public services (or "amenities") or, alternatively, to provide amenities of the national aver-

Reprinted from A. D. Scott, "Federal Grants and Resource Allocation," *Journal of Political Economy*, Volume LX, No. 6 (December, 1952), pp. 534–536, by permission of The University of Chicago Press.

[1] *Journal of Political Economy*, LX (1952), 208–17.
[2] *Economica*, XVII (1950), 416–22.

age level with low local taxation. These amenities, I had argued, are largely social services and thus, through their impact upon the lower-income workers, distort the supply of labor in the various areas toward relatively excessive supply just where productivity is least. Buchanan has contended that we cannot classify all such funds as transfers from rich areas to poor merely as amenities in the social service sense; a closer inquiry would show that some increase the skill and productivity of workers through better education, while others increase their productivity by attracting additional capital and enterprise (by lower taxes, preferential treatment, and other devices made possible by the grants). Such grants may therefore increase the national product more by being transferred to the poor states than if they were distributed to the richer ones. My objection to this argument is that it relies heavily upon there being sufficient natural advantages in the poor area to justify the immigration of capital and enterprise, and the application of training and education, in comparison to the returns similar investment, training, and migration would yield in richer provinces. Consequently, Buchanan's more general analysis does not alter the fundamental shortcoming of federal grants.[3]

II

There is no doubt that behind both our treatments of the problem lies controversy about the nature of the national labor market. This I see as consisting of a set of smaller national markets for each trade and skill, each of which is further divided into regional markets for each skill. It is implicit in both discussions that the supply curve of labor in each market is perfectly elastic at some reserve price, so that, when the price falls below it, labor seeks other opportunities, at home or elsewhere. The bundle of government-provided amenities will be the same whatever job is taken within an area, but the worker will add it to the wage when he is comparing his lot with the rewards of opportunities in other areas. The greater the federal transfers, the greater this bundle of amenities, and the lower must local demand (marginal productivity) sink before outside opportunities become attractive to the worker.

So far as I can discover, Buchanan agrees with this view of labor supply as far as it goes. His first point of difference is that the federal grant may not add to the local amenities, in the sense of social services, but may take the

[3] The entire discussion is based on long-run tendencies. In the short run the possibility of less than full employment must be faced. In order to make the best use of federal grants, it is necessary to spend them where (a) the local marginal propensity to consume is high; (b) the marginal propensity to "import" from other parts of the federation is high; (c) the marginal propensity to import from outside the federation is low; (d) the federal grants plus the local matching taxation have redistributive (marginal propensity-raising) effects; (e) the local government is willing to finance as far as possible by deficit; (f) the local government is willing to expand expenditure; and (g) government spending is not offset by a fall in the local marginal efficiency of capital, when it is hoped to raise the level of national aggregate demand in the short run. Cf. Professor Somers' "Government Expenditures and Economic Welfare," *Revue de science et de législation financières*, Vol. XLIII (1951).

form of educational subsidies. When greater educational opportunities are present, the local population moves out of the category of unskilled labor and into the category of better-educated workers. The demand for and marginal productivity of such labor may well be higher, and the reward consequently greater. In addition, the existence of a new supply of skilled labor may itself raise the local demand, that is, may cause an inflow of investment and enterprise, and reinforce the above consequence. My comment on this point is that, even if matters did have such a happy outcome, it would not be a point against the resource-distortion argument. Briefly, it is not a question of whether the provision of capital, enterprise, and training will pay dividends in the poor provinces. It is a question of whether the same resources will pay greater dividends in poor provinces than they would if transferred to rich provinces.

The second point of difference is about the demand for the various local supplies of labor. We seem agreed that demand is based upon the marginal revenue productivity of each kind of labor. My point was that the poorer the area (in *my* sense, poor in natural resources), the lower the demand curve will be, and the lower local rewards will tend to be. Buchanan's point was that (for any fixed local endowment of natural advantages) the more that capital can be induced to immigrate, the higher the demand curve will be. The two points are formally compatible. I conclude that mobile factors should shift to where demand is highest. He concludes that demand should be raised where resources are fixed.

Yet there is no doubt that it is *his* case, the introduction of capital and enterprise into areas of given natural resources, which Buchanan considers important. He speaks of the ratios of capital to labor, in its various grades, and to entrepreneurship. He is prepared to admit that it may be desirable that these ratios should be adjusted by the emigration of relatively abundant resources and by the immigration of scarcer ones. He then sets forth reasons for believing that, if capital and enterprise are relatively scarce, fiscal measures which attract and fix local labor may attract them also. It seems clear that he has the Southern States in mind, and this analysis, which in my paper I likened to the infant-industry argument for tariffs, may well apply there.

In thus concentrating his attention upon the ratio of capital to labor, implicitly assuming a uniform endowment of natural advantages throughout the federation, Buchanan ignores the opportunity cost of the mobile factors, which may be greater than their yield in the poorer states. In unitary states only one thing is geographically permanent: the location of natural resources. In federations the geographical data are given in *two* respects: the location of natural resources and the boundaries of the federal states. Some states will thus inclose rich resources, others poor. Buchanan's scheme of equalizing fiscal pressures cannot equalize natural wealth and thus will result in aiding the poorest province, attracting there, as he has so clearly shown, capital and enterprise, as well as fixing unskilled labor.

The whole argument, in fact, resolves itself into whether or not the provinces receiving the federal grants are the best fields for such aid, from the income-producing point of view. Buchanan's implicit assumptions that natural resources are adequate, awaiting only development, and that labor in poor areas requires only training and experience for its efficient utilization lead him to reject my argument that transfers will lead to an inefficient use of national resources. My own assumption was that *both* natural resources *and* the other factors are scarce and that national product will be highest when the scarce labor capital and enterprise are attracted to the best soil, ports, mines, sites, etc., and that federal transfers will frustrate this attraction unless the cynosure of fiscal attraction happens to be, by coincidence, the optimum location of production.

III

In his last section Buchanan discusses the weight of resource-allocation considerations in policy-making. He objects to policies contrary to "commonly accepted ethical standards" and urges that opposition to "harsh and oppressive measures" to distressed and blighted areas should not be lessened on grounds of allocative efficiency alone. He urges that equity, national interest, and the preservation of minimum standards of the public services (surely another aspect of equity?) should be the primary trinity of motives for federal transfers.

I do not, of course, urge allocative efficiency as sole grounds for transfer or any other policy. The science of public finance has become recently very sensitive on this subject, as Buchanan's own recent contribution on the pure theory of public finance shows, and the extent to which the economist should take his cue from the legislature and the press in discussing specific measures is still a matter of some controversy.[4] It still seems to me that the economist may usefully point out that some federal decisions have costs as well as benefits, for example, that the rejection of the St. Lawrence Waterway Project, while benefiting New England and the Atlantic Coast, may, in aiding these "distressed and blighted" areas, do a disservice to the maximization of the national product, or that the people of Tasmania might serve the Australian commonwealth better if they lived where their work was more useful. Economic policy is likely to be wrong if it does not consider these matters and balance them against more pleasant considerations. The amount that any federation can invest in its weaker members is limited, even in the United States; and the profitability of reinforcing strength rather than weakness should join Buchanan's trinity of co-ordinate (not alternative) objectives.

[4] J. M. Buchanan, "The Pure Theory of Government Finance," *Journal of Political Economy,* XLVII (1949), 496–505.

d. A Reply

James M. Buchanan

Professor Scott's stimulating comment has clarified certain points of difference between the analysis of the allocative effects of federal grants contained in my paper and that of his earlier treatment.[1] But the basic argument of my paper is not affected. I did not state, and I did not intend to imply, that income-transferring grants will tend in all cases to promote a more efficient allocation of economic resources. The part of my paper under discussion concluded only that "no general pattern of resource distortion can be established," and the final paragraph of the paper included the statement: "It has been shown that . . . no universally applicable conclusions [may] be drawn." The original argument by Scott, and the one which apparently he still supports, is the more general. Hence, the burden of proof rests with him; he must demonstrate that his model is not only the representative but also the prevalent one. There may exist real world situations fitting Scott's model. "Detailed empirical inquiry" would reveal these, but it would surely reveal also other situations more closely approximating the conditions of the model imputed to my analysis. My concentration on the role of income-transferring grants in improving resource allocation was designed to accomplish the negative purpose of refuting the more commonly held views.

Despite the fact that the logical structure of my analysis does not require that I do so, I am willing to defend the model attributed to me as being more descriptive of reality than that opposed to it. There is no apparent disagreement on the actual effects of grants on resource movement. Social service grants tend to encourage labor to remain in recipient states; other income-transferring grants tend to encourage the shifting of capital investment to the low-income recipient states. But, for this shifting of capital to be efficient, there must be assumed to be present in these areas sufficient natural advantages to keep the marginal social productivity of this capital investment equal to or above that prevailing for like units of capital invested in other geographical locations. In my opinion, this assumption is justified for the poor regions of most federal countries. Scott does not accept this assumption as warranted, and this appears to be the significant point of difference between us. His emphasis on the importance of natural resources does serve to bring out a deficiency in my paper in that I did not make this assumption as explicit as

Reprinted from James M. Buchanan, "A Reply," *Journal of Political Economy*, Volume LX, No. 6 (December, 1952), pp. 536–538, by permission of The University of Chicago Press.

[1] A. D. Scott, "A Note on Grants in Federal Countries," *Economica*, XVII (1950), 416–22.

possible.[2] There is no important disagreement concerning the nature of regional labor markets or of the desirability of including efficiency considerations in all matters of economic policy.

Scott seems to agree that the relatively poor geographical areas in federal countries are characterized by both a relative scarcity of nonnatural resource capital and a relative surplus of labor, especially of the unskilled variety. His point is that these areas may also be so poor in natural advantages that any additional capital investment would be socially inefficient; therefore, the outmigration of the surplus population is the only desirable resource adjustment. It seems to me that the paucity in natural advantages for any geographical area already characterized by a labor surplus could scarcely ever be sufficient to reduce the marginal productivity of all supplementary capital investment below that prevailing elsewhere. The productivity of capital depends on the supplies of the complementary resources with which it works. Although natural resources are complementary to mobile capital, they are no more important, and probably considerably less important, than labor in determining marginal productivity. As Scott implied in a footnote to his earlier article,[3] natural resources may well be much more significant in determining average productivity. A lack of natural resources in a region may serve to keep the average product of capital relatively low; it is not likely to keep marginal productivity below that found in other regions provided labor is in excess supply. The type of capital investment which will tend to be most productive in, and thus will tend to be the first attracted to, the areas poor in natural resources will be investment in operations which utilize a high proportion of labor and which exploit the natural advantages that do exist as fully as possible. Investment in heavy industry would be inefficient in regions deficient in power potential regardless of the degree of labor surplus; investment in light industry requiring little capital equipment per worker would probably be efficient in regions possessing surplus population no matter how inadequate the natural resource base.

If the concept of social productivity, as different from private productivity, is considered, the tentative conclusion that some capital investment will be efficient is reinforced. Scott speaks as though labor were the only mobile factor, when, in fact, labor is less mobile than capital. The social losses involved in labor mobility are significant and cannot be completely overlooked. This does not imply, as is suggested, that I consider desirable the fixing of the labor supply in areas where this resource is found in abundance. It does imply that resource adjustment should normally run in two directions and that the whole burden of adjustment should not be placed on labor except in rare instances. The comparative importance of labor outflow and capital inflow in attaining resource equilibrium will be dependent, in part, on the adequacy of the natural resource base. The movement of the cotton textile industry

[2] This deficiency in my paper has been pointed out to me by Professor H. P. B. Jenkins.
[3] *Op. cit.*, p. 419.

to the Southern States during the same period in which southern labor has continued to move northward typifies the type of resource adjustment needed in this country. In this case, it is clear that the two-way resource movement has taken place in the almost complete absence of federal income transfers of the sort discussed. The argument advanced by Scott is obviously not applicable in such circumstances.

In a more general sense, the diversity of approach between Scott and myself probably stems from a fundamental difference in the manner of classifying resources. Scott appears to adopt the traditional trichotomy — and (natural resources), labor, and capital — and his views seem colored with the Ricardian idea that natural resources are somehow "original and indestructible." This leads him to devote special attention to the role of natural resources and to overemphasize, in my opinion, the geographically optimum allocation of resources. I prefer the Knightian classification of resources into two broad categories, labor and capital, with natural resources included as a subdivision of the latter. Invested capital seems clearly to be a more important subdivision in the consideration of most economic problems. There are few resources which cannot be produced and destroyed in an economic sense; investment can produce soil and even climate to a degree. For example, the Florida Everglades are now scarcely able to support the tribes of Seminole Indians, but, with substantial investment in drainage, this region might be transformed into a highly productive agricultural area. With the advent of scientific rain-making and the possible peacetime utilization of atomic energy, the importance of natural advantages in determining the efficient location of production will be further reduced.

Section B

CURRENT POSITIONS ON STATE AID

In the consideration of state grants for education, there is a difference of opinion on whether a fixed-unit plan, i.e., the type proposed by Strayer and Haig, should be used or whether a percentage scheme is to be preferred. Johns and Morphet (Selection 36) provide an extended discussion of an extremely difficult problem, namely, how to establish the amount of the foundation program. This is a problem that was left unresolved in the Strayer-Haig proposal.

Wisconsin was the first state to adopt a percentage-equalizing grant for general-purpose aid — in 1949. The Wisconsin plan is actually the implementation of the Updegraff proposal made in 1922 for Pennsylvania. In Selection 37 Kahl and James discuss the workings of the plan.

In 1961, Paul Mort and his associates urged the adoption of a percentage-equalizing program in New York State (Selection 38). Of particular interest is the special treatment advocated for high-density areas. The publication of this report marked the turning of a circle. In 1906 it was the rural areas that — in Cubberley's view — stood in a disadvantageous position; now it is the great cities that appear to need special consideration.

36

Developing the Foundation Program

Roe L. Johns and Edgar L. Morphet

A crucial but difficult task in designing a Strayer-Haig plan is the estimation of the dollar value of the foundation program. In reading this selection, it is well to bear in mind that Professor Morphet, University of California, and Professor Johns, University of Florida, have had considerable experience in conducting the processes of measurement they describe here.

If a foundation program plan is to be sound and is to work the way it is intended, it must be carefully and scientifically devised to conform to sound principles and criteria. Failure to do so is almost certain to create problems and inequities. Two basically sound ideas as to how a foundation program should be developed are discussed briefly in the paragraphs which follow.

The Dollars-per-Unit-of-Need Approach. The idea back of the "dollars-per-unit" approach to the development of a foundation program is that, if a defensible cost per unit of need can be established and if valid procedures are used in determining need, in arriving at the amount required, and in apportioning funds, each local school system will be in a position to provide and finance the essential educational opportunities encompassed in the foundation program. This idea is sound. However, there are several problems which should be faced realistically, such as (1) determining the unit of cost to be used, and (2) convincing lay citizens, including legislators who must make the appropriation, that the cost per unit decided upon is needed to purchase the essential educational opportunities included in the foundation program. If people are not agreed on the opportunities which should be financed, they may have difficulty in agreeing upon the unit cost to be included.

The original plan for determining the unit cost of the foundation program provided for ascertaining the amount expended in typical or average districts in the state — that is, those districts presumably neither especially handicapped

From Roe L. Johns and Edgar L. Morphet, *Financing the Public Schools*, pp. 273–287.

nor especially favored because of their local ability. While this plan provides an objective basis for determining costs, it has some limitations which have been recognized for several years. Two of the most serious are (1) average practice is affected by existing customs and legal limitations and thus may not be desirable practice, (2) those who believe there are inefficiencies in the organization and administration of education may not consider average practice acceptable. Many may believe it is far beyond what should be provided in less wealthy districts whose expenditures have been considerably below the average. Furthermore, if revisions were made periodically on the basis of average practice, the unit cost figure would eventually become highly artificial since the standard for each revision would automatically be forced upward by the last previous revision.

More recently, much greater attention has been given to other means of determining unit costs. Attempts have been made to take into account trends in prices and wages, financial handicaps imposed on the districts, and other similar factors.

Perhaps the most promising approach has grown out of the cost-quality studies. These studies show that (1) low expenditure districts cannot finance a satisfactory program of education, and (2) there are expenditure levels below which essential educational opportunity cannot be provided. Thus, an objective basis is provided for determining a unit cost figure not directly affected by or related to average practice.

The advantage of studies of this type is that they begin to direct attention to what it takes to provide adequate educational opportunities and away from practices which may be affected by limitations involving insight, understanding, or ability. One of the difficulties is that many people may not be willing to subscribe fully to the theory that greater expenditures for education tend to result in better education. The center of attention is necessarily still on the amount of dollars required per unit of educational need. This figure can be derived readily by experts but may not be easily understood by laymen who must support the program if it is to be adopted. To the extent that the amount proposed per unit is accepted and understood generally, the idea is both sound and practical. If, however, too many people question the findings and opinions of the experts, the unit appropriation may be limited or reduced and the program thus handicapped.

As taxes become higher and competition for the taxpayer's dollar becomes keener, more people may be inclined to raise questions concerning the amount of dollars per unit required to provide the essential services. The deductive definition of the kind and quality of education which can be purchased by a given number of dollars per unit may need more substantiation than has sometimes been provided.

The Services-and-Facilities-Needed Approach. The authors, in working with lay commissions and legislators in a number of states, have sometimes encountered considerable difficulty in convincing laymen and even some educators that a certain amount of money per weighted pupil or per weighted teacher is necessary to finance the foundation program. They have been concerned also about the problems and implications in using average practice. Gradually another procedure has been evolved for arriving at a defensible cost of the foundation program.

This procedure may be illustrated as follows: A committee of educators and laymen concerned with the development of a foundation program, and with a plan for financing that program, begins to work on the problem of determining what is needed for a satisfactory program of education in any school or school system in the state. One of the first questions raised usually is: How many children can be taught satisfactorily by an elementary or high school teacher? The committee is likely to be interested in the findings of research studies and in reactions of teachers, pupils, and parents in their own community and state.

Eventually, after much study and discussion, members of the committee may reach a conclusion which may be stated about as follows: "Some teachers can teach more children than others and do a superior job. However, other things being equal, the average teacher in a large school should not be expected to have more than 27 to 30 pupils in her class if she is to do a good job of teaching and to work effectively with individual pupils. The average class load should therefore generally not exceed this number of pupils. If it is much larger than this, both teachers and pupils will be handicapped. In the smaller schools the number of pupils per teacher should be somewhat fewer than in large schools, if the teachers are to do an equally good job. Of course, in a one-teacher school a teacher is needed even though there may be only ten or twelve children. However, small schools are expensive to operate and the foundation program should recognize the smaller pupil-teacher ratio only for necessary small schools."

From consideration of the teacher-pupil ratios the study usually moves on to such questions as: What quality of teachers and teaching is needed, and what preparation should be expected for good quality teachers? What other services are needed for a good program of instruction, such as principals, counseling services, librarians, and so on? In these discussions, most attention is usually centered on the instructional program, as it should be. Eventually, however, people begin to recognize, as a result of their studies, that many other services, as well as adequate facilities, are needed for a good program of education. They begin to develop the understanding necessary to reach agreement on services and facilities needed. When the essential services are agreed upon, these can be translated into costs and the cost per unit can be determined on a reasonably objective basis.

Advantages and Disadvantages. In the latter approach, the attention is centered on services and facilities needed and out of this study grow conclusions as to cost; in the former, attention is centered on cost, and on the basis of the figures arrived at, assumptions are made as to the services and facilities which can be provided.

The procedures used in developing such foundation programs as those found in Florida, Kentucky, and Ohio illustrate the "services-and-facilities-needed" approach. In Kentucky, for example, under the guidance of a state committee, local lay-professional committees were organized in practically every district to discuss the characteristics of a satisfactory foundation program of educational opportunity. These studies and discussions were continued in many cases for several months. The reports were then transmitted to the state committee, which summarized the returns. One interesting development was that in many cases more than 90 per cent of the people involved were agreed on some of the basic features of an essential program of educational opportunity. On the basis of these agreements the foundation program was approved by the legislature.

This procedure, too, involves some problems and difficulties: (1) Considerable time is required for large numbers of people to become informed and to establish bases for agreement; (2) some people may react on the basis of preconceived notions or prejudices and may not be willing to think through the problem; (3) there is a possibility that insufficient attention may be given to the findings and conclusions of studies that have been made in various parts of the country; (4) there is some danger that legislators may try to compartmentalize the program.

A foundation program developed in this manner has sometimes been called a "budget-based program." However, the procedure is designed to be used in *developing* the program, *not in attaching restrictions and limitations* to various aspects of the program. In fact, there is no greater need or justification for placing requirements and limitations on various aspects of a program based on a study of services and facilities than on a program developed on the basis of a "dollar-per-unit" approach. A unit cost figure can be derived in either case. A sound foundation program of educational opportunity can be established through either procedure.

Since the legislature must finally authorize the program and the financial support necessary to implement the program, it would seem that even greater attention must be given in the future to procedures which will result in widespread understanding of the problems and needs than has been necessary in the past. The question that must be resolved in each state is, What procedures will most likely result in the insights and understandings necessary to assure the adoption and financing of an adequate and satisfactory foundation program of essential educational opportunity?

MEASURES OF EDUCATIONAL NEED

One basic step in developing a satisfactory foundation program plan is to establish objective, equitable, and valid measures of educational need. If the measures of need are subjective, the determination of need is likely to be influenced by the judgment of state officials, and this, of course, might introduce inequities. If the measures of need are invalid, they would also be inequitable and would have adverse effects on the educational program.

While there is agreement that sound measures of need must be developed, there are differences of opinion as to whether a single measure should be used for determining all aspects of educational need, and as to the extent to which average practice should be used in deriving measures of need.

The Single Measure. Theoretically, a single measure for determining all aspects of need is desirable. Mort originally proposed the derivation and use of a single, all-encompassing unit. Studies have been made to determine the feasibility of developing such a unit, and on the basis of these studies a single unit of measurement has been proposed.[1] If a community is sparsely populated it will either have to operate small schools or provide extensive transportation, or perhaps operate some small schools and still provide some transportation. The cost per pupil in such communities would necessarily be greater than the cost in more densely populated communities.

The development of a single unit for measuring educational need would have advantages in analyzing the expenditures in different types of districts and among different states and in developing foundation program laws. Unless carefully developed, however, the single unit could serve either to retard consolidation because insufficient allowances were made to cover the cost of transportation and construction or, under different circumstances, it might unduly stimulate consolidation. When properly drawn, based on sound study, the law would neither reward nor penalize consolidation.

Most states have found it desirable to use two measures — one for current expense and capital outlay, and a separate measure for transportation. Several states use entirely different measures for current expense and for capital outlay, although this does not seem to be necessary. In fact, studies have shown that there is a long-range continuing relationship between expenditures for capital outlay and those for current expense.[2]

Units of Measurement. The pupil-teacher ratio is necessarily much smaller and the cost per pupil in attendance or in membership is much greater in small schools, in certain types of classes, and for certain grade levels than for regular classes in larger schools. It is therefore necessary to develop either a weighted pupil unit or an adjusted classroom unit for use in measuring educational need and in arriving at the foundation program cost. These units should be derived on the basis of careful studies if they are to serve satisfactorily as measures of need. Arbitrary compromises based on expediency are almost certain to result in inequities.

[1] See, for example, William P. McLure, *Effect of Population Sparsity on School Costs*, Contributions to Education No. 929 (New York: Bureau of Publications, Teachers College, Columbia University, 1947).

[2] F. E. Grossnickle, *Capital Outlays in Relation to a State's Minimum Educational Program* (New York: Teachers College, Columbia University, 1931).

The chief problem with the weighted pupil unit is that it is difficult to interpret to legislators and other laymen. The adjusted classroom unit, although it is directly related in its derivation to the weighted pupil unit, is much easier for laymen and even teachers to understand. They can readily see the relationship between the number of teachers needed and program of services or facilities to be provided. This relationship is not so obvious in the case of the weighted pupil unit. More important than the question of which unit is to be used (a matter which can be appropriately decided by the leaders and the legislature of each state) is the method used in deriving the unit.

Either unit may be derived on the basis of average practice. However, as pointed out by Mort and Reusser,

> This has two very serious faults. First, practice on which the weightings are based varies from decade to decade. Second, it varies from state to state. The most serious variations are in the weightings given to secondary pupils as compared with elementary pupils. Sparsity corrections appear to be more uniform from state to state and more stable from decade to decade.[3]

Average practice provides definite criteria which may be used in developing units for measuring need. However, existing practice may tend to perpetuate undesirable and uneconomical practices and may indirectly even retard improvements.

Because of these difficulties, which have vigorously been pointed out from time to time by the authors . . . , increasing attention has been given during recent years to the derivation of units on the basis of service needs. The adjusted classroom unit seems to be well adapted to this approach.

The weighted pupil unit is usually used as a unit of cost for the foundation program as well as a unit of need. Thus, attention is centered on cost from the beginning, and people who are particularly tax-conscious may tend to resist improvements because the unit is directly associated with cost. This has usually not been the procedure in developing the adjusted classroom unit. Experience indicates that many people tend to be less concerned about the cost after they understand and have agreed upon the need than is the case when cost is an obvious consideration from the beginning.

Deriving and Implementing the Adjusted Classroom Unit. There are two points of view relating to the derivation of the adjusted classroom unit. One holds that the units should be derived in "pure" form from the studies and discussions and should cover needs for all employees and services. The other holds that the classroom unit should be "built up" in terms of services needed, starting with classroom teachers, then taking into consideration other pertinent factors and finally arriving at the same single-unit formula as would probably be derived if the first procedure were followed. The latter procedure will be used to illustrate how the unit is developed and what it means for measurement of educational need.

3 Mort and Reusser, *Public School Finance*, p. 493.

As previously explained, the committee responsible for a state-wide study, with the help of consultants, usually obtains evidence from studies of present and desirable practice in various types of communities, considers proposals regarding desirable programs made by local committees of educators and laymen which have been studying the problem, and eventually proceeds to develop a statement describing essential instructional and related services. This statement then becomes a guide for the development of classroom units to be used for measuring need. The statement tends to be both idealistic and practical. It usually envisions better services than are provided in the most backward districts but may not include the quality of services desired by the most progressive school systems. At any rate, it is not unduly restricted by considerations of average practice, although the committee will undoubtedly study data regarding these practices.

Units for regular teachers. Attention is usually centered first on the number of full-time teachers needed for regular classes in the larger schools (usually schools having more than 300 pupils). In most states the conclusion has been reached that there should be one teacher for about every 30 pupils in average daily membership, or for about 27 or 28 pupils in average daily attendance. Surprisingly enough, the number of pupils per teacher which has been accepted as desirable has usually been about the same for high schools as for elementary schools. The number in junior or community colleges has usually been somewhat less.

Attention is next usually directed to the small schools — that is, those having fewer than 100 to 150 pupils in attendance. In most cases the committee and consultants have agreed that where small schools are necessary because of sparsity of population and isolation (but not because of existing district boundary lines) sufficient units should be provided to enable such schools to conduct a satisfactory program, and that this will mean fewer pupils per teacher than in the larger schools. It is obvious that for any necessary one-teacher school there should be one unit. For other necessary small schools the formula developed usually provides for from 15 to 25 pupils per teacher, depending on the size of the school. For non-isolated small schools the same formula is used as for larger schools. (Provisions for determining isolation of small schools will be discussed later.)

Thus, suppose a district with 3,000 pupils in membership in several large schools (more than 300 to 400 pupils each) had one non-isolated school with ten pupils, an isolated one-teacher school with eight pupils, a non-isolated school with 30 pupils, and an isolated school with 100 pupils. If the conclusions from the illustration above are used, the district would have 100 classroom units for the 3,000 pupils in larger schools, one unit for the isolated one-teacher school, five units for the isolated 100-pupil school, one for the non-isolated 30-pupil school, and one-third of a unit for the non-isolated one-teacher school; or a total of 107⅓ units. These would be classroom units based on need for regular full-time teachers.

Units for other teaching personnel. Unfortunately, many state programs have stopped at that stage and have not provided units for other needed instructional services. This has meant that the only way those instructional services could be provided would be to increase class size and, therefore, presumably lower the quality of the instructional program. For a realistic and comprehensive foundation program, it is necessary to provide units at least for kindergarten pupils, for exceptional children instructed in the schools, for vocational education, and for adult education. Suppose, in this district there are 300 kindergarten pupils, and kindergartens are operated on a half-day basis. There would thus be five additional units for kindergarten teachers. There might be four additional units for teachers working with exceptional children, four units for the equivalent of four full-time vocational teachers, and 2⅔ units for full-time teaching equivalents for adult education. The district would thus have 123 classroom units for teachers.

Units for other instructional and administrative personnel. This still would not meet the need, because no provision would have been made for librarians, counselors, principals, supervisors, or others primarily concerned with instructional services. Studies in a number of states have shown that one additional classroom unit for other instructional services should be provided for each eight to ten classroom units for direct teaching services. In the district considered above there would be from 12 to 15 units which should be added if it is to have a realistic program. Thus, instead of 123 classroom units the district would have approximately 135 units.

Studies have shown that classroom units derived in this manner can also be used readily to measure the need for other current expense (except for transportation) and for capital outlay. However, the classroom units should include in all cases units for regular teachers, units for other teaching personnel, and units for other instructional and administrative personnel.

Measuring Educational Need for Small Schools. If the same plan is used for measuring educational need in all small schools, one of two things will happen:

1. When the formula used for determining units of need in large schools is used, every small school will be handicapped in that it will have to provide more teachers and other instructional services than included in the formula if it is to operate satisfactorily. Thus, the necessary small schools will be penalized along with those that are not necessary. Some states have used this plan.

2. When a small-school formula is used for all small schools, each school will have sufficient units to operate reasonably satisfactorily and thus, the unnecessary or non-isolated schools will be encouraged to continue. There would thus be incorporated in the formula a reward or incentive which would tend to perpetuate these schools. A number of states have used this plan, with the result that the people of the entire state are confronted with the necessity of having to help pay the extra cost of operating these schools.

The tendency during recent years has been to attempt to devise an objective plan for determining which small schools (that is, those having fewer than 100 to 150 pupils) are isolated and should be continued. This has no bearing on the question as to whether the non-isolated schools will continue to operate, because that is a matter which probably should be left for local determination. However, the people living in a district which chooses to continue the operation of such a school should pay the extra expense of operating the school.

Several states, such as Florida, Kentucky — and to a more limited extent, California — have devised and are using formulas of isolation as a basis for determining which small schools are to be allotted units on the small-school formula for the foundation program. For a one-teacher elementary school to be isolated, for example, one or more of the following conditions should apply: (1) It should be 18 or more miles from another isolated or large school; (2) pupils would have to be transported over roads that are impassable or extremely hazardous during part of the school year; (3) more than 10 per cent of the pupils would have to be on the bus more than three quarters of an hour, morning or evening. The distance may be decreased slightly for somewhat larger schools. In the case of small high schools, both the distance requirement and the time on the bus are usually increased somewhat.

Other Factors to Consider. Attendance during current year. In developing foundation programs or other state support formulas, the traditional practice has been to use the attendance of pupils during the previous year for determining need. This practice is not realistic, because rapidly growing districts may be seriously handicapped. For example, suppose a foundation program is developed on the basis of attendance of the previous year in a district which is entitled to 500 classroom units. If the attendance increased by 10 per cent during the year and no provision was made for recognizing this change, the district would have to provide an additional 50 teachers out of its own resources, or overload classes and teachers, as a means of carrying on its program. Most state aid formulas revised during recent years have included provisions for additional units based on increased attendance during the current year. This can readily be done by basing the first apportionment on the attendance of the previous year, then making adjustments for increases in attendance when later apportionments are made during the year. Provisions for this adjustment should be incorporated in all state foundation program plans.

Attendance or membership? Another difficulty arises in states that base their units for the foundation program on average daily attendance. The attendance (and consequently the units) in certain districts may have decreased during a particular year solely as a consequence of epidemics or inclement weather. Several states have made adjustments to take care of this situation by (1) basing units on attendance during the first two or the best two months, (2) maintaining for each district, for the three preceding years, the ratio between average daily attendance and average daily membership and automatically correcting to the average for the district during any year when the ratio drops below its own average, or (3) changing from average daily attendance to average daily membership.

Services beyond regular school year. A third factor, which has been overlooked in developing many foundation programs, is the educational services which may be needed beyond the regular school term. The units for the foundation program are customarily computed on a nine-month basis, or in a few cases on the basis of a nine-and-a-half or even a ten-months period. However, more and more districts are operating summer schools or continuing certain educational services during the summer months. Provision can and should be made for adding fractional units sufficient to meet the needs during these months. Thus, if there is a six-week summer school and the attendance would justify 90 classroom units on the basis of the six weeks, this would be the equivalent of 15 additional units based on a nine-month program. Units can be added for principals on the basis of one month for each additional month of service and for other instructional services on a somewhat similar basis. Unless these units are added to the foundation program, the less wealthy districts will generally not be able to provide the services and the program will be handicapped. The basic question is: Are these services needed to provide the essential educational opportunities which should be included in the foundation program? If they are, provision should be made to include them.

TRANSLATING NEEDS INTO COSTS

Traditionally, in developing a foundation program plan, the cost elements have been built into the unit. Thus, when the number of units is determined, all that is needed is to multiply this number by the foundation program cost allotment per unit to determine the cost of the foundation programs. However, as indicated above, there are some inherent disadvantages in having the cost unit built into the unit for measuring need.

When the unit of need is based on a study of services and facilities necessary for an adequate foundation program of education, the cost must be determined separately. The units merely represent the educational needs for a foundation program. When it is found that a district has a certain number of units of need, there is no way, until further steps are taken, to determine how many dollars this need would represent. Translating units of need into units of cost, then, constitutes a separate step.

One way of determining the value which should be assigned to each unit of need would be to use the average cost per unit based on the current expenditure for education in the state. This would merely mean that the foundation program is to be set at the level of the average expenditure in the state. This procedure has sometimes been used.

A more common procedure has been to develop the cost unit allowances very much as the units themselves are developed. This is not done or should not be done as a means of controlling the program or expenditures but merely as a realistic means of developing understanding of financial needs and of making adequate provision for costs to be included in the foundation program. It would be a serious mistake in any state for those who are developing the foundation program to assume, or for the legislature to accept the idea, that steps taken to develop cost units should be used as devices for controlling or restricting foundation program expenditures in the districts.

Instructional Salaries. A question with which discussion of salary needs usually starts is: What should be the beginning salary of a properly certificated teacher who is a college graduate and has had no previous teaching experience? The next logical question is: How much, on the average, should properly certificated college graduates be paid, considering the fact that some of them have had no experience and some have had many years of experience? Other pertinent questions are: Do many districts employ teachers who are not college graduates? What would be a reasonably adequate salary for such teachers? Should most teachers have had training beyond college graduation? What would be a reasonable salary for such teachers? What about salaries for instructional personnel beyond the customary nine- or ten-month term? (That is, the amount for additional service provided through extra units for summer programs or service, as previously explained.)

Several state committees have agreed upon a fixed amount per unit which should be included for instructional salaries. Other state committees have taken the position that if a fixed amount is included for all districts, those which are now employing poorly prepared teachers probably would use the money in developing salary schedules for their presently employed teachers. Once that is done, they would not be in a position to attract better qualified teachers, because the only way they could raise their salary schedule would be to increase local effort. Some state committees, therefore, have decided to assign a somewhat lower value to a unit which is used for teachers who are poorly prepared and a somewhat higher value to units used for teachers who are particularly well prepared. Districts with poorly prepared teachers could thus increase the amount of their foundation program allotment by employing better qualified teachers.

Two arguments used against using this differential in most states are: (1) Districts should be assured of an adequate amount of money per unit, then should be free to determine how the money is to be used, and (2) the more alert districts will employ a higher proportion of well qualified teachers and consequently receive a somewhat larger share of the funds than the others. People in some states, in which a substantial proportion of the teachers are poorly qualified, may conclude that a differential is necessary for the present but should be discontinued at a later date. The evidence seems to indicate that reasonable differentials have stimulated improvement in the preparation of teachers in many areas where standards previously had been quite unsatisfactory.

Current Expense Other Than Salaries and Transportation. In many foundation programs, the amount included for current expense other than instructional salaries and transportation has been far too limited to meet the needs. Studies made in a number of states show that about 25 per cent of the amount needed per classroom unit for instructional salaries should be included in the program to meet the necessary expenses of administration, operation, maintenance, and other related current expense. The entire program may be handicapped if the amount included for such expense is too limited.

Transportation Expense. . . . In a number of states, the cost of transportation is not included in the foundation program plan. In a few, a separate foundation program has been established for transportation. It would seem that the only defensible procedure would be to develop a sound plan for determining the cost of transportation, then to include the allowable cost in the foundation program for each district in the state.

Capital Outlay. Only a few states have included capital outlay in the foundation program thus far. There is still some difference of opinion as to whether it should be included in a general program or as to whether there should be a separate foundation program for capital outlay. . . . If capital outlay is to be included, the amount needed per unit can be determined as explained later and that amount added to the other unit figures to arrive at the total value of the classroom unit, except for transportation.

Cost of the Foundation Program. The value of the classroom unit thus becomes the total of the amount included for instructional salaries, the amount for current expense other than salaries and transportation, and the amount for capital outlay if that is to be included in the foundation program. The cost of the foundation program for any district, then, will be determined by multiplying the total value of the classroom unit by the number of units in the district and adding the allowable cost of transportation. The cost for the program in the state can similarly be determined.

Some authorities have advocated cost-of-living adjustments in the value of the unit for school systems where such variations are found. The problem unquestionably needs further study. However, no state has provided a direct adjustment thus far in the current expense portion of the program. Most people point out that, when all factors are considered, variations within a state are usually relatively minor. Communities in which the higher costs are found usually have somewhat higher ability and hence greater local leeway, can more easily attract competent teachers, and have a number of advantages over the less favored areas. In fact, some contend that an adjustment should be made, as has already been done in some countries, to provide for higher salaries for teachers in the more isolated schools.

Proposals have also been made to provide in the law for the value of the classroom unit to be increased or decreased each year as the value of the dollar changes. The use of such an index would probably receive more serious consideration in a number of states if (1) the foundation program were financed at an adequate level, and (2) some way could be found to make the index applicable to both local and state funds involved in the support of the program.

37

The Wisconsin Plan

A Combined Selection

The several unique features of Wisconsin's plan of school aid are discussed in the two following statements. Dr. Kahl is assistant state superintendent and bears a major share of responsibility in administering the program. Professor James of Stanford University formerly was assistant superintendent and administered the plan in its early years of operation, i.e., 1950–54.

a. Wisconsin's State Support Program

William Kahl

A state support philosophy which seeks to develop local initiative and to encourage schools to provide an ever-expanding and higher quality program must be implemented through a rather complex formula. Although the present state support program for schools in Wisconsin may appear to be somewhat involved, the complexity can be justified in that it permits the operation of factors which can be directed to facilitate an equitable distribution of school aid to local school districts.

Adapted from "Wisconsin's State Support Program," in Committee on Educational Finance, *Problems and Opportunities in Financing Education,* Washington, National Education Association, 1959, pp. 62–67. Copyright 1959 by The National Education Association.

Underlying Concepts

Several assumptions underlie the Wisconsin program of school support. Because education is seen as a state function, the state has a direct responsibility in contributing financially to the support of all administrative units or districts offering a satisfactory educational program and exerting a minimum local effort to finance an adequate program.

Equality of Opportunity. Equality of educational opportunity, while never a complete reality or achievement, should be recognized in the formulation of any state support program. Through the equalization principle, Wisconsin places a guaranteed valuation back of each resident child in average daily attendance. In districts with low valuations, the state attempts to equalize educational opportunity by providing an adequate per-pupil valuation base. If the district has insufficient equalized property valuation, the state makes up the difference and thus assures an adequate base. The degree to which the state assumes responsibility for equalizing educational opportunity can be measured to some extent by the proportionate shares of the equalization valuation assumed by the local district and the state.

Local Ability and Effort. The property tax load can become excessive, and the state support program attempts to keep tax levies within certain limitations. While it may be difficult to determine the point at which a property tax load becomes excessive, the state support law has defined a required operating levy for current operation of 15, 20, and 25 mills, respectively, in certain types of districts to be excessive. When maximum limits for current operation are reached, the state support program assumes any excess current operation cost.

Quality of Education. The quality of the educational program is a basic concern in determining the amount of state support paid to the local school district. In order to provide an incentive for local districts to enrich and improve the educational opportunities for children, the financial effort exerted by the state is greater in districts providing an integrated-level program than in districts offering a basic-level program. The application of this concept of quality education is carried out in districts.

Organizational Pattern. The state support program included in its original philosophy an incentive feature which was clearly related to the organizational pattern of the school program. This concept has resulted in a greater degree of state support to districts that provide an integrated-level program and that are organized on a k-12 or 1-12 grade pattern.

Requirements for State Support

In qualifying for state aid, school districts must place a minimum levy upon the equalized valuation of property in the school district. Elementary districts offering grades k-8 or 1-8 and union high schools must levy at least 3 mills. School districts offering k-12 or 1-12 must levy at least 5 mills.

For state-aid purposes, school districts are classified as qualifying for state aid on a basic or on an integrated level. School districts on an integrated level provide a better quality of education for children. Teachers are better qualified to teach in their respective positions. The course of study includes more subjects in more fields as well as better facilities. Music, art, and kindergarten are a regular part of the offering. The high school must employ more than five teachers, and must provide an adequate offering in the vocational fields as well as in the academic areas of science, mathematics, English, and social studies. Physical education, guidance and counseling, health services, special classes for the handicapped, audio-visual aids, and library services represent additional services. Reasonable pupil-teacher ratios must be maintained so that class loads will permit effective teaching.

Flat Aids

Two basic factors are involved in the computation of flat aids: the number of children in average daily attendance and the amount per child as set forth in the statute. The flat aid in terms of existing statutes may be illustrated thus:

Type of Aid Classification	*Grants per Pupil in Average Daily Attendance, 1957–58 and 1958–59*	
	Elementary School	*High School*
1. Basic k-8 or 1-8	$28	. . .
2. Basic 9-12	. . .	$35
3. Basic k-12 or 1-12	28	35
4. Integrated k-8 or 1-8	35	. . .
5. Integrated 9-12	. . .	44
6. Integrated k-12 or 1-12	35	44

Let us assume that a school district offering kindergarten through grade 12 qualifies for state aid on an integrated level. The district has 500 resident elementary-school children and 200 high-school students in average daily attendance. The equalized valuation of the district totals $21 million, of $30,000 per resident child. Since this amount is greater than the guaranteed valuation of $28,000 for integrated k-12 districts, the district qualifies for flat aids. The present flat-aid schedule provides $35 in state aid for resident elementary-school children in average daily attendance and $44 per secondary-school student. The state aid for the elementary-school children would total $17,500 (500 × $35), while the high-school portion of state aid would be $8800 (200 × $44). Total state aid to this district would be $26,300. The difference of $9 between the flat aid for elementary-school pupils and high-school students is due to the higher cost of education per high-school student. Consequently, $35 and $44 in integrated k-12 grade programs would represent approximately the same per cent of support at each level.

EQUALIZATION AID

The basic factors which produce equalization aid rather than flat aid are (a) the equalized valuation of a school district, (b) the number of resident children in average daily attendance, and (c) current net operating costs.

The state statutes require that the minimum equalized valuation back of each resident child in integrated k-12 districts should not be less than $28,000. In the case cited above to illustrate flat-aid grants, $21 million divided by 700 students equals $30,000. Since the valuation back of each child exceeds the state requirement of $28,000 by $2000 per child, the district falls in the flat-aid area of state support.

Equalized valuation per resident pupil in integrated k-12 districts (on the basis of the 1956 data) varied from a low of $5800 in one district to a high of $82,000. Those districts exceeding $28,000 fell in the flat-aid area.

Now let us assume that the flat-aid district used in the earlier example lost $7 million of its equalized valuation, and had only $14 million in back of 700 children. The result would be an equalized valuation per pupil of $20,000, or $8000 less than the guaranteed valuation set forth in the law.

At this point it is necessary to determine the *net operating cost* per pupil, so that a *required tax rate* for current operation may be established. Let us assume that the net operating cost is equal to $336 per pupil. Since the guaranteed valuation by law is $28,000, the required operating levy rate would be equal to $336 divided by $28,000 or 12 mills. Since the district has $20,000 of equalized valuation per resident child, it could produce $240 ($20,000 × 12 mills) of the amount needed, and the state would provide $96 ($8000 × 12 mills). Through the guaranteed valuation, the state and local district have raised the $336 needed to meet the current operating cost of educating each pupil. The state aid paid would be equal to $67,200 (700 × $96) of a required net operating cost of $235,200.

The only difference between flat aids and the equalization aid is found in the local property tax base. The flat-aid district has $21 million or $30,000 per resident pupil and the equalization-aid district has $14 million or $20,000 per resident pupil. The state aid paid to the flat-aid districts would equal $26,300, and the state aid paid to the district receiving equalization aid would total $67,200. It is important to note that the flat-aid district receiving less state money is operating at a lower local tax rate. In order to produce $336 on a $30,000 guaranteed valuation, the local required tax effort would be 11.2 mills; the local required rate for the same cost in the equalized district, as indicated previously, equals 12 mills.

STATE SUPPORT AND LOCAL NEEDS

The wide variations due to economic and school population distribution factors require a state support program which has a marked degree of flexibility. As noted previously, the property valuation per resident pupil of the various school districts gives a measure of the wide range in their ability to finance adequate educational programs. To provide any semblance of equal educational opportunity, it is evident that resources other than local must be brought into play in low-valuation school districts.

Flexibility in state support can be and is being achieved through two possible avenues. First, the local tax impact can be reduced materially by increasing the guaranteed valuation per resident pupil. The biennial adjustment of the guaranteed valuation per pupil permits a realistic adaptation of the formula. Should the state have chosen to increase the guaranteed valuation to $36,000 rather than $28,000 during the 1957–59 biennium, the required property levy would have been reduced by 2.77 mills, and the local effort for current operation would have been 9.33 mills rather than 12 mills. This flexibility feature of the state support formula permits an opportunity to adjust the burden so that increased costs of education can be met while still permitting local initiative to improve educational opportunity. In fact, the application of the state support formula in Wisconsin with its unique equalization factor has served as an effective instrument in keeping the tax pressure within reasonable bounds. The flexibility of the state support program permits the per cent of state support to range from zero in some districts to as high as 80 per cent in other districts.

An integrated-level k-12 district was used to illustrate the program because more than 75 per cent of the average daily attendance in the state is recorded for this type of aid classification district. The formula operates in a similar manner in the other five aid classifications. The variation in flat aid and guaranteed valuations merely takes into account the type of district organization, variation in cost of education, and the incentive feature which tends to improve the quality of educational programs. The guaranteed valuations for the various aid classifications is shown below. The illustration used previously applies to districts represented in line 6.

Classification of District	*Guaranteed Valuation per Resident Pupil, 1957–59*
1. Basic 1-8	$23,000
2. Basic 9-12	55,000
3. Basic k-12 or 1-12	23,000
4. Integrated 1-8	26,000
5. Integrated 9-12	65,000
6. Integrated k-12 or 1-12	28,000

A second factor in the Wisconsin state support program which takes into account the limitation of local resources is found in the state's willingness to assume the total portion of the cost beyond a local maximum effort. In a small district, for instance, with sparsity of population and low enrollment, the operating cost of education might be such as to require a high tax rate. A net operating cost of $504 in such a district could require a rate as high as

18 mills. The state, you will recall, considers any required operating levy rate for k-12 grade districts which exceeds 15 mills excessive. Therefore, in our example, the 3 mills in excess of 15 mills would be assumed by the state.

The foregoing discussion makes no attempt to give a complete picture of state aid for education in Wisconsin. Rather it has sought to describe the distinctive qualities by which the aid system seeks to give some equality of educational opportunity to Wisconsin's children. Because of its flexibility we can say that the Wisconsin system of state aid for education realistically distributes the financial load between state and local school districts so that school districts are able to provide ever-improving educational programs.

STATE AID FORMULA

In conclusion, it may be well to reduce the Wisconsin state-aid formula to an algebraic expression applicable to school districts classified on the integrated k-12 level. The factors will vary in each district, and the effect will result in variations in terms of state support.

State Support Formula, Integrated k-12 Level

Factors	*Numerical Value*
A = Resident elementary-school ADA	500
B = Resident high-school ADA	200
C = Guaranteed valuation for resident ADA	$28,000
D = Net operating cost	$235,200
E = Equalized valuation	$14,000,000
F = Nonresident high-school ADA	0
G = State aid per high-school ADA	$44
H = State aid per resident elementary ADA	$35
X = State aid payment	

Equalization Aid Formula

$$X = \frac{D}{(A+B)\ C}[(A+B)\ C] - E + FG$$

$$X = \frac{235{,}200}{(500+200)\ 28{,}000}[(500+200)\ 28{,}000] - 14{,}000 + (0 \times 44)$$

$$X = \$67{,}200$$

Flat Aid Formula

$$X = AH + (B+F)\ G$$

$$X = (500 \times 35) + (200 + 0)\ (44)$$

$$X = \$26{,}300$$

b. Analysis of Wisconsin's School Support Program

H. Thomas James

This analysis will consider the Wisconsin school support program in relation to those characteristics it shares with the programs of most other states and those characteristics which are unusual and, in one instance at least, unique among school support programs. In addition, it will offer other ways of viewing the program, which may change the initial impression that Wisconsin ranks low among the states in revenue made available for the operation of local school systems.

A necessary first step in the analysis is the translation of special terms used in Wisconsin statutes into the common terms used by the U. S. Office of Education and by students of school finance in discussing programs of support.

Wisconsin makes *general-purpose grants* and *special-purpose grants* to local school districts. This analysis is confined to the general-purpose grants, which amount to about three-fourths of all state funds going to local school districts.

General-purpose grants are of two kinds: *flat grants* and *equalizing grants*. Wisconsin distributed a larger percentage of its general-purpose grants on a flat-grant basis than did the nation as a whole in 1953–54, but has moved sharply toward the 1953–54 national norm in the last four years. Equalizing grants accounted for only 30 per cent of the general-purpose grants in 1953–54, but had risen to 47 per cent by 1957–58.[1]

The Distribution Pattern

The following elements form a system for distributing state support funds: (a) a measure of educational *need*, (b) a measure of taxpaying *ability*, (c) a standard of educational *effort*, and (d) a standard of educational *adequacy*.

Educational Need. Like most states Wisconsin measures educational need by average daily attendance. It should be noted, however, that exceptions

Adapted from "Analysis of Wisconsin's School Support Program," in Committee on Educational Finance, *Problems and Opportunities in Financing Education*, Washington, National Education Association, 1959, pp. 67–72. Copyright 1959 by the National Education Association.

[1] Hutchins, Clayton D., and Munse, Albert R. *Public School Finance Programs of the United States*. U. S. Department of Health, Education, and Welfare, Office of Education, Misc. No. 22. Washington, D. C.: Superintendent of Documents, Government Printing Office, 1955. 251 p. (Half the general-purpose grants were distributed nationally as flat grants and about half as equalizing grants in 1953–54. I have not seen the 1957–58 national norms. Thirty-eight states made some general-purpose flat grants; and thirty-nine, some general-purpose equalizing grants in 1953–54. Only one state was listed as making no general-purpose grants that year.)

occur, as they do in most states, which can trap the unwary person who assumes that ADA is a standard unit of measurement for free use in interstate comparisons. So, while Wisconsin uses ADA, it is ADA as defined by Wisconsin statutes.[2] As a generalization, however, we may say that Wisconsin measures need on the ADA scale if we recognize that the scale is specially defined.

Taxpaying Ability. Taxpaying ability is measured in terms of the valuation of taxable property per child in ADA. This contrasts with seven states that have developed indexes of taxpaying ability, but does conform to practice in the majority of states. Wisconsin, however, like a small but increasing minority of states, determines through a state agency the "full" or "true" value of property, and measures ability in terms of the full valuation rather than the valuation assigned to property by local assessors.[3] The state is thereby guarded against two types of erosion of the property tax base which plague states entirely dependent upon local assessors: (a) competitive underassessment among multiple tax districts within school districts and (b) deliberate underassessment to create advantages for the district in the competition for state funds.

Local Effort. In common with many states Wisconsin prescribes a minimum standard of taxpaying effort but deviates from general practice in expressing the standard in mill rates on full valuation of property.[4]

The state grants no general-purpose aid to any district that does not meet the standard. It is interesting to note that the yield of this state mandatory property tax levy for schools in the 1957–58 school year approximated $65 million, more than three times the total flat grants made, more than four times the total equalizing grants made, and almost twice the total general-purpose grants made that year. I shall return to this point later to suggest some implications of viewing this required levy as a part of the total funds mandated for the support of public education in Wisconsin.

Like many other states, Wisconsin sets a maximum standard of local property-tax effort, but its manner of doing so introduces some unusual features. First, the limitation is on the levy *required* to support the costs of current operation, not on the total levy. Thus, a district may levy 30, 40, or more mills

[2] This includes special treatment of two categories of kindergarten, inconsistent treatment of two levels of nonresident pupils, a special category of schools in which ADA is computed on the basis of one week in the current year for aid purposes instead of on the previous year, its own special handling of adjustments for epidemics and drop-outs, and some special limitations on pupil-teacher ratios which incorporate elements of the classroom unit rather than the ADA basis for distributing some funds.

[3] Wisconsin's practices in the equalization of assessments helped place the state seventh from the top in the nation in the percentage which assessed valuation of property bore to full market value — about 57 percent in 1954. I understand, though, that there has been some decline in this percentage in Wisconsin as there appears to have been generally in the past few years.

[4] Three mills for 8-grade districts, 4 mills for high-school districts, and 5 mills for 12-grade districts.

in a given year, but if the net costs of current operation in that year require more than 15 mills in a k-12 district classified as integrated, or 20 in a high-school district, or 25 in a k-8 district, the state returns to the district treasury the difference between the yield of the maximum mill rate specified and the net costs of current operation. This provision, I believe, is unique to the Wisconsin program. It involves computing the cost of current operation for the year and reducing that cost by federal and county aids, normal state aids, tuition transfers, other receipts allocable to current operation, and the yield of a 15-mill levy (k-12 district). Any such excess, if found to exist, is borne in full by state funds. The uniqueness of this provision lies in the willingness of the state to allow a local community to define an educational program, and then to guarantee support of the program, even though its cost may run beyond the normal revenue expectations of the community and far beyond the normal costs per pupil for the state.[5]

Three comments are in order at this point:

1. Students of school finance in other states who knew of this provision and understood it were skeptical of it when it went into effect in 1947. The principle, however, has stood the test of time, and in the 12 years of its operation it has in fact been extended and strengthened.

2. Owing to Wisconsin's relatively high assessment practices, 15 mills on the full valuation of property is a very heavy tax indeed, comparable perhaps to 30 on assessed values in Illinois, 75 in California, and 165 in Minnesota. The normal diligent effort to keep local tax burdens bearable have therefore had their effect in keeping within bounds the state burden resulting from this provision.

3. The principle, as it has operated over the past 12 years, has been essentially a correction-for-sparsity factor, and thus has affected only a very small number of districts.[6]

The second observation to be made of this provision for maximum effort is that the state discriminates sharply between the maximum effort necessary under the preferred system of district organization — 15 mills for k-12 districts classified as integrated — and the maximum effort prescribed for the less encouraged systems, which are set at 20 mills for high-school districts and 25 mills for elementary-school districts. This differential has been a potent factor in the extension of k-12 district structures, particularly in areas of low economic ability.[7]

[5] Note that a k-12 district under the regular equalization program is guaranteed an income per child for the current operations from state sources alone, if the program requires it, of $420 per pupil, which is higher than the average expenditures per child for current operations.

[6] I recall that about 33 districts came under the provision the last year I worked with administering it. Improvements in the equalization formula as well as improvements in district structure since 1954 should have reduced that number. The cost, as I recall it from the last time I checked it, was about half a million dollars, and that, too, probably has declined.

[7] In Wisconsin over the past decade the number of school districts has been cut almost in half, and the limitation on maximum local effort has played its part in this reduction.

Educational Adequacy. Wisconsin deviates from general practice in the way it establishes its standard of adequacy. The typical state foundation program set its minimum program in terms of a fixed amount of money per pupil, frequently ranging from $200 to $260 per pupil, or in terms of a number of dollars per classroom unit. Wisconsin, however, has preferred to define standards for several levels of educational programs, review local programs and classify them annually on the basis of these standards, and then assure the income from a guaranteed tax base for each type of program. The localities thus are responsible for the decisions (a) on the level of program they will aspire to and (b) on expenditures (and therefore tax rates) which affect the size, within broad limits, of the state contribution.[8]

Local decisions typically require more than the $140 minimum guaranteed per pupil for current operation in integrated districts, however. The program provides for state sharing of costs up to 15 mills on the $28,000 base, or up to $420, so that again a district with more than that base would provide all of the cost up to 15 mills, whereas a district, if one were to exist, with no valuation could expect to draw up to $420 from the state in equalization aids. Any net additional costs beyond the yield of 15 mills would, as noted above, be borne by the state.

Thus, despite its apparent complexity, the Wisconsin foundation program bears definite resemblance to the generalized pattern of foundation programs if it is recognized that the standard of adequacy employed is not rigidly prescribed by the state except at the minimum level, and that beyond that minimum the standard is flexible and determined in large measure through local decisions.

SOME OBSERVATIONS

The Wisconsin legislature has repeatedly affirmed its intention to keep the major portion of the cost of education on property tax and to use state funds to equalize those costs which the legislature determines are an excessive burden on the property-tax base.[9] Within the framework of this legislative decision, which appears to be the only framework we can use in what is essentially an area of value judgment, we find the following factors to commend:

[8] Thus, a k-12 system classified as integrated has met certain standards of quality and quantity of educational program to achieve that classification. The state currently establishes a guaranteed valuation of $28,000 back of each pupil and requires a 5-mill levy on the valuation of the district, thereby assuring from local or state sources or both, an absolute minimum of $140 per pupil. The $140 is shared between state and local taxes in proportion to the ratio of the per-pupil true value to $28,000, except that a district with more than $28,000 value per pupil provides the entire $140, and, at the other extreme, one with no valuation would draw $140 from the state.

[9] The wisdom of this decision may be questioned by those who see the property tax as an anachronism in our present-day economy and by those who see income and sales taxes as more effective and efficient taxes on the economy and as taxes which bear more equitably on the taxpayer. As Wisconsin's metropolitan units expand and multiply, the volume of these questions may be expected to increase.

1. The property-tax base is soundly administered. Wisconsin probably ranks near the top in the nation in the quality of its property-tax administration. Evil effects of competitive underassessment are minimized, and the state school support program is designed so as to keep it from becoming one of the erosive factors on the property-tax base.

2. The flexibility of the support program is one of its most striking features, wherein state funds are allocated on the basis of ability, in the range from none at all in the most economically favored districts to very high percentages of current costs (I recall one instance as high as 95 per cent) in the least economically sufficient districts. This flexibility is maintained through biennial adjustments of the guaranteed valuation to economic change.

3. Quality, efficiency, and effort are richly rewarded in those districts eligible for equalization aids. Though the inducements are slight in the large majority of districts eligible only for flat aids, the annual review of district programs in the light of state-prescribed standards of quantity and quality of education has proven a powerful incentive to educational improvement.[10]

4. Independent indicators of the effects of a state support program are difficult to come by. However, two items from 1954 data seem worthy of mention: (a) Wisconsin ranked twentieth in income per capita that year and fourteenth in expenditure per pupil in ADA. This suggests to me that Wisconsin is probably a little better than holding her own in expenditures for education among her sister states. (b) In that same year Wisconsin ranked thirty-eighth in the nation in the relationship which expenditures for education bore to expenditures for all services of state and local governments. This suggests to me that if Wisconsin citizens come to value education as highly as they apparently value other services of government, they might do even better by education.

On the critical side, Wisconsin, along with other states, is frequently chided for providing no equalization of the costs of capital outlay. Again I would point, not in defense of the decision but in simple justice, to the framework of property-tax support in which Wisconsin practices must be judged, and say that under the state's high assessment policies and liberalized debt limitations, the legislature repeatedly has satisfied itself that the buildings needed are being built without local levies or debt burdens that are "excessive."

Let me close by returning to my earlier comment on the $65 million yield of the state-mandated levy on property. I would like to suggest, again within the value framework of a state bent upon resting most of the cost of education on property, that a legislature also concerned with establishing a high minimum standard for local school programs would find available revenues for support of that state-defined minimum in such short supply that it would find it convenient to pre-empt some portion of the yield from the property

[10] No school administrator or board of education would lightly contemplate the possibility of a reclassification of a district to a lower level, for even though the financial consideration might not appear important, the prestige factor of the higher classification has been shown repeatedly to be of enormous importance to citizens of the district.

tax to accomplish this state-defined purpose. I would like to advance two observations for purposes of discussion:

1. The state share of the Wisconsin foundation program is not $35 million generally reported as the total of the general-purpose grants for 1957–58, for instance, but that amount plus the $65 million derived from the state-mandated tax on property; not $64 per pupil, but more nearly $190 per pupil from state-mandated taxes; Wisconsin is not in the low group in terms of state support of schools at all, but is in fact in the high group.

2. Were the state to decide to shift a substantial portion of the costs of schools to other sources of revenue, this entire yield of the mandated tax on property could be shifted without impairing any of the relationships now contributing to local control of the schools, local initiative, or local effort.

38

Unification of Fiscal Policy in New York State

Paul R. Mort

Long a powerful advocate of the Strayer-Haig plan of aid, Professor Mort shifted his interest in his last years to percentage-equalizing grants. His 1961 proposal for New York, passed in substance by the legislature in 1962, was the final major plan he devised.

It is the belief of the Conference Board that the time has come to modify the basic State support structure for public schools in such a way as to bring it into line with the problems and needs of the times. The broad technical details of 10 proposals . . . are discussed briefly below. . . .

The present State aid formula, originally adopted in 1925, calls for periodic determinations of a fixed minimum level of school support per pupil as a basis for figuring the State's share of the cost of public education in a school district. During the decade of the 20's, when the level was being increased by predetermined steps, and during the relatively stable period of the 30's, this arrange-

Adapted from A *New Approach to School Finance*, Albany, New York State Educational Conference Board, 1961, pp. 9–20. Reproduced with permission.

ment operated quite satisfactorily. During the decades of the 40's and 50's, however, it has not been able to meet the financial stress of new forces. Population increases, continuous inflation, rising living standards, heavy demand for college graduates in other occupations, and the awakening to the need for improving the quality of the schools (more excellence) have caused school costs to mount every year.

The level of support used in the State aid formula did not rise automatically with the cost increases. Only population increase was in any degree reflected in the formula. Inflation, rising living standards, the pressure upon teachers' salaries, rapid expansion in facilities, and the fever for improving the schools were dealt with piecemeal. They were attacked as small independent fires without recognition of the fact that they were manifestations of a single pervading conflagration. The result was a multiplicity of modifications of the law and special provisions to correct specific aspects of the weaknesses. The result has been high local tax rates or curtailment of school quality in many school districts.

The piecemeal modifications and special laws have reached a level of complexity where they have overshadowed the idea that a basic statewide fiscal policy does in fact exist. Emphasis on these minute details of the finance program has militated against due consideration of the wholesomeness of the whole fiscal policy and structure. Also, because of the increasing involvement of the State Education Department in the meticulous decisions required to administer such laws, it is resulting in a subtle shifting of control from the local school districts to the State.

1. State Sharing in Total Expenditures

It is proposed that in the future the basis for figuring State aid be the legally incurred expenditures of the school district and that both the State and district share in each such dollar of expenditure (except as provided in Recommendation #6) in such a way as to equalize the ability of school districts to support their schools.

It is proposed that the aid to be paid in any year be that justified by the budgeted expenditure of that year. The fall payments would be made in terms of the budgets of the school districts then available, would be subject to correction in terms of information available later in the year, and would be subject to final adjustment made as a part of the payments of the following year, after reports are available on actual expenditures.

The essential changes from the present State aid program plan are these:

> Subject only to the limitations contained in Recommendation #6, the State would share in all legally determined expenditures — not just in a limited foundation program; the State would share in all legally determined expenditures — not just in operational expenditures. In other

words, debt service, capital outlay translated into debt service, transportation of children in all districts, and all the specific expenditures now made the subject of special aids would be included in the over-all figure of expenditures shared in by the State.

The proposed plan retains the ability-to-pay principle as in the present foundation program plan but applies the principle to all expenditures.

The approach is not particularly novel. In its full sweep it has recently been adopted by Rhode Island, and Maryland and Delaware have such a broad plan under consideration at the present time. The idea was proposed by Updegraff in the New York Rural School Survey in the early 20's, just prior to the adoption of the present foundation program design. The State of Wisconsin has used the plan for some years but sets a limit (a local tax limit) beyond which the State pays 100 per cent of approved expenditure. The State of Washington has utilized the idea in its capital outlay aid.

. . . .

2. Transition from the Present Laws

It is proposed that the present State aid system be allowed to continue as a minimum guarantee until all districts profit from the new system. To assist districts not immediately qualifying under the proposed new plan, it is recommended also that aid under the existing foundation program be increased by 5.0 per cent for the 1962–1963 school year.

School districts making average or more vigorous effort would be entitled to receive aid immediately under the new plan.

School districts making less than average effort would continue to receive aid on the old plan with a 5.0 per cent increase. Pressures of school costs not taken care of in the present plan would soon bring such districts under the new plan within two or three years in most such cases.

3. Gradual Replacement of Special Aids and Special Provisions

It is recommended that in districts receiving aid under the plan proposed here, all other aids to education from the State and Federal governments shall be counted as part of the State's share under the new plan for the years in which they are paid.

The other alternative is to reduce the number of weighted pupils used in computing ability by the same procedure as recommended to reflect transportation expenses in the number of such pupils. In this case the State would share in local expenditures less such amounts.

a. *Adjustment for Heavy Debt Service.* Since the State's sharing in the costs at the rate determined by the ability formula will in some instances leave a school district still heavily overburdened for debt service, it is recommended that a special provision be made providing for the payment by the State of 75 per cent of any residual debt service in excess of that which could be met by a tax of $2 per $1,000 on full value of taxable property.

The cost of this is minor but the importance to a few districts is material.

Because of the difference in practice among communities in the matter of bonding for schoolhousing or using a pay-as-you-go policy, the policy adopted by Rhode Island for dealing with capital outlay not financed by borrowing is recommended. This policy is to pay one-twentieth of the outlay for each of twenty years. In New York State thirty years could be used.

4. The State Share

It is proposed that the State percentage share shall be the difference between 100 per cent of the budgeted expenditure of a school district and the local share as determined under Recommendation #5 but not less than 25 per cent.

The formula for determining the local share presumes a State average share of 42.5 per cent. However, the adoption of all proposals herein made will raise this to about 50.0 per cent.

The 42.5 per cent State share is the percentage, on the average, which the State paid in 1960–61 as estimated by the Diefendorf Committee's *Interim Report*. From the standpoint of statewide policy, this is the most strategic item in the formula. The determination of what this figure should be is related to the effects of State and local financing of all government. Using a larger percentage would in effect reduce the burden on the property tax and shift it to other tax bases. An analysis of the present balance of tax loads on the various bases, actual and potential, indicates that property is now relatively overburdened. This implies that the percentage of the cost of education carried by the State should be higher than the figure indicated here or that some appropriate step be taken in the financing of municipal government to bring about such adjustment. It would appear that the 42.5 per cent benchmark figure will make demands on State taxation appropriate for the present needs for correcting balance. It would appear that the further needed correction for the overburden of property should be obtained by an extension throughout the State of local taxing powers already in use by New York City and certain other counties and cities. For a further discussion of the implications for education, see Recommendation #7.

5. THE PROPOSED FORMULA FOR MEASUREMENT OF ABILITY

It is proposed that the *local* percentage share of each dollar budgeted for educational purposes in the current year shall be determined by the following formula:

$$\left.\begin{array}{l}\text{Local percentage share}\\ \text{of each dollar budgeted}\end{array}\right\} = \frac{\text{Local ability}}{\text{State average ability}} \times \begin{array}{r}57.5\%\ \text{but not}\\ \text{more than } 75\%\end{array}$$

The ability figures in the formula represent ability to support education in terms of the tax base made universally available to school districts — real property. Local ability is the full value of real property, as determined under the present plan, divided by the number of pupils weighted to take account of factors such as extreme population sparsity that cause the same level of education to cost more in some districts than in others.

It will be noted from this that a school district with the same ability as the State average would pay 57.5 per cent of its cost locally and would receive State aid amounting to 42.5 per cent. A community with a third of the State average ability would pay only 19.2 per cent locally and would receive 80.8 per cent from the State. A community with ability a third higher than the State average would pay 76.7 per cent locally and would receive 23.3 per cent from the State. However, in conformity with the present policy of allowing a minimum flat grant, it is recommended that the State share in no district shall be less than 25 per cent.

It is recommended further that the two components of the ability factor be corrected to reflect (a) extreme variation in the impact of municipal government on the local tax base and (b) variations in the cost of a like program of education sufficient to handicap districts in their efforts to provide adequate education.

Such corrections are of greater significance if the present foundation program is continued, since the remaining inequalities of ability to go beyond the foundation program are not meliorated as they would be under Recommendation #1.

Under the present plan the State has sought to get a refined way of equalizing burden for an always too limited foundation program. For expenditures beyond this, all the great variations in local ability come into play. Accordingly, every facet of the program for which a case could be made as affecting some districts more than others was a candidate for inclusion in the measures of cost of the foundation program, or, for the equivalent of this, special aid outside the foundation program. There was no other way to equalize the burden. Under the proposed program the State will participate in every dollar spent. Under this plan minor inequities in the measurement of ability will not have drastic impact on individual communities. Accordingly, it is to be expected that corrections to the cost or valuation figures for aspects of the program, the differential impact of which is, say, less than 10 per cent of the cost of the program (and having no more than 4 per cent effect on the State's share) will be rejected, since such corrections are well within the error inherent in the basic valuation figures.

If the new plan can divert energy from efforts to get minor adjustments in State aid over to local grappling with the great challenges to education in this day which, as determined locally in this plan, would be shared in by the State, it will strengthen the educational posture of local administration and public alike. This it should help do, since the cost of whatever the community decides to do will be shared in by the State in such a way that no community will have a fiscal barrier to advancement even if its ability measure may fall short of perfection. Educational advancement, not meticulous equity in a limited sphere, is the goal of the proposed plan.

a. *Correction for Impact of Municipal Government.* It is recommended that the valuation of taxable property of a school district used in computing local ability, but not State average ability, shall be reduced to offset the encroachment of municipal government costs on ability to support schools. The reduction shall apply in any school district in which the percentage of per capita local tax revenues for non-educational purposes (municipal, town, county and region) exceeds the State average outside of cities of over 125,000 population and the counties contiguous to such cities. Specifically, it is recommended that in such districts the true valuation used shall be reduced by a valuation reduction ratio (VRR) determined by use of this formula:

$$\text{VRR} = \text{The excess, if any, of M over .332}$$

in which M is the ratio of the per capita (resident weighted pupils) amount of local revenue for non-educational purposes to the sum of (1) this amount and (2) the average expenditure for education for the entire State. It is recommended further that the figures used shall be a five-year average, using the year 1959–60 for the first year, and then adding a year each year until the five-year basis evolves.

The application of this correction to valuation in any district will have the effect of reducing the ability figure used in determining the percentage of all expenditures to be carried by the State.

In districts making up the State outside of the great cities and their contiguous counties, the M in the formula is .332. For a district with this value of M, or less, there would be no correction.

For the six large cities and for a few districts in metropolitan areas, the value of M and the correction figures expressed as percentages are:

	M	VRR		M	VRR
New York City	64.2%	31.0%	Syracuse	55.3%	22.7%
Albany	59.2	26.4	Scarsdale	54.4	21.2
Rochester	58.9	25.9	Yongers	52.1	19.9
Lynbrook	56.8	23.6	Green Island	45.6	12.4
New Rochelle	56.4	23.2	Johnson City	41.0	7.8
Buffalo	55.6	22.4	Lancaster	39.3	6.1
White Plains	55.6	22.4	Williamsville	37.9	4.7

This is the proposed correction for the valuation of the district (the percentage of reduction in its tax base) to be used in determining its ability in the application of the proposed fiscal policy. Applied to New York City, it would mean that New York's valuation per pupil would drop from $29,308 to $20,252. New York City would be paid the following percentage of the allowed expenditures:

$$100\% - \frac{20{,}252}{25{,}300} \times 57.5\%, \text{ or } 100\% - 46\% = 54\%$$

instead of

$$100\% - \frac{29{,}308}{25{,}300} \times 57.5\%, \text{ or } 100\% - 67\% = 33\%$$

Implicit in the long-time practice of using the total property tax base of the district in computing ability to support education is the assumption that other demands on this tax base are fairly even throughout the State. . . . It appears to be clear that the cause of the squeak in the core cities of our metropolitan areas, and to a lesser degree in the suburban areas, may be identified more surely in the tax base than in the variations in the cost of a like program of education.

At its roots this is a problem of municipal government, not of educational government. The fundamental answer to this problem would be a major step forward in the revision of the financing of municipal government, bringing into the ken of the State's fiscal policy for municipal government the problems of metropolitan core districts and those of suburban areas and other population impacted areas to the extent that municipal costs bring them into the picture. When this is done, the destructive effects on the schools of a too limited tax base will be corrected and we might expect all districts to face up to their problems of supplying school buildings where needed, the maintenance of plants and the provision of an adequate complement of teachers — issues which at present seem to overwhelm those in control of policy in all out-sized cities.

But compared with financing education, the financing of municipal government on a State-local partnership is still a new field. Accordingly, until such time as the municipal house can be put in order it seems essential that the differential impact of municipal government, wherever it becomes disturbingly excessive, shall be taken into account in computing the ability of school districts.

b. *Correction of Pupil Measure for Cost Factors.* For determining the district's ability for the purpose of this plan, it is recommended that the weighted pupils used in determining the State average ability shall be the same as in the present law, with three modifications as specified below:

(1) Resident Attendance. Attendance counted shall be that of residents in the district attending public schools in the district or in other districts.

(2) Small Schools. For certain districts additional units shall be allowed on account of *actual attendance* in small schools.

For schools with elementary attendance of 350 or less, add 9; for such schools with elementary attendance of more than 350 but less than 377, add 1 for each 3 the attendance falls short of 377.

For schools with secondary attendance of 575 or less in grades 7–12, add 60; for those between 575 and 720, add 5 for each 12 the attendance falls below 720.

For schools with secondary attendance in the junior high school years only and with secondary attendance less than 288, add 30; for those with secondary attendance between 288 and 360, add 5 for each 24 the attendance falls below 360.

(3) Transportation. There shall be a further addition for transportation. The addition shall be that proportion of the total WADA *computed on attendance (not resident) pupils,* and supplemented by the small school correction, which the expenditure for transportation in the preceding year bore to the total current expenditures other than that for transportation.

Provision (2) is of major importance to rural schools and to enlarged city districts that have a considerable amount of sparsely settled territory.

The recommendation on transportation would mean that transportation in all districts would be taken into account in computing ability and would be reimbursed at the percentage rate set in the general formula. For those schools now receiving 100 per cent on transportation, this will not represent a reduction, since the inclusion of the equivalent weighted pupil units in determining ability will increase the percentage of State aid for all expenditures in an amount to make up for the reduction from 100 per cent of transportation. Under the present law, transportation costs are dealt with outside of the foundation program; also, they are not dealt with in the same manner for all districts.

6. Definition of Expenditures and Rate of Increase in Aid

In order to avoid State control or approval of local expenditures and to assure the prudential use of State monies it is proposed that (a) a limit be placed upon annual increases in per pupil expenditures in which the State will share, (b) municipal or municipally controlled school expenditures be excluded, and (c) increases in State support resulting from the new law be tapered.

a. *Limits on Current Year Shared Expenditure.* It is proposed that the maximum increase over the preceding year's expenditure allowed in any year shall not exceed $50 per weighted pupil. The effect of this is to require the district to carry fully for one year any increase in excess of $50 per weighted pupil unit. However, it is proposed that this limitation shall not apply to any district operating schools in excess of $50 below the minimum expenditure level to be specified by the Board of Regents in accordance with the equalization of educational opportunity provision.

b. *Exclusion of Certain Expenditures.* It is proposed that expenditures for schools not a part of the school budget and expenditures for municipal functions, even though they are a part of the school budget, shall not be acceptable for State sharing under this act.

> This would rule out expenditures for functions normally considered school functions but handled in a given district by the municipal government. To be subject to State sharing, it would be necessary to make them a school function. On the other hand, it would rule out school expenditures for functions normally municipal except where there is no municipal government with jurisdiction.

c. *Rate of Increase in State Aid.* It is recommended that districts entitled to receive aid under the new plan on account of expenditures already in being when this act is passed shall receive one-third of the increase in 1962–63, two-thirds in 1963–64 and the whole amount in 1964–65 and thereafter.

It is further proposed that this "⅓–⅔" rule apply also to increases of aid due to the adjustment proposed in Recommendation #5a.

This limitation is not proposed for expenditures in 1962–63 that represent an increase in expenditure per weighted pupil. Such expenditures would be subject only to the $50 limitation proposed in Recommendation #6a above.

7. Broadened Local Taxing Powers for Property Tax Relief

It is recommended that the efforts be continued to broaden local taxing powers for school support.

> The strength and effectiveness of local self-government in school affairs depend upon having sufficient taxing power to meet pressing problems without waiting for State action. The recommendations of this report will reallocate some of the burden as between the property tax and State tax bases. . . .

8. Fiscally Responsible School Government in Large Cities

It is proposed that, for any city with a population in excess of 125,000 to be eligible for the advantages of this act, arrangements approved by the Commissioner of Education must have been made to place full responsibility for educational affairs in the board of education, including arrangements for earmarking that proportion of revenues (1) raised by local taxation and (2) received for any or all purposes (other than for activities under the control of the board of education) from State and Federal governments which were expended for education in the last fiscal year next preceding January 1, 1961.

It is further recommended that such arrangements include earmarking for school district purposes a proportion of the total borrowing power of the city under the constitutional debt limit, which proportion shall approach as nearly as possible the proportion recommended for current revenues, but in no case shall it be less than 25 per cent of the borrowing capacity of the city under such limit.

It is further proposed that, on failure of any such city to honor the agreement in any year, State aid payable for municipal purposes be diverted to the school board in the amount required to make up the deficiency.

It is further proposed that the law prohibit the board of education of any such city from receiving grants from municipal authorities in excess of those provided by such earmarking.

> This provision envisions the disentangling of municipal and educational government in the big cities and the assurance that increased aid shall build up local tax leeway for schools and for freeing the overburdened municipal government from fiscal responsibility for schools. It presumes that the basic fiscal problem of the schools is a State problem, not a municipal problem, in these cities as in the remainder of the State.
>
> If it was allocating 32 per cent of its total revenues as herein defined for school district purposes, the city would be required to continue to do so. If it had a borrowing power of $44 million, a total debt subject to the limit of $12.0 million, and a debt for school district purposes of $2.0 million it would have to allocate at least 25 per cent of the $44 million for school district purposes.

9. Strengthening the Leadership and Fiscal Responsibility of the Board of Regents and of the State Education Department

There is urgent need for strengthening the leadership and responsibility of the State Education Department with respect to: (1) Assuring that children in no community shall be denied what the law presumes they shall have. (2) Assuring that the State fiscal policy operates in a way as wholesome for all the school districts in the State as the law envisions.

a. *Equalization of Educational Opportunity.* It is proposed that a required minimum level of operation be established for each year by the Board of Regents and that it be determined after a realistic analysis of those districts which now, for one reason or another, are operating schools below the average level of effort.

We usually think of the present system as an equalization law. At the time of its adoption in the middle 20's, the idea of assuring a minimum of education was properly emphasized. What was not foreseen at the time was that a system of financing, which required increases in State aid to all districts just to raise the minimum, might operate to divert attention from those districts which for one reason or another were not providing schooling of the quality essential for our time. And as a matter of fact, the law was never made strict enough actually to require the minimum presumed. The basic reason here is that the compliance permitted counting debt service as part of the minimum and the problem of building aid was never adequately dealt with in the law. This new proposal disentangles the concept of equalization of educational opportunity from the equalization of burden concept and at the same time removes the schoolhousing problem as a deterrent to advancement. Equalization of burden, all of it, is central in this new proposal but it is not subordinate to the minimum program idea. By the same token, the State's fiscal policy and the operation of the State Education Department in leadership in laggard districts can be pinpointed under this new plan.

Under the new plan there will be no question of the ability of any district to meet the minimum standards of support. The problem here will be for the State Education Department to help communities achieve a minimum of educational opportunity with as much concern as that agency has exercised so successfully over the years in the reorganization of school districts. In setting the minimum level of support, the State Board of Regents can thus be guided directly by the considerations of quality of the educational program and the concern of the communities in meeting them.

Achievable standards should be set and then provisions made to meet them. Our present practice of penalizing by withholding aid should be abandoned. In its place more drastic action should be taken to deal with misfeasance or malfeasance.

b. *Wholesome Operation of the Finance Program.* (1) It is proposed that the State Education Department be directed to make a continuous study of the operation of the new law.

(2) It is further recommended that the State Education Department and the Board of Regents as its policy body be charged with the responsibility of establishing policy for enhancing the wholesomeness of the operation of the State's school finance law based upon such studies within the range of principles established by law, so long as the changes in any factors in the formulas are general in their application and do not entail changes in the total State aid of more than 5 per cent.

This implies that the Board of Regents be empowered to modify the formula for determining the relative ability of districts or to adjust the formula to temper the effects of sudden change in valuation, population or other factors. They would be required to report annually to the legislature, governor and the people the actions taken and recommendations for legislative action where needed action falls beyond the regulatory powers of the Board.

(3) It also is recommended that the Board of Regents be directed to develop and enforce standards for minimum complements of professional staffing both as to numbers and qualifications appropriate to various expenditure levels or other controlling conditions.

A distinct advantage of the foundation program of support, as it has operated in this State, is its freedom from provisions tending to warp local decisions on such matters as numbers of teachers employed or the amounts to be spent on this or that educational function. Recently this policy of maintaining freedom for local boards has been encroached upon in the establishment of various special aids. With the operation of the proposed program, the restrictive character of special aids will disappear and, when and if additional special aids are adopted, they will tend to disappear in their effects because of the general operation of the plan. As proposed, the plan would have no effect on the policy of setting minimum salary schedules except that it would assure State participation in meeting this and other mandates.

There are certain other areas in which policy varies greatly in the State and where consideration may well be given to the setting of some prudential norms. Outstanding among these matters is the variation in the complement of professional employees provided for a given number of children. While there is no set ideal number for all communities, there would appear to be little question that districts with higher expenditure levels are spending on higher levels to no small degree because of the employment of a larger complement of professional workers. Certain districts, under pressures of low availability of funds even in the midst of wealth, particularly but not exclusively the large cities, have warped the balance between numbers and salaries to the disadvantage of the quality of their schools. The race against disaster in which understaffed school systems are now engaged in the treatment of pathological cases, in the creation of which the understaffed schools have had a part, can be corrected by the provision of staff and housing commensurate with the educational task they face today. The plan of financing proposed will remove any valid excuse for any school system lagging in either staff or buildings.

10. Study of Internal School Government Improvement

It is recommended that for the five-year period beginning July 1, 1962, there be appropriated the sum of $300,000 annually for use by the State Education Department on studies and (with the approval of the Board of Regents) for grants to large cities for experiments designed to improve the system of public participation in the development of local school policy by the decentralization of public responsibility over functions that can be controlled as satisfactorily or more satisfactorily by lay bodies made responsible for those functions in limited areas within the cities.

Both the work of the cooperative board considered as a prototype of the large city board of education and the work of the Bronx Park Community Project and other large city experiments in decentralization raise critical questions with respect to the effectiveness of the present system of school government in large cities.

Section C

MEASUREMENT OF LOCAL NEEDS AND RESOURCES

The two selections in this section offer further analysis of the assessment of local needs and resources. Only as these variables are accurately assessed can grants-in-aid serve rigorously the objective of equalization.

D. S. Lees and his associates argue the merits of percentage grants vs. fixed-units aid (i.e., subventions in Strayer-Haig form). The question turns on the practicability of finding a dollar expression of unit cost of local services that is applicable for the different kinds of communities that are likely to be found in a state.

In Selection 40, Burke deals with the measurement of local resources. He makes a strong case for the use of equalized property valuations. This is preferable, in his opinion, to the use of an income measure.

39

Percentage Versus Unit Grants

D. S. Lees

This masterful analysis was sponsored by the Institute of Municipal Treasurers and Accountants (Incorporated), England. The central government in that country has experimented considerably with both main types of aids.

The ideal grant would have the following characteristics: it would be simple, intelligible and equitable; it would encourage local economy in the use of public funds; it would leave a wide area of local autonomy in the administration of local finances; and it would enable central departments to control, in at least a general way, the standards of the services for which they were ultimately responsible. The ideal grant does not exist and cannot exist; it is not possible in practice to preserve all the characteristics together in their entirety and it may not be possible to preserve some of them at all. Just where the emphasis should lie is a matter of judgement. Throughout this study we shall maintain that "equity" should be the over-riding consideration. We shall do so because we think that equity is of paramount importance in principle and that, in practice, no arrangement that is manifestly inequitable can be in the best interest of local government or of the services which it provides. We shall see that equity may be in conflict in particular with economy.

The principle of equity can be divided into two parts.

1. *Equity as between Individual Local Authorities.* First, three basic facts can be stated.

(a) That local authorities have no discretion in the provision of many local services and only limited discretion in the minimum standards of service to be provided.

(b) That the expenditure per head of population required to attain these minimum standards differs from one local government area to another due

Adapted from *Local Expenditure and Exchequer Grants,* London, Institute of Municipal Treasurers and Accountants (Incorporated), 1956, pp. 3–7, 156–160, 168–177. Reproduced with permission.

to causes outside the control of local authorities — this we are calling the "needs" problem.

(c) That the rateable value per head of population available to meet this expenditure differs from one local government area to another — this we are calling the "resources" problem.

Stated generally, the present purpose of Exchequer grants is to enable and encourage local authorities to provide services at standards regarded as reasonable by Parliament and public opinion without undue strain on relative local finances. In other words, the grant system has the dual function of promoting the development of local services, and of equalizing as between areas the benefits and burdens arising from the provision of local services. The promotional function goes back to the beginnings of the grant system in the 1830's. The equalizing function, on the other hand, is of comparatively recent origin. . . . This is a reflection of the modern concern with equalization in general fiscal policy. Furthermore, from a financial standpoint, Exchequer grants may be regarded as subsidies to local authorities and it is a well-recognized principle in the equitable distribution of subsidies that they should discriminate in favour of those who, by some criterion, have the greatest need. It thus seems a reasonable generalization that more Exchequer funds should be directed to areas with low resources than to those with high ones and to areas with high needs than to those with low ones.[1]

2. *Equity as Between Local Authorities Collectively and the Central Government.* Here two issues are involved.

(a) Equity at any given time. At any given time, the total cost of services attracting grants will be divided in some proportion between the central

[1] These ideas, which today seem unexceptional, first found their full expression in Lord Balfour's Minority Report to the Royal Commission on Local Taxation (Final Report, Cmd. 638, 1901). "The conditions to be observed [in the distribution of Exchequer grants] would appear to be the varying circumstances of the different districts as regards, *first*, ability to raise local funds, and *secondly*, necessity for expenditure upon the services assisted. Having established criteria of these two conditions the grants should be distributed in such a way that most would be given to those districts which have the lowest ability and whose expenditure is necessarily high, and less to those with the greatest ability and less necessity for expenditure" (p. 74).

"Now the ability of any district to bear the burden [of expenditure] can best be measured by the value of the property subject to rates. I do not assert that this test is absolutely accurate as regards the ability of the individuals concerned, but it is by far the best measure of the ability of the district, i.e., of the local resources available to meet the burdens of local government" (p. 75).

"Even if two districts have the same number of inhabitants, yet the real and inevitable requirements in the way of local services and the cost of carrying out those services may vary considerably. To meet this consideration it is reasonable to take into account also the expenditure actually incurred . . . . Actual expenditure is the best test of the burden actually borne . . . and, therefore, while any application of this criterion should be carefully safeguarded, it cannot be wholly disregarded" (p. 76).

"While there is such extreme disparity in the local resources of different districts, it is hopeless to expect and impossible to insist upon uniform efficiency in the administration of national services, unless the State subventions can be used as a means of equalization and a lever for securing improvement" (p. 85).

government and local authorities. It is impossible to say *a priori* what an equitable proportion should be, and in practice the proportion differs from service to service and from time to time. For example, at the present time the fire service grant is 25 per cent, the police grant 50 per cent and the education main grant almost 60 per cent. . . .

(b) Equity over a period of time. Here it is possible to be more definite. Assuming the proportion of the total cost of a service borne by the Exchequer to be equitable, that proportion should be maintained from year to year as the cost of the service increases through causes outside the control of local authorities. These causes may be two-fold. First, local authorities may be obliged to increase the scope and/or quality of services. If grants do not rise in proportion to the additional expenditure required, then self-evidently the financial burden on local authorities will rise more than proportionately. Secondly, the value of money may fall. Total expenditure will rise (unless the scope and/or quality of services are reduced) and the local financial burden will show a disproportionate increase unless grants rise as the value of money falls. The inequity of keeping grants fixed in amount as prices rise is seen more clearly if we suppose that prices are stable and the money value of grants is reduced. In all essentials the two situations are the same.

. . . .

PERCENTAGE GRANTS

The English grant system is predominantly a percentage grant system. The reason for this is to be found in the purpose of grants. Since their inception in 1835 the primary purpose of Exchequer grants to local authorities has been to initiate and to improve local services. As we hope to make apparent in the following discussion, this purpose has favoured specific rather than general grants and percentage rather than unit grants. It is upon the latter that we shall wish to lay particular stress.

We shall state briefly the arguments for and against the percentage grant system and examine the background, content and validity of criticisms commonly made of it.

The percentage grant has the following advantages:

(a) It is simple and intelligible.

(b) It is efficient in starting a service and in dealing with new developments within a service.

(c) It maintains what we have called "equity over time." This has been of special importance since 1945, with a rapidly rising price-level and substantial improvements in the quality of many services.

(d) It is equitable as between authorities in that it reduces absolute differences in the *necessary* costs of providing services. For example, if authority A needs to spend £105 per unit of service and authority B £95 per unit, a percentage grant at a rate of 50 per cent will reduce the absolute difference of £10 to £5. To anticipate later discussion, a 50 per cent unit grant based on an average cost of £100 would leave the absolute difference in unit costs the same and the proportionate difference larger.

(e) It enables and encourages the more progressive authorities to improve standards of service (that is, to increase the number of units of service or to increase unit costs) without undue impositions on local rates.

(f) It provides scope for different methods of tackling problems. Opinions differ, for example, on whether boarding out or residential homes is the better method of child care. The latter is more expensive than the former and a percentage grant reduces the difference in cost for those authorities who prefer it.

(g) It deals automatically with expenditure on connected services. For example, there is an intimate connection between expenditure on domestic help, on the one hand, and expenditure on welfare of old people, child care and maternity cases, on the other. Again, local authorities are encouraged to choose the method which, in their view, is the most desirable, and the most desirable method is not unfailingly the cheapest.

(h) It does not require standardized forms of accounts or uniformity in the allocation of expenditure. On the former in particular there are widely differing opinions on the correct form, and discrepancies in the allocation of expenditure to the various heads are familiar enough.

The main arguments against the percentage grant are twofold:

(a) It is disequalizing as between local government areas in that it enables authorities with high resources to take more advantage of the inducement to spend given by percentage grants than authorities with low resources. . . .

(b) It provides insufficient incentive to economical spending; it is responsive to *any* increase in expenditure, whether that increase is necessary or not. If an authority is economical and reduces its expenditure, its grant automatically falls. The percentage grant does reduce cost differences between local government areas but it does not differentiate between those costs which are necessary and those which are not. In short, the percentage grant system contains no automatic assurance of economy. In order to ensure the economical use of Exchequer funds, central departments are compelled to supervise local expenditure in some detail. Local autonomy is thereby endangered. This is the core of the "control/economy" problem.

Now it is pointless to ask whether percentage grants encourage "extravagance" by local authorities, . . . for we have no idea how much specific operations by local authorities *ought* to cost, and despite the fact that the controversy over "extravagance" has continued since the early 1920's, very little is now known about "necessary" or "unavoidable" costs. Yet it is not until such information is available that discussion of "extravagance" can be meaningful, far less fruitful. All we know at present is that local authorities spend as they do and that some spend more than others.

Nor is it possible to identify "extravagance" even in a limited way by instancing authorities with high unit costs. High costs may be due to peculiar local circumstances. Certain sparsity conditions, as we have seen, make small classes unavoidable; teacher/pupil ratios are high and thus costs per pupil are high. Secondly, high costs may be due to high standards of service. Merthyr Tydfil, for example, has small classes as a matter of policy and its costs per pupil are akin to those in sparsity counties. This could be deemed "extravagance" only (a) if classes were smaller than the Ministry of Education thought necessary and (b) if, at this high standard of service, Merthyr were inefficient in its administration. The former case does not apply as no minimum size of class has been fixed by the Ministry. The Ministry is exhorting authorities to reduce the size of classes and this Merthyr has done with spectacular success and at no negligible cost to its rates. It is progress of this kind that the percentage grant is particularly apt in assisting. About the latter case — of inefficiency — we know nothing at all.

The point about high costs due to high standards of service is an important one. Economical spending is not the same thing as low spending; economy means an absence of waste, the avoidance of unnecessary expenditure. Thus if an authority is supplying a service at a standard above the average, and is doing so at a minimum cost, that part of its expenditure above the average is unnecessary only if the high standard of service itself is unnecessary. It would indeed be possible, even if in practice difficult, for central departments to define some average standard of service and to say to local authorities "whatever you provide in excess of that standard will be financed entirely from local rates." It could be done but it is highly unfamiliar doctrine and the reason is not far to seek. The scope and quality of grant-aided local services have increased persistently in the present century and the aim of official policy is to increase them still further. But the rate of increase among local authorities is not even; some local authorities are less willing, and, for various reasons, less able to raise their standards than others. The standards that official policy wishes to achieve are set by the authorities who progress quickly and not by those who lag behind. Given the aims of official policy, it would be the height of folly and inconsistency to penalize the authorities that are achieving the aims most successfully.

It is a comment on, rather than a criticism of, percentage grants that they are promotional. If official policy is to raise standards, then percentage grants are an admirably appropriate form of financial assistance. But the issue here is not that of percentage versus unit grants. If — and this is a large "if" — central departments could define for each local government area the scale of unit costs necessary to provide services at the corresponding scale of standards, they could pay an amount of grant per unit according to the standard of service actually being provided. Arranged in this way, unit grants would be as promotional and as capable of furthering the purposes of official policy as percentage grants. The critical difficulty is that of ascertaining the *necessary* unit costs for each local authority.

. . . .

With percentage grants, local authorities have to meet a proportion of any increase in expenditure. The crucial question is at what point this proportion becomes a real incentive to economy. The closer the proportion to 100 per cent, the greater the incentive to economy; the closer the proportion to zero, the greater the incentive to spend. It is impossible to lay down any critical proportion *a priori*, but a permissible generalization might be that as long as local authorities have to meet at least half of any increase in expenditure, there is sufficient incentive for them to be careful in their spending. . . .

. . . Conditions since 1945 have not been normal. Education expenditure is by far the largest item in local budgets and it has increased rapidly since 1945. Here the *absolute* amount left to be financed from rates, rather than the proportion, has provided a firm assurance of careful spending. The chief cause of the absolute increase has been a 50 per cent rise in the general price level, reinforced by expansion in the quantum of service and improvement in quality. Thus it could be argued that it is the pronounced degree of inflation that has ensured economy with the 60 per cent rate of grant. If the government should stabilize the price level for any longish period, pressure on local finances will be relaxed and the need to introduce some other safeguard may arise. . . .

Unit Grants

The over-riding claim made for unit grants is that they ensure economical spending by local authorities. The general notion is that a unit cost is determined for each local authority; the unit cost may be the same for all authorities or it may be adjusted, for reasons we shall discuss, to suit the circumstances of individual authorities, or groups of authorities. However that may be, grant is paid as so much per unit, say, 50 per cent of the unit cost that has been determined. The total grant of an authority then becomes the amount of grant per unit multiplied by the number of units.

The incentive to local economy is self-evident. If an authority spends more than its determined unit cost, the excess falls entirely on local rates and not, as with a percentage grant, partly on the Exchequer. If an authority spends less than its determined unit cost, the saving accrues entirely to the local authority and not, as with a percentage grant, partly to the Exchequer. Put another way, expenditure above the unit cost means a rate of grant of less than 50 per cent and expenditure below the unit cost a rate of grant of more than 50 per cent, whereas, with a percentage grant, the percentage remains a constant 50 per cent no matter what the level of expenditure. Since economical spending is assured by the form of the grant, central departments have less need to scrutinize local expenditure in detail or to make inquiries about it.

We have seen that, if the value of the units is adjusted year by year, departments will have at least as much need to scrutinize and inquire at the estimates stage with unit grants as with percentage grants, and possibly more. The Exchequer is required to pay grant equal to a certain percentage of all local expenditure on a service and there is no reason to suppose that it will be less concerned about the total amount of grant if it is distributed on the basis of units rather than on the basis of expenditure. Scrutiny and inquiry are likely to be less at the grant claim stage with unit than with percentage grants, but our evidence is that the scope for reducing inquiries at this stage by substituting unit for percentage grants is negligible.

Unit grants do not share many of the important advantages, listed in the previous chapter, which accrue automatically to percentage grants. These advantages will be illustrated briefly in relation to unit grants.

Advantage (a). Whether the unit grant is simple and intelligible depends upon the variations in unit costs between local government areas, factors causing these variations and the account that is taken of these factors in fixing the individual or group units. The more diverse the variations and the more complex and obscure the causal factors, the less simple and intelligible (to all but the experts fixing the unit costs) the grant becomes.

Advantage (b). An important limitation of unit grants is their impotence in starting a new service or new development within a service. The reason is that, in these circumstances, "it is unlikely that the costs can be estimated or forecast with any degree of accuracy — the cost per unit of service performed or demanded is likely to vary very widely between authorities, it may fluctuate a good deal from year to year and is likely to be rising at an unforecastable rate."[2] This is obviously significant, for example, for the education service, where the degree of experimentation at present is high and very variedly spread among authorities. Although this is a service in which the present rate of grant, on a percentage basis, may be thought too high of itself to ensure economical spending, this consideration alone would be sufficient to rule out the replacement of the present percentage grant by a unit grant.

Advantages (f) and (g) can be subsumed here. As long as local authorities are allowed discretion by central departments to deal with problems in a variety of ways, the scope for the operation of unit grants will be small, for there can be no uniformity of costs where there is no uniformity of method. Under local health legislation, in particular, local authorities are left with a wide measure of discretion in the ways in which (and the extent to which)

[2] Chester, *Central and Local Government*, p. 214.

they perform their duties. For unit grants to be feasible, there must be close departmental control over local methods. This is a curious outcome of a type of grant which, it is claimed, will gain local authorities more freedom from central control.

. . . .

A unit grant will share advantage (c) only if the value of the unit is adjusted from year to year. Units may be difficult to fix in the first place and in time of inflation strains on the central budget could be relieved simply by a refusal to revise the value of the units. If the units are adjusted from year to year, there will almost inevitably be a time-lag between the rise in expenditure and the rise in the unit value of grants, due simply to the problem of ascertaining the value of the units in any particular year. . . .

A unit grant will share advantage (e) only if it is finely attuned to the differing standards of local authorities. This will be difficult in practice, both because a "standard of service" is an ambiguous concept and because the minimum expenditure relating to a particular standard of service in a particular local government area is extraordinarily hard to define. To the best of our knowledge, it has never been attempted, far less achieved.

Advantage (h). To determine what unit costs actually are requires standardized forms of accounts, standardized statistical returns and uniformity in allocation of expenditure. These requirements are not met at present. Until they are, any unit grant system will suffer from the sheer lack of primary statistical data.

Finally, a unit grant will share advantage (d) only if it is finely attuned to local conditions to take account of the differences in necessary costs. We are using the term "necessary costs" to mean those costs which, under the most efficient administration, are necessary to achieve any given standard of service.

This is the most important problem in any unit grant system — to measure whatever unit is chosen so as to make an equitable contribution to the expenditure of local authorities. This means in particular making full allowance for differences in necessary costs, for the central idea of unit grants is that they ensure that local authorities will incur the lowest expenditure consistent with the provision of services at some standard. Now it is agreed on all sides that necessary costs differ as between authorities so that, even if all authorities had the same standards of service and were all equally efficient in administration, this fact would cause their unit costs to differ. Official opinions on these differing costs, and comments of our own, will be given in a moment. But first it is both possible and necessary to state that a unit grant based upon a simple average of the expenditure of all local authorities is unacceptable. It is unacceptable because it would be highly inequitable as between individual authorities and because its chief purpose — that of ensuring economy — would be achieved in a haphazard way, if it were achieved at all. It would be inequitable because high-cost authorities would be penalized for reasons outside their control. They would have ample incentive to spend economically and would be able to maintain an average standard of expenditure only by levying above-average rate poundages. In other words, the rate of grant on their expenditure would be less than the average. Low-cost authorities, on the other hand, would receive an unwarranted bonus — they would be rewarded for reasons outside their control. They would now be able to achieve average standards of service while levying below-average rate poundages. The additional grant would be in the nature of a free gift, to be spent or used to lower rate poundages as the authorities thought fit. In other words, their rate of grant on expenditure would be above the average. It is by no means clear that, for all authorities taken together, the cause of economy would be furthered. Pressure to economize would be strengthened for high-cost authorities and weakened for low-cost authorities. The former would tend to spend less freely and the latter more freely. If the latter spent their bonus within the grant-aided service, *actual* costs would tend towards equality as standards of service between the two groups diverged. But there would be no need to spend the bonus within the service for which it was granted; it could in effect be spent to improve purely local, non grant-aided services. The additional grant then, far from tending to diminish as unit costs converged, would be a perpetual gift for general use in the locality. Overall, more and not less Exchequer money may be spent under this than under a percentage grant arrangement, for a percentage grant cuts the impositions of high costs and the bonuses of low costs by the percentage element in the grant. Here, at least, the principles of equity and economy are not in conflict.

. . . .

In its Costing Statistics of Pupils (1950), the Ministry of Education said: "The circumstances which determine the cost per pupil differ widely from one area to another, and no experienced reader will be likely to fall into the error of supposing that it is possible without knowledge of those circumstances to deduce a standard figure of cost above which any expenditure should be regarded as excessive and below which it should be regarded as inadequate. It is impossible that the tables should themselves bring out the special causes which operate in individual areas to make expenditure comparatively high or comparatively low."

. . . .

In 1922 the Board of Education said: "the search for a standard expenditure per child is unavailing because of the great range of variations in the necessary cost as between one area and another."[3]

[3] Memorandum submitted to the Committee on Exchequer Grants, Cmd. 2571, 1926, p. 9.

The Committee on Local Taxation (1914) said: "Apart from the difficulty of finding suitable units the [unit grant] system is open to the objection that the expenditure per unit depends upon many factors besides the ability of the district, and that it varies from locality to locality within very wide limits. The result is that an average is of very little use, and would be as much too large in one case as too small in others; while a series of units, as has been suggested, applicable to different sets of localities, would involve endless difficulties of inquiry and classification, and would probably in the end produce rather an appearance than a reality of fairness."[4]

. . . .

While one need not accept these views as correct, they should at least dispel facile notions about the use of average and standard expenditure. But the idea of a standard, as of an average, expenditure dies hard.

[4] Report, p. 22.

40

Measurement of Taxpaying Ability

Arvid J. Burke

Dr. Burke, Director of Studies, New York State Teachers Association, holds a substantial reputation for his writings on school finance. Some of his most powerful arguments have been brought to bear on the question of the measurement of local ability.

The theory of equalization in public school finance requires a measure both of fiscal need and fiscal capacity. In a plan involving central control, the objective is to measure state or local ability to finance a specified program or level of service. In a plan based upon both decentralized control and operation, the aim is to determine ability to provide a specified level of support for the budget of the operating unit.

FUNDAMENTAL PROBLEMS

Just as it is impossible in central finance to do more than approximate local fiscal needs, so it is impossible to determine precisely the fiscal ability of states or local units. Too frequently it is assumed that there is a general type of taxpaying ability, such as income, which can be measured for purposes of financial equalization. If there is a definable general ability to pay taxes, it cannot be measured. Ability to pay taxes involves physical, psychological, and other factors which are difficult to define. Indeed, the budgetary process and the purposes of central finance impose conditions upon a satisfactory measure of local taxpaying ability that go beyond considerations of measurement of ability to pay taxes alone. For purposes of central finance, state or local taxpaying ability has to be defined in specific terms and to be administratively possible. Often these necessary practical approaches to the problem are confused with ascertaining the general fiscal ability of units of government.

State policy in public school finance has come to depend increasingly upon the measurement of local taxpaying ability. The ability measure is used not only for purposes of equalizing support but also for distributing general aid or sharing state-collected taxes. The latter results from using a local share of the cost of the equalization program well below that necessary for equalization purposes. The "state and local partnership" concept of state support for schools almost always uses the equalization program or foundation program for purposes of sharing state-collected taxes with all local units. To the extent that such formulae use a tax rate for local support of the program below that necessary for complete local support of the program in the well-organized and most-able local units, general aid is distributed within the formula in proportion to local ability. The more-able localities receive more general aid per unit than those with average or below-average ability.

It is possible that some states have placed too much confidence upon imperfect measures of local fiscal capacity in combining equalization aid and general aid in the same formula. It is possible that sharing state taxes on a per capita basis would involve much less inequity in some states. Although it is necessary to have an adequate equalization program no matter how crude the measure of local ability, the errors of measurement can be minimized in such cases by limiting the equalization formula to local units where the general aid, plus a reasonably high local share for equalization, will not produce the level of support made possible by the formula.

States which have developed economic indexes of local ability cannot be certain as to what they are measuring by such indexes. These indexes are no substitute for accurate estimates of the yield of a specific local tax system with uniform rates. Although property valuation is not a perfect measure, it can be made to meet more criteria than economic indexes or income as a measure of local ability.

. . . .

Property Taxation as a Measure

For many decades the only tax generally authorized for local support of schools was some form of property taxation. In most states this condition still exists. Thus, measures of local taxpaying ability in equalization formulae usually have been limited to the actual or hypothetical yield of a specified property tax. Although the measures always have not been expressed as a property-tax rate, the effect of other measures based upon property valuation alone are the same. Techniques have been developed for computing the yield of such a tax for central-finance purposes. The most advanced of these, if utilized, could improve vastly the extent to which the property-tax base conforms to the criteria of a satisfactory measure of local taxpaying ability.

The use of these techniques to produce a result which would conform to the demands of the criteria to the fullest possible extent depends largely upon the concept of the property tax. If the tax is conceived as a real-property tax, the problems are not insurmountable. If it is defined as a general-property tax, it is practically impossible to overcome the difficulties. It is virtually impractical to assess the thousands of kinds of personal property and intangible property rights which the economy makes possible. This precludes any practical way of correcting for differences in the assessment of personal property among local units. Even if localities are authorized to levy personal-property taxes or general-property taxes, the measurement of relative yield of specified rate of property tax should be limited to the real-property component of the property-tax base.

. . . .

Advantages. The use of good equalized (full) valuation of real property to compute the hypothetical yield of a specified tax rate in a local unit probably conforms to more of the criteria of a satisfactory measure than any other that has been used. Nevertheless, it is not a perfect device.

Among the advantages of this measure are these. It is possible to obtain the data every year in small states and in states with county assessments and close state coöperation in fixing the assessed valuations. In other states the data could be kept within two to five years of being current. The data can be assigned to local school units. The tax is one which is authorized for all local units. It reflects a source of tax revenues which all can reach. Data can be obtained for all local units, no matter how small they may be. The full or equalized valuation cannot be manipulated by the local unit to gain an advantage. It is one of the most stable of measures available, and the use of a moving average after each periodic revision would lend additional stability to the measure. The tax is one which people have come to accept. If opportunities are provided for local units to be heard on proposed revisions of the equalized valuations, and if they can secure justifiable changes in the proposed valuations based upon fact, confidence in the measure is attainable.

Limitations. The major criticisms of property-tax yields as a measure of local ability to support an equalization program are directed at the one criterion, equity. These criticisms begin with the premise that property taxes must be paid out of income earned from the property or income derived from other sources, or from credit. This is followed by illustrations of varying income yields per thousand dollars of valuation of various economic classes of property. The effects of the tax upon individual homeowners of varying income status, such as the retired on fixed incomes, are stressed. Where rent controls operate to hold down the value of rental properties, the favorable status of tenants relative to homeowners in a period of rising incomes is used to clinch the inequity criticisms.

The underlying assumption of many of the criticisms of the property-tax measure on grounds of inequity is that another measure is available or could be devised to correct these inequities. . . . No other measure would meet the other criteria as well as the property-tax base. The equity of the property tax might be increased by better administration and by economic classification of property. It might also be increased by homestead exemptions for the retired, but this hardly seems necessary when the liberal exemptions for the retired under income-tax laws are considered. It is possible that equity could be increased, especially where rent controls exist, by supplementing the property-tax base by nonproperty-tax yields.

The property-tax measure merely indicates what a given tax rate will yield relatively among various local units. This does not necessarily indicate equity or payment according to ability. There is no way of determining to what extent a given tax rate per thousand represents in equal sacrifices or equal taxpaying ability in an economic or individual-taxpayer sense. To do this would require an analysis of the economics of each class of property on the tax rolls of ever taxing jurisdiction and a study of the financial status of all taxpayers. Both of these are impossible of application. Whatever equity can be achieved must be secured through improving the legal concept of the tax and improving its administration.

Another problem is the selecting of the tax rate to be used in the formula. Here the key considerations are local tax leeway, the relative emphasis upon equalization, the extent to which state-collected nonproperty taxes are to be used to supplement the property-tax base, and state and local sharing of the cost of the equalization program. Local leeway is necessary for local initiative and adjusting to local cost variables which cannot be accurately determined in the measures of need. It is affected not only by local taxing powers for schools but also by the extent to which the property tax is used by other units of government. The degree of equalization emphasis in the formula is determined by how high the rate is. If it is set at a level which would support the equalization program entirely from local funds in the large fiscally able units, the formula provides equalization aid only. If it is set so low that such able units receive substantial aid from the state, there is considerable general aid in the formula apportioned according to valuation per pupil. This means that the state is providing local nonproperty taxes to supplement the property-tax base instead of granting such powers to the local units. No matter what rate is fixed, it determines what proportion of the cost of the program the state will pay.

. . . .

Income as a Measure

Measurement of income, in theory at least, would seem to be the nearest approach that could be made to the determination of state or local taxpaying ability. Unfortunately, income is a much more elusive thing than is generally realized. If it could be measured for a state or local unit, its usefulness as an index of ability would be very limited, for reasons explained below.

Defining Income. The discussion of taxable capacity revealed that income may be monetary or nonmonetary. A person with high nonmonetary income and low monetary income will be better able to pay local taxes than another person with equivalent income but all monetary. The latter is harder hit by the federal and state tax system. Most persons do not know what their income is because they do not keep accurate records of income from all sources whether received in cash, in kind, or credited to their accounts, or of the expenses incurred in producing or earning the income or the losses incurred which deplete the income.

If the recipients themselves do not know what their income really is, what is the basis for the figures on income of individuals which we have? They come from three sources: (1) census reporting by persons who do not know or, if they did, would not be inclined to reveal; (2) income-tax reporting which is incomplete, largely unaudited, and subject to all of the errors that result from lack of knowledge and accounting, unintentional or planned evasion, and ability to afford avoidance; and (3) estimates of income at source accompanied by guesses or approximations as to where the estimated income should be allocated according to residence of individuals. It would take a high level of individual accounting to trace all wages, nonmonetary benefits, salaries, pensions, annuities, fees, service charges, profits, interest, dividends, royalties, rents, credits, capital gains, and other forms of income actually paid or accruing to each individual according to his residence.

Income payments to individuals or personal income according to residence, even if either could be determined for states and local units, would account for only part of the income out of which any local tax is paid. There also are corporate income, partnership income, institutional income, trusts, and a variety of forms of income which may not be distributed, or may only be partially distributed, to individuals. The tax systems of a local unit or a state may reach income of residents of another unit or state.

The accounting of all income payments to individuals by residence and all other forms of income by situs would hardly be worth the effort, if it could be done, for measuring state or local taxpaying ability. As indicated earlier, income figures without a great deal of information on such matters as dependency load, health, creditor and debtor status, nonmonetary income, incidence of federal taxes, climatic demands upon living standards and costs, habits of spending and saving, and many other factors do not reveal taxable capacity.

In an economic sense income has to be measured in terms of the goods and services which can be obtained with it. This is real income. It is not just a matter of money or cash in any one year. It involves the price level in the particular market. Equivalent goods or services may be priced higher in high-income markets than in low-income markets. The income of certain persons may vary from year to year. Past low-income periods and future prospects for income have to be averaged to get at real income. This involves past obligations, debts, and losses as well as future credits or gains. Although not received as cash income, assets may appreciate or depreciate in value. This affects credit or money value of assets if placed upon the market.

The income figures generally available for states or counties are estimates of personal income or income payments to individuals. Insofar as payrolls are reported for unemployment insurance or social security (both have upper limits), the payroll segment is fairly good. How accurately payrolls are assigned to state or county of residence is uncertain. Arbitrary allocators such as census data, which soon get out of date, have to be used. Farm income is estimated, and the value of food produced and consumed on the farm is most uncertain. State totals are based upon arbitrary allocations. Local totals involve a still further arbitrary allocation of the data. The income of the self-employed is estimated. The estimates of income from business activity are probably nothing but approximations. Allocation by residence is especially difficult as it relates to profits, dividends, interest, royalties, and similar items.

Limitations. The first difficulty encountered in using income in a measure of taxpaying ability is securing accurate data by residence or situs. Census reporting is handicapped by lack of information by the person reporting, reluctance to reveal true income if known, and the necessity of using sampling. The data obtained are grossly underestimated or understated, and they are out of date for long periods. Data are lacking on the many important factors, such as nonmonetary income and price level essential for translating the data into a measure of taxpaying ability for individuals. The data do not reveal other forms of taxable income which the state or local tax system can reach.

The only type of income data that could be obtained for all local units of government other than census-type data is that derived from income-tax returns. The purpose of these returns is not to obtain a report on the income of all individuals, but to collect as much tax as possible with the funds made available for collecting the tax. The federal income-tax returns are the only ones which could be obtained for all local units, assuming the forms were changed to reveal residence by local school units. These are required only from those subject to the tax, but the extent to which all such persons file depends upon the effectiveness of enforcement.

Income-tax compliance requires a high degree of literacy and maturity. The yield of the tax depends more upon voluntary compliance and morality than upon ability to enforce the tax at a reasonable collection cost. Self-reporting, ease of evasion, ability to avoid, the limitations of auditing, the high cost of field checking, and the cost of enforcement all limit the usefulness of income-tax returns as a true indication of income. There are striking differences between certain kinds of income as obtained from source data and as obtained from income-tax returns. Part of these differences result from the lack of proper net-income accounting by most individuals. Part result from the very nature of the tax and the impossibility of enforcing it at a reasonable cost. Tax returns have very little value in revealing nonmonetary income.

Income as reported and estimated from source may have value in assessing trends, but it has very little value in measuring differences among states and local units. Although better data on payrolls are becoming available, such data are not complete and they do not reveal residence of the recipients. The devices used to allocate payroll data according to residence are crude even when applied to states; they are subject to wide margins of error when applied to local units. Estimates of farm income, self-employed income, part-time-job income, casual income such as taking in boarders or selling flowers, and income in kind are subject to wider margins of error particularly as applied to individual states and localities. They require accurate accounting and reporting which does not exist. Attempts to allocate estimated rents, royalties, interest, dividends, and profits to residents in individual states are highly questionable as to their accuracy.

Total income of a unit of government, even if it could be obtained, would not of itself indicate the taxpaying capacity of a state or local unit. The distribution of the income among the taxpayers would be even more important — the relative proportions of low incomes, average incomes, and very high incomes. Two units with the same per capita income might have very different taxpaying ability, depending upon the distribution of income. Another crucial factor in considering states is net income after federal taxes. This not only involves the federal income tax but the incidence of other federal taxes. In applying income on the local level, the incidence of both federal and state taxes has to be considered.

Income data do not necessarily indicate the taxpaying capacity of a local unit. Few local units have power to tax any income at all. None have the power to levy taxes which would reach the higher levels of income. On the other hand, both states and local units can levy taxes which have to be paid out of the income of nonresidents.

The degree of equity that can be achieved through income taxation has been exaggerated greatly. Aside from the problems of evasion (intentional and unintentional) and avoidance by those who can afford it, there are many other sources of inequity. Many of these are due to imperfections of law, such as inequities among occupational groups as to allowable deductions of expenses incurred in earning the income. A factory or an office worker who must drive twenty miles one way to work gets no allowance for transportation, but a salesman with equal income has considerable leeway in writing off the expense of automobile ownership.

The degree of equity that can be achieved by using income as a measure of relative taxpaying ability is equally misunderstood. Persons with highly fluctuating incomes must average these to maintain a basic standard of living. The standard of living that must be maintained under varying natural or climatic conditions varies. There are geographic differences in nonmonetary income. These factors, together with differences in the price level of like goods in different markets, result in the same money income representing different amounts of real income and taxable capacity. The economics of earned income and unearned income are quite different. Money income earned currently may reduce future prospects for income as a result of occupational disease, impaired health, loss of occupational mobility, or effects upon mental outlook resulting from earning that income.

The use of income as the sole measure of relative fiscal capacity assumes that all production of goods and services enters the free market. This ignores the family, the farm, the neighborhood, and other institutions where goods and services are produced without any monetary exchange. Attempts to correct this deficiency in income data by estimation are handicapped by lack of data for making good approximations.

Income data have an appearance of scientific accuracy which is dispelled when the assumptions, sources of data, and methodology underlying the figures are examined. If regarded as the best approximations which can be had with the data available, they are useful statistics. As a measure of relative taxpaying ability, they have only two assets — simplicity and objectivity. The estimates cannot be manipulated locally. If they are acceptable as a measure of relative ability, it is because the concept of income is not fully understood. Although income is the most unstable of any measures available, this can be overcome to some extent by averaging over a period of time.

PART FIVE

The Problem of Productivity in Education

Under the logic of economics a more efficient scheme of production is always preferred to a less efficient one. This statement applies with as much force to the management of educational expenditures as it does to the management of an industrial operation. Recognition of the efficiency criterion does not mean that education will necessarily become a mass production affair or that broad objectives, such as character development, will be slighted. If the goal of education is to assist in the development of the child in accordance with his particular abilities and aptitudes, then this is a matter for educational philosophers to state. It is within the prerogative of educational policy makers to define "development of the individual" as broadly as they wish. Once the goals of the educational establishment are set, efficiency considerations should then — but only then — become the ruling criteria for the management of resources in our school systems.

Until the last few years the techniques of education appeared to be subject to gradual change only. Textbooks were more attractively printed, improvements were made in the lighting and ventilation of classrooms, and the standards of teacher training were raised. These changes occurred slowly and did not seem to represent sharp departures in the conventional concepts of the process of education. Now, we hear much of a "technological revolution" in the schools. New arrangements in the grouping of staff and students are employed; various types of equipment (language laboratories, teaching machines, television, etc.) are brought into play; and school architecture is modified to accommodate the changes in staffing patterns and in the use of equipment. No doubt these new practices which are already in use in some school systems will spread across the land. It is hard at this time to say anything about the pace at which yet other innovations will appear over the horizon.

All of this leads to the following conclusion. The concern about quality of education in our country in the postwar period has been reflected both in an increase in the amount of resources placed at the disposal of school systems and in an examination of the processes of instruction. That examination has been directed to the end that a higher volume of educational output is obtained from any given volume of resources. It is eminently fitting that both routes to higher-quality education — a greater volume of inputs and a search for a more efficient use of the inputs available — have been taken.

Inevitably, the changes in educational technology that we are beginning to see about us will have an impact on the career patterns of teachers and on the schemes of remuneration under which their services are obtained. It is very likely that there will be a greater degree of specialization in the teacher's role. Inevitably, the changes will lead to a refinement of the budgetary process in school systems, with greater emphasis being placed on various types of program and performance budgeting. In turn, these tools depend on the more fruitful employment of cost accounting in education.

There are basic difficulties in the rationalization of educational processes. First, it is hard to measure inputs in quantitative terms that are meaningful. For example, it is an uncertain task to try to relate an increment in salary expenditures to an increment in quality of labor input. One can speak of the higher levels of training and experience possessed by newly hired teachers in a particular district, but how well such measures can predict actual classroom performance is not clearly established. Second, as is well known, it is extremely difficult to measure educational outputs — or even to agree on what the relevant outputs are. Third, there is the further problem of how to relate specific changes in outputs (assuming that they can be measured) to specific changes in the cluster of inputs. It is in recognition of such difficulties that the federal government has undertaken to subsidize research in the technology of education.

Education has multiple goals. These goals are defined at the present time with varying degrees of precision. In pursuit of its goals, the educational establishment yields multiple products. Multiple variable inputs are employed in what are actually a whole series of processes. Baldly stated, the efficiency criteria consist of (1) cost minimization in specific processes, (2) the weighing of alternative processes to choose the one of lowest cost to yield particular products, and (3) the weighing of alternative products to choose the set of lowest cost to meet the goals of the establishment. This is to be done while taking account of short-run constraints in productive capacity. It is a formidable problem.

PART FIVE • THE PROBLEM OF PRODUCTIVITY IN EDUCATION

Section A

THE PROBLEM STATED

Writing in 1957, Johnson (Selection 41) posed a series of "economist's questions" about the management of the educational enterprise. He stressed the importance of weighing carefully the alternative use of scarce resources to accomplish the given ends of school systems. As shown in the later article by Ruark (Selection 42), it is no longer true that the educator is bound by time-honored conventional practices. Indeed, there is no dearth of new techniques to be evaluated by school districts. If school administrators could be admonished to choose among alternatives in the use of resources in 1957, it can only be said that the range of alternatives has now been considerably broadened.

In Selection 43, Kershaw and McKean present their scheme, based upon "systems analysis," to improve economic decision making in public school systems. Should he desire, the reader may compare such a type of decision making with the processes of choice he has observed in actual situations in school systems.

41

Economics and the Educational System

D. Gale Johnson

In clear and precise language Professor Johnson of the University of Chicago treats the general concept of efficient allocation of resources in school districts. He draws special attention to the need for improvement in the schemes of payment of teachers.

Education is a big industry in the United States. In recent years governmental expenditures on education have been at least twelve billion dollars, and expenditures by private educational institutions have been well over two billion dollars. It is at once evident that educators, especially administrators of educational institutions, and economists have a great deal in common. Economics is primarily concerned with the use of scarce resources — labor, land, buildings, machinery, fuel, and blackboards. Education requires vast quantities of each of these plus many more things. The economist is concerned with understanding how such scarce resources are used, while the educational administrator is involved in the actual process of making decisions relative to the use of labor, buildings, and other facilities for the purpose of carrying out a specific function, namely, educating the youth of our country.

Economists' Concern with Scarcity

What does it mean when we say that economists are primarily concerned with the use of scarce resources? First, we need to be clear about what we mean by scarce resources. "Scarce resources" means anything that does not exist in sufficient quantity to enable us to use as much of it as we would like without being concerned about the amount that is left. Thus, in the middle of the Atlantic Ocean we would not be concerned about the amount of ocean water that we used for any purpose, since the use of any conceivable amount would not result in our being concerned about the amount remaining. In

Reprinted from D. Gale Johnson, "Economics and the Educational System," *School Review*, Volume LXV, No. 3 (Autumn, 1957), pp. 260–269, by permission of The University of Chicago Press.

other words, we would not have to economize in our use of ocean water. However, in the irrigated agricultural areas of California, water is scarce, and, if more water is used on one field, less water would be available for use elsewhere.

The concept of scarcity is a purely relative notion. Anything, a good or a service, is scarce only in terms of the uses which it is serving. My actual or potential output as an artist would be scarce in an absolute sense; the total number of paintings that I could complete in my lifetime would certainly be numbered in the dozens. Yet, given the quality of the paintings and the absence of any desire on the part of anyone else to purchase the paintings, they could not be classified as scarce goods. Scarcity implies that there is less of a good or service than people would wish to have or use if the good or service were free.

The fact of scarcity confronts all of us with the necessity of continually choosing among alternatives. As individuals we must choose among various alternative ways of spending our income as a means of achieving whatever may be our ends. We realize that, if we spend more on an automobile, we shall have less to spend on housing, food, entertainment, or furniture. If we do spend more on our automobile, we presumably do so because we believe that such an expenditure gives us more satisfaction than if we had used our income in some other way. Economists are interested in scarcity from several viewpoints. Only two will be noted here.

From one viewpoint, economists study the effects that changes in relative scarcity have upon the behavior of producing and consuming units in our society. The basic concepts of supply and demand are important tools in understanding the impact of scarcity. If less wheat is produced because of a crop failure in the Great Plains, our knowledge of the demand for wheat permits us to indicate the probable change in the price of wheat and of certain other similar products as well as the changes in the various uses of wheat. If a new and cheaper method of producing wheat becomes available, the economist is interested in studying the effect that the change will have upon the supply of wheat and upon the various areas that produce wheat.

From another viewpoint, economists are interested in the rather detailed types of choices among various alternatives which a given farm or business firm or school system must make. Most people who have been trained as economists are employed by businesses or governments to help their employers make choices among alternative ways of doing things. An automobile company is interested in producing a car of a given quality as cheaply as possible. To do this requires the talents of many individuals. The economist can help by determining whether the costs can be reduced by using different materials, by buying from other sources than those now used, by using a different inventory policy, or by organizing the production line somewhat differently. In addition, the economist may be able to help his employer by determining whether a car of a different type or quality might not be more acceptable to consumers and thus result in greater sales and profits for the company.

EDUCATION LIKE AND UNLIKE OTHER BUSINESS

Most of the aspects of scarcity that the economists study are those that are reflected in the market. In our type of economy most of the choices amongst alternative uses of scarce resources are made through the spending of money in the market by businesses and consumers, and thus the results of their decisions are reflected in prices at which goods and services are bought and sold. However, many decisions that affect the use of scarce resources are made through the political mechanisms of our society. These decisions are of two general types. One type is the use of regulations that affect the way in which members of the society can use their resources. These regulations include such items as building codes, zoning ordinances, fire regulations, and speed limits for cars. The other type, which is of more immediate concern to us in the present context, is the collective decision to provide certain goods and services with little or no direct cost to the persons using the goods and services. In the United States most of our educational services are provided in this way. We do not permit individuals to determine how many resources should be devoted to education by buying and selling education in the market. Instead, educational services are provided primarily by governments, and tax powers are used to pay for these services.

In many respects a city public school system is like any business that operates in that city. It must use scarce resources to produce a service. It has to organize its activities, and it must pay for the goods and services that it uses. It differs from the usual business, however, in that it is not allowed to charge for its services. The "demand" for its educational services cannot be determined in the market place. Instead, the demand is reflected by the funds that the relevant political agency, presumably reflecting the wishes of voters, appropriates for the use of the school system. Nonetheless, the school is in competition with all other businesses for the sale of its services. When a community votes taxes to pay for schools, the citizens of that community reduce the amount of money that they have to spend for other things.

If an economist were hired by a school system, I think that he would try to find the answers to the following questions: (1) Is the school system producing its product — educational services — as cheaply as possible? (2) Is the school system providing the amount and the quality of product — educational services — that are desired and will be paid for by its consumers, namely, the taxpayers?

Before you assume that the answers to these questions would imply paying the lowest possible salaries to teachers or the provision of education of minimum quality, let me try to indicate how an economist might approach each of these questions. I hasten to add that there is nothing unique about the approach that the economist would take in answering these questions, except that he would emphasize the necessity of considering alternative ways of accomplishing a given end and the desirability of considering whether the end actually chosen is the appropriate one. By "end," in this context, I mean the kind and the quality of educational services provided.

Producing Educational Services. Two special problems are involved in trying to determine whether a school is producing educational services in an efficient manner. The first problem is the difficulty of defining and measuring the product that is being produced. Thus we may find that two school systems have quite different costs per pupil, even when the salaries paid to all personnel and other prices are the same, but it is difficult to prove that the quality of the education provided is the same. Consequently a frequently used, important approach, comparing different businesses producing the same product, is difficult to apply.

The second problem results from the economic nature of the school system. The special economic nature of school systems consists of two elements. On the one hand, a public school system in a given city is a monopoly, and thus competition from other schools does not exist as an effective pressure to maintain efficiency and low costs. On the other hand, the receipts of a public school system come from government appropriations rather than from the market. Schools do not operate on a profit-and-loss basis; in ordinary businesses operating in a competitive situation, the existence of losses implies that elements of inefficiency probably exist.

I am not arguing that public schools should be organized differently. I only wish to point out that the task of maintaining efficiency in public school administration is a relatively difficult and continuing problem and that, in studying efficiency, certain guideposts that exist for other producing units do not exist in the case of schools. These considerations, I would argue, place a special responsibility upon school administrators to be continuously alert to possible alternative ways of providing educational services that may permit of lower costs without a sacrifice of quality.

Economists are often interested in determining whether a given type of business has been able to achieve an increase in output, while holding constant the quantity of scarce resources used, over a period of time. To my knowledge, no systematic study of this kind has been made of education. From the records available to many school systems, it should be possible to determine whether costs, after taking into account changes in the value of the dollar, have declined over the past several decades. My expectation is that, contrary to the situation in manufacturing and agriculture, little change in the real costs per pupil has occurred over the past several decades in city school systems.

The preceding paragraph ignores one important aspect of the problem of measuring changes in costs relative to the services produced — whether the quality of the service has changed. Since there seems to be a great deal of dispute among educators on this point, it might be well if efforts were now made to conduct measurements and studies that would allow reasonably effective comparisons of primary and secondary education today with the education that will be provided in the decades ahead.

There are many other problems in attempting to determine if a given quality of education is being provided at reasonable cost at a particular time. One important question that the economist might raise is whether the present salary policies of school systems are effective in achieving this objective. I am sure that most of you know of the recent study of salary and wage procedures in the armed forces. Two suggestions, among many others, were made. One was that the armed services should recognize that some of the skills that they required were much more expensive to acquire than other skills. The armed services have paid truck-drivers more or less the same as electricians, radar and radio specialists, and mechanics, despite the fact that in civilian life the latter jobs command more than does truck-driving. As a result re-enlistment among men with these desired capacities has been very low, while there has been a plentiful supply of truck-drivers. Is it not possible that the present shortage of science teachers in the high schools is due to our following the same kind of policy?

Another suggestion in the armed services study was that much greater emphasis should be put upon ability and skill rather than seniority in determining promotions and pay scales. Admittedly, such a policy is much more difficult to administer than one based mainly on seniority. To a degree, school systems have tried to avoid placing complete reliance on seniority by emphasizing training and education in their pay scales. However, we all know that different individuals with the same education may vary greatly in their productivity as teachers.

One of the basic difficulties of administering any school system is the high rate of turnover of personnel. Part of this turnover rate is explained by the salaries paid school teachers relative to salaries paid in types of employment that require similar skills. Salary levels are such that almost all teachers in elementary schools are women, and women generally remain in the labor force for a rather small portion of their lifetime. It does not necessarily follow that salaries should be sufficiently high to attract men into primary school teaching in significant numbers. Yet it seems appropriate for school administrators to consider the possibility. Administrators might also consider whether somewhat higher pay scales might not reduce turnover among women teachers by reducing the exodus to better-paying jobs.

Providing the Amount of Educational Services Demanded. In the usual business there is no particular problem in determining whether the amount and the quality of product are what consumers are willing to pay for. This is readily evident from a comparison of the production rate with the rate at which the good is purchased by its consumers at the prevailing price. If the production rate exceeds the consumption rate, one or both of two things will happen: production will decline, or the price will fall.

In the case of public education there is no obvious way of determining whether the amount and the quality of education made available are those desired by the taxpayers. In the short run, most of what is known is whether there are enough classrooms and teachers for the number of students that come to the school. Whether or not there are enough classrooms and teachers depends, in part, upon the standards that are accepted concerning the student-teacher ratio. In the longer run, the amount and the quality of education are determined by the political process, which involves, among other things, the determination of school budgets, local tax rates, and aids or grants from other governmental units.

Economists do not consider that they are especially qualified to evaluate all or most of the political decisions that result in determining the amount and kind of educational services demanded of a given school system. However the economist might well want to determine how the amount and the quality of educational services are related to the level of income of the community and to the distribution of the population by age, occupation, and perhaps ethnic origin. The economist might also study whether the support of public school systems is related to the availability of substitutes, especially parochial schools. Frankly, some of the results of these analyses might be of only secondary interest to the school administrator as he is concerned with the day-to-day operation of a school system. However, the studies might well help him to understand some of the basic factors that may explain the amount which local taxpayers are willing to pay to support public education.

An additional area that an economist in a large city school system might want to investigate would be the following: What influence has the quality of education provided by large cities had on the movement of people to the suburbs? This would be an extremely difficult question to answer, and several social scientists would probably have to work together in trying to find the answer. About all that I know of the subject results from observing the behavior of some of my friends and the casual observation that one of the important advertising points made by a large number of growing suburbs relates to the quality of their public schools. If it is true that the quality of education has an important effect upon decisions to leave the central city for the suburbs, it probably means that the school systems are not providing the quality of education that many people are willing to pay for. Thus it might be that cities would find it to their advantage to provide a better quality of educational services as a means of increasing local property values and, thus, the tax base. However, the latter conclusion may not be valid. It may be that the persons who care about having better public education and are willing to pay for it represent a sufficiently small minority that it would not be possible to induce taxpayers to pay for this quality of education for all school children.

One final question might be posed at this point: Do educators provide their consumers with sufficient information to permit them to make a rational decision concerning the amount and the quality of educational services that they would like to have?

When a family buys a new refrigerator, they have a fairly clear conception of what the product will do for them and what the services are worth to them. But when taxpayers are asked to vote additional funds for schools, I suspect that they have little conception of the value of these additional funds. If the money is required because there are more children per thousand families, this reason is probably understood fairly well. But if the funds are requested for an improvement in the quality of the education, the people probably have little basis for making a rational decision. I have no idea how the appropriate information can be obtained or how it should be presented. Yet I believe that we educators have tended to take it as a matter of faith that more and better education is always desirable. This faith may be valid, but there is no reason to believe that those who have to pay for the education, in competition with many other uses for which they may utilize their income, will automatically adopt our creed. If I were a marketing specialist, which I am not, I might suggest that we educators take a few lessons from Betty Crocker.

What I have tried to stress are certain special problems that would interest the economist in the study of a school system. These special problems arise because of the nature of the school system as a producing unit. This special nature exists because public schools generally have a monopoly in any given area and because the direct users of the schools do not pay for the services received, but instead the community as a whole makes the payment. I am sure that school administrators recognize these special features of the economic unit of which they are a part. Yet it is all too often true that we really fail to understand the familiar.

If there is anything unique about the approach that economists make to their subject matter, it is that economists continuously emphasize the necessity of considering alternatives. Many of the techniques of analysis used by economists are devised to indicate which of a number of alternatives is the appropriate one to choose in order to reach the desired objective. Most of the problems that economists study are problems that involve choices among alternatives. The idea of economizing, stated simply, is basically that of choosing the alternative that is least costly for a given result or that results in the greatest gain product or satisfaction for a given cost.

I do not wish to argue that, if school administrators approached their problems within the same framework as economists might, our educational system would be revolutionized. Yet I do believe that, if school administrators were always on the lookout for alternative ways of accomplishing their objectives, some desirable changes might result.

42

Technology and Education

Henry C. Ruark, Jr.

The range of innovations in education is discussed in this article. Mr. Ruark is consultant for instructional materials, Oregon State Department of Education.

Advancing technology is forcing better organization everywhere, and education is no exception. Probably at no other time has the American educational system undergone as agonizing a period as that in which we work; there is a continual clamor for change, a demand for action arising from one simple fact:

Education has been too slow to meet the changing demands of the modern world.

Three accelerating forces can be identified as major causes of the stresses and strains so easily observed:

1. Rising birth rates, leading to rising enrollments.
2. Expanding knowledge in many fields, with its modifying effects on the curriculum.
3. Advancing technology and its influence on the instructional process.

The effects of these three forces are inescapable facts of modern educational life. We can do little about the first. The others demand from us, first, professional efforts to understand what is happening, and second, action as educational leaders to make certain that the inevitable impact is made to serve well our long-field educational objectives.

In 1869, Thomas Henry Huxley spoke out on the scientific education of his day. He said:

> As industry attains higher status in its development, as its processes become more complicated and refined and competition more keen, the sciences are dragged in one by one, to take their full share of the fray; and he who can best avail himself of their help is the man who will come out uppermost in that struggle for existence. . . .

Adapted from "Technology and Education," *Phi Delta Kappan*, Volume XLII, No. 9 (June, 1961), pp. 387–392. Reproduced with permission.

Huxley made his statement in the midst of the First Industrial Revolution, which was the product of inventive genius.

In 1960, Admiral Hyman Rickover spoke out on education. He said:

> Because we do not fully comprehend the changes brought about by the rise of totalitarianism and technological progress, we continue to think and act as if we were secure. . . . We forget that technology has wiped out distance as a factor in war.[1]

Rickover made his statement in the midst of the Second Industrial Revolution, which is the product of scientists and technicians. The admiral points out that we no longer have a real choice between policies of political isolation as against involvement in world affairs; neither do we have a real choice between policies of economic isolation as against involvement in world markets.

The admiral, characteristically, failed to point out that the technology which has brought these political and economic changes has also brought just as sweeping advances in communication, and has created potential changes in the instructional process which may well wipe out many present-day limitations on learning, including those he often cites in arguing that not every American should be afforded opportunity for self-development to whatever level he can attain. It is thus valid to say, perhaps, that we may no longer have a real choice between policies of the past in education as against involvement in the development demanded by the modern world.

It is generally conceded that there is a twenty-five to fifty year lag between initiation of an educational idea and its widespread acceptance in practice. What many persons, both in and out of education, fail to realize is that we are living in an era of fantastic change. This is a fact, one that we must understand and live with, but even constant repetition does not convince everyone.

This educational lag simply cannot be tolerated any longer. It cannot be tolerated because, like it or not, education has become our first line of defense. We neglect it at our peril, not only as a bulwark against atomic destruction, but also as our sole determining force to shape the world as we believe it must be shaped, if free men are to remain free to pursue the goals about which we dream.

New concepts of what constitutes education for competent citizenship today, new methods and materials of instruction, new demands for different and increased teaching skills are crowding in from every side.

Developments in communication have revealed great potentials for making the instructional process more effective and more efficient; among the many tasks demanded of us today, perhaps none is more urgent than assessing the role of new educational media in improving instruction.

Educators could not ignore these developments, even if they wished to do so. The child who comes to school today is not the same child who came to

[1] Hyman Rickover, "Your Child's Future Depends on Education," *Ladies Home Journal*, Oct., 1960, pp. 98–102.

school yesterday. He is substantially, although subtly, different; the impact of change in the world, brought to him through his communication experiences, makes him so.

Today's student pays a price for his new knowledge. His experiences are to a large degree secondary and vicarious, rather than primary and direct; much of his new knowledge is neither profound, meaningful, nor accurate. Selectivity necessarily exercised by the media, imperfect absorption by the learner, and other factors too often lead to distortion and misunderstanding. But education must build on the foundation laid by these communication experiences, and in the process correct and extend these learnings.

The instructional process is the heart of education, of course, and instructional materials can give shape and substance to the curriculum, control its content, and vitally affect the teaching-learning process. Re-examination of communications developments has greatly extended the meaning of the term "instructional materials." A few decades ago, the "older" medium — print — was supplemented by "audio-visual" materials such as motion pictures, filmstrips, slides, radio, and disc recordings. These materials appealed to both the visual and auditory senses and offered teachers a splendid means of enriching and accelerating the learning process. More recently, "newer" new media — audio and video tapes, language laboratories, educational television, and teaching machines — have revealed still other instructional potentialities.

Two Major Trends

As these media are used more and more widely, not only for enrichment and acceleration but also for basic instructional communication, two major trends are evident. One is toward mass instruction, wherein learning experience takes place in larger groups, utilizing many basic media of communication, with some emphasis on projected still and motion pictures or educational television. The second is toward individualized instruction — learning experiences on a "machine and me" basis — with heavy emphasis, even basic dependence, on automated devices such as the language laboratory and the teaching machine.

The impetus for these developments comes in large part from a currently strong interest in developing new curriculum materials in a number of subject-matter fields, and an equally strong drive toward better utilization of staff and student time.

It is significant that major subject-area studies use the new instructional media to up-date subject matter. For instance, new instructional materials of many types are being prepared by the School Mathematics Study Group at Yale, the Biological Sciences Curriculum Study at the University of Colorado, the Wayne State University Modern Foreign Language Project, the Physical Sciences Study Committee at Massachusetts Institute of Technology, and the National Science Foundation.

THE "PACKAGED COURSE"

A corollary development arising from this basic concern with curriculum and content is the "packaged course" concept, exemplified by series of films now available in physics, chemistry, biology, and mathematics. Some series are the result of film recordings from television classes based on the "master teacher" concept, bringing to mass audiences highly skilled presentations by a subject authority. Still other materials, designed to deal with attitudes and appreciations rather than skills and knowledge, are being produced to exploit the recognized powers of the motion picture in this field.

National interest in better utilization of staff and student time is reflected by the development and widespread use of "team teaching" and other new approaches. Decrying the "manpower waste" in the schools, the Fund for the Advancement of Education has embarked on many experiments in utilization of teacher and student time; most revolve around use of group instructional tools and materials. Thus we see the overhead projector and the motion picture used with groups of 250 or more, or the classroom use of televised instruction to bring the same program at the same or different times into classrooms in a whole school district, a whole state, or even a whole region. This approach is usually coupled with small-group and individual work for other aspects of learning.

It is evident that mass use of the newer instructional media reflects the basic concepts of mass production, the "newly traditional" answer in our Western world to all problems involving the same quantity-quality dilemma: "Standardize it, make it quickly, use machine tools, produce in huge quantity — and distribute widely."

But education deals with the most plastic of materials — the human individual. The same "machine tools" of educational technology which make possible this mass approach may also, it is now evident, create individualized instruction, in some cases self-instruction, and permit a very near approach to the time-honored Socratic or tutorial situation, involving each student in close contact with a patient and untiring teacher who draws out correct and carefully sequenced responses to skilled and probing questions. The teacher, of course, is really the person or persons who program the content material for whatever machine is used to present it.

This second trend, toward individualized instructional instrumentation (to adopt technologically-oriented language!) has been organized on an ascending scale of sophistication by Dr. James Finn: individual reading pacers and similar devices; individual viewing and listening equipment for existing slides, filmstrips, motion pictures and recordings; language laboratories of all types; specifically programed printed materials such as scrambled textbooks, programed texts, etc.; and true "teaching" machines of the Skinner and Pressey type.

Teaching Machines Everywhere by 1964?

Programed material presented through automated devices and "teaching" machines represents a dramatic instructional innovation. It has been said that "the trouble with teaching machines is that they either sound like robots and scare everybody, or they sound so innocuous that nobody realizes they are revolutionary." But it has also been said that "the development of a successful machine that will teach a person the complex of interlocking symbolic and verbal knowledge which is the mark of an education is equivalent to a general theory of learning and teaching."[2] Dr. Eugene Galanter, author of this statement, predicted in 1960 that teaching machines would begin to come into general use in education within four years.[3]

The program is the heart of the machine technique; the machine serves only to control presentation of the program, to prevent students from cheating, and in some cases to record student learning rates and errors.

Today there are literally dozens of teaching machines of varying degrees of complexity and automation; most reflect either one or a combination of two basic approaches to the organization of learning materials into a program.

Whatever the program, it takes the form of either multiple choice responses or constructed responses. Very rarely are these two combined, since each represents a different viewpoint of the learning process. In a multiple-choice program, the learner chooses one of several responses. After he has committed himself, the machine reveals whether or not his choice was correct. If correct, he can go on to the next step; if not, he must choose another response until he discovers the correct one. In a constructed response, the learner writes or builds his response by manipulation of the machine. Again, he is immediately informed of correctness and can proceed only if his constructed response is accurate.

In both types of programs, cues, prompts, or hints can be used to further guide the learner. Proponents of the multiple-choice form (Pressey, Crowder) insist that some errors are natural and necessary; advocates of the constructed response (Skinner, et al.) try for "errorless" learning, with such small program steps ("frames") and liberal use of cues and prompts that the student is not allowed to make an error. The latter method is sometimes designated a "linear" program, since it moves the student straight ahead in a carefully guided line which is the same for all learners, except for rate of progress "down the line." The test of ability is not the degree to which a concept is understood but how quickly it has been grasped. For example, if such a program is truly valid and effective, while the average youngster is moving along in elec-

[2] Eugene Galanter, "The Ideal Teacher," *Automatic Teaching*, Wiley, 1959, p. 1.

[3] Eugene Galanter, "The Mechanization of Teaching," *Bulletin of the National Association of Secondary School Principals*, April, 1960, p. 304.

tronics and the slow learner is dealing with Newton's Laws, the gifted may be moving well into nuclear physics.

Branching off the main line onto a sidetrack and back again is possible with the multiple-choice approach. If a student's responses show that he is confused, he can be branched off through a succession of smaller and simpler steps until he demonstrates full and complete understanding, at which point he is brought back to the main line again. Or, if he demonstrates by rate and choice of responses that he has a background for certain learnings, he can be branched around a part of the main line program and moved ahead to more complex learnings.

Branching programs are sometimes called "contingent" programs, since the sequence of the program is contingent at all points upon the student's last response. Contingent or branching programing normally uses multiple-choice responses which facilitate automatic scoring; place little emphasis upon step size or cueing; assume that a student should be allowed to make mistakes; and provide the potential of different remedial instruction for different types of errors.

SKINNER AND THE "CONSTRUCTED RESPONSE"

Skinner at Harvard is adamant in contending that the constructed response is the only way to make sure the student is not merely identifying the most likely response, while advocates of multiple-choice response and branching see advantages in a more natural and more flexible learning approach.

There is no definitive evidence to support one school of programing over the other at present. It appears likely, however, that in cases where there is strong internal logic in a subject, or where close adherence to a sequence is desirable for other reasons, Skinnerian linear programing offers real advantages. There are other learning objectives where it may be desirable to allow the learner to go his own way, so long as his performance meets acceptable standards; for instance, he can do so in areas where there are no unequivocally "right" answers, such as problem-solving situations in the social studies.

A third position on programing suggests that it should be linear where possible and branching where necessary, with assessment made of the learner's performance after a sequence of frames. At this point a judgment would be made, either by the machine or the student, to continue in a small-step linear program if the student has made many errors, or to branch ahead if he has made few errors.

Programs can be presented on paper as sheets or notebooks or as scrambled or programed texts; or on film, as motion pictures, filmstrips, microfilm, or slides. The paper forms, often less expensive, are usually expendable in use; film forms, although more expensive originally, can be used for many students and are adaptable to presentation of visual and auditory stimuli.

Research in the new media, stimulated by the tremendous upsurge in interest throughout the educational system and supported by large numbers of grants from foundations and from Title VII of the National Defense Education Act, is rapidly adding to our knowledge of specific capabilities, of differential applications, and of integration of these new materials and media. These significant new findings are being reported widely in the educational press and will be even more widely disseminated through federal and other channels. Added to the large body of experience and research already available to us, there seems little doubt that the result will be a broad response throughout our school system.

Another major factor is the support for new media of instruction specifically included by definition within the scope of special equipment and materials to be acquired by schools under Title III of the NDEA. Many states report a heavy emphasis on basic media resources in local district applications. For example, just before the passage of Title III the U.S. Office of Education reported just over sixty language laboratories in public schools; within the first two years of Title III programs the count shot up to well over 500 and has been growing larger ever since. One Western state estimates that at least 20 per cent of total expenditures under Title III are going into printed supplementary and basic audio-visual materials. Other states have reported similar experience.

Potential Great, But Future Fuzzy

There appears to be little doubt that these new media of communication are potentially powerful educational forces, that utilization of instructional technology both in the classroom and increasingly in the home is probably inevitable, and that education can be made more effective and efficient if these new tools of learning are widely and wisely used.

In a society increasingly characterized by technological advances, the shape of education in the coming years is certainly neither distinct nor fixed. Some persons who study current trends see tomorrow's classroom characterized by automated instructional methods; others have some reservations about mechanizing the instructional process.

Not Merely AIDS to Teacher

A significant point often overlooked is that the new media can no longer be regarded merely as *aids* to the teacher. Since they now store and disseminate subject matter in ways never achieved before, they are performing functions which were for a long time the exclusive domain of the teacher. The media can now illustrate, discuss, analyze, present content, form concepts, and build generalizations; they can even systematically prescribe areas for continued student inquiry.

These newly programed capabilities of the new media force a reformulation of the conventional role of the teacher in the classroom. Just as industry discovered that it could not attain present high production flows without major changes in the organization and employment of human effort, so will education require development of similar major changes before the true potentials of present-day and future technological devices can be achieved. The teacher will no longer be principally a communicator, presenting facts, constructing concepts, and guiding skill development; increasingly, the teacher will work with individual students on a tutorial basis, directing their learning and using machines for much presentation and routine exposition, pointing out further resources, and encouraging the student to accept increasingly higher levels of responsibility for his own educational growth.

Not everyone agrees with this view of things to come; some who are skeptical about the desirability of mechanizing parts of the instructional process, or question its value, call attention to the highly experimental nature of some of the newer devices and point to the almost total absence of learning theory undergirding use of these newer media. One author says that we seem to be witnessing a movement toward a learning theory based on an "automatic" model of man, and fears that modifications of educational goals and procedures may subvert "ultimate" or "eternal" values. Others decry the large financial investment and costs of maintaining new media, especially highly technical systems such as are required by various forms of television. Some fear that democratic values, such as the worth of the individual, may be lost amid the technological devices.

Still others are concerned that mechanization may bypass the essential elements of learning, such as readiness and motivation; that it may deny the student the social developments to be gained through contact with human instructors; and that it may lead to regimentation and a degree of curriculum rigidity such as we have never experienced.[4]

Those who advocate full use of the new educational media maintain that technology can offer the overworked classroom teacher relief from some routine, repetitive presentations of materials and that, since much of the information-dissemination part of teaching would be done by mechanical devices and teacher aides, the professional teacher would be released to serve as a sensitive guide for the learner. They maintain that the student would thus take greater responsibility for his own learning, and that the teacher would be freer to use her critical and creative talents to individualize instruction still further.

THIS IS THE "SYSTEMS APPROACH"

One author foresees still another development in classroom technology: a combination of the media for mass instruction with the media for individual instruction, to create a true "systems approach" in education. This demands thorough analysis and long-range planning; application of personnel, machines, and materials to the point of saturation of the instructional situation; and complex interplay of control and concentration of effort, on the basis of feedback of information from all stages of the process-flow within such an organ-

[4] Gene C. Fusco, "Technology in the Classroom," *School Life*, March-May, 1960.

ized learning system. This would demand the application to education of the new "operational research" patterns which attempt to strip a problem down to its bare essentials, create a mathematical model of it, and then solve for the best answer. Methodologies from other sciences are also used in this type of analysis for planning purposes. As an example, the producer of a film series for a certain course and the manufacturer of a teaching machine might together develop a teaching machine program of multiple-choice response items, based on the material presented in the films. The films might be projected hourly on closed-circuit television, and students would work under program assignments with machines located in individual instruction spaces throughout the school building.[5]

Proponents of the application of the new media emphasize that no new technological break-through is needed to bring about the instructional transformation they envision; the present state of the communication arts makes the so-called "automated classroom" possible today.

Regardless of the enthusiastic hurrahs of proponents, or the equally vocal skepticism of the critics, it appears that instructional technology is here, and that it is here to stay. It also appears evident that no *one* of these technological developments will completely resolve our continuing quantity-quality dilemma. We will have to integrate and combine a variety of teaching-learning methods, materials, and devices to buttress our attack on educational problems as they exist, and we will probably need to provide for more effective individual counseling and guidance than ever before.

It would seem that the issues of classroom use of the new media will revolve around the same old problems of organization, staff, space, finance, and program with which we have become so painfully familiar.

Overseeing the media and machines in the classroom and controlling the flow of materials and programs will certainly require a growing body of specialists highly skilled in materials and resources. Such specialists will perhaps be based in an instructional materials center combining the facilities of the present school library and audio-visual services with the addition of small-group and individual learning spaces and the facilities demanded by local production of unique learning materials. They will be key personnel in a developing team of educators and sub-professional aides.

In many ways, the new media will demand more of the teacher than he has yet been asked to give. Finding out what a pupil's response to a stimulus actually is has never been an easy part of the teacher's task; and it will be even more difficult if the child spends any of his time learning from a technological device. The teacher will have to work more closely than ever before with the individual pupil to discover what effects the new methods are having on his attitudes and emotions.

Given the context of automated teaching, it becomes all the more vital for a teacher to discharge distinctly human responsibilities, too. If the values of

[5] James D. Finn, "Technology and the Instructional Process," *Audio-Visual Communication Review*, Vol. 8, No. 1, Winter, 1960.

a democratic society are to be preserved, the teacher must concentrate even more earnestly on responsibilities of developing the full potential of every child by stimulating his imagination, broadening his vision, stretching his powers to build his confidence, and helping him to appreciate the ideas of democracy.

NEW BUILDINGS ARE REQUIRED

The new instructional program probably cannot be effectively administered in conventional school buildings, and efforts to design them to accommodate the new media are already under way. Total flexibility of instructional spaces probably cannot be built in; expense may be too high, and acoustical difficulties may be too great. Above all, tomorrow's needs are impossible to foresee. On the other hand, the administrator cannot close his eyes to rapid changes in instructional technology and the modifications in instructional spaces that will be needed. It is obvious that some practical guidelines are badly needed, and they are being provided through various publications, one of the best being a Title VII research project recently completed under the direction of Dr. Amo De Bernardis of the Portland (Oregon) Public Schools.[6]

Financing is always a major concern in education, of course. It has been estimated that although a simple type of teaching machine can be built for $20, the production of the manuscript for a single program on that machine, say in arithmetic for one semester, will probably cost as much as $50,000. The installation of a sophisticated language laboratory can cost thousands of dollars, as can the purchase of just one among the many film series being offered. Costs of an in-service TV system range from several thousand dollars to more than $250,000. Clearly, instructional technology, although it will probably improve the instructional process, will certainly increase the operating costs of the schools.

But is cost to be the deciding factor? Many who advocate use of instructional technology in classroom teaching maintain that to use skilled teachers for the routine aspects of teaching, even though they can carry out the tasks for less than the machines will cost, is to waste precious human abilities and qualities. Educational technology promises to provide the teacher with greater opportunities to perform more creative functions, for more sensitively human ends. Can our society afford not to make the very best and most productive use of its greatest resource, its human materials?

COST IS NOT THE QUESTION

Perhaps the difficult question is *not* how much will the new media cost, but how we can best use them to upgrade the teaching-learning process through more significant learning experiences to such an extent that the cost factor becomes secondary.

[6] Amo De Bernardis, et al., *Planning Schools for New Media.* Division of Education, Portland State College, Portland, Ore., 1960.

After all, we are the nation which has traditionally faced the problems of providing the greatest educational opportunity for all to move toward the highest goals of which they are capable. Difficulties, costs, and dilemmas are not new to us.

We have left to the last a key question — that of programing and control. It is always poor programing, rather than the medium itself, which must bear the brunt of criticism in any discussion of the new media.

Teachers have had relatively wide latitude in selecting textbooks for a given subject field. Even if a text is not entirely satisfactory, creative teachers can supplement it with reference and resource books. In selecting audio-visual materials, teachers have been somewhat more restricted. High production costs and the limited market (until very recently) have made it difficult for a manufacturer to produce films, filmstrips, recordings, and the like at a low unit cost. The enormous cost and the centralization demanded in planning and designing materials for the new media inevitably raises the question of curriculum control. The preparation of motion pictures, TV programs, audio tapes, or teaching machine programs requires the services of highly specialized persons and the outlay of large sums of money. Such materials are revised only at great expense, and this barrier to flexibility has alarmed some persons who see a possibility of "freezing" the curriculum once an investment in these materials has been made by the local school district. Others point to the danger that a national curriculum might materialize; or that agencies not accountable to the public for their actions could produce standardized instructional materials in package form that could not easily be modified to meet the needs of local school districts. The same concern about the possible weakening of existing curriculum control always arises in connection with large television programs such as the state, regional, and airborne projects now underway.

It would appear that the answers to these problems are yet to be developed, but that the problems themselves vary only in degree and complexity from similar problems long ago faced in education. It would appear that we may expect somewhat similar solutions to be developed. One basic principle learned from experience with the new media does emerge: New media, just as other teaching materials, must be under the control of the teacher, who should select them for the unique contribution they can make to the teaching-learning situation as it exists in the classroom, for a particular group of learners. Basic principles underlying all good teaching and learning apply to the newer as well as the older instructional materials.

Administrators must first of all ensure that the purposes and goals of education in a democratic society will be protected and preserved; maximum development of each pupil must remain the basic goal of any instructional program; and the purposes of education as revealed in the instructional program of local school districts should determine which instructional tools will be used and how they will be used.

I think we can agree that the influence of technology on education emphasizes the words of Whitehead, who said: "It is the business of the future to be dangerous."

Certainly technology is now making the future course of instruction capricious and hazardous. If we would be leaders for education, we must look forward, and not present what Herbert Muller has noted as "the curious spectacle of civilized man forever marching with his face turned backward — as no doubt the cave man looked back to the good old days, when men were free to roam, instead of being stuck in a damn hole in the ground."[7]

The good old days of education are gone, too. The days of the future will be what we make of them.

[7] Quoted in Finn, *op. cit.*

43

How to Make School Decisions

Joseph A. Kershaw and Roland N. McKean

How can a school district make efficient choices among alternative resource-using processes? Kershaw and McKean sketch a system of analysis for dealing with this significant problem.

Suppose that your district decides, for one reason or another, to improve pupil performance in mathematics. This improvement will require more dollars for your math program. As a result, you are immediately faced with an important decision: to spend new money or to make funds available by taking them away from something else in your system. Next, you must choose the method, or methods, you'll employ to do the job.

This will involve a second decision based on an examination of all the ways of improving math performance. For example, should you:

1. Obtain better teachers (which may involve higher pay)?
2. Install television as a means of using your best teachers more effectively?
3. Hire teacher aides to release teachers from non-teaching chores?

Reprinted by permission from "How to Make School Decisions: An Outsider's View," *School Management*, Volume IV, No. 5 (May, 1960), pp. 67–69, 118, 121.

4. Change the curriculum to give added emphasis to math?
5. Reduce pupil-teacher ratios in math classes?
6. Supply better classroom equipment?

To make an intelligent choice among these possibilities, you must have an idea of *how much each technique will cost* and how much each will accomplish — what the cost and output of each technique will be. In addition, you must have some understanding of the good and bad *indirect* effects of each suggested alternative on other parts of your school system. From these considerations you can determine which course of action provides the most of what you want for a given cost.

Keeping the Dollar in Focus

Well-meaning people often assert that cost is not important — that what does count is finding ways to improve education. Once you find these, they say, communities will somehow pay the necessary costs. This is simply untrue.

Without question, we could improve our high school education substantially by having one teacher for each four or five students. This would be theoretically possible; it would "simply" require increasing the high school faculty about fivefold and setting starting salaries at around $15,000 or so (to attract that many teachers). No one suggests this, of course — precisely because society is unwilling to pay this price.

So there is nothing wrong with affixing a dollar sign to your alternatives. All you are doing is seeking policies that appear to yield the greatest output from your anticipated budgets. And the way to hit upon such policies — even if precise measurements never become available — is systematically to consider *alternative* ways to use direct resources.

Problems of Choice

Compare your situation with that of a business executive. Business management has multiple aims just as school management has, but the dominant pressure on business management is to increase profits. The selection of a firm's actions is still far from simple, but the *criterion* of proper policy is straightforward compared to yours.

Your course is rarely so clear. The educational objectives of parents, taxpayers and educators are multiple — not focused neatly on a single, well-defined aim. And measuring progress toward these objectives is typically difficult and in some instances impossible. Yet it is possible for you to think systematically about the options open to you, provided you keep these factors in mind:

Every Decision Is a Choice Among Alternatives. When a school board decides to add a psychologist, it is by that act deciding not to do many other things that cost the same. The money earmarked for the psychologist's salary could just as well be spent repairing the gymnasium, buying typewriters, raising custodial salaries or replacing worn-out band instruments. It may sometimes happen that alternative uses for the same available money are close competitors — buying a new school bus vs. reconditioning an old one; often they will be quite unrelated. But the point is, whenever a positive decision is made, a decision *not* to do an almost infinite number of other things is made with it.

Every Alternative Should Be Evaluated. It is not enough to ask, "Is this proposal a good one?" Instead, your question should be, "Is this proposal better than all others that might be equally costly in resources?" Every decision to spend money, or to use existing resources in a different way, should face up to the question of whether the proposal advances the system toward its goals more than other alternatives would.

Decision Making Has Side Effects. In something as complex as a school system, changing one of its elements is likely to affect the cost of performance of all the others. For example, a decision about building design would influence the costs and the benefits resulting from the introduction of television into the educational program. You must be aware of these indirect effects.

But what if you cannot measure how much each alternative will produce? (And at present this is rarely possible.) You can still make personal estimates of *output* under alternative policies whenever you make a choice. Too often this explicit consideration of alternatives is bypassed in favor of concluding somewhat mystically that the school "needs" (in an absolute sense) a particular policy or piece of equipment. The need is there, of course, but so are many, many others.

ALTERNATIVE PACKAGES

In order to consider alternatives systematically, it is helpful to think in terms of those that cost approximately the same. A 12-room house produces more comfort and costs more money than a six-room house. But these facts alone do not help much in choosing between them. The question that must first be answered is, "What alternative *packages* of things could I buy with the same resources required for the 12-room house, and what value or 'output' would each of the packages probably yield to me?"

In our earlier example, if using teacher aides to get average math achievement raised by a designated amount costs $13,000, and reducing pupil-teacher ratios to obtain the same results costs $9,000, it is wasteful to use teacher aides. The other $4,000 has other productive uses to which it can be put. We use cost as part of our criterion not to pinch pennies or to find ways to cut the total budget, but because this is the way to judge efficiency. It is always efficient to do a specified job with the lowest expenditure of resources, or to get the most output from them.

In examining cost (or output, for that matter), the *extra* or "incremental" amount resulting from each policy alternative should be identified. It is tempting to allocate a slice of joint costs — such as administrative or research expense — to each course of action even if those expenses would not actually be affected. What should be estimated, however, are the truly incremental effects of each alternative.

What Are Your Goals?

Suppose we look briefly at the measurement of output under alternative policies. The difficulties here, of course, are enormous, but let's focus our attention for a moment on output in terms of only one of the administrator's aims — instruction of pupils in the basic subjects. This is more difficult than

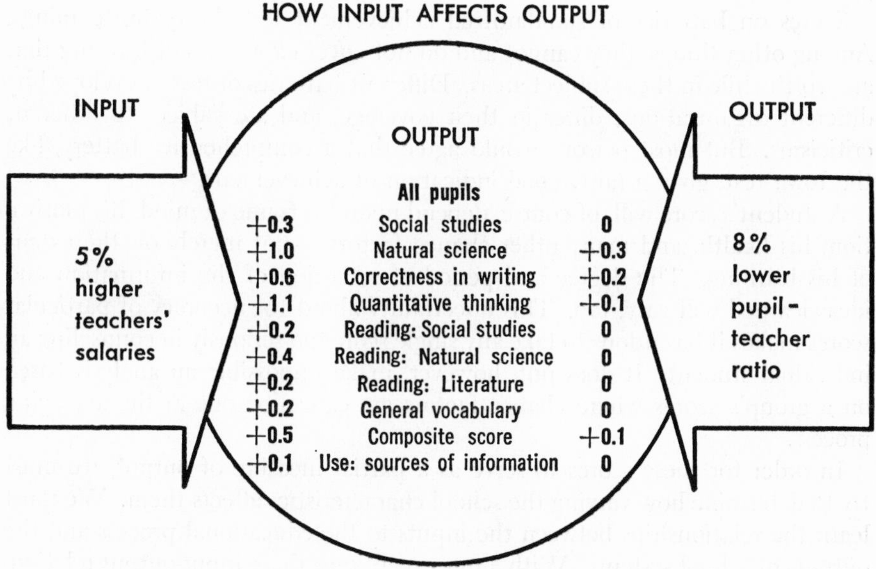

Note: The Iowa Tests are used here merely as an example. The scores shown are hypothetical — after allowing for effect of other factors — but they are drawn up so as to be consistent with certain plausible hypotheses — e.g., that higher teacher salaries would improve scores in mathematics and science particularly, because they would alleviate the "shortage" that affects those subjects especially. These numbers represent changes in raw scores — not in scores that have been converted into percentiles or other relatives.

Separate analyses for different ability groups (pupils with IQ's above 120; those with IQ's from 100 to 120; those with IQ's from 75 to 100) could show impacts on pupils in those groups.

was implied in our example about improving performance in mathematics. To elaborate just a little: Slow and bright students will be differently affected by many innovations — which students do you want to improve? And suppose you can improve the bright youngsters in math by letting their history slide — is this good or bad? Or again, how much improvement do you want? Presumably if a school did away with everything except math, its graduates would be outstanding in math. If this is absurd, how far *does* one go in that direction?

A PARTIAL MEASURE OF OUTPUT

Measuring the effects of alternative policies on test scores would give data about one major dimension of educational output. While they would not make possible *definitive* conclusions about a district's practices, they would help an administrator make his choices by showing him *part* of the effects of various policies. And, if he wished to "buy" greater scholastic achievement, he would know (approximately) what steps to take to get a designated improvement.

Scores on batteries of standardized achievement tests have shortcomings. Among other things, they cannot and do not cover *all* aspects of learning that are worthwhile in these subject areas. Different batteries of tests, developed by different organizations, differ in their coverage, and are subject to different criticisms. But most persons would agree that a comprehensive battery, like the Iowa test, gives a fairly good indication of achievement.

A student's score will, of course, depend upon his frame of mind, his motivation, his health, and many other chance factors — not merely on the extent of his learning. The degree and period of retention of the information and ideas learned will vary, too. This uncertainty about the accuracy of particular scores makes it hazardous to take any single score too seriously in counseling an individual student. It does not, however, make impossible an analysis based on a group's scores where chance factors are cancelled out in the averaging process.

In order for these scores to serve as a partial measure of output, we must try to determine how varying the school characteristics affects them. We must learn the relationships between the inputs to the educational process and the outputs of school systems. With a few exceptions, these input-output relationships in education are simply not known at present.

ESTIMATING INCREMENTAL OUTPUT

We think it would be possible to learn quite a bit about these relationships. What we have in mind is an analysis of pupils' test scores as a function of differences in school characteristics (or inputs). Allowance must be made, of course, for the effects of the non-school factors that influence performance.

To reveal much, this sort of statistical analysis would have to be on a fairly large scale. (A start on a study of this nature is being made by the University of Pittsburgh and the American Institute for Research in connection with their Project Talent.)

Such a study would try to relate a rather long list of school characteristics and control variables to the test scores of students.

The control variables or "covariates" would be the non-school factors — such as intelligence and home environment — that influence pupil performance.

When the calculations were made, the first results would indicate the significant differences in outputs due to variations in inputs. One could go even further and derive estimates of the size of these significant differences, using this material.

Statistical Analysis

Let us see what such a statistical analysis, if successful, might show about the incremental output from changes in a hypothetical school system.

(The numbers that follow are, of course, hypothetical too.) The analysis would show the average effect of designated policy variations, given various school characteristics as they initially existed and given certain non-school factors (home environment and pupils' intelligence).

Officials in a particular school system could first determine which combination of non-school circumstances and existing school characteristics best fitted their situation. Then they could find in the exhibits the estimated effects of making policy changes in such a school system.

Extracting Data

The accompanying table (see page 395) illustrates how the data extracted in this fashion might be arranged. It presents the predicted effects of two changes in System X. One is a 5% salary increase, and the other an 8% decrease, in average class size.

The salary increase would presumably give the system a wider range of applicants from which to choose, especially of applicants trained to teach science and mathematics in the secondary schools. The result would be an improvement in the quality of instruction over what the system could otherwise provide.

In the second change to be considered, it is assumed that the smaller classes — within the range under consideration — would increase pupils' achievement modestly in certain subjects. (Past studies suggest that this impact is slight, which explains why the changes in test scores due to the lower pupil-teacher ratio are modest in the table.)

ESTIMATING INCREMENTAL COSTS

The incremental costs of introducing innovations or modifying school policies would be essential elements in quantitative comparisons of alternative systems. In this illustration the same two changes in System X are designed so that each would raise system costs by $150,000.[1]

These are comparatively uncomplicated examples of the estimation of incremental costs associated with policy changes. The calculation of extra annual cost becomes more complex for policy changes, such as the introduction of television, because this would affect still more variables simultaneously. With care, however, reasonable estimates can be made of the incremental costs of almost any adjustment in the school system.

NEW LOOK AT ALTERNATIVES

This information on cost and output is useful in comparing alternative policies. Of course, the aim of such comparisons would not be to discover ways of cutting the total budget or even of staying within the limitations of existing budgets. School budgets will almost certainly continue to rise. These comparisons would aim at helping school officials get the most out of such future, higher outlays.

To compare the two changes, they must be constructed (or adjusted) so that they cost the same. Then the system yielding the larger output for the same total cost can be determined.[2] In drawing up this illustration, we have already designed the changes so that they entail the same incremental cost, $150,000. What about the effect on output? For our purposes, we can take the estimates of these effects directly from the table. According to these hypothetical estimates, raising teachers' salaries would (in the long run) improve test scores more than the alternative policy costing the same amount.

In the interpretation of such comparisons, the qualifications mentioned before should be kept in mind. There are pertinent considerations other than costs and test scores. But this sort of analysis would reduce one set of important and complicated considerations to a meaningful and relatively simple form. Given the tremendous difficulties connected with decision making in education, progress along this line would be a most welcome step forward.

[1] In making these calculations, we assumed a certain size for System X, a unified salary scale for its elementary and secondary teachers and no changes in administrative salaries. The 8% decrease in the pupil-teacher ratio meant that the system would employ 30 more teachers and that there would be an 8% decrease in class size on the average, not in each course.

[2] The systems might also be constructed (or adjusted) to yield the same output to determine which one produced that output at the lower cost.

PART FIVE · THE PROBLEM OF PRODUCTIVITY IN EDUCATION

Section B

ECONOMIC ASPECTS OF THE TEACHER'S ROLE

The five selections in this section have to do with various aspects of teachers' pay. Salaries of teachers is by far the largest single item in school budgets. It is likely to remain so for some years in the future. No consideration of use of economic resource in education can afford to overlook the system under which teachers are presently paid and the problems associated with their remuneration.

Knezevich and Fowlkes (Selection 44) describe the single salary schedule and also raise certain key questions about its limitations. Spears and McElligott (Selection 45) present a modern version of the single salary schedule that was recently adopted by the San Francisco public schools. In Selection 46, Barr brings to light some of the complex issues that are involved in assessing the productivity of teachers. Lieberman (Section 47) offers a national plan for merit pay. A proposal for use of a modified form of rank classification in education, developed by the Center for Field Studies for the Concord (Mass.) schools, is shown in Selection 48.

44

Salary Schedules

Stephen J. Knezevich and John Guy Fowlkes

Two distinguished professors of school administration make a critical survey of present practices in the payment of teachers. It should be noted that the discussion is aimed not at the level of salaries but at the methods used in determining how much one teacher shall receive as compared with another.

The authorization of a contract for personal services is the first step in the management of salary payments. All contracts must be issued by the board of education. Where the law requires that contracts be in writing, oral contracts are not recognized as valid legal documents to be used as the basis for salary payments. In the absence of specific statutory commands to the contrary, oral contracts are as valid as written contracts.

One of the most significant developments in personnel administration in recent years has been the growth and use of salary schedules. Salary schedules for instructional personnel are a twentieth century phenomenon. In 1918–1919, less than one-half of the cities had salary schedules. But by 1922–1923 approximately 65 per cent of the city schools studied by the National Education Association had schedules for salary payments to instructional personnel. A most prophetic statement issued in 1922–1923 declared: "It is safe to assume that scheduled salaries are to be a permanent element in the administration of American schools."[1] This prophecy is approaching reality, for by 1956–1957, 97 per cent of the city school districts had developed and used salary schedules. Many of the smaller school districts do not have schedules for salary payment. It is predicted that within the next 25 years, there will be hardly a school district in the United States without a salary schedule for instructional personnel.

By and large, the salary schedule is a development of local school systems. Some states have statewide salary schedules for teachers. The relative slowness

From *Business Management of Local School Systems*, by Stephen J. Knezevich and John Guy Fowlkes, pp. 75–77, 83–84.

[1] National Education Association, Research Division, "Teachers' Salaries and Salary Trends in 1923," *Research Bulletin*, Washington, D.C.: NEA, 1923, *1*:36.

with which statewide salary schedules change has made it necessary for local systems within these states to develop local schedules based on more realistic payments to teachers. In this sense, the state schedule is a minimum salary law rather than a true picture of teachers' salaries in the state. Over two-thirds of the states have minimum salary requirements for teachers but not all of these have salary schedules. A few states have minimum salary regulations which are so low as to make the law obsolete.

The salary schedule is a statement of policy on remuneration for personal services. As a policy adopted by the local board of education in most states, the board has a right to modify or abolish its salary schedule. In the few states having a statewide salary schedule for teachers local board action cannot abolish state schedules or pay below state prescribed minimums. If the salary schedule establishes that teachers of similar qualifications must be given similar salary consideration there can be no discrimination. Salary schedules facilitate to a great degree the administration of salary payments.

Many reasons have been offered for the development of salary schedules. Among these are (1) to secure teachers who are personally competent and professionally well prepared, (2) to encourage professional growth of teachers, and (3) to retain competent teachers. A salary schedule is a formally adopted plan for the payment of the school employees. To a large degree it determines the beginning salary, the amount and number of yearly increases, and the maximum salary to be received by various groups of teachers, or other groups of employees with specified qualifications.

There are many factors involved in the development of a salary schedule. It is not the purpose of this chapter to justify or develop any of the philosophical bases upon which salary schedules are founded but merely to indicate some of the problems in the development and use of salary schedules.

Policies and Procedures Related to Schedule Preparation

The action of individuals or groups such as the superintendent, teachers' organizations, and lay groups usually motivates the study of salaries with the objective of preparing a new schedule or revising the existing one. Such requests to begin preliminary work should receive the formal approval of the board of education. The appointment of personnel to execute the systematic study preliminary to actually writing a schedule should rest with the board. This group should include the superintendent, representatives of the entire staff, members of the board of education, citizens other than the board members, and special consultants as necessary.

The responsibility for drafting a schedule must be fixed either in the committee making the study or in the executive officer of the school district. Although the primary burden for making the study should rest with a specially appointed committee, the entire teaching staff should be called upon for assistance as needed. The board of education has the ultimate responsibility to adopt and execute the schedule and, therefore, should be given the opportunity to review and criticize proposed drafts of the schedule.

The committee or individual charged with the responsibility of preparing the salary schedule must assemble and consider certain information germane to the determination of local salary policies. This includes information on (1) the salary schedule already in effect with a review of its strengths and weaknesses; (2) minimum, maximum, median, and average salaries and increments paid in other school systems, particularly those similar to the one under consideration or in close relationship to it; (3) salaries in occupations other than teaching; (4) the age, sex, marital status, living standard, income, expenditures, dependents, etc. of the present teaching staff; (5) the professional preparation and evidence of recent growth among staff members; (6) teacher turnover and teaching load; (7) trends in costs of living; (8) and property assessments, tax rates and collections, municipal expenditures, school expenditures, and other factors related to financing the proposed salary schedule.

Policies must be formulated to stipulate what groups of employees are to have salaries specified by the schedule. It must be determined whether the staff, superintendents, administrative assistants, and others are to be included. Policies on local standards to be used in determining qualifications for appointment to positions of school service — the training, native ability, personality, and experience requirements — must be spelled out in sufficient detail to make the schedule workable.

Among the more important decisions to be made is whether the salary schedule shall be a position type, a professional preparation type, or a combination type of schedule. There is a definite trend toward the professional preparation type of schedules. Whatever the type, the minimum salary and maximum salary to be paid must be stipulated. Most authorities recommend that the maximum be at least twice the minimum salary.

The number of the increments or salary raises a teacher will receive in moving from the minimum to the maximum salary is still another important aspect of the problem. This includes the determination of the total number of increments in each salary class, the spacing of increments at annual or at longer intervals, the size of the increments, and whether there shall be uniform, smaller, or larger sized increments at the beginning or end of the schedule.

Some of the unsettled problems which inevitably create lengthy discussions in schedule development are: (1) Should men and women of equal qualifications be paid equal salaries for equal work? (2) Should merit or teacher efficiency be recognized in the salary schedule? If there is to be a super maximum or merit raise, what should be the size of increment, the maximum salary with efficiency rating, and the super maximum salary granted to teachers of outstanding efficiency? (3) Should special teaching assignments be recognized with special minimums and maximums on a separate schedule or should special assignments for teachers be recognized on the same schedule with a bonus above scheduled amounts? How do you define special assignments such as those for head football coach, director of student plays, or advisor to the school annual staff?

. . . .

The preparation or single salary schedule and the position type of salary schedule are the two basic types with many variations and combinations possible from these. In the single salary schedule, the basis for variation of salary payments to classroom teachers is preparation and experience. The single salary schedule is a direct contrast with the position type of schedule. In the position type of schedule salary will vary according to the grade level at which the teacher teaches and also with the subject taught. High school teachers receive more than grade school teachers, and band men might receive more than English teachers in a position type of schedule.

In 1918–1919, no city school system had a single salary schedule. As early as 1919, the National Education Association went on record in favoring a single salary schedule for teachers. By 1922–1923, 16 per cent of the city school systems had single salary schedules. There was little change in the years that followed, and by 1930–1931, only 17 per cent of the city school systems had single salary schedules. In 1940–1941, 31.3 per cent of the city systems had single salary schedules, and in 1950–1951, 97.1 per cent had them. By 1956–1957, the proportion of any type of schedule other than the single salary schedule in city systems was negligible.[2] There seems little question but that the single salary or preparation type of schedule is now in use in the overwhelming majority of all school systems that have any type of a salary schedule.

. . . .

Differentiated School Staffs and Differentiated Salary Scales Needed

The question can well be raised as to whether the existing concept of the kinds of workers needed in local school systems will ever provide the professional services, or make possible essential or what clearly seems desirable differentiation in payment for workers in schools. Local school systems are the only institutions of comparable social importance, complexity, and size that substantially have only one classification for an overwhelming majority of its workers. In other words, local school systems are suffering from a monolithic classification, and hence a monolithic salary schedule.

The title "teacher" is so broad and diverse in terms of work assignments teachers assume that it is not surprising to find so low a degree of specialization among nearly all of the staffs of local elementary and secondary schools.

[2] National Education Association, Research Division, "Salaries and Salary Schedules of Urban School Employees, 1956–57," *Research Bulletin*, Washington, D.C.: NEA, April, 1957, 35:90.

Teachers are now expected to stimulate and direct learning by children, and at the same time render high-level secretarial, clerical, and mechanical service necessary, toward a level of learning which admittedly with many boys and girls is far short of their capabilities.

It is not surprising that marked differences are found in the competence of teachers to fulfill responsibilities that have been assigned to them. It is not uncommon to find an elementary teacher who will teach the music or art class in another room in exchange for the teaching of arithmetic or science by another fellow teacher. Similarly, members of school custodial staffs particularly are enjoined to "fix" items of instructional equipment ranging from projection machines to impaired globes, because some teachers simply are not "good with their hands."

As a much wider utilization of electronic and other types of learning and teaching machines is made, the importance of what might be called school technicians will become increasingly essential toward maximum effectiveness among teachers and learners. Also, if those who enjoy the tutelage of boys and girls are to serve increasingly as diagnosticians, counselors, resource staff, and advisers as opposed to policemen, nursemaids, prescribers, and exhorters, teachers must be emancipated from secretarial and clerical work which requires peculiar professional skill, if the more specialized teacher functions are to be available to the degree needed.

INSTRUCTIONAL TEAMS SEEM TO BE DEMANDED

In connection with the previous discussion, it seems clear that a different and what promises to be a much sounder approach might well be made on the organization of essential school staffs around what may be called instructional teams. Some experimentation in the direction of organizing instructional teams for teaching has been conducted during recent years with results which suggest that all concerned work more efficiently with more effective learning resulting.

Three illustrative types of instructional teams seem appropriate of mention here:

1. The mere assignment of two present-day workers known as teachers given joint work assignments; as for example, two teachers to two fifth grades; this arrangement while it obviously gives no relief in connection with secretarial, clerical, and technical services needed does seem likely to stimulate a higher level of planning and encourages the fuller utilization of strengths for a pair of teachers working as a team than when they work substantially separately. Also, such an arrangement tends to reduce the excessive effort necessary for a teacher to attempt teaching something for which he, himself, feels his ability and preparation are inadequate.

2. An instructional team composed of what might be called a teacher-chairman or team leader, a teacher associate, an instructional secretary, and

the part-time service of a technician in the care and use of instructional and learning equipment. With such a team, recent experimentation has suggested that again more effective work is done by all concerned even when the traditional pupil-teacher ratios of relatively small numbers of children are multiplied from two to four times the ratios usually insisted upon as desirable.[3]

3. If instructional teams are more preferable units of organization than the individual teacher, it seems clear that institutions responsible for the preparation of teachers must include experience in team teaching in connection with what is traditionally called practice teaching. Consequently the instructional team just suggested might be modified to include one or two teaching interns in lieu of the associate teacher.

These are illustrations of what seems to deserve much thinking and actual experimentation in the establishment of instructional staffs in local school systems and the attainment of differentiated staffs and differentiated salary scales or schedules.

It is apparent that the plan of merit would hold under a policy including instructional teams and hence differentiated salary policy, as well as under the existing prevalent monolithic staff and salary schedule policies. However, it might be that differentiated staffs and corresponding differentiated pay schedules would be highly beneficial toward the recruitment of more competent workers in the classrooms of local school systems and would also make it possible in terms of economics to pay more appropriate salaries to various kinds of workers.

More Exact Classifications of School Staffs Seem Needed

It is an established matter that large numbers, particularly of women, even during the time of their college preparation and work toward the gaining of certification, frankly indicate that they do not expect to remain in teaching very long — often for not more than two to five years. Also, no small number of men similarly declare they do not intend to make teaching a career. Many of our young men and women who both by design or the turn of circumstances spend only short periods of time in the classroom are able, professionally minded, and high-level workers. However, those who spend only a short period of time as members of local school staffs hardly seem to deserve salary and welfare policies commensurate with those who intend to make their life's work the role of a school staff member. It would therefore seem, assuming that the beginning salaries for all school workers in any connection are of sufficient levels to enable them to live in keeping with their qualifications, that a longer period of service than that now found in most cases might well be required before they are recognized as "career workers."

[3] J. Lloyd Trump, *Images of the Future*, Washington, D.C.: The National Association of Secondary School Principals, 1959, pp. 15–18.

In this connection, the recommendation has been made that a minimum of five years teaching experience be required before a permanent teaching certificate (or license) is granted.

At any rate, in consideration of the development of a more satisfactory policy in the classification of school staffs and their corresponding remuneration, it seems clear that existing legal requirements in connection with the certifying of teachers should also be examined toward needed revision.

45

Found: An "Automatic" Salary Schedule

Harold Spears and Joseph P. McElligott

It is not uncommon for school administrators to be paid under a "ratio plan." Superintendent Spears and Chief Budget Officer McElligott of the San Francisco Unified School District show how a ratio plan can be employed to set the salaries of the entire professional staff.

The San Francisco school district has a simplified salary structure that requires a minimum of study in its annual consideration. It is based on the ratio plan.

San Francisco's single salary schedule meshes together all parts of the school system. By dropping a hundred dollar raise into the slot — the first step of the first classification of the basic schedule — a complete revision is automatically set in motion. The teacher on the top step of the last classification pockets $190, the elementary principal collects $262, and so on all around the professional circuit.

By this relatively simple action, the board, by a single decision, adjusts the salaries of all 3800 certificated employes except the superintendent, who is employed on contract.

Reprinted, with permission, from *The Nation's Schools,* March, 1962.

Table 1

SINGLE SALARY SCHEDULE IN RATIOS AND SALARIES

Rating	Classification 1		Classification 2		Classification 3	
(Steps)	Ratio	Salary	Ratio	Salary	Ratio	Salary
1	1.000	$5060	1.079	$5460	1.162	$5880
2	1.048	5305	1.136	5750	1.229	6220
3	1.097	5550	1.194	6040	1.296	6560
4	1.145	5795	1.251	6330	1.364	6900
5	1.194	6040	1.308	6620	1.431	7240
6	1.242	6285	1.366	6910	1.498	7580
7	1.291	6530	1.423	7200	1.565	7920
8	1.339	6775	1.480	7490	1.632	8260
9	1.387	7020	1.537	7780	1.700	8600
10	1.436	7265	1.595	8070	1.767	8940
11	1.484	7510	1.652	8360	1.834	9280
12	1.533	7755	1.709	8650	1.901	9620
13	1.581	8000	1.767	8940		
14	1.629	8245				

Table 1 shows the San Francisco basic single salary schedule both in ratios and salaries. The figures indicate there is a ratio of 1.9 between the beginning salary of $5060 (the bottom step in Classification 1) and the maximum salary of $9620 (the top step in Classification 3). The three classifications show the various gradations of academic preparation. Within each classification there can be uniform vertical advancement through increments for added training and experience.

THREE CLASSIFICATIONS

The San Francisco basic single salary schedule involves three preparational classifications, with these qualifications: (1) the bachelor degree or equivalent; (2) the bachelor degree or equivalent, plus 30 semester hours or equivalent units, and (3) bachelor degree or equivalent, plus 60 semester hours or equivalent units.

In principle, the three classifications indicate, in numerical order, gradations of preparation promising maximum teaching contribution. Each gradation is rewarded accordingly.

In addition to this provision for horizontal advancement in training and compensation, the salary schedule provides for vertical advancement on each of the three classifications by added training and experience.

To foster continuous improvement in service, and as a basis of eligibility to vertical increment advancement, the teacher must satisfactorily complete six semester hours of work for each three school years in Classification 1; six semester hours for each four years in Classification 2, and six semester hours for each five years in Classification 3.

This basic schedule encompasses all full-time, regularly appointed teachers except those at City College, which is the junior college.

RATIO PLAN

In March 1961 the board of education, upon the recommendation of Supt. Harold Spears, adopted as the salary schedule the ratios shown in the accompanying tables. The salaries in the tables represent the application of the ratios, based on the beginning step of $5060 of Table 1, the basic schedule.

This means that if at any future time the board wishes to increase the salary provisions of the schedule, it will determine a monetary raise to be applied to this beginning step; the other salaries will be determined automatically.

To apply the ratios, annual salary amounts are rounded out to end in zero or five, and to provide a uniform dollar increment within each classification.

JUNIOR COLLEGE

The schedule of salaries for the junior college (or City College) parallels Classification 3 in maintaining the following relationships: (1) the same number of steps between minimum and maximum; (2) the same monetary increment between ratings, and (3) the same monetary difference between each rating of Classification 3 and the City College schedule. The ratio ranges in 12 steps from 1.253 to 1.992 (Table 2) as related to the lowest step (1.0) of the basic schedule.

Table 2
SALARY SCHEDULE FOR JUNIOR COLLEGE

Rating	Ratio	Salary
1	1.253	$ 6,340
2	1.320	6,680
3	1.387	7,020
4	1.455	7,360
5	1.522	7,700
6	1.589	8,040
7	1.656	8,380
8	1.723	8,720
9	1.791	9,060
10	1.858	9,400
11	1.925	9,740
12	1.992	10,080

Table 2 shows the ratio and salary range for City College instructors. The lowest step for the junior college represents a ratio of 1.253 when compared with the lowest step in the basic salary schedule for teachers. It rises in 12 steps to 1.992, which is equivalent to a salary of $10,080.

Table 3
ADMINISTRATORS' SALARIES BY RATIO IN SINGLE SALARY SCHEDULE

Position	Minimum	Maximum
Base		
Teacher Maximum (Class. 3–12)	1.000	1.000
Central Office		
Administrative adviser	1.904	2.270
Assistant superintendent	1.641	2.006
Chief, division of budgets	1.641	2.006
Coordinator A	1.573	1.875
Coordinator B	1.441	1.681
Director	1.441	1.681
Asst. chief, division of budgets	1.441	1.681
Supervisor AA	1.310	1.549
Supervisor A	1.087	1.378
City College		
President	1.772	2.138
Coordinator	1.511	1.744
Dean of instruction	1.429	1.663
Dean of men & student activities	1.367	1.601
Dean of women	1.367	1.601
Registrar	1.367	1.601
Director of placement	0.870	1.155
Director of testing & research	0.870	1.155
Assistant registrar	0.846	1.046
Secondary and Elementary		
Principal, secondary	1.253	1.538
Principal, elementary	1.087	1.378
Asst. principal, secondary	1.087	1.298
Asst. principal, elementary	1.000	1.133

Table 3 shows how salaries of the various administrators are blanketed into the teachers' single basic salary structure by ratio. The lowest salaried administrative position begins with the highest step of Classification 3 of the teachers' basic schedule. Thus, a ratio of 1.000 is equivalent to a salary of $9620. Further application of the ratios to administrative salaries is illustrated in this article.

CHILD CARE

Besides the 135 regular schools, San Francisco has 25 child care centers that provide for the care and supervision of children for working mothers. In the new salary structure, the child care teachers were geared into the basic schedule by ratio. It was determined that the maximum salary in the child care program would be equal to the fifth step of Classification 1 of the scale for regular teachers.

This guarantees continued professional status to child care service teachers and, at the same time, distinguishes between the higher professional demands of the regular classroom teacher and those of the child care teacher, as recognized by the state code. Child care teachers who aspire to higher salaries than those established for employes in this classification are encouraged to qualify and apply for positions as regular teachers in the San Francisco schools.

Gearing the child care schedule into the basic single salary schedule in this manner meant establishing ratios for the steps in the existing child care schedule. The base point in this meshing of schedules would be Classification 1, Rating 5, of the basic single salary schedule and the maximum of the highest classification of child care. This point, therefore, has been established as 1.000 in the ratio. As it is the maximum step of the child care schedule, all lower steps in the schedule will be stated as something less than 1.000, depending on their relationships to the maximum. The beginning step of child care is 0.742.

ADMINISTRATIVE SALARIES

Also blanketed into the structure by ratio are all administrators in the central office, in the City College, and in the secondary and elementary schools.

The following summary shows both the number of classifications and the number of positions in each area:

	Classifications	*Positions*
Central office	9	46
City College	9	13
Secondary and elementary schools	4	213
Total	22	272

There are five ratings in each classification; advancement through the ratings is based on service within the classification. In the sole case of the classification of assistant elementary principal, there are only three ratings because of the narrow range between the minimum and maximum salary.

In gearing the elementary assistant principal into the salary structure, the lowest salaried position begins at the same salary as the highest step of Classification 3 of the teachers' basic schedule. Table 3 carries all the ratios.

The following figures show the application of the ratios in Table 3 to representative positions.

	Minimum	*Maximum*
Assistant superintendent	$15,790	$19,300
Supervisor A	10,460	13,260
Principal, secondary	12,050	14,800
Principal, elementary	10,460	13,260
Assistant principal, secondary	10,460	12,490
Assistant principal, elementary	9,620	10,900

Basic Principles

Underlying San Francisco's basic salary schedule were these considerations:

1. *Inservice work*, by the very requirements of the salary schedule, implies value that will be carried over into the teacher's classroom.

2. No *bargaining privileges* are given the superintendent in the schedule (applied as a single salary schedule).

3. So-called *longevity increments* are ruled out. In the case of money to be put into the salary schedule to benefit the maximum number of teachers (they are most in need of a proper living allowance), it would be well to concentrate upon the regular schedule with the number of classification lanes now provided, rather than to add so-called longevity increments. Good salaries are reflected in quality teaching, and such teaching should be effected as early as possible in the teacher's career.

4. The setting up of *separate schedules for splinter groups*, such as guidance counselors, home teachers, and attendance officers, was avoided. It would be extremely difficult to judge this service more important than classroom teaching. That the teacher of any pupil, in or out of the basic classroom group, is a specialist is the standard that must be adhered to in the improvement of salary schedules.

5. New San Francisco teachers with *full-time outside teaching experience* receive one increment credit for each two years of such experience, not to exceed a total of two increments.

San Francisco has been fortunate in its supply of teacher candidates. We have been able to maintain a high degree of selectivity. The written examinations for teachers, which are a hurdle for acceptance to the local schools, stand as an exception to general school practice and indicate the high standards that we are able to maintain.

The present practice of a maximum of two increment steps for previous experience enables the district (1) to distribute more of its salary funds to *career teachers*, and (2) to balance its teaching staff in age by employing each year a noticeable number of young teachers at the bottom of the schedule. In the case of Point 1, a greater distribution of the total salary money to beginning teachers with experience would invariably handicap the district in holding out higher salaries at the upper levels of the schedule.

6. The policy of setting advanced classifications by 30 and 60 hours of work beyond the bachelor's degree represents certain advantages over the M.A. and doctoral requirements for advanced classification placement. Degree requirements tend to deny teachers the rights to the higher salaries, whereas a salary structure should promote growth study. The San Francisco plan enables the teacher to select his advanced work to serve his immediate teaching needs, and at times these needs change suddenly. He can procure inservice units in courses planned by the local district in relation to the instructional program.

7. The determined relationship by ratio of the highest step of the basic schedule to the beginning step has been set at 1.9. In our opinion, this is a fair ratio for a single salary schedule, providing automatic advancement with the minimum of inservice work required.

By its basic single salary plan, the San Francisco school district has taken a long step in simplifying the annual consideration of salaries. As the question of salaries for 1962–63 is faced this spring, the new structure that has been adopted will serve as a firm bridge to the new year.

46

Problems in the Measurement and Prediction of Teacher Effectiveness

A. S. Barr

This excerpt is drawn from the introductory section of an important study on merit pay directed by Professor Barr at the University of Wisconsin. The depth of the problems in the assessment of teachers' contributions is clearly revealed.

To select, recruit, educate, and assign teachers to particular teaching positions in an acceptable manner, one must have more precise information about the many meanings associated with teaching, in general, and in particular situations; and how to identify the personal, academic, and professional prerequisites to effectiveness.

Part of the difficulty associated with the development of an adequate program for the measurement and prediction of teacher effectiveness arises from the facts that teaching means many different things, that the teaching act varies from person to person, and from situation to situation. Teachers teach different subjects and at different grade levels; they may not teach sub-

Adapted from "The Nature of the Problem," in *Wisconsin Studies of the Measurement and Prediction of Teacher Effectiveness,* Madison, Dembar Publications, Inc., 1961, pp. 5–8. Reproduced with permission.

jects but direct activities; besides classroom instruction they are presumed to be friends and counselors of students, members of a school community, and members of various local, state, and national associations of professional workers. With the situation as it is, the researchers interested in the measurement and prediction of teacher effectiveness have basically two choices: one, to seek the essence of teaching found within a wide range of activities called teaching and the means of predicting efficiency in a variety of situations; or second, to measure efficiency in particular learning and teaching situations and predict these particular efficiencies. These particular situations may be carefully controlled situations as found in experimental research or the uncontrolled situations of particular schools, classes, and school systems. The first problem is one of definition; one must define teaching before it can be evaluated and effectiveness predicted.

A further difficulty arises out of the fact that the concept of efficiency is nowhere well defined. Here as with the definition of teaching there are many different concepts of efficiency. The opinions are so varied among teacher educators, administrators, and teachers that each person can be said to have a more or less private system of evaluation all his own. This is not a mere statement of opinion but a matter that has been amply substantiated by research. The amount of divergence that one would expect to find in a particular situation would depend, of course, upon the composition of the group making the evaluation, the extent to which an attempt has been made to standardize criteria and provide training in their use, and the particular teacher or aspect of teaching being evaluated. In uncontrolled situations the judgments of a group of supervisors, administrators, and teacher educators, all observing the same teacher at the same time, under identical conditions, may vary so much that some observers may rate a particular teacher as among the very worst teachers that they have observed. Much that is important in providing good schools depends upon the accuracy with which teachers are evaluated.

There are many predictions made in the course of selecting and recruiting persons to be trained as teachers, in the education of teachers, and in the placement and employment of teachers. Many persons have failed to realize that so many predictions are made in the procurement and management of the teaching personnel. When admission standards are set in teacher educating institutions, in effect a prediction is made, namely, that persons meeting these standards do have the potential to be good teachers; when curricula are established for the education of teachers, a prediction is made, namely, that persons who pursue these curricula will become good teachers; when the superintendent employs an experienced or inexperienced teacher, he assumes, or at least hopes, that she will succeed. The employment score for some administrators is not very high in this respect.

The problem under discussion involves many psychological considerations. First of all, attempts to measure and predict teacher efficiency make assumptions relative to the nature of human abilities. As one examines the literature, it can readily be observed that human abilities have taken on many meanings. Sometimes they are thought of as physical processes and sometimes as symbolical processes. Sometimes they are referred to as psycho-physical entities and sometimes as operations. They are sometimes considered as something very specific such as the ability to read the temperature from a very sensitive thermometer or as something very general such as the ability to do certain types of mathematical calculations. Sometimes they are spoken of in even more general terms as when one speaks of academic intelligence, mechanical intelligence, or social intelligence. Sometimes abilities are referred to as primary and sometimes as secondary; sometimes as deep and underlying operations and sometimes as easily observed surface or superficial events. We shall look upon all such use of the term as matters of convenience but shall at all times attempt to keep the reader informed about the meaning intended.

The nature of human abilities cannot be adequately defined without some reference to the mind-body relationship. We shall assume that mind and body are one and discuss teaching effectiveness, chiefly, in terms (1) of operations, processes, and behaviors, (2) of conditions, internal and external, considered essential to easy, smooth, and efficient operations, and (3) of end products, outcomes and results, that follow from operations. When words like intelligence, tact, forcefulness, forthrightness, or cooperation are used, they will, in general, be used to describe behavior rather than innate qualities or traits. The conditions, both external and internal, under which teaching takes place will be treated as far as possible on a factual basis and in a manner such as to include both psycho-physical processes and socio-physical environment factors and their many interrelationships.

The above very general statement may be rendered somewhat more meaningful by a further discussion of certain aspects of the problem. Consider, for example, the personal internal condition essential to efficient operations so generally lost sight of in teacher efficiency studies. Proper physiological functioning, including sensory processes, neurological processes, circulatory processes, digestive processes, excretory processes, and glandular processes, is assumed to constitute a basic source of conditions that limit and facilitate efficiency in teaching. The psychologists are not ordinarily directly concerned with these but they are nonetheless important and need much more consideration than they ordinarily receive. They constitute, doubtlessly, the most important single source of causes of efficiency and inefficiency in teaching. These processes underlie many of the causes of effective and ineffective teaching frequently discussed at a more superficial level by psychologists and in a manner that may be quite abstract and ambiguous.

In this connection, a point should be made of the fact that many persons interested in effective classroom instruction will not be content to merely study behavior. Much can be learned from the study of behavior and as a psychological operation it certainly is a vast improvement over the study of the stream of consciousness which characterized psychology at the turn of the century. Many will desire, however, to know how behaviors come to be, their concomitants, and antecedents. Much of the current theorizing about behavior and other psychological uncertainties arises out of the unwillingness of many psychologists to look beyond and back of events. The point here is that much can be learned about teacher efficiency from the study of psychophysical processes.

Another critical point in the study of human abilities will be found in the sensory processes and perception. Much attention was given to the testing of the sensory processes at the turn of the century in attempts to measure intelligence but not with too much success. Those studying the matter did find out, however, that individuals differed, and laid the basis for further investigation. As the matter has been pursued further, and with better investigational procedures, much new information has been had. Among the broader generalizations that have arisen from this study is the concept of early learning. In a certain sense, sensory perceptions are learned and much that will condition human behavior and efficiency will be learned in the first few years after birth and during the pre-school period. The nature and functioning of perception needs careful study as it relates to teacher efficiency. In a more complex and more highly generalized level, fruitful research has already been conducted with reference to such matters as social perception, self-perception, and the teacher's perception of all sorts of teaching situations. This would appear to be closely related to any basic attack upon the measurement and prediction of teacher efficiency.

Another critical point in human behavior and efficiency will be found in the ties that have been established between physical and symbolic manipulation in each individual teacher's way of thinking and behavior. The building of these connections comes chiefly in preschool and early elementary school education. This being as it is, the matter has been generally looked upon as water over the dam and not amenable to further study and improvement. But, presumably, the connection between the physical world and the symbolic world is faulty or inadequate in many instances. Many people live in a world of symbols that have little connection with the realities of life. As a matter of fact, much of the discussion of teaching is quite remote. Possibly a study of just how teachers perceive the many things associated with teaching, the concepts that they hold, and their ability to manipulate verbal symbols might provide new insights into teacher efficiency. Teaching involves an immense amount of verbalization.

In the immediately preceding discussion, attention has been focused upon the antecedents of teacher efficiency. The researcher who purports to assess human abilities must be equipped not merely with lists of the concomitants of ability but he must have ideas about how these are categorized and structured. One of the theories about structure is that ability can be thought of as some general power (Spearman called this general factor g) plus a host of special capabilities. Other theories emphasize the importance of group factors. Thurstone, for example, stresses the importance of what he called the primary mental abilities. The manner in which he structured these abilities, useful as it seemed to be for certain purposes, may or may not be helpful for the evaluation and the prediction of teacher effectiveness. Much has also been said about the dimensions of abilities. Thorndike, for example, emphasized the dimensions of breadth and depth. Guilford has pursued this matter intensely for many years and has suggested a much more elaborate structure. It would seem that the researcher in this area must give some consideration to structure.

More use should be made of psychological theory. It is an important source of ideas about teaching ability and competency, but the other side of the coin is equally important, that is what is done must be workable, practical, or useful in a situation composed of many factors other than psychological theory. Besides the skepticism that many practitioners have of psychologists and their theories, there is the need that theory be set forth with more objectivity, and in a manner that is more meaningful to practitioners. For one thing, theory must be simplified; this usually comes with more insight. What is frequently lost sight of is that theory by its very nature tends to emphasize the generalizable and to neglect the specifics. Practitioners are seldom allowed to forget specifics. The researchers involved in the investigations here summarized would appear to be generally familiar with the theories of the structure of human abilities but their specific assumptions in this respect are frequently inadequately set forth.

Even when one is clear about the various ways of categorizing and structuring human abilities, different vocabularies may be employed in talking about the matter. This would appear to be particularly true of the discussions of the special talents presumed to be prerequisites to different teaching assignments, wherein teachers teach many different things under a variety of conditions to pupils with different capacities. It is not generally assumed that the special talents required of teachers are possessed in equal amounts by any particular teacher or that they are highly intercorrelated. This latter point becomes exceedingly important in correlation studies where traditionally low correlations are generally assumed to be undesirable. . . . Correlations cannot be taken at face value. At this point it is emphasized that the talents of individuals are highly diversified and that it is doubtlessly psychologically unsound to expect many high level talents in any particular individual or that they will be highly intercorrelated. It is probably sound to assume that there is a considerable number of one-talent teachers. There is a lesser number of two-talent teachers; and very few many-talented teachers. In light of current theories of the structure of human abilities, it is probably best to hypothesize that teaching ability is composed of some particular combinations of special and general abilities. Much of the research relative to the evaluation and prediction of teacher effectiveness does not seem to reflect this point of view to any considerable extent.

Besides the foregoing problems there are the discrepancies between potential and observed efficiency that one must expect. For many reasons many individuals do not live up to expectancy. These discrepancies may arise from many reasons: lack of interest in pupils, teaching, and the subjects taught; lack of physical energy, determination, and drive; lack of adaptability, flexibility, or the ability to adjust to different needs, persons, and situations; personality conflicts, rigid value systems, and attitudes unacceptable to majority groups: teachers, parents, pupils, administrators, supervisors, and all others with whom the teacher may come in contact. These deal chiefly with the feeling components of behavior and are part of the potential except that measures of potential have dealt chiefly with its cognitive aspects. Since, for various reasons, people do not live up to expectations, those who would predict efficiency must include in their machinery of prediction some of the non-static aspects of behavior.

Possibly some thought should also be given to the nature of measurement. Measurement is a device for eliciting behaviors under standard conditions. Most of the behaviors studied through the so-called standardized test are verbal behaviors and while teaching may be studied by means of direct observation, measurement is frequently nothing more or less than the counting of the number of verbal acts correctly performed under a given set of conditions. Very great attention has been given to the quantification of these verbal exercises and the statistical treatment of data secured through them. All statistical calculations involve, however, assumptions and these assumptions need most systematic study as they relate to the measurement and prediction of teacher efficiency. Whether these statistical-verbal operations are profitable or not for measuring and predicting teacher efficiency needs further consideration and more study, notwithstanding the very great amount of time and effort already devoted to it.

Finally, a problem that must be of continued concern to those interested in the measurement and prediction of teacher effectiveness is that of an adequate criterion. By and large, and with many exceptions, two criteria have been used: (1) efficiency ratings of one sort or another, and (2) measured pupil gains. Both present real difficulties. Over all, general ratings of teacher effectiveness have been shown to be, under current conditions, exceedingly unreliable. Depending upon one's point of view, this unreliability provides a substantial road block or a challenge to the researcher interested in this area of research. A further difficulty arises out of the fact that where a number of subjects are employed, as is usually the case, drawn from a number of different school systems, or even from the same school system, the teachers rated are generally not rated upon the same performance. That is, they do different things. While the differences in what teachers do are not ordinarily as extreme as juggling acts and memorizing non-sense syllables, they are nonetheless different. Thus, to use efficiency ratings, even with well developed scales and highly trained raters, one must assume a large amount of transfer from one set of tasks to another (tasks which may be called teaching), to measure and predict teacher effectiveness.

The use of measured pupil gain as a criterion of teacher effectiveness also presents very real difficulties. First of all, each teacher in the modern school, within very broad limits, chooses his own purposes, means, and methods of instruction. These ordinarily vary from one school system to another and within named grade levels and subject fields. Regardless of the validating data reported in test manuals, the tests used in developing the pupil gain criterion will have varying degrees of operational validity, except as the teachers agree to pursue certain stated objectives which can be defined with sufficient clarity to provide like meanings to all the participants. A second difficulty arises out of the fact that, notwithstanding over a half century of effort, many of the outcomes of learning and of teaching are poorly or inadequately measured. The gaps in the criterion arising from inadequate tests with which to measure pupil gain will be found to be considerable. Finally, tests measure effects but not causes. The sources of the effects observed are not readily ascertained, even under carefully controlled experimental conditions. Some of these effects will reside in the pupils, some in their general and special capabilities, some in their previous training, and some in motivation. A few of the effects are doubtlessly traceable to the home environment: socio-economic status, respect for school education, and direct assistance rendered by various members of the family. A few of the effects will be traceable to the school and community: In some, teachers' and pupils' morale is high and in some it is low. The physical facilities of different schools and communities vary greatly. And finally, there are the direct and indirect effects of the teaching of other teachers, both in the same and related subjects. One of the very best measures of a teacher's effectiveness will be found in what his students do in subsequent course work. Accordingly, the problem of establishing an adequate criterion of pupil gain will not be an easy one.

47

A Foundation Approach to Merit Pay

Myron Lieberman

This is a radical departure in the thinking about merit pay and, indeed, about the career patterns of teachers, broadly considered. Dr. Lieberman, the author of Education as a Profession, *has a notable reputation as a writer on educational topics.*

Merit pay (or "merit rating") is really a cluster of problems growing out of one major issue confronting public education. Most school systems pay all teachers strictly according to their level of training and years of experience. This policy is commonly referred to as "the single salary schedule." As a rule, the policy makes no allowance for the subject or grade level taught. An elementary teacher, a teacher of driver education, and a physics teacher, each with an M.A. degree and five years of teaching experience, receive the same salary in communities adhering to single salary schedules.

Single salary schedules vary from community to community. They may differ in their minimums, their maximums, the size of the increments from year to year, the number of steps on the schedule, the allowable credit for prior teaching experience, and other factors. Nevertheless, wherever they are used, teachers are not paid according to any judgment of their effectiveness as teachers. They are employed, retained, or fired on the basis of such judgments, but fewer and fewer are compensated on this basis. In 1956–57, less than 5 per cent of the public school teachers in cities of 2,500 or more population were employed under salary schedules which made any provision for merit pay. Less than half of the school systems which authorized or specified higher pay for superior service were actually paying any teachers for such service.[1]

Single salary schedules inevitably result in relatively low maximum salaries.

Adapted from "A Foundation Approach to Merit Pay," *Phi Delta Kappan,* Volume XLI, No. 3 (December, 1959), pp. 118–122. Reproduced with permission.

[1] This statement is based upon an estimate made in a letter to me from Hazel Davis, associate director, Research Division, NEA, dated August 25, 1958. The best recent summary of the extent and nature of merit pay may be found in NEA Research Division, *Superior-Service Maximums in Teachers Salary Schedules,* 1956–57 (Washington, D.C.: National Education Association, 1957).

Since all teachers are eligible to receive the maximum, and since teachers are a large occupational group, any schedule with high maximums encounters strong community opposition. Communities are, or may be, willing to pay outstanding teachers outstanding salaries, but they are not going to pay *every* teacher such a salary.

Teachers' organizations and probably most school administrators are opposed to salary differentials among teachers on the basis of merit or alleged merit. Merit rating is usually a divisive factor among teachers themselves, because there appears to be no commonly accepted procedure to implement it. If school administrators decide who gets the merit raises, teachers become unduly subservient to the administrators, and there is always the possibility if not the fact of favoritism in awarding merit increases. Many school administrators do not relish the task of singling out the "better" teachers for salary purposes, especially if they have to work with those who are turned down for merit increases. If teachers decide who get the merit raises, they end up wrangling among themselves.

A school system might conceivably employ consultants or an outside agency to evaluate its teachers. This procedure presents a dilemma. In order for the outside evaluators to make competent judgments, they would have to observe the teachers several times a year. However, if each teacher were visited only once a month by an evaluator, the costs would be enormous. As an illustration, consider the costs of evaluation in New York City, which has approximately 40,000 professional employees, of whom well over 30,000 are teachers. Sound personnel policy would require that the evaluators be at least as well qualified, and presumably as well paid, as the teachers they evaluate. The costs of visiting each of 30,000 teachers ten times per year would be prohibitively high under these circumstances.

It would be possible to reduce the over-all cost of merit rating by operating on a somewhat different plan. A school system might consider for merit raises only teachers who had been employed a certain number of years, and fewer than ten visits per teacher per year might be required. However, teaching is not an assembly-line operation. Even good teachers have their share of bad days. For this reason, few teachers would care to have important decisions about their future made on the basis of only a few visits a year. It is obvious that the fewer the visits, the more likelihood that non-merit factors will determine who gets the best ratings.

Earlier, I stated that merit rating was really a cluster of problems rather than one narrow and well-defined problem. A workable plan for merit rating must solve such issues as who shall do the rating, what shall be the criteria for rating, how often shall rating be carried out, who shall be rated, how much of the salary budget shall depend on merit rating, and what differentials are to be paid for what differences in rating. Practically all plans for paying teachers according to merit have eventually been rejected because one or another of these problems was not solved to the satisfaction of school boards or teachers or both.

Who Shall Do the Rating?

Although there is no unanimity of opinion on any of these matters, the biggest stumbling block has probably been the question of who shall do the rating. Regular administrative personnel in a school system, such as department chairmen or principals, could do it without heavy additional expense, because their routine work usually requires them to evaluate teachers. Also, their daily presence in the school affords them many excellent opportunities to do so. However, reliance upon ratings by regular staff personnel is not likely to become widespread; too often severe tensions and poor morale are the outcomes of this solution. Administrator domination of teachers, even in their non-classroom activities, is also pronounced under this procedure. And since the employment of outside personnel is too costly, the situation appears to be hopeless. This stalemate has been a disaster to the teaching profession.

Can High Salaries Reduce Budgets?

The opponents of merit rating have often contended that it is a device to reduce school budgets. High salaries for the few are allegedly used to justify low salaries for the many. This argument overlooks the historical fact that the economic position of teachers has been declining for several decades and that this decline has taken place during a pronounced shift away from merit rating to single salary schedules. Also, plans for paying teachers according to merit vary in so many ways that there is little point to blanket condemnations of merit rating. Nevertheless, such condemnations are the rule at teachers' conventions where the subject is considered. In taking this attitude, teachers have failed to realize the harm done to our educational system by the absence of high top salaries in teaching (I am referring to salaries in the $10,000–$25,000 range, not the $8,000–$10,000 range which seems to concern most teachers).

So far as I know, not a single public school teacher in the country receives $15,000 per year, which is a conservative estimate of the average income of the medical profession. There are well over 1,000,000 public school classroom teachers in the United States, but it unlikely that more than 200 of them make $10,000 per year from their regular teaching salary. What is even more crucial is the fact that there are no income ceilings in medicine, law, engineering, and most other occupations which compete with education for personnel. Thus education fails to get its proper share of the most able, energetic, and aggressive persons. Since there are about 1,300,000 persons engaged in public education, it is obvious that many of them must have outstanding ability.

Nonetheless, the tremendous disparity between top salaries in teaching and in other fields drives away from teaching many individuals who would pull up the entire group.

One cannot measure the loss to education merely in terms of the number of good teachers lost in this way. One must visualize it in terms of its impact upon the professional standing of teachers and upon the loss of able educational leadership. For these reasons, even those who criticize current proposals for merit rating should be exerting every effort to develop a feasible way of implementing it. Certainly, we should not waste any time on those who believe that good teachers are immune to economic considerations.

NATIONAL SPECIALTY BOARDS

What, then, is the solution to the problem of merit pay? A partial solution may be found in the establishment of national specialty boards comparable to those in the medical profession. The latter provide special recognition in the form of a diplomate to physicians who achieve outstanding levels of skill and knowledge in a particular field, such as surgery or psychiatry. The procedure for acquiring the diplomate in a given field is handled by the national organization of specialists in that field, e.g., the American College of Surgeons sets the requirements and processes the examinations for the diplomate in surgery.

In education, such a plan might work in this way: The national organization of teachers in a given field, for example, the National Council of Teachers of Mathematics, could set up an examination procedure for the diplomate in their field. These examinations should be comprehensive and rigorous. They should test the applicant's knowledge of his subject and his ability to diagnose and prescribe for various kinds of teaching problems. They should include observation of the applicant in actual teaching situations and also evaluation of any instructional materials prepared by applicants. The entire procedure should be such that only outstanding teachers are "board certified."

The use of board certification would eliminate favoritism, boot-licking, horse-trading, and all the other evils inherent in merit rating procedures whereby teachers are rated by other personnel in their own school system. Since it would not be possible for anyone in the system to give or take away board certification from a teacher, the basis for the undesirable practices just mentioned would not exist. Furthermore, the fact that a teacher could carry his board certification with him to a new position would mean that his professional advancement would not be tied to the subjective judgment of particular administrators in particular school systems. The standards for board certification would have to be high and distinctive enough so that both the non-certified teachers and the public would regard board certification as a defensible basis for salary differentials. This would happen if there were a nationally recognized body which administered the board examinations under conditions scrupulously designed to achieve this purpose.

Notice also that a system of board certification should eliminate the opposition to merit rating by teachers' organizations. School administrators would not be in a position to coerce teachers' organizations by granting or withholding merit pay to particular teachers. There would be little occasion for squabbling within a teachers' organization over who should receive merit pay.

Opposition to merit pay based upon board certification might develop in the AFT if the organizations which administered the specialty board examinations were departments of the NEA. AFT members might fear that examinations under the control of organizations affiliated, albeit rather loosely, with the NEA might be prejudicial to AFT members.[2] I believe this organizational problem could be solved in several different ways. The examinations might be administered by an independent testing agency, such as the Educational Testing Service, or they might be administered by subject-matter organizations not affiliated with the NEA, such as the American Physical Society or the American Mathematical Association. Certainly, if any teachers' organization were to oppose such a plan merely out of its organizational fears, it would be rendering a great disservice to American education.

Should Be Extralegal, Nationwide

Specialty board certification should not become part of the state certification structure. It should be an extralegal process, so that the specialty boards could make necessary changes from time to time without going through legislative channels. It would also be essential that the specialty boards rigidly adhere to a single standard for teachers all over the country. In this way, any school system or college which employs a board certified teacher would be assured of getting a highly qualified professional employee.

A system of specialty boards would meet many of the objections to current proposals to pay salary differentials to superior teachers. The specialty boards would eliminate the morale problems inherent in having teachers and administrators evaluate their colleagues for salary purposes. Using board certification as the basis for merit pay would also eliminate the expense to school systems of evaluating teacher competence for purposes of salary differentiation. With a national specialty board, the cost of the examinations would be borne by the teachers, just as the cost of board certification in the medical profession is now borne by the doctors. The reason would be the same — the board certified teacher would receive substantial benefits from his new status. All that would be required of the school system is a policy decision to pay higher sal-

[2] At the 1958 Annual Convention of the AFT, I suggested the introduction of educational specialty boards to several AFT leaders. None objected to it *in principle* as a merit rating plan.

aries to board certified teachers. The salary differentials for such teachers would have to be large enough to make it worthwhile for them to strive for board certification at their own expense. I believe that many school boards would pay such differentials if they had confidence in the specialty board procedures.

RELATION TO TEACHER EDUCATION

The establishment of educational specialty boards might also help to solve some of the most pressing problems of teacher education. . . . Teacher-training institutions have yet to solve the problem of providing adequate supervision for student teachers. The supervising teachers in the schools are usually persons who lack advanced training. They are often selected haphazardly, without any real inquiry into their ability to help beginning teachers. To supplement the supervision they give, the teacher-training institutions send out supervisors who go to a different school every day to catch a fleeting glimpse of prospective teachers in action. This is a costly and inefficient procedure; the colleges cannot stand the financial burden of providing effective daily supervision for every student teacher. As a result, student teachers are seldom observed more than once every three or four weeks by a college supervisor.

If educational specialty boards were established, student teachers could receive their practical training under the guidance of board certified teachers. As supervisors, the board certified teachers could be treated as adjunct professors of the teacher-training institutions. Indeed, the extent to which a school system employed board certified teachers would be an indication of the caliber of that system. This would also follow medical practice, where the extent to which a hospital or clinic employs board certified specialists is widely accepted as an indication of its caliber. Many other professions have established procedures to identify their most competent practitioners.

Let us turn next to the problem of how to transform the idea of educational specialty boards into an operating reality. The proposed solution will illustrate the role which the foundations might play in remaking the structure of American public education.

First of all, the foundations might bring together the leaders of a few national organizations of specialists in certain fields. The most effective procedure would be to bring together leaders of the national organizations of professors and public school teachers in the same field. Thus in the field of mathematics there should be representation from both the American Mathematical Association and the National Council of Teachers of Mathematics. If the leaders of these organizations were agreeable, as I am sure they would be, the foundation could make relatively modest grants, say of $25,000, to these organizations to draw up proposed plans for board certification in their fields.

In due course, these organizations should draw up fairly complete plans for the operation of a specialty board in their subject. The plans would include provisions for who would conduct the examinations, the nature of the examinations, where and how often they would be given, the budget for the specialty board, the fees to be charged, the qualifications required of applicants, and so on. The foundation grants would make it possible for the organizations to secure the very best advice on these matters from teachers, leading scholars in each subject, and others with ideas to contribute.

When the plans are completed, they should be disseminated to school administrators and school boards over the country. The participating foundations might then convene a large number of leading classroom teachers, school superintendents, and school boards to assess their reactions to the proposals, either in a series of regional meetings or in national conferences or both. At these meetings, educational personnel would become fully acquainted with the proposed boards. After everyone concerned had ample opportunity to study the proposals, and after they had been changed in whatever ways seemed desirable in the light of these reactions, the issue of participation should be put squarely up to teachers' organizations, superintendents, and school boards. Naturally, local, state, and national organizations would be expected to encourage lay and professional acceptance of the proposed specialty boards.

Function of the Foundation

At this point, the attitude of the foundations should be something like this: Whenever a given number of school systems agree to pay at least a specified higher salary to board certified teachers, an additional grant would be made to cover the costs of specialty board operation for several years. After that time, the specialty boards would have to be self-supporting or supported by other sources. And if it were not possible to get a number of school boards to pay a substantial differential to board certified teachers, the foundation should indicate that it would abandon the enterprise.

This is only a skeletonized version of the strategy which might be employed to effectuate specialty boards, but it does illustrate some important points. One is that the foundations supporting such a project would not be trying to ram a particular change down anybody's throat. They would be making it possible to develop an idea, to discover whether it had widespread support, and to put it into effect if it did have such support. They would be foolish to push the idea of specialty boards past a certain point without support, but they would be fully justified in giving the idea an opportunity to catch on.

Advantages of National Approach

It would be easier to introduce board certification as a basis for merit pay on a national basis than on an isolated, local basis. It is always easier to get a school board to approve a change when many other boards have also approved it. Teachers are not likely to undertake the intensive study needed to pass their board examinations before they know how much more school systems will pay teachers who pass these examinations. School systems are not likely to pay an adequate differential to board certified teachers unless the boards are launched with unimpeachable professional and public support. All of this requires national planning and publicity.

The establishment of educational specialty boards would not be a complete answer to the problem of rewarding superior teachers. For one thing, the boards would not be geared directly to the teacher's actual performance on the job from year to year. A teacher who had passed his board examinations might nevertheless lie down on the job. Some outstanding teachers would never get around to securing board certification. Despite these and other potential weaknesses, the specialty boards could provide a reasonably objective way of distinguishing and rewarding outstanding teachers. The big danger would be the degeneration of board standards, such as would take place if board certification were based upon the accumulation of credits, travel, service to the community, and criteria of this nature. It might be feasible to begin with boards which examined only the teacher's knowledge of his subject. This seems to me to be unduly restrictive, but it would be better than no boards at all.

In evaluating the idea of educational specialty boards one should not assume that the idea is not feasible unless the boards provide an unerring guide to teacher competence. Nor should it be thought necessary that the boards remove all need for evaluative judgment within a school system. Merit is not always rewarded in other occupations. Some persons receive more than their due in every occupation. It would, however, be a blunder to reject merit rating in principle because no current way of implementing it promises absolute accuracy. For that matter, even the supporters of the single salary schedule admit that it results in many inequities. We are urged to endure these inequities only because nothing better has been proposed. This may be, but the long-range harm resulting from single salary schedules should stimulate everyone to search for a better plan to compensate teachers.

My proposal for educational specialty boards has two objectives: first, to illustrate a possible answer to an important problem of professional compensation, and, second, to illustrate how the foundations might act to change the structure of American education. Let me conclude by discussing the latter objective briefly.

Like the people in the field, the foundations are characterized by an unwarranted faith in a community-by-community approach to educational reform. In their case, it is reflected in an emphasis upon "demonstrations" or "pilot projects." This faith is all the more plausible since, for some purposes, demonstrations or pilot projects are the only feasible way to get improvements. Nevertheless, reliance upon demonstrations and pilot projects has a tendency to narrow the scope of needed foundation activities. At the national level, you cannot demonstrate the wisdom of certain changes by "pilot projects"; you either make the change or you don't.

The changes which the foundations must support will threaten vested interests of all kinds — professional, religious, political, racial, and economic. A great deal will depend upon the foundation trustees. They must provide the climate within which the permanent staff of the foundations can support the bold action that is needed. For this, the trustees must have a vision of what public education can be, and they must be persons not easily bluffed by legislatures, investigating committees, disgruntled applicants, or vested interests of any kind. Their difficulties and dangers will be great, but their opportunity is immeasurable.

48

A Salary Plan

Harvard Center for Field Studies

This is a salary plan proposed by the Center for Field Studies for the Concord, Massachusetts, school system. It offers an approximation to position classification of public school teachers.

Basic Assumptions

A *salary* is usually defined as a payment for a certain amount of human service rendered in the present period of time. Several recommendations are made in this report, and reasons are given to support each one. To help the reader consider the recommendations and reasons for them, certain basic assumptions on the remuneration of personnel must be understood and accepted. The underlying assumptions are:

(1) People who offer their services in return for a salary normally have alternatives in making their offer. They may choose one of several lines of

Adapted from Harvard Center for Field Studies, *A Salary Program: Studies of the Concord Public Schools*, Cambridge, Graduate School of Education, Harvard University, 1959, pp. 1–2, 21–24, 26.

work[1] such as engineering, business, or education. Additionally, a person may have choices as to where he wants to offer his services and to whom he desires to make his offer. In public education, these two choices are usually made at the same time. A person also is able to pick a specific work assignment within a given line of work. For example, he might choose to be an elementary classroom teacher or an assistant principal, both of which are in education.

(2) Level of salary is one of the major measures of the relative attractiveness of a line of work, of the place of work, and of a particular work assignment.

(3) In a line of work, some work assignments are "more demanding" than others. Some carry extra-heavy responsibilities; some require a rare kind of inborn talent; some are based on acquisition of highly specialized training; and some are unusually exhausting.

(4) Among people with the same training and experience who hold similar work assignments, there will be observable differences in the contributions they make as individuals to the task at hand.

(5) Aside from level of salary, security is considered to be a major factor in the attractiveness of a line of work for a large number of people.

Because of the first two assumptions, school authorities need to pay salaries high enough for education to be in a favorable competitive position with other lines of work that employ college graduates. . . . Public education is so vital to contemporary American life that it should draw the talents of the most gifted of college graduates. This is a long-range goal for staffing schools.

. . . .

Furthermore, because of the third and fourth assumptions, extrinsic (monetary) rewards are desirable in order to encourage some members of the staff to undertake the "more demanding" work assignments and to recognize the exceptionally high contribution that some members of the staff make in a given work assignment. The problem for Concord and other communities is not just how to attract outstanding individuals to its staff but also how to provide a work climate within which they are likely to continue to use their talents in an effective way.

The foregoing line of reasoning may lead to advocating that salaries should be determined annually for each individual. Every staff member's pay ideally would depend upon an assessment of the complexity of his assignment and of his performance in it. In view of the fifth assumption, however, the study staff believes that the expectation of an orderly advancement from a beginning salary to a reasonably adequate maximum salary according to a schedule is a major attraction in public education for many people. . . . The sensible

[1] The phrase "line of work" is used to describe an activity such as public education. The more common term, occupation, would require that public school teachers and public school administrators be considered as separate groups.

course is for the Concord schools to continue to compete for the services of outstanding individuals who place a high value on security. An attempt to determine salaries on an individual basis would also be hampered by limitations of administrative staff. A complete salary program, therefore, would include elements both of a schedule under which advancement is largely automatic for the majority of personnel and of a plan by which salaries are determined individually for personnel who meet certain extraordinary criteria.

. . . .

Payment on the Basis of Differentiated Work Assignments

In the process of analyzing the salary policies and practices in the Concord schools and preparing recommendations for a future salary program, the study staff has come to view the maximum salary opportunities as especially important. The establishment of a justifiable and competitive maximum salary in any line of work is difficult when one or more of the following conditions prevail: (1) The salary program is being developed for a large rather than a small classification of workers. (2) Workers in the classification perform approximately the same function. (3) The level of training, experience, or education is sufficiently high to permit the quality of personnel sought to have a choice among several career patterns. (4) An accepted method for determining differences in productivity or competence among those engaged in the enterprise is lacking. (5) Salary or wages are derived from local tax sources. (6) Practice makes it possible for all, or a high percentage, of those engaged in the enterprise to reach maximum salary by one procedure or another. (7) The expectation of all within the classification is that progression to maximum is automatic.

. . . .

The conditions listed above that have served as barriers to the recruitment and retention of competent career-minded teachers have been recognized by school officials in recent years. . . . The most common way to get around them has been the promise of, or actual promotion to, an administrative position. By this procedure, desired personnel are at least held within the ranks of education. Aside from the loss of competent teachers from the classrooms, the relative scarcity of administrative positions within a school system has made this a limited solution.

A second method of overcoming the conditions is awarding supermaximum salaries to teachers whose classroom performance has been at least satisfactory and who have by faithful service reached the limit of the salary schedule. While this type of reward may be justified for the majority of teachers, this technique does not contribute to the solution of the basic problem which is the need to create a salary policy which permits a career progression comparable to other professions and occupations.

Third, the Concord schools with other systems have attempted to enhance careers in teaching through a form of an Outstanding Service Award. This award is a close relative to "merit schedules" found in salary programs in the country. These kinds of provisions should be included in a complete salary program even though such features are inadequate to establish significant differentials in salary by themselves. Nationally, $200 is usually the largest amount granted above regular schedules for outstanding service. An important reason for such small salary differentials appears to be the inability on the part of school officials to defend paying *markedly* different sums to teachers who are performing what is defined as the same task.

If markedly higher salaries for outstanding teachers become common practice in the future, certain other inadequacies in the present concept on "merit schedules" will likely become troublesome. For example, the highly paid teacher might become a model for the inexperienced one. The present operation of "merit schedules," however, does not provide clear guides on what patterns of training and experience should be followed to become an outstanding teacher. Furthermore, evaluation of the job of the teacher as a "general practitioner" is a highly subjective process. Because of this reasoning, a cardinal rule for "merit schedules" has been that the plan of evaluation must be worked out for each school system. Each plan ideally has to be constructed by local teachers, administrators, and board members working together. The localism in "merit schedules" implies that a person can expect at best "local success." Superior performance is evaluated according to standards of one particular school system. Under this practice, uncertainty would always prevail whether a teacher judged to be outstanding in one school system would receive the same high rating in another. Local success may be sufficient inducement for a person in one of the "fee-taking" professions such as medicine or law to devote his life to the profession; but a teacher is an employee, and he needs more assurance that good work in one place opens up for him the opportunity to bid effectively for attractive positions elsewhere.

Though a single salary schedule has been proposed for continuation in the Concord Public Schools as a basic feature of its salary program, the study staff has concluded that this plan of payment will sooner or later have to be modified to permit a division of labor, differentiation of jobs, or specialization. At the present time the staffing arrangements in the Concord schools and in the vast majority of school systems throughout the United States assign equal basic responsibility to all teachers. Differentiation of jobs other than by grade level or subject area is generally not attempted. The beginning teacher is expected to carry the same approximate responsibility as the experienced teacher. This kind of situation is not found usually in other professions or work areas which offer a lifetime career to the workers. As an illustration, when a thoroughly experienced teacher retires who has had the benefit of extensive training, he will likely find that the full responsibility for the duties he performed in the classroom are passed along the following year to a new member of the teaching staff who has had no experience and only the minimum amount of formal training required for certification. . . .

The replacing of highly trained and experienced personnel by the relatively untrained and inexperienced does not prevail in business, law, or engineering. Whereas the meaning of a "career" may not yet have been closely defined in the literature, the concept assuredly includes the following requirement: A person has a career if, when he hands over his work to another person, he is either replaced by an individual of substantial training or experience, or it is explicitly recognized that the position he held is not fully manned. Under this requirement, the public school teacher today does not have a sustained career.

If certain tasks in education can be established that call for an outstanding level of ability, training, and quality of experience, then the performance of these particular tasks by those teachers who have the necessary qualifications could serve as a reasonable basis for substantial differences in salaries. The time has come for working out new ways to place values on educational specialization similar to those with which specialists are rewarded in other fields. The proposed salary program for the Concord Public Schools is a beginning step in this direction. The program provides competitive minimum and maximum salaries for *all* teachers selected to teach in the Concord schools, and it opens ways for additional responsibility and compensation for *certain* teachers. The descriptions of differentiated jobs which follow are only suggestive, outlining an approach to start putting into practice that aspect of the recommended salary program which is designed to provide a purposeful and sustained career progression for teachers in the Concord schools and in other systems. These kinds of jobs really can only be established after extensive developmental work and careful examination of the needs of the schools.

(1) Demonstration: Teachers might work with other instructional staff members in areas of their particular competence and knowledge. In addition these teachers might assist newly employed teachers in adjusting to the Concord schools.

(2) Research: Teachers would conduct research in areas of special knowledge and competence that would assist in the development of the Concord educational program.

(3) Planning: Teachers would help plan programs in areas requiring liaison between various educational institutions. For example, closed circuit television teaching might require the cooperative use of knowledge from a university staff, technical workers, and these local personnel.

(4) Performance: Teachers could undertake particular teaching activities on the elementary level such as instruction of gifted children, special remedial

Career Specialist Program Outline

Phase I	Phase II			Phase III			Phase IV
	A	B	C	A	B	C	
2 years	5 years	1 yr.	3 years	5 years	1 yr.	4 years Minimum	Balance of Career
Apprentice	General classroom teacher	SABBATICAL YEAR #1*	General Teaching	½ time teaching in special area	SABBATICAL YEAR #2*	½ time teaching in special area	½ time teaching in special area
Teaching ⅔ time	Teach full time		Teaching full time	½ time general teaching		Supervise practice teachers	Supervise apprentice teachers
Attend seminars	Committee work		Committee work	Committee work		Assist in Research	Direct Research
Observe exp. teachers, etc.	$4000 to $6000/year		$6500 to $8000	Curriculum revision		Committee work	$14,000 to $18,000
Attend meetings	$500/year increments		$500/year increments	$8500 to $10,500		$11,000 to $12,500	$500/year increments
$3600/year				$500/year increments		$500/year increments	
No increments							
Automatic advancements as long as training requirements were met.					Selective process and needs of school system determine advancement in these phases.		

Assume the current (1959) cost of living in considering the above.

*Sabbatical year: ½ salary paid by the community
½ tuition paid by the community
¼ tuition paid by the university
¼ tuition paid by the teacher

classes, large group instruction, and in areas requiring unique teaching methods.

(5) Instruction: Teachers could be responsible for instruction in areas requiring exceptional levels of training in subjects like those necessary for advanced college preparatory groups. These teachers might also assist in the vertical articulation of subject areas.

(6) Programming: Teachers may assume new responsibilities for seeing that each child is placed in contact with the more appropriate members of the instructional staff and materials at the proper time in each subject area.

Teachers who may be selected for their skills and competence in these suggested areas or in others to be determined by school officials should be designated as teacher-specialists. These jobs as outlined above would not require full working time, as a teacher-specialist engaged in one of the areas listed will continue to have a primary identification as a classroom teacher. The specialist jobs foreseen are not entirely instructional. Some career teachers with the teacher-specialist designation can be expected to make their greatest contributions in classrooms, others may be capable of research and planning functions. Flexibility in the assignment of specialized tasks will be necessary to have full utilization of the unique competencies of these selected teachers.

While the teacher-specialists should not have to possess doctorates as prerequisites for specialized jobs, they should have an inclination and ability comparable to those necessary for such advanced graduate study. The teacher-specialist in instruction will likely become recognized not only for his ability to pass on old knowledge but to suggest innovations in teaching specific areas; to introduce new learnings; and to point out those sections of the instructional program which need revision. While the general classroom teacher will remain the foundation for an instructional staff, the teacher-specialist may be recognized more as the creative innovator.

PART FIVE · THE PROBLEM OF PRODUCTIVITY IN EDUCATION

Section C

BUDGETING AND FISCAL PLANNING

In the area of fiscal planning in public activities, the major development of the 1950's was the introduction of the concept of performance budgeting. The basic aim of performance budgeting is greater efficiency in the use of resources in specific public tasks. (Program budgeting, which is actually a refined form of functional classification, is concerned, on the other hand, with effective choice among alternative outputs.) Burkhead (Selection 49) discusses the strong points — and also the limitations — of performance budgeting. Haberstroh (Selection 50) deals with a closely related matter, namely, the use of electronic data processing to improve public decision making.

The last two selections in this section deal with capital planning and debt management. Ovsiew and Castetter (Selection 51) describe capital budgets and show the advantages the use of that instrument bestows on school systems. The material in Selection 52 from the Educational Facilities Laboratories, prepared with the assistance of Edward Edelman, treats the question of how to reduce interest costs on long-term debts.

49

The Characteristics of Performance Budgeting

Jesse Burkhead

Professor Burkhead, Department of Economics, Maxwell Graduate School of Citizenship and Public Affairs, Syracuse University, has been director of the Carnegie Project for Research in Educational Finance. In this selection Burkhead gives an appraisal of a new tool in budgetary practice.

There is no precise definition for performance budgeting; it has come to mean something different in every jurisdiction which puts it into operation. In particular, there has been a tendency to make program budget and performance budget synonymous terms, and this has contributed a good deal to the terminological confusion.

In an attempt to clarify what is meant here by program and performance, definitions will proceed along organizational and hierarchical lines. For present purposes, program will be defined in relation to a higher level of organization than performance. A program embraces a number of performance units. A department or agency may conduct or participate in several different programs, whereas organizational (performing) units below the bureau or division level within a department conduct the derivative activities and are directly responsible for performance. Program costs are broad summary costs which may be built by aggregating the costs of performance units. On the other hand, a program budget might stop with broad program costs; it need not be extended to or built on performance units, and in some cases performance detail may serve no useful purpose.

Program and performance may also be distinguished according to their time dimension. Budgetary programs are inherently forward-looking, a projection of the economic and social policies of a government. Performance must be based on the past — on the record of prior accomplishment. In the preparation of budget estimates, program determinations should precede and set the framework in which the measurement of performance can be undertaken.

Reprinted with permission from Jesse Burkhead, *Government Budgeting,* New York, John Wiley & Sons, Inc., 1956, pp. 139–155.

In accordance with these definitions, a program budget serves a different purpose than a performance budget. A program budget is useful for review and decision-making at and above the departmental level. It is adapted to the requirements of over-all budgetary planning — to central budget office review, review by the chief executive, and by the legislature.[1] The performance budget may also provide useful information for review, but in addition, it must serve management purposes at and below the departmental level. Performance classification and analysis seek to measure the cost and accomplishment of detailed activities, and by so doing improve the implementation of programs.

In the discussion which follows, the term performance classification will be used to describe a specific technique for organizing and reporting budget data for administrative units within departments and agencies. The nature of this classification will be examined prior to an appraisal of its role and significance in the budgetary process.

A performance classification differs from other classifications. The intent of a performance classification is to assure that the things bought by a government are no longer to be counted or classified solely by type, as things in themselves, but are to be organized and aggregated according to the activities they serve. Objects bought and used are viewed as activity factors or components, and the object is deemed significant and classified in relation to what it is used for, not in relation to its specific character.

At some point any budgetary system must be concerned with things bought, with objects. The difference between a performance classification and the traditional object classification lies in the way things bought are viewed and grouped. In a performance classification a ton of cement is potentially a section of a road, a dam, or a concrete building and is so classified. The emphasis is on process, or on purpose or achievement. A ton of cement in combination with other materials, some equipment, and the physical activity of men, becomes a specific end product for the implementation of program decisions. Performance classification provides the link between the things bought and the things done or accomplished. This is what has become obscured in the traditional object classification as government activities have moved from the simple and small to the complex and large. In a performance classification expenditure data are reorganized to assist, rather than confuse and detract from, management responsibilities. It is then possible to relate the myriad of things bought to the myriad of things done or to the end products effected.

The end products or things done may be reports filed, roads built, infantrymen trained, tons of food transported, acres of trees planted, tax returns audited, labor disputes mediated, school lunches provided, pennies minted —

[1] Roland N. McKean, of RAND Corporation, has suggested, in correspondence with the author, that program review in terms of costs and benefits, even where the latter are difficult to measure, is the greatest gain which can come from this kind of budgeting.

in fact, any tangible thing that government does. This tangible quality of the end products which may be listed in a performance classification is of greatest significance. Herein lie both its potentialities and its limitations.

It is always possible to identify an end product in a government activity; the things that are done are always recorded in some fashion or other. The difficulty is that frequently the objective things that are done are nonsignificant as a measure of accomplishment under a program. For example, every labor dispute mediated by a government agency is recorded in the files of that agency. In a given fiscal year it is always possible to count the number of disputes which have been mediated; the information is available and easily measurable. Unfortunately, this is largely irrelevant information for budgetary purposes. In some years the disputes may be difficult to settle; in other years easy. In some years there might be but one case mediated, but this might significantly affect the national economy. In another year there might be no disputes at all because the disputes of the previous year had been so very well settled that all labor-management issues had been disposed.

On the other hand, there are many governmental activities where the end products are identifiable, measurable, *and* significant. Tons of garbage collected, gallons of water provided, and numbers of trout hatched are meaningful measures of performance for the governmental units which conduct these activities. And, of course, there is the middle range of governmental activities, where the measurable and identifiable end products are only reasonably significant in determining accomplishment. Numbers of children graduated from the eighth grade, or property tax assessments completed, or building inspections performed are examples of this sort.

What it comes to, then, is that performance classification based on end products can often create an illusion — the illusion that program content and accomplishment can be measured by the discrete things that are done by a government. This is by no means the case. Regardless of whether or not the end product in a performance classification is meaningful in terms of program content and accomplishment, it cannot measure performance in any value sense.

The facts of performance are not judgments about programs and should not be regarded as such. Value judgments are made in the minds of men. These may partially rest upon the number and type of things done, but they can reside in them only by imputation. Therefore, it is useless to search for a homogeneous end-product unit that will measure "better education," "better defense," or "more economic and efficient personnel recruitment." The best that can be done is to measure a variety of specific accomplishments, which may facilitate judgment as to whether governmental services are improving, in relation to the costs of such improvement.

Performance classification in and of itself does not assure more desirable government programs at a lower cost, although this is frequently implied in discussions of the subject. At best, performance classification provides factual evidence which may be of assistance to all levels of management in determining effectiveness. Performance data, when properly grouped in relation to larger programs, can also be of assistance to legislators and citizens as they select desirable government activities and programs. Performance classification can point up the concrete things done and the dollar cost of these, but the value judgments about them are made in the politic mind — and, for society, in the political process.

SELECTING THE PERFORMANCE UNIT

Just as it is difficult to generalize about the difference between program and performance, so is it difficult to generalize about the technique of performance classification. The complex nature of performance is implicit in some of the definitions that have been used. To quote from an unpublished memorandum prepared by the U. S. Bureau of the Budget:

> A performance budget is one which presents the purposes and objectives for which funds are required, the costs of the programs proposed for achieving those objectives, and quantitative data measuring the accomplishments and work performed under each program.[2]

As this definition implies, measuring accomplishment and measuring work performed are not the same thing. Work performed is the process or the activity; accomplishment is the end product and, as noted, the end product may or may not be a significant measure of the character of the program.

In the selection of the performance unit it will always be possible, however, to discover a number of government programs where the end product is significant and measurable. Municipal government programs frequently have performance characteristics of this type. Garbage collection is such a case. It is relatively easy to ascertain the specific number of tons of garbage collected in a municipality during a fiscal year and, on the basis of a number of years' experience, to forecast tonnage for the forthcoming budget year. The trucks and manpower used for collection are not likely to be devoted to any other activity, and therefore the costs per ton can be computed and accurate full-cost budgets set forth in these terms. Certain problems of homogeneity may still remain, however, and may be sufficiently serious to partially invalidate the year-to-year comparability of the performance measurements. The volume of commercial garbage, which is relatively easy to collect, may change in relation to the volume of residential garbage, which is more expensive to collect. Some homes may install garbage disposal units, making the stops for pick-up less numerous this year than last.

There are other government programs that produce specific and significant end products — a reforestation service which plants a specified number of

[2] Quoted in Chester E. Glassen, *Development of the Performance Budget Structure in the Department of the Army* (unpublished master's thesis), Syracuse University, 1953, p. 34.

trees in a given period, a reclamation service which adds each year to the number of acres of arable land in a given area, or a highway department which constructs a number of miles of new roads. Again, homogeneity problems will enter. In one year the trees may be planted on the hillsides, in another year in the valleys. Acres of reclaimed land may be of better quality in one year than the next. The new roads this year may be better (or worse) than the ones last year. Technological changes also intrude with improved methods, and get mixed with the changing nature of the end product, to produce performance units which are noncomparable in cost terms over a period of time.

Nevertheless, the end-product approach to selecting the performance unit can provide significant information on program content in a number of cases, and can serve as a relatively firm basis for budgetary planning. Where it can be used, it provides information of great service to management. It permits a determination of whether program costs are increasing because more work is being done or because costs are higher for the same volume of work. The measurement of activity costs cannot do this.

The end-product approach, however, cannot dominate performance classification for the reason already noted — definable, homogeneous, and significant end products do not exist in a great many cases. For many programs the work process or the activity must serve as the performance unit. This situation is well illustrated in the case of a staff function such as a personnel office.

The general responsibility of a personnel office is to contribute to an improvement in the level of skills, effectiveness, and morale of employees subject to its jurisdiction. It implements this responsibility through its programs for recruitment, examination, training, and employee relations and by means of continuous studies of job classification. It may also be charged with the administration of welfare and retirement programs; it will customarily devote a considerable part of its energies to maintenance of employee records. For a personnel office there are no end products which will effectively measure the discharge of these responsibilities. The same general situation obtains in governmental research programs. In ordnance development the number of tests and experiments conducted during the year is a meaningless performance unit.

In these cases performance must be measured in terms of activities. For a personnel office, activities might be described as follows:

01 General administration
02 Recruitment and examination
03 Reclassification
04 Training
05 Maintenance of records
06 Employee relations
07 Research in classification
08 Administration of welfare programs

To each of these activities dollar cost figures should be attached for past, current, and future fiscal years. In the budget justification each activity should be described and, where possible, changes in work load indicated.

Performance classification in terms of activities will provide a great deal of information about "what government is doing," will center management attention on program, and should help to make management cost-conscious. Activity classification can be refined to great detail if this is desired. Refinement, however, runs the risk of obscuring the major outlines of an agency program and of transforming budgeting to a detailed exercise in accounting.

What activity costs can do is to show the relative dollar emphasis on the components of a program. But like an end-product classification, activity costs cannot, in themselves, provide the value judgments which are necessary for budgeting. The dollar figures in the above example for "04 Training" will not tell the personnel director of the central budget office or the legislator whether the training programs this year are better than the ones last year. The costs of "01 General administration" may be lower this year than last because personnel officers are unavailable for hire at the prevailing salary rate. The total of activity costs will show only what it costs to conduct the whole program. The success of the personnel office in improving the morale and effectiveness of employees will have to be determined primarily by administrators who see the results of what the personnel office does. And this is more likely to be based on what is observable around the office than on what appears in the activity schedules.

With all their limitations, the activity schedules are nevertheless likely to serve as the unit of performance measurement in most governmental programs. They are flexible and usually fit in well with existing organizational structures. Activity schedules have served as the unit of measurement in much of the performance budgeting work that has been done in the federal government. Table 1 shows such a schedule for Marketing Research and Service, Agricultural Marketing Service, U.S. Department of Agriculture.

The obligation basis of reporting used by the federal government in these schedules shows the commitments which have been or may be undertaken for the conduct of the activity during the fiscal year. Obligational authority permits agencies and departments to award contracts, hire personnel, and place orders for materials and supplies. Obligations do not measure the liabilities incurred; these depend on the delivery of materials or the provision of personal services. And neither do obligations nor liabilities measure the cost of an activity in terms of the rate at which goods and services are used. Federal government activity schedules are useful for control purposes, since obligations are incurred in point of time before costs are incurred, but these schedules are not an accurate measure of activity costs.

In the federal government a further problem is encountered in combining the activity schedule with a listing of the sources of funds, as illustrated in Table 1. In this case the program for Marketing Research and Service is financed from three sources: appropriations directly to the Agricultural Marketing Service, reimbursements from the Commodity Credit Corporation, and reimbursements from other agencies. These sources are separately designated and totaled. To find the total of obligations for any one activity it is necessary to add the amounts which may be provided from one or more of the three sources of funds. This makes the activity schedule complex, just as the sources of financing for federal programs are complex.

In the federal government the term activity has been broadly applied to mean, under various circumstances, process, purpose, and project. For example, the budget presentation for the Soil Conservation Service, U.S. Department of Agriculture, lists under "Flood prevention" the activity of "Preliminary examinations and surveys." This is a process approach to classification. The same activity schedule also lists "General basin investigations in the Arkansas–White–Red River and New England–New York areas." This is a project approach. The Veterans Administration's activity schedule in the program for Inpatient Care, Maintenance and Operation of Hospitals, shows a threefold breakdown, (1) neuropsychiatric hospitals, (2) tuberculosis hospitals, and (3) general medical hospitals. This is a purpose classification.

In a complex government there is no other solution. It is not possible to define all activities in terms of purpose, process, or project. Under these circumstances the activity schedule must retain flexibility in the measurement of components of programs.

Whether the unit of performance is established on the basis of end products or on the basis of activities, it is easier to develop this type of budgeting if programs and organizational structures are synchronized within departments and agencies, and within divisions or bureaus of these departments and agencies.

In every government a number of programs are conducted jointly by two or more administrative units. This means that administrative responsibility is divided and the hierarchical lines of authority are not clear. Neither specific activities nor specific end products can be assigned to individual organizations, and the responsibility for performance cannot be readily determined. In other cases a single administrative unit will conduct a number of different programs. Here the costing becomes difficult and requires the allotment of employee time by the use of time slips or some other form of record-keeping where such detail is justified.

Difficulties in the synchronization of organizational structure and program arise most frequently in those governmental units where professional skills are recognized organizationally. A state public service commission is a typical example. Here the commission may be organized in terms of an engineering division, an accounting division, and a legal division. Personnel from all three divisions will work on rate cases and on the enforcement of service standards. In fact, working teams specifically drawn from each division may be assigned to specific cases. The end product is a regulatory order; the activity is utility regulation. Both the end product and the activity are of a

Table 1

OBLIGATIONS BY ACTIVITIES, MARKETING RESEARCH AND SERVICE, AGRICULTURAL MARKETING SERVICE, U.S. DEPARTMENT OF AGRICULTURE

Description	1954 Actual	1956 Estimate
Direct Obligations		
1. Marketing research and agricultural estimates		
(a) Marketing research	$ 3,884,253	$ 5,469,200
(b) Economic and statistical analysis	862,850	1,309,200
(c) Crop and livestock estimates	3,667,596	4,202,600
Subtotal	8,424,699	10,981,000
2. Marketing services		
(a) Market news service	3,399,294	3,653,000
(b) Inspection, grading and classing, and standardization	6,223,386	6,002,000
(c) Freight rate services	155,074	161,000
(d) Regulatory activities	1,560,676	1,549,000
(e) Administration and coordination of State payments	28,529	50,000
Subtotal	11,366,959	11,415,000
3. Obligations under reimbursements from non-Federal sources	240,174	348,900
Total direct obligations	$20,031,832	$22,744,900
Obligations Payable Out of Reimbursements from Commodity Credit Corporation		
1. Marketing services		
(a) Inspection, grading and classing, and standardization	$ 1,267,032	$1,645,000
Obligations Payable Out of Reimbursements from Other Accounts		
1. Marketing research and agricultural estimates		
(a) Marketing research	64,389	10,000
(b) Economic and statistical analysis	381	2,900
(c) Crop and livestock estimates	14,414	16,000
Subtotal	79,184	28,900
2. Marketing services		
(a) Market news service	48,421	700
(b) Inspection, grading and classing, and standardization	149,323	192,000
Subtotal	197,744	192,700
Total obligations payable out of reimbursements from other accounts	276,928	221,600
Total obligations	$21,575,792	$24,611,500

Source: *Budget of the United States Government for the fiscal year ending June 30, 1956*, p. 359. (The column for fiscal 1955 is omitted.)

joint character. Performance for the commission as a whole cannot be broken down into specific programs, without a detailed and cumbersome costing system, unless separate divisions are created for electric companies, gas companies, street railways, and so forth, with a rearrangement of engineers, accountants, and lawyers in these divisions.

Important as performance classification may be, it would be unwise to recommend that all governmental agencies should be reorganized in the interests of defining performance units. The measurement of performance should contribute to effective administration, not impede it. An organizational structure based on professional skills may make performance classification difficult or even impossible, but it may be the best way to administer the organization. In every case it is effective administration which is the goal, not the classification as such.

The relationship of performance classification to other types of classifications is shown in generalized form in Chart 1. As defined here, a program classification is broader than a performance classification, and each program

Chart 1
PERFORMANCE CLASSIFICATION

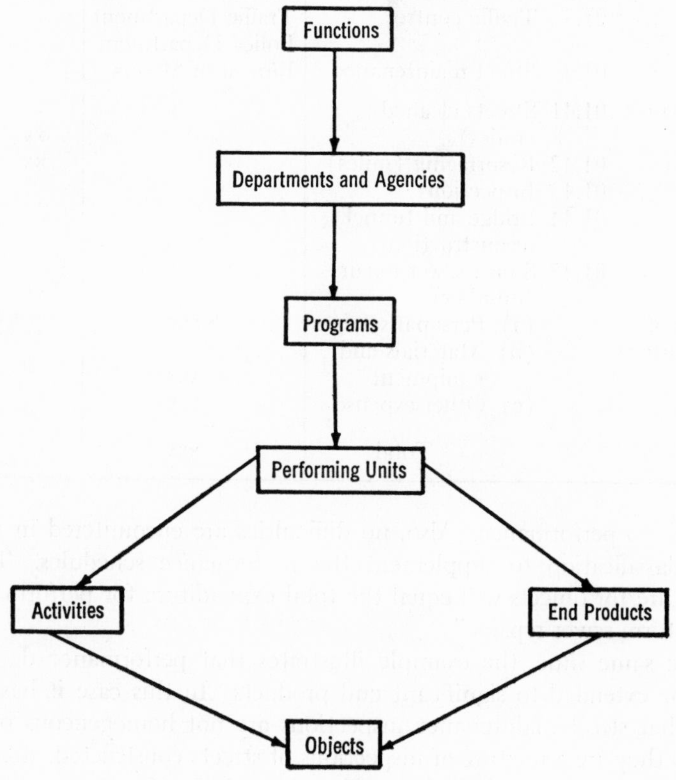

embraces a number of performing or organizational units. Chart 1 shows that performance can be measured in terms of either activities or end products, and that objects of expenditure can be grouped on either basis.

These relationships are further elaborated in Table 2, based on the hypothetical but typical municipal function, "Provision of streets and roads." The hypothetical case is relatively uncomplicated and is intended to demonstrate the interrelationships of function, program, performance, and object classifications.

As Table 2 demonstrates, it is possible to move with relative ease from a functional classification which cuts across agency and departmental lines, to

Table 2

PERFORMANCE CLASSIFICATION IN A CLASSIFICATION SYSTEM

Function			Department or Bureau	Number of Units	Total Cost
Function	01.	Provision of streets and roads			
Program	01.1	Street construction	Bureau of Streets		$ xxx
	01.2	Street lighting	Bureau of Streets		xxx
	01.3	Traffic control	Traffic Department Police Department		xxx
	01.4	Street maintenance	Bureau of Streets		xxx
Performance	01.41	Streets cleaned (miles)		xx	xxx
	01.42	Resurfacing (miles)		xx	xxx
	01.43	Inspections		. .	xxx
	01.44	Bridge and tunnel reconstruction		. .	xxx
	01.45	Storm sewer repairs (number)		xx	xxx
Objects of expenditure		(a) Personal services	$ xxx		
		(b) Materials and equipment	xxx		
		(c) Other expense	xxx		
		Total	xxx		

programs, to performance. Also, no difficulties are encountered in using the object classification to supplement the performance schedules. The total expenditure for objects will equal the total expenditure for performance unit "01.45 Storm sewer repairs."

At the same time, the example illustrates that performance data cannot always be extended to significant end products. In this case it has been assumed that street maintenance inspections are not homogeneous over time, and that they are a mixture of inspections of streets constructed, streets maintained, storm sewers, and the like. Therefore, this performance unit must be established on an activity basis. The same lack of homogeneity has been assumed for the performance unit "01.44 Bridge and tunnel reconstruction." That is, it has been assumed that bridges and tunnels in a typical city differ greatly in size and in the costliness of reconstruction.

In practice the administrator is the person best equipped to make the arbitrary assumptions and decisions as to whether an end product or an activity is the better unit for measurement. If the maximum potentialities of performance budgeting are to be realized, its applications must be worked out flexibly. Nothing is gained in budgetary classification by overrefinement of detail. In fact, the overrefinement of detail is a positive evil — it detracts from the importance of program and destroys the perspective of decision-makers. Performance budgeting should not become a victim of self-strangulation.

The Measurement of Cost

The uniform measurement of the full cost of end products of activities is logically required, to convert a system of performance *reporting* into a performance *budget*. The distinction is this: performance reporting is the identification of activities or end products and the measurement of changes therein. This may be done either in terms of work units or in terms of dollar figures. Performance budgeting goes beyond this. The identification of programs and the measurement of changes therein are set forth on a cost basis so that performance costs are equal to total costs for budgetary purposes. Performance reporting is selective; performance budgeting is comprehensive. Most governments are likely to find that a full-cost performance budget is impractical.

For performance budgeting to be complete it must embrace the supporting agency accounts, to provide a harmonious accounting framework starting with appropriations and continuing through the accounts that are used for recording obligations and disbursements. These must all be established and maintained on a basis of performance within programs, so that they may be used by management for purposes of observing and controlling the rate of budget execution.

Performance *reporting*, as defined here, need not extend to a reclassification of financial accounts. Performance data can be developed by management independently of the budget and control accounts, and dollar figures may or may not be attached thereto.

This kind of performance reporting has long been used in government operations, particularly in the justification of budgetary requests. It has also been used as a management control for measuring cost and progress in those operations where work is homogeneous and routine. In such cases, the technique consists of identifying units of work load and showing changes in the quantity of such units as a basis for analyzing financial requirements. The management control and budgeting for institutional care — hospitals and correctional establishments — has often been developed on this basis. The number of patients per hospital, the number of beds per hospital, or the number of inmates per prison are measured and projected as a basis for budgetary requests and for cost control.

A simplified example of this kind of performance reporting is shown in Table 3, which reproduces data from the budget presentation of the U.S. Forest Service.

Table 3

MAIN WORKLOAD FACTORS IN RESOURCE DEVELOPMENT, U.S. FOREST SERVICE (in acres)

Description	1954 Actual	1956 Estimate
Planted to trees (annual)	22,750	22,000
Planted to trees (cumulative)	1,372,084	1,416,084
Still to be planted (total)	4,000,000	4,000,000
Reseeded to range grasses (annual)	41,491	40,000
Reseeded to range grasses (cumulative)	550,638	630,638
Still to be reseeded (total)	3,449,362	3,369,362

Source: *Budget of the United States Government for the fiscal year ending June 30, 1956,* p. 359 . (The column for fiscal 1955 is omitted.)

Performance reporting of this type is valuable in providing information on program and accomplishment. It is not a performance budget as the term is used here.

In the development of the cost figures which make up a performance budget, all costs should be included. Ideally, this requires an accrual system of accounting for the measurement of past program costs, and estimates on an accrual basis for the budget year. In turn, this would mean that inventory should be maintained on an accrual basis and that the portion of capital equipment used up in each fiscal period should be charged to the performance costs for that period.

The requirements for full costing in terms of accrual accounting are more than most governments are prepared to meet. Government accounts are traditionally maintained on the basis of obligations, showing the commitments which are or may be undertaken during the year, or on a cash disbursement basis, showing the amount of goods and services paid for during the year. A shift to accrual accounting, which would show the goods and services used during the year, is invariably difficult and costly, and most governments will avoid it unless there is a clear demonstration that outstandingly better management results will thereby be attained.

In the absence of accrual accounting, the measurement of performance cost becomes most difficult in government programs where capital expenditures are a significant part of total costs, and where the capital outlay portion is not constant from year to year. A state highway department is one example; a municipal public works department is another.

In cases of this sort the ideal measurement would be full annual cost per mile of highway or per mile of streets and roads, with mile of highway or mile of street defined precisely in terms of a standard construction unit of specified composition, width, and durability. It would then be possible to charge to each year's budget the costs incurred in that year, as each mile of highway or street was used up, and it would be possible to determine whether the highway plant was in better condition at the end of the fiscal year than at the beginning and by how much.

This ideal condition is not likely to be attained. Apart from the problems encountered in accrual accounting, there are conceptual problems. A standard highway unit this year is not a standard highway unit next year. In practice, therefore, the measurement of performance costs that are a mixture of current and capital outlays must be based on activities, with a separation of outlays for maintenance and repair from outlays for new construction, and with no effort to annualize all capital costs. Under these circumstances performance budgeting becomes a technique for decision-making about different kinds of activities. The segregation of capital outlays is desirable, not for purposes of arriving at cost figures, but for purposes of improving decision-making in budgeting.

Apart from highways and some other types of public works programs, the conflict between traditional cash accounting and the cost measurements required for effective performance budgeting are not always sharp. In a great many general government departments and agencies, the difference between cash and accrual accounting as reflected in the treatment of inventory or in depreciation on capital assets is not likely to be significant. Where the bulk of an agency's expenditure is composed of wage and salary payments, the difference between cash and accrual measurements will not be of sufficient importance to invalidate the cash basis for purposes of performance budgeting. For government enterprise, accrual accounting is very likely to be employed for all accounting and budgeting purposes; no change in the basis of reporting is required for purposes of performance budgeting.

There are other problems in cost measurement. The activities of any agency will include certain common staff functions such as personnel and accounting, and an unapportioned activity which must be classified as general management or executive direction. Costs recorded for these staff functions are not always capable of explicit further breakdown in terms of specific activities. However, the usefulness of performance budgeting is not substantially diminished by the presence of unapportioned cost items of this sort, provided that the composition of the unapportioned element remains reasonably constant from one year to the next. That is, the composition of activities or end products must remain roughly comparable to facilitate the cost comparisons which are the rationale for performance budgeting.

The measurement of program costs is sometimes complicated by the existence of joint products and activities, a problem similar to that of apportioning general management expense. An agency engaged in a specified number of activities may wish to add an additional activity. This will require only slight additions to cost. In the case of a central statistical agency, for example, a new type of data may be added to existing data-gathering activities at small additional (marginal) cost. A reapportionment of the cost of activities to include the additional one will make programs partially noncomparable from one year to the next.

It is evident from the foregoing cases and examples that full cost measurement is impossible in all circumstances. Whether it is of sufficient importance to force a complete reorganization in government accounting, and whether it is worthwhile to attempt to refine performance costs, are questions that must be answered in relation to the needs of particular governmental units, and in particular, in relation to the requirements of administrators, whose interests must be served by performance budgeting.

The Installation of Performance Budgeting

By way of summary, it might be well to set forth the steps that are involved in the installation and operation of a performance budgeting system. These are as follows:[3]

First, the central budget office and the administrators of departments and agencies must cooperate in the identification of work programs that are meaningful for management purposes. The central budget office should attempt to preserve uniformity in terminology and should provide some general advisory service at this stage, but program identification is the administrators' responsibility.

Second, programs, once identified, should be examined in relation to organizational structure. Where it appears desirable in the interests of more effective administration, some organizational realignments may be called for to assure a greater harmony between program and hierarchy.

Third, the units of performance should be identified within each program. In some cases this unit will be a specific end product; in most cases it will be an activity. In every case the unit should be as homogeneous as possible over time.

Fourth, consideration should be given to the full measurement of performance costs. In some circumstances it will be desirable to introduce accrual accounting for inventory and capital expense.

Fifth, a system of internal reporting should be established so that progress under the program can be measured throughout the fiscal year. Accomplishment must continuously be compared with plans.

Sixth, the legislation that authorizes the budget should be drafted in

[3] For other discussions of installation procedure see Donaho, *Municipal Finance*, February 1950, pp. 103–106; Cope, *Tax Digest*, December 1950, pp. 415–418; Frank A. Lowe, "How to Initiate a Performance Budget Program," *Performance Budgeting and Unit Cost Accounting for Governmental Units*, Municipal Finance Officers Association, Chicago, 1954, pp. 1–7.

program terms. Appropriation structures should be simplified so that each program, where possible, is financed from a single appropriation.

Seventh, the accounts maintained to control and record the disbursements of moneys should be established on a program basis, subdivided by performance units. This, together with a simplification of appropriation structures, will establish a single set of accounts to support all phases of the budget cycle.

During the installation phase the central budget office must be available for assistance and consultation, but the administrators themselves must have major responsibility for the definitions if the performance budget is to accomplish its purpose of orienting management toward program. The applications cannot be worked out in the central budget office and imposed on the agencies.

At the same time, the agencies are not wholly independent in the development of performance units and performance costing. The central budget office must assure some patterns of uniformity throughout the whole of a government. A standard terminology needs to be employed, so that such concepts as program, subprogram, and activity have a uniform meaning in relation to the organizational hierarchy. For example, it might be decided that departments and bureaus of departments would conduct programs and subprograms, and that units of performance would be established within the subprograms. A uniform coding system must be developed to accompany such a standard classification.

It should be emphasized that performance classification is not useful for the summary budget accounts. Performance classifications are agency-level and division-level. For a large government the number of budgeted programs might amount to several hundred, and the number of budgeted activities or end products to several thousand. These may be meaningfully summarized only in terms of broad functions and organizational units.

Despite all of the difficulties that may be encountered in the installation of a performance budgeting system, it has one very great advantage in that it can be introduced in a step-by-step process over a period of years. There is no necessity for a rapid conversion to performance classification in any government. The techniques developed in the departments and agencies where the task is relatively simple can be adapted to the more difficult areas. As one writer has said, "The performance budget process in government . . . is not a destination but a pilgrimage. . . ."[4]

The Consequences of Performance Budgeting

The development of performance budgeting has been characterized by a widespread popularization of the term, by definitional variety and operational flexibility in its application, and by a relatively slow rate of progress in adoption. The reason for this is not hard to find. Performance budgeting is ex-

[4] Seckler-Hudson, *Advanced Management,* March 1953, p. 32.

tremely difficult and requires an almost complete reorientation in the administrator's "way of life." It has been said that, "The budget is a psychological device to make people in an administrative organization think. . . ."[5] But a reorganization in thinking takes time and can be accomplished only if those who must do the thinking are flexible and receptive and understand the reasons for reorganization.

The most important consequence of performance budgeting is that it increases the responsibility and accountability of management. A performance classification provides an additional tool of analysis, which should enforce on administrative units a consciousness of their contributions to departmental programs and the cost of their contribution. The program analysis required should provide perspective for the department head, and the cost-consciousness it entails should facilitate the administrator's control over his financial operations. The performance budget enhances the role of management, but at a price — budgeting may no longer be treated as a peripheral assignment, but is now at the center of management responsibility, and the administrator must be willing to assume this responsibility. This should lead to an improvement in the quality and quantity of budgeting at the level of operations.

[5] Quoted in John A. Perkins, "Preparation of the Local Budget," *American Political Science Review*, October 1946, p. 949.

50

Electronic Data Processing and Administrative Organizations

Chadwick J. Haberstroh

Improvement of school administration calls for the analysis of increasing quantities of data. Fortunately, the new types of equipment for processing data open the range of possibilities for quantitative analysis in almost fantastic degree. Professor Haberstroh is in the Department of Industrial Management, Massachusetts Institute of Technology.

The Organization as a Task Oriented Social System

The bulk of the current literature on computer applications focuses on the tasks to which the computer can be applied. This may consist of surveys of how the job is done or analyses of how it can be done better. This focus is also evident in the papers presented at this conference. Sometimes, but not typically, the discussion is carried as far as the human problem of using the new technology to get the task done.

The "how to do it" focus is dictated of course by the mutual interest of both the writers and the readers of this literature. Most of them work in organizations and on just such tasks as are described. A large portion of work in this field is necessarily done by people with a thorough knowledge of computers and programming techniques. Other writing may rest instead or as well on an expert knowledge of the field to which the computer application is being made. As more and more applications take place, however, there has occurred a greater realization that characteristics of the organization as a social system are exceedingly important determinants of the outcome. These factors arise from the "human nature" of the individual members of the organization and also from its "organization nature" as a system of action.

It is not hard to concede the existence of these factors, nor even to go

Adapted from Chadwick J. Haberstroh, "The Impact of Electronic Data Processing on Administrative Organizations," *National Tax Journal*, Volume XIV, No. 3 (September, 1961), pp. 259–269. Reproduced with permission.

further and recognize that they govern the choice of tasks and the application of the technology. One can accept these points and then ignore them by relying on the magnificent degree of flexibility for which the human being and organizations of human beings are well known. But if people and organizations are adaptable, they are also rigid. If change and new patterns can be imposed, they can also be resisted. Successful organizational design is not likely to be achieved by the same techniques used in designing a machine or in programming a computer. Rather, it requires some degree of recognition of the fundamental laws that govern such systems. Nevertheless, many designers in the scientific management movement insisted on treating people like machines, and many designers of the electronic computer school are undoubtedly trying to program them like computers. The result then and now is a limited degree of success and an enormous degree of waste.

TASK AND TECHNOLOGY

Our first problem is to explore the meaning of the new information technology itself for the organization and its members. To do this, we will need three levels of concept. We need at the first level the idea of the objective possibilities for action. This we must distinguish from the second level, the present state of the art, society's knowledge of the techniques for action, which we will label *technology*. The computer experts assure us that contemporary developments have extended objective possibilities well into the domain of what used to be pure fantasy and well beyond the present state of technology. An acceptance of this point has been a great stimulus to research in computer hardware, programming technology and systems analysis. It is hard to say whether society will ever close the gap between its established technological ability and what is believed by experts to be possible. It is equally hard to say that technology has not already outstripped the general public's perception of the possibilities for action.

The distinction between the state of the art and public appreciation thereof brings us to the third level concept and the most important for the remainder of this analysis. This is the *task model* of a particular organization, one of the systemic characteristics that influence organizational behavior. The *task model* is the organization members' shared perception of what the task is and how it should be accomplished. A given task model may incorporate the latest technology or it may be quite archaic. In any concrete case, it is almost inevitable that at least some elements of the task model will lag appreciably behind the best available technology. Nevertheless, the most important influence on any organization task model is the state of technology and the research process in society as a whole. The problem of innovation into specific organizations is a secondary consideration. This is even true in fields where technology is changing rapidly and substantially.

Technological advance is never limited to one field; an advance in one area generates needs and ideas that inspire work in other fields. Just as advances in computer hardware stimulated the development of programming techniques not dreamed of by the computer's inventors, so the development of the whole field of information technology is stimulating applications to organizational problems, most notably in systems analysis and simulation. We must not, however, make the mistake of regarding the computer as the only impetus to change in organizational techniques. Consideration of the psychological factors inherent in work relationships has inspired such innovations as job enlargement, participative management, profit sharing, group incentives, Scanlon plan, employee centered supervision, etc. The growth of organizations in recent times to their present enormous sizes has generated another group of techniques designed to achieve decentralization and control. These and other organizational developments interact with developments in information technology and with developments in all other fields to create opportunities for innovation and oftentimes considerable economic and social pressure to do so.

If research does not automatically result in innovation, it would be well to mention right at the start two perfectly rational factors that preclude this. The first is the organization's commitment to sunk costs. It takes time, effort, and resources to build a new technology into an organization. This is quite obvious when the technology is incorporated into machinery or buildings. Present machinery at scrap value may give service at lower cost than new and superior machinery that would have to be bought at manufacturers' list prices. Or a forecast of further technological change may prevent any adoption of intermediate forms of technology. These same considerations apply equally well to aspects of the task model that are not incorporated into physical capital but are situated in the beliefs and practices of the personnel. These also represent sunk costs and any attempt to change them will require further expenditure. In addition to these rational factors, there are other barriers to innovation that arise from the social character of the organization.

Social Aspects of the Task Model

The task model has been defined above as a shared way of perceiving and acting in relation to the purposes of the organization. It includes not only such things as instructions for doing the physical labor involved, but also beliefs as to who should give or change instructions, limitations on the range within which instructions may be given, perception of the purposes and subgoals of the organization, standards of performance, etc. These ideas taken as a whole form a consistent and unified pattern of response. Each individual knows a portion of the task model in great detail and has at least some general knowledge of the remainder. He holds these ideas in cooperation with others, perceives the others as depending on his knowledge and himself as depending on the knowledge of the others. The fact of sharing his ideas with his fellows provides "social reality" for them, i.e., gives him an acceptable basis for believing in the factual or moral correctness of these ideas.

Certain characteristics of the task model itself may greatly modify its susceptibility to planned revision or unplanned gradual evolution. Any organization has some capacity for change built into its task model directly. This may be something as routine as the replacement of workers by other workers. On the other hand, an organization may use a research and development branch of an organization-planning office for the specific purpose of routinely generating changes in the technical or organizational aspects task model. Any organization, however, will exclude some parts of its task model from deliberate review and change. In many organizations this even extends to the identity of individual occupants of positions above the lowest level. Any death or resignation poses an un-planned-for problem and the task model is patched up from crisis to crisis. Thus there can be a considerable range of variation in the degree to which the task model is statically or dynamically oriented. Many, if not most, organizations tend to regard their task as fixed and their way of going about it as the most efficient possible. The increasing pace of change in our society may, however, be pushing more organizations into incorporating dynamic elements into their task models.

One of the most fundamental findings arising in many studies of organizations is the tendency of their members to place a positive value on the procedures they use. This goes beyond the fact of valuing procedures as means for the achievement of ends. Although the task model of a successful organization is unquestionably a valuable property in this sense, this tendency of personnel to value and defend their specific ways of proceeding has often been found to impair the realization of the over-all purposes of the organization. When this phenomenon comes to public attention it is labeled "red tape" and universally deplored. It is not always easy, however, to distinguish between the virtue of a workmanlike concern for protecting and maintaining one's tools and the sin of an idolatrous attachment to the same objects at the expense of legitimate values.

The problem of a purely emotional attachment to means is compounded in the organization situation by the overriding need for stable organizational norms as a basis for effective operations. Effective, coordinated action is possible only if members can form reliable expectations as to the performance of those others who must enable or complete the work. The problem is further compounded by the possibility of a genuine conflict of interest between the organization as a whole and any particular individual or group in it. The case of the skilled employee whose status and material welfare are based entirely on his virtuosity in organizational practices that may be rendered obsolete is the most obvious example. The same principle applies at top management levels, too, although different aspects of the task model would be cathected.

It is not necessary to look up an old-timer in the organization to demonstrate the operation of this principle. Computer technologists are frequently criticized for lack of realism in their applications. There is no reason to think that this is all a plea for the defense. Computers, too, are easy to fall in love with, and a computer technologist probably would not be in that field if he did not have an appreciation for the sheer abstract beauty of a rigorously logical and efficient programming job. It is also possible for him to develop an unreasonable attachment for the techniques that he learned in school or for a previous successful solution to a somewhat different problem. These things may create an inability to adjust to realities outside of the expert's own model and a resulting tendency to demand more adaptation from others than is really necessary.

Personnel accustomed to the existing organization procedures, on the other hand, are impressed with the demonstrated workability of old procedures, the ease of working with what is familiar as opposed to the disruption and uncertainty of a proposed change. The old way may be what *they* learned in school, or it may be the same procedure followed by other organizations.

The net result of the strong defenses against change found in most organizations is preservation of the *status quo* against all but minor evolutionary changes, except under conditions of crisis. A number of studies have shown a direct relationship between felt stress of organization members and their willingness to innovate. It may be expected that the more profound types of change will occur only under stresses uniformly regarded as serious by all relevant personnel.

The Impact of Information Technology on Task Model

Viewing information technology as a possible change in the task model of an organization, we can define two alternatives for effecting the change. New personnel can be brought into the organization who have a prior commitment to the new elements in the task model, people having prior training in computation methods or experience with applications. Alternatively, an effort can be made to change the task model of present members by training programs or reinstruction on the job. Either method of change could be accomplished within the structure of the current task model, by invoking recruitment programs in the first case or established indoctrination procedures in the second. This is not to say that the changes are all thought out in advance and integrated with the old task model. On the contrary, once a commitment to a certain degree of change is made, it is likely to carry the organization farther than was originally intended. Unforeseen problems and newly opened opportunities will stimulate new activity. On the other hand, what might at any stage seem like a logical extension of a new program may encounter resistances of the type suggested in the last section. Resistance may not only block extension, but may also prevent realization of anticipated gains even though the change has apparently been successfully made. This blockage may be permanent unless the interests that are being defended can be discovered and effectively neutralized.

Whether change is introduced by new personnel or not, the new elements have to be related in some way to the existing task model in the on-going organization. How this relation is structured and which personnel option is chosen are important factors in determining the depth to which change will extend and the smoothness with which it will be executed. Conversely, these choices become the first arena in which the policy of commitment to change and the nature and strength of vested interest are tested out.

The most common way of introducing computer technology into an existing organization seems to have been to regard it as a substitution for clerical labor. Management is used to considering working-level personnel as means to get the task done. Accustomed to dealing with labor turnover and the substitution of different kinds and degrees of skill and with the acquisition and replacement of various types of office equipment including complex mechanical punched card equipment, management finds it easy to contemplate a new type of machine and a few new skills as an economic substitution for an old way of doing the job. The definition of the job, however, and the procedures for accomplishing it do not necessarily change. Management may still preserve its old way of doing things, merely accomplishing this with a different balance of labor and equipment. Such organizations typically even have a procedure for getting rid of redundant personnel involving reduction in force by attrition and retraining of present personnel. This approach causes minimum disruption and need not require the hiring of a single technical expert, if training and outside consultation are preferred.

Sometimes an economic application requires a genuine rethinking of the work-flow system. Organizations that have gone so far as to take this step have usually estimated that the systems study generated savings of the same order of magnitude as those yielded by the mechanization itself. This process encounters more resistance, however, and the resistance comes from more powerful places. If the innovation is being implemented as a departmental program (in business it is typically a part of the controller's department), it is fairly certain that the rethinking of procedures will stop at the boundaries of that department. Even if the innovation proceeds from a broader mandate, management will frequently still go to great lengths to avoid violence to such parts of its task model as the number of departments in the organization, the autonomy or duties of important managers, the functional basis of departmentalization, etc.

The redesign of a work-flow system is a task that an organization is not likely to undertake — unless it has previously developed a high degree of sophistication about planning — without bringing in new members who have the appropriate specialized skills. Computer experts can frequently make the necessary contributions in systems analysis, and most systems analysts come prepared with a thorough understanding of modern computers. Thus, an organization that contemplates work-flow redesign would tend to bring in new personnel with these skills to achieve it; and — conversely — an organization that brings in computer technologists is likely to find that it has created pressures toward a thorough replanning of work-flow systems. The result of innovation will frequently include unanticipated consequences as the innovation impinges on more narrowly organizational aspects of the task model (discussed in the next section) and mobilizes the defensive interests vested therein. Nevertheless, fairly profound changes in work-flow can be implemented without compelling a re-examination of the organizational aspects, as managerial ingenuity discovers ways of reconciling the new with the old.

Some organizations do go so far as to review basic, organizational features of their task models. This has arisen most frequently in the past from crises in organizational effectiveness, rather than from computer innovation. As experience with electronic data processing grows, we can expect to see more experimentation with organizational forms and adoption of some . . . as especially appropriate in conjunction with new methods of information processing. From past experience with organizational changes, there is every reason to expect that the economic gains from innovation in this area are also of a large order of magnitude. If so, we must expect long-run pressures toward improved organization, as well as toward better work-flow systems and computer applications.

. . . .

Organizational Features of the Task Model and Their Relation to EDP

Many ideas as to how an organization should be set up achieve a high degree of acceptance in society. Certainly the most widespread and venerable of our ideas about organization are those of "line" and "staff." Others like "decentralization" enjoy only slightly less popularity. For others, like the principle of "functional specialization," there may be widespread agreement coupled with diversity of opinions as to what functions should be specialized. Other ideas, such as "task force" or "project" organization, are less widely appreciated. None of the ideas mentioned above owes anything to the development of electronic data processing. On the other hand, the presence of data processing techniques may determine whether a given form of organization will succeed and vice versa. Several of our introductory quotations speculate on the compatibility of specific organizational forms and information technology. These refer to long-run solutions; what combinations will occur immediately will be largely a matter of historical accident, although conscious experimentation cannot be entirely ruled out.

An important set of questions concern the implications of EDP for decentralized organizations. Decentralization appears to have developed historically as firms grew very large and were still forced to adapt to changing conditions in order to survive. The essence of this innovation in task model is the establishment of a substantial degree of autonomy in decision making at a department level, reserving only certain functions to top management. There are two main aspects of this innovation that require analysis. Both are conditioned by the fact that decentralization did not supersede the older concepts of line authority, but instead was tacked on and made consistent with them.

The first line of analysis starts from a principle in control theory. One way of stating this is that where a complex job of regulation must be done, a regulator of commensurate complexity is required. The operations of a large organization require a degree of complexity that cannot be attained by a single top manager or management committee. With increasing complexity, a single man or committee cannot even cope with it on the basis of a distinction in the task model between "important" and "routine" matters, leaving "routine" to be dealt with by subordinates according to rule. However, I think there is evidence to show that the older concepts of the line system prevented management from perceiving decentralization as a transition from one-man or committee rule to rule by a complex executive organization. Although decentralization placed great weight on the decisions of department managers, the "line" concept prevented them from being regarded as an integral part of top management, and their relations with the rest of top management regarded as an organized system. Thus we might surmise that a substantial part of the effectiveness of decentralization stems from the organizational characteristics of this complex executive system, rather than from any magic in the process of "delegation." If this is so, these relationships are themselves susceptible to systems analysis and computerization. Such a process would undoubtedly force restructuring of the division manager's functions as part of top management. It would also reduce the number of personnel required at this level and give more effective control over subsidiary operations. Such a development would certainly be viewed as "centralization."

Another line of analysis concerns an alteration in personal relationships between general manager and division manager. Under decentralization, although the nominal line relationship was maintained, the "responsible" officer in general management was not engaged in "supervising" the work of the division managers in any meaningful sense. The results of freeing a subordinate from direct dependence on and subservience to a superior have been studied intensively, mostly by psychologists. The results that can be reliably expected are increased morale, self-reliance, and initiative on the part of the subordinate. This in turn can be a source of increased efficiency. If centralization should occur because of improved information technology and within the concepts of the "line" system, then this second trend could be reversed with concomitant reduction in the degree of improvement to be expected. The inherent fallacy in the line concept is the equating of a department with its head officer. If this equation is accepted, then top management's very real need to maintain control over the organization is resolved into a need to maintain domination over the man.

The principle of functional specialization is wellnigh univeral in organizations, as is the idea of calling some of the functions "staff." Some specialties, like accounting, finance, production, sales, purchasing, are almost equally universal, but a great deal of variety can be discovered after one leaves these domains. Research and development, manufacturing analysis, operations research, training, and planning are all sufficiently widespread to be recognizable, but are nothing like universal among organizations. The older specialties have a firm social base in professional or educational institutions. The newer ones are gradually attaining that basis. Information technology itself is generating some such bases of specialization.

When specialists are needed in small numbers, they are usually designated "staff" and asked to advise some line executive. The "staff" designation in an organization committed to the concepts of the line system permits expert advice to be used centrally, yet denies the advisor the power and status inherent in central line positions. Staff designation also can provide the same kind of autonomy that decentralization gave to the subordinate line manager. Both the central position of staff and their autonomy can help organization effectiveness. As the work-load of a staff specialty increases, however, additional personnel are required and systems of super- and subordination develop. Soon a complete department is in existence with chief officers largely engaged in administration. This blurs the distinction between line and staff specialties and eliminates any advantages that might accrue from staff autonomy. At this level of complexity, the line-staff concepts again obscure the *de facto* organizational and work-flow arrangements that undoubtedly, as in the case of decentralized organizations, contribute to the effectiveness of the organization as a whole.

The information handling capacity of computer systems may give added impetus to the choice of planning as a strategic function around which to build a department. In the past, planning has most commonly been relegated to the darkest "staff" corners. Plans have been accepted only with the approval of top line management and that approval has not usually been easily given. As such activities have proven their worth, however, they have tended to take on more and more *de facto* autonomy. The culmination of this process can be seen for example in the cases of the Atwood Vacuum Machine Company, which has assigned a planning unit action responsibility for the coordination of job-lot cost estimation, manufacturing, and purchasing, and the International Shoe Company, which has its planning unit coordinate sales estimates, production, inventories, and purchasing. In both reports, the company officers specifically mention rejecting the previously held idea of planning as a "staff" function.

Another organizational innovation, which has received some recognition as a means of introducing computerization, is the "task force" form of organization. The rationale here is that a specific task is assigned to a relatively small group which is expected to be disbanded upon completion. The strong point of this form is its flexibility in permitting people of different interests and abilities to be grouped together with very close coordination among them. Another important feature, perhaps equally significant, is the fact that each individual retains his identification with his "permanent" functional department. This is undoubtedly conducive to a retention of specialized skills in the new situation and also serves to free the individual from excessive subordination to the task-force director. Some authorities go so far as to recommend systematic rather than *ad hoc* use of task forces with the permanent functional organizations serving as a corps of technically competent manpower to be allocated to the task forces.[1]

Another aspect of task force or project organization is the necessity for giving a coordinative function of very broad scope to a comparatively low-level manager. This form and decentralization both have the merit of providing appropriate experience for senior management positions. The same cannot be said of the strict "line" system that keeps individuals working within one narrow specialty even though at fairly high organizational levels. The success of the newer organizational form in task accomplishment and in management development raises the question as to whether management itself is not a function that could be specialized, professionalized, and organized into a functional corps. This seems to be well within the range of possibility and is a basic presumption of the more forward-looking programs in university education for business.

DYNAMICS OF THE EXTERNAL SYSTEM

Although we are primarily interested in consideration of the internal administrative system, perhaps some additional attention needs to be given to the ecology of the organization. Earlier we gave some attention to the development of new knowledge in society as an influence on the innovations made in the task model of a specific organization. Going somewhat further than that, the environment can compel innovations as well as make them possible, if the innovations do in fact permit lower cost operation. In the case of business firms, the forces of competition and the quest for profit create this pressure. In public administration, administrative and political factors tend to produce the same effect.

In addition, the social environment conditions the pressure toward and direction of innovation by creating external economies, services available from outside at lower cost than a single organization could provide them

[1] Bernard J. Muller-Thym, "Practices in General Management, New Directions for Organizational Practice," *Journal of Engineering for Industry* (Part of report, "Ten Years' Progress in Management, 1950–1960").

internally. The development of a profession is one instance of such a factor that influences forms of organization. The profession, as a social entity, lowers the cost to any given organization and employing professionals by itself examining the degree of qualification of personnel and enforcing standards of conduct. By standardization it permits technology developed in one organization to be transferred to another and — beyond this — it provides, through educational programs, meetings, publications, and informal contacts, the specific means of communication by which this transfer can be effected. Increasing professionalization will thus have a considerable impact in determining the direction and speed of innovation.

In addition to or aside from professionalization, as the process of administration becomes more and more complex, many organizations may find it necessary to make use of training facilities and consulting services from outside. The type of service available may well exert a significant influence on the type and amount of innovation.

Another hypothesis, and a most intriguing one, is suggested by Alan O. Mann.[2] He envisions that information processing will tend to become a regulated public utility, with standardization of format and equipment permitting encoded transmission of data between supplier and customer, tax office and taxpayer's accounting office, etc. Data processing for small business and individuals would be contracted for by banks, credit agencies, or accounting firms.

Future developments may also exert a substantial influence on our society's mores concerning occupation. As the norms change, organizations will encounter pressure to which they must adapt. Consider the influence of professionalization on the present notions of "career" and "status." Now it is customary for an individual to commit his career completely to one organization, and consequently be rewarded with a degree of managerial control over the organization's affairs. The most radical prospects would appear to be a divorce of managerial functions from organizational status and an acceptance of mobility between organizations as a normal step at any stage of a career. If these developments should happen in future society, the "organization man" would go the way of neanderthal man and many of our most widely accepted "principles" of administration would follow him into oblivion. Although it is precarious to make specific guesses, even as specific as these, we can be certain of profound change in social norms in the context of our working lives within the foreseeable future.

[2] Donald G. Malcolm and Alan J. Rowe, eds., *Management Control Systems, Proceedings of a Symposium Held at System Development Corporation, Santa Monica, California,* Wiley, 1960, p. 245 ff.

51

The Capital Budget

Leon Ovsiew and William B. Castetter

It has sometimes been held that school authorities do not place sufficient emphasis on long-range planning. The capital budget, here described by Professors Ovsiew and Castetter, is a highly important instrument in that task.

Current and long-term budgets are the means through which all educational planning is forged into reality. Through these instruments, present and future educational needs, and plans for financing them, are organized and expressed in concrete terms. Long-range plans for capital outlays can be crystallized through what has come to be known as the "capital budget," i.e., a long-term plan which projects the capital improvement projects to be undertaken, the nature of their costs, and the methods by which they are to be financed.

Many long-term budgets are planned for at least a six-year period. Within this period long-term budgets may be altered to fit certain economic and other conditions peculiar to the community. Without a long-term plan for financing proposed expenditures, the planning which does take place will probably be, at best, of the emergency type.

Emergency building is invariably expensive, especially in time. When building problems pile up, when split sessions, overcrowded classrooms, and church basements threaten, boards and administrators drop everything to concentrate on housing. Unfortunately, other problems do not really disappear, they only seem to fade away. Ignored for a time, they reassert themselves in new emergencies.

Of course building problems are complicated, for they include such complex factors as long-term population projection, financing, planning the school curriculum, site selection, administrative organization, and architecture. In some districts resources for planning are not commensurate with the problems, and for many districts where resources may be good, time for research and planning is hard to find, unless it is "stolen" from other activities. In such cases a school district is well-advised to seek the help of a professional survey

From Leon Ovsiew and William B. Castetter, *Budgeting for Better Public Schools,* pp. 156–160; 184–185.

group. Many universities provide such service, and there are also a number of competent persons in private service agencies. Usually such professional service saves more than its cost, since the survey report provides the basis for a planned capital improvement program.

Regrettably, school systems — again because of chronic neglect of the planning function — often engage survey services a year or more later than they should. Even so, the emergency can at least be partially delegated in this way.

. . . .

Capital Budget Procedure

The capital budget, like the current budget, involves three component plans — educational, revenue, and expenditure. The general sequence of capital budget development also parallels in some respects current budget procedure in that a budget must be prepared, reviewed, adopted, and administered.

The several steps involved in capital budgeting, as well as the sequence in which they occur in the budget cycle, are summarized in the tabular outline on page 464. In the sequence illustrated, the essential steps in the capital budget process include:

(1) *Defining Need.* The first step in the formulation of the capital budget is the determination of the capital needs of the school district for a given period. This involves a consideration of the purposes of the school, the educational program necessary to achieve purpose, and the capital needs which are involved in the program.

(2) *Developing the Capital Improvement Program.* The second step in formulating the capital budget is the preparation of the capital improvement program. This phase consists largely of transforming the list of capital needs into specific capital projects. In brief, each project in the capital needs lists must be reduced to specifics. What the project is, why it is necessary, the specific elements of the project, and its relationship to the comprehensive plan are matters which must be transformed into specific plans.

(3) *Establishing Priorities.* If steps 1 and 2 are carefully prepared, it is more than likely that the list of capital projects will be greater than the community can finance in any one year. Some will be more urgent than others. The third step, then, is designed to establish relative urgencies for each project in terms of priorities. It is at this stage that the capital budget begins to take form, for the projects will have to be spread out over a five- or six-year period. Some projects will be listed in the first year of the capital budget, which actually become the capital improvements to be included in the operating budget.

(4) *Integrating Physical and Financial Plans.* The capital improvement program has now reached the stage where capital needs are known, priorities established, and projects phased over a five- or six-year period. At this point

GENERAL SEQUENCE OF CAPITAL BUDGET DEVELOPMENT

1

Define Need

- Assign staff planning responsibilities
- Appraise total capital improvement needs
- List all improvements needed to attain purpose without regard to cost or urgency

2

Develop Program

- Summarize capital needs — what, why, where
- Specify each need in terms of detailed project
- Coordinate planning with other governments

3

Establish Priorities

- Determine relative urgency of each project
- Phase program over 5–6 year period
- Accord priorities to all projects
- Allocate priorities by years

4

Link Physical and Financial Plans

- Estimate cost of each project
- Project expenditure estimates by years
- Project revenue estimates by years
- Adjust proposed expenditures to financial ability
- Develop capital budget document

5

Present

- To board, community, lay groups, other governmental agencies
- Encourage public understanding and appraisal
- Revise in light of appraisal

6

Adopt

- Board adopts first year of capital budget as part of operating budget
- Adopts total capital budget in principle

7

Administer

- Implement operating phase of capital budget
- Develop project budgets
- Revise capital budget annually
- Extend capital budget one year as first year is incorporated into operating budget

each project is given a price tag or cost estimate, so that the tentative costs of the program can be ascertained for each year of the capital budget.

At the same time that the expenditure plan is being developed, it must be linked to a revenue plan. Estimates of school revenues available for capital improvements must be made. Hence, there is a necessity for a balancing of the educational, expenditure, and revenue plans so that they are economically and educationally defensible. It is at this stage that the several plans are fashioned into a capital budget document for presentation to reviewing authorities.

(5) *Presentation.* Like the current budget, the capital budget should have official sanction of the board of education. As a matter of fact, broad participation by the community in all phases of capital budget formulation should be encouraged. Further, efforts should be made to coordinate school improvement planning with the plans of other governmental agencies, such as city, county, or regional governments.

Presentation to the foregoing groups provides an opportunity for appraisal and possible readjustment of plans before adoption by the board of education as a guide to capital improvement planning.

(6) *Adoption.* Formal adoption of the capital budget generally means that the first year of the capital budget actually is transferred to the operating budget in the form of capital improvement items. The remaining years are adopted in principle, but are subject to review and modification during the next budget cycle.

(7) *Administration.* The final step in the capital budget process is to implement the plans called for in the capital budget. In addition, one more year must be planned so that there will always be continuous budgeting five or six years in advance of the operating budget.

. . .

Advantages of Capital Budgeting

The changes which are taking place today — technologically, industrially, economically, institutionally — are such that school plants and programs must be developed in terms of decades rather than by single years if blunders and financial waste are to be avoided, and the largest possible return in usable school plants is to be achieved.

From a practical standpoint, there are a number of desirable outcomes to be achieved through employment of the capital budget procedure. Some of these are listed below:

> The capital budget is planned in light of the educational program toward which the community should direct its efforts. Stress is placed upon educational goals to be achieved — a "what should we buy" concept rather than "what can we afford?"

Continuous attention is placed upon unmet needs.

The capital budget provides a systematic method of integrating and projecting educational, building, and financial plans into a single comprehensive program.

The capital budget provides a means for continuous appraisal of all phases of the school system.

The procedure may involve extensive use of lay groups, which will simplify the tasks of interpreting the nature of the educational program to be achieved and securing public financial support necessary to carry on the program.

The capital budget provides both the public and the school administrators with a view of the entire educational enterprise, and furnishes guidelines to both groups for future planning.

Indebtedness can be scheduled so as to minimize the accumulation of debt service charges during any single period.

Revenue and expenditure plans can be coordinated. Funds are more likely to be available for school projects if the financial needs are defined and planned for in advance.

The board of education can acquire adequate school sites in advance. A planned program of improvements tends to lessen the potentially adverse effects of some pressure groups.

The capital budget emphasizes needed improvements to the extent that the likelihood of their being neglected is lessened.

School plant planning through the capital budget can be coordinated with master city or town plan.

The capital budget, with its emphasis on long-term planning, reduces the possibility of mistakes and blunders. When projects are placed on a priority list, impetuous action toward the development of a "pet project" is minimized.

By use of the capital budget procedure, a gradual shifting to a pay-as-you-go policy of financing school plant construction may be possible. Where statutes permit, the possibility of accumulating reserve funds might be feasible.

Unforeseen needs are less likely to occur if improvement needs are carefully planned. When they do occur, they usually impede or thwart total planning efforts.

It should be noted, in summary, that capital improvement planning is but one aspect of educational planning. This chapter will become more meaningful if it is considered in terms of the totality and integrity of all foresightful educational planning.

52

Interest Rates and School Borrowing

Educational Facilities Laboratories

To obtain a lower rate of interest on school bonds is a genuine economy in the management of educational resources. There is, after all, only one quality of money. This selection includes several suggestions to that end.

At an interest rate of 4 per cent, it costs over $1,650,000 to retire a million dollar bond issue in 30 years. A 1 per cent advance in the rate of interest would add another $160,000 to the cost. Borrowing adds substantially to the total price of a school building. The alternative to borrowing, of course, is to put all construction on a pay-as-you-go basis or to have built up reserve funds which can be drawn on for just such purposes. But few school districts (and few individuals buying a home) are either willing or able to pay for a building outright. Since school districts often are already under the shadow of past debts, to change to a pay-as-you-go plan tends to place an unduly heavy burden on today's taxpayer. Yet, pay-as-you-go is a prudent policy and can be used with discretion to meet part of capital outlay expenses. Such items as site acquisition, site development, minor additions, and renovations are among those which can often be met by expenditures from current funds.

The pay-as-you-go system is rarely feasible. The use of reserve funds is not often the answer either. Theoretically at least, the acquisition of reserves during periods of little or no construction and the use of these funds, either exclusively or in conjunction with long-term borrowing, enables a local school district to spread out the cost of capital outlay programs more evenly. Not only is the local tax rate less subject to fluctuations and instability, but the interest cost is also reduced. Historically, however, reserve funds have suffered from mismanagement, from diversion to other uses, and from the argument that the taxpayer himself could earn more on his money than the interest which the school district is able to secure. Moreover, school boards usually meet taxpayer resistance when they attempt to levy taxes for indeterminate future needs.

Adapted from *The Cost of a Schoolhouse,* New York, The Laboratories, 1960, pp. 114–124. Reproduced with permission.

As for states, the pressure on their finances is usually too great to set up construction reserve funds of hundreds of millions of dollars for payment to local districts as future building needs may require. In fact, the trend is for state legislatures to tap existing reserve funds to put public works programs into action. Reserve funds are consequently disliked by the financial community unless the funds are free of a public body or public control and are in the hands of a trustee. Such funds do not represent the same kind of tangible security as school bonds.

For almost all school districts borrowing is necessary. And borrowing usually means the issuance of long-term obligations. These long-term loans in the form of bonds may be for 10, 20, 30, and even 40 years. Short-term loans for a period of 1 to 5 years or less are sometimes used as a temporary measure to tide a district over to a better marketing period. These temporary loans must be paid off with the proceeds of long-term bond issues. Many states have not yet passed legislation permitting such short-term financing of school construction.

When a school district wants to borrow money, it is competing with all other classes of borrowers, including financial institutions, private corporations, and other governmental bodies. In order to get the best terms, i.e., the lowest interest, a school district must make its offering as appealing as it can to as many classes of potential investors as possible. This is one of the reasons why the serial bond is the type of bond used by school districts. A serial school bond issue consists of bonds, usually of $1,000 denomination, so scheduled that some bonds fall due each year for the length of the issue, the number depending on the repayment schedule. The serial bond attracts a greater variety of customers. It is of interest to those preferring either 1–10 year bonds or 10–20 year bonds, as well as to those who wish to invest their money for periods from 20 to 30 years. Commercial banks, which represent the largest single investors in school issues (holding some 30 per cent) and which head many of the bidding syndicates, prefer to invest their own money in the short 1 to 10 year maturities. Savings banks, on the other hand, would rather have longer serial bonds, as would casualty and fire insurance companies. Pension funds and certain insurance companies frequently prefer 30 year obligations.

MARKETABILITY OF SCHOOL BONDS

School bonds represent a substantial portion — close to one-third — of all municipal bonds being offered in the money market. The price which investment bankers are willing to pay for them is determined by a variety of factors, including the credit of the district, the demand for school bonds of similar quality originating in the same state, and the current condition of the money market at the time the bonds are issued. School districts can secure better bids, that is, lower interest rates, if they understand the preferences and requirements of people in the securities business and, so far as statutes and regulations permit and the needs of the school district allow, design their issues to fit these requirements.

Although their tax-free income gives school bonds a particular appeal to certain groups of investors, these bonds still lack the highest degree of marketability because the bond market tends to favor obligations backed by the credit of the state. The most important factor in marketability is the *credit rating* which a bond carries. These ratings are prepared by firms which specialize in studying and evaluating the relative investment quality of all kinds of bonds, those of private corporations as well as those of public agencies. The rating of securities takes into account such factors as the present outstanding debt of the district, its general economic level and social conditions, and the cost of its current operations. Moody's Investors Service, on a rating scale which starts with Aaa, generally rates school bonds Aa, A, and Baa. School bonds rated Aa and A generally command a lower interest rate. Standard and Poor's Corporation, another major rating service, applies quality symbols which for school bonds range usually from A1 to $B1^{+}$.

Marketability of bonds is often increased as school district boundaries become larger or if the districts are coterminous with cities or communities of high repute. Programs for district consolidations or plans which provide for the financial strengthening of local school districts will often raise credit ratings and help insure lower interest rates.

Marketability can also be strengthened by direct state action. It is for this reason that some states, such as Florida, issue bonds on behalf of the counties. On January 27, 1958, the Florida State Board of Education offered a group of bond issues which totaled $7,855,000. Each bond issue was stated to be "for and on behalf of the county" with 11 counties participating in the group of issues to be sold. Each of the issues was to be secured by a "first, prior, and paramount lien on state motor vehicle license taxes . . ." In this example, the state, while not using its own credit, agreed to the use of certain state funds for the payment of the bonds offered on behalf of each participating county.

New York State now requires the State Comptroller to withhold from State aid due a local school district such funds as may be necessary to pay both the principal and the interest on any default by the district. As soon as the announcement of this legislation was distributed in April, 1959, there was strong positive response nationally by prominent investment banking houses, both in their releases and in their advice to investors. This is credited with having helped the stability of New York school bonds in May and June of 1959 during a weak bond market. In effect, it resulted in their upgrading.

Any way in which the state can be brought into the picture will improve the rating of the thousands upon thousands of relatively obscure school districts. And at 4 per cent interest, a favorable change in rating can mean an interest saving of 1/5 to 1/4 of 1 per cent. On one million dollars over 30 years, this could mean a saving of $40,000 to the taxpayers. Consequently, one key to economy in capital financing is raising the rating of a school district's obligations.

Another central problem in the marketability of school bond issues is the narrowness of the demand for them, coming as it does largely from investors in the state or region in which the bond issues originate. Unless the individual school district carries a name well known and respected nationally, it is a virtual stranger to the bond market outside its own state. This is partly because of the sheer number of local school districts in the United States and partly because of the complex (and confusing) names carried by some consolidated districts. The smaller the demand, the higher will be the interest rate bid by the investment bank or syndicate, to enable it to sell the bonds with a reasonable profit.

In order to broaden the school bond market, New Jersey recently published a report for investors entitled "New Jersey Schools — Invest for Your Future Security." Similar publicity by other states can help acquaint the investment field with the desirability of their school bonds.

A school district is also aided in the sale of its bonds by the use of nationally recognized bond counsel. Bond law and bond proceedings are complex and unique, and the preparation of bond issues requires the use of lawyers specially trained in the skills of this field. Investment bankers and commercial bankers heading the syndicates, which bid on school district bond issues and all other types of public securities, require that the proceedings be prepared by a firm of nationally recognized municipal bond counsel and that the counsel's opinion approving the bond issue be delivered to the successful bidder. A refusal by such counsel to deliver an unqualified legal opinion, due to irregularities in the bond proceedings, bond election, or bond law, will usually nullify the sale. In a number of school districts the local attorney for the district is employed at substantial expense to aid in the preparation of the bond proceedings. This is often an unnecessary expenditure since the local attorney must normally depend upon expert bond counsel for his forms and often for the actual drafting of the papers.

Another aid in the sale of a district's bonds at a satisfactory interest rate is the use of a prospectus. Knowledge of relative economic and social conditions is fundamental to an investment syndicate's evaluation of a district's bonds. Type of community, kind of industry present, population data, assessed valuation, total tax levy, tax rate, tax collection record, total debt statement, and amount of state aid are all among the factors which should be analyzed in detail. Since the sole security behind the school district bond is the taxing power of the district, property valuation data on all private property within its limits should be presented in detail. If there is a particularly large taxpayer, such as a public utility or an industrial plant, its assessed valuation and a description of its property as a taxable entity should be given. It is helpful also to present a judicious estimate of the future need for additional schools.

If no additional classrooms will be required for many years, that fact is of vital importance.

The prospectus should also present the debt of other public bodies, including water districts, sewer districts, and fire districts, which overlap the school district or lie within its borders. It should include complete details on the bonds presently being offered, including the maturity schedule, the place of payment, and provisions for redemption before maturity.

The mistaken idea that a simple one-page circular is adequate needs to be abandoned. The analytical investor in municipal bonds knows little of the economic and financial soundness of each individual district. The prospectus should awaken his interest in the bonds of a public body previously unknown to him and should provide him with sound factual material which will prove the bonds are a good investment.

The Timing of Issues

The interest cost of a bond issue depends on its timing as well as on its marketability.

In periods of temporary stress it may be advisable to delay offering a bond issue and to wait for a better market. If many school issues are being offered for sale at the same time, it may be wise to time an offering so it is not made in the same day or week as other large ones. There have been recent periods when there were no offerings for two or more weeks, and then many offerings from a single state were made in one day. Since most issues are bid by the same syndicates and it is difficult for syndicates to tie up large funds in more than three or four issues, proper timing is particularly important, especially for large issues. Recently, for example, a single issue for $11,270,000 was offered and sold by one school district alone. Such timing, of course, requires a general knowledge of the level of activity of the bond market.

The attempt to take advantage of money market conditions in order to secure the best possible interest rates has led some districts to rely heavily on short-term loans. While short-term issues have been used as a mechanism to wait for more preferred rates, this is a mechanism with built-in problems, and it should be used with caution. One reason for this is that after it is used once, such short-term financing usually cannot be repeated. But more important is that in a period of rising interest rates on bonds the delayed sale may cost the district more in the long run. Many school districts which tried a few years ago to outguess the money market now need to refund their short-term obligations at a time when long-term interest rates are hitting new highs.

A further danger in the "wait and see" method of short-term financing is that in trying to outride a period of high money rates school districts issue a large amount of short-term debt. Too much short-term debt which must be refinanced into long-term obligations at any one time reduces the favorable position of a district. A number of school districts which have used short-term loans are now facing serious refinancing problems.

What If All the Bids Are High?

If competent advice suggests that the bid or bids on a school district's long-term issues appear to be high, then it is sound policy to reject the bids and to reoffer the bonds at another sale or to finance temporarily if the statutes permit. It is necessary to analyze those factors which were responsible for the unfavorable response and to take positive steps to correct them. Bids may be high because of lack of competition. This is particularly true of rural districts where only one bid may have been received. In such a case it is probably wise to reject the bid. Indeed, it can be stated as a general proposition that whenever possible a district should never sell its bonds if it receives only one bid. Unless it has other bids for comparison, it is at a loss to know whether or not to accept the offer. If not enough parties have indicated interest in the bonds, better data and wider advertising in financial journals may be called for. Or it may be that the maturities were set improperly for the immediate needs of the market. A district may be offering 15-year serial bonds when issues with longer maturities are in demand. There are fluctuating conditions in the money market, and a district needs to know them in order to tailor its offering to the best advantage. Another possibility is that the issue may be too large. If so, it might be advantageous to offer it in two stages.

So that school districts may be able to avail themselves of the most promising methods of long-term financing, several states have begun to establish financial advisory services. Such services can render important help in improving marketing procedures for school bond issues. They hold a promise of yielding substantial economies to the local taxpayer.

Limitations on School District Borrowing and Alternative Solutions

Almost all states impose some debt limitations based on property valuations. These are usually written into the state constitution, and range from a 2 per cent limit in Indiana and Kentucky to 10 per cent in Missouri and 20 per cent in Florida.

Ratios between assessed valuation and the actual market value of property frequently differ strikingly between school districts — all the way from 10 per cent to 90 per cent or more. Therefore, the very same debt limitation may permit a debt for one school district in an amount many times the size of that which another district with the same estimated total market value of property is allowed to incur. In some cases, the law requires that all property be assessed at true and fair market value, and there are some communities where this is done, but they are a very small minority. Wisconsin and New

York require that debt limitations be based on equalized full valuation. Other states should move in the same direction.

One method sometimes used when debt limitations are excessively restrictive is that of permitting a district to borrow "outside the debt limit." Usually this needs to be done by state legislative action or on authority of a state emergency finance commission. Such devices are subterfuges at best, since the financial community is primarily concerned with the district's rating rather than with technical statutory limitations.

The problem of constitutional debt limitation has led to the use of various devices by which the local school district tries to circumvent the borrowing restrictions under which it must operate. One of the first of these to be used successfully was the Kentucky leaseback plan. Under this arrangement a private school building corporation is created for the benefit of the local school district. The private corporation purchases sites, erects buildings, leases them to the district, collects rents for their use, and uses the rents to pay back the principal and interest on its bonds. When the indebtedness has been retired, the nonprofit corporation deeds the school building to the district. The corporation's project is financed through the sale of bonds, and, since the debt is not a debt of the school district, it is not subject to the local debt limits. The fly in this ointment, however, is that the corporation does not have a top credit rating. It is, therefore, expensive for the local district to use it. But the district does use it because it has no choice. Its own low debt limit requires such a plan.

The building corporation has a number of other weaknesses. The most important is that its securities are not local government obligations and, therefore, are no stronger than the willingness of the local school district to continue its lease-rental payments. The bonds thus have limited marketability, and this makes them more expensive. This is an example of how a low debt limit structure can actually add to the cost of schools. Nevertheless, the Kentucky plan has been widely and successfully used in that state for the past 30 years. It has also been used extensively in Indiana.

The private building corporation is the direct predecessor of the school building authority. This type of structure has been most fully developed in Pennsylvania, both on the state level and on the local level. The Pennsylvania constitution limits the amount of money that can be borrowed by a school district to 7 per cent of the assessed valuation of the taxable real property. It is estimated that the State average for real estate assessments, exclusive of the large cities, is approximately one-third of true valuation. This valuation and the 7 per cent debt limit make borrowing problems for many Pennsylvania districts and have led to the creation of school authorities.

The Pennsylvania State Public School Building Authority combines the lease-rental plan of the corporation with State aid payments to the local school district. The corporation pays off the bonds from the proceeds of the lease-rentals it has collected from the school districts. Although the bonds do not pledge the credit or the taxing power of the Commonwealth, they are tied to State aid payments, which gives them a better rating than those of the private corporation. If a school district defaults on its payments to the State Authority, the State is authorized to withhold from the district an amount of rental aid equal to the default and to make such payment directly to the Authority.

Several other types of school authorities have been developed in Pennsylvania which operate on a local rather than on a state level. These may be independent local authorities for individual school districts, or they may be authorities set up as *joint* school authorities to build projects for several school districts. Joint school boards are created by voluntary resolutions of the individual school boards who wish to join together. The joint district through its joint board creates a local joint school authority. Many authorities in Pennsylvania are now of this type, and this plan has become one of the strongest motivating forces for school district consolidation.

While the Pennsylvania local authority system of financing school building construction has been both praised and damned by financial experts, the consensus is that it represents an awkward financing device. This view holds that, while it is feasible and workable, it is expensive in terms of interest costs and does not furnish any evidence of saving over conventional school district financing; its higher interest costs are directly transferred to both the state and the local property owner who bears the real estate tax burden. The Pennsylvania local authority system is illustrative of the way restrictive conditions force legal inventions or adaptations which are not always efficient or economical.

In contrast to, or in conjunction with, the various devices designed to get around state imposed debt restrictions are the programs of direct state action.

STATE PROGRAMS FOR PUBLIC SCHOOL CONSTRUCTION

State Bond Issues for Loans. California is the outstanding example of a state which has used its own bonding power to finance local school districts. Since 1949 it has issued bonds for school construction amounting to $615 million.

The provisions for repayment of a school district loan to the State of California are such that a district is not required to make any repayment to the State in a year when the district's total levy to meet prior bonded debt is 4 mills. However, if a 3-mill levy ($3.00 per $1,000 valuation) will meet prior bonded debt in that year, the district is required to repay the State an amount equal to a 1-mill levy.

State loans to school districts in California must be paid off in 30 years and any debt unpaid at the end of 30 years is automatically written off by the State. The district's annual repayment to the State is to meet both principal and interest on the State's loan to the district, but no interest payments on the loan are required after 25 years.

Maryland and Michigan also issue state bonds and then lend these funds to the local districts for their building projects. The Maryland plan, like that of California, began operation in 1949. The original authorization was for $50 million, and additional authorizations of $20 million and $75 million were made in 1953 and 1956. Maryland law requires that each school construction loan shall be repaid in full with interest and that a sufficient annual levy be made on the property within the county to retire the loan. The State Comptroller withholds, from the annual State aid payment due the county, an amount equal to the county's payment due on its loan. All the counties in Maryland have participated in the program, and it has been necessary to give the State additional bonding power from time to time, to enable it to continue this financial assistance.

In 1955 Michigan created a $100 million State loan fund for the payment of both interest and principal on school district bonds. The plan permits any school district needing construction funds, *when its tax rate becomes more than 13 mills for debt service in any year,* to apply to the State for a loan representing the difference between the amount the district would actually require to pay principal and interest in that year and the amount provided by a 13-mill tax rate. The peculiarity of the Michigan plan is that a district may apply at the time it issues its bonds *regardless* of its then current tax levy for bonded indebtedness. For example, a district may have only a 7-mill tax rate at the time its bonds are issued. But it makes application at the time of issuance, anticipating that in a future year it may have to push its rate up to 13 mills; and in any year in which its rate goes over 13 mills the State steps in to help. Almost all districts issuing bonds apply for State assistance even though very few of them need it at the time of issuance. This Michigan program represents a cheap "standby device," and as such has many desirable features.

Other State Funds for Loans. Some states have revolving loan funds for aid to local districts. These funds are set up with monies from current revenues, special appropriations, or other sources exclusive of bond issues. Arkansas has such a fund from which it grants small loans, the maximum being $50,000 to any one district. Almost all the districts in the State have used the fund since its establishment 12 years ago. The same type of fund exists in North Carolina, where it is called the State Literary Fund, but the North Carolina fund has been used by very few school districts because of strict requirements and a low maximum limit on loans.

Virginia's loan fund, also known as the State Literary Fund, has been used by most of the districts which have let contracts for school construction since 1950. Loans up to 100 per cent of the cost of construction have been made with relatively low interest rates. Annual repayments on the principal are made over a period of 30 years. Under this arrangement more than $36 million was committed to school districts in the years between 1950 and 1957.

State Grants. In addition to loans, state bonds have been issued to finance all or part of a program of direct state grants in a number of states, including South Carolina, Delaware, Vermont, and Washington. These states have used their general credit to borrow money for school purposes and have allocated the money to local school districts.

Another group of states has insisted that local school districts use their own borrowing capacity and issue their own bonds without the aid of state bond issues. These states, however, have been liberal in giving assistance to the districts to meet debt service payments on their bonds.

In Massachusetts, for example, annual appropriations are made from State general revenue to finance direct State grants for school construction. The grants may be used in two ways. The State may give funds directly to the district towards the cost of school construction. Or, on the other hand, if the bonded indebtedness exceeds more than 50 per cent of the cost of the project, the amount of the grant is divided by the number of years the indebtedness will remain outstanding, and the grant is paid in equal annual installments during the period in which the bonds are being retired. Connecticut has a somewhat similar program using State general funds.

Other Types of State Aid. In 1958 New Jersey authorized a fund to be used to purchase a school district bond issue when a default is anticipated, or to pay interest on such bonds in the hands of outside holders so long as the district is unable to make such payments. Although this fund is relatively small, totaling only $18 million in 1958, it definitely has been a strengthening factor for marginal school district bonds of that State.

The New Jersey plan has certain advantages over that of Michigan. It is more flexible in that the State can move in at any time to bolster the bonds of a district (thereby protecting all its districts) by taking a weak issue out of the regular market. In comparison, Michigan requires stricter conformity to its eligibility regulations before a school district can qualify for aid, in that a district must qualify its bonds long in advance of the time when default troubles could arise.

. . . .

It is clear that the trend since 1945 has been toward further centralization of school district financing in the state capitals. One state after another has come forward with some plan to help local districts finance their bonds. These plans have ranged from help in meeting interest payments to the purchase of the bonds themselves to the taking of some type of loan contract obligation of the district in lieu of bonds. These plans may eventually result in more financing by states and state agencies and less financing by the local districts.

Does this mean that the voters and the local school board members will be satisfied with less control over spending? Will the traditional small school district bond issue become extinct? Probably not. Both the short- and the long-term outlook for school district bonds appear good. Debt service obligations of currently outstanding school bonds will be met with ease by most districts. Moreover, the high quality of these bonds will be recognized even more generally in future years as many states follow the lead of Michigan, New York, and others in making the investor aware that school bonds are among the finest investment media the market affords.

A NOVEL

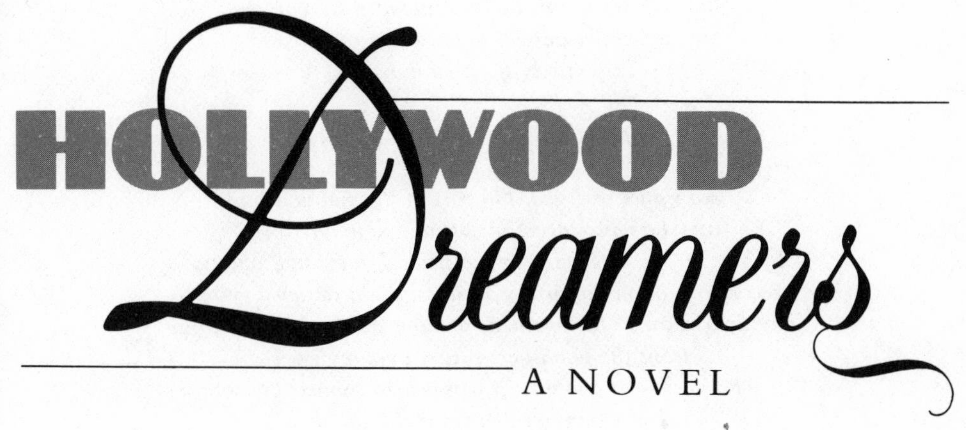

JUDY SPENCER

BEAUFORT BOOKS • *Publishers* • *New York*

No character in this book is intended to represent any actual person; all the incidents of the story are entirely fictional in nature.

Library of Congress Cataloging-in-Publication Data
Spencer, Judy.
Hollywood Dreamers.
I. Title.
PS3569.P452D7 1986 813'.54 85-26752
ISBN 0-8253-0355-9

Published in the United States by Beaufort Books Publishers, New York.

Designed by Christine Swirnoff / Libra Graphics, Inc.

Printed in the U.S.A. First Edition

10 9 8 7 6 5 4 3 2 1

For Harry and Sophie,
thanks for the chromosomes

Prologue

December 1985
New York

"ARE YOU ANYBODY?" A girl screamed out as the limos pulled up in front of Radio City Music Hall. Barricades dotted the avenue and mounted police wheeled around on their big horses, all in an effort to keep the crowd under control, but it all added to the general confusion. The National Association of Theater Owners were giving out their awards tonight and the crowd knew they had chosen the winners with their own box office dollars. Karen Singer had won for top female box office draw and her fans, known for their loyalty, were out in droves. They would have given anything just to catch a glimpse of her.

Karen Singer was sitting in her limo, caught in gridlock around the Rockefeller Center area. "I used to practically live *in that store," she told the slim black man sitting beside her. "C'mon Sid, wouldn't you like to jump out of this car and shop your brains out?"*

"You're babbling," Sid said, "and I haven't quite got your blush the way I want it. Hold still." He moved a big, fluffy brush against a smooth expanse of cheekbone. In his day, Sid had been a legend as the finest makeup man in Hollywood. He was pleased to see that he hadn't lost his touch. "Dear one, if I say so myself, no one does your face the way I do. I saw your new film. You were wonderful as always but what's with this natural look bullshit? I like a woman who wears a little makeup."

"Sid, you don't like women."

"I like them, I just don't want to sleep with them," Sid qualified. "There. You're perfect." He squeezed her hand affectionately. "I can't help thinking about the first time I met you. Nobody else could take their eyes off Lake, but I knew my girl was going to

win all the marbles." Then he could have cursed himself for even mentioning Lake's name.

Sure enough, Karen turned to stare out the window.

"Don't, my love," he told her in a gentle voice. "What's done is done and there isn't a man alive who's found a way to rewrite the past. This is your night. You earned it, now enjoy it."

"Somehow, I feel if Lake was still with us, none of this would have happened to me. It all feels like a mistake, like this should be her *night, not mine."*

"Look!" Sid commanded, holding up a mirror. "This is what all those people are waiting to see tonight. You."

Her hazel eyes with their curious up-tilted corners flicked at her reflected image in the mirror, taking in a long graceful neck, high cheekbones, and her trademark hairstyle, a short, gamine cut. Her hand idly stroked the rich fur bordering the neckline of her gown, the only trim on the off-the-shoulder ivory dress. It clung to her lithe body like a second skin and looked vaguely medieval in design. The long sleeves came to a slight point over her hands. The gown was beautiful, but it also accentuated that slight feeling of otherness Karen had always possessed. She had always seemed to feel things in a deeper way than most people did, which was probably why Lake had sought her out and why they had been such close friends, despite all the difficulties.

To get her mind off of Lake, Sid asked, "Don't you wish Johnny was here to hold your hand?"

"Well, sure, but he hates these things. He's much happier staying home, teaching Mark how to dive. You should see that kid." She spoke with obvious pride. "We're talking Olympic material."

"Don't you dare pull out any baby pictures or I'll hit you." The limo came to a halt. "I think it's time for your big entrance."

The crowd went crazy as they stepped from the limo. In a second, Karen had ducked under the red velvet rope separating the crowd from the celebrities and was busily signing autographs. Sid marvelled at her fearlessness, but she emerged from the crowd intact if disheveled.

A practical man, Sid grabbed his makeup case and ran after her.

"Are you anybody?" a girl screamed at him.

"Heaven forbid," Sid muttered. He caught up with Karen and they were quickly ushered to a backstage dressing room. There, Sid straightened out her hair and dabbed a little more deep rose

gloss on her lips. He stepped back for a moment to survey his work. "Don't look so serious," he moaned, "you look as if they're going to take you out and shoot you, instead of giving you a very prestigious award. Now give me a movie star smile, you're making my makeup look bad."

Her eyes were piercing. "Sid, do you know what day it is?"

"Monday."

"That's not what I mean. It's December 23rd."

"So?" His gaze dropped guiltily. Damn, why did they all feel so responsible when it came to Lake? Why did they all feel there should have been something they could have done to save her? "It's just the day before Christmas Eve. That's all."

"It's a little more than that, Sid. It's the anniversary of Lake Eastman's murder."

Part 1

1

September 1971

LAKE EASTMAN shored herself up on one elbow and stared dismally at the young man doing push-ups on her. She was bored. And disappointed. After all, this young man was top dog on campus. Best athlete, highest grades, best body, and, rumor had it, the most well-endowed boy in the school. For all these reasons Lake had chosen him. It appeared she was wrong. Again.

He emitted a squeak like a rusty hinge and flopped down next to her. The young man was not an idiot. He knew better than to ask, "Was it good for you, baby?"

She got up and quietly began to dress. Long platinum blonde hair curtained her face, hiding her expression from him. Displaying the easy style that had made him a campus legend, he reached out with light fingers and pulled that platinum shade. Her eyes, glowing sapphires, were empty.

"Don't." She pulled away, then immediately realized how coldly she was acting. "I'm . . . sorry." She was, too. More than he would know or believe.

Things should have been easy for her, but they never really were. They'd kidded her about her name in grade school. "Lake Eastman, Lake Eastman," they would chant raggedly, "I'm gonna swim in Lake Eastman!" But under the taunts and jeers they were scared of her.

Because Lake Eastman was a goddess passing among the mortals. An earthbound angel. Words pale, but the most commonly used phrase was "My God, that girl is gorgeous." She was. She was an adman's dream of an infant, a beautiful child, an adolescent unacquainted with braces or Clearasil. Platinum hair that never darkened. Sapphire eyes fringed with impossibly dark lashes. Perfect skin, perfect teeth. Perfect, perfect, perfect. She was a freak of nature, and nobody was going to give her any sympathy.

Boys were terrified of her. Girls hated her perfect guts. She walked the high school halls alone, conscious that everyone was staring at her. For years she thought her slip was hanging out. She stopped wearing slips. They still stared.

College was a little better. The men tried harder to be cool. *Yeah, we see goddesses every day. Nothing unusual there. By the way, will you marry me?*

The young man now searching for his underwear had been the coolest of the cool. He didn't look very cool now. He looked like a little boy who'd just lost his ice cream cone.

"It's not you," she said, trying to be kind. "It's me, really it is." She meant to be kind, dammit, she always meant to be kind; it just never came out that way.

She had a dream, a waking, fleeting hope that this moment would be different. The young man would turn to her, motion her to sit down next to him. "Talk," he would say, "tell me. I want to understand." And he would listen.

But this time was no different from the others. Lake paused, her shirt in her hands. Her head was bowed in the attitude of prayer.

Talk, the young man would say, tell me. I want to understand.

The young man was looking at her. "You know what your problem is?"

And he would listen.

"You're a cunt."

I want to understand.

"A real frigid bitch." His voice took on assurance. "Yeah, I was warned. I knew all about you before I walked in here tonight. The old male ego made me think I could melt the famed icebox, but I really don't think that can be done." He was being so nice, charming even. He was helping her. "You're like a sexual Cinderella trying to find the right cock to fit your glass slipper."

"It was the prince who was searching for the right fit," Lake said softly, smiling to herself.

"You should examine your motives." Now he was her friendly therapist. "If no man can satisfy you, then an answer suggests itself immediately, doesn't it?"

Yeah? How about most of the guys I sleep with are egotistical jerks who don't give a shit about me. They just want to sleep with the best-looking tush on campus.

He was gathering steam. "What you need is a nice lady. There are plenty of attractive dikes on campus, particularly in the art department." He reflected a moment. "I don't know why that is. Ah, yes!" He brightened. "All the nude models, of course. Sisters of Sappho, 101."

She smiled at him. "These attractive dikes," she purred. "Did they give up heterosexual love after a night with you?"

"Good, Lake." He laughed with some bitterness. "Good one."

"Of course, *your* nasty comments were psychological insights."

"So, I'm a bastard." He shrugged. "Women line up just for one kiss from me. Being a bastard never ruined anybody's life. Your problem"—he grinned—"just might."

Whistling, he put on the rest of his clothes and left.

On the drive back to Darien, Connecticut, she reached a decision. She made this particular decision about a hundred times before but she'd never had the guts to see it through. Maybe today would be a first.

She parked her car and walked slowly up the drive, hugging her books to her chest like a very little girl. She always felt like a very little girl when she was home. Well, this would be the last time she walked into that house. Better to live someplace else, anyplace else, even though her father had made it very clear that the family funds would be cut off if she left home. Still, she was scared and not just of him. Twenty years old and she could count on the fingers of one hand the nights she'd spent away from home. Scary nights full of dark, horribly real nightmares. Easier to stay at home where the demons at least wore familiar faces.

"Today for sure," she promised herself, "I am leaving."

The housekeeper opened the door for her and she ran upstairs. "Mother?" she called out.

Evelyn Eastman looked up from her needlepoint. She could work for hours on the torturously close work; it was one thing she did well and seemed to enjoy. Evelyn also liked jigsaw puzzles, but never ones over five hundred pieces. When Lake was ten she had a mild stroke. She had recovered physically, but her mental capabilities had been sadly diminished. She could not read above a child's level, preferring picture books. Sometimes Lake read to her.

"He's home," Evelyn said, "you'll have to dress for dinner. He likes to see you dressed up."

"Life is full of little disappointments."

Evelyn smiled timidly. "I think you look fine. You always

look pretty to me. Like the roses in the garden. See? I stuck my finger on them." She held out her hand for inspection.

Lake sighed. So, not a good day for Evelyn. She would have liked to have said goodbye to her mother and see more in Evelyn's eyes than dust-filmed sweetness.

"Mother," Lake said gently, "I may go away for a while."

"Oh, he'll be angry," Evelyn said, poking her needle through the canvas with exaggerated care.

"He'll have to get used to it. I just wanted to tell you, let you know what I was planning."

"Will you be gone a long time?"

Lake nodded. With luck, she would never be back. After a week or two, Evelyn would probably forget she'd ever been around.

Her mother stared at her with big, serious eyes. "You have to look out for youself."

"I will."

"Yes, you're very smart." She went back to her work.

Lake felt her eyes begin to sting. What had she expected anyway? Evelyn did the best she could. It was nobody's fault. She was simply incapable. "Will you miss me?" she asked her mother.

"Oh, yes." Evelyn's voice was soft and placid. Her eyes did not move from her work.

Lake put her arms around her mother and hugged her gently. "Careful of the needle," Evelyn warned.

"I am." Suddenly, Lake was assailed by a wave of self-pity. There is no one in this house for me, she thought, not one soul who cares for me. She pushed the thought out of her head, and went to wash up for dinner.

It was time to leave, and nothing was going to stop her. This time.

It would make a great feature in *National Geographic,* their little family dinners. Lake could just picture it. *Our reporter discovered the last stronghold of the American Dream. At the head of the table sits Karl Eastman, a self-made millionaire. Next to him is the lovely wife, Evelyn, the lady with the vague expression. And sitting there in solitary splendor is the lovely progeny, Lake.*

"Pass the . . ." Evelyn seemed to forget what she was asking for.

"Salt?" Lake offered.

Evelyn smiled, fuddled but gracious. "Yes. Thank you."

Servants glided, proffering trays. Baby lamb chops, teeny-tiny peas, new potatoes. A lot of things had died young so the Eastmans could have this lovely repast they were enjoying so much.

"I have an announcement to make." Her voice sounded weak and Lake hated herself for that weakness. "I'm going to Manhattan. To study acting. You said after I got my Associate in Arts degree at the community college, I was free to pursue whatever study I wanted. Well, I've decided."

"Oh, really?" Karl chuckled dryly. He never guffawed, never ho-hoed. He chuckled. Dryly. "And where are you going to live?"

"I'll find a place. Greenwich Village is pretty affordable."

Karl chuckled some more. Evelyn chased peas around her plate.

"I have some money saved up, and there's my trust fund . . ." Lake started to panic. Why wasn't anybody saying anything?

"You can't touch that trust fund until you're twenty-one. Correct me if I'm wrong, dear, but didn't you just turn twenty? By my calculations that gives you almost an entire year before you can get your hands on that money." Karl stabbed a chop. "Surely you didn't expect me to *give* you money? Oh, no, that would be out of character for such an independent spirit."

Lake folded her napkin and put it on the table. "That's fine, Dad. I'll manage. Matter of fact, I think I'll go upstairs and pack. You don't have to worry about how I'm getting to the train. I can walk, thank you."

Karl smiled at his plate. "You're making a mistake." His manner excluded Evelyn completely. She seemed rather grateful for that. "You and I both know you belong here with us."

"You don't know anything about me." Lake spat the words out.

His smug self-satisfaction was maddening. "Who knows a daughter better than her own father?"

"I am *leaving.* For good." She started up the stairs stiffly.

He went after her, standing so close she was sure he was smelling on her the boy she'd spent the afternoon with. Lake held her ground.

"All right," he said tonelessly, "if you have your heart set on going, I suppose there's nothing I can do about it. Your room will be waiting for you when you come back." Calmly he rejoined his wife at the table and went back to his dinner.

Lake drifted into her father's study, toying with the idea of ripping the place to shreds. What good would that do? A servant would quietly come in and pick up the debris. There was no way she could touch him.

The desk was big, mahogany. It weighed a ton. The kneehole was so huge that Lake had yearned to make it her own personal hidey-hole when she was a little girl. But Karl did not allow her into his study, his place of secrets. Well, she was here now. And like it or not, old Karl was going to give his daughter a hand in starting her career. She spun his desktop Rolodex, hurriedly copying a name and phone number onto a sheet of paper.

Richard Dano
872 W. 47th St.
555-7982

Heavy footsteps sounded in the hall. "What are you doing here?" Karl Eastman demanded angrily. "You know I forbid you to come in here."

She laughed at him. "I assure you, it'll never happen again." She went to her room to pack.

Karl collapsed into his chair, arms hugging the desk possessively. Tenderly he pulled open the drawer, feeling along the bottom, where an envelope was taped. It held canceled checks, letters, receipts, personal papers, a diary. He shut the drawer, shaking a little.

She had been so close! So close to discovering all his secrets locked up in his desk.

She would be gone soon, and while that was safer, it was not necessarily what he wanted. He smiled deep in his wolf's heart. No matter where she was, no matter how far she ran, she would always belong to him. He knew it and she knew it, though she pretended not to.

Who knows a girl better than her daddy?

January 1972

Karen Bloom was moving to New York to lose her virginity. Her mother was under the impression that Karen was going to

New York University to study (shudder) acting, but eighteen-year-old Karen had decided 1972 was the year for some lucky guy to cop the famed Karen Bloom cherry. Toward this end Karen had (A) applied only to colleges far away from the parental home in Chicago, (B) had her nose fixed in the hopes of attracting a better class of candidates vying for the K.B. cherry, (C) prayed a lot.

She had a nice composite in her mind of the guy who would finally "do the job." He would be incredibly non-Jewish looking. (Karen's mom always spoke of this fixation as the "lure of the stranger." Translated, it meant Jewish girls got the hots for guys who didn't look like one of the tribe.) He would have broad shoulders she could cling to while they were "doing it." He would have a cute little tush. He would, of course, be madly in love with her. There was only one problem. Karen did not know how to "do it." Oh, she knew slot A went into tab B, but she really didn't know *how.* What should she do during the foul deed? Should she talk? Grunt? Sing? Would she have to keep her eyes open? Would she have to touch it? Would she want to touch it?

It would have been nice if she'd had an older sister to go to for advice. Mom was not exactly a wealth of sexual information; upon the occasion of Karen's first period, she had told the girl, "If you kiss a boy now, you can get pregnant." This had upset Karen greatly until she'd checked out the scoop herself.

Men seemed to be all Karen could think about. Men. Hundreds and hundreds of big, strong men with their muscular arms and mysterious bulges. Thousands of them, all waiting in New York City for the express purpose of fucking Karen Bloom.

One way or the other.

IT WAS SURREAL, staring at all those little Lake Eastmans grinning up at her glossily. Finally she made her selections, choosing the allotted two poses from the contact sheet (two 8 × 10s were included in the photographer's fifty-dollar fee), and shelled out a few more bucks for one extra print. That one had a special destination.

The photographer put down his greasy coffee mug. It bore the legend "Genius."

In the hallway of his picturesque (*i.e.*, falling apart) East Village apartment, another actress was waiting, presumably to see his portfolio. He was making her wait a long time.

"Do you like the prints?" He picked up the cup again, using it as a prop, tonguing the rim as he stared at her.

"Yes, they're fine."

He seemed a little peeved that she wasn't going into rhapsodies over his work. Lake could tell the pictures were a little better than the ones she'd come to town with, but they were still light-years away from the flattering poses she'd seen other actors flash. Maybe she just wasn't photogenic. She smiled at the photographer, still moodily licking his mug. "Thank you." She paid him, noting that she had $1.87 and two tokens in her purse. Time to get a job. A job-job, not just running around for open calls, where she made a fool of herself. A job to pay for acting lessons and singing lessons and everything else a novice actress needed for survival.

Carefully she pulled out the third print and studied it.

"Be lucky for me," she whispered. She started walking to the subway.

Richard Dano was a great name for an actor. That's what Reni

Damiano had thought back in the fifties on his way to Hollywood. Richard Dano had been destined for stardom. And he had almost made it. It had been a question more of poor timing than of lack of ability. Not that he had ability; good actors were a dime a dozen. Richard Dano had charm.

They stopped buying charm in Hollywood in the sixties. They didn't want Richard Dano hanging out on the beach with Annette and the kids; he looked too much like Frankie Avalon, and he wasn't California enough to look like a legit surfer. He bought a limo and started chauffeuring the established stars around. It kept him in résumés and dental floss. He got a walk-on on *The Dick Van Dyke Show,* playing a delivery boy. Then things got really black.

They weren't going for tall, dark, and handsome. Ugly and ethnic were in. Richard Dano had a rep as a no-talent womanizer. He wasn't. As a womanizer he was tops. Acting ability was another story. The studios were dying, and the starlets were getting off their backs and into the boardrooms. On top of all that, some bastard broadsided the limo. His beautiful Fleetwood was totaled, and he wasn't feeling too hot, either. One leg was broken, he sported a variety-pak of cuts and bruises, and his insurance policy had expired the week before. They might as well have taken his dick; they had everything else.

What happened next was astounding. They guy who had broadsided him (not entirely his fault either, Dano had to admit) offered to pick up the tab. First aid for the Fleetwood, for Dano, and a confidentially whispered, "Let's keep the insurance companies out of this, eh?" Dano thought that was a reasonable request.

The guy came to see him in the hospital. There was Dano, plaster of Paris smeared on every area the sun shines on and a few it doesn't. The guy leaned close, smiling. "Mr. Dano," he said pleasantly, "you owe me."

Dano agreed and asked what he could do for the guy to make it up to him.

"Nothing right now, Mr. Dano," the guy said. "I'll let you know." He smiled again, but it wasn't so friendly this time.

Dano got into his reconstituted Fleetwood and drove to New York. There he sold the Fleetwood, kissed Hollywood good-bye in his heart and soul, and once and for all gave up acting. He became an agent.

Lake rapped on the door timidly. Her father and Richard Dano had once invested in a well-intentioned musical flop based on the life and times of Joan of Arc. It seemed people weren't quite ready for an execution set to music, even on Off Broadway.

"Hello, dear." He brushed past her in the hall and went into his office. Lake gritted her teeth and followed. The office looked like a filing cabinet had exploded in it. Everywhere were stacks of "pix and résumé" lovingly stapled together by anonymous hands praying for a little notoriety. *Somebody, please, look at me.* So many of them, covering the desk, piled on the floor, one dog-eared stack employed as a doorstop.

Every picture stands for a person, Lake reminded herself. God, it was depressing. She held out her own picture, hoping he wouldn't condemn her to the pile. He took it from her and dropped it on the desk.

"Lake—" he began. It didn't sound good.

An incredibly plain-looking young man stuck his head into the office. "Hey, Richard. Did you get—whoops, sorry, didn't know you had company."

Dano's lips began to whiten. "Lake Eastman, this is George Nichols, my assistant."

He shook Lake's hand gently. "I'm sort of an agent in training." George looked at his boss brightly. "But even I can tell a winner when I see one. We better hurry up and sign this beauty." He waggled his eyebrows at Lake. "How else am I going to get her phone number?"

"George . . ." Dano said in a bored voice.

George was still grinning at Lake. Not in a nasty, lascivious way; he just seemed so damn glad to be in the same room with her.

"George." Dano's voice was approaching the danger zone.

"Right," George said. "I must have a hundred things to do. Miss Eastman." He held her hand, admiring it. "I hope to see you again before you pick up your Academy Award." He made a hasty exit after Dano treated him to another particularly vitriolic glare.

Dano was holding out her picture. He was giving it back. I can't believe this, Lake thought. I really can't believe this.

"Oh, sure, you're pretty. This is New York City. Every pretty girl on two continents is here trying to break into acting. Here you're just another pretty face. Nothing special. You want to see pretty faces?" He grabbed a stack of pictures—there had to be at least a hundred there—and thrust it at her. She jerked her head away, shocked. Why was he doing this to her?

Dano looked tired. "You should go home, where you're something special. Where people care about you. Nobody here gives a damn." In a crazy way she got the feeling he was trying to be sincere. "This is not a very nice business, Miss Eastman. You should go home."

She took her picture back very carefully, sliding it into its envelope. "You have to be very careful with these pictures," she remarked conversationally. "One little scratch, and every copy will have that scratch. I'm going to make lots of copies, hundreds and hundreds"—she smiled at him confidingly—"so I can let all you agent shitheads see just what you're missing!"

She kicked the doorstop pix out of the way so she could slam the door on her way out. The tears came as she was waiting for the elevator. At least Dano wouldn't know he'd made her cry. A small victory but a valid one. Sure, she'd laugh about it . . . in about ten thousand years, when she picked up her Academy Award.

"Miss Eastman?" George Nichols stood there, holding a blue cardboard cup of coffee, looking plain and awkward and concerned. "What's wrong?"

Lake hoo-hooed an involuntary wail and fled into the elevator. The last thing she wanted right now was somebody being nice to her.

George hit Dano's office at full tilt. "What did you do to that girl?"

Dano cleared his throat. "George, this has nothing to do with you."

"The hell it doesn't!" George bellowed. "This is it! I've had it up to here!" He sprayed the room with coffee. "I quit!"

Dano smiled. "Where you gonna go, George?"

George jerked his thumbs toward his chest, tugged at imaginary suspenders. "I might just open my own agency. In California."

"Yeah, George." Dano was unruffled. "Why don't you go to California? Hollywood is waiting with her legs outstretched for George Nichols." Just like she had for Reni Damiano, and who'd gotten screwed that time?

"I'm not kidding, Richard." George sounded uncertain. "I will quit."

"Nichols." Dano gave him the grin stardom had passed up. "You already have."

When George left, it got quiet. Dano made a phone call to a direct line.

"Karl Eastman speaking."

"Eastman?" Dano rubbed his upper lip with his forefinger. "I don't owe you anymore."

She walked home the long way, surprised at how long it took her to come to herself. She'd always thought she'd bounce back, quick and resilient. Nobody keeps this girl down. That man had been a friend of her father's, a fellow investor, and that was as close as Karl got to anyone. Why did he do that to her?

Unless she really was missing that vital ingredient that made one person stand out from the crowd. She remembered staring at the mobs that had showed up at any audition she'd gone to, trying to pick out the one or two who would actually make it. Dano was right. Everyone was pretty. Everyone looked like a winner.

She sat down on the stoop of a town house. The way George had looked at her, didn't that mean she had something special? Or did it mean she should find some nice guy like George and settle down?

"To hell with you, Richard Dano," she said softly. "You're not going to ruin my life. You're not even going to ruin my day." First things first. A job. On her way to see Dano she'd passed a restaurant with a "Help Wanted" sign. She walked around the area, trying to remember exactly where it was. It was in the window of a place called Camille's. It did not look like a place she would ever want to eat in, but she needed work desperately.

The bartender, who was also the day manager, read her the riot act. "You gals is singing waitresses. Don't let that confuse you." His voice was surprisingly deep and resonant. "You wait tables, and when you got a free minute, you sing. You ain't gonna get discovered here; this place ain't gonna make you a star. No percentage in that shit. You're here to sell whiskey and veal parmigiana. That's it. Period. If you can't remember that, you're out." He sighed a deep "What's the use?" sigh. "Wait a sec, lemme introduce you to Raoul." The bartender waved over a young man sporting a truly amazing pompadour.

The maître d' looked very put out. "All right, Lake." He said her name as if he didn't believe it was her name. "You're hired, I suppose. You realize I won't stand for any flirtation with my waiters, I simply won't."

"Of course," she said with quiet dignity. "My job is to sell whiskey and veal parmigiana, not to seduce your waiters or further my career. Gentlemen, if you'll excuse me, I have a few errands to run."

"Bitch," Raoul whispered.

The bartender guffawed. "Stop talking about yourself, Raoul. It's getting boring." He poured a shot of Dewar's and downed it, smacking his lips. Pretty girls came and went, he thought wisely, but liquor was dependable.

When Lake got back to her small Christopher Street apartment, another surprise was waiting for her.

Tina, her slim dancer roommate, was lying on the floor naked, Tina's preferred posture for meditating. "Hi!" Tina said, still on the floor. "I'm moving out." She got up and started crawling into her bra and panties. "I got a gig with a bus-and-truck tour. *Oklahoma.* Principal dancer. I leave in five weeks."

Lake swore softly. She wouldn't miss Tina, but she certainly would miss Tina's half of the rent. Well, she would just have to put another ad in the paper. That was how she had gotten the lovely Tina to begin with.

Tina was looking at her, annoyed. "Well," she demanded, hands on her nonexistent hips, "aren't you happy for me?"

Lake collapsed into a chair. "Thrilled," she answered.

"Please sit down," the incredibly gorgeous blonde said.

Karen sat down, barking her shins on the glass coffee table. She was nervous. If the beautiful girl didn't want Karen for a roomie, it was back to Aunt Sophie's in the Bronx. Aunt Sophie was a lovely lady with the personality of a guard dog, and what she was guarding so zealously was her niece's virtue. Karen had to get the hell out of there fast.

"You're Karen, right?" The blonde smiled kindly. "I'm Lake Eastman."

"That's a great name," Karen gushed and then could have kicked herself. *Idiot!* She was eighteen, for crissakes. When was she ever going to learn a little cool? "I'm going to be going to NYU—"

"That's only a short walk from here," Lake pointed out. "The neighborhood may look a little strange, but believe me"—she laughed, bell-like, and Karen listened, fascinated—"Christopher Street is pretty safe, at least for us."

"Why is that?"

The blonde sighed. "A lot of people here are gay."

"Oh, homosexual." Karen nodded wisely. "My mom will be glad to hear that. She's terrified I'll be attacked by the Greenwich Village rapist or something."

"Not in this neighborhood."

Karen laughed. "What about your family? Did they freak when you moved to the city?"

There was an imperceptible pause while Lake mentally shifted gears. Karen even imagined that the blonde recoiled slightly. "I don't . . . speak to my family," Lake said finally.

"Oh." Karen looked down at her folded hands. "I'm sure you'll patch it up."

"No, I don't think so." Again she smiled pleasantly. "What are you studying at NYU?"

Karen brightened. "Acting. I got a scholarship and everything."

"I'm an actress, too."

"How nice." I hope we are never up for the same role, Karen prayed. "Have you been in New York long?"

"Three months. I had a roommate, but she's leaving to go on the road, so I'm in a financial bind."

Karen nodded sympathetically. "Well, I've got my scholarship money, plus some savings . . . " She plunged on a little frantically. *Please, Lake, Aunt Sophie is driving me crazy.*

Lake rose gracefully. "Let me give you the guided tour. You'd have your own room, lots of privacy, good closet space . . . " Almost as an afterthought she turned to Karen, her elegant mind working methodically. "You know, you really are pretty," she said slowly. One hand reached out and touched Karen's long light-brown hair. "But you should get your hair cut, maybe halfway down your neck, a pageboy. Wispy bangs. Your hair's very fine."

"Yes, I know." Karen felt embarrassed. She certainly was *not* pretty. "Uh, thanks."

"Now you'll think *I'm* queer." Lake laughed. "See what this neighborhood does to you?"

"Oh, no, I think you're great!" More gushing. Karen, you fool! she berated herself. "Well, I'd better get going. Aunt Sophie's pot roast is bad enough before it dries out. You'll let me know?"

"Either way." Lake nodded. "Good-bye. And good luck!"

"You, too. And I hope you make up with your parents." *Jerk!*

"Oh, wait." Lake called her back. "Do you"—she hesitated, reluctant to ask—"have a boyfriend?"

"Oh, no." Karen laughed. "No, no, no."

"It's not a terminal condition."

"Keep telling me that. Uh, why'd you ask? Is it important?"

For a moment Lake's facade of sophisticated ease slipped.

"I . . . I've had this recurring nightmare since I was a kid. I'd sort of like to have a roommate who's around at night."

"Well, unless something changes drastically, I'll be around at night. All night. Every night."

"What are you doing today?" a bored voice inquired, raking a metal comb through her hair. Karen's eyes flicked over and above her reflection in the mirror.

"I want it cut," Karen said firmly, "to about here." She indicated with a hand to her neck. 'Like a pageboy style with"—*wispy*—"wispy bangs." She settled back confidently.

Fifteen minutes later Karen fell in love with her own reflection. The spiky bangs framed her large hazel eyes to perfection. She sighed contentedly. "That's fine, Emile," she told the blond perm. He gave her a hand mirror so she could see the back of her head. "Just fine." Karen paid the receptionist and then, without hesitation, gave Emile an extravagant tip. "Thank you very much."

He pocketed the tip, looking down at the floor. "Good luck in your career, Karen."

She laughed. "I guess I'll need it. Thanks." She admired her reflection one last time before heading for the door.

"How could you cut your beautiful hair?" Aunt Sophie screamed. Actually she liked the haircut, but she'd already yelled about Karen not calling to say she'd be late, and she'd already cried about the pot roast drying out, so the haircut was the only thing left to get upset about. Aunt Sophie was not one to let a golden opportunity slip past. She screamed about the haircut. "What am I going to tell your mother about your beautiful, beautiful hair?"

"Tell her I cut it."

"I promised your mother I'd look after you." Aunt Sophie clutched her chest. "Oy," she moaned, "it'll break your mother's heart if I have to tell her about the shiksas you run around with."

"What shiksas?"

"Shiksas!" Aunt Sophie raved. "You can't tell me 'Lake Eastman' is a name for a nice Jewish girl. What kind of a name is 'Lake Eastman' anyway?" the aunt asked philosophically. "Sounds like a good place for a bungalow colony."

"How do you know Lake's name?" Karen demanded.

"Don't yell! In my house only I can raise the voice!"

The girl bit her lip anxiously. "I'm sorry, Aunt Sophie. Did Lake call?"

"Can't wait to go run off with your shiksa friend? Well, young lady, let me tell you—"

Karen spied a scrap of paper on the end table and pounced on it. It bore a phone number identified only by the scrawled epithet "SHIKSA!" Good old Aunt Sophie. Salt of the earth.

While the parent-in-absentia tirade continued, Karen dialed the number. By the time the phone started to ring, Aunt Sophie had retreated, mumbling, to the kitchen, apparently to take a hacksaw to the dear departed pot roast.

"Hello?" Even over the phone Lake sounded like a tall, gorgeous blonde.

"Hi, it's Karen. Returning your call. I know it's kinda late, but first I had to get the message from my Aunt Sophie, which was no easy feat." She took a quick breath. "If you're lucky, you will never, ever meet my Aunt Sophie. Ummm, why did you call?"

Laughter issued from the telephone. Soft, educated, blonde laughter. "The apartment share is yours if you still want it."

"If I still want it!" Karen whooped. "You bet I do. This'll be great! Oh, hey, I cut my hair like you said, and it looks really good. Now I need some new clothes. We can go shopping together!" Another breath. "Guess I better shut up before you change your mind. I'm just . . . so excited," she finished lamely.

"Me, too," Lake said confidingly. "Well, roomie. When can you move in?"

"Is tomorrow too soon?"

"Tomorrow's fine," Lake said. "See you then. 'Bye."

"'Bye." Great, Karen thought exultantly. All I need now is the boy.

Aunt Sophie came out of the kitchen wielding an electric carving knife. "You've got a funny look on your face." She whirred the knife threateningly. "What are you thinking about?"

Sex, Aunt Sophie. Hot, raunchy, squishy sex in my new bachelorette pad. Demurely, like a placid little Jewish nun, Karen sat down on the plastic-slip-covered couch. "Nothing, Aunt Sophie," Karen said sweetly, "nothing at all."

Heh-heh-heh.

Karen was putting her clothes away, getting accustomed to her new home, and swearing she would never again take a suitcase on the New York City subway system. Lake had just arrived back from an audition in time to let Karen in. They were both starved so Lake was in the kitchen, heating up a can of tomato soup, while Karen unpacked.

"There's some leftover tunafish," she called to Karen. "How's that?"

"Fine."

Lake had just retrieved the bowl from the refrigerator when the bell rang. Tina breezed in. "Hi, just came to pick up a few things I left."

"Thanks for phoning ahead," Lake said sarcastically. "Considerate as always."

"I'll just be a minute," Tina sang, heading for the bedroom. "God," she said, seeing Karen, "she didn't waste any time getting another girl in here. Where'd she dig you up from?"

"Chicago."

"I guess that explains it." She disappeared into the closet. "Hope you don't mind, I left some of my shit here. Jesus, how old are you anyway, twelve?"

Karen bristled. "I'm eighteen."

"Calm down." Tina emerged from the closet with an armload of clothing. "Look, I made the same mistake you're making, moving in with this nut job."

"Some of those things are mine," Karen pointed out helpfully. "I just hung them up."

"What? Oh yeah, well some of this stuff is mine, I'll just go through it." She sat down on the bed, folding her long legs under her. "Shit, I don't think any of this is mine, except for the bathrobe."

"I told you." Karen went over to the dresser and pulled out a stack of folded leotards. "I think *these* are yours, I found them in the dresser."

"Thanks." Tina frowned at the leotards. "No wonder I left these behind, they're awfully ratty." She pushed them to one side and fumbled in her bag for her cigarettes. "She's completely nuts, Miss Connecticut Royalty." She jerked her head toward the kitchen. "At first I thought, this is a great deal. She's got money, if I'm ever late with the rent, she can always bail me out, not that she's seen dollar one from them, they're as crazy as she is. Okay, money isn't everything, a roommate's good for company, right? She's real moody, like I've never seen in my life. Every other night, she'd wake up screaming from some nightmare, keep me up half the night. If you were smart, you'd find someplace else to live. Have you got any matches?"

"Sorry."

"Figures. You look like a dyed-in-the-wool non-smoker. I

wouldn't smoke, either, except if I don't smoke, I eat. So I smoke. Look," Tina sighed, "I'm not trying to be a bitch, not that I can't be, I just want to let you know what you're in for." She shrugged lamely. "I'm selfish, but I'm not malicious. There's a difference, you know."

"Thanks," Karen said, "I'll keep what you said in mind."

Tina nodded. "Yeah. Well, good luck." She dropped the cigarettes back in her purse, gathered up her leotards and took off.

A minute later, Lake came in carrying two mugs of soup. "The tunafish was moldy. I'm afraid this is it."

"It's fine." They sipped in silence for a while.

"Look, Karen," Lake began hesitantly, "I wasn't exactly eavesdropping, but Tina has all this stage training and her voice really carries."

"She almost walked off with half my wardrobe," Karen pointed to the tangle of clothes on the bed. She busied herself rehanging them. "That Tina's a real character."

"Karen, please sit down. I want to talk to you and it's a little difficult with you bouncing all over the place."

She sat down. "Okay. Here I am."

Lake took a deep breath. "I've had other roommates in here. Tina lasted the longest out of the bunch, and that was strictly because she just wasn't here all that much. I'm not a very warm person. I don't know why that is . . . suffice it to say that I'm the logical product of a very looney family. I came to New York to see if I could escape that legacy, and believe me, my father's got a very long arm when it comes to looking out for me. All I want from a roommate is a little friendship, but I don't know how to *be* a very good friend. When you answered my ad, I was hoping so hard that you'd want to be my roommate. I was so thrilled when you called me back. But I'd understand if you want to change your mind. Tina didn't lie to you about me."

"Lake," the younger girl said softly, "I don't know a soul in New York and I don't have any place to stay. It's either you or Aunt Sophie, and you haven't met my Aunt Sophie. I don't want to spend my whole life being the same person I was in Chicago. So, I guess we're both going through some changes. Anyway, if Tina is normal, I think I'll stick with the lunatics. It'll all look *so* much more interesting in my autobiography, which I'll write when I'm incredibly rich and famous. And who told you I was so normal anyway? My mother decorates with plastic fruit."

"My mother would eat it," Lake said dryly.

They both burst out laughing. "Is she really that bad?" Karen asked.

"She's not the swiftest. But my father . . . let me put it this way. My mother would be *in* the looney bin, but my father would be running the place."

"Much more interesting than mine," Karen laughed. "My dad wears at least six different kinds of plaids per outfit. He looks like a test pattern."

Gingerly, Lake picked up one of Karen's sweaters, lying in a heap with her other things on the bed. "Does that explain why you dress for life in a subterranean cave?"

"I feel uncomfortable in bright colors."

"Maybe we can find something in between fire engine red and fungus grey. Where do you shop anyway?"

"I'm not telling. I don't want you laughing at me."

"History. You're in New York now. Home of Bendel's and Bergdorf's, not to mention Macy's, Bloomingdale's, Gimbel's, Altman's, Sak's Fifth Avenue—have I left anyone out? Grab your jacket. We're going shopping."

Connecticut wasn't that far away from the city. Lake had been in the big department stores before on many occasions, but it was fun to see it all again through Karen's amazed eyes. She marvelled at Bendel's elaborate set-up of small stalls, perfectly mimicking the feeling of little European shops. Even the clientele seemed to fascinate her; fur-clad even in September, languid in their movements as they lazily picked over bright silk scarves. To Karen they were like creatures from another world.

"I've figured it out," Karen whispered to Lake. "These women are perfectly accessorized. Shoes, bag, even the nail polish goes. Must take hours." She stared hungrily at a woman's exquisite pearl choker. "I could get into it."

Lake inspected a pair of leather gloves. "No, you couldn't. What do you think of these? Mink-lined." She tossed them aside. "Too ostentatious. Hmmm, we really do have a lot of other stores to hit," her eyes darted through the elegant mob, "but first, I think we need a little perfume." She sauntered over to the perfume counter, littered with tiny glass bottles of every size, shape and color, from the square-cut Joy to the slimmer shapes of Chanel. Pushing her sweep of blonde hair to one side, Lake touched the stopper of one bottle to the nape of her neck. "Chanel No. 19, I've always loved it." She held the stopper out to Karen.

"It's wonderful," Karen agreed, "but it's not me."

"Close your eyes," Lake selected a scent and dabbed it behind Karen's ears. "Like that? It's Joy."

Karen inhaled deeply with obvious pleasure. "Very well named."

"Glad you like it. You can buy some after you make your first million, it's very expensive." She put the bottles down reluctantly. "As for me, I've only got to wait a year before I get my hands on my trust fund."

"Is it a big trust fund?"

Lake grinned. "Like an elephant. Although I can't say I'm suffering too much. Money never meant much to me."

"That's because you've always had it," Karen observed. "Rich people *are* different. They don't worry about the same things."

"That's not it," Lake argued. "The only difference between rich people and the rest of the world is that rich people are terribly rude. They don't need common courtesy, they have servants. And they get away with murder, because everybody else thinks, if you're rich, you must know what's going on. Also you can hire better lawyers, just in case they *do* catch you. Come on, we've got Saks, Lord and Taylor and Altman's to cover. And that's just on Fifth Avenue."

"But I *like* it here," Karen protested as Lake pushed her out the door.

"Don't argue," Lake said, reaching into her purse. "Let's cross the street. Fast."

"Why?"

"Humor me." She darted across the street, laughing. "Here, a present." In her hand was the bottle of Joy. "Go on, take it. I swiped it for you. Joy's not my style. Take it," she said impatiently, "I can't very well take it back."

"I can't believe you swiped this."

"Why? Don't you believe rich people swipe things?"

She smiled. "Thanks. I never had anybody swipe anything of this magnitude for me. Usually it's Bic pens and Zippo lighters. I'm moving up in the world."

"Absolutely," Lake declared. "Where shall we go next?"

A man veered over to Karen and whispered something in her ear. A very shocked expression resulted.

"He wanted me to abuse him," she reported to Lake.

"Not in the mood, huh?" Lake commiserated.

Another man approached the brunette.

"No, no, no," Karen waved her hands frantically, moving out of his path. He followed her doggedly.

"Take it easy," the man murmured, shoving a flyer into her hand. "What are you, from Ohio or something?"

Lake took the crumpled paper from Karen's hand and read it. "Perfect!" she exclaimed. "Want to go to a fashion show?"

"Yes!"

"Can you run twenty blocks in ten minutes?"

It turned out they both could, arriving at the boutique specified in the flyer breathless and laughing. Racks of expensive clothes had been pushed to either side to make room for rows of folding chairs and a makeshift runway jutting down the center aisle. The dressing rooms were being employed by the models; from time to time a slim arm could be seen, poking through a sleeve as the models hurriedly dressed. On each folding chair was a small bright-red shopping bag filled with free samples of shampoo, hand lotion, skin cream, even a miniature tube of brilliant pink lipstick, and a handful of pamphlets relating the life stories of the participating designers, specialities ranging from fur coats to jewelry.

"Hello." A young man, his sports coat as bright as the little shopping bags, smiled at them anxiously, holding out a tray laden with steaming cups of coffee. "Would you care for some coffee?"

The coffee was followed by trays of butter cookies. Unabashed, Lake grabbed a huge handful. "Have you got a clean handkerchief?" she asked Karen. "We can have these tonight."

Karen was mortified. "Lake!" she hissed.

"You're twice as broke as I am. Besides, you don't know how these shows work. If we don't eat these cookies, they're just going to go to waste. They'll just throw them out; the models certainly can't eat them. You don't want to waste food, do you?" The cookies were wrapped and went into Lake's handbag.

"Ladies," a capable-looking woman in a beautifully cut deep blue suit announced. "We'll be starting our fashion show momentarily. Please keep in mind that everything you see on our runway today, including jewelry and shoes, can be purchased in the boutique."

With that, the music started and the first model glided onto the runway. She was a sleek blonde clothed in a buttery-soft sweater and skirt of winter white. Three ropes of pearls of varying lengths hung around her neck.

"Nice," Lake remarked. "We can put that on our list of things to get after we make our first million."

"It'll be out of style by then."

The next model came out, a broad shouldered brunette with

a headful of curls that reached halfway down her back. Her outfit suited her sultry look perfectly, a jungle-print sheath with a fuchsia hip-wrap. She whirled, smiling at the blonde before they both disappeared to make room for another girl wearing a velvet-collared suit reminiscent of an English riding habit, down to a bowler hat with a fingertip-length veil, her shiny hair bound in a ponytail at the nape of her neck.

"You're prettier than any of them," Karen told Lake loyally.

"This is runway modelling," Lake explained. "It's more important to be an exact size and type than drop-dead gorgeous. You should see the girls who do the print work, you know, magazine ads, commercials. They're unbelievable."

"You won't have any competition." She squeezed Lake's arm. "Now, *that* I like." A redhead slinked onto the runway wearing the brand-new fantasy look, an iridescent aqua gown with a ruffled neckline pulled off the shoulder to display a creamy neck adorned with a brilliant diamond choker.

"Too much material," Lake frowned. "You're too little to carry off that much dress. Stick with the English riding habit."

"Ugh. So boyish."

"Gamine," Lake corrected.

The first model appeared again, wearing a grey wool trouser paired with a white silk ascot blouse fastened with a pearl stickpin. A grey fedora slouched on her head in approved Bogart-style. When she reached the farthest point of the runway, she took a quarter out of her pocket, tossed it and caught it a few times like a 1920's gangster, much to the audience's delight.

It was an education for Lake. All the girls were beautiful; they could all strut and smile, snap their heads to make their hair fly as they spun. Some of the girls just seemed to have a little extra, an added fillip of personality. They pouted, tipped their hats down over one eye, twirled their necklaces like long-gone flappers. They *acted.*

I can do that, Lake thought with confidence. In the space of one day, she felt like her entire life had turned around. Maybe all a person needs is a friend, she mused.

Karen was squeezing her arm again. The whole crowd was oooh-ing and aaah-ing madly.

"Although our model is wearing a traditional headpiece and full-length veil, this gown would be perfect for a second wedding with just a simple white silk flower to tuck into your hair . . . "

"Oh, wedding gowns," Lake said in a bored voice, "not for me."

"Be honest, everyone wants to get married."

"I never will," Lake declared. "Nobody marries for the right reasons anyway."

"What do you mean?"

"They marry for money," Lake explained airily, "or lust, or maybe companionship."

"What about love?"

"Sorry, my dear, that's still lust."

Karen's eyes never left the veiled model twirling on the runway. "I'd like to get married," she said wistfully, "if anybody ever asks me. And I want a big wedding, just so I can wear a beautiful gown and have a long white veil."

Lake shrugged. "Doesn't do a thing for me. Look! There's more food coming!"

The young man in the red coat was returning. This time his tray was laden with sandwiches, crusts neatly trimmed. Lake nearly cleared the whole tray. The young man stared in amazement.

"We're terribly hungry," Lake said sweetly. "Cook is on vacation in the Bahamas, and her replacement is simply not working out. You know how it is."

He went away shaking his head.

"Lake, maybe we should go, I think some of the people here are starting to stare."

Lake hefted her bag experimentally. "We might as well. I couldn't fit anything else in here if I tried. Getting late anyway. Sandwiches for dinner, okay?"

They started to walk home, Lake carefully shifting her bag on her shoulder to keep the sandwiches from disintegrating. At a street corner, Karen insisted on buying them both big, salty pretzels. She ate hers with mustard.

Karen sighed contentedly. "This has been the best day of my whole life," she announced.

"Mine, too," Lake said, suddenly realizing how true that was. Now, all she had to worry about was the night.

Karen heard the screams around 3:30 A.M. She wasn't a particularly light sleeper so it was possible Lake had been screaming for a good few minutes. Karen went into her room and turned on the light. "Lake?"

She sat up immediately, but still seemed somewhat disoriented. "I'm sorry," she croaked, her voice still heavy with sleep. "Did I wake you?"

"It's all right. Come on." Karen guided her into the kitchen and started messing around the stove.

"What are you doing?"

"Making you some hot milk."

"Going to force me to drink that, aren't you?"

"Yep," Karen nodded. "Just take a minute here . . . how do you feel?"

"Fine," Lake said a little irritably, "I'm fine as long as I'm awake. Which I am now."

Karen poured the milk into a mug. She brought it over to Lake. "Do you want to talk about it?"

"Definitely not." She sipped, grimacing. "This is truly godawful."

"Supposed to make you feel better."

"I doubt it."

"You know, they always say it's better to talk about the things that trouble you."

"I've never found that to be true at all. I remember when the Jesus freaks were out in full force. They were always trying to save me. I guess I look like I need saving pretty badly. Anyway, they were always telling me that you had to accept Jesus, you had to say his name *out loud.* Because when you put words to a thing, you *make it real.* I don't want to make the things that I dream real."

"I won't bother you again about it," Karen said softly, "but I don't agree with you. One of these days you're going to have to talk to somebody about these nightmares."

"One of these days I will." Maybe it was the power of suggestion but the milk *was* making her sleepy. "After we're rich and famous and we've been friends for a couple hundred years, we'll talk about everything that's ever happened to us. If I told you now, you'd run screaming into the night and I'd have to find another roommate which would really screw up my life."

"I'm tougher than I look."

"Good," Lake yawned, putting her head down on the table. "I'm not."

3

NEW YORK UNIVERSITY was terrifying. Everyone seemed to know where they were going. The first day of school had always been a prime source of anxiety for Karen, whether it was kindergarten or high school. She saw no reason that college should be different.

Getting to class late didn't help her frame of mind, either. Bodies were strewn on the floor of the acting class. Except for the even breathing that bellowed their chests up and down, the scene was reminiscent of a battle going the wrong way.

"Excuse me, excuse me, excuse me." Stepping carefully Karen found a bare patch of carpet to call her own and stretched out on the floor with the other student actors. The instructor, wearing more Irish wool than an Aran fisherman, moved among the class, smiling happily.

"That's right, breath deeply. In . . . out . . . don't think of anything just yet . . . " He maneuvered his fawn-colored Hush Puppies slowly through the fallen. "Now"—the instructor's smile grew in anticipation—"I want you to imagine that your body is filled with some delicious substance, like chocolate milk shake or—"

"Rice pudding?" One of the bodies spoke to a soft ripple of laughter.

"Whatever you like. Slowly this delicious substance is being siphoned out through your toes . . . "

He droned on. Karen felt a little sick imagining rice pudding draining out through her toes. She kept feeling imaginary little rice particles sticking to the inside of her feet. She gave up and turned her head to the side. A very good-looking boy was lying next to her. Dark blond hair, green eyes. Nice build, even lying down. Especially lying down. He smiled at her. She smiled back, got embarrassed, and quickly turned her head away.

"All right," the instructor said, "whenever you feel ready, one at a time, stand up and act as the person who has criticized you the most."

A beautiful girl with a waist-length mane of hair got up like a sleepwalker. She had an Eastern European accent of some sort. "Vy you have to do this?" the voice said sorrowfully. "Get up on stage, embarrass us. You are a whore! That a daughter of mine should become a whore, you have hurt me so . . . "

"Now tell him off," the instructor said softly.

"I'm not a whore!" she cried. "I'm an actress! An actress! Why can't you just love me! I love you! I hate you!" She punched the air virulently. "I love you! I hate you! I love you!" She dissolved into tears and slowly melted to the floor, then stretched out prone again, calm and smiling.

"We can see," the instructor said, "how love and hate often spring from the same source."

A guy who looked like he pumped iron for breakfast, lunch, and dinner got up and whined how his father had never loved him. Then he, too, burst into tears. Another boy got up and put his arms around the muscleman in a comforting gesture.

"Don't be afraid to trust each other," the instructor admonished.

"I am." A small voice spoke up from the prone bodies.

Karen hiked up on one elbow and looked around for the voice's owner. A girl who bore a startling resemblance to Winnie the Pooh slowly got to her feet. She looked at the other student actors fearfully. "I'm afraid to trust the others."

"Why?"

"Because they're the competition."

"Not right now," the instructor said. "Right now they're your adoring public. Let's have a little commotion!"

The class whistled and cheered for Winnie the Pooh, who looked considerably happier. Karen was now sitting up watching the whole scene in a detached manner. Her mind was going click-click-click, a million miles an hour.

The good-looking boy next to her tapped her arm. "What are you thinking?" he whispered, his voice holding a trace of a drawl.

"Look at their faces," she hissed back. "Everyone's applauding *themselves.*"

It was true. All eyes seemed to be on Winnie the Pooh, but they were really turned inward. Thirty private little universes. All that self-congratulation. The good-looking boy started to laugh. He applauded Karen for her insight. She applauded him, for his recognition of that insight. They applauded each other. Winnie the Pooh beamed and took her place on the floor. Karen applauded Pooh and the excellent way she had sat down. Pooh giggled.

"How do you feel?" the instructor asked Karen, singling her out.

"Stupid!" She laughed.

"That's right!" People began to quiet down at the sound of his voice. "This is the way you behaved when you were a child, before you were socialized and regimented and forced into a little gray box. You feel silly, but my God, you people look more attractive than you did when you walked in that door. This is the way you were meant to be. In touch with your emotions. In touch with this very moment, not what happened this morning, not what's going to happen this afternoon. This moment!" He smashed his palms together like cymbals. "That is acting. If you can understand that, my God, Olivier will be out of a job."

A few people laughed ruefully. The general opinion appeared to be that Olivier was safe.

Next the class was directed to break into couples for an exercise called "Mirrors." Most of the class buzzed knowledgeably, veterans of many acting classes. "Mirrors" was strictly old hat. This was Karen's first acting class. What the hell was "Mirrors," anyway?

"Partners?" the good-looking boy asked Karen, smiling.

"Sure." *Thank you, God.* Karen sneaked a surreptitious look out of the corner of her eye at the other couples.

"I'll lead first," the boy suggested.

Karen nodded. Watching his eyes carefully she duplicated every movement the boy made. She began to feel her body warming up as she stared into those beautiful green eyes. Suddenly he smiled broadly, and she giggled in return. Her mouth fell open softly as she concentrated on regaining her serious demeanor. His gaze slid from her eyes to her mouth, and she brought her lips together primly, blushing a little, spreading the warmth from her body to her face.

Now it was the boy's turn to mirror Karen's actions, all the time keeping his eyes locked on hers. A little half-smile played on his lips. He's probably got a girlfriend, Karen thought, or else he's an absolute bastard. How could those green eyes belong to a bastard?

"Okay, very good!" The instructor's voice intruded. "Now . . . " He led them through a few other exercises: get up and act like your favorite comic book character (Karen chose Astro Boy, a Japanese cartoon character); act like little kids; act obnoxious, scared, shy, arrogant, belligerent, psychotic, catatonic, compulsive-neurotic . . . act, act, act. Then, as a finishing touch, the instructor put on a record that sounded like the soundtrack album from *Sheena, Queen of the Jungle,* and the class got up and gyrated and jumped on chairs and screamed.

Sometime during this excess of motion and emotion, the instructor hied himself and his Irish wool to some other hither, and the class, slowly catching on, began to disperse. Karen looked around, discreetly, of course, but the good-looking boy was gone. Sighing, she gathered up her things and pushed her way into the hallway.

He was there.

"Hi, I was waiting for you."

He was waiting for her. *He was waiting for her.*

Thank you, God. I swear, as long as I live, I'll never talk back to my mother, I'll even try to be nice to my Aunt Sophie . . .

"Have you got time for a cappucino?"

She'd never had a cappucino. "I'd love to."

He grinned, that sweet, sweet smile. "I was hoping you'd say that. Great." He held the door for her, and she slipped past him, wishing she had the guts to brush up against him.

"By the way, my name's Harry Townsend," he said cheerfully.

"That's a nice name," Karen said softly, hugging her books to her chest.

"I'm sure yours is nice, too."

Karen looked at him blankly. "I can't seem to remember what it is." Frantically she dug in her wallet for some ID. "Ah, here it is! Karen Bloom. Yes, that's it! Doctor, I'm cured!"

He laughed. Definitely not the laugh of a bastard. "I'm real glad to hear that, Karen." He held her arm courteously as they skirted some of the more unusual looking denizens of Washington Square Park. A real Southern gentleman.

In the café he waited until she sat down before he did. They both had cappucinos, which arrived in beautiful glasses that fit into metal filigree holders. The drinks were capped with a cinnamon-dashed froth of bland steamed milk, but the coffee underneath was strong and bitter. Karen liked cappucino very much.

"It must be tough," Harry was saying, "coming in on the second semester."

"Yes, everyone seems to know everyone else by this time." Karen licked milk foam from her spoon. "I really feel like the new kid on the block."

"I know how that feels," Harry commiserated. "My dad was career army, and I was the new kid on the block about three times a year. My dad was real against my being an actor. That's how come I'm older than most of the kids here. It took me a while to save up the money but I wasn't going to spend the rest of my life in Hixson, Tennessee."

"You must be very determined."

"I sure am." He laughed. "If hard work means anything at all, Harry Townsend is going to get everything he wants." He signaled the waitress for two more cappucinos. "There were a lot of other schools I could have gone to, but I wanted NYU. You know why?"

"Because it's a good school?"

"Nope." Harry shook his head emphatically. "You know how many successful film and television directors and producers come out of this school? Maybe I'll do a student film with one of these guys, and when he goes on to better things, maybe I'll go with him."

Karen thought about all those self-possessed kids she'd seen rushing around that morning. "I wouldn't count on it, Harry."

"I'm not, but you always gotta hope." He smiled into her eyes. "I auditioned for this guy's senior film project. He's still looking for the female lead; you should read for him. Here"—He scribbled on a paper napkin. "You call him, tell him you want to read for him."

"Thanks, but I don't know if I'm ready for an audition yet." He was still holding out the paper napkin, so she took it and tucked it into her purse. "I'm just curious, why are you doing this?"

He looked offended. "'Cause I'm a genuinely nice guy." He leaned closer. "And you've got beautiful eyes. Bet those eyes give you away every time."

She looked up at him and then quickly down at her cappucino. "I guess they do."

"You've got something special, Karen," he said quietly. "It's sweet and innocent and shy"—she looked up again, raising her eyes like a searchlight—"and underneath, steel."

She was puzzled. "I don't understand."

"Neither do I." Harry laughed. "How 'bout another cappucino?"

"Come on," Lake pleaded. "What have you got to lose?"

Karen glared at her, looking deeply offended. "How dare you? How dare you interrupt *Gunsmoke?* People get deported for less."

"Pph, no you don't." With her usual grace Lake leaped at the television set, punching the off button. "You've been avoiding this too long. Did you call that guy at school about being in his student film?"

"Nooo . . . "

"Have you gone to any audition since you moved to New York?"

"Nooo . . . but I don't have a monologue, and I haven't really found a good song for auditions, and I'm still in school anyway—"

"Sorry, kiddo, it just won't work." Lake pursed her lips like an old-lady schoolteacher. "Lots of auditions have cold readings, you can sing anything you can remember the words to, and if you can't remember the words, make 'em up. I'm no diva, but it doesn't stop me from going up there and making a fool of myself. And as for school"—she grabbed the *TV Guide* Karen was pretending to read and slapped it down to the coffeetable—"acting is an early-entrance business. People start acting when they're still in diapers."

Karen looked at her seriously. "Are you trying to tell me that Marshal Dillon wets his pants? . . . Wow." She shook her head sadly. "If Miss Kitty ever finds out—"

"You're impossible." Lake switched on the TV and went into the kitchen. "Forget it. You're on your own. Go on, hide in NYU. They write a lot of parts for sixty-year-old graduate students."

"Lake?" Karen found herself talking to the TV. Suddenly its incessant chatter was annoying. She turned down the volume, watching Jim Arness move around soundlessly. "Lake, I'm scared," she said in a small voice.

"Well, join the club." Lake had a container of milk in one hand and a pack of Sunshine Hydrox cookies in the other. She plopped them down on the table. "Do we need glasses?" she asked doubtfully.

"We'll just have to wash them later."

"True." Lake ripped into the cellophane wrapper, offering Karen a fistful of cookies. "Look, everybody's scared to go on their first audition. That's why you have to get it over with as fast as possible. You wouldn't have believed how scared I was."

"Really?"

"Really-really," she teased. "It was a hair commercial, my first honest-to-goodness audition, and it turns out to be a national commercial. I thought I was going to die."

"Yeah?" Karen tipped the milk container so she could dunk her cookie. "So what happened?"

"Well, first of all, I walk in wearing old blue jeans and a ratty old sweater. Real professional, right? The room is filled with gorgeous girls of every size and shape. All with big boobs"—she held her hands out in front of her to demonstrate the size of the aforementioned—"all blondes. And the clothes! Here I am, practically disappearing in a ratty old black sweater, and these girls . . . These girls are in all the right blonde colors—"

"Blonde colors?"

"You know." Lake waved her hands vaguely. "Coral, aqua, all those drippy little pastel shades that are boring as hell."

"Aha." Karen nodded sagely. "Blonde colors."

"You sign in, and they give you a sheet of copy to memorize. Immortal literature it is not. I think this one went . . . " Lake pouted coyly, twining her hands in her hair. ". . . a full length mink for my pampered body, beluga caviar for my educated palate, and for my hair, Silken Lustre shampoo. Oooh. Because every woman deserves a little luxury. Oo-oooh." Lake crossed her eyes.

Karen's smile was faint. She still looked terrified at the prospect of auditioning.

"They take me in to read," Lake continued. "They have the copy written on a big card, stuck onto the camera with a big hole in the center so the lens can poke through. And here's the director, cheerful as all get-out, saying, 'Make love to the camera, darling!' I swear he said that. Naturally I read the whole thing backwards. I wound up washing my hair with beluga caviar, eating the mink, and wearing Silken Lustre shampoo oo-oooh. Needless to say they did not call me back." She drank from the carton, sprouting an old man's mustache. "But I lived to go to another audition."

"Maybe I won't."

Lake sighed a little tiredly. "Trust me, you will."

"Oh, I know." Karen munched thoughtfully. "To really end life you usually need to get hit by a car or run into a mugger with a large knife. But what if I'm terrible? What if I'm so bad that people laugh at me? I *will* die if I can't be a good actress—part of me, anyway."

"You'll never know unless you try."

"I don't want to know if I'm terrible."

Lake waved the milk carton threateningly,"How about a milk shampoo-oo?" she inquired sweetly. "Look." She set the container down with a thump and reached for the blue-bannered copy of *Backstage.* "There's an open call tomorrow for a new musical, *Friday's Child.* Open call, Kar, as in nonunion. Every single person within commuting distance with the nerve to call himself an actor will show up. All you need is an eight-by-ten and sixteen bars of standard show music. You'll be very lucky if you get through all sixteen bars. Most of the time you don't. So. What do you say? You've got that much nerve, haven't you?"

"No."

The milk carton hovered.

"Wait! I'll go, I'll go!" Laughing, Karen tucked her legs under her like a small elf. "I just . . . " She scooped her hair behind one ear and touched the tip of her nose with her finger. These signs usually meant that Karen wanted to say something serious, which was either one of two things: how was Karen Bloom going to find romance in this cruel, heartless city or . . . how was Karen Bloom going to become a star as in not being able to walk down the street without getting mobbed by thousands of adoring fans? Ah, the self-centered absorption of an eighteen-year-old, Lake thought from the lofty vantage point of twenty. "Lake, why do you want to be an actress?"

She was a little taken aback. "I don't know. Why do people want to be anything? Why does anybody want to be, say, a plumber?"

"Because they're good at it, or they want to make a lot of money," Karen said reasonably, "or their father's a plumber so the opportunity is there. That's why people become plumbers. Acting just isn't like that; don't ask me why."

"I just like acting," Lake said slowly, feeling her words bounce like sonar someplace deep inside. "I think I like being other people. Sick, huh?"

"Twisted," Karen agreed. "I don't know why I want to be an actress. I just know I want it so badly that every day I'm not a star, I die a little, I really do. It's like . . . you never fit in anywhere. Not home, not school, not with your family, not even with your friends. But when you're acting, you fit. You belong. And it's the finest feeling on earth. Do you know what I mean?"

"Yes," Lake whispered. She didn't like hearing these things out loud. She didn't like hearing that they all felt the same way, that none of them was truly different. She certainly didn't like hearing her private thoughts coming out of the eighteen-year-old mouth of Karen Bloom. As much as she liked Karen, and she did—Karen was nice and funny and a good person—Lake just didn't feel Karen had it. She was a sweet kid, but that wasn't what people paid to see when they went to the movies. Maybe she was wrong to urge Karen to go to the *Friday's Child* open call. Oh, hell, everybody had to take their lumps. Better to let her find out now. Karen had school to fall back on. She was bright; she could probably go pre-law or pre-something else that could lead to a nice career.

No, Lake was pretty sure Karen did not have it. On the other hand, she had no doubt about herself. It occurred to her with a jolt that every actor, good, bad, and indifferent, probably felt the same way.

"Go to sleep," she said suddenly. "We'll have to get up early. I bet people are lining up for *Friday's Child* already."

"Hey," Karen said. "I just realized . . . since I moved in, you haven't had any nightmares."

"No, I haven't." Lake grinned at her. "Not a one. How 'bout that?"

Karen shook her head in wonder. "Am I a terrific human being or what?"

"You're terrific," Lake agreed, flipping off the light. "Now go to bed!"

At five o'clock in the morning, the city could be the most beautiful place on earth. Streets were deserted and quiet. If you were just coming in from a night on the town, you could feel the whole city was exclusively yours. If you'd been up all night, pondering your fate, you could look out your window and watch faint gray light wash the city new and hopeful again. Then you could go back to sleep for a few more hours and wake up ready to face the world.

If you were just waking up at five o'clock on a nasty February morning, to go wait in line with fifty thousand other unemployed actors in the slim hope of achieving overnight stardom on Broadway, the city was a nasty old whore with an asthmatic cough, a runny nose, and a penchant for drooling. And February all by itself was no treat. It had the great distinction of being the most popular month for suicides. The holiday people had done their best, they had stuck Valentine's Day in there, but it was no use. February was about as attractive as New York City, viewed from the wrong side of five o'clock a.m.

As Lake had suspected, a few hearty souls had camped out overnight to ensure a low number on the list. Not everyone held with this theory; first seen, first forgotten, they said.

At any rate, when Lake and Karen showed up at seven-thirty a.m., they were numbers 130 and 131 respectively. That was on the unofficial list, started by the actors numbers 1, 2, and 3.

They shivered in line for two and a half hours. Then someone official prompted a stampede to transfer names onto the one-and-only, this-is-it, real list. After that madness many of the actors with high numbers went off to their day jobs, to make rounds, whatever. They wouldn't be seen for hours, anyway. The low numbers and the ones with nothing better to do were led into the basement of the theater. It was big, reasonably clean, and, praise the Lord, *warm.*

One sweet-natured boy offered to run across the street for coffee. He was deluged by requests, his face growing longer in direct proportion to his list.

Shortly afterward, a paper cup of liberally sugared coffee in her hand, Karen was perking up. With interest she watched the antics of the actors around her.

A long, graceful girl lowered herself into a perfect split, her face a mask of detached concentration. Next to her another girl sang scales, trying to shake the morning fog from her vocal chords. Not too distant from her a small group was trading information: the absolute best dance teacher, a fabulous coach for Shakespeare, a marvelous therapist who was unbelievably cheap and wonderful with the creative persona. And, of course, they talked about other auditions.

"Did you go to that call last week for *Angel's Song?*"

"What a zoo! I never saw such terrible organization. Honestly, if they can't run an audition properly, can you imagine what the show must be like?"

"That was nothing." Appointment books were pulled and consulted. "Last Tuesday I was scheduled to do a cold reading for some Off-Off Broadway showcase. They asked people to do improvs. Why? They didn't even have a script."

Knowing nods were exchanged all around. "Dead giveaway," someone said.

Other actors were coping with the long wait by meditating, eating, tweezing eyebrows, painting faces, doing the time step, learning the time step from somebody doing it, reading scripts, writing scripts, catching up on correspondence, and, that all-time favorite pastime, stapling résumé's to the backs of 8 × 10 glossies.

One boy did T'ai Chi, an Oriental form of exercise that looked like an underwater ballet. His movements blurred gracefully, one pose melting into another, seemingly without end. He didn't pause even when the monitor came down and called the first ten names on the list.

"Give me your pictures and résumés, please. And be prepared to sing sixteen bars, up-tempo."

Lake grimaced. "I hate singing." She nudged Karen. "You're worried? I'm the one who shouldn't be here." Karen grinned weakly.

"Do they want belt or legit?" somebody called out, eliciting an abundance of replys, opinions, and outright speculation.

Karen looked panicky. "I don't even know what that means."

"Relax." The boy who'd brought coffee was smiling at her. "Legit voices are like Shirley Jones, and belt is Ethel Merman."

"And Jolson?"

"Yeah, Jolson." The boy grinned. "Your first time?"

"Does it show?"

He patted her shoulder. "Take it easy. These are good people to audition for. Not all of them are."

Lake caught his eye to give him a friendly smile. Kinship, he and she, looking after the novice. He smiled back briefly, looking a little awkward. His focus shifted quickly to the floor. He was scared of her.

"Good luck, little one." He ruffled Karen's hair and turned away.

"I wish people wouldn't treat me like a puppy," Karen said in an annoyed tone.

"Here, Fido, good Fido," Lake said in a high, squeaky voice. She made kissy noises through pursed lips, sounding just like a Park Avenue matron talking to her poodle. "Be a good puppy-wuppy or there'll be no cookie-wookie—"

Karen threw her empty coffee cup at Lake. "Okay, Eastman. Forget about ever borrowing my genuine silk blouse."

"You don't have a silk blouse."

"See? You forgot already!" Karen snickered good-naturedly. "Lord, I am so funny, I can't stand myself."

Lake tossed back the coffee cup. Before Karen could retaliate, more numbers were called, swiveling heads throughout the room.

The coffee boy picked up his shoulder bag in preparation for the upstairs trek.

Karen waved to him. "I'll listen for you. What are you singing?"

"Promises, Promises."

"Good luck!" Karen called out in her earnest young voice.

Lake felt her face grow warm with embarrassment. *Not "Good luck," you idiot,* she almost said, *everybody knows you're supposed to say "Break a leg."* Karen didn't know. She didn't know anything. Lake hung on and resisted her impulse to rap Karen squarely on the head. The feeling passed, leaving only a vague unease. Maybe it was better, to be the way Karen was. It was just too bad that things were in no way wonderful and Karen was in for a cruel awakening. Maybe we should just go home, Lake thought.

"Hey." Karen was watching her closely. "Why do I feel like I just walked into the middle of a movie? Come on, give. What were you thinking about?"

Lake yawned, an elaborate show of cat stretch and teeth. "The laundry. I have no undies for tomorrow."

"Liar."

"No, honest. Not a single pair."

From upstairs came the strains of a miserable baritone massacring "Promises, Promises."

Karen looked up, frowning. "Oh, poop," she said. "You'd think a nice guy like that could at least sing decently."

"No such luck." Lake yawned again, this time the real article. "What are they up to, number fifteen? Wake me when they get to the nineties."

She leaned back, closing her eyes.

At a little after four o'clock, numbers 130 through 139 were called. As they climbed the narrow stair, Karen felt the familiar symptoms of nerves assail her. Her palms were cold, her underarms were damp, and whatever had screamed "star" from the mirror in her bedroom in Chicago was on permanent vacation. The first mistake she'd made was coming to this audition at all. Your first audition should not be for a Broadway show. You were supposed to start small and work your way up. The second mistake was auditioning right after Lake. 130, 131. You couldn't argue with numbers.

From the wings she watched Lake. In Karen's eyes her roommate was all cool disdain as she tossed out "My Heart Belongs to Daddy" in a kittenish growl. Karen had been living with Lake long enough to know that the blonde did on occasion fart and, like everyone, go to bathroom, but she just wasn't sure Lake actually perspired. She certainly didn't seem nervous now.

From Lake's side it looked a little different. She was nervous, she was crazy, she was one huge puddle of sweat. She couldn't sing, she never could sing, and on Broadway things like that tended to stand in your way. She knew just enough to get by, acting sexy and coy, making her voice husky and suggestive. All the technique in the world couldn't hide the fact that she just couldn't sing.

"Huh," one waiting actress whispered vindictively. "I guess if you look like that you don't need talent."

Karen didn't hear the weakness in Lake's trembling soprano. She knew Lake was going to be the biggest star ever. She, on the other hand, was probably going straight back to Chicago, where she would gain three thousand pounds and become a professional mother's helper.

Lake walked back into the wings, breathing a monumental sigh of relief and rolling her eyes. "See?" She grinned shakily. "Nothing to it. Go on out there and break a leg."

"I'm a dead woman," Karen moaned. Somehow she managed to put one foot in front of the other without falling down. She stepped out onto the stage and felt . . . *I am home.* Not thought, but really felt *home.* The stage was bare. Only the work light required by union rules shared the vast space with her. She was on a real Broadway stage, and the feeling was magic and special.

"Karen Bloom?" a not unfriendly voice asked from the darkness. "Can you stand on the tape, please?"

There was a tape "X" near the work light. She lined her toes up on it. "Okay?"

"That's fine." The darkness whispered for a moment. Pens scratched. "You can give your sheet music to Bob, our accompanist."

"Oh, I don't have any. This is my first audition ever, and I—" She took a deep breath. "Is it all right if I sing a cappella?"

"That'll be fine, Karen."

They're friendly, Karen thought with delight, they're on my side.

She sang "You Made Me Love You" because she never forgot the words. Her dad used to play his Jolson records all night for her when she couldn't sleep. Karen had had this bizarre childhood insomnia because she had liked to lie awake at night to see if she could hear her bones growing. Either that or she just liked Jolson. And her dad.

It felt like her voice was going straight out the top of her head. She had no technique, no sense of theatricality, but her voice was sweet and clear; a cleanly drawn picture of a little girl listening to Jolson with her dad at four o'clock in the morning.

They let her sing the whole song.

The silence was broken by cheers from the wings. It wasn't until then that Karen thought maybe she had done all right. Darkness spoke again. "We'll be calling people back in the next week or two. We'll also be keeping a file for replacements as the show goes along. Thank you very much."

"Thank you," Karen said politely. Reluctantly she left the stage.

Lake was waiting with tears in her eyes. "You were wonderful," she whispered, hugging Karen tightly.

"I was." Karen's voice was filled with astonished pride. "I really was. Oh, Lake, thank you for making me come today. You're the best friend a girl ever had."

No, I'm not, Lake thought with anguish, I'm no friend at all.

She just hadn't expected Karen to be that good.

4

MATT SINGER liked the voice on the other end of the telephone. A lot.

"Harry Townsend—he's in my acting class," Karen said hesitantly. "He said you were doing a student film and that there was a part open for a woman. Uh, could I read for you? I'd really like to."

Matt grimaced a little wearily. Why not? This film was turning into his own personal albatross. He'd read everybody in NYU for the part, including some of the foxier cafeteria ladies. Why not the body attached to the voice on the phone? "Sure. What about tonight?"

"Tonight?"

"Eight o'clock. At Weinstein."

"That's the dorm, right?"

Sigh. "Right. I'll meet you in the lobby."

"What's this movie about, anyway?" Karen asked.

Sigh. "It's about a man who accepts a bet from his buddy that he can hide from the buddy for three days. But the buddy really wants to kill this guy. The part you'll be reading is this girl the hero picks up. He thinks she's a hitchhiker, but she's really working for the buddy. At the end she falls in love with the hero and helps him escape."

"Sounds great!" Karen tried to sound enthusiastic and extremely professional. After all, she had recently survived her first Broadway audition. She hadn't gotten a call back, but that was a mere technicality. "See you at eight." She banged down the receiver. "Yayy! Another audition!"

Lake, curled up in a chair, began to laugh. "Karen you dope! You never told him your name!"

"Is this the mystery lady?" Matt said as Karen came flying into the Weinstein lobby in her usual disorganized style.

"I'm so sorry. You must think I'm crazy—"

"Well, yes." He unwound from the low lounge chair. "But most actors are." He was still unwinding.

"Oh, my."

Matt grinned shyly. "Six foot four, though you don't ask. Now, may I ask you a question?"

"Anything."

"What the hell *is* your name?"

"Karen Bloom." She offered her hand to the giant. Matt was tall and skinny. He looked like a woodcut of Ichabod Crane. He was so gawkily plain it was almost endearing, but there was a whole other bright, sharp life going on behind his glasses.

This guy's going to make it, Karen thought with a sudden jolt. As sure as I live and breathe, Matt Singer is going to be a very successful director.

Quickly Matt introduced her around. This guy was the D.P. (director of photography), another guy was some other set of initials, and the girl with the cropped platinum hair was simply "sound." Harry was there, and he gave her a friendly wave. They were both handed photocopied scripts and sent to an empty room to practice the scene.

"I'm so nervous," Karen confided.

"Nothing to it, that's the secret," Harry said.

"What?"

He tapped the script. "You want to be an actress?"

"You know I do."

"Don't ever let them catch you at it." He winked. "This script, any script, all we have to do is be ourselves. You and me, nothin' else."

"Okay, Harry," Karen said trustingly. "Let's go do it, you and me."

Matt watched his young actors closely. He watched them as a unit, how they reacted together, how they listened to each other. He made them do the scene again with a slightly different inflection. The D.P. called out a direction. With a coolly concealed flash of anger, Karen turned to the D.P. "I'm sorry," she said calmly. "I only listen to the director!"

"That girl is hired!" Matt yelped to general laughter. He'd needed to see that flash of anger. He'd needed to know whether Karen's sweet shyness was tempered by a little spice. The fire was there. He gave the actors another scene.

Karen skimmed it quickly. "It says here we're supposed to kiss," she said to Harry doubtfully.

"I don't mind." Harry laughed. "How 'bout you?"

She muttered something unintelligible, blushing. Sure she wanted to kiss Harry. She just hadn't counted on an audience. All through the scene Karen was in a quandary. A kiss, sure, but what kind of kiss? An auntie kiss, a prom-night kiss, or a parking lot kiss? What kind of kiss did Harry have in mind, for that matter? Karen didn't want to be left with her tongue hanging out, so to speak.

Harry put his hand on her shoulder, turning her toward him. He wasn't a big guy, but Karen's slight build made him look like John Wayne. She was looking down, and he tipped her chin up so she would look into his eyes. Sweet, green eyes.

Just you and me, kid.

He bent his head to hers and kissed the tip of her nose. It tickled. Just as a little smile parted her lips, he kissed her. Her mouth opened to him, and her arms automatically reached for his shoulders and rested there, relaxed and natural. He tasted of coffee. For the rest of her life, regardless of circumstance, the taste and tang of coffee reminded her of sex.

They pulled away slowly. Without the shelter of Harry's shoulders, she felt nakedly exposed.

Matt was watching her with an odd expression. "Thank you very much," he said. "I'll let you know as soon as I can."

"Well," she sighed, convinced she'd never hear from Matt Singer again, "good luck with your movie."

After the actors had left, the D.P. turned to Matt. "Why'd you give them that second scene?"

Matt shrugged. "I wanted to know if they were boyfriend and girlfriend."

"So?"

"That was a first kiss if I ever saw one."

"So?" the D.P. repeated.

"So," Matt said, "I'm going to marry that girl."

The D.P. looked at him. "I guess that means she got the part, huh?"

"Yuck." Lake took off her slipper and swatted a roach as it strolled along the kitchen wall. "Damn bugs." The slippers were hideous, fluffy pink affairs. Karen had bought them for her, purchasing a blue pair for herself.

"Damn bugs," Karen agreed, pouring hot chocolate into two mugs. One said "Gorgeous Blonde." The other read "Gorgeous Brunette."

Karen sat down. "It went well, I think. Good Lord." She peered into her cup. "It's just not the same without the marshmallows, is it?"

Lake eyed her. "What's on your mind, Karen? I know it isn't marshmallows."

"Lake," Karen said slowly, "did you ever make love to a man?"

"I'm not a virgin," Lake said. She felt herself grow cold and distant. She had to protect her secrets.

"Well . . . what's it like?"

It's like nothing. It's like being cold and dirty inside like an old fireplace that needs sweeping out. "What do you mean?"

"Does the first time hurt?"

"A little. But it hurts less if you're relaxed, honest it does," Lake hastened to add, seeing Karen's horrified expression. "It's really . . . nice."

Karen laid her cold little hand on top of Lake's. Cold hands, warm heart. Karen has a warm heart, Lake's mind mumbled idiotically. *Lake has a cold box. Hey, boys, Lake frozen, skating today!*

"Lake, were you raped or something?"

"No." She laughed. "Why?"

"Because every time we talk about sex, you get this very strange look on your face, like you're remembering a visit to the dentist. For root canal."

"I believe," Lake said in measured tones, "that sex with the right person, someone you love and trust, can be a wonderful experience."

"You don't sound too sure. Do you really believe that?"

"No." Lake waved her fuzzy slipper. "But I hope." She drained the last of her hot chocolate. "I do hope."

5

AH, YES, she could see the headlines now:

LAKE EASTMAN HAS SINGING DEBUT AT CAMILLE'S THOUSANDS DIE TRYING TO ESCAPE

She hung on the piano until her knuckles turned white, but it was no use. They were still going to make her sing, even after what Lake considered her disaster at *Friday's Child.* The piano player winked encouragement.

"Go on, doll," he whispered. "With your looks they'll never hear the flat notes."

"I wish."

He played her intro. She missed her cue. Gentle laughter filtered through the diners. They looked up from their plates and glasses expectantly. Lake learned a valuable lesson: one way to get your audience's attention was by screwing up.

"Sorry." She spoke into the microphone, trying to adjust her voice as it boomed back to her. "Guess I'm a little nervous." The intro came around again, and she pounced on it a few beats early. The piano player covered smoothly; he'd been doing this a long time.

"Embrace me," she sang in a husky soprano, "my sweet embraceable you." She knew enough to stick to Gershwin or Cole Porter; the material practically sang itself. And she'd learned to stay calm. Nerves tightened muscles, which cut off your air. She pushed the nerves down consciously, and her voice got stronger.

The applause was decent. At a table for two in a corner, Penny, another temporary waitress, dealt out salad Niçoise and chicken parmagiana, then applauded like mad. Not a table for two, Lake corrected herself, a deuce. Waitress lingo. It felt great having lingo. It felt like belonging.

She met Penny at the bar. They both put in their drink orders to the surly bartender, who, according to some accounts, was a failed opera singer.

"You were fabulous!" Penny gave Lake a quick hug. Penny had trained Lake, and they had fallen into an easy "work buddies" relationship. Nothing deep or demanding, just looking out for each other.

Penny went up to the piano to hand Mr. Music her lead sheets to look over, while Lake delivered her drink order to a table full of tourists. That was all they ever got at Camille's, tourists and lowlifes.

They both went to the kitchen to pick up their orders. "Look out for the two guys at table fourteen," Penny whispered to Lake as she grabbed a tray off the stack. "Especially the one in the red plaid."

"He seems okay."

Penny shook her head. "He's drinking straight vodka. Stolichnaya. Stolichnaya drinkers are always trouble."

"Always?" Lake teased, claiming her fish. "I need a baked potato, please."

"Always." Penny was serious. She grabbed two salads and drizzled orangey-red French dressing over both. "So you watch out. Comin' out!" she yelped, pushing her way through the swinging door.

Another waitress, Joyce, wagged her head philosophically. "Penny thinks she knows it all, but don't let her scare you. Drunks tip good, anyway." She laughed. "If they're far enough gone, they can't tell a ten from a twenty."

Lake nodded slowly. She didn't like Joyce. Joyce had been in New York for six years, and the city had won. She knew all the tricks because they'd all been played on her. Lake was scared of Joyce because the only difference between the two of them was bad luck and bad timing. Joyce wasn't one to take advice from.

Table fourteen ordered more drinks. Resignedly Lake gave the order to the bartender. "Do you think we should cut off the Stolichnaya brothers?"

The bartender wiped the bar with a sad-looking towel. "They look okay." He shrugged. "Use your judgment."

Thanks a lot.

"You're so pretty," the red-plaid brother said, curling his hands around the glass Lake had just set down.

"Thank you," she murmured.

"Do you know *how* pretty you are?" The drunk leaned over.

People are liars, Lake thought absently. Vodka does have an odor. "Sure, I know," Lake said coolly. "You just told me."

"Sharp chick," the drunk told his friend, grinning wolfishly. "Sharp chick, slick chick, hip chick . . . "

"He's a lyricist," his friend explained.

"Excuse me."

Lake spun quickly in response to the voice at the table behind her, expecting more trouble. It was Joyce's station, but she was getting ready to sing so Lake figured it was okay to handle her table.

The man smiled at her. He was sitting alone, and he seemed very comfortable with his own company. His dark, luxurious hair was styled in no particular fashion; it just seemed to fall in perfect, deep waves. When something caught his attention, his gray eyes regarded it unself-consciously. He was clean-shaven, though a bluish shadow was visible on his slightly square jaw. His clothes weren't fussy, but the cut and fabric suggested money well spent. Gray-green tweed jacket with leather patches at the elbow, corduroy trousers, and a well-cut shirt. He caught Lake mentally cataloging his wardrobe and looked amused.

"That's a lovely jacket," Lake stammered. "I couldn't help wondering where you got it."

"Donegal, Ireland. That's where I developed a fondness for Guinness stout." He held up his empty glass. "Could you bring me another, please?"

"Of course." She took his glass and set it on her tray upside down.

"Oh, Penny," Lake moaned at the bar, burying her face in her hands, "I just acted like such an idiot!"

"Join the club." Penny laughed. "If I didn't act like an idiot at least twice a day, I wouldn't know it was me."

"Who is that guy?"

"Isn't he cute? That's one of Joyce's regulars." Penny waved at the Guinness drinker. He waved back.

Lake was mortified. "I'm going to die."

"Gorgeous hair."

"At least you got to the hair." Lake turned over a tray for the beer. "I got stuck on the jacket."

Joyce was conferring with the piano player. Lake had never heard her sing before, and she was curious.

Penny nudged her. "I just love her voice. So intense," she whispered. "She's doing one of the songs from *Follies.*"

Lake hadn't seen *Follies.* Even if she had, it wouldn't have prepared her. Joyce sang beautifully. Whatever spark had been crushed out of her lived on in her voice. It was better when you closed your eyes. If you left them open, you could see it was still Joyce, angry and bitter. But when you closed them . . . oh, God, she was good. Lake was so enchanted with Joyce's singing that she had completely forgotten about the Guinness on her tray. She inched forward slowly and deposited the mug on the tweedy man's table. He was reading something and didn't look up.

The red-plaid brother lightly touched Lake's back, dragging his forefinger down the length of her spinal column. She shivered. He waggled his empty glass at her.

"Wouldn't you like some coffee?" She tried to sound persuasive, but the Stolichnaya brothers weren't going for it.

"Are you cutting us off?"

She smiled pleasantly. "I'm afraid so."

Red-plaid grabbed her arm. Hard. Lake got scared. He was strong, and the horrible thought came into her mind that if she pulled away quickly enough, the bones in her arm might snap like kindling. "Please let go."

"Bring us our drinks." He was smiling. The other hand was reaching out, and there were a limited number of places he could be interested in.

The tweedy man reached over and hauled red-plaid out of his chair. His buddy just sat there complacently. The tweedy man grabbed the drunk and shook him the way a cat shakes a mouse. The drunk tried to fight back in slow motion. The tweedy man pushed him back effortlessly, watching the drunk's arms flail windmill-style. The drunk plowed forward, and the tweedy man tapped him in the solar plexus. He doubled up, groaning, and collapsed on the floor. His buddy looked down at him calmly. "Hey, man, pull yourself together."

The manager was rushing over. He looked upset. "What the hell's going on? Lake, what the hell are you doing?"

"Me?" Lake managed to choke.

Unbelievably, the manager began to apologize: to the Stolichnaya brothers, the tweedy man, everyone but Lake. Finally he turned to Lake and started to scream at her. She stood there dumbly, taking it.

The tweedy man touched her shoulder lightly. "Go to your locker and get your things. You just quit."

"I did?"

"Sure." He grinned at her. "You don't want to work in a dump like this, do you?"

"Nope." Lake went to the stairwell that led to the basement locker room.

Lake didn't have much in her locker: her purse and her coat. She took a moment to brush her hair, not really seeing herself in the mirror. But she saw Joyce, quietly shutting the door behind her.

"His name is Daniel Fox. He's a writer—TV, screenplays, very well-connected. He'll do a lot for you." She sat down next to Lake and began to comb her own hair. She did it carefully, moving each layer of hair artfully. "I've been waiting on him for almost two months now. I had a throat infection, so this was the first time I've really been in voice for a long time." Suddenly she collapsed, head sinking onto her arms. Harsh, noisy sobs erupted from her.

"I'm so sorry." Lake patted the girl's shoulders in clumsy comfort.

Joyce picked her head up, and the hate in her tear-wetted eyes made Lake recoil in horror. "What do you care what happens to me?" Joyce hissed. "When I fall, I'll go down alone. There'll always be somebody there to catch you. And I can sing, I can really sing." Tears slipped down her cheeks and collected in the hollow of her throat. "I can sing better than you ever will." Sobbing, she slammed a locker door. It jumped away from her, clanging.

"You do sing beautifully," Lake said softly.

Joyce turned away. "Don't be *nice.* Don't take the hate away. Don't take that away from me, too."

Lake walked out onto the street like a sleepwalker. He was waiting for her. Suddenly the street looked very good: the atmospheric set of an arty little film critics love to love. The handsome dark-haired man with the blue-black Dick Tracy jaw, waiting for the love of his life, whom he has only just met. He stands, lighting his cigarette like the Marlboro man, basking in the neon light radiating from the wall of the Spanish restaurant he leans against.

Daniel Fox was walking toward her. "Where to?"

"I don't really know the neighborhood very well." She laughed. "How about the cuchifrito place across the street?" She'd never been in there. Everything in the window looked like fried chicken, but she was pretty sure it wasn't.

"I know a place," he said abruptly. "Your name?"

"Lake Eastman." She winced, waiting for the usual joke or gibe.

"Yes." He nodded; somehow it was what he expected. "Lake. I am Daniel Fox." He took her arm lightly, but she could feel the strength, the energy in his body. She shivered, this time with excited apprehension.

He took her to a quiet, dark little bar that specialized in imported beers and had sawdust on the floor. The bartender knew him and seemed glad to see him. He brought Lake coffee and Daniel a martini, its iciness coating the glass with silvery beads.

"When are you going to write a story about a bartender?" he cracked to Daniel.

"One of these days." Daniel smiled. He lit another cigarette and leaned back in the booth casually. "You have it, you know," he said to Lake.

She laughed. "I hope it isn't catching."

"Don't be a silly girl." He smashed out the cigarette he'd just lit. "You know damn well what I mean. Of course you're quite pretty—you don't need me to tell you that. I wouldn't insult your intelligence or mine. Lots of girls are pretty, but—" He cupped her chin in his large, powerful hand, tilting her face up into the light. She closed her eyes, concentrating on the feel of his gentle fingers on her soft throat. His grip tightened ever so slightly, and he shook her. "Open your eyes." Slowly she did. "Look at me." She countered his keen stare, very conscious of her breathing. It was at that moment that she knew how much she wanted him. She could imagine the hand at her throat traveling over her body, could imagine a lot of things.

He took his hand away. "Yes, you really have it," he said softly. "The intrinsic quality. The thing that makes people stars. Without it all the talent in the world is just so much shit. Let me see your head shot."

She took her picture out of her bag and handed it to him. He ripped it up, took one of his cards out of his breast pocket, and scribbled on the back of it. "Be at this address tomorrow at ten o'clock—sharp, he's a busy man."

Lake shrugged helplessly. "I really don't have the money for new pictures. Without the waitress job . . . "

He handed her a hundred dollar bill. "I made you lose your job. Don't worry about the pictures; I'll take care of that."

"Why are you doing this?"

"Oh, I don't know. Maybe I like playing Pygmalion. Maybe I've fallen in love with you. Stranger things have happened."

"Not to me."

He was still holding out the money. "I forgot to leave you a tip, anyway."

"Then that should be Joyce's."

"Joyce?"

"The girl who sang the Sondheim. Wasn't she good?"

"Pretty voice," he said absently. "But she doesn't have it. You do."

"Do I?" Lake said slowly. "Do I really?"

He walked her home. It wasn't far, but they took the long, winding way around. From time to time he would stop and study her in the light of street lamps, always taking her chin in his hands. It was like a signal.

She was at her door. "Will you be at the photographer's tomorrow?"

"I'll be there, Lake," he said softly. "I'll always be there for you. You must go to sleep now so you'll be fresh for the camera."

"All right."

He went down the steps and waited until she was safely indoors. Then he walked away slowly. She watched him from the bedroom window.

"Karen," Lake whispered, "wake up."

The lump under the covers on Karen's bed moved sluggishly. "Pepsi," the lump said.

"How can you drink that stuff in the middle of the night?"

"Pepsi?" the lump moaned.

Lake went into the kitchen and poured Karen some soda. She walked back to the bedroom and gave Karen the cup.

"Hello," Karen said blearily. "What's up?"

"Karen, I met a guy." She plopped down on Karen's bed. "I mean a man. An incredible man."

"Yayyy!" Karen hugged Lake, managing somehow not to spill any soda. "Tell me everything."

A WEEK AFTER the photo session, Daniel Fox became everything Lake had never had in her life and so desperately wanted. It started with a knock on the door.

"I'll get it," Karen sang. She could be maddeningly chipper in the morning, singing made-up songs as she prepared for school.

Lake, wallowing in her tangled bedclothes, heard Karen unlock the door. She heard it creak open. Then she heard, "Holy cow!" The statement was repeated for greater emphasis. "Hooolyyy cooow! Lake!" It didn't exactly sound like a rape or an abduction, so Lake managed to grab her robe before galloping to the door.

"Holy cow," she agreed weakly. "What do they want?"

"You, I think," Karen said, still goggling. "Won't you sit down?" she asked the entourage politely.

The entourage thought about it. There was a liveried chauffeur, a tough-looking lady wearing a coat that could only be monkey fur, and a younger woman, whose prime function seemed to be kissing up to old monkey fur.

The chauffeur stepped forward, removing his cap. "You ought to put on something warm, miss." he told Lake. "It's pretty cold out. You ought to put on some boots and a hat, too. Heat escapes through the extremities."

Monkey fur laughed deeply. "You don't know what the hell's going on, do you, toots?"

"No, I don't," Lake answered. "Would you mind telling me what you're doing here?"

"Dan Fox thinks you're going to be the next great whatever, so today, sweetie pie, you're getting the works. Only the top people. Jon-Paul for the hair, Galina H. for makeup and skin care, and for wardrobe, well . . . " She stroked her monkey fur modestly. "Like I said, honey, only the top people. You can call me Mac. This"—she indicated the younger woman—"is my assistant. *You* don't call her; *I* do." She looked at Lake hard and long. "Size seven." It wasn't a question. Frowning, she glared at Karen. "Size five or three?"

"Depends." Karen was fascinated. "Sometimes one, sometimes the other."

"You're short," Mac said flatly.

"Thank you."

"Good eyes, though." She snapped her fingers, and the assistant handed her a cigarette. "Not good enough!" she warned Karen, "but good." The chauffeur produced a lighter.

"I gotta write this down!" Karen muttered. "I need something good for my creative writing class. Where's my notebook?"

"Miss Eastman?" the chauffeur said politely. "I don't mean to rush you, miss. But you ought to think about getting ready to go. You've got appointments to keep."

"Excuse me." Lake ran to the kitchen, where Karen was frantically scribbling in her notebook. She moved her lips when she wrote.

"Karen, what should I do?" She shook the girl so hard that Karen's teeth rattled.

"Look," Karen said with dismay, "now I've got squiggles all over the page." She closed the notebook. "Are you insane, girl? Go with them! Do you know how much Galina H. charges for a facial? Fifty bucks! Go, have a wonderful time, and—"

"I know," Lake said wryly, "tell you everything."

Four hours later Jon-Paul, Galina H., and an assorted cast of underlings, assistants, alchemists, and anybody else the beauty industry could conceivably employ were all sitting around sipping champagne and admiring their work. Mac, her monkey fur, and her assistant had taken measurements earlier and beat a hasty retreat.

"A good job," someone said.

"Good raw material," another said.

Lake looked in the mirror completely and totally in awe of herself. It was practically a religious experience. "Oh," she breathed softly. "That"—she tapped the mirror with hopeless devotion—"is gorgeous." Amazing what you could do with six kinds of eyeshadow, two shades of lipstick, and all the other marvels of modern science. The soft coral pink sweater, shot through with the glimmer of gold thread, set off her coloring to perfection, and the deeper coral skirt was short enough to show off her legs.

Daniel arrived quietly while she was adoring herself and indulging in a few hosannas. She saw his reflection come up behind hers in the mirror. "I don't know why you're doing this." She smiled at the mirror. "But I think I love you."

He kissed the top of her head. "That's why I'm doing it." He turned to the assembled group. "Thank you all. You've done an excellent job. And now, how about lunch?" He offered Lake his arm.

As soon as Lake and Daniel had left, the beauty technicians began to file out.

Galina, the makeup artist, was struggling into her coat. She had been a great beauty in her youth. She was still a handsome woman with flaring Slavic cheekbones and thick, iron-gray hair wound into a coronet of braids. Jon-Paul, the dapper hairstylist, gave her a hand with her coat. She turned to him questioningly. "Tell me, my charming Frenchman, what has Mr. Dan Fox got on you?"

The Frenchman hesitated, then smiled roguishly. "A young man, but I mean a *young* man. Fifteen years old." He sighed, recalling past delights. "But very mature for his years. Pity his father was not. And you, *ma petite Russe?* What is your crime?"

"I cannot say," Galina whispered.

"Then you should not ask what you are unwilling to answer."

She dropped her proud head, ever a woman of honor. "I have a daughter," she said in the same hushed tone. "She is autistic, so I must keep her in a special place, where they know how to take care of her. Her father . . . if he could find her, I believe he would kill her. Yes." She nodded her head. "I believe he would. She is a great shame to him." She smiled strangely. "Fathers can be terrible creatures. Demons, they can be. Daniel Fox said he would tell her father where I have hidden her." Her eyes dimmed slightly, but she was still smiling. "I have no doubt at all that he would."

The host at the Russian Tea Room led them to a choice table and held Lake's chair for her, smiling at her. Daniel sat with his back to the wall like a gunslinger. Lake mentioned this to him, and he favored her with his secretive smile.

"You'll soon see why," he told her.

As new arrivals came in, Daniel could pick and choose those whom he wanted to make eye contact with, preamble to a tableside swoop and an introduction to Lake.

She felt like Alice going down the rabbit hole to emerge in a new world populated by unusual creatures. No one was ordinary. Everything Daniel Fox brought to her was strange and entrancing. A man stopped by the table to say hello. He spoke by holding a small microphone up to a hole in his neck. Cancer of the larynx, Daniel explained to her later. The man was a Broadway angel who had a knack for success, if not health. He gave Lake his card, expressing in his death-rattle voice how pleased he was to meet her. Smiling, he went off to work another table. A set of sixty-year-old identical twins, blue-haired grandmothers. They would not sit, but remained standing, arms intertwined as they talked.

"She's lovely, Dan!" one gushed.

"Just lovely," the other gushed.

"More than a friend?" one tittered.

"Are we to be attending a wedding?" the other tittered.

Lake was glad when they scampered off, but still . . . it was fascinating. And the attention was intoxicating.

There followed: a surprisingly polite rock star, a canny husband-and-wife team of agents, a mink-coated widow all of twenty-three years old, a very charming professorial type who was drunk out of his mind and told Lake that he had a member of mythic proportions.

"It's very sad. Women just want a crack at old Jasper there." He looked down at his crotch with a mixture of sadness and regret. "Nobody loves me for myself."

Lake burst out laughing.

He went away. The husband-and-wife agents came back.

"All right, you pirate," the wife told Daniel, "talk. Where did you find this divine creature, and who is she signed with?"

Daniel leaned back, toying with the remains of his shashlik. "Ask Lake. She's the brains of this outfit."

"Well, darling," the wife said to Lake, "you're on."

The Russian Tea Room made some particularly lethal vodka drinks. Lake had enjoyed a few, and while she wasn't exactly drunk, she was certainly feeling a little reckless.

"What do you want to know?" The words came out of her mouth like molasses.

"Where are you from, dear?"

"Albuquerque, New Mexico," Lake lied smoothly. "There's a perfectly wonderful seafood restaurant there called the Zuider Zee. You wouldn't think to find a seafood restaurant so far inland, but there it is. You should try it the next time you're in Albuquerque," she advised the agents wisely.

The wife laughed. "I certainly shall."

"Of course, I'm not from there originally."

Daniel was smiling encouragingly. He was enjoying her little game.

"I'm from Mars." She grinned at her empty glass. "Mars is nice this time of year."

"Pink snow," Daniel agreed, gravely nodding his head.

"I went to Albuquerque for the rodeo," Lake went on, "but even *that* got boring, so I came to New York. To be a private detective. Loss prevention, that's where the real money is." A tunic-clad waiter hovered close, and Lake collared him, pointing to her empty glass. "Bring me something blue," she commanded grandly.

The husband and wife looked at each other and shrugged. "Ah, Daniel," the husband said softly, speaking for the first time, "you do bring out the best in all of us. Nonetheless, if she photographs half as well as she looks in person—"

"She will," the wife said, eyes glowing.

"Bring her to the office tomorrow morning," the husband said, standing. "We'll have some paperwork to get out of the way."

"What's this all about?" Lake asked as soon as they had gone. "What am I signing?"

"A contract with the biggest modeling agency in New York." He laughed at her expression. "Why do you look so surprised?"

"They want to sign me after my little performance?"

At that moment the waiter came over, looking bewildered. "I'm sorry, I can't find anything blue. Could you give me a hint?"

"Oh, that's all right," Lake said hastily. "Maybe you just better bring me some coffee.

Daniel traced the delicate veins on the back of her hand with his finger. "Tell me. I want to understand. Everything. How you feel, how you think . . . I want to know."

She closed her eyes. "You don't know how long I've waited to hear somebody—anybody—say that. I don't know why I acted that way." The coffee came; and she fell silent until the waiter went away. For some reason, she could think only about the way Daniel was stroking her hand. "I don't know why . . . " Her voice trailed off.

"Don't you?" His eyelashes were long; she hadn't noticed that before. "Do you know why people follow rules?" An answer wasn't required from her. "Because it's easier. So much of life is just showing up. Show up for the train. Show up for work. Everybody doing the expected thing at the expected time. Easy and safe. And if somebody doesn't want to live by the rules?"

"They get locked up?"

"No," he said. "They do as they please. They base their actions on the intuitive, not the intellectual."

"Daniel." She laughed uneasily. "Everybody can't just run around doing as they please."

"Not everyone," he said serenely, "just special people." His eyes bored into her. "You can do whatever pleases you."

"Because you say so?" she teased.

Dead serious, he answered, "Why not?" The answer seemed to please him. "Why not?" he repeated.

His apartment was tastefully if sparsely furnished. Real investment pieces. Good sculpture that begged to be touched. Lake drifted through the dark living room, handling things, willing her mark to be left in this place. A sketch was taped to the wall. She stopped before it. Even in the dark she knew it was a sketch of her own face.

"Why, Daniel?" she whispered. "Why me?"

In the dark he began to pace. "Because I *do* understand, don't you see that?" He was angry, frightening her a little with his intensity. "I know about others, how they grab and paw at you, offer you foolish worship, then defile you for showing them to be the weaklings they are. Clamoring for beauty. Offering nothing."

She snapped on the light, staring at the sketch until her eyes went into soft focus. "God, that's good," she murmured. "Is that the way I look to you?"

"No. I could never do justice to you. Silly to try." He laughed harshly. "Clamoring for beauty."

She turned off the light. "I dreamed," she said in dreamy tones, "that someone somewhere would care about me, who I am, what *I* care about. But no one did for so long that I stopped caring about things. Something has to anchor me to the earth."

"There's a party tomorrow night," he said irrelevantly. "Important people, fascinating people. Would you like to go?"

"Did you hear me?"

"Yes. What about the party?"

"All right." She swung her head so that her hair fluttered like cornsilk. "If you want." She walked toward him, feeling heat rise from her body. Her head felt hollow, a balloon ready for flight. He was standing next to the couch. She jumped onto it lightly, pulling him toward her, his face nuzzling her breasts. Through the fabric her nipples became hard, trying to thrust their way through her bra.

"Poor Daniel," she breathed, "living on the edge all the time. How is it there?"

"Pink snow." With one fast motion he ripped her blouse away. The cloth was thin and gave easily. He wrapped both hands around her hips and lifted her into the air, her waist aligned with his shoulders. She bowed her head, looking at him, the silken curtain of her hair caressing his face. He seized it in his teeth and pulled until she brought her lips down to his. He kissed her deeply, thrusting his tongue into her mouth. Under her ass his hand began to work, first pulling the skirt up out of his way, then massaging her. With a little moan she wrapped her legs around his waist, hiking herself up so she could fumble with his belt buckle.

He sat down in his desk chair, still holding her. The chair had no arm rests but a very high back. Back arched, hair streaming, skirt bunched at her waist, she slowly lowered herself onto the hard shaft rising from the open zipper of his trousers. She pulled at his shirt, popping buttons, clawing at him, sucking on his nipples. Her own felt like they were going to burst. Moaning in his own private delirium, he seized her hands and locked them onto the back of the chair, behind his head. Using that for leverage, she thrust against him, she the man, he the passive one this time. He laced his hands at the small of her back, pressing into her, filling her completely. She came, roaring like the ocean.

He was still hard. Knowing how wet and ready she was, he put her down on the carpet and had her again, savagely ramming into her. Sweat soaked her hair. When his frantic motion prevented her reaching for him, she sucked on her own fingers. Their juices mingled, running from the creases and folds of thigh and pubis to the carpet, staining it a deeper hue. He spread her legs and drank her dry while she screamed and laughed. In her voice was triumph. I can feel! she thought exultantly. I can feel!

Finally spent, he lay down beside her, wriggling out of what shreds of clothing he still had on. That done, he lay back, hands behind his head. Lake raised up on one elbow and looked at his body.

It was a fine body, fine-made and finely honed, marked only by the fierceness of her lovemaking. Smiling to herself, she traced the clean line that lead from neck to shoulder, the girdle of muscle that sat above his hips, pointing to his lovely cock. She studied the intricacy of the wrinkles on the skin of his testicles. Like silver foil bunched up tightly, then flattened out. She nosed their softness, inhaling his scent.

She meant to stay up all night, just watching him, but eventually she fell asleep. She slept so soundly that she did not hear him get up, around three a.m., and go into the other room.

From memory he dialed a number.

"Hello?" a sleepy voice said.

"Fox."

"Sure," the voice rumbled. "Who else would it be at this hour? So whose grave are we digging this time?"

Daniel grinned a tight smile. "Your choice of words would be unfortunate if I taped these conversations."

The voice yawned. "How do you know I don't? Lots of private dicks do."

"Not you." Daniel laughed. "The name is Lake Eastman. Darien, Connecticut. See if Mommy or Daddy has any skeletons I can rattle. Just in case."

"Fuck that shit," the wife agent snarled to her husband. "No one, but no one stands me up."

"Stands us up," the husband corrected mildly.

"Sorry, dear."

"That's quite all right."

"Jesus!" she exploded. "Can you imagine if we signed this little Eastman prima donna, booked her for a gig, and then she pulls her disappearing act? We'd look like idiots! We simply cannot take the risk."

"No, we can't," the husband agreed sadly.

Still fuming, the wife sat at her desk. "I wonder what happened? Do you think she got rushed by another agency?"

"No," the husband said thoughtfully. "I just think Danny doesn't want to share this one with anybody. He's always been a little crazy—"

"Amen to that." The wife agreed.

"But I think with this one he's really going over the edge. Poor girl."

"Why do all you poor, deluded men feel sorry for the pretty girls?" The wife sniffed.

The husband shrugged. He thought about pink snow on Mars and how pretty it must look.

Lake didn't wake up until four o'clock that afternoon. In Daniel's bed she stretched luxuriously, taking her sweet time to come to full consciousness. She was quite alone. "Daniel?" She wrapped the sheet around her lithe body and padded to the kitchen. Coffee was made and she helped herself, finding cups in the cabinet above the counter.

"Daniel?" She sipped her coffee and aimlessly wandered around the apartment. "Dammit, where are you? This is a heck of a way to thank a girl for a memorable evening!"

He came in when she had just finished her second cup. "Good, you found the coffee. Sorry to take off like that but I had a few errands to run."

"I wish you had told me you were leaving."

"You were sleeping so peacefully I couldn't bring myself to wake you. Here." He held out a box wrapped in gold paper. "Go on, take it, it's for you."

"So that's what you were up to all morning," Lake said in a pleased voice.

"Afternoon," he corrected, "it's twenty to five."

"I can't believe I slept so late—" she opened the box and removed crumpled sheets of pink tissue paper. "Oh, how beautiful." She held up the little glass globe, peering at the miniature seascape within. A small boat crested oddly shaped waves. She shook the globe back and forth, causing a miniature pink snowstorm.

Daniel smiled, watching her. "I had it made up just for you."

"Thank you," she whispered. "But Daniel, I can't stay. I've got to get home. I think I've already missed an important appointment." Her eyes widened. "Those people last night, wasn't I supposed to meet them?"

Daniel shrugged, unconcerned. "I wouldn't lose any sleep over it."

"Obviously I didn't." Hastily she pulled her sweater over her head. "Will you call me?"

He didn't respond.

Lake stopped dressing and turned to look at him. "Will you?"

"Of course I will."

"Just like to see me sweat, don't you?"

He found her shoes near the bed and handed them to her. "Run along home." There was just a touch of mockery in his voice.

"I'm never sure whether you're being serious or not." She slung her handbag over one shoulder. The glass globe she cradled delicately in both hands, fearful of shattering her treasure. "I really do love my present, Daniel."

In one quick movement he was at her side kissing her deeply, passionately. "Sure you don't want to stay?"

"You're a terrible tease but I can't."

"Then go so I can get a little work done."

She lingered in the doorway. "Call tomorrow," she said in a playful way, "or I may just turn up on your doorstep and you won't get any work done for a long time. 'Bye."

After she'd gone Daniel went into the bedroom to play back the day's messages recorded on the phone machine.

"This is Karl Eastman," the voice on the tape announced. "I think we should talk, Mr. Fox. It's about my daughter. I don't want you seeing Lake anymore."

Daniel Fox smiled. He rewound the tape, set the machine and dialed his old friend again.

"It's Fox," he told the detective, "it seems I'm going to need that Eastman report sooner than anticipated."

7

KAREN WALKED DOWN the highway, a small pack slung on her back. Taped to the pack was a cardboard sign reading "Hollywood" in big block letters. She wore a blue and white checked skirt, knotted at the waist, and a pair of cutoffs. It was approximately thirty-five degrees with a nice north-northeasterly wind.

On cue Harry pulled up slightly behind Karen, leaned over, and rolled down the car window. He was wearing a light shirt and jeans. They were both freezing their respective tails off. "I'm only going as far as Anaheim."

Slowly Karen turned around and looked at Harry. She gave him a gingerbread smile, sweet and spicy. "Okay." She hopped into the car, and they drove away.

"Cut!" Matt yelled. The car kept going. The camera crew started jumping up and down, waving frantically. The car turned around and obediently crawled back to the crew. Karen hung out the window, a down jacket draped around her shoulders. Matt walked over to the car, smiling. "Great. That was just great. You guys want some hot coffee?"

"Coffee?" Harry came to life. "Someone mention coffee?" He threw the heater up to high. "Karen, get back in the window so we can get this heat circulating."

Karen was staring up at Matt, shivering a little. "You didn't like it."

He handed her two drippy paper cups. "I'm going to get you guys a walkie-talkie so the crew can communicate with you when you're in the car."

"Good idea," Harry put in.

"Oh, Karen," Matt said casually.

She snapped to attention. "Yes?"

"Why don't you roll up the window?" Matt grinned. "You guys must be freezing."

"We're definitely going to have to kill him." Karen shook her head, throwing herself at the window handle. "God, it's freezing!" On the dashboard coffee sloshed dangerously.

"Easy!" Harry warned, rescuing the cups from their precarious position. "We did that scene just fine. You know it, and I know it."

Karen sighed. "Maybe it could have been . . . more so."

"More so what?" Harry flipped on the radio. Van Morrison was yodeling away. "You, mah brown-eyed girl," Harry sang along. He put his arm around Karen and rocked back and forth in time to the music. She would have liked to have thought his action was spurred by affection, but he was probably just trying to keep warm.

One of the camera crew, bundled up in muffler, a cap, and a down jacket, rapped on the window. "The last take was real good," he informed them, "but you guys got to do it again. Director's orders."

"I knew it!" Karen punched Harry's arm.

"More freezing to death," Harry moaned, throwing the car into gear.

"Show biz!" Karen giggled. She felt suddenly giddy, the result of getting up at five that morning, the excitement and strangeness, even the attention, which she simply wasn't used to. "Want to go to Hollywood and make movies with me, Harry?"

"Holly-weird." he corrected.

"Holly-weird," she repeated. "Well, how 'bout it?"

"I don't know," Harry said doubtfully. "Is it warm there?"

"Sure! Sunshine, palm trees, the Manson family . . . " She leaned forward to turn off the radio, brushing against Harry, noting, absently by this time, the electrical thrill that pulsed through her body every time she touched him. *That's it. That's what was missing in the scene.*

Harry ruffled her hair. "What are you grinning about?"

You, my dear. "I think we're going to be perfect this time." She scrambled out of the car, bare legs flashing.

As soon as she'd left, Matt ambled over to the car, cranking his long body down to peer into Harry's window. "Harry," he said slowly, "would you do something a little different this time?"

Harry looked a little startled. "Uh, sure. You're the boss."

At her mark Karen watched them curiously. After a moment Matt loped away.

"Quiet on the set!" Matt yelled. He rose, head and shoulders, above the rest of the camera crew.

"Sound!"

"Speed!"

"Camera!" Matt cried.

"Speed!"

"Action!" At the director's command Karen started her trek down the road. This time for the money, she thought. She was going to give Harry the sexiest, sizzle-your-socks look since Dietrich in *Blonde Venus.* Karen revved her motor. So did Harry. Except this time he pulled up a little too close, careening into a large mud puddle. Icy water splashed over her bare legs. A few drops even managed to nestle beneath her bra. She was too surprised to scream; all she could do was just stare numbly at Harry, who was merrily cracking up.

"Uh, sorry, miss. The least I can do is give you a ride. Hop in."

She stared.

He patted the seat coaxingly. "Come on."

"Okay," she managed to squeak and got in. Harry peeled out, still laughing.

"Cut!" Matt raced over, wearing a big grin. "Guys, that was perfect. Okay, we're going to move the camera around to do Harry's close-up, so Karen, you can take a very fast shower and get ready for the interior scenes."

She was staring at him, big eyes uncomprehending. "Karen?" Matt said kindly, "is there some problem?"

Oh, not really. I kind of enjoyed you two high-spirited lads putting your heads together to make a fool out of me. "No problem, Mr. Director," she said smartly, turning her back on Matt and Harry. In a fine temper she marched off to the van.

"I'd keep an eye out for some well-planned retaliation," Harry advised the young director. "That girl's got revenge on her mind."

"She won't do anything until the shoot is over," Matt said confidently. "No actress worth her salt would jeopardize her close-ups."

"I wouldn't bet on it." Harry laughed. "Karen's a real nice girl, but I figure her for a short fuse." He spun the radio dial, vainly searching for a song the deejays hadn't played out. Mostly what he was getting was a lot of static. It seemed to irritate Matt. He reached into the car and turned off the radio.

"You've got her all figured out, have you?" His comical Ichabod Crane features were still stretched into a disarming smile, but Matt's eyes remained distant and watchful. Harry was beginning to get the feeling that Matt's interest in Karen was more than professional.

"Nope," he said cheerfully. "I just see that little flash in her every now and then. You know what I mean?"

Behind his glasses Matt's eyes lost their suspicious gleam. Once again he was the friendly scarecrow. "Harry, you're a real student of human nature."

Harry Townsend winked. "You bet."

Karen stepped out of the shower, skimming her hair back with both hands. Automatically she grabbed at the towel rack. No towels.

"Karen?" That was the platinum blonde at the bathroom door. "How long you gonna be?"

"There are no towels!" Karen yelled, but the blonde had vanished. Judging by the ruckus in the other room, the camera crew must have arrived. "I need towels!" When this elicited no response she started singing. Karen sang "All God's Chillun Got Towels." Nobody seemed to care for that tune, so she segued into "If I had a towel, I'd towel in the mor-or-ning." She was all set to launch into "The Towel that Got Away" when she heard amused laughter at the door.

"Matt?"

"Nope."

"Harry?"

"Yep."

"You better have a towel on you," she warned.

"Yep. Open the door."

"I can't! I mean, I don't have anything on," Karen stammered. She felt like an idiot. If only she had a better body. Then she could let Harry in, he'd say, "My God, Karen, you have a gorgeous body" and ravish her, they would achieve multiple simultaneous orgasms (she'd read that in some magazine) and walk off into a Technicolor sunset, and Matt would have to find two other actors to finish his stupid movie.

"Karen," Harry said a bit tiredly, "Open the door a little. I'll hand you the towel. I promise I won't look, for Christ's sake."

"Okay." She was starting to shiver, anyway. There wasn't even a bath mat; the tile floor was cold and wet. And slippery. Just as she grabbed the corner of the towel Harry was gallantly holding out, she started hydroplaning on the tile floor. As she skidded around, her mind kept playing the same embarrassing scene over and over again. She would fall, crack her head on the sink, and die. The cops would be called in: the hardnosed cynical I-seen-everything-twice pro and his gee-whiz rookie partner. They would look down at her naked, dead body, and the rookie would say, "I give her a 7.5. Whaddya think?"

The hardnose would shrug. "On a scale of one to ten, or one to a hundred?" Then they would walk out, laughing.

In a last ditch effort Karen grabbed at the towel rack on her way down. It decided to keep her company, neatly detaching itself from the wall with a minimum of plaster fallout. Karen hit the floor with her right shoulder first, the rest of her following shortly, along with the towel and the towel rack.

"Karen! Are you okay?" Harry tried to push his way through the door, mashing Karen's foot.

"Owww! Wait a second!" She wrapped the towel around herself and crawled to the door. Harry fell over her and hit the floor in a pretty fair imitation of her own tailspin. Somehow Karen managed to scoot to a sitting position, her back against the tub. She rubbed her sore shoulder, which was sporting a nice bruise.

Harry touched her shoulder gently. "Anything broken? Does that hurt?"

"Of course it does, what did you think?" She started giggling uncontrollably. "Are you all right?"

"Yes." He was laughing so hard he was shaking. He looked nice when he laughed. She was about to tell him that when Matt poked his head past the bathroom door. He looked at them both coldly, but Karen was getting the worst of it.

"Five minutes, in costume please," he told her in icy tones. "And dry your hair, Karen." He closed the door.

"He hates me," Karen wailed. "The director hates me! Harry, what am I going to do?"

He kissed the tip of her nose. "The first thing you're going to do is dry your hair."

"I think we need to talk."

Karen looked up, surprised. The day's work over, the cast and crew had assembled in the D.P.'s parents' home for dinner and a night's lodging. They were munching out on Kentucky Fried Chicken, cole slaw, and biscuits. A few people had taken their plates into the living room and were clustered around the TV. Harry was slouching on the counter, waiting for the kettle to boil so he could make instant coffee. The last thing Karen had expected was "I think we need to talk" from Matt Singer. She looked over to Harry for some kind of support.

He yawned and turned the flame off under the kettle. "Guess I'll take a nap."

"Thanks, Harry," Karen muttered under her breath. She shrugged. "What do we need to talk about?"

"I want you to know why I changed that scene."

"Oh," she said, acid-sweet, "you mean why you told Harry to deliberately splash me with mud."

He grinned. "Yeah. I thought you'd like to know why."

"I'll admit I'm curious—a little," she hastened to add, smiling back in spite of herself.

Matt paused, collecting his thoughts. "This is basically an action film. Most of the time you're being chased by killers, running for your life, that sort of thing." He leaned forward intently, bony shoulders hunched, his whole face becoming animated.

This is his one love in life, Karen realized. Making movies.

"There's very little time for character development," Matt went on, "but if the audience doesn't like you and Harry, the whole thing dies right then and there. Harry's easy, he's the hero. But what about you? Here you are, all ready to vamp this guy—"

"And you make a fool out of me!"

"No!" He slammed his fist down on the table. "We make you human. Karen, don't you see? That's your gift. You're not the prettiest girl in the world—"

"Thanks a lot!"

"But you are pretty enough." He steamrolled over her objections. "And sweet, and there's something about you people like almost immediately. All I did was make that a little more obvious."

"By humiliating me?" She stood up quickly, but he grabbed her arm, holding her loosely.

"Karen, you're going to have to learn how to control your temper! Do you honestly think I'd jeopardize my film for the purpose of humiliating you? Not that I have any desire to humiliate you in the first place!"

"You don't?" she faltered. "I thought you didn't like me."

"That's got nothing to do with it," he maintained stubbornly.

"You are here because you've got a good quality for this role. And I will do whatever it takes to catch that on celluloid."

"Even if it means manipulating your actors like we were dumb animals?"

"Of course. That's an actor's job."

Karen laughed. "Well, it takes a little skill, you know."

The young director shrugged. "Not really. All an actress needs is to be attractive and charming, which you are."

Karen couldn't answer; she wasn't sure whether she was being insulted or complimented.

"At any rate, I doubt you'll be satisfied as an actress."

"I won't?" Karen asked, mystified.

"You're too damn bright. You'll probably wind up in some aspect of production."

"I will?"

"Sure. What do you do besides act?"

"Go to school." She thought of something but quickly rejected the thought.

He was watching her keenly and caught it. "What were you thinking?"

"Oh, nothing." Somehow the words forced their way past her lips. "I used to make up these dumb stories. They were really stupid—"

"There you are!" Matt crowed triumphantly. "A writer!"

"I'm not a writer." Karen laughed. "Besides, I really love acting."

"Why?"

Because it's a golden opportunity to kiss and hug good-looking non-Jewish boys. She looked down at the table. "I just do."

He nodded his ungainly head. "That's a good reason—for now. It may not hold up ten years down the road."

"You may not even want to direct, either," Karen pointed out.

"Probably not. It's too much work. I hope to produce," Matt said promptly.

Karen laughed. "Matt, you are too much. But I get the crazy feeling you get what you want."

He smiled strangely. "We'll see."

"Is that all you wanted to say?" She got up and dumped her paper plate into the garbage.

"One more thing," Matt said slowly. "I didn't think this needed to be said, but I'm constantly amazed at how insecure actors are. You were cast because I chose you, and I chose you because you were the best."

"You were right," Karen said quietly. "It needed to be said." She caught herself in mid-yawn. "'Scuse me, I think I'll go to bed now. Good night."

"Good night."

I guess he's all right after all, Karen thought sleepily, closing the bedroom door behind her. She *did* find Matt attractive in a strange sort of way. Not like Harry, with his good looks and Southern charm. Matt's appeal was different; he was a study in contrasts. His awkward appearance belied his quick, inventive mind and business savvy. A nice guy who wouldn't hesitate to use a little coercion to achieve his goals. No, he wasn't like Harry. Matt was going to make it; he was the future. Harry could very easily wind up lost in the shuffle. He was . . .

"Hi, you busy?"

. . . at her door.

"No, come on in."

He sat on the edge of her bed. "Did you-all have a nice chat with the director?"

"You-all?" she mimicked.

He tugged her hair playfully. "Don't tease."

"I guess we had a nice talk," Karen said. "But I just don't understand him very well. At least I don't think he hates my guts."

Harry laughed. "No, I don't think so, either."

"What's so funny?" she demanded.

"You are." He leaned into her so they were almost touching noses. "Why do you find it so hard to believe that anybody likes you?"

She looked away. "Because I'm nothing special," she said in a low voice.

He tipped her chin up so their eyes met. "You're very special, and I'm glad to be here with you." He stroked her hair gently. She moved a little nearer, closing her eyes.

I must remember this, Karen vowed. I must remember every sound and feel and flavor, and I must remember it as long as I live, because this will probably never happen again.

Harry rested his jaw on the top of her head. He tended toward a five o'clock shadow, and she could feel the scratchy bristles against her scalp. If she could have died right then and there, in his arms, Karen Bloom would have considered it a life well spent.

"I like you, too, Harry," she said softly.

"Good." He kissed her lightly, one hand brushing the nape of her neck. "So sweet," he murmured, "you even taste sweet."

That's my Crest toothpaste, she almost blurted out. Instead she chuckled in her throat.

"What's so funny?" he asked her, teasing, as he bent to kiss her throat. He followed the sculpted line of her collarbone with his tongue, and it nearly took her breath away. A little moan whispered past her lips, and she clung to him, trying to press him closer.

Somehow they were lying down, glued together, frantically kissing and touching each other. Somehow her blouse wound up on the floor. Karen thought it looked nice there. The bra followed shortly. Because the blouse was lonely, Karen reasoned. Harry pulled away from her for a second to pull off his T-shirt.

"Harry . . . " She hesitated a second. "There's something I have to tell you."

"You don't have to worry," Harry said, pulling his wallet from his back pocket. "I've got protection." From the wallet he removed a small foil packet bearing a ring-shaped imprint. The wrapper read "Trojan." She wasn't exactly sure what it meant, but she was willing to make an educated guess. Harry waved the packet, grinning. "My dad always said to be prepared, just like the Boy Scouts."

"Harry, I'm a virgin."

"Oh," he said finally. "Do you want to stay that way?"

She ducked her head, embarrassed.

"'Cause if you do," he said softly, "it's okay with me. I would never force my attentions on a lady. It just seemed to me you needed a little attention. Besides, there's a whole lot of other stuff a man and a woman can do—"

"I don't know what to do," Karen said miserably. "I just know I don't want you to leave."

"Okay," Harry said with his usual good humor. "I didn't want me to leave, either. Come here, you." He reached for her, and in seconds she had wriggled out of her jeans like a graceful little fish. He stretched out alongside her, rubbing the crotch of her cotton panties. She wiggled against his hand, feeling her panties dampen under his touch. He worked his hand under the cloth, resting his warm palm against her pubic hair. One finger ventured deeper, into uncharted territory, and Karen pulled away, embarrassed.

"It's okay," he said soothingly. "See? Nobody's gonna hurt you." He guided her hand down to his cock, wrapping her fingers around the shaft. It felt like a tree trunk to her. "There, is that an instrument of torture?" he teased.

"My God, Harry, it's so big!"

He laughed delightedly. "Music to my ears, girl."

Karen was intrigued. She'd never seen a penis up close and personal. "Does it hurt when I touch it?"

"Nope."

"Would it hurt if I rubbed it?"

"Not at all." Harry hastened to relieve her fears. "Try it."

She rubbed experimentally. "Harry, I think it likes it!"

"Sure, it likes you." He stretched out to accommodate her ministrations better. "Oh yeah, that's great, Karen. A little faster . . . harder . . . harder . . ."

"I don't want to hurt you," Karen said doubtfully.

"It's okay!" he panted, head thrown back in ecstasy. "The equipment's designed to take a lot of p-p-p-pressure!"

She rubbed harder. The head of his penis was now a lovely shade of purple. It was so hard that Karen figured it could hit pop flies out of a ball park. There was a little slit on the head, which Karen eyed curiously. As she bent closer, the damn thing spit at her.

"Ugh!" She jumped back, convinced Harry had pissed on her. It wasn't piss, though. She had sticky white stuff on her face. She put out her tongue and tasted something like tears.

Harry was breathing hard. He seemed exhausted. "Harry, are you all right?"

"Oh, yeah." Still sighing contentedly he grabbed his T-shirt from the floor and wiped Karen off. "Such a good girl." He kissed her. "Such a good, sweet girl."

"That's being a good girl?" Karen laughed. "Boy, has my mother been lying to me."

Harry kissed her with renewed vigor. As he held her close, she could feel his cock getting hard again. "Now, I'll be good to you," he promised. He cupped her breasts, kissing them wetly. One hand played between her thighs.

Whenever she became embarrassed, he seemed to sense it almost before she did, murmuring endearments and compliments —such a good girl, such a beautiful girl, such beautiful breasts, nipples, belly button—until she stopped being embarrassed. Until he put his mouth betwen her legs.

"No!" She yanked at his hair. "It's dirty down there!"

Harry looked at her with real pity in his eyes. "You poor kid. It's *beautiful* down there. It looks like . . . " He searched for the right image. "Orchids!"

"Orchids?"

"Well, one orchid." He thought a moment. "Or a pink tiger lily. What's up, tiger lily?" He bent down and nuzzled her.

"Don't, Harry," she protested weakly, ". . . really, don't."

He looked up. *"Really* don't?"

"Nooo."

He grinned and went back to work, lapping at her like she was an ice cream cone. "Mmmm," he gurgled happily, his hands reaching for her breasts. It looked funny, his head buried between her legs while these two detached hands snaked along her body like fast-growing vines. She started laughing, her stomach pumping in and out like a miniature high tide. Then the waves came faster and faster until she fell back, clutching the rumpled blanket, not sure whether she was laughing or crying.

Harry gathered her in his arms, pressing her close. She was sure now. It was crying.

"That was your first one," he said, pride evident in his voice. "You *came.*" He chuckled. "I came again just listening to you. You're a very sexy lady."

Who, me? Karen nuzzled her head just below Harry's chin. She could feel his breathing slow to normal and even out as hers did.

"Harry?"

"Hmmm?"

"What I did to you," she asked him innocently, "what's that called?"

"Uh, you sure you want to know?"

"Yes."

"Well, it's called a hand job. Y'know, you . . . jerked me off. And what I did to you, that's going down. Girls do it to guys, too."

"Hmmm." Karen was thinking. She kissed his neck affectionately. "Okay. I'll try that tomorrow tonight."

He looked at her in feigned shock. "My God, I've created a monster."

She fell asleep, smiling.

Every night, Harry came to Karen's room and performed for her the various numbers in his vast sexual repertoire. She would have done anything he asked, except give up her virginity. Everything in her body was his to touch, tongue, kiss, and fondle. Everything but that one thin membrane. No matter how much he begged, and it did come to that, she stuck to her guns.

Karen couldn't bring herself to tell Harry why she wouldn't let him deflower her; it was an embarrassing, shameful, secret. She wouldn't let him fuck her because he wasn't Jewish and because he was a struggling actor with little hope for the future. And Karen knew that if she gave him that one thing, she could not possibly, ever, walk away from him.

She would have been irrevocably in love with him, and she did not want to be in love with an actor, particularly one of the unemployed variety. She did not want to starve with somebody and watch love die in a studio apartment in the East Village.

This was the shocking truth. In 1972 Karen Bloom took shameful advantage of one Harry Townsend, a sweet, innocent Southern boy.

Of course, Harry thought it was the other way around.

Matt Singer wasn't exactly sure *how* he was going to get Karen Bloom to fall in love with and subsequently marry him. He only knew he was going to. The fact that she and Harry seemed to have had a reasonably torrid affair during the filming didn't faze him. Harry had his own career to worry about; he couldn't devote all his time and energy to courtship. Matt would.

He was unusual. His own mother marveled at him. Never had there been a child so independent, so self-sufficient. At a fairly early age he proved himself quite capable of cooking his own dinner. It wasn't duck à l'orange, but he could broil a chop without setting fire to the house and open a can of peas and carrots without requiring major surgery. He never whined for expensive clothes or a car. He never came home drunk or high. When he wanted something, he worked for it with a quiet intensity that was pleasing to watch. He had a long way to go, but he was all right.

In the whole world only two things frightened Matt Singer. One, that he would never get a chance to display his cinematic abilities. Two, that he would never fall in love. No high school crushes, no posters of movie stars tacked up on his bedroom wall, nothing. Oh, he *liked* girls, had *tons* of them for friends, had even slept with a couple. For some unknown reason though, he had never given his heart. He had never been in love. But when he met Karen, he was quite determined to win her, in his methodical way.

"Hi!"

"Oh, hi!" She always ducked her head in that slightly embarrassed way, pushing a strand of hair behind her right ear. "Been a while, hasn't it, Matt?"

"I haven't seen you since the wrap party." He fell in step beside Karen. She had an armload of books, but he couldn't figure out how to gracefully offer to carry them for her, what with women's liberation and all. Obviously she was perfectly capable of carrying them herself.

"Are you done editing the film?" Karen asked.

"Not yet. By the end of the month, I hope." He threw etiquette to the winds. "Here, give me those books. You look like you're struggling."

"Thanks." She surrendered them gratefully. "I keep forgetting that being liberated does not make you a weight lifter."

"What about lunch?" he asked abruptly.

"What about it?"

"Are you too liberated to let me treat?"

Karen laughed, taking his arm. "I'm too broke to protest. Actually, if you hadn't come along, I was going to skip lunch. Lucky for me."

"Lucky," Matt agreed.

There was no need to tell her how he'd bullshitted his way into the registrar's office and surreptitiously looked up her schedule. Her class had let out ten minutes late. He'd been waiting, patiently, for twenty. "Coffee shop?"

"Sure."

He held the door for her because he figured that if she liked a guy to carry her books, she probably liked a guy to hold doors open. He wasn't going to blow it on a technicality.

They both ordered burgers, coffee for her, a glass of milk for him. She fussed with the coffee a lot. Milk, to dye the coffee to just the right shade of tan. Paper napkin meticulously ripped in half, one half slipped between cup and saucer to prevent unsightly drips. He watched her, mesmerized. The girl had a real sense of order in the world.

Another minor production ensued when the burgers arrived. Carefully she scooped out the contents of the little container of coleslaw onto the burger, further decorating *that* with a measured plop of Heinz's finest. Pleased, she began to eat.

"Do you still see Harry?"

Karen choked a little. "That's a funny thing to ask."

"Not really." Matt shrugged. "He moved, and I just want to keep my contact sheet up to date. I was wondering if maybe you knew what he was up to?"

Karen smiled at her ornamented burger. "You could leave a message on his service, I guess."

"I guess." He was looking at her rather directly.

She sighed. "It's difficult for us to get together. I mean, we're both so damn busy with our careers. Harry left school, you know."

"I know."

"To look for acting work full time," she explained, feeling a little foolish. "Lord," she sighed, "how can it still be so cold when spring is just around the corner?"

Matt shrugged. "March is like that. The days may seem like spring, but the nights are definitely winter. So. About Harry . . . "

She met his eyes. "Harry and I are buddies. Period. If that's what you wanted to know, why didn't you just ask?"

"I did." Matt grinned. "I asked you what Harry was up to. You told me. Thanks."

Mollified somewhat, she went back to her burger. "You were right, Matt."

"Of course I was." He thought a moment. "About what?"

"At the wrap party, when we saw the rushes? The scene when I got splashed?" She sipped coffee daintily. "It was . . . *right.*"

Matt leaned forward intently. "I'm so glad you understand. One thing I know about is making movies."

"Yes," Karen said thoughtfully, "I believe you do." She ducked her head in that embarrassed way. "Sometimes I think that's the big love of your life."

"Nope." He smiled easily. "You are."

"Well! You certainly made my day!" She laughed it off. "I can die a happy woman! The soon-to-be-great director Matt Singer is in love with me!"

"Sure," he said. "Why don't you marry me?"

Karen threw her hands in the air. "How about tomorrow? I can cut astronomy; when am I ever going to need astronomy in my adult life?"

"Not too often," Matt agreed. "Unfortunately, tomorrow's not good for me, not for a wedding, anyway. What about lunch?"

"Tomorrow?"

"Tomorrow."

She couldn't think of a reason to refuse. "All right. But I'm warning you, I'm just like a cat that way. Once you feed me, you may never get rid of me."

Matt smiled. "Promises, promises."

It was Karen's first show in New York City. Not a great show, not even a good show. To tell the truth it was a lousy show with a truly rotten script, a mediocre set, and nonexistent direction. The rest of the cast exhibited a motley assortment of psychological disorders.

But it was a show! Praise the powers that be, she was finally in a show! And they were going to be reviewed.

Karen had forgotten one little detail. She was a god-awful actress in a god-awful show. The reviewer picked up this little tidbit of information like it was the game ball at the Super Bowl and ran with it. He unabashedly, wantonly, joyfully crucified her in print. The reviewer wrote that he had a Chippendale desk that was less wooden than the performance turned in by the unfortunate Miss Bloom. He would up his review with the fervent hope that Miss Bloom would limit her acting to doing impressions of furniture because that was obviously her forte.

Karen cried a lot. Not only was she hurt, she was mortified. Everyone else in the show had most certainly read the review. They all seemed terribly sympathetic, but Karen could see the thinly veiled triumph in their eyes. She vowed never to return to the theater. Her feet insistently carried her there. She went on, but her confidence (what little had been there to start with) was crushed. In the vernacular, she stunk. Worse, she had invited Matt to the show, so there was a witness to her failure. He found her crying in the communal dressing room. She held out her arms to him blindly.

"Help me," she sobbed. "Make me a good actress."

He held her until the flood of tears subsided. "First thing, a lousy review, even when justified, only means you were bad in one show in one theater on one particular night. Okay?"

She nodded, sniffling into his shirt.

"Okay. Second thing, you *are* good. You may even be very good. You will be working long after this show and these people are a bad memory.

"Third and last, I can't make you a good actress. Nobody ever teaches anyone else a thing. They can only tell you how they got there. And that just doesn't matter. Make your own rules and have the guts to stick to them. If you screw up, even on stage, you'll survive and you'll *learn.* You're pretty tough, Karen; it's part of your charm. Uh, you can blow your nose on my sleeve; I really don't mind."

"Thanks." She blew away, then made a nice effort to gather her shredded dignity into a manageable pile. "What can I do to be better in this show?"

He went through the usual facial contortions that signified deep thought in the mind of Matt Singer. "This is what you do: relax. Above all, relax. Don't play the jokes. They're so pallid, they might as well be invisible. Chances are nobody will notice they're gone. Make her lighter, more flirtatious. It'll make you look good, and that's all we care about. As for your fellow actors, since they're not giving you any help out there, fuck 'em. Don't set up their jokes, don't give an inch."

"I don't care to do that," Karen said stubbornly.

"Karen, when somebody shits on you, fair play goes out the window."

"No," she said. "That's my rule, and I stick to it."

"Karen." He kissed the top of her head. "I guess that's why I love you."

"Oh, Matt, I—"

"No." He cut her off. "What you are is grateful. I know you don't love me just yet. But you will. You'd be silly not to."

Karen laughed. "Okay, let's blow this dump."

The next show she was a little better. No one commented, no reviewer was present, no mention was made. But Karen knew, and it was a private victory. Not a gift from Matt. It was an important distinction, and it made her understand a lot of things. If there was a moment, a pinpoint in time when she really did begin to fall in love with Matt, it was the moment of that understanding.

And he was Jewish. It would have been a lie to say that that didn't make it easier to fall in love with him. And loving Matt Singer was starting to look like a sweet deal.

So why was she still thinking of Harry?

Harry seemed to be on everyone's mind. A few weeks after Karen's disastrous review, Matt gave his old leading man a call.

Though his days at NYU seemed like ancient history, Harry agreed to meet Matt at the school because A) he wanted to see what Matt had completed of the film so far, and B) Harry regarded his relationship with Matt as insurance. *Just in case* Matt ever got anywhere, Harry wanted the option of going along for the ride.

Matt greeted him with about as much warmth as anybody got from the young director. "Sit down. I've only got about five minutes done, that's all I can show you."

Harry enjoyed it anyway. He always liked to watch himself and it was obvious that even as a neophyte director, Matt knew how to flatter an actor's profile. "Looks pretty good to me. Karen looks great on film."

"Yes," Matt nodded absently. "You know I asked her to take a look at this screenplay I've been working on and in no time flat she had straightened out all my problems, storyline, character development, the works. Even that change I made in our film, in the hitchhiking scene, I wouldn't have thought of that without Karen. She kind of inspired me."

"So," Harry said delicately, "you guys are . . . seeing each other?"

"Yes."

"Well, that's great." *Why don't I feel great about this?* Harry wondered. In a way he liked Matt, and he certainly respected his abilities; he just got the feeling that Matt went home, peeled off his skin and hung it up in the closet. The guy could be a little detached, not exactly sub-human, but . . . Karen was all too human. "She's a really sweet girl."

"You look awfully surprised, Harry."

"I'm not."

"Don't take this the wrong way, but you're not that good an actor. Strange as this may seem, I really do respect your opinion concerning Karen. She considers you a good friend."

Harry couldn't help but feel pleased. "I feel the same about her."

"So why do you think my seeing Karen is so strange?"

"Because the two of you are so different," Harry hedged. "You're real single-minded about the career, and I always had the feeling Karen would chuck it for the house and kids routine."

"You don't know her as well as you think you do."

"Maybe," Harry conceded. "It's just . . . well, she's a lot more emotional than you are. You're . . . ," *from another planet,* "kind of reserved."

"I love Karen. Just because I don't display my feelings openly doesn't mean I don't have them. Everyone in my family is a emotional exhibitionist. They scream a lot, wave their hands around, and nothing ever gets done. I'm just different. Does that seem so strange?"

"No." Still, Harry felt very uneasy. Why was he so concerned about Karen's future anyway? She would probably marry her nice Jewish NYU student, move to Scarsdale, raise some nice kids and he'd never see her again. Good. Great. Girls like Karen could be a real pain. Girls like that weren't happy until they got married. And yet . . . she'd been so sweet in bed with him. He'd sort of loved her a little bit then.

"I don't think you're going to make her happy, Matt," he said plainly. "I know you believe you love her, *she* may even believe it, but I sure as hell don't."

"You're wrong!" Frustration showed on Matt's face. "I really care for Karen. She's the only girl I've ever felt this way about."

Harry shrugged. "I'm not the one you have to convince. I don't know why you feel the need to talk about this shit with me anyway."

"Just wanted to let you know."

"What the fuck for?"

"In case you were thinking of giving me a little competition."

He started to laugh. "Jesus. One word from me and you think she'd come running. Karen doesn't want a guy like me. She wants stability."

"So do I, Harry."

"Then you'll both be very happy together." He couldn't seem to stop himself. "I just think—" What? That maybe Karen was better off with him? "Ah, I don't know shit about people."

"And here I thought you were a real student of human nature." Matt's eyes glittered.

"Guess not."

"I wish I could make you understand how much Karen means to me. I work better, I think better—"

Sounds like a new wonder drug, Harry thought sourly. *That's not love, is it?* Painstakingly he searched Matt's earnest face. *Maybe it is—for him.*

He held out his hand to Matt. "Hey, good luck. She's a great girl. You're a lucky guy." His mind started playing movies again, private screenings, only one customer. He could call Karen. Matt was right; if Harry called, she'd come running. He could save her from a fate worse than death. In a moment however, his sanity returned and he realized that it was none of his damn business.

"THE SLIP comes off," Mac said firmly, "and the little Lollipop panties, too."

Lake looked to Daniel for support, but he ducked out of the room, laughing a little.

"The slip," Mac said. She was a tough old bird, and she hadn't made a name for herself as a top designer by being a pussycat. She was doing Dan Fox a big favor, coming to his apartment to outfit his newest little tootsie. Still, it looked like this time Danny boy had grabbed the brass ring.

Mac snapped her fingers, and her little assistant scurried forward and dropped a dress over Lake's head. It was a silvery green floor-length gown, heavily beaded. It weighed forty pounds and squashed her breasts flat against her rib cage. Mac peeled the dress away from Lake's body and sewed in a pair of falsies with quick basting stitches. Lake wondered if even Raquel Welch's boobs could stand up to forty pounds of bugle beads. Mac eyed Lake critically, then slapped her sharply between the shoulder blades. "Stand up straight."

"This dress weighs a ton," Lake complained.

The designer laughed. "Suffer." She gave Lake another whack on the back and sent her out to the living room.

Daniel took one look. "No," he said shortly. Lake could have kissed him.

"Why not?" Mac exploded. "That dress is a knockout."

"That dress," Daniel said serenely, "is trying too hard. Here." Carelessly he grabbed a dress from the gaudy pile strewn on the couch and tossed it to Lake. "Try that one."

She loved it. It was uncanny how Daniel seemed to know her

taste. She came prancing out of the bedroom, spinning around, showing herself off. The copper color of the dress curiously set off her skin and hair, making her look like molten gold. The short length was light and comfortable. The style was fairly demure, until you got the back view. The back was almost completely bare, stopping just short of the cleft of her ass. Lake posed *à la* Betty Grable, peeping over her shoulder. "Notice the lovely Lakeside view?"

Daniel turned to Mac. "Why didn't you show me that one first?" he asked softly.

The little assistant sat up very straight.

Mac shrugged. "Didn't think it was right."

Daniel walked over to the assistant, eyes level with hers. "What do you think?"

"It looks beautiful," she said quickly, looking anxiously at Mac.

"Did you think it wasn't right, like Mac said?"

The little assistant knew she was being pushed. She'd fought so hard just to get her job with Mac, and Mac had a difficult nature. She wasn't going to blow it now.

"We agreed," Mac said, twisting the knife, "that that's a tough color for a blonde to carry."

"Did you?" Daniel asked the assistant, an amused smile playing around his lips.

"Yes. Mac and I agreed." The assistant started gathering up the discarded dresses. "I'll take these down to the car." Mouselike, she left.

"You old bastard," Mac yelped, pummeling Daniel on the shoulder. "Trying to steal my talent?"

"Why not?" Daniel laughed. "You've been stealing your assistants' designs for years. What's amazing is how long it takes them to wise up. Looks like this one's going to take it for a long time."

Mac grinned. "I only hire people who are terrified to leave me." She gathered up the rest of the clothing that had not met with Daniel's approval. It was quite a pile. She gave Lake a queer grin. "Lake, dear, I'd say stay as sweet as you are"—she winked at Daniel—"but I'm too much of a realist. 'Bye all."

"You must be tired. Why don't you take a bath?" Daniel settled down with one of his scripts, and within seconds was deeply absorbed.

"You knew that assistant designed the dress," Lake said

slowly. "You knew Mac was taking advantage of her talent and inexperience."

"Hell, yes." Daniel spoke a little irritably. He hated to be disturbed when he was working. "Mac ran dry years ago. All she's got left is a name and a formidable reputation. I gave the assistant a chance to gamble on her own talent. She chose to play it safe, stick with Mac."

"Why didn't you just help her?"

He put down his script. "She didn't ask. If you want something, you have to ask."

"I didn't ask for you," Lake said, half joking.

"You don't have me." He got up, went into the bathroom, and started to run the water. "You'll feel better after you bathe. There's some nice bath oil here. Help yourself. I have to work."

She slipped out of the shimmering copper dress and stood before him, naked and willing.

"Come on," he chided gently, "get in before the water gets cold."

Embarrassed, she crossed her arms over her breasts and tried to shrink into the wallpaper.

"Lake." He took her hands. "You know you are lovely and desirable. Now take your bath!"

She got into the tub obediently and started splashing around with a woebegone expression. He started to laugh. "What would make you happy?" He rubbed her shoulders.

Ravish me. "I don't want to go to this party."

"It'll be fun." He dribbled oil into the water. "You can tell them all about the ski season on Mars and laugh at their bewildered expressions." He stood abruptly. "I really must get to work."

She splashed aimlessly for a few minutes. Usually a hot bath relaxed her, but just being with Daniel kept her keyed up. She toweled off quickly and joined him in the living room. Again he had returned to his private world, where she couldn't intrude. She touched his hand. He flicked her away absently. She persisted.

He eyed her evenly. "What is it you want?"

Lake sighed. "Take a wild guess," she said sweetly.

"You want something, you have to ask for it."

She hooked her fingers around one of the couch's loose pillows. "Daniel," she said in the same honeyed tones, "fuck me!" She slammed the pillow into his face and fled, screaming in mock terror. He snagged the edge of her towel and pulled it away from her body. She couldn't match his strength, and he quickly pinned her, squirming, to the carpet.

"You want to play rough?" He knotted the towel loosely around her wrists.

"Oh, nooo!" Lake howled. "Not that!" Her toes dug at his jeans insistently. "Get those pants off, mister. I'm giving the orders around here."

"Oh, yeah?" He laughed, unbuckling his belt. "Who tied up whom?" He playfully bit her shoulder.

"Careful, don't mark the merchandise." She slipped her arms out of the towel and reached for him, but he grabbed her wrists and threw his full weight against her. He was a big man, and she couldn't budge. He raised up and stared at her, smoldering.

"Daniel, you nut," she said with a laugh, "what are you doing?"

He wouldn't answer. He waited until fear began to seep into her eyes and then swooped, laughing, to kiss her neck, her eyelids, her collarbone sculpting the flesh into plains and valleys. "Tell me what you want me to do to you," he whispered, face buried against her navel.

She told him. She told him in the language of the gutter. No matter what she asked, he complied. Lake wasn't inexperienced, but most of the men she'd been with had treated her like a fragile little doll. Daniel seemed to be trying to inhale her. She felt his teeth and nails raking at her, and she liked it. She liked listening to her voice rising into an animal scream. She liked the insanity.

"Yes," she growled, laughing in his ear. "Yes, yes, yes!" He exploded in her and then flopped down next to her, breathing heavily.

He reached over her to grab the towel and draped it across their legs. "Sleep." He curled up next to her, penis glued to her ass. Cozy. Soon his breathing became even and regular.

"Daniel?"

No response.

"Daniel." Annoyed, she speared him with her elbow.

"What?" he sighed.

"You said I didn't have you."

"You don't. But you will."

"When?" she whispered. "When?"

He smiled, eyes closed. "When I have you."

"Body and soul?" She tried to sound light.

He was asleep and would not answer.

"How do I look?" It had to be the tenth time she'd asked.

"Perfect," Daniel said calmly. "Perfect." He cupped her chin in his hands in the old, much-loved gesture. "Party masks on!"

She smiled, practicing, as they stepped out of the limo. The doorman nodded respectfully and ushered them into the elevator. The building was quite old but beautifully kept up; the mahogany bench in the elevator was well polished, its pillow invitingly plumped. The elevator opened directly into the penthouse. Striking but ostentatious, Lake thought as she handed her wrap to a liveried servant. Definitely a show of what her father would call "new money."

"Look sharp," Daniel said. "Here comes your host."

A heavyish man in his fifties, wearing a well-cut tuxedo that looked a little ridiculous on his blocky form, was approaching them, eyes fastened on Lake. He was, Lake remembered, an Extremely Rich Person. ERPs, Karen called them.

Lake shook his hand politely. "Thank you so much for inviting me to your home."

He beamed. "My pleasure, dear." Hungrily he stared at her copper-clad breasts. Lake sighed. Only a true ERP could get away with such behavior. "I'm very happy to have a future movie star standing right next to me. A year from now I'll have to make an appointment to see you. An appointment at the box office, ha-ha!" He nudged her slyly, doing his damnedest to graze her breast. Restlessly her eyes scanned the crowd.

"Matt!" she yelled. "Hey, Matt!" She turned to the two men. "Would you excuse me?" she asked and ran off, her long, smooth back flashing whitely against the copper of her dress.

Matt was at the bar. His sweater, patterned to resemble a tuxedo front, didn't quite jibe with the other guests' black tie. He didn't look too happy. "The usual," he instructed the bartender. With a straight face the bartender poured a tall glass of milk and presented it to him.

"Hello, Lake," Matt said. "Nice dress."

"What are you doing here?" Lake asked, delighted to see a friendly face.

"The host is my uncle," Matt said glumly. "I'm supposed to be making future contacts, but I'm not very good at this. I wish Karen were here, but she's got a show tonight."

They both looked at the milling guests, furiously wheeling and dealing. "Some party," Lake said doubtfully.

"Mmmm," Matt agreed. "Tons of ERPs."

They both laughed.

She realized Matt was looking over her shoulder with a thoughtful expression. Lake whirled around. Daniel was watching them. Carefully. Intensely, with no readable expression on his face.

"Your escort?" Matt said in a low voice.

Lake nodded slowly. "Matt? What do you know about Dan Fox?"

"Fact or fiction?"

"Both, please."

"Okay. He really is a fine writer—does thorough research, has an understanding of character that is unbelievable. He knows everybody in the business and has tremendous influence. When he bets, he wins. He's charming, intelligent, a fascinating conversationalist. Married once, divorced. I think she lives in France. A sculptress. Refuses to discuss him."

"Discreet lady," Lake murmured, signaling the bartender for a glass of champagne.

"Or a terrified one," Matt said. "I think Daniel Fox is crazy. Certifiable."

"Fact or fiction?" Lake said coolly.

"All right," Matt admitted, "it's just my humble opinion. He loves controlling people. If he can't get them to do what he wants by his influence, he finds *other* ways. I see a great potential for violence in him."

"You're wrong," Lake said sullenly. "He's wonderful. He makes me feel alive. Those are just rumors from jealous rivals. Anyone who's doing well in this business has a few enemies."

Matt shrugged. "You asked, so I told you. Watch your step. Karen will kill me if I let anything happen to you."

Daniel appeared at her side. "There are other people here you should meet." Without a word to Matt, Daniel grabbed Lake's hand and towed her along behind him.

"Hello, Winston." Daniel saluted a sixtyish man who wore his thick white hair combed straight back from his high forehead like an orchestra conductor. He looked bored.

"Daniel." They shook hands warily. Dead silence, punctuated by the cheerful conversations of the party going on around them.

"This is Lake."

Winston did not offer her his hand. He didn't even look at her. "I know what you're up to, Daniel," he said coldly, "and I don't care for it one bit. I choose my students carefully, only the most promising graduates of the foremost drama schools. I have no intention of playing acting coach to your latest conquest."

"I'm much too well brought up to slap you," Lake said angrily, "so, if you'll excuse me . . . " She poured her drink over his beautiful hair and walked away in her copper-colored dress. It was a great walking-away dress.

"Well?" Daniel grinned. "Is she motivated enough for you, Win?"

The acting teacher wiped champagne from his eyes ruefully. "She's definitely got more fire than the average bubblehead you favor. But I can't promise anything, Dan. There's no telling if she has any talent; the pretty ones rarely do."

"That's your prejudice, you pretentious snob. You'll coach her?"

"You knew I would." Winston curried his hair with his long fingers. "We know each other's secrets, Dan. How can I refuse you? Oh, well, might be a challenge."

"You won't be sorry, Win. This one is different."

"Yes." Winston eyed Daniel closely. "I believe she is. I've never seen you so—" His sharp eyes picked out Lake, cooling her heels at the entrance, still wearing a murderous expression. "You'd better hurry, Dan. I think your young lady—"

But Fox was ahead of him. He saw Matt helping Lake on with her coat at the elevator.

Smoothly he cut between them. "I think you've had enough party."

Stubbornly Matt held his ground.

"It's all right, Matt." Lake dismissed him. He slouched away reluctantly, still watching them.

"You have to get up early tomorrow," Daniel said lightly. "Winston is a stickler for punctuality."

Her mouth practically flew open. "After the way he treated me, what on earth makes you think I'd study with him?"

"Because I'm telling you to," Daniel said pleasantly, "and you trust my judgment."

"I'm tired of your games, Daniel." She tried to get the elevator door to close so he couldn't get in. She knew how it would infuriate him. But he was too quick.

"You love my games." His hands caressed her bare back. "Games are fun and exciting, aren't they?" His eyes bored into her like rivets. Her body grew cold with fear, and peering around the edge of that fear was a terrible excitement. He pushed her down onto the mahogany bench and pulled the copper dress up around her hips.

The elevator landed with a hydraulic hiss on the main floor. Lake pushed Daniel away and bolted past the astonished doorman and into the street. She could hear Daniel behind her, running easily, laughing from time to time. She felt cold air on her teeth and realized she was laughing, too.

It *was* a game, a wonderful game—fantasies sprung to life. She was a defector fleeing over the border to political asylum and her yearning lover. She was a doe flushed from her thicket by cruel hunters. She was a great hero, once loved, now falsely accused, desperately trying to find sanctuary, banging on midnight doors behind which the public who had deserted her huddled in cowardice.

She dashed into the street, into the headlights of a truck. Part of her mind registered a squeaky sound. Haunted house doors. No, no, a truck's brakes squealing. She stared up at the cab, where a man's head had suddenly grown.

"Jesus, lady!" the man yelled. "Didn't you see me coming? I coulda killed you!"

She tapped the engine grill. It blew warm air in her face. "Close," she told the grill, "but no cigar."

"Take her home, Mac," the truck driver called to Daniel. "Let her sleep it off."

"I'm not drunk," she insisted as Daniel led her away from the traffic. "I just felt . . . "

"Invincible."

"Invulnerable." She kissed him quickly. "I used to read Superman comics."

"That is my magic spell," he whispered against her ear. "Nothing can hurt you while I am here."

It was crazy; it had to be crazy. They walked through Central Park at three in the morning. She dragged her coat in one hand, loving the feel of cold air on her bare back.

"You're a veritable treasure trove," he said with a laugh. "Platinum"—he touched her hair—"copper"—the dress—"white gold"—fingers shivered on her back. He took the coat from her hand and spread it under a tree. She sat down on it, working her dress up over her hips. She wore no underwear, just a garter belt and stockings. Between her spread legs the platinum triangle gleamed. "Feels good," Lake murmured, pulling the dress off her shoulders. She stuck a finger in herself, then offered it to him. He licked it clean and came to her, hurriedly lowering his pants. He slid into her, teasingly grinding his hips, stirring her insides. She was all liquid, dripping onto the lining of her coat. She kissed him, stroking the roof of his mouth with her tongue. His rhythm became faster, and she grabbed double handfuls of his hair and sucked on his tongue furiously.

Suddenly she opened her eyes and shrieked. Standing above Daniel was a man wearing a ski mask. He was holding a knife.

"Gimme your money, man. I want the watch, too, and the cunt's jewelry."

Daniel started to get up.

"Slowly, man, slowly."

He kept his movements slow, reaching for his wallet. Then he reached out and closed his hand *on* the blade. His other hand slammed into his attacker's stomach. As the man buckled, Daniel pounded into him again, heedless of his injured hand. He began to laugh, deep and low in his throat. The mugger scrambled to his feet and ran.

Lake had been watching quietly. She got to her feet and having no cloth to bind his wound, pressed her own hand over the cut. "Why?" she whispered. "You could have just given him the money."

"I won't have things taken from me," he said simply.

The telephone jangled insistently in the Sunday morning still of the apartment.

Karen raced to answer it, knowing how Lake's customary hangover was progressing.

"Hello?" she whispered into the receiver.

"Hi! It's a beautiful day! Aren't you guys up yet? I've got breakfast right here." Karen smiled at Matt's cheerful voice on the other end of the line.

Lake stumbled into the living room, making little mewing sounds. She stared malevolently at the phone in Karen's hand. "Whoever that is, have them shot."

"It's Matt. He's got breakfast."

"Good stuff," Matt promised, "and a surefire hangover cure."

Karen related this information to her hurting roomie.

"What's he pushing this week?" Lake demanded suspiciously.

"Nova Scotia lox."

Lake moaned. "Nothing personal, Karen. I'm just not up to Jewish soul food."

"Come right over," Karen said into the phone, hanging up quickly. "You need some cheerful company," she said to Lake with equal speed, "after hanging out with Foxy all night."

"Arghhh . . . " Lake said indistinctly.

"Come on, you like Matt, don't you?"

"More than you like Daniel," the blonde said sweetly.

"Oh, please, let's not fight over him again." Karen looked anxious. "He's just a bit of a ghoul, you know? Somber. You need the Singer and Bloom comedy team to perk you up!"

"Bloom and Singer," Lake corrected. She tugged Karen's hair affectionately. "Okay, doctor, whatever you say. Why don't you scoot into the bathroom and put some blush on before the boyfriend gets here."

"Nooo!" Karen screamed in mock terror, crumpling her lithe body into a fair approximation of Quasimodo. "He mustn't see me without my makeup!" She limped off to the bathroom. Before Matt got there, she managed to put on blush, mascara, and lip gloss. She even managed to get the lip gloss off her fingers so she could open the door when he buzzed.

"Morning!" she sang, taking the paper bag from him and standing on tiptoe to receive a kiss. She spirited the bag away to the kitchen while Lake mumbled an appropriate greeting.

"And for you, Miss Eastman . . . " He offered her the contents of another, smaller paper bag. "I slipped into your neighborhood bar and asked the bartender to whip up his favorite, time-tested hangover cure."

Lake skeptically eyed the Styrofoam cup in the bag. "What is it?"

"Looks like tomato juice, smells like tomato juice, but it's *not*—"

"I don't want to know." Lake cut him off. "At this point I'll try anything."

"Lake!" Karen yelled from the kitchen. "Can you give me a hand?"

The blonde waved her cup at Matt. "Thanks, you're a pal." She shuffled into the kitchen, where Karen was busily preparing coffee. They both wore their big fluffy slippers.

"Let me do that." Lake smiled. "You make shitty coffee."

"I'm so offended I may shrivel up and die," Karen said blithely. "Isn't he terrific? In your honest opinion, of course."

Lake sipped her tomato juice. "Marry him."

"Yeah?"

"Absolutely." Lake nodded. "I think one of us should get married, and I've decided it should be you. Besides, Matt's intelligent and charming, and he adores you."

"Yes, he does," Karen said modestly. "Not that I can figure out why."

"Stop that or I'll puke on you."

"How unladylike." They both giggled. Suddenly Karen got serious. "If I do get married, would you be my maid of honor?"

Lake was genuinely touched. "I would be happy to." She touched Karen's arm.

Karen darted forward and hugged Lake. "I love you. Do you know that?"

"Oh, honey." Lake felt herself dangerously close to tears. "Why does it sound so easy when you say it?"

"Well, well," Matt said in his amused way, "I should have brought my camera. You guys should see yourselves getting all weepy over the lox. If I'd known you were so emotional, I'd have stuck with the whitefish."

"Lake eats whitefish now," Karen piped in.

"Sure," the blonde said sheepishly. "I even eat gefilte fish. Next, stuffed derma."

Matt grimaced. "*I* wouldn't eat that stuff."

"Gangway." Karen squeezed past with a laden tray, leaving Matt and Lake in the kitchen.

"So tell me, Matt," Lake said smartly, "would you happen to have an older brother stashed away somewhere?"

He looked at her with an odd expression. "No offense, Lake, but girls like you never seem to want guys like me until you see us being nice to somebody else. Then, all of a sudden, you feel terribly lonely and unloved."

"Thanks for the insight," Lake said coolly. "I'm sure it'll give Daniel a laugh or two."

Matt saluted her. "Glad to be of assistance. Humor is key in a relationship." He went out to join Karen at the table. "Hey, gorgeous." He stroked her hair.

She looked up, smiling shyly. "Who, me?"

"Yes, you. How 'bout the movies tonight?"

"Great!" Karen smeared cream cheese on a bagel half. "Ummm . . . Lake?" She waved to Lake to join them. "Would you and Daniel like to join us?"

Lake laughed shortly. "I don't think so. Thanks, anyway."

They both looked relieved. "Come on," Lake cried. "Is he that bad?"

"No, no, no," Karen said hastily. "We just like *you* better. You come to the movies with us."

"I think I'll pass. Oh, the coffee. I forgot all about it." But Lake didn't go directly to the kitchen. She went to the phone and hating herself all the time, dialed Daniel's number. Hung up. Dialed again.

A woman answered, sleep heavy in her voice. Lake slammed the phone down. She let a second crawl by, then acting involuntarily, dialed again.

". . . you've reached the answering machine of Daniel Fox. I'm not in right now . . . "

She hung up.

"Lake?" Karen sat down on the floor. "Is something wrong?"

"Nothing." *Everything.*

"Come out with us tonight," Karen implored. "We'll have fun, the three of us."

"The three of us," Lake repeated. She made her mind slow down. There was a reason, probably a very good one. Things happened with good cause. Besides, relationships hinged on trust. Karen trusted Matt with her life. All she had to do was trust. There, she was better now.

She went out with them. It was just as bad as she had imagined.

9

"MY PARENTS are out of town for a while," Matt said. He didn't say it with a leer, but she got the message. The parental mansion, with hot and cold running beds, was up for grabs. For weeks Karen had been stalling Matt's innocent advances. His dorm room was too small, too dirty, too cramped, too small, too . . .

"Won't your folks be mad if you have a girl over while they're gone?" she faltered.

"Are you kidding? My father would be thrilled. For a bar mitzvah gift he got me a subscription to *Playboy.* Come on," he coaxed, "I'll broil something and open up a can of peas and carrots. Gourmet living."

In the space of four seconds, her mind ran down her options like a rat in a maze. She could decline Matt's invitation completely, in which case she'd better have a darn good excuse. She could accept, and if things got too heavy, sweetly tell him she had a yeast infection or her period.

No good. The dauntless Singer could decide to slog his way through either problem. Men were very resourceful when it came to a little nookie. The only viable solutions were to either flatly tell him no or go through with it. Idly she wished for the fortuitous entrance of a mad scientist who would transfer Matt's psyche into Harry's gorgeous body.

"Okay," she said slowly, "but let's order in Chinese."

"But I don't speak Chinese." He laughed at his own joke. "Okay. See you whenever you get here. 'Bye."

" 'Bye."

She found herself staring into her bedroom closet. Hmmm, what do you wear to a seduction, anyway? She had a nice pink button-down-the-front blouse, but that made her too accessible, and she didn't want him thinking she was easy. As for leotards, well, they were tricky. There you were thinking you were practically rape-proof, but one good tug at the old scoop neck, and the hooters were let loose on an unsuspecting public. No leotards, she decided; they were too much of a tease. Nothing with ruffles, either. She could just see Matt chewing on her frills as he vainly tried to figure out how she'd gotten in there in the first place. After all, she didn't want to discourage him *completely*.

After much deliberation she chose a mauve sweater. It had a high neck, ending in a soft picot stitch at her throat, but it also had a long back zipper. Then, to further confuse him, Karen put on a bra that hooked in the front. Just in case she wanted to chicken out.

Just as she was leaving the apartment, the phone rang. "Oh, poop." Karen raced back to grab the phone. "Hello?"

"Hey, it's me!" a jubilant voice proclaimed.

"Harry?"

"You bet!" he crowed. "And I've got great news!"

"What's the terrific news?"

"I gave the best audition of my life today." He took a deep breath. "I know the producers were impressed. It's down to me and *one* other guy, but I know I'm going to get it; I can *feel* it."

Right then and there Karen got a pretty strong feeling herself, a bad one. "You don't know how this thing's going to turn out, Harry—"

"I can feel it in my bones," Harry said insistently. "So when I was thinking who I wanted to celebrate my good fortune with, naturally I thought of you. After I get off from my waiter job, I'm going to take you someplace strange and wonderful. How do you feel about Indonesian food?"

I'm sure it goes well with Chinese takeout, Karen thought dismally. "I have plans for the evening."

"Oh." He was quiet, thinking. "Then join me later for a drink."

Now she was quiet.

"Please?"

"Sure, Harry," she said warmly. "Where shall I meet you?"

"I may get out of work late, so just let yourself into my apartment. One twenty-six Sullivan Street, apartment three B. I always leave the key under the mat. Karen?"

"Yes?"

"I'm real glad to be seeing you again." He hung up.

"Oh, poop," Karen said, about nothing in particular. She went back into the bedroom, pulling the mauve sweater over her head. She found an ivory V-neck that she'd always thought was a little too low-cut and put that on. At her throat she knotted a silk scarf of the same shade.

As she brushed her hair, she looked at her reflection in the mirror. "You have no idea what you're doing, do you?" she asked her reflection. "Ha! Easy for you to say. I'm the one who's going to pay for your antics."

She turned off the lights and carefully locked the door behind her.

"That's a really nice sweater," Matt said, consigning the last of the subgum wonton to the garbage.

Karen winced. "You've already said that."

"Have I?"

"Six times."

Matt studied her. "Well, it is a nice sweater. Not your usual style."

She threw silverware into the sink with wild abandon. "Oh, for Pete's sake, it's just a sweater. How can it be usual or not?"

Matt thought this out with his customary deliberation. "Well, usually," he said slowly, "you've covered up to your chin. I never knew you had collarbones. Really, I'm very flattered you dressed up for me."

If you only knew, you poor deluded man. "Well, I'm glad you're glad." She drifted into the living room and turned on the television.

Matt's parents had a very large coffee table with a variety of adult toys on top of it. There was a large chunk of coral, two small chunks of coral that had once been part of the larger piece, an oversize brandy snifter filled with souvenir matchbooks, and a cigarette lighter in the shape of a gleaming stainless-steel apple.

It was that gleaming apple that fascinated Karen. She was turning it over and over in her hands when Matt sat down beside her on the couch.

"Put that down. You'll set fire to something one of these days, I know it." He took the apple out of her hands and set it down on the table. Leaning across the coffee table, he flipped channels until the familiar theme of *Hawaii Five-O* blared through the apartment.

"Book 'em, Danno," Matt advised the TV set, adjusting the

volume to a low level. He put his arm around Karen, and she snuggled against him. He turned to her. "Don't you think Danno should book 'em?"

"Book 'em, Danno," she agreed, a little tiredly. Enough audience participation already. Was she going to be ravished or not? She leaned forward, lightly running her tongue along his lips.

"Stop reading those dirty books, Karen," Matt frowned. "I can't keep up with you."

She giggled and bit his ear.

"Ow! You little runt!" He pushed her down onto the couch, one long arm pillowing her head, his mouth glued to hers. His other hand was under her sweater, inching toward her breasts. Rhodes scholar that he was, it did not take him long to figure out that her bra hooked in the front. He was eating a lot of wool in the process, but he was getting there. After a moment she impatiently pulled the sweater over her head.

Karen unbuttoned his shirt and pulled it free of his pants so they could crush their bare chests together. She could feel the crotch of his jeans tighten as he came erect. She rubbed the bulge, and in response he thrust his tongue deeper into her mouth. He moved her legs apart slightly, laying his long body on top of hers. As he hugged her tighter, Karen got the sneaking suspicion that he was—

"Watching TV?" Karen screamed. "I'm getting all hot and bothered, and you're watching TV over my shoulder? Matt, how could you?"

He sat up, looking very uncomfortable. "I'm sorry, but it was some really interesting camera work. It just sort of caught my eye."

"I'm lying here half-naked, and you're watching camera angles?" Angrily she squirmed into her sweater. "Thanks a lot, Matt, thanks a lot!" She hunched forward and started toying with the apple.

He watched her patiently. "Karen, what's on your mind?"

"You."

"Really?" He seemed flattered. "I'm causing all this consternation?"

"I'm just not sure what's going on with us. Maybe you don't like me, maybe I'm not like the girls you dated in high school.

"I didn't date a lot in high school," he said. "How about you?"

"Not a lot," she admitted.

"So we're even." He took the apple from her hand and put it back in its rightful place.

"Why don't you marry me?"

"What?"

"You heard me. I'm a nice guy, I can cook, I'm crazy about you—"

"Are you?"

"Of course," he said, annoyed. "Can't you tell?"

"Not always."

"Because I don't jump on your bones every chance I get?"

"Something along those lines."

"I love you more than anything, Karen. I don't know what to say to make you understand that. Being rich and successful wouldn't be any fun without you and I *am* going to be rich and successful. That's another reason why you should marry me. I'm a great investment."

"Like IBM." Her voice was overly bright. Well, this is it, she told herself, this is what you've always wanted.

"Marry me, Karen. I love you and I'll take good care of you."

"I need time to think, Matt." She saw his face fall. "Just tonight. Can you meet me tomorrow morning? We can have breakfast."

"I have classes until two. How about three o'clock at the coffeeshop on West Fourth?"

"All right."

"Think you'll be able to give me an answer then?"

She nodded feeling trapped. This was going to be the most important decision of her life. Why was she so confused? It should be an easy choice. Matt was perfect for her.

Matt got her jacket and helped her into it. "Brownie points," he winked at her. "Figure I better rack 'em up while I can." He walked her to the door, kissing her lightly. "Say yes," he urged her.

"Tomorrow," she managed to stammer. "I'll give you my answer tomorrow." She ran all the way to the subway.

Harry wasn't in yet. His window faced toward the street, and she could see it was still dark.

Karen raced up the steps, found the key under the mat, and let herself into Harry's apartment. Not knowing exactly what to do, she sat rather gingerly on the edge of Harry's bed. It felt strange to be alone in someone else's apartment.

The place was Spartan neat. It wasn't so much that Harry was such a good housekeeper; he had so little that it would have taken a dedicated slob to make the place look like a wreck. No books, just a neat pile of theatrical scripts on top of a large dictionary.

Stuck into a corner of the mirror on top of the bureau was a photo of Harry with his arm around a girl. They were holding up an obviously homemade cake that bore crooked icing letters. "Happy Birthday, Harry and Jackie." The girl looked so much like him. A twin sister.

She opened the top bureau drawer. Underwear, socks, most of it in pretty bad shape. In the second drawer she found a loose-leaf ring binder. The way it was scribbled up, Karen figured it went back to high school days, maybe earlier. Inside, in a manila envelope, the kind any actor uses to send out his picture and résumé, was a packet of letters. The return address was the same on all of them.

MRS. JACKIE HABER
261 ORCHARD ST.
SALINA, KANSAS

She opened one at random.

Dear Harry,

Hi! How's the famous actor? Is New York as wonderful as I always thought it would be? It sure does feel funny to have my twinny so far away for the first time ever. I was telling Mommy, and she just laughed and said we'd keep in touch with that crazy radar we have. I guess so. I keep thinking how you knew I was going to marry Douglas. It sure was a surprise to me! Still is sometimes.

Anyways, radar or no, I expect lots of letters and so does Mommy, though she don't admit it. Is your apartment nice? Living in Greenwich Village sounds so glamorous . . .

She put down the letter and sifted through the pile until she found one with a recent date.

Dear Harry,

So low today, I really wouldn't bother writing. Oh, Harry, you don't know how smart you were to run while you could. I can't believe God ever invented a place like Salina, Kansas, unless it was to punish poor souls like me who don't have the guts to get the hell out of here! How can one deadly dull, boring day be so much like the next? I feel like my whole life is taking care of Douglas and the boys, and when the boys grow up and move away, it'll just be Douglas and me. The thought of that don't exactly have me looking forward to my old age. Lord, I feel like I'm there already.

The only sunshine in my life is knowing that you got out, Harry, you got out for both of us. So now you got to make it for both of us.

I love you so much, you are a part of me. I guess it is so, what they say about twins. When you succeed, it feels like I'm succeeding, and right now, Harry, you're all the hope I got.

Love,
Jackie

P.S. I probably shouldn't send this dumb letter, but what the hell, I know you'll understand.

Karen packed up the rest of the letters and put them away. She'd read enough. She stretched out on Harry's bed and fell asleep.

A sudden thump in the hall jolted her awake.

She bolted upright. "Who is it?" Karen called out.

"S'me."

"Harry?"

"Where's my key?" He was stumbling around in the hallway. It sounded like a big, clumsy dog was out there, snuffling at the door.

"Karen?"

"Yes?"

"Open the fuckin' door."

"Right." She opened the door, and he practically fell on top of her, drunk and smelling charming. There was no way she could control his bulk, so she just watched him crash around the tiny apartment.

"Harry, what's wrong?" she asked from her relatively safe perch on the bed.

He laughed harshly. "Guess?"

She didn't say anything.

"The other guy got the part." He was still laughing, chuckling to himself as he fell onto the bed next to her. "So, like a fool, like a complete idiot, I asked them why they chose the other guy. I mean, what was wrong with me? And they told me." His eyes were squeezed shut; he was hiding from her. "They said I didn't read masculine enough."

"Harry," she said quietly, "that's a crock, please take my word for it. You could be a poster boy for the Marines." He didn't laugh. "Those people don't know anything. That show will probably fold in previews."

"I know." Bedsprings creaked as he curled his body around hers, his head resting on her thigh. "I know all the right things to say to myself: what a big mistake those guys made not casting me, how many other shows, better shows, I'll get a crack at, how I'm the best goddamn actor in this shitpile of a city." Tears dotted his lashes. Karen felt tears start to her own eyes. She knew the feelings. All she could do was stroke his hair, appear sympathetic, and wish he'd shut up.

"I'm just so tired of giving myself the little pep talk," Harry went on, rubbing his face. "It's only treading water. The second I stop believing in all my fragile hopes—that I *can* act, that I *will* get work—I will go under. I'm just so damn tired of treading water, tired and scared."

"Everything will be okay, Harry, because you're a good, sweet man, and that ought to count for something, even in *this* business. And if fate doesn't pay you your due, then I guess I'll have to do something."

"What will you do?"

"Whatever I can, and that's a promise." She bent and kissed his hair.

"Crazy girl," he said indistinctly, "I almost believe you." He started snoring softly.

She eased away from him, mindful of her light-colored sweater. Not wishing it to become soiled, she pulled it over her head, folded it neatly, and left it on top of the bureau. She found one of Harry's shirts, a light-blue plaid with pearl snaps, and put that on. Then she crawled back onto the bed and curled up with him like they were spoons in a drawer, his front to her back.

He was asleep, and she was sure he couldn't hear. "I love you, Harry," she said.

At a quarter after three, Karen walked into the coffeeshop on West Fourth. She found Matt stationed at a corner table, watching the door, trying very hard to look calm. He pointed to his watch.

"I'm sorry. I just—" she slid into the booth.

"You're here now, that's all that matters."

"I watch a lot of old movies," she said suddenly, as if they were in the middle of a conversation.

He waited for the rest of it.

"In a lot of old movies," she went on, "there is this scene where the heroine, in the course of the story, begins to doubt the hero, whether he is a good man, whether he really loves her. Or the hero"—she licked dry lips—"believes that his lady loves someone else. Because he finds a gift-wrapped tie in her apartment." She looked down at the china cup. White stoneware with a maroon stripe. "Of course it's for her father, or something like that. All that bother just to fill two hours before the happy ending. I *hate* those scenes. I always thought that if the boy and girl would just talk to each other, they could avoid so much heartache."

"Okay, let's talk."

"Matt, do you still want to marry me?"

He laughed. "Yes, Karen, I still want to marry you. I do love you."

"Will you be faithful to me?"

Again he laughed. "Those are the rules."

"So I've always heard." She was dead serious. "Now it's my turn." With an effort she collected herself and plunged. "I love you, Matt, maybe for all the wrong reasons, not the least of which is that you love me. I realize how much I need that. But you deserve to know the truth. I'm a virgin—" She held her hand up, cutting him off. "Please, hold your applause," she said with a wry smile. "If I marry you now, you'll be the only man I'll ever be with. I'm scared I won't be able to be faithful to you. I look at other men, even just walking down the street. I think about them. So if you don't want to marry me anymore, I'll understand."

He looked at her incredulously. "Excuse me, are you running for Pope?"

"What?"

"Nobody, but *nobody* can say for sure that they can be faithful." Some of the other diners were looking at them with mild interest. Matt lowered his voice. "It's all a gamble. I love you, and I promise you I'll do my best to make you happy. And since you need a little romance in your life . . ." He got down on one knee, looking like a very noble scarecrow, and took her hand. "Will you marry me?"

"I warned you," she sighed. "Let this be on your head. Yes, I'll marry you."

★ ★ ★ ★

It wasn't until she was in a cab heading home that she realized she was still wearing Harry's shirt. Matt had never said a word, although surely he must have noticed. Her admiration for him doubled.

10

GEORGE NICHOLS (who?) called Lake to have lunch, after she remembered who he was (Richard-Dano-the-agent's-assistant), Lake agreed to meet him for a fast cup of coffee; her schedule was tight. She had a photo session that morning, modeling wedding gowns. They were the worst. Even with the fan going full tilt, the veil had to be pinned to the backdrop. She was literally trapped in that gown for hours.

Then Daniel had quizzed her. Where was she going? And to meet whom? For reasons she didn't quite understand, she lied to him. She said she was meeting Karen for lunch. After all, the wedding was only a month away. As Karen's maid of honor Lake had a lot of plans.

"Sorry I'm late," she panted, sliding into the coffee-shop booth. It was a glorious April day, still a little chilly, but the warm sunshine steaming through the window made them blink.

"That's all right." George looked well. Tanned. "So, how've you been?" he said awkwardly.

"Oh, fine." She ordered coffee. "Yourself?"

He waved his hand modestly. "Not too bad, if I say so myself. I opened an office on the Coast. I'm only in for the day. California is great." His eyes lit up. "You'd do wonderfully out there. Lake, you should really think about it."

She laughed politely. "That's nice of you, but I'm doing fine in New York."

"Are you?"

She steeled herself. "What do you mean?"

"I've heard some rumors . . ." He gulped hot coffee. "Not that I'm one to listen to rumors, so I checked these stories out. . . .

Lake!" he burst out, "you should be the hottest new model to hit this town since Suzy Parker. Haven't you ever wondered why things aren't happening for you?"

"I hadn't noticed," she lied.

"It's Daniel! For every step forward you take, he drops you back two. You've offended some of the biggest agents in the business"—she thought of the missed appointment with the husband-and-wife agents—"your behavior is erratic and irresponsible"—a hundred separate incidents popped into her head.

"Maybe I just don't have what it takes," she said coolly.

He started to laugh. "Holy cow, Lake, we're not talking about Lady Macbeth's mad scene! For modeling you've got the right stuff. I've seen the little work you've done since you came to New York, and it's primo. You should be the number-one girl in this town. You would be if it wasn't for Daniel Fox." He leaned across the table so suddenly that it startled her. "Haven't you figured it out? I don't have any business in New York today. I came to see you. Lake, you have to get away from Daniel."

"I'm sorry, George," she said in that frozen, formal voice. "I really have to go now. I have an acting class with Winston Lowe at three, and he's an absolute bear if I'm late. Thanks for the coffee." She stood up, angrily grabbing her purse.

George pleaded with her. "Please, Lake. Just tell me you honestly believe Daniel is doing right by you."

She lifted her chin defiantly. "I'm in love with him. Does that answer your question?"

His reaction surprised her. He was looking at her with pity in his eyes. "You don't know him, you don't know him at all. I wish I could make you see him as he really is."

"And how is he really?" Her anger was miles away, detached, voices echoing through the wires of a transatlantic phone call. She liked that; it proved she was in control of her emotions. He wasn't bothering her at all.

He knew if he pushed her, she'd bolt. George backed down. "He's a lucky bastard," George said softly, "to have a girl like you to stand up for him. I'll never forget the way I felt, seeing you for the first time in Richard Dano's office." He reached into his pocket. For one ridiculous moment she thought he was going to pull out a ring. It was a business card. "Look me up when you get to the Coast. Hollywood can always use another beautiful blonde."

"We have no plans to visit the Coast."

"You'll go there. Everybody does." He reached for the check.

"In the meantime, I'm staying at the Plaza. I hope"—he smiled a little too brightly—"well, don't hesitate to call."

"Look, George, let's be friends. I can't stand this la-how-jolly sophistication." She leaned toward him, touching the back of his hand. "Don't take this the wrong way, but it looks lousy on you, pal."

He smiled, and it was real.

"Friends, okay?"

He squeezed her hand warmly. "Friends. Always, I hope."

"And maybe we will come to California soon. For business. And to visit friends." She felt almost shy. "Will you be glad to see me then?"

He practically choked on his reply. "You know I will."

"All right. Let me get to my class before Win pitches a fit." She got up, gathering her things.

"Lake, be careful."

She smiled. "You sound like a bad actor in a spy thriller."

"Sure, that's me," he croaked miserably, "a bad actor. Didn't you know that's where agents come from?"

"Just as I've always suspected."

They walked out together.

Daniel was waiting in a cab across the street. Lake turned back to look at George, his face open and readable. It hit her, the differences in the two men, the realization that all the common-sense people in her life, Matt, Karen, and now George, did not like Daniel. They were frightened of him.

"Tonight," she said to George, surprising herself as much as him, "dinner?"

"Sure." George tried hard to look cool. He smiled at Daniel across the street; no need to be unfriendly. Daniel smiled back. With his right hand he tapped his breast pocket, almost like patting a gun.

George took a deep breath. His imagination was getting the better of him. He watched her get into the cab and found himself waiting on the curb long minutes after the cab had pulled away.

Daniel gave the cabbie the address of Winston's Soho loft. "Did you have a nice lunch?" he asked Lake. "You and Karen?"

"Yes. Thanks." Her heart was beating so loud she was positive he'd hear it.

He was humming something under his breath. "Party tonight," he said, humming his strange little song.

"I can't make it," Lake said quickly.

"Other plans?"

"Of course not." She laughed. "I just want one solid evening to work on my new monologue. Win did everything but throw the kitchen sink at me on this one. I think he's just waiting for me to fall on my ass—" Too much, she told herself. Slow down. "You know how much I want to earn his respect."

"Yes," he said, cupping her chin in his hand, "I know." His hand moved to her throat. "Don't ever lie to me again, Lake. I'll always find you out."

He was deep in her eyes, going through them to all her secret places, until it was all she could do to keep from screaming, "What is it you know, Daniel? What?"

"Lake," Winston sighed, pressing his fingertips together like a cage, "if you cannot commit the lines to memory, don't bother wasting my time."

She'd been stammering through her monologue, watching Winston do his slow burn. Finally all the words just deserted her. She sank into a chair, murmuring apologies.

"Oh, for pity's sake." Winston got up and brought her a cup of coffee. "I'm giving you two minutes to get it together so you can massacre Inge again. I think the old boy's still breathing."

"Winston." Lake peered at him over her cup. "You and Daniel go back a long way, don't you?"

"The Neolithic Period."

"Where did you meet?"

"What has that got to do with William Inge?"

"I don't know. Was he there?"

"No," Winston answered sharply, "he was off writing this bloody monologue so you could make a mockery of it today."

She set her cup down and walked behind his chair. "I don't know why you do it, Win," she purred, rubbing his shoulder, "giving poor, untalented me the benefit of your wisdom and experience. Why *are* you doing this, Win?"

"The monologue," Winston said inexorably.

"Why?" she went on sweetly.

"I enjoy the challenge, trying to make an actress out of a model. The monologue, Lake!"

She slipped around to the front of his chair, staring intently into his eyes. He looked cool, he was even smiling a little, in an annoyed sort of way. But Winston was an actor. Only the faintest sheen of sweat at his hairline gave him away.

"Why, Winston?"

"A favor to a dear friend." He made an elaborate show of his righteous indignation. "Now, can we get back to work?"

She laughed softly. "You should get an Academy Award for that performance. You're full of shit, Winston. A favor for a friend is arranging an audition, not three months of private coaching for free. What has Daniel got on you?"

"Careful, Lake." Now he was playing her fellow conspirator, voice barely audible, body tipped forward. Here it was, the truth to set her free. "You're a very high-strung girl. You have to be careful not to let these delusions take over. I can recommend an excellent therapist—"

"Bastard!" With one wild swing Lake knocked over cup, table, and a small chair that had the misfortune to be close at hand. The damn cup wouldn't break. It rolled around on the floor making clumpy sounds. "There is nothing wrong with me! It's Daniel, not me! It's him!"

He was offering her a scrap of paper. "Please call Dr. Mandel as soon as you can. He's particularly good with this sort of thing. Please call him, Lake. I have no particular faith in your abilities as an actress, but I've nothing against you personally."

She kept her voice low and even. "I hate you, Win, and that should worry you."

He laughed heartily. "Why on earth should it?"

She was playing the moment, watching the movie from the back row. "If I don't like you," she said with a catlike smile, "maybe Daniel won't, either."

It was then that she saw fear on his face and knew she'd been right about everything.

She left Soho and started toward midtown.

Galina H.'s receptionist smiled brightly at the girl in front of her. The blonde was absolutely stunning, but the receptionist knew everybody who was anybody, and she did not know the blonde. She had to be a gorgeous nobody or girlfriend to somebody. Either way, she was stubborn as hell. "I'm sorry," the receptionist said for the umpteenth time, "you cannot see Galina without an appointment."

"Just tell her it's about Daniel Fox."

The receptionist sighed. "If you don't have an appointment—"

"Just tell her." Lake sat down and started leafing through *Vogue.* She had gotten through only the first ten pages when the receptionist trotted back, looking miffed. "Right this way."

Galina's office had a mirrored wall reflecting a myriad of rouge-dyed brushes, bottles of makeup, and tiny compacts of bright shadows. Magazine articles displaying Galina's techniques and products were framed on the walls. These, too, danced in duplication in the mirrors.

Lake closed her eyes, fighting vertigo.

A cool hand touched her shoulder. "You are all right?" The consistency of Galina's appearance was reassuring. The same coronet of iron-gray braids. Soft dress of lavender gray. She sat down, smiling kindly at Lake. "So? There is something I can help you with?"

"Yes." The more she thought about it, the more ridiculous Lake's mission seemed. Galina wasn't going to help her any more than Winston had. "Please, don't tell me I'm crazy, but I think . . . I feel there are things about Daniel that I should know."

"Do you love him?" Galina asked bluntly.

"Yes." Her answer was automatic, without thought.

"Then there is nothing else you need to know."

"Galina." Her voice faltered. "I said I love him. I've been saying it so long that it's starting to sound like the truth. All I really know is that I need him, maybe not in a good way. Please, tell me the truth."

Galina's eyes searched. She was thinking. If I tell, what will happen to me? Will he seek me out for vengeance? Why tell at all? Why should I help her when no one stepped forward to save me? But someone should have.

She got up and closed the door. "When I first came to this country, that was when I first met Daniel. I needed his help. He offered it graciously, with an open hand, but I could not help but feel something was wrong. In all the time I knew him, it was like watching an actor play many parts. I never saw the man behind all the masks. When I asked his friends if they felt this, too, they would laugh and say, 'Galina, you are imagining things.' I believed them. I prayed that someone would have the courage to tell you the truth. From the first time I saw you, I wished this with all my heart." She went over to the mirrored wall, soberly studying her reflection. Her graceful hand went to her throat in a protective gesture. "I have so little courage," she said apologetically to her reflection, "but enough, I think." Again she checked the door.

"If you repeat what I tell you to anyone, anyone at all, it is my life," she said simply. "Do you understand?"

Lake nodded numbly.

"All right." Galina smoothed imaginary wisps of hair away from her brow. "And after I have told you my little story, promise me you'll get the hell away from Daniel Fox."

Forty-five minutes later, as she was leaving the building, Lake felt dazed but better. The first order of the day was to get her career back on the right track. Then, if that went well and she was feeling confident, she would call Daniel and tell him it was over. Then she would have dinner with George, and he would pet her and tell her she'd done the right thing and make her feel good. George was going to be good for her, she could feel it. Everything was going to be fine.

Daniel was waiting for her across the street.

She almost screamed. Then she realized it couldn't possibly be Daniel; he'd told her he'd be home working the rest of the day. It had to be someone else wearing a coat of a similiar design. The man melted into the crowd.

"So, you see," Lake wrapped up, "while I certainly can't excuse my behavior, I would like to apologize."

The husband and wife regarded her with unblinking eyes.

Lake took a deep breath. "I've done a lot of thinking lately, and I hope I've matured a bit. At any rate, if I can do anything to revise your opinion of me, please let me know. I . . . I'm genuinely sorry for the way I've acted." She folded her hands and looked down at them contritely.

"Oh, hell," the wife said, pacing double-time. "What's life for if not second chances? You still look like a dream, honey." She patted Lake's hair. "It's a damn shame you're a schizophrenic, but who's perfect? Tomorrow." The wife gave Lake an address. "It's a go-see."

"Thank you ever so much," Lake gushed, putting a little grovel into it. "I won't let you down, you'll see."

"Lake?" The husband spoke, his voice sharp in a moment's silence. "If you do let us down, there won't be another chance."

She lifted her chin, answering his challenging stare. "I understand." Proud as a queen she walked to the elevator, dissolving into childish whoops and giggles when she was safely inside. She saluted herself. She congratulated herself. She dubbed herself a knight of the round table. "I did it!" she yelled in the elevator. Obligingly the doors opened, and a very dignified Lake Eastman got out, smiling mischievously.

She bought a hot dog from one of the street vendors, something she never did because, God knows, those things were full of germs. On her instructions the vendor slathered it with mustard and sauerkraut. Nothing was going to taste better than that dog, she thought, bringing it to her lips.

There across the street was Daniel Fox. She stuffed the hot dog into the trash and walked away quickly.

"Hello?"

"Hello, Daniel? I know you've been following me."

"I haven't." There was genuine surprise in his voice.

Panic began to rise in her. Forget it, she told herself. He's just trying to drive you crazy. Forget it. You have other matters to discuss.

"Daniel." She kept her voice rigidly controlled. "I'm just coming by to pick up a few things I left at your apartment. And then that's it, Daniel. I never want to see you again."

"All right, Lake," he said pleasantly.

She hung up. The lining of her coat was terribly stained, and she could not remember when or how that had happened. She smelled the stain. Old sex. Horrible, dirty smell of hotel linen. She began to shake uncontrollably and could not calm herself for a long time.

"Hello, Fox?"

"Here."

"Yeah. I did like you said. Though it ain't in my usual line. Private investigations is my job, not gaslighting pretty blondes."

Daniel laughed. "You followed her?"

"Wearing your coat and hat. Just like you said. Hey, did you get Daddykins off your back?"

"Yes." He rubbed his jaw, smiling in remembrance. They had come to an understanding. They both had secrets to protect.

"I'll call you when I need you." He hung up and moved his desk chair so that it faced the door. Then he sat down and waited.

"Hello." George Nichols smiled at the desk clerk at the Plaza. "Any messages for me? Room 1206." Life was wonderful. The Plaza was wonderful. Dinner was wonderful, and—. The clerk handed him a piece of paper, the kind you would rip out of a spiral-bound notebook.

George—
Sorry, I can't make it tonight.
Lake

"Shit." Disappointed, George reread the short note, hoping the words would change if he stared at them long enough.

He had never seen a sample of Lake's handwriting. It never occurred to him, as he folded the note and shoved it into his pocket, that he still hadn't.

As soon as Lake came through the door, she realized she had made a terrible mistake. She could tell by the look on his face as he sat there, waiting for her and smiling. She turned to run, but he was out of that chair faster than she would have thought humanly possible. He hit her. No one had ever hit her before, and it hurt like hell. How do boxers take it? she wondered distantly. He hit her again, in the stomach, drummed on her ribs, kicked the soft muscles of her calves. She went down, too surprised to fight back. He started dragging her toward the closet.

"No!" She dug her nails into the carpet, but his strength was formidable. He shoved her into the closet and locked the door. She heard scraping and scratching outside and realized he had pulled his chair up against the closet door. She heard him sit down and settle himself for the night.

He was humming.

Morning. She had been locked in that closet all night. "I need to use the bathroom, Daniel," she said evenly.

"Of course." He took her to the bathroom, politely held the door for her, then locked it. He waited outside.

She peed quickly, looking around for a makeshift weapon. Her eyes lit upon an aerosol can of shaving cream. Menthol. She grabbed the can and rapped on the door. "Finished."

He opened the door. She sprayed the shaving cream in his eyes. As he was bellowing in pain, she ran past him out into the hallway, the stairs, the street. Blessed luck, there was a traffic cop on the corner, and she collapsed against him, incoherently sobbing.

Daniel did not come out of the building.

A few hours later Lake was finally on her way home from the

police station. It was dark. She unlocked the apartment door and flicked on the light. On the coffee table was a small stack of messages, all in Karen's scrawl, all from the husband-and-wife agents. Nothing from George. Another liar.

Lake would have wept, but she was all cried out. She went into the kitchen, snapped on the light, and drank juice out of the container while she stood over the sink.

She went into the bedroom, pulling her sweater over her head, fumbling for the light switch on the wall.

Daniel Fox was sitting on her bed waiting for her. She screamed, turning, knowing how hopeless it was, how fast he was. He tackled her in the hallway. She kicked furiously, met the yielding flesh of his genitals. He crumpled, and she ran for the door.

"Help!" she screamed. "Somebody call the cops, please!" Down the hall she heard one of her neighbors bolt his door. Daniel struck her across the jaw, and she saw stars. He flopped down on top of her, his knee pressing her legs apart.

"I'm sorry, but you have to be punished," he said in an ordinary voice. "You lied to me, and you know I won't have that." He sounded sane; she sounded like the lunatic.

"I'll never do it again, Daniel," she sobbed, weakly fighting him off. "I swear I won't."

He hit her again. She felt herself slipping away. He was undoing his belt buckle.

Lake heard more screams, and they weren't coming from her. Fingers sank into Daniel's shoulders, ripping him away from her.

It was Matt.

Karen was on the phone calling the police. Her voice was low and steady, but tears were streaming down her face. Daniel turned to her, and seizing Karen by one thin arm, he flung her across the room. She was light and fairly flew, smacking against the wall. She lay there, dazed.

Matt was doing his damnedest to pin Daniel's arms, but Daniel was fast and crazy. Daniel twisted around in Matt's grip, smashing the heel of his hand against Matt's glasses. Blood began to flow down Matt's face, but he still hung on.

Laughing a little, Daniel kicked at Matt's knees, knocking him down. He kicked his ribs steadily.

Dimly Lake noticed Karen was no longer there. Where had she gone? A second later Karen came charging out of the kitchen, waving the biggest knife she could find.

"Stop it!" she screamed, slashing the air in front of Daniel's nose.

He watched her, considering. Would she or wouldn't she? He was still considering when the cops came in, trying to sort out the merry scene that greeted them. Matt was on the floor, bleeding. Not too far away Lake was nursing her own bruises. She was naked from the waist up. Karen and Daniel were locked in their own variation of a Mexican standoff.

A nice policewoman was there, and she gave Lake her jacket while her buddies handcuffed Daniel and led him away. He was docile and wished them all a pleasant evening.

"Hey there, professor," one of the cops said to Matt, "how you doing?"

"Not too bad," Matt said from the floor, "but I think I'll stay here for a minute. Okay?"

"Fine," the cop said.

Karen ran to the kitchen, put the knife back in its place, and got a wet paper towel. "Oh, Matt," she wailed, "your face is a wreck!" She sat down next to him and washed his face gently.

Lake was quietly telling the policewoman what had happened.

"You were great," Matt told Karen as he sat up gingerly. "You had *me* scared. I really thought you were going to kill him."

"Oh, no." Karen was shocked. "I'm not a violent person." One of the cops laughed, and she gave him a withering glance. "I'm *not.* Am I?"

Lake came over and put her arms around her friends. "You were marvelous, both of you."

The two girls got into the back of one cop car, Matt in the other. Karen held Lake's hand. "Everything's okay now," she whispered. "That asshole will go to jail where he belongs, and he'll never bother you again. It's all over."

It didn't feel over, not to Lake. It wouldn't feel over until twenty years later, and even then it wouldn't feel over until Daniel Fox was in his grave, and even then . . .

11

"DOES IT LOOK OKAY?" Karen asked anxiously.

"Oh, yes." Lake smiled. "You look beautiful."

Karen turned to her, careful of the satin. "Good. Do you know how much this crap costs?" She stroked the billowing skirt affectionately. "It is pretty, though." The only ornate thing about the gown was the fabric. The style was simple: a fitted bodice with a scoop neck tapering to a slightly pointed waistline. The skirt flared out, buoyed by a crinoline slip. Long sleeves covered her slim arms. Karen had found a garland of small white silk flowers. With netting sewn on it, it made an admirable veil. "You should see Matt in his tuxedo." She grinned at Lake. "Extra tall, of course."

"Of course. Are you nervous?"

"Of course!" Karen laughed. "I guess I wouldn't be normal if I wasn't. Not that things will change that much. Matt knows I'm not going to give up my career." What career? "Well, my hopes of a career, anyway. I better get out of this thing before I ruin it."

Lake unzipped her and helped her step out of the dress. "Are you sure about quitting school? You're so smart, maybe you should just stick it out and get the degree. Thrill your parents to tears."

"Three years of my *life,*" Karen exclaimed melodramatically, "just for a dumb piece of paper? No thanks. This way I can go to work and support Matt, because he's going to be up for an internship as soon as he graduates next month. Interns don't get paid, you know. Then, as soon as he's making decent money, I'll quit my job and look for acting work full-time."

It sounded like a recipe for disaster to Lake. "Can't your parents help out?"

"Oh, no." Karen looked aghast. "You can't ask your parents to support you when you're *married.*"

"Why not?"

"Because you can't."

"Why don't you graduate and then get married? I'm sure Matt will still like you then."

Karen gave her a very pained expression. "I want to get married now, before I chicken out."

"Do you love him?" Lake asked in a low voice.

"Yes, I do," Karen said thoughtfully, "but I always thought love would be more passionate. You know, the kind of things you can't imagine your mother doing."

"You can imagine your mother with Matt?" Lake laughed. "Kinky." She sobered. "No, I know what you mean. The nice guys, the good ones who'll take care of you and treat you right, they never seem to set you on fire. For that you need a bastard. I don't know why it is that way. Is Matt good in bed at least?"

"I sure hope so."

Lake stared. "You mean you don't know?"

"Nope."

"You really are a brave soul."

Karen sighed. "What I am is an idiot. Probably."

She looked so forlorn standing there in her slip, Lake couldn't help herself. "It's not too late, Kar. Don't marry him if you're not sure. You'll find someone else, somebody's who right for you."

"No, I won't!" Wailing, she sat down on the floor. "I don't look like you, I'm not brilliant, I'm not witty. Who else is going to come along? This is my one big chance. I'm so lucky to have Matt. He's going to be famous, he loves me, he's a wonderful, intelligent person and he's extremely tall."

"Then why are you crying?"

"I don't know. I'm such a jerk!"

"No, you're not," Lake defended her staunchly, "You're dear and sweet and Matt's one hell of a lucky guy. Just remember, if you change your mind," her eyes twinkled wickedly, "you've got until tomorrow night to seduce some handsome young stud. Unless of course you've got someone stashed away on the side."

"No such luck," Karen grumbled.

He seemed very pleased to see her. Everything he had in the world was packed up in one small suitcase and a rucksack. He looked like he was going camping, not moving to California permanently. Holly-weird. "I'm glad you're here."

"I couldn't very well have you leave with nobody to see you off," Karen said lightly. "Are you sure about going to LA?"

Harry shrugged. "I'm not doing so hot here. It'll be nice just to be someplace warm for a change." He touched her cheek with his finger. "What about you? Are you sure?"

"I better be. The wedding is tomorrow night."

"So . . ." he said uncomfortably.

"So . . ." she echoed, looking down at the floor. "Oh, Harry," she burst out, "I'm not sure of anything. I'm so nervous I could die! I love Matt, I really do, but I keep wishing I'd slept with you! And now it's too late!"

"Poor you." He put down the suitcase and held her, but it was awkward and not much good. "That's just maidenly jitters. You'll get over it. I always figured marriage to be a tough gig."

She shook her head. "I don't know if I can do it."

"Yeah, well . . ." Very gently he pushed her away. "You got to be true to your school, you know what I mean?"

"Yes, I know."

His bus was pulling up now. He picked up his suitcase. "But if you do make a mistake, you gotta forgive yourself."

"I really don't know if I can," she said seriously.

He looked over at the bus, then back at her, standing there so small and somber. Dropping his suitcase he covered the two steps between them and kissed her. It was a kiss with a whole history behind it, the kind of kiss anybody would want to be on the receiving end of.

He held on to her for a moment. "Karen, if you don't love him, don't marry him."

Her eyes widened. *"What?"*

"If you have doubts, maybe you should wait a while, you know, date around a little."

"Date around?" She started to laugh. "My God, Harry, I'm supposed to get married tomorrow. My entire family flew in for this. Exactly when am I supposed to do this dating around?"

He grinned weakly. "Guess you better step on it. Shit! Don't cry, Kar, it was a stupid, lousy joke. Look, I better jump on this bus before it takes off without me—just don't marry him if you don't love him."

"Why are you doing this to me?" she cried.

"Because I like you, we're friends."

"You don't do things like that to your friends, Harry. You just don't."

"Please Karen, I've got a bus to get on." He lowered his voice. "I just think you can do better than Matt Singer. You're really something, Kar. I never told you this, I probably should have, but the only thing that can shoot you down as an actress is your own lack of confidence, and marrying Matt is not going to make you feel confident. My sister married a guy she thought was going to make it all better. It doesn't work that way."

"What have you got against Matt? He's a wonderful guy. Why did you start this, Harry? What do you care who I marry?"

"I care."

She grabbed him by the shirt collar. "You're going to have to do better than that. This is my life we're talking about."

"That bus driver does not give a shit whether I am on that bus or not—"

"Neither do I. You talk to me *now.*"

He squirmed away from her grip. "What is it you want me to say, Kar? Huh? I like you. You're a nice girl, a great girl. Somebody *should* marry you, but it won't be me. I just don't want the responsibility—oh, please, don't cry. If you cry, we can't talk and I'm going to miss my fuckin' bus as it is. You can do a lot better than Matt, and a lot better than me. I'm just a selfish prick actor and Matt . . . well, that boy has got no heart. That's why he needs you, but *you* don't need him. You've got to try to remember that, Kar."

Her voice was tired. "Go catch your bus."

"Don't be angry." He shoved his hands into his pockets. The bus driver honked his horn and Harry glanced over to him. "Just a minute!" he yelled. He turned back to face Karen again. "I'll never forget how sweet you were to me when I didn't get that part. You were so good I just wanted you around forever. I really loved you for a while, Kar, but I know I can't give you what you need."

She smiled faintly. "Harry, you're a jerk. One of these days, you're going to have to be responsible to somebody. That's what happens when you fall in love."

"Today is not that day."

"Don't put it off too long, Harry."

He kissed her again. It was more than a little desperation on both sides.

The bridal procession began. It was strictly an amateur production. The bridesmaids giggled their way down the aisle, each accompanied by a terrified young usher. Most of Matt's friends were NYU students. Two of them were under the influence of the wicked marijuana plant. All of them were positive some portion of their formalwear was on backwards. They were not going to be happy until the bar was open.

Lake got a good deal of attention, most of it from Aunt Sophie, solidly squashed into a front row seat. Clad in an amazing concoction of purple satin, the Aunt glowered. She spent the entire ceremony giving Lake evil, evil looks.

Accompanied by his parents, Matt seemed to be the only member of the wedding party genuinely glad to be there.

Then Karen made her grand entrance. Demurely, she walked down the aisle to the appropriate oooh's and aaah's. She looked very sweet, her light brown pageboy halo'd with silk flowers. She also looked terrified.

Before they reached the altar, Mr. and Mrs. Bloom kissed their daughter goodbye and left her standing in the aisle for her husband-to-be to claim.

Looking very spiffy in his black tuxedo, Matt took Karen's arm to lead her under the wedding canopy. Aunt Sophie stopped glowering long enough to nod approvingly. A nice Jewish boy. What could be better?

"You're standing on my veil!" Karen whispered to Matt.

"Sorry."

Karen turned and handed her bouquet to Lake. Lake squeezed her hand. She almost felt like saying "it's not too late," but the wedding was in full gear and in all honesty, it *was* too late. Suddenly, Lake felt very sad. Her eyes flicked over to Matt. Sometimes she thought they were two of a kind, she and Matt. Cold people, hard to understand, difficult to get close to, but not totally devoid of emotion. Funny how Karen seemed to understand both of them so well. Lake smiled at the groom, feeling a certain kinship.

The rabbi began the ceremony. The Hebrew words sounded very strange to Lake, solemn and masculine. Karen's parents, small faces lined with anxiety, stood quietly by. Matt's family was somewhat better off financially; the Blooms felt a little overwhelmed but pleased at their daughter's choice. It was obvious they felt Karen was marrying into a better life. *Poor kid,* Lake thought, *trapped on all sides.*

Bride and groom drank from the cup of wine. A glass, wrapped in a napkin was placed on the floor, (Karen had told Lake it was really a light bulb since it made a satisfactory pop) and Matt stamped on it to a chorus of Mazel Tovs.

"Good luck," Lake whispered.

"Let's have a nice round of applause for the new Mr. and Mrs. Matthew Singer!" The bandleader yelped enthusiastically.

Nothing.

Guests started looking up from their fruit cup.

"Excuse me." Lake got up from her seat with a little note. She handed the note to the bandleader.

He looked at it and sighed. "Hooo boy, these liberated women are driving me nuts. Okay! Let's hear it for Matt and Karen!"

She moved over to the bar and got a vodka on the rocks.

"You are gorgeous," a young man next to her said approvingly. "Not one of the Singer clan I bet."

"Friend of the bride," Lake said, sipping her drink.

"Groom's cousin. Some party, huh?"

"Some party," Lake agreed.

"Real surprise. Bride's a cutie. Some shocker Matt getting a honey like that. I didn't think he'd ever get married."

She was suddenly interested. "Why's that?"

"Just a loner. A real loner. Guess he's not alone anymore." The cousin smiled. "Lucky guy."

"Lucky," Lake echoed, feeling the familiar pangs of jealousy. Lucky Matt had bailed out of what would probably have been a miserable life. He had escaped. She wouldn't so easily.

Daniel . . .

My God, was she still in love with that crazy man?

"Care to dance?" the cousin was asking.

"No thanks."

He shrugged and went away.

Matt and Karen waved to Lake as they danced by. Lake waved back. She got a fresh drink and contemplated Matt's happy expression. *Will I ever feel that way about anyone,* she wondered?

"Thanks for sticking it out to the bitter end," Matt said. He and Lake were schlepping wedding gifts out to the car. "I'd hate to have to do this with Karen's dad."

"Bad back?"

"Lousy conversationalist." He shoved yet another Mr. Coffee into the trunk. "So tell me, Matthew," he boomed in a hearty, artificial voice. "What is it you do? Movies? Any money in that? You gotta make plenty of money to take care of my little girl right." He went back to his normal voice. "Try making conversation with that."

"Pretty tough, huh? What are you going to do with seventeen Mr. Coffee's?"

Matt shrugged. "I don't know. Mate them and start a corporation." He gave her a quick, hard glance. "Are you okay?"

"Yes." She laughed a fraction of a second too long. "Of course I am."

"You just seem sort of shaky after that incident with Foxy."

Her smile crumpled. Tears came unbidden. She tried to hide her face in her hand but it wasn't much use.

Matt put his arm around her awkwardly. "It's okay now. He won't bother you anymore."

"That's not it." She turned and buried her face in his shoulder. "Daniel was the only man I ever cared about and it wasn't exactly a healthy relationship. What if all my other relationships are like that? Maybe I can only fall for guys who bring me down. Self-destructive tendencies, huh?" She wiped her streaming eyes on his jacket.

"Don't be silly, you'll find somebody nice . . . somebody sane."

"Maybe it should have been you." Her eyes, deep-sea colored, met his evenly. "Maybe I was just a little too slow on the draw." She moved to kiss him. Horrified he pushed her away.

"Don't," she said unsteadily, "don't push me aside. I can't take that anymore. We're a lot alike. I understand you, Matt. I understand the loneliness and now you're taking Karen away from me. Can't you see how I feel?"

He shook his head angrily. "You're crazy. You're just not happy unless you're ruining somebody's life. You could at least confine yourself to screwing up your own. What if Karen had seen that?"

"I wasn't thinking of that," she mumbled. "I just wanted somebody to hold me, be nice to me. It just came out wrong."

"You just want to hurt Karen, that's what you want."

"No." Her smile was sepulchral. "She just keeps getting caught in the crossfire. You'll see. You'll hurt her and none of it'll be intentional. It'll all be crossfire. I told you, we're an awful lot alike."

"Hey!" Karen was running toward them wearing jeans and a sweatshirt. "Are we all packed up?"

"Pretty much." Matt slammed the trunk closed. "Lake, do you need a lift?"

"No, I have a ride back to the city," she said tonelessly. "Thanks just the same."

Karen hugged her tightly. "You were a wonderful maid-of-honor. Thank you for everything. Matt? Give my buddy a kiss." Karen gave her a new husband a little push towards Lake. "Go on," she prompted.

Matt bent and gave Lake a chaste little peck on the cheek. Karen watched them curiously, saying nothing. After some more prolonged goodbyes they got in the car and drove away.

A few miles passed in with the only sound coming from the radio. After a while, Karen snapped it off.

She looked out the window and bit her thumbnail.

Lake walked around the parking lot, not really caring if she missed her ride home. Gravel chattered beneath her feet making a homey sound. Across the lot there was an answering chatter. Lake peered into the darkness, seeing a familiar shape. The tiny hairs along the back of her neck began to rise.

"Daniel?" she whispered.

Nothing answered.

"Daniel?"

Whatever she thought she saw, disappeared.

Lake closed her eyes and thought of California.

There is some truth in advertising, Karen thought with satisfaction. Holiday Inns are pretty darn accommodating. She bounced up and down on the hotel bed. "Matt?"

"Yes?" He was at the desk counting the cash gifts from the two hundred-odd guests. Generous guests. "The first year's rent," he exclaimed exultantly, "if we're careful."

"Ma-att," she said playfully, "come to bed."

"In a minute."

"Now."

"Just a sec."

"Now."

"Okay."

Forty-five minutes later Matt finally got into bed next to her. Shaking off sleep she turned to him warmly. "Hello."

He kissed her forehead. "Go to sleep."

"Not *that* tired." Her hand, resting on his stomach, traveled downward. His member was flaccid but quickly sprang to attention under her touch.

"Karen, I really am tired. You probably are, too." He rolled over onto his side, turning his back on her. She persisted.

He lay down on top of her and gave her a few quick kisses. She wrapped her legs around him, and this seemed to encourage him. He entered her and began to push farther in. She was tight and dry and felt him dig his toes into the sheet so he could bore deeper.

There was no blood, but it hurt horribly, and she was so glad when it stopped that she almost cried with relief.

He cuddled next to her, one arm under her neck, the other thrown across her body. That part was okay.

"It'll get better," he said quietly. "The first time is always the worst; everyone says so."

She didn't really care. Matt was good and kind, and he would take care of her. The sex wasn't important. It didn't matter. And she didn't really think it was going to get better. If she was very lucky, it would just get . . . infrequent.

It didn't matter, she told herself, tears stinging her eyes, it didn't matter at all.

When Matt and Karen returned from their honeymoon, a letter was waiting for them:

Dear Karen,

I tried very hard to wait till you came back so I could tell you these things in person, but you know me. After I made up my mind to go, it was all I could do to stay long enough to pack.

Karen, this isn't fair of me to ask, but I have to. Please, please, no matter what happens, no matter what I do, don't forsake me. That is your gift, you can forgive. Most people can't. My father never could.

I need you, in ways I don't understand myself, so don't leave me out here all alone. If you do, then I will be lost.

I wish you and Matt all the happiness you deserve. And I do love you. I don't know why I could never say it. I think you knew.

Lake

There was no return address.

Part 2

12

April 1974

HARRY TOWNSEND was feeling very frustrated. He had broken his ass courting the great George Nichols. For two years solid he'd sent postcards, flyers, even a large chocolate airplane on one desperate occasion. Finally he'd simply hired a limo to pick up the agent and deliver him to Harry's showcase, an evening of absurd theater. The reasons that absurd theater got its name were all painfully evident that night. Harry went out and got drunk. By three o'clock in the morning, he felt a lot better about himself and was ready to go knocking on George's door prior to popping him a good one on the nose. Luckily, he did not know where George lived.

The next day there was a message on his service. George Nichols would like to see him for an interview. Lying on his bed in a very old apartment in North Hollywood, Harry played the scene in his head.

First of all he would not be kept waiting. Not more than twenty minutes. Well . . . say a half hour. Tops. They would shake hands, Harry's grip being the firmer, but not boastfully so. *And then* . . . and then Harry would grin, painting the scenario in his head, imagining it all. George would be singing his praises. He'd be down on his knees thanking Holly and Al Townsend for the conception and subsequent care of the greatest box office draw since . . . since . . .

"You're very good, Harry," George Nichols was saying earnestly. "But unfortunately I've just signed a young man who is a similar type."

Since Lassie, you asshole. Harry cursed himself and his prior vivid imagination. Forty minutes sweating in the reception area to hear this? "We might be similar types," Harry said, reminding himself to smile, "but no two people are the same. I'm sure if I could show you a broader range of my work—"

"Harry, at this point I wouldn't be sending you up for a major film role. For commercials and under-fives on soaps, it's strictly looks."

"Nonetheless," Harry maintained stubbornly, "I feel that if you would just give me the chance . . ." He was going into pity overload. "Oh, hell. Look, George, why did you ask me in here?"

"Because I think you're a pretty good actor. I also think you're not quite ready. How old are you?" The agent leaned close suddenly, peering intently into Harry's face. "Twenty-seven?"

"Exactly. That's pretty darn good."

"When you deal with actors as much as I do . . ." George shrugged modestly. "Twenty-seven is an in-between age. Long in the tooth for a juvenile, lightweight for a leading man. It shows. It shows on you. If you can hang out for another three years without going nuts, build up the body a little, trim the hair, I think we've got something big."

"I need work now," Harry said softly. "Couldn't you work with me on a freelance basis?"

"Even if I did send you out freelance, I would have to think of my client first. You'd be cheating yourself, Harry. Better to wait the few years—"

"Can you guarantee that you'll sign me in three years?"

"You know I can't." George felt uncomfortable. Nothing was worse than an actor laying aside his charm and showing you the sweat and desperation beneath. The truth was, he genuinely meant everything he was telling Harry. George saw great potential in the young actor. He just needed a little seasoning. Either that or a facial scar. Nothing vulgar, just a little crease along the chin or a thin line skating along a cheekbone. Something to hint at a dark and wicked past. Something women would fantasize about as they clutched their pillows to their breasts at night. Something . . . fascinating. "In three years," George said brightly, "I'll probably be standing in line to see you."

More than likely, I'll be parking your Porsche for you at Ma Maison, Harry thought.

"Why don't you give me a call in two weeks," George said, a trifle less brightly, "and I'll see what I can do."

"Sure. Thanks." Harry held out his hand, feeling numb, which was a lot better than feeling like a complete washout.

"Going to make an appointment for that haircut?"

Harry laughed, trying not to sound bitter. "As soon as I can afford it."

Without hesitation George got out his wallet and held some money out to Harry. The action was completed before George realized that what he was doing could be interpreted as an insult.

Harry pulled himself together. "Come on now, Mr. Nichols," he drawled, "don't you know better than to lend money to an actor?" He picked up his portfolio. "See you around."

George hoped so, but he doubted it. He knew what made stars, and it wasn't ability. It was luck. Harry Townsend didn't strike him as a particularly lucky guy.

On the other hand, George was a very lucky guy. He consulted his appointment book for the eighty-fifth time that day, unable to keep his mouth from sliding into a big, happy grin.

11:45 Lake Eastman.

He remembered her voice on the phone, the hesitant whisper when she asked if he remembered her. He had to choke back a laugh. Remember her? Sure he remembered her. She'd been all he'd been able to think about for two years. He even found himself following strange blondes down the street, hoping.

No more hoping. The moment was at hand. Lake Eastman was sitting on his Haitian cotton couch in his tastefully furnished reception area, looking at his jazz festival posters from New Orleans. Putting lipstick prints on a Styrofoam cup filled with overbrewed coffee. Elegant fingers stroking the pages of *Variety* or the *Hollywood Reporter.*

Oh, hell, the way his memory painted her, Lake wasn't sitting on the couch, she was probably floating six inches above it. Glowing. No mortal woman could possibly be as beautiful as the picture in his mind. As he reached for the intercom button, he prepared to be disappointed.

The receptionist was chatting up the great-looking actor who'd just come out of George's office. She answered the buzzing intercom with some annoyance, unwilling to turn away even for a second. "Yes? I'll send her right in. Miss Eastman? You can go in now."

The blonde on the couch got up. "Thank you," she whispered.

The good-looking boy talking to the receptionist smiled at Lake. "Hope you have better luck than I did."

A very small smile touched her face as she raised her eyes to meet his. "That's kind of you," she said in a soft voice that went through him like ice. Harry had never been a great believer in love at first sight. Four words from a woman he'd never seen before, and he was willing to swear that he'd met the only woman he would ever love. Crazy. He waved a jaunty good-bye to the smitten receptionist and walked out the door, mentally kicking himself for not taking George's money. He really needed that haircut.

Lake knocked on George's door timidly, then let herself in. She started to laugh. George's office was decorated in early paper airplane. Made from balsa wood and Styrofoam, painted tin and plastic, executed with the skill of a craftsman and the loving clumsiness of a determined two-year-old, toy airplanes were everywhere, hanging from the ceiling in colorful profusion. His desk was a landing strip. A small, painfully detailed air-control tower sat on top of a filing cabinet.

George pointed to it with pride. "Correct to the smallest detail. If you look inside, you can see the teeny-tiny air controllers popping teeny-tiny Valium."

She peered inside. He wasn't lying. "That's amazing."

"So," George said awkwardly, "what've you been up to these past two years?"

"Oh, I just felt like disappearing for a little while. It was very pleasant."

It had been bliss. She had dyed her hair brown, found a quiet little town on the coast, and moved in. A vacation from herself. She got a job waiting tables in a small café. Every morning she swam in the ocean, fighting the current with a certain satisfaction, dyed hair packed neatly into a white bathing cap. The café was never awfully busy. They got the kids who had staked out the beach as their own personal surfing and sunning domain. The kids ate burgers with ketchup and mustard on them. Sometimes tourists cruising up Big Sur would come in for lunch or a late breakfast. The other waitresses were friendly to the quiet brown-haired girl from the East. One hazarded a guess of an unhappy love life. The brown-haired girl had no boyfriend and didn't seem to be looking for one. She lived as chastely as a cloistered nun, sharing an apartment with another quiet waitress who stayed home nights reading her hometown paper.

Lake enjoyed her new life. She tried grits for the first time in her life and liked them. She changed her hairstyle as well as the color, wearing bangs for the first time since childhood, all of her hair trimmed shorter, the ends turned neatly under, like a pageboy.

She would catch herself looking in the mirror, almost believing she was looking out from someone else's face, someone else's body. All she felt was a deep, abiding gratitude for the rest. A perfect vacation.

Finally, one day, she had simply had enough vacation. She bleached her hair back to blonde, brushed the bangs away from her eyes, and left her home of two years. It took a pitifully short time to pack. Lake had not personalized her rented bungalow with pictures and knicknacks. She packed her clothes, a hair dryer, and a small bag of cosmetics. She also packed a stack of mostly unanswered letters from Karen. Lake knew she should break her ties with Karen, but it was easier said than done. She compromised by writing sporadically and giving Karen a box number to respond to.

She found a cheap hotel in Hollywood, parked her suitcase, and called George, feeling flattered, pleased, and terrified at how happy he sounded just to hear her voice. And here she was. Among the airplanes.

"The casting for pilots is really over by this time," George was telling her, "but I think I can keep you busy with commercials and things like that. First we just build up your visibility. Then we shop for a good pilot, something perfect for you—"

"George," she said with a laugh, "you make it sound so easy. What about being a struggling actress?"

"That's for other people." He grinned. "You're special. Get used to that idea." His face went puppy-soft. "I never thought I'd see you again. Oh, I dreamed about it, but I'm a pretty realistic guy. I just didn't think I'd hear from you. Well, here you are!" He laughed happily.

"Yes, here I am," she murmured. On impulse she leaned forward rather suddenly, pressing her cool lips to his. "Thanks."

"What for?"

There was no answer for that, so she let it go.

He rattled on about his plans for her future, how nice California was, how well she looked. She played with one of the airplanes, a hand-made wooden model, listened to him, and smiled gently to herself.

He asked her where she was staying, and if she hadn't made any other plans, would she care to have dinner with him?

She didn't hesitate when she answered yes.

George took her to one of his favorite restaurants. The owners had renovated a beautiful old stone farmhouse, decorating the interior to suit the continental cuisine. Mellow peach walls glowed against dark wood. Each table had a small bouquet of dogwood blossoms in a tiny glass vase, as well as a hurricane lamp. The effect was old-fashioned and charming.

"It just kills me when some bright-eyed kid walks into the office and tells me he's only interested in acting as an art."

"Why?" Lake twirled linguini with pesto sauce around her fork.

"If that were really true, they'd be happy to perform anywhere—a high school auditorium, the local playhouse, anywhere. If you come here to make it in movies or TV, it's because you want the whole package—the fame, the money, all of it. You gotta take the Devil's name if you play the Devil's game."

She looked at him steadily. "Is that what you think I want?"

"You?" His eyes were thoughtful. "No, I don't think I'd presume to know what you want."

"Am I that complicated?"

He laughed. "You dropped out for two years. *Two years.* I thought, maybe she's in trouble, maybe she needs my help, but I didn't even know where you were. Then, all of a sudden, you call me up like we'd spoken only a few days ago. I'm flattered as hell, but I'm curious. People do things for all sorts of reasons. I haven't begun to figure out yours."

She leaned forward, covering his hand with hers. "Maybe I just wanted to see you, George."

He smiled wryly. "My lady, that's darned nice of you, but I find it hard to believe it took you two years to come to that conclusion. It's okay to say you want the whole ball of wax. Everybody else in this town does."

"There isn't a great deal in this world that I'm sure of." She gave up on the pasta, setting her fork down alongside her plate carefully. George noted that all of her actions were executed with the exaggerated care of a drunk. *See? Just like all the other people. No problem here.* Her voice heightened in intensity though it did not become louder. "I think when a person is a star"—she spoke a little more cautiously now, eyes darting around, nailing other patrons with blue arrows—"she creates her own little niche, a place where she irrevocably belongs. *And nobody else can take her place.*" She was shredding a piece of bread into fluffy bits, then compressing each bit into a white pill. "I need that more than anything, to know that I can belong someplace. To prove that I'm not an outsider."

"Prove to whom?" George said quietly. "You may find—"

"What?" She laughed, quicksilver in her throat. "That the only place I belong is Mars during the ski season?" The image of Daniel Fox, dangerously alluring, grew in her mind. She pushed it away with some anger. A mound of little white pills clustered at her fingertips. She swept them into her palm and deposited them in the ashtray. "I'm glad I called you, that's all."

"That makes two of us." He spotted the waiter hovering nearby. "Do you want coffee or dessert?" he asked Lake. She shook her head, so he got the check from the waiter and they left.

"You can't hurry love," Harry sang along with the juke, "no, you just have to wait, she said love don't come easy, it's a game of give and take."

It was late enough for the bartender to be sick of the Supremes, sick of his job, sick of sunny Southern California, and sick of actors who had to get drunk on beer because they couldn't afford anything else. The bartender had a number of old Diana Ross albums at home he intended never to play again.

The bar was pretty quiet, which was normal for the dark side of morning. At one end a boy and a girl sucked up Bloody Marys and fondled each other cozily. At the other end a steady customer (and dedicated lush) held on to his Rob Roy for emotional support. In the middle of the bar sat the actor with the thing for Motown.

A nicely dressed lady, whom the bartender knew as an occasional patron, sat at a small table. She liked sweet drinks and would try several different kinds in the course of an evening. Brandy Alexander. Green crème de menthe. Ramos Fizz. Tonight he had made her a strawberry daiquiri, which she sipped at. She tipped nicely, and the bartender thought her a real lady.

The Supremes lapsed into silence.

"Goddamn," Harry swore, "would you believe I'm out of quarters?" He eyed the jukebox longingly.

The bartender squelched a smile. He wasn't expecting a tip from an out-of-work actor, but you never knew. Actors always wanted you to remember them when they made it big. He looked at Harry's empty glass. Never mind out of quarters, this guy didn't have enough for another beer.

"Don't you like the Supremes?" Harry smiled winningly at the bartender. "Wanna spring for a tune or two?" The bartender shook his head.

"Come on!" Harry swiveled on his barstool to face the cozy Bloody Mary drinkers. "Nobody here to stick up for good old Motown, the sound that made us what we are today?"

Without a word the stylishly dressed lady got up and went over to the juke. Smokey Robinson's distinctive voice exhorted her to "shop around." She smiled at Harry, moving slightly to the music.

They started to dance, a lazy shuffle of feet and arms. Not touching, swimming through the air with a cool bop, admiring each other's style.

She was about twelve years older than he was, Harry guessed, twelve prosperous years. (Later he found out his guess had been conservative. She was solidly in her forties.) Harry wouldn't have known silk from polyester, but he knew from the fit of her suit and the drape of her blouse that she wasn't doing her shopping at K-Mart. Expensive clothes tended to fit well; that much Harry knew about fashion. Good fit or not, he could only guess at the shape her body was in; all he could see was her legs. They were slim, not muscular but shapely. Harry was hoping he'd hold up as well in twelve years.

"Join me?" She motioned to her table with a manicured hand. The smile brought out a few lines around her eyes. So she wasn't a twenty-year-old babe, so she wasn't the blonde he'd seen in George Nichols's office. At least she appreciated Motown. "You're an actor." Her low voice stated the fact with assurance; it wasn't a question.

He laughed. "Does it show?"

"Oh, I deal a lot with people in the industry," she said casually, fishing in her clutch purse for a pack of cigarettes. "Actors have that certain look to them—you know, larger than life." She looked at him with frank speculation. "Are you larger than life?"

He couldn't resist. "Only where it counts." He took her lighter, thumbing the tiny flame into action. When she bent her blonde-streaked head to touch cigarette to flame, she moved closer, letting her sweet-smelling hair sweep along his shoulder. An errant strand brushed his bare neck, and he shivered. She felt it.

"I'm getting to you, aren't I, handsome stranger?" With a flip smile she reached under the table, lightly running her fingernail up and down his leg, from hip to thigh.

"You're no shrinking violet, I'll say that."

"I'm a Scorpio," she said, continuing her below-table massage. "Very hot sign. What's yours?"

"Dollar sign. Anything else you need to know about me?"

"Yes." She was using her fingertips now, brushing dangerously close to his groin. "How easy are you? I mean, do I have to buy you dinner?"

"I've had my dinner." He grabbed her hand and guided it where he wanted it. "Buy me breakfast."

"My goodness," she murmured, "you *are* larger than life." She gasped a little as his hand traveled up her skirt with startlingly accurate aim. "My name is Chris Hargreave."

"Harry Townsend. Hello, Chris."

"Hello, Harry. Wanna fuck?"

"I thought you'd never ask."

They stumbled out to her car. It was a four-door sedan, a roomy job. She leaned against the side of the car, pulling him toward her. They kissed deeply. He moved his hips against her, rubbing his erection against her mound. Through her bra her nipples poked at him. "Chris," he gasped against her neck. "let's get in the back seat."

"The back seat?" She started to laugh. "I haven't done *that* since high school."

"I can't wait, Chris." He brushed the hair away from her ear and took her earlobe between his teeth.

"I love that," she moaned. "How did you know?"

"All Scorpios love that," he mumbled around her ear. "The keys, Chris."

She unlocked the door, and they tumbled into the backseat, each pulling at the other's clothing. Harry got her elegant blouse off in record time. The front closure of her bra snapped open, releasing her breasts with charming alacrity. He put his lips to each in turn, delighting in her little cries of pleasure.

"Now for you," she rasped, dry-throated. She worked his pants down, scooting her body lower in the seat. The car was filled with the rustle of her fine clothes and the smell of her expensive perfume. She wore no panty hose. He wrapped his arms around her bare legs, kissing her inner thigh, where the skin was very soft.

She reached for him, stroking and fondling him until he thought he'd lose control. One leg was draped over the headrest of the driver's seat. The other she appeared to be trying to thrust through the rear window. Her arms outstretched, she pulled him closer until his chest just brushed the tips of her fine, large breasts. Against his ear she whispered, "Be nice to me," as though she had suddenly turned into another woman.

"Be nice." Her eyes were closed.

"Look at me, Chris."

Obediently she opened her eyes.

"Poor Chris," he said. "Sure, I'll be nice to you. It's a hard life for all of us, girl."

She smiled, a little half-sad smile. When he penetrated her, it was very gently, with great tenderness. She matched his rhythm. After she had become slick and wet, he pulled away teasingly. She put her hands on his buttocks and drew him in again, making herself a refuge. "Angel," she whispered over and over again in a tiny voice, "sweet angel." For some reason it affected him more deeply than any sexual acrobatics she could have pulled out of her bag of tricks.

"Angel."

When he came, she held him close, then washed him all over with her tongue, like a mother cat. She didn't come, but he believed she was content.

He rested against her, cooling off. She stroked his hair and murmured in her own language. It seemed like the nicest thing anyone had ever done for him.

After a while they untangled, and she climbed into the driver's seat and drove him to her house. It was, as Harry expected, a darn nice little place. Pool, jacuzzi. In the living room there were two framed sketches next to each other.

He pointed to one. "I like that."

She smiled indulgently. "I got it for twenty dollars in Venice. California, not Italy. The one next to it is a Dali. Worth a nice bit of change."

"I still like this one better," Harry maintained.

"You'll never get rich that way." She moved about, taking off earrings, draping her suit jacket over the back of a chair. "Actually I'm not mad about the Dali, either. I just bought it as an investment. Got a girlfriend?"

"Nope. Wouldn't have done what I did with you if I had."

"Honorable."

"Nope. Scared shit of getting killed by a jealous lady."

She smiled. "Oh, I like you. You make me laugh."

"Are you married?"

"Divorced." Her answer was curt. He assumed she didn't want to talk about it, but she went on. "We were married twenty-three years," she said quietly. "He's got a lovely little girl now. I think she's about nineteen. Great big eyes, lots of long, shiny hair, little breasts like a boy. Really a lovely girl. What's today, April twentieth? They were married a year ago today." She put her arm on Harry's shoulder. "You'll stay the night, won't you? I hate to wake up alone."

It was the black and purple dream.

She twisted in her sleep, wishing the dream away, but it would not go. Sighing, she resigned herself to it. Let it play itself out and pass into mist. Like a hundred times before. The dream was familiar, a nasty-toothed old friend, but the terror was always fresh.

She fell through the black and purple void with stomach-lurching speed, faster and faster, until she thumped onto her bed. A dream bed of soft white pillows. The linens were embroidered with an entwined "O" and "P." The bed was in the middle of a busy pedestrian crosswalk. They rushed around her, ignoring her, their speech a cacophony of buzzing consonants and odd clicks. A woman in an orange tabard turned to stare at her. The woman had no face. Skin flowed smoothly from her hairline to her collar without any form of indentation. No eyes. No mouth.

All the people were like that.

Except Lake.

The woman in orange clicked to her companions. They began to cluster around the bed, bumping sightlessly against the clean linen. Lake wanted to scream, but the people shoved their fingers in her mouth, their flaccid fingers, the tips unmarked with whorled prints like hers, like normal people. She choked, feeling their rubbery arms turn into manacles. Around her arms, around her legs. Across her forehead, binding her to the white pillow. She could not move.

Standing at the foot of the bed, the woman in orange waited patiently. Lake felt her toes begin to hurt, a strange, intense pain. As much as she could, she looked down. The lower part of her legs was disappearing.

But it still hurt.

Her toes had vanished, but she distinctly felt that crushing pain in her feet. A steamroller was cruising up the length of her body, higher and higher. Calves, knees, thighs, finally onto the trunk of her body, squeezing more than life out of her. Fingers began to vanish.

The woman in orange held up her hand, fingers outstretched. Fingerprints were appearing. She pulsed her hands eagerly. Waiting for more. Waiting for Lake's soul.

The steamroller was up to her throat. It stole her voice. It sealed her mouth. It crushed her cheekbones.

A red mouth bloomed on the other woman's face. The mouth smiled. Soundlessly Lake began to cry. Tears dripped from her lashes onto the bed. There was nothing else left of her. Worst of all her mind was changing. Cohesion of thought was ebbing. She was ceasing to be. She thought dimly, if only the pain would end, that would make losing herself worth it. And yet she was still frightened to go into the void.

The last thing she was aware of were her own blue eyes, staring back at her from another face.

"Wake up! Wake up, Lake, it's only a dream." George was holding her, letting her cry herself awake. "Okay now? You want a glass of water?"

"Whatever for?" She started laughing, wound up hiccupping. "Why do people always want to give you water when you have a bad dream?"

"Because they don't know what else to do," George said reasonably enough. He patted her shoulder. He wasn't half bad at it. "Maybe it's just sleeping in a strange place. I just couldn't let you stay at that fleabag hotel another night."

She'd been willing to follow his lead when he suggested she spend the night. Lake hadn't expected George to graciously offer her his guest room. Perhaps he was frightened she would reject him.

"Is there anything I can do for you?"

"No. I've had this dream before. It's nothing."

"Are you sure there's nothing I can do for you?"

She kissed him lightly. "You could make love to me."

The breath caught in his throat. He bent his head and returned her kiss in a restrained fashion. "Lady, there's nothing I'd like better, but I get the strangest feeling you wouldn't respect me in the morning. Just another snorting, pawing male anxious to jump your lovely bones. No, I think we'll get to know each other a little better first. I can wait. All right?"

"You're really special, George."

"Either that or the world's biggest idiot. Think you can sleep now?"

"Yes."

"Sure?"

"Uh-huh." She pulled the blanket up to her chin. "Good night, George. If you keep acting like Sir Galahad, I just might fall in love with you. Thought it only fair I warn you."

"Aha, I think the lady's on to us. Good night." He was up for a long time, pretending to read in his own bedroom, puzzling over what recurring dream was haunting her so. He felt sure there was some great mystery in her personal history. If he could just unravel her secret fears, she would fall in love with him, he was certain.

When he woke up the next morning, she was gone. She had taken a sheet of his stationery and fashioned a clumsy paper airplane, which she left on the kitchen table. That was it. No message. He thought of her moving around his quiet house in the early morning, touching his things, and felt her presence still there.

Bemused, he sat at his kitchen table holding the paper airplane. He'd waited two years for her to come to him. He wasn't going to wait another two years.

They made love again in the early morning, and when they woke up gummy-eyed at noon the next day, Harry was still fond of Chris. The unflattering light of day was showing total impartiality, but she still looked good to him. And those breasts would have looked good to a blind man. He padded naked to the bathroom, peed, and showered. In her closet he found a big terrycloth robe. It was hers, but the oversize styling didn't make him look too foolish. At least it wasn't pink.

He followed the sound of Chris's voice to the kitchen. She was on the phone. He rubbed her shoulder affectionately and started making breakfast. Necessity and a growing taste for the good things in life had taught him a few basic recipes: omelettes with tomatoes and basil, good French toast with vanilla-scented cinnamon. He found fresh basil growing in a little pot on the windowsill and decided on the famous Harry Townsend's tomato omelette. There were fresh flowers on the counter, in a cobalt blue vase. He pinched off a few blossoms and decorated her plate.

She was off the phone. "I don't eat breakfast as a rule. Too many calories."

"Break a few rules."

"Cooked in butter, I suppose?" She eyed the dainty plate hungrily. "Oh, hell, damn the cholesterol. I wasn't planning to live forever, anyway." Her eyes widened at the first bite. "This is darn good."

"Basic bachelor survival skills." He poured coffee for both of them. "This sure is a nice house. One of these days I'd like to have a place like this."

"Good coffee."

"Thanks."

She devoted her attention to his excellent omelette. "I have some dealings with people in the industry," she said. "Very often I have functions to attend—parties, premieres, boutique openings. Some women in my position have paid escorts, pretty boys who wind up going home with the bartenders. There's no . . . dignity to it. As for single men my age—well, let's just say this is a bad town to turn forty in." She kept her eyes on her plate. "I think you know what I'm getting at."

"More coffee?" Harry asked, feeling a little stunned.

"No thanks. Maybe later. We could help each other, Harry. Not that there's anything like a free lunch. It may sound old-fashioned, but I'd expect fidelity. I won't have people laughing at me. Not again. But in return I'd take care of you in style, Harry. I'd dress you like a king. I'd use what influence I have to help your career, although I can't make any promises in that area. There's a Jag sitting in my garage collecting dust. Part of my settlement. My ex was very fair, I must admit. I never drive it. And I'm sure we could work out something nice concerning pocket money." She cut a tomato with her fork and tucked it into her mouth. "I'm not looking for true love, Harry. I just want company."

With an effort he tore his eyes away from her fork traveling calmly from plate to mouth. "Chris, I appreciate your generosity, but—"

"Think it over. Give yourself a little time. Go out today, make your rounds, do whatever you have to do. You're welcome here tonight. I want you to know that." She picked a flower off her plate and brushed the soft petals against her lips. "You're very welcome here. Any time, whatever you decide."

Harry thought. "What color is the Jag?"

"Green." She smiled. "Like money."

Harry Townsend was having lunch with an actor pal. It was about a week after his first tryst with Chris Hargreave. He hadn't exactly been suffering.

"Jesus," the pal said, "look at you! A rich relative die and leave you a bundle?"

"Something like that," Harry said, stroking the collar of his new Ralph Lauren jacket with self-conscious pride.

"Something like that?" The actor pal laughed. "Give."

They both picked up their bloody rare burgers and munched.

"I met a lady," Harry said after a while. "A nice, generous patroness of the arts."

The actor pal looked like his eyes were going to fall onto his plate. "Before you go any further with this sordid little tale, could you please let me know if she has a sister?

"Jesus, Harry!" He started to laugh. "Most of us would kill for a setup like that. Is she decent-looking, or do you have to put a bag over her head?"

Harry gave him a sour look. "It happens she's a very attractive lady with a truly respectable set of knockers. Articulate, intelligent, does the *L.A. Times* crossword puzzle in ink, actually knows where Madagascar is—"

"If you blow this deal, buddy, you better grab the next bus back to East Shitkicker, Texas, or wherever the hell you came from. Marry the girl next door. Get a job in her daddy's feed store. Your kids can join the local 4-H club, raise pet steers. Sounds perfect."

"Hey, don't knock the 4-H club," Harry kidded.

"Is that the life you want?"

"No," Harry said slowly, "but I didn't figure to make a living off a sugar mommy."

"She's old enough to know what she's doing," the pal said. "Come on, Har. It'll all look wonderfully sordid in the autobiography."

"Thanks." Harry grinned. "You're always a source of moral inspiration." He picked up the check. The pal did not even make a show of protest. They parted amiably.

Harry got into the green Jag and pointed it toward the rich part of town. Every now and then he caught sight of his eyes in the rearview mirror. No new wrinkles. No evil light in them to mark his fall from grace. He looked well rested and well fed. He looked like a working actor. "What's the matter, pal?" He taunted his reflection. "You waitin' around for true love?'"

He spun the radio dial, trying to avoid the disco sound, which was everywhere. The local retro-rock station offered Buddy Holly. Almost twenty years gone, and he was still the best thing that ever happened to rock and roll. *And* he'd been a Texan.

The beautiful blonde from Nichols's office flitted through Harry's imagination, ethereal and yet terribly real. She *was* real. At the very second he was driving down Wilshire Boulevard, she was alive and breathing someplace else. Eating dinner, perhaps by herself. Sleeping on cool white sheets, hopefully by herself.

Somehow he was going to find her again . . . *and you're gonna love me, too.* The trade papers were on the seat next to him; at the next red he flipped them open and began to page through.

The light turned. Cars began to honk at the green Jag blocking traffic.

In the trades, on page sixteen, was a sketch of the mysterious blonde. *His* mysterious blonde. Bold print announced:

THIS WOMAN IS WANTED
for a promising career in films and television.

$10,000 REWARD
for any information concerning
the whereabouts of this woman!

CONTACT: George Nichols Agency

"George," Harry sighed, "I don't want to upset you, but this girl's *mine.*"

Before he went home, he picked up some flowers for Chris because he thought she might like that.

Sid Fraser had come to Hollywood before it was fashionable to be gay or black. Now, in the enlightened seventies, he was fashionable as hell on both counts. In his younger days he'd played at being an artist, complete with a trendy Greenwich Village loft infested with trendy Greenwich Village roaches. At least the roaches were decent about sharing their space with the rats. Sid cared deeply, passionately about everything. Especially his art. After three years of poverty and a variety of minor sexually transmitted infections, Sid came to the sad conclusion that he was no artist and no great judge of character. (At least where personal cleanliness was concerned.)

He moved to Hollywood hoping nobody would notice another homosexual black. It was 1959. People noticed. He got beat up a few times in various parts of Southern California. Eventually he found people like himself and through them a job. In '62 Sid found his niche. That was when he started his career as a makeup artist, so skilled that nobody cared if Sid Fraser went home and slept with his pet gorilla. Actresses fought over him, with quite a few actors joining in the fray, as well. Sid could take ten hard years off your face in one hour. He could disguise weak chins and nasty habits. He was a miracle worker.

Suddenly, inviting the dapper black makeup artist to your

party was the hip thing to do. *Just be careful not to leave him alone with your husband . . . tee-hee.* The famous, the rich, the brightest lights in the brightest town in the world wanted to be his friend. Sort of. One night, after one too many drinks, he had poured out his life story to an eminent screenwriter, a man known for his sensitive portraits of losers, the emotional and physical cripples of life. It was a mistake. The writer was looking for material, not a friend. Not a lover. Fortunately Sid's story was too racy even for Hollywood.

He began to decline invitations, making the excuse that his new lover (imaginary) was simply not quite the social butterfly. Sid was not so much hurt as disappointed. In public he twittered and flitted to the general delight of his clients. It was what they expected, and he believed in giving the people what they wanted, so long as he could keep his private life private. None of his clients really knew anything about him; where he lived, what he enjoyed doing in his spare time, if he was in love or hoped to be.

Now he was forty. If he had few illusions left, he still enjoyed his life. He had a very nice house with a beautiful garden, something he'd always wanted. He took good care of himself; no red meat, alcohol in moderation, forty-five minutes of exercise every morning to keep his slight build at a manageable 148 pounds. He still found his job rewarding. At night he went home alone (most of the time; Sid was no saint) and watched himself evolve from a quiet, well-mannered man into a fussy old eccentric. A fussy old homosexual eccentric. "The Lord surely has a strange sense of humor," Sid's mother had said when he'd informed her of his sexual preferences.

He was inclined to agree.

"More coffee?" The brown-haired girl who'd been waiting on him for the past month held a steaming pot aloft.

Sid held his cup out. "Thanks, dear." For the past month he'd been working on the new John Allison flick, lensing on location, in this case the nearest stretch of California coastline the producers could get cheap.

He watched the girl retreat to the waitress station, where she discreetly scratched her head with the eraser tip of her pencil. A dye job, he noted, an amateur one. Her scalp was dry from the harsh dye preparation. Probably a blonde underneath there. A blonde who didn't mind working the late shift in a dead quiet café while most of her peers were out boogying their buns off.

"Lake!" another waitress called out, "I'm going home now, okay?"

"Okay, see you tomorrow." Sid's girl scratched her head again, frowning a little.

It wasn't so much that she intrigued him, Sid reasoned; she *beckoned* to him. His emotions were not easily provoked. No matter how much he enjoyed his work, it all came down to another face to be painted, light shaped by shadow. Dark to recede. Light to come forward. It was a science, exacting and cold. It wasn't so much that she was the perfect canvas for his art. He did want her, though not like other men. The industry's most beautiful women had cheerfully offered their bodies to him. *C'mon Sid, you just haven't met the right girl.* He had not been tempted. But he did want *this* girl. He wanted to be her friend. He was lonely just like she.

She brought over his scrambled and bacon. "There you go, Sid."

"Why don't you draw one, or whatever you waitress gals call it, and join me." He smiled invitingly, folding up his *Variety* and tossing it on the table. "I'm simply starved for a little intelligent conversation."

She shook her finger at him. "Serves you right for going into show biz."

"Please." He batted his eyelashes comically. Sid had enough charm to do things like that and not look like a total idiot. "I'll let you steal my toast, you wretched child."

"Sinking to bribery?" She poured herself a cup and sat down. "How's the movie doing?"

He shrugged. "Let's just say it's not Oscar time." He offered her a piece of toast, which she absently dunked in her coffee.

"I'd never even heard of John Allison until you started coming in here."

"*Nobody* had heard of John Allison a year ago. One season on the soaps, and they pack him off to la-la land to make movies. Not that the precious lad can act, but when you're nineteen and possibly the most gorgeous male a smiling God ever created . . ."

"Is he a real pain in the ass?"

"Of course, dear one, but he's not really a bad boy when you get to know him. Very sweet but terribly wild. He's a damn sight better than the leading lady. No redeeming social value there, I'm afraid. Honestly, you could walk in and do the part. You're certainly pretty enough."

"Oh, no," she said hastily. "No show biz for this girl."

"Why not? They'd want to blonde you up a bit—"

"No." She took another piece of toast and nibbled, looking a little ashamed. "Sorry, I didn't mean to bite your head off."

"Well, enough of me and my sterling priceless opinions. I suppose you've got loads of amusing chatter. Working in a diner is second only to working in a beauty salon for good gossip. Now what dirt did you overhear today?"

She sat back stiffly. "I don't invite confidences. I guess people don't take to me."

Sid handed her another piece of toast. She looked down at his plate. "Stop this. I'm eating your whole breakfast." Still she took it.

His bright face looked amused. "You're chock-full of mysteries, aren't you, sweetness? I suppose that's why you don't invite confidences, as you put it. You've no wish to reciprocate with a secret or two of your own."

"What makes you think I'm mysterious?"

"Oh, things." He fanned himself with his copy of *Variety.* "Just things."

"What things?" she countered, taking a scrap of bacon from his plate.

"For one, why a lovely like you spends her nights working in this tacky little dump when you could make a fortune selling toothpaste. Or why there's no sweet young man waiting around to walk you home."

"We're in Southern California," she told him teasingly. "All the sweet young men are more interested in you than me. And I don't see anybody waiting to walk you home."

He winked at her. "I'm working on John Allison. Do you think he kisses on the first date? Ah, well, he's in love with someone else."

"Himself," they said together, laughing.

"The shoot ends in two weeks," Sid told her. "Aren't you going to miss me *terrrrribly?"* He slapped her hands away from his last piece of toast. "God, you're fast."

"I'll cry into my pillow every night." He was watching her with an expectant expression. "What, Sid, what? You've been sitting there all night with that charming I-know-something-you-don't-know look on your face. What is it?"

He folded *Variety* over to page sixteen and placed it in front of her. "You've been holding out on me." This time, when she groped for his plate for the last bit of toast, he let her.

"Weeelll." She let out a long, slow breath. "Some people find the most interesting ways to get a girl's attention. Thanks for letting me know."

"Is that all?" he exploded. "Tinseltown's top agent is scouring the countryside for you, and that's all you have to say for yourself?"

"That's it," she said dryly. "More coffee?"

"Sit!" he commanded. *"Tell."*

"There's nothing to tell. I met George a few years ago when I was modeling in New York. He was very sweet to me. When I got in touch with him in L.A., he was just as nice. The only problem is . . . oh, God, I'm never exactly sure why I do half the batty things I do. I think he wants a relationship, which I'm not ready to get into. I really like George. I don't want to hurt him."

Sid roared. "Let me get this straight. You're afraid of breaking an agent's heart. How *novel!* Did it ever occur to you, oh, egotistical one, that our Georgie may only be interested in you professionally? That he just wants to make a buck off your gorgeous hide?"

Her face went blank. "Well, no—"

"Look, angel." Sid was pure business. "It's all fine and good to be the darling kook I've come to know and love these past few weeks, but what's wrong with being a millionaire kook?"

"It's not that easy," she protested weakly. "I don't want to get into something I can't handle." Still her mind raced. If he wants me back so badly . . . "There are other things to consider."

"Like the rent," Sid said pointedly. "I don't know how to get this through your head, but there's nothing wrong with being rich. It's actually a preferred state of existence." His voice softened. "Look, I happen to know George, professionally of course, and he's a good agent and a decent human being. If you're going to be pursued, he's the cream of the crop. Why don't you call him? It takes two people to have a relationship, sweetness. You don't have to start anything you're scared to finish. Go on, call him. I'll hold your little hand while you talk to him, if that'll make you feel better."

That was precisely what she had him do. "Hello, George." She laughed uneasily into the pay phone receiver. "Guess who?"

There was one moment of dead shock. "Hello, sweetheart," he said. "I knew you'd come walking back into my gin joint someday. I'm a patient guy, sweetheart."

"That is possibly the worst Bogart I have ever heard."

"I like it better than your Jesse Owens. Are you going to come back like a good little girl so I can make you a star?"

"Yes, George." A giddy feeling bubbled up in her. *A star.* Sid was right. This was going to work out fine.

"I'll send a limo for you."

"No, I'll take a bus. I like the bus."

"Lake—"

"Trust me, George," she said evenly. "I said I'm coming back. Trust me on this, and the rest will follow."

"All right. Tomorrow then?"

"Tomorrow." She hung up.

"There." Sid patted her shoulder with maternal concern. "Don't you feel better?"

"No." She laughed. "I feel scared, but it's a whole lot better than feeling nothing at all. Oh! I guess you get the reward."

"Name your first child after me." He paid his check, put down a tip, and preened a little, checking his reflection in the chrome napkin holder. "Other than that"—he grinned—"I would *love* to get your face in my hands, professionally speaking. What I could do with those cheekbones. 'Bye, dearest; be good. Failing that, at least be careful."

He walked out onto the beach and aimlessly pointed himself back to his hotel. He wasn't sleepy, but the town was so small that the movie theater didn't have a midnight show. Sighing a little, he resigned himself to a small dose of small-town ennui.

The phone was ringing as he got his key out. "All right, all right!" he told the phone. "Can't you hang on a minute?" He picked up the receiver, not waiting for the voice at the other end to identify itself. "George," he said wearily, "not only are you unbelievably impatient, but you do the worst Bogart anybody ever heard anywhere."

"I was practicing that Bogie for weeks." He chuckled. "She's coming back, Sid, she's coming back!"

Sid slipped off his shoes, wiggling his toes to get the blood moving. "She's not back yet," he cautioned. "You couldn't wait for me to call you? I barked my shin trying to get to the phone in time. She's as lovely as you said, and you know I've seen them all. You'd better go slow, George. That's the only advice I'll give you on this."

"Bullshit." George laughed. "I know you better than that. You live to give advice." They went back a long way, to George's Greenwich Village days, when *he* wanted to be an actor. "On the level, Sid," George was asking, "what did you think of her?"

"Oh, God, I'm no great judge of character."

"Sure you are. You've already made all the major mistakes of life."

"Thanks a lot," Sid said tartly. "Well . . . I like her—it's impossible not to like her—but she's so troubled. She's not right with herself."

"You want to translate that into English for me, Sid?"

"You asked for my opinion." Sid was beginning to feel irritated. "I'm sorry if I can't express myself better than that. This girl may have originated the phrase 'identity crisis.' She'll be very dependent on you, but the second you get close, she'll run." He paused a second. "Are you in love with her?"

George's answer took too long. "I barely know the girl. I like her. You said yourself that it's impossible not to like her."

"Then like her. Be her friend, her confidant. But if you're looking for a long-term relationship, find someone else to love."

"I barely know her," George repeated. "I gotta dash, Sid. Thanks again for helping me out. You're a great guy and a hell of a dancer. If I were gay, I'd be chasing your butt all over town."

"You're too ugly for me, George.'

The agent sounded hurt. "You used to say I was just your type."

"I didn't know you were going to leave me for a blonde. Honestly, George, how tacky." Sid yawned, hinting inelegantly. "Haven't you got something to do, deals to make, starlets to attack?"

"Absolutely. I'll call up half a dozen or so. Take care, Sid. Try not to get crabs."

"Same to you, my friend." His hotel room had a small terrace, just big enough to stick a lawn chair and a small table on. Still, the tiny space caught a refreshing breeze from the ocean. Sid sat out on the terrace, trying to figure out why George's call had disturbed him. It hit him after a while. Sid really did love George, as his oldest and closest friend; maybe in another way he didn't care to admit to himself. Why complicate his life further? Sitting there in his little lawn chair, letting the sea breeze scent him with salt, it hit him that in finding his friend's mysterious lady love, maybe he hadn't been doing George such a big favor after all.

13

MATT AND KAREN had spent the first year of married life driving each other completely crazy. Financially supporting your husband sounded noble and admirable on paper. In reality it meant no money for recreation, clothing, or red meat. About once every two weeks Mrs. Singer drove into the city with huge care packages. Monthly parcels arrived from Mrs. Bloom in Chicago, containing carefully packed baked goods and on one bizarre occasion, a ten-pound sack of raw rice. An explanation came later: that week Mrs. Bloom had had a terrible cold and had sent *Mr.* Bloom to the market. Mrs. Bloom promised never to get sick again. Even Aunt Sophie would send over the dreaded pot roast every now and then.

Right about the time Lake had made up her mind to go back to George, life in New York began to smooth out for Karen and Matt. Matt got a job as an associate director on a children's television show, *Hurdy-Gurdy*. It was a mixed blessing: a steady paycheck left Karen more time for her career, a career that could certainly be helped by a husband in the business. On the other hand, *Hurdy-Gurdy* rarely hired any actors over the age of twelve. Her one hot connection shot to hell. At least Matt wasn't likely to be seduced by any luscious young starlet unless he was developing a penchant for pedophilia.

Still, they were doing all right. They could afford to eat out twice a week, if one meal was at McDonald's. They went to the movies, carefully analyzing each film afterward over hot chocolate in the winter, root beer floats in the summer. Karen had never believed she would love anyone so much. There was only one problem.

Matt would not make love to her.

In their first months together as man and wife, they made a few disastrous attempts, always at Karen's initiation. It hurt a lot down there. She knew it was supposed to hurt less as time went on, but they never seemed to reach that point. After a while she stopped asking. It was too much like begging.

She was philosophical. She was willing to believe that all of Matt's passion belonged to his work. He's a workaholic, she would tell herself proudly, a sure sign of future success. Matt was going to be somebody; all she had to do was stay married to him, and she'd be somebody, too. She was lucky to have him. He was kind and gentle, supportive of her career. He was her best friend, her personal manager, and what woman wouldn't kill to have that kind of marriage? If she worked at it hard, she could make herself believe these things. Deep inside she was dying a little, drying up and blowing away like a white-headed dandelion.

Matt was so good; the fault had to lie with her. Avidly she read every magazine she could get her hands on that offered advice on clothes and makeup. She dressed better, paying attention to her body type and her coloring. For the first time in her life, men watched her as she walked down the street. There was something untouched and fine about her, a wistful innocence. Men watched her, seeing a pretty young woman with a serious expression and a dancer's slight build. Their catcalls and whistles embarrassed and frightened her, but she would not wear shapeless clothing or go out with no makeup. She would sit at her mirror dedicatedly stroking mascara onto her lashes. Careful about her appearance she most assuredly was, but deep inside was the irrational, fervent belief that if she could just get the mascara perfect, her husband might want her.

These were Karen's most secret thoughts. She tried not to dwell on them, and she shared them with no one. She loved her husband very much, and she knew he loved her.

From the outside it looked like a perfect marriage.

The morning had started out chilly, but as the day wore on, it promised to turn into a scorcher, too hot for early June. Karen regretted wearing her jacket, but she'd left the apartment early to make rounds. Looping her jacket over one arm, she went over to a pay phone on the street, praying it wasn't broken.

"Eastman residence," a disinterested voice intoned.

"Hello, this is Karen Bloom. May I speak to Mrs. Eastman?"

"She's unable to come to the phone now."

"Well, she'd invited me over for tea this afternoon. I just wanted to check and see that everything was all right."

"One moment, please."

Cursing, Karen fed more change into the pay phone before the housekeeper came back with a curt, "Mrs. Eastman is looking forward to seeing you this afternoon."

Five cents extra just to hear that. She counted her money, figuring trains and the odd cup of coffee at Chock Full O' Nuts. Two dollars ahead of the game, easy. With her usual quick step she walked the four blocks to her next appointment. In between the grand Broadway theaters were little doorways leading to decrepit office buildings. Some of the agencies housed there looked like they hadn't prospered since vaudeville died, but they survived.

Karen knew this particular agency was on its last legs. There was no receptionist, everything was covered with dust, and the leather chair behind the desk was cracked and ancient. Still, this agent had consented to an interview. He had been cordial on the phone, and though Karen had never met him before, he sounded nice. His long Dutch surname was loaded with double vowels, so Karen just waited in the doorway.

His watery blue eyes lit on her. "Yes?" He was abrupt but not nasty. "You are?"

"Karen Bloom." She offered her hand, which he regarded mildly before he enclosed it in his. "We spoke yesterday afternoon?"

"Of course." He motioned her to a folding chair. "You have some pictures?"

She handed him her head shot and résumé, answering his questions about her training and experience. He inquired about her personal life, and again she answered as honestly as she could: yes, she was married; yes, she loved her husband very much. He gave her some dialogue to read and stared at his knobby fingers as he fed her the cues. Afterward he was silent for such a long period of time that she thought he had fallen asleep or quietly taken a stroke on her.

"Miss," he said eventually, "you're a dear, sweet girl. I believe your husband is a lucky man. Go home to him."

"Sir?"

He smiled kindly. "You understand how this business works. An illusion. I present an illusion, you present an illusion. All the same, yes? You are to give me the illusion that a pretty young girl like yourself is . . . willing. Understand? You are not supposed to sit there telling me about how happy you and your husband are. That is no illusion. You see? You cannot be successful in this business unless you offer the illusion."

"The illusion that I would sleep with you," she said in a flat voice. "And what if I did? You'd help me then?"

He came around the desk and stood in front of her. "You're a very pretty girl." His large hand moved over her hair lightly. She could hear his breath whistling in his nostrils. "Very pretty hair. You wash it every day?"

"Most times. It's no bother."

His hand became heavy, bowing her head. Karen forced her body to stay glued to the chair. What was the big deal? She wasn't a virgin, and she needed the work. How bad could it be? She could close her eyes and pretend she was someplace else.

"Very pretty. A little like some of the stars of my day. Fragile. Like a little flower." One hand fumbled at his zipper. The other pressed her head forward.

"No!" She leaped to her feet and began to run, sobbing wildly.

When she was halfway down the stairs, she saw another girl coming up, treading carefully, balancing portfolio and purse on her shoulder. She was a little older than Karen, a little hard-eyed but pretty. A big girl with plushy hips and a pillowy chest. Her makeup was heavy but attractive, big dark eyes and a red mouth. She stared straight ahead with a resolute expression.

When she got to the top of the stairs, the girl set her portfolio down, fished a Kleenex out of her purse and wiped her lipstick off.

She set her face in more cheerful lines and opened the door. "Hi! Any work today?"

Evelyn was waiting in what she called her sitting room. It was a small room off the more formal living room. The decorator had been expressing her cluttered English garden look. When Evelyn was actually in the room, she looked like a pale orchid amid the riotous prints of roses and petunias, if you could find her at all. The decorator thought it was one of the biggest mistakes of her career. The lady of the house was not supposed to be overwhelmed by the wallpaper.

"Hello," Evelyn chirped, as Karen tried to locate her. "Did you have trouble getting here? Please, sit down." She pointed to a well-upholstered chair, its plump little legs daintily skirted.

"Thank you." Karen sank so far into the chair that her toes

barely touched the rug. 'That was nice of you to send a car to pick me up at the station." Despite the fact that she and Lake had been roommates, this was the first time Karen had met Lake's mother. Lake *never* spoke about her family. Understandably, Karen was curious. As she'd thought, Evelyn was very pretty in a vague sort of way. Her face was like a big baby doll's—pink, with very regular features and a blankly pleasant expression. Her skin was very pale and perfect, with remarkably few wrinkles. The eyes staring innocently up at Karen were a light brown. I suppose she gets the blue eyes from her father, Karen thought. It took her a minute to realize that despite the languor, Evelyn was a good-size woman, taller and heavier than Karen herself. "Mrs. Eastman, I was wondering—"

"Tea?" Evelyn said in a bright voice."You will have some tea, won't you?" The housekeeper pushed a tea cart into the sitting room.

"Yes, thanks."

Scowling a little at Karen's request for three sugars, the housekeeper, a clear-eyed lady of mammoth proportions, served up the tea and a few small sandwiches. Karen hoped there was more to come; she was starving. Eveyln touched the housekeeper's hand in her hesitant way. "Amanda's been with my family since I was a child. I'd be lost without her."

"Yes, you would," Amanda said. She left with a heavy tread, glaring at Karen over one meaty shoulder.

Evelyn leaned forward as if she were about to impart a great secret. Karen leaned toward her eagerly. "She used to live on a farm," Evelyn whispered.

With great disappointment Karen sat back. "Mrs. Eastman, I was wondering if you'd heard from Lake. I haven't heard much from her since she moved to the Coast, just a few letters and I was getting a little worried."

Light eyes stared indifferently. "Lake's in California."

"Yes, I know. It's just . . . well, two years is a long time. Surely she's written you to say where she is, how she is . . ."

Evelyn was nodding in agreement. "Do you know"—again she spoke in that confidential whisper—"I don't like to speak on the telephone. That's why I didn't come to the phone when you called earlier. I didn't want you to feel badly about that."

"I don't. Lots of people don't like the telephone, I guess. It always takes you out of the bathtub for one thing." I am definitely sounding like an idiot here, Karen told herself. Calm down and stick to the facts. Something told her Evelyn could digress just fine on her own.

The lady in question was smiling into her tea. "Lake is fine."

"That's certainly a relief. Where is she? What's she doing?"

"I don't know."

"Did she write? Or call?"

"I don't speak on the phone. I think I told you that."

"Then how . . . you haven't heard from her at all?"

"Lake is fine," Evelyn repeated. "I feel it in my heart. There was no need to call or write."

"In two years," Karen burst out, "you've made no effort to get in touch with your only daughter? I think that's a little strange, Mrs. Eastman, if you'll forgive my saying so. It's not the way I would have handled things."

"You're not like us," Evelyn said. "You don't think people could be happier away from their families. I think she is. She was never happy here."

You're not like us. Karen looked at the grand surroundings. Her own mother had decorated with plastic fruit and fake cut crystal. Karen had always wanted to live in a fine house like the Eastman mansion. However irrational, she wondered how Lake could have been so unhappy with so many fine and beautiful things around her.

Evelyn plucked aimlessly at the sheer fabric of her sleeves. Her hands were large, in defiance of her overall daintiness, large and mottled slightly with brown spots. "She would walk through this house"—eyes cast to the side, Evelyn visualized scenes from the past—"not like a for-real child. Not . . . noisy and forever breaking things, exploring. She was like a pretend child, a little visitor. Like some other people had left her with us and would someday come and take her away. She was always so careful. Like a little visitor. I never really felt she was ours. Karl—Mr. Eastman—understands." For a moment the vagueness receded. "My memory is not very good. I think it was at one time better than it is now. But I *do* remember . . ." She changed her mind abruptly. "I think Lake is happier away from here."

"Don't you miss her? Don't you worry about her?"

The pale woman was silent.

"Don't you love her?"

"I love her as much as I can," Evelyn said slowly. "But you have to understand she was never really ours. Karl understands, he really does. I'm glad she's not here anymore." She motioned to the gleaming tea service. "More tea?"

"No. Please excuse me," Karen said numbly. "I have to be getting back."

Evelyn held out her hand, the queen marking the end of an audience. "Thank you for coming to see me." As Karen ignored her hand, Evelyn lifted it to the brooch at her throat. It was a pretty piece of jewelry, silvery initials "E.P." against onyx.

"I didn't." Karen said. "I didn't come to see you at all." She couldn't find her jacket anywhere and reluctantly decided to ask Amanda where it had been stashed. As she mounted the grand marble stairway, she heard Amanda the faithful cursing a blue streak upstairs.

"To hell with you, bitch!" came the angry retort.

"I'll give you bitch," Amanda answered, showing a spectacular lack of imagination. "I'll give you bitch so good, you won't know which end is up."

Curiosity got the better of her. Karen ran up the stairs, anxious to see who had the guts to stick up to American Gothic. Amanda's opponent was a lively black girl about Karen's age. Pinned to her uniform was a NOW button. "Look, I am just here for today," she told the belligerent Amanda. "How was I supposed to know not to clean in here?"

"You know, you know darn well!" Amanda's face was turning purple. "We never clean in the Mister's office, and you know that!"

"If you don't say anything, I sure won't."

This did nothing to calm the irate housekeeper. "You come in here and make a mess of the Mister's office, and I'm supposed to say nothing!" Amanda had a full head of steam, and she seemed determined not to let it go to waste. "If it weren't for your mother . . . look at this mess you made! Just look at this!"

One desk drawer had been pulled out. It was resting on a chair.

"Look at what?" the black girl said. "I was putting some pencils away, you came by and started hollering . . . You got me so crazy I pulled the drawer out by mistake. Big deal. It slips right back in. It's not like I broke anything." She turned and saw Karen standing there. "What's your problem?"

"Karen Bloom, just visiting."

"Okay, just visiting, help me get this drawer back in. This sucker's heavy."

Amanda stood by stolidly, watching as each girl grabbed an end and wrestled the drawer back to its rightful place. "I want you out of here," she announced, her remark apparently aimed at both. "Out of here as soon as you finish that." Her heavy step signaled her departure.

"A pleasure," the black girl grumbled. "I wouldn't work here if my life depended on it."

"Are you temporary here?" Karen gasped. That damn drawer *was* heavy.

"No, my mom works here, and she had to go to the dentist today. She asked me to fill in for her. But I don't care if all her teeth fall out, this is the last time I'm ever going to do this. Careful, I don't want this thing falling on my toes."

They inched the drawer onto its track. Karen put her hand underneath the drawer to steady it. Her stomach fluttered. There was an envelope taped to the bottom of the drawer; she could feel it. For a moment she toyed with the idea of just ripping the envelope free. Her new pal wouldn't protest; Amanda, still fuming in the hallway, was another story. Reluctantly she slipped the drawer, secret envelope intact, back into the desk.

"To hell with this place," the girl said cheerfully. "The people here are all crazy." She pulled off her apron and dropped it unceremoniously onto the floor. "Let Amanda have a hissy fit about *that;* this girl is out of here." She looked around the office, shaking her head. "Certifiable. Every last one of them."

"Absolutely," Karen agreed. "Lucky they were born rich."

"No," the girl said slowly, "there is no luck in this house." Her face brightened. 'I'm up for a burger and fries. What about you?"

"Sounds great."

Fifteen minutes later, in a diner a few miles away, the two girls had exchanged thumbnail biographies and were chatting away over hamburgers and Cokes.

Her name was Rena. She was going for a Master's in psychology, working her way through school any legal way she could. The last thing she wanted was to spend her life cleaning up after white people the way her mother did. Nope, she was going to get the same white people on the analyst's couch and make a fortune off them. Poetic justice. Of course, until she got her degree, there wasn't anything wrong with helping her mother out every now and then. Rena had worked for the Eastmans sporadically since she was in high school.

"Then you knew Lake," Karen said excitedly.

"I saw her around," Rena corrected. "I would not go so far as to say I knew her. She was very quiet. And then, out of nowhere, she would just do something really hairy."

"Like what?"

"Like disappear for a day or two. And the nightmares. God, she had terrible nightmares. Wake up screaming, the whole bit."

"Lots of people have nightmares. I don't think that's so strange."

"That's not all. She would take things."

Karen stared at her in disbelief. "Lake never stole anything."

"Not that you knew," Rena reminded her. "I remember once, I must have been about eight or nine, my mom took the two of us to Rye Playland. She bought us both these little plastic mirrors with these tacky little sea shells glued all around. I mean, these things were horrible, with these blue and green and pink shells. Well, I thought that girl was going to have heart failure. She did everything she could to yank that dumb mirror out of my hands. Between mom and me we kept her away, but a few days later you better believe I couldn't find that stupid little mirror anywhere."

"That doesn't make any sense," Karen protested. "Why would anybody steal anything they already had?"

"That's just it," Rena stated triumphantly. "She didn't want me to have the mirror because it was *exactly* the same as hers. Don't you get it? The girl has a major identity problem. Let's say she has a boyfriend and you got a boyfriend. She's going to want what you got."

"So?" Karen said, feeling a little uneasy. "Don't a lot of girls go through things like that, stealing each other's boyfriends, petty jealousies?"

"It's not the same," Rena insisted. "Lake doesn't know who she is, right? So she goes after your guy because, well, maybe things are no good with her guy and yours is a decent sort of person. *He's* the one she should have gotten, but *you* were there first. A case of mistaken identity.

"Somehow you took her place, and she's trying to get it back." Rena took a bite of her now cold hamburger and swallowed quickly. "I love psychology. I can't wait till I can start practicing. My professor thinks I have a real gift for it."

"I'm sure you'll be very good," Karen said weakly. "I think Mrs. Eastman's a little weird, too. Is she, ah . . ."—she groped for a suitable term—"father-fixated or anything interesting like that?"

"She's a real sad case. She had a stroke when Lake was a kid, so she's a little incapacitated. Her memory's not too good. She's very impressionable; I think she still believes in Santa Claus. It's really kind of sad. Mr. Eastman, he just ignores both of them. Not that he isn't a little strange himself. I didn't pull that drawer out for nothing. Do you know what I found in there once? A membership card to Phantom's."

Karen pretended she knew what Phantom's was. From Rena's expression, it was obviously a cross between Studio 54 and the Marquis de Sade's rumpus room.

"Poor Lake," Rena sympathized. "No wonder she's totally fucked up. Is she in trouble? Did she kill anybody?"

"Oh, no," Karen, said, aghast at Rena's clinical delight in Lake's twisted psyche. "She's just disappeared."

"I wouldn't worry. I don't think she's self-destructive. But if I were you, I'd keep my distance. People like her are a terrible drain on your own energy."

Karen nodded in feigned agreement. Something was bothering her. She would have killed for a picture of Karl Eastman. "What does he look like?"

"Who?"

"Mr. Eastman."

"Old Karl?" She thought a moment. "Good-looking in a very corporate way. I think he wears three-piece suits in the tub. What's up?" She laughed. "You like older men?"

Karen shrugged. "It's just fun to see which parent your friends take after."

"That's your idea of fun?"Rena mused for a second. "I think Lake takes after her mother more than her father. But he is handsome, with that wavy brown hair and those deep-set brown eyes."

Karen looked at her in mild surprise. In high school she had been shown how to determine genetic traits with Mendel's square.

"Rena, isn't that unusual, two brown-eyed parents having a blue-eyed child?"

The other girl laughed. "No."

"What about Mendel's square? I remember that from science class."

"That doesn t even work for hamsters. No, she's old Karl's kid, all right. They're both warped."

Matt got home late. The apartment was empty, but the TV was on, as well as every light in the house. Since Karen and the laundry basket were both missing, Matt came to the brilliant conclusion that she and the laundry might be in the laundry room in the basement, where he found Karen transferring clothes from dryer to basket.

"Oh, poor you." Karen chuckled softly. "You look like you've been through the wringer."

"Here, let me do that." He took an armload of towels from her. Grimacing, he checked his watch. "God, is it really eleven o'clock?"

"Sure is. Everything come out okay?" She opened dryer number three and hauled out the linens.

"Eventually." He took two corners of the flat sheet she offered him and backed away. "How was your day?"

"Well, Lake's mother was awfully strange."

"Besides that."

"Par for the course. A lecherous agent, a pornographic playwright, nothing I couldn't handle." She put her corners together, Matt did likewise, and they walked together. Corners met, Karen bent slightly and folded the sheet in half. "Matt, is there something on your mind?"

He found a hand towel and made a big production of folding it. "You know those little stories you write?" he said a shade too casually.

"Sure. Matt, if you're going to spend all night folding that one little towel, I'd just as soon you didn't help me." She took the towel from him and tossed it into the basket.

"I showed your stories to a couple of people at work—"

"You didn't! How could you? Those stories were private. They were just about stupid things—my growing up, you and me, me and Lake." She fell silent a moment. "Uh . . . what did they think? No!" she added rapidly. "If anybody said anything horrible, I really don't want to know. But if anybody said anything nice or helpful, I can handle that."

"Everybody loved your stories!" He cranked his long body forward with such haste that he nearly knocked over the laundry basket. "I talked to a few people. . . . Well, they're willing to give you a test drive as a writer for *Hurdy-Gurdy.* No promises, but I'm sure once they see your work—"

She slammed the dryer door shut. "I don't *want* to write for *Hurdy-Gurdy.* I don't want to write at all. I want to act. All you do is push me toward this writing business, which I know nothing about, and could care less. I never knew you were so against my acting career."

"Your acting career"—he opened the dryer door and pulled out a sock she had missed—"is bringing you nothing but grief and some juicy anecdotes to put in your memoirs someday. You like dodging old leches who think they own you just because you need a job? You like that life?"

She started to cry. If Karen had one gift, it was probably that she didn't look hideous when she cried, the way most girls did. Her nose didn't get red and drippy. She cried like Mary Pickford in her heyday as a silent film star. Very quietly. After two years of marriage this was always her best shot, going for sympathy.

"I don't know what else to do. This is what all the other girls do: make the rounds, fend off the passes. Why can't I handle it as well as they do? I feel like I'm trying to get across the river and the bridge is washed out. What do I do?"

"Build a bridge, my love. Become your own connection. Besides, there's a lot more glory in being a struggling writer than a struggling actress."

"I don't know if I can do it."

"Well." Matt shrugged. "Do you know if you can't?"

"I don't know that, either."

"See?" He smiled. "You're halfway there."

She kissed him. "I love you."

"Yeah, sure. You're just using me for my connections."

"Not at all. It's your manly strength that drives me wild." She shoved the filled laundry basket at him. "Go on, impress the hell out of me."

In the empty apartment upstairs, the TV continued to play. Gliding spectrally into their small, cluttered living room, amidst Karen's papers and neatly boxed résumés, Matt's file cabinets, and old copies of *Variety*, peeping into the jars and pots like a visitor left alone to explore, the figure of Lake flickered from the set.

"Witchcraft perfume," she whispered huskily, holding a tiny flask to one sculpted cheekbone, "because all's fair in love and war."

A few weeks later Karen sat down to write a letter.

6/20/74

Dear Rena,

I hope you don't mind me writing you. I figured if I sent the letter care of your mom at the Eastmans', it would reach you okay.

Anyway, how are your studies going? You really got me interested in the human psyche—you know, why people do things, etc. etc. I was wondering if maybe you could recommend some good books for a lay person. Don't laugh too loud, but it seems that I'm going to be doing a little freelance writing for a children's television show. So anything on child psychology would be great. Well, I will make this short, as I am sure you are very busy. Thanks for your time, and I do hope you write back. I just love writing letters.

Karen Bloom
608 East 78th St.
NYC 10028

P.S. How are your mom's teeth?

7/2/74

Dear Karen,

I was surprised to hear from you, but it was a pleasant surprise. I've been really crazy here because I'm packing up to actually go to fuckin' Australia (can you believe it?!?) to study with this fabulous lady who's the leading expert on phobia work. I've enclosed a bibliography that I hope will be helpful. The titles that are underlined are particularly easy to read. Some of them can get pretty technical.

I'm also enclosing my address in Sydney, so you can keep me posted. There are a lot of books I'd love to recommend to you. Seeing how I'm moving halfway across the world, I could use a friendly letter every now and then. I love to write letters, too.

Yrs. truly,
Rena Wheaton

P.S. Mom had to have a root canal, but she's okay now. Sweet of you to ask.

14

September 12, 1977
LOS ANGELES

"HEY, SILKY!"

Lake grinned, waving madly to the young men in the convertible. They all wore T-shirts that read "U. S. Olympic Drinking Team." "Silky, we love you!"

She blew them a kiss, laughing. She was riding high. *The Girl Upstairs* had originally been a summer replacement, just another jiggle-vid sitcom in a summer filled with T and A. It was George's first attempt at producing, though, and he was determined to succeed. Based very loosely on *The Seven Year Itch*, with a dash of Walter Mitty thrown in for good measure, *The Girl Upstairs* had the best writers money and flattery could buy. George was starting a literary department, this sitcom was his first package deal—his actors, his writers. George liked it.

The glory, however, was all Lake's. Silky Shaugnessy ("Sounds like an Irish con artist," she'd joked) bounced into America's living rooms once a week with her Gracie Allen witticisms and her Marilyn Monroe wardrobe. Silky was the one they recognized and loved. Lake finally had her identity. Everybody loved Silky.

She parked her red Porsche and breezed up to the office, waved jauntily to the receptionist, collected her personal mail (she insisted everything be sent c/o George), and barged cheerfully into George's office without knocking. Rank had its privileges, and the turquoise suede jumpsuit she was wearing deserved a little attention.

He was on the phone. "No, no. I've got to have that contract on my desk Monday morning at he latest." She curled her arms around his chest and chewed on his ear. "Hey, come on." He put his hand over the receiver and tried to shoo her away. "Just hold that thought till I wrap this up." He turned back to the phone:

"No more excuses. Monday morning, right? . . . Terrific, knew I could count on you. I'm looking forward to this project a great deal." He put the phone down with a grin on his face and turned his full attention to Lake. "Hello, gorgeous. To what do I owe this midday visit?"

"Lunch, remember?" She laughed. "As in, are you buying me some?"

"You're early."

She picked up a small wooden airplane and toyed with the flaps. "Well, I'm usually late, George," she sighed. "I thought I'd shake you up and be on time for once."

"But you're early."

"I miscalculated. Aren't you glad to see me?"

"Thrilled as always. If you can just give me five minutes—"

"No." She stuck her tongue out.

"Sweetheart, I'm doing this for you. *The Girl Upstairs* is only the beginning. I've got something very interesting percolating."

" 'Percolating?' " she teased.

Very carefully he removed the airplane from her grasp and set it down. "There's a play that's doing particularly well in London right now. I'd give my eye teeth to produce it over here, maybe even do a movie of it. Story is about an unfaithful wife and her husband and her lover. We change the wife to the husband, and *voilà,* there's a plum role of the lover for some deserving girl to play." He wrapped his arms around her, feeling silk against his chin as she nuzzled close. "The only problem is, Albie Weiss is trying to bring the show over with the English cast minus one. That spot he's holding open for his number-one boy, John Allison."

"John Allison is a spoiled brat."

"No argument here. Weiss seems to control him; I think he's a definite surrogate father."

"Maybe more than that." Lake put her face inside George's suit jacket. He always smelled nice.

"Sid says no. And Sid thinks *everyone* is gay."

"If Sid says no, then no it is." She was in such a good mood, she was willing to let Sid be the ultimate authority on human sexuality. "Go on, attend to your five minutes of business and then feed this poor starving girl. I've got my mail to go through, anyway." She blew him a kiss, much as she had the "U.S. Olympic Drinking Team," then began sifting through her letters.

She knew Karen's stationery by sight. It was pale blue. The paper was very fine and expensive. Even when she was broke,

Karen would save up to buy a costly item rather than a cheap if more immediate purchase. Even when her wardrobe had consisted of just jeans and leotards, she wouldn't buy costume jewelry or a cheap vinyl handbag. She had a Coach bag and a very small ring with a genuine if microscopic opal. And now, of course, she had a real gold wedding band and a very small diamond engagement ring.

They hadn't seen each other now in over five years. Karen wrote several times a year, long, newsy letters about Matt's career, which was doing pretty well, auditions, always in a cheerful vein. Karen did not complain. In response Lake had Karen's name put on the office mailing list. On all major holidays the Nichols office wished Karen Bloom and Matt Singer the appropriate sentiment. Karen couldn't have sent a letter to Lake's home, anyway. Lake had never given her the address.

9/9/77

Dear Lake,

Here it is September again. I always think of September as the beginning of the year (left over from school, I think), except of course it isn't. Anyway . . . we are all well here. Matt is freelance now, and he's up for something pretty big. Thank God. I've been waiting years for nepotism to pay off. I'm still with Hurdy-Gurdy *(you haven't lived till you've tried to write dialogue for a six-foot panda), and I am still teaching that adult education course at the New School. It pays, and at least my students are toilet trained, which is more than I can say for* Hurdy-Gurdy's *viewers. So, I guess I can't complain too much. I'd rather be acting, but . . . I ain't starving.*

In all the time I've been writing you, I never mentioned my friend Harry Townsend (he's an actor, of course), who moved to L.A. around the same time that you did. If you ever run into him, say hi for me. We write, but it's not the same as being there. I guess you know that. He's a really sweet guy. We were in Matt's NYU movie together. (God, that was a hundred years ago.) I guess I was pretty smitten with Harry.

Anyway . . . after five years it has finally occurred to me that if you wanted to keep in touch you would have. Matt points these things out to me, for which I could kill him, but I know he's right. So I won't be writing anymore unless, of course, you write me first.

I guess I just wanted to be friends more than you did. I wish you only happiness and success.

Love,
Karen

P.S. We watch your show all the time. It's really funny.

Lake looked at the letter rather absently. She supposed she'd always known that eventually Karen would give up on her, but she'd miss those letters. Funny how she'd hung on to them, almost imagining Karen seeing her read them. Well, it was over. There's an end to things, she thought idly.

. . . my friend Harry Townsend . . . I guess I was pretty smitten . . .

Maybe there was one last act of sisterly sharing yet to perform. Lake pulled out the *Players Guide* and flipped to the leading men. There he was. Nice-looking. Not extraordinary. The picture could be old, too. Many times George would call in an actress on the strength of her picture and have a lady walk in who was obviously ten years older. Maybe Harry Townsend hadn't stood the test of time. Pulling a piece of paper from George's memo pad, she scribbled down Harry's service number.

"Hey," George said brightly, holding something behind his back, "what's a girl like you doing in a place like this?"

"Slumming." She shuffled the piece of paper in with her mail. "What have you got there? A concealed weapon?"

"Heh-heh." He leered. "I don't keep my concealed weapons behind my back, m'dear." Shyly he brought forth a little jeweler's box.

"George, you don't have to . . ." Her voice trailed off weakly. While he beamed at her, she opened the box. It was a very lovely sapphire ring, simple and elegant. He hadn't wanted to scare her off with the more traditional diamond.

"You and sapphires go together." He took the ring and slipped it on her finger. "Kind of like strawberries and champagne."

"I can't accept this."

"Why not?"

She clutched her mail a little closer. "Because . . . you know damn well why not."

"It's not an engagement ring, Lake. It's just a ring. That's all."

She took it off. "That's a crock, George."

George began to laugh softly. "Well, what if it is? What if I want something more than dinner and a sleepover once or twice a week? What if I'm in love with you?"

"Don't be."

"Easy for you to say." He noticed the *Players Guide* on the desk and put it away without a second's thought. "I need more, Lake. I need a commitment. It's a normal progression: people see each other for a couple of years, they like each other, they start thinking about a future together."

"Why can't things stay the way they are? For the first time in my life, I'm happy. The show's doing fantastically; I care for you more than I've ever cared for anyone else. I trust you; isn't that enough?"

"No."

"Then I'm sorry." She got up to leave.

He jumped to his feet hastily. "Please," he begged, "take the ring, anyway. I bought it for you; I want you to have it."

"I'd rather not."

"Please, Lake." His eyes were sad. "Please. Just a gift."

Reluctantly she allowed him to put the ring on her finger. She did not have nice hands and as a rule did not care for rings.

"And now," George said, "let's forget about it and have a nice lunch."

She smiled at him, relieved. "That sounds wonderful. I'm starved." The ring *did* look very pretty, and now that things were straight between them, Lake recaptured her earlier euphoria. They nodded a pleasant good-bye to the receptionist and rode down in the elevator.

He saw her slip a few letters into her purse."Anything good in the mail? Somebody die and leave you a million?"

"Letter from Karen."

'Oh? That's nice. What's your little pal up to?"

"She says she won't be writing anymore." She spoke in such a cool, ordinary tone that George stared at her in amazement. He'd always thought Karen still meant quite a bit to Lake; she looked forward to those letters. Sometimes he was painfully aware of how little he really knew her. It was beginning to scare him. That's how it'll be with me, he thought, as soon as it stops being fun. She'll forget I ever meant anything to her. Like we never met at all.

"It's such a beautiful ring," she whispered softly. "You're so good to me, George." She rubbed her cheek against his shoulder, silk against tweed, with such genuine affection that he forgot her passions seemed to be as temporary as the moon's phases.

They had a nice lunch, talking of inconsequential things. It was an uneventful afternoon. The only item of note was when Lake excused herself to go to the ladies' room. There was a bank of pay phones in the ladies' lounge, and it was from there that she left a message on Harry Townsend's service.

Chris had planned an early start, but she seemed nervous as hell about leaving, despite her careful preparations. "Have I got everything?" She fluttered, her manner contrasting with her solid body. Even her wardrobe was not as carefuly coordinated as usual. She'd gotten word that her mother was ill, and she was flying home to Lexington until the crisis passed. Her mother was a hypochondriac and a pretty unpleasant lady from all accounts. The only family member taking her seriously was Chris.

It was six-thirty in the morning. Harry had gallantly offered to drive her to the airport, but she'd told him to get his beauty sleep instead. Still, he missed her warmth in bed and got up to make her breakfast.

He took her hand and molded it around her coffee cup. "At least drink the coffee. You've got to have something."

She smiled at him wanly. "I've really got to get going. Are you going to be all right here alone?"

"I'll manage. You call me if you need anything."

She said nothing.

"I'm sure it's nothing, Chris. A lady in her seventies gets a cold, and the relatives start making funeral arrangements."

She smiled gratefully. "At the very least it'll be nice to see the old beast again. Not that we ever got along, but you can always hope, right? Well, I'm hitting the road." She gathered up her handbag (her suitcase was already in the trunk) and went out to the car.

He heard her drive away. Idly he reached for the phone and dialed his service. Last night he'd neglected to call. Since he'd moved in with Chris, Harry had been very lackadaisical about his career. He was too damn comfortable.

"Box 419, please."

Silence at the other end.

"Box 419."

"I heard you," an annoyed female voice said. "Here's your message. 'Will you meet the lady of the lake at Avalon.' "

"What?"

"That's your message, Harry. You got a friend who's really into King Arthur?"

He hung up, feeling confused as hell. *Avalon?* Harry was a reasonably intelligent guy. He called up the information number for the ferry to Catalina, revved up the green Jag, and took off.

It was a glorious morning. The Santa Ana winds were doing their thing, the ferry chugged along at a nice clip, tourists were at a minimum. Harry bought coffee in a Styrofoam cup and a Danish. He saw no woman who could be his lady of the lake.

Three hours later they pulled up at Catalina. It was a beautiful little island, greenery standing out in relief against white sand reflecting sunlight. It had been a favorite retreat of a millionaire, who had preserved a good deal of the natural flora. There were a number of small bungalows pressed close together, where some lucky people lived, and, as Harry remembered, there was a beautiful town for the very wealthy at the top of the hill. It was called Avalon.

He began to walk around aimlessly, dodging the odd rented bicycle or golf cart. He was beginning to think somebody was having a good laugh at his expense. There was an arcade on the main drag that caught his attention, filled with pinball and video games, as well as other cheap attractions. He went in and blew a few quarters on the crane-claw thing in the glass case. You operated the crane-claw, hoping to pick up a Crackerjack-quality prize. The prizes were piled up, plastic debris six inches deep at the bottom of the case. He spent two dollars winning a plastic ring with a big paste diamond.

"You came," a softly insinuating voice said at his back. 'You actually came for me."

He turned around even though he knew the owner of that voice. The woman who'd had the starring role in his sexual fantasies for the past two years, the woman he'd sworn would one day be his. *His* lady of the lake.

"Oh, Silky," he breathed."Somehow I always knew I'd be seeing you again." He laughed softly to himself, expecting . . . what? Expecting her to say that she loved him, that she'd been looking for him all these years?

She stood very close. Close enough for him to see how beautiful she really was, how perfect her skin was, a thousand different shades of precious metal in her hair. "I've taken a room at the hotel." Her hand, her ringless hand, brushed his cheek, smoothed the hair away from his forehead. Stubbornly it fell right back. "You're much nicer than your picture." She moved even closer, her hips lightly grazing the front of his jeans. "Let's go. The hotel's down the street." She hooked her fingers through his belt loops and pressed herself against him hard.

He gasped a little as the sensation of warmth radiated up to his throat. "You're very sure of yourself."

"Always," she murmured, kissing him deeply, thrusting her tongue into his mouth. She was shocked to feel him push her away. Gently, but a definite push. Her eyes widened comically.

"Sorry,"he said genially. "It's just . . . the last thing I expected from you was a rape scene. I think I liked you better as an unattainable dream—you know, something to look forward to." His eyes moved over her with great reluctance. "You are the most beautiful woman I have ever seen. If anybody had told me two years ago that this would happen, well, I'd have had to say they were crazy. Guess I must be the crazy one, walking away from you. Anyway, I live with a lady; I think I owe her a little loyalty." He took a few steps away. "Would you believe I've never been here before? Think I'll rent one of those little golf carts, give myself a tour. It's been real interesting meeting you."

Still in shock, she ignored his proffered hand and watched him stroll away whistling, a happy man, his pride intact.

Lake felt like a total fool. "Shit," she said softly. "This time, my girl, I think we went too far." She went out the back of the arcade and ran as fast as she could, a smile growing on her face.

Harry was debating whether he wanted to try his luck picking a pearl-laden oyster from a tank in a jeweler's window. For a nominal fee the jeweler would set your pearl in a ring or a pin. If you found a pearl in the first place. Harry was trying to figure if he felt lucky.

"Your limo, sir," Lake called out brightly from her golf cart, cruising along next to him. She patted the seat next to her. "Come on, I won't bite you. I'm sorry I was such an idiot, and anyway, you're stuck here until the ferry gets back, and that isn't till five-thirty. I promise I won't try to rape you again unless you beg me."

He approached her cautiously. "What exactly am I getting myself into here?"

"A golf cart."

"Ha-ha."

"I can't say, Harry." She sighed. "Life is a strange and beautiful thing. Why don't we just leave it as a pleasant afternoon in a place you've never been before?"

"Can I drive?"

"No."

"You're a hard case, Silky." He eased himself into the golf cart.

"I've got a name, you know." She nudged the golf cart up to its top speed of twenty-five miles per hour.

"I know. Lady of the Lake Eastman."

"That's it," she said firmly. "You're buying lunch."

High in the hills they found a place that looked like someone had tried to make a little chapel in the woods. There were logs to sit on and a cross made of two sticks lashed together. Through the trees you could look down and see the dock; water shining around it, people walking up and down the main street.

Lake sat down on one of the logs. "What's she like?"

Harry had been pretty honest about his relationship with Chris. "Chris is a good kid. She's a tough businesswoman, but it's all cover. She's a marshmallow."

"What does she do?"

"She shops for a living." He grinned at her reaction. "She actually runs a shopping service. One of these days she wants to open her own boutique, but right now she shops. For people who are too busy to shop, people who want to know the right things to buy, people who have too many other people to buy things for. Only in L.A."

"Not true. I bet Bloomingdale's in New York had it years ago." She picked up a pebble and tossed it from one hand to the other. "Do you love her?"

He hedged."She's been very good to me. I'm grateful."

"It's not the same."

"I know that. I know we're all out there looking for the big love of our lives, but . . . I'm so damn *comfortable.* For the first time in my life as a struggling actor, I'm comfortable. It's so nice having that live-in cheering section. Chris thinks I'm great. Olivier and Redford rolled into one. It's hard to walk away from all that emotional support. That and the money."

"You're very honest."

"It's easy with you."

"Really?"

"Sure. We'll probably never see each other again. Nothing to lose."

The pebble made a little tapping sound as it struck the band of her sapphire ring. "Maybe you'll grow to love Chris. That happens."

"I don't believe it does." He took the pebble from her. "Rose quartz. Pretty, isn't it?" He tossed it through the trees. "When you really fall for somebody, I think it hits you right away."

She leaned against his shoulder; his skin was very warm from the sun. "That's very childish."

He grinned happily. "Ain't it, though? One thing they can't do is make you grow up."

"Well, it's nice to meet a fellow case of arrested development." She smiled at him. "I think you're right, though. I think it does hit you right away, no matter how indebted you are emotionally to someone else."

He kissed her. Her arms went around his neck as if it were the most natural thing in the world. In some other world they had always been together. It wasn't a first kiss, it was a reunion. She burrowed against his warm neck and hid there for a while. The sapphire ring burned on her finger. She worked it free and let it drop to the dirt.

He broke the silence. "Why did you call me?"

"For all the wrong reasons. Does it matter?'

He didn't have to think long. "No, it doesn't matter at all."

They didn't speak much on the ferry ride home. Lake liked to ride in the bow, feeling the wind in her face. He stayed with her, his arms wrapped around her.

"Hey," she said, "you like me, buster, don't you?"

"Yeah, I like you." He laughed.

"What if I told you I'm a pretty terrible person?"

He laughed again. "I'd believe you."

"You don't have many illusions."

His answer was lost in the roar of the ferry's motor.

So she went home with him, which was what she'd wanted in the first place for completely different reasons.

Whether out of a sense of insecurity or a cagey cynicism, Harry had held on to his bachelor apartment. They drove over in his car. Lake left hers at the pier, saying she could send someone to pick it up later. Harry's apartment was reasonably clean, but it had that unmistakable emptiness of a place not lived in.

She shivered a little.

"Pretty bleak here," Harry agreed. "Most of my things are over at Chris's." Street noise filtered through the window.

She gave herself the guided tour while he attempted to spank dust out of the couch. She was a little flattered that he was abusing his couch in an attempt to please her.

The bedroom was plain, but the sense of abandonment was not so sad. It was more the empty room of a child grown and gone away to school. Next to the bed was a small two-shelf bookcase holding last summer's best-seller and a very old Hardy Boys book. Amused, she picked up the book to check on the exploits of Frank and Joe. A folded slip of paper skated to the floor. It was a torn newspaper page. *Variety.* George's paper search for her.

"I used to lie on my bed and dream about you." He was standing in the doorway. "I used to dream about becoming real famous, because then I was sure I could win you." He sat down next to her. "We have a mutual friend back in New York, Karen Bloom. Well, Karen Singer she is now. You were roommates, weren't you?"

"Yes."

"I almost wrote that poor girl, asking her to give me your address. She would have, too."

If she'd known it, Lake amended silently. "Why didn't you?"

"Because it would have been like sucking up to somebody to get something out of them. You know, being nice to the school geek so you could cheat off him in geometry."

"So you didn't ask her."

"Nope. It's too damn hard to shave in the morning if you can't look yourself in the eye."

She stroked his hair. "You're a nice guy, Harry."

"Nah, I just keep one eye closed."

"I'd have to keep both eyes closed."

"It's a good thing you don't have to shave."

She pulled his hair, not hard but not very gently. "I'm trying to tell you I'm not a very nice lady."

He bolted upright. "You mean you're not a virgin? That's it, I want my money back."

Laughing, she pounced on him, seeking to regain her hold on his hair. He fended her off, grabbing her wrists and wrestling her to a prone position. Even in play he was very careful, very mindful of his greater strength. "I'm not any nicer than you are. I'm just trying to get by. Just like everybody else."

"I'm not like other people."

"You're better-looking than most. Other than that you seem pretty normal."

She smiled faintly, shifting to a sitting position. "That's the nicest thing anybody's ever said to me." Earlier she had braided her hair back in one long plait. Now, with an easy grace, she undid her hair, the action as particularly female as a cat's stretch is feline. "Do you know what I wish?" She pulled her blouse free of her jeans and began to unbutton. "I wish I was a nice average lady in Kalamazoo or Milwaukee or someplace like that, and I've been married for ten years, and I'm just coming home from a hard day of work. Wouldn't that be great?"

He thought about Marie Antoinette playing at being a milkmaid.

"Well, that's what I wish." She wriggled out of her jeans. "I can really see this, just like I'm actually living this woman's life. She—" Lake smiled. "*I'm* around thirty-five, a little thick in the waist, but really, a decent-looking lady for thirty-five. I come home. I don't know whether my husband's home from work yet, but he's really upstairs, only I don't know it. And he's very, very quiet, so I think I'm all alone in the house." She skinned her underwear off and began to work on his clothes. Her hands were light and fast. For the first time he noted that her hands were not particularly attractive. Funny that such a beautiful woman was not perfect. "Anyway, the children are all away—either they're still at school or staying over at friends. Maybe it's our anniversary or something. I'm thinking about our time together, looking back over the years, kind of wondering to myself if I made the right decision. I go into the bedroom; I'm very preoccupied." Her face glowed. "I'm looking in the mirror, noticing the gray hairs and the crow's feet, and all of a sudden he comes in, and he says how I look just like I did when he married me ten years ago." She moved closer, her hair, rippled slightly from the braid, falling around her shoulders almost like a bridal veil. "And I say, 'darling, I love you.' And then he says—"

"I love you, too," Harry said quietly. "I always will." He pulled her close, against his bare chest.

She turned her face toward him, shining with eagerness, enveloped with the warmth of belonging. They kissed unhurriedly, awash in their fictional life, nestling together, the hollows of one filled by the curves of the other. Her swan's neck curved over his shoulder. She sighed contentedly, like a little cat, when he entered her. The thin sheath of muscle along his back moved under her fingers; she delighted in his lithe body, his slim hips cushioned on either side by her soft thighs. His thrusts were very fluid, like a wave flowing deep inside her. She moved her hands to the small of his back and felt his rhythm begin there, the first curl of the wave. He moved even deeper inside her, forcing a small gasp to escape from her. Reflexively her hands moved to his neck, holding on for support. "Now," she whispered, against his ear, salt trickling from his body to hers, "please, now."

At her gentle urging his movements became faster. He rocked against her, instinctively knowing the places that felt good to her. At one thrust she felt tears come to her eyes. She who was so detached and distant. At the next thrust a shivery, liquid quiver flowed upward from her groin. A second later she felt him shake uncontrollably with the force of his own orgasm.

He kissed her cheek and tasted tears. "Hey, are you crying?" He licked the tears away. "You got a complaint with the service?"

"Oh, no." She reassured him with a kiss. "It's just, I wasn't expecting . . . I never felt this way before."

"Aha, you *did* lie."

She was seized with panic. Lie? Did he know more about her than he'd let on? "What do you mean?" she demanded coolly.

"You *were* a virgin."

She relaxed into his arms. "Found me out, huh?"

He smoothed the tangled hair away from her face. "I was crazy about you from the first time I saw you in George Nichols's office. We were meant to be together, Lake. All those times we could have met back in New York, then to move out here and run into each other. I believe in fate. Especially when it tells me what I want to hear."

"I have somebody," she sighed. "Somebody I'm grateful to, just like you are to Chris. But I want you. I want to be with you as much as I can."

"I know. We'll just have to be smart about this," Harry said thoughtfully. "No sense in hurting people if you don't have to, right? For now we just take it slow."

"As long as I can be with you." She flicked his ear lobe with her tongue. "Harry. What a wonderful, old-fashioned name." A thought popped into her head. "Were you very close with Karen?"

He seemed surprised. "Karen? Oh, I think we're closer now. Then we were just kids. I think she had a crush on me."

"Egotist."

"You're probably right. We write. When I'm in New York, I go see her and Matt." He smiled in remembrance. "She got very pretty. You haven't seen her in a few years; she really looks good."

"I guess marriage agrees with her."

He shrugged. "Maybe. I always thought Matt was a cold guy. Now there's somebody who's definitely going to succeed. No doubt in my mind."

"You think Karen's going to make it?"

"If I thought so, I probably would have given Matt a run for his money." He grinned at Lake. "I'm a mercenary bastard. She sings beautifully, though. I heard her sing in some dive the last time I was in New York. Sent shivers up my spine. But her voice is all wrong for disco, and she doesn't know a soul in the business. No, I don't think Karen will ever get the breaks, and she won't do what you or I would do to make the breaks happen. No, she'll be the power behind the throne."

"She has Matt. That's enough."

"I don't think so. But I'm probably wrong."

Lake squirmed against him. "Don't you think we could find something better to do than reminisce about an old friend?"

She stayed the whole weekend. They ordered in Chinese food and Tex-Mex takeout. Harry ventured out to the corner bodega and bought provisions. He made her omelettes and grits, which they both loved. They made love and dreamed about the future, scheming how they could steal time to be together. Lake slept well at night; no bad dreams deviled her sleep. At night they slept pressed together like spoons in a drawer. The only other time in her life when she had been free from the awful nightmares had been when she lived with Karen.

Late Sunday night or early Monday morning, Harry let himself into a dark house.

Chris was sitting in the kitchen. All the lights were out. Harry got the strongest impression from the posture of her body that she was stoned. Paralyzed in some way.

"Chris? Are you okay? Is anything wrong?"

"Don't turn on the light." A heavy sorrow throbbed in her voice. The sound of old tears.

He sat down next to her and reached for her hand.

"Where were you?" she sobbed. "I called and called. I left three messages on your service; nobody knew where you were. I thought you were hurt."

'I was just hanging around with my old friends—you know, boys' night out." He pressed her hand, feeling how she'd bitten her nails to the quick. "I'm sorry, Chris. I didn't think you'd need me over the weekend."

"My mother died. She died the day I got there."

His stomach churned with shame. All that time he and Lake had been romping in sexual abandon, Chris had needed him, and he'd let her down. "I'm so sorry, Chris. I didn't know." He put his arm around her stiff shoulders. "My poor girl, all alone at such a bad time."

"She was gone by the time I got there," she whispered. "I

never even got to say good-bye." She buried her face in his shoulder and cried.

"Oh, my heart is broken," Harry's mother had sobbed when his father died. He had never thought the words stagey; they were horribly real. He was seven years old at the time, and he knew her heart was broken because she could not stop crying. Seven-year-old logic. He would have given anything to stop her tears.

"Don't cry, Chris. It's over and done with. Nothing you can do to change what's past." He couldn't reach the tissues without abandoning her, so he handed her a paper towel.

She hitched in a shuddering breath and blew her nose. "I would have given anything just to hear your voice." She laughed shakily. "So much for casual relationships. I guess I wasn't built casual. God! I would have killed just to talk to you."

"I'm so sorry, Chris." He was sure he'd said that at least twice before. "It won't happen again."

"Please, Harry." She gave him a wan smile. "Don't make promises you can't keep."

Oh, my heart is broken, her voice sang to him like a keening Irish widow, and never will it be whole again.

"I can keep this promise." Harry could never bear unhappiness; he had no defense against it. "Marry me, Chris. I love you."

"They found her car," George said, clutching a coffee cup. "How far could she go without her car?"

Sid knew an answer was not required. George was just ranting. Sid was there to provide fresh coffee and a sympathetic ear. Sid's ears were very tired. It was very late, and he dearly wanted a nice stiff drink—fuck the I'll-just-have-a-white-wine school of thought. The problem was that he did not want to offer George a drink. George didn't drink particularly well, and a drunk George was no thrill. He tended to get sentimental, and Sid just wasn't in the mood.

"Something must have happened to her," George insisted. "God, I hope she's all right."

"I'm sure she is."

"How can you be so sure?"

Sid sighed, weary to the bone. "Because Lake is a big girl and she can take care of herself. Because the police didn't find a body. Because the car was locked, the radio was turned off, and she took the keys with her. I watch *Columbo.*I know this stuff."

"Okay." George lumbered into the kitchen to get more coffee. "Then what happened to her?"

"Maybe she just wanted to be alone to think."

"Think about what?"

"God knows, George," Sid said tiredly. "God knows what anybody thinks about—" He stopped suddenly. "George, are you sure you left your machine on? Your phone machine."

"She'd call the office," he said slowly. "I mean, I assumed she'd call the office. Maybe I left it on. Jesus, I can't remember. *Maybe* it's on. I don't know, what do you think?"

"I think you should go home and turn your fucking machine on, George. That's what I think."

"Oh, shit," Geroge said faintly. "But what if she calls *here* while I'm *there* because my machine is off?"

"Ehhhhh!" Sid screamed. "Then I will call you *immediately* and tell you every little pearl that fell from her precious lips. *Go,* George. The affection I have for you is rapidly waning."

Sid thought he'd be thrilled to get George out of his house, but the silence depressed him. He turned on the TV and got a late-night rerun of *The Rockford Files.* He picked up the cups, deposited them in the sink, turned off the coffeemaker, and got out a bottle of Southern Comfort, reserved for special occasions only. He poured a small shot into a glass and trekked out to the living room and Jim Rockford.

Lake was sitting in his chair.

He nearly dropped his glass. "God! You almost gave me a heart attack. Where the hell did you come from?"

"I was waiting outside until George left." She was shivering. Her hair was braided away from her pale skin; she looked like an unearthly beautiful waif. "Can I have some of that?"

"Wait, I'll get you a glass."

She stared numbly at the television until he came back. "George gave me a ring," she whispered. "A beautiful ring, and I lost it. He's going to be angry with me. I was hoping to be with him tonight."

"He won't be angry. Not for long, anyway. Besides, lost things can be found. Where were you?"

"Does it matter?"

"If you want to find the ring it does. We can retrace your steps."

"I don't remember. I wasn't anyplace in particular. Just wandering."

"Even wandering is going someplace," Sid said reasonably. "You had to actually *be* somewhere."

"George must have been so worried."

"What do you think?"

"Is he angry?"

"Of course not. George could never get angry at you. Not for more than three minutes, and that just for show. You know that."

"I felt so bad about the ring." She was rattling on, not listening to his responses, completely tuned in to an inner dialogue. It was like listening to a little girl prattle, oblivious to what was going on around her. "He gave it to me as a token of his friendship. When I lost that ring, I felt like I'd lost George a little bit, too. I can't lose George. He's the best friend I have."

"Where were you, Lake?" He moved on to the big question. "Who were you with?"

"No one, no place. I told you. I wish I hadn't lost that ring."

"Who were you fucking?" He lashed out at her.

She stared at him. The little child behind her eyes vanished. She was a hurt woman, and she would strike back if she had to.

"Who was he, Lake?" Sid asked softly.

"No one you know." She sank into the chair, defeated. "He isn't important. A one-night stand."

"A whole weekend does not a one-night stand make. A whole weekend is living cheek to jowl and still finding each other fascinating. A whole weekend is a little romance." He poured more Southern Comfort for both of them. "George and I go back a long way, and he's one of the world's few decent people. Despite your recent behavior you're not such a hard case. I don't know who hurt you. Maybe you had a bad daddy or a nasty mommy so you feel compelled to repeat this little family drama for the rest of your life. That's none of my business; you do as you like. You fuck who you like. This is Hollywood. Everybody looks good and everybody's available. But if you love somebody else, you come out like a decent person and tell George. You let him walk away with a little pride."

"I can't," she said. "I need him." Lake knew she could never explain to Sid the feeling of total abandonment she'd felt when Harry left. As soon as he'd gone, it was as if he'd never existed. If she lost George, there'd be nothing left but a series of nightmare-filled nights.

"Then you have to tell your little boyfriend good-bye. George has been a good friend to me, and I won't stand for—"

"You're in love with him." She smiled. Here at last was ammunition. Something she could use. "Oh, poor Sid, George is it for you, isn't he? The love everybody waits for. Poor Sid."

His face hardened. "Poor Sid will be watching you, angel. I'd rather be your friend, but I'll play it any way you want. Look, I don't expect you to be a saint, but the second you go over the line, I'll personally help you pack your bags. Do we understand each other?"

She nodded, sipping her drink. "You're going to look after me."

"That's right."

"He'll never believe you, Sid. If it comes down to you or me, who do you think he'll choose?" She smiled at him. "I can make your life very miserable if I want to." She drained her glass. "And I had hoped we were going to be friends."

"Any way you want it," Sid said evenly. He'd dealt with people like Lake before. The most dangerous people were the most wounded. He'd pity her, but he'd also be very, very careful.

She got up. "I do care for George," she said, watching Sid all the time. "Maybe not the way he wants me to, but I do care."

"You need him, Lake." Sid moved to get her jacket. "You need him to keep you safe from all your dark dreams and fears, and when you find he can't do that, that nobody can do that for you, you'll push him away. And it'll kill him. My dear angel, something about you shines like the sun, and it isn't just your celebrated beauty. But that glow is eclipsed by whatever madness pursues you. One draws people to you, the other forces you to destroy them—and yourself, one fine day. Find a way to be right with yourself, and you'll find the man you really need."

She laughed as she took her jacket from his hands. "I am right with myself, Sid. This is who I am."

He thought of the waitress he had met at the beach. "No," he said confidently, "you're not."

For a moment she seemed to struggle quietly with herself, weighing what part of herself to reveal to him: frightened child, destructive woman, abusive adolescent. Her face went blank. "I'm sorry," she said in a toneless voice. "We're not going to be friends."

Harry was in her thoughts constantly. She schemed, trying to find ways for them to meet. A few months later an opportunity presented itself to her, and she grabbed it.

They were having dinner at Lake's—George, Lake, and Sid, a cozy little threesome. Sid was watchful, but George's eyes were glued on Lake. He didn't notice anything else.

"I have found a script for you," George announced over dessert.

"A script. You mean a feature? George, that's wonderful. I'm getting a little sick of Silky, to tell you the truth."

"That was fast," Sid muttered.

"Wait a second, lady," George protested. "The script does need a little work, I'll admit that; good writers are scarce in this town. And we'd have to shoot while *The Girl Upstairs* is on hiatus; no sense in throwing out the million-dollar baby. We're talking about a pretty hectic schedule for you."

Lake cuddled up to George. "I can handle it. Is it a good story?"

"I think so." He beamed. "I really think so."

Lake frowned, chewing on her full lower lip. "George—oh, this is horrible, but I promised Karen I'd ask—"

"Are you guys writing again?"

"Well, sure," she lied smoothly. "I know I act a little crazy sometimes, but I like to think I've come to my senses."

Sid laughed very quietly.

George glared at him. "Honey, since your little disappearing act you've been a changed girl. Maybe you just had to get it out of your system." He looked into her eyes lovingly.

"Ahem." Sid cleared his throat loudly. "What was it you promised your friend, Lake?"

"Oh!" Lake laughed self-consciously. "Karen has an actor friend out here—Harry Townsend, I think his name is. I promised her I'd ask you to audition him for something. I know that was presumptuous of me, but—"

"Not at all. That was really sweet of you to help out a friend. Most people forget their old friends as soon as they make it big. Hell, we'll send Karen a plane ticket. I'll give her an audition as well!"

"Karen doesn't act anymore," Lake put in quickly. "I guess she couldn't take the insanity of the life. She's just a very sweet, simple person."

"What's she doing now?" Sid asked.

"She writes for a children's show in New York."

George digested this information. "That's nice. It's always good to know a writer."

"So you don't mind giving this Harry person an audition?" she wheedled, knowing George would never suspect she was being devious.

"Not at all." He squeezed her hand.

She squeezed back, smiling at him. "Would you excuse me

for a second? I just want to get a drink of water." She got up and walked toward the kitchen.

"George—" Sid started.

"I don't want to hear it." George cut him off. "If you've got anything negative to say about Lake, you can take it someplace else."

"My God, George, what has happened to your mind? You know damn well what's been going on at the set ever since her 'little disappearing act.' She's practically shooting down your sitcom single-handedly. If she's not late, she's stoned. The only thing she doesn't do is shoot up, and I think it's only a matter of time, George. She's lost all interest in the series."

"Creative people get bored easily," George said. "You can't expect a girl like Lake not to have a few problems."

"Why not?" Sid asked, mystified. "Why can't you expect a girl like Lake to be a normal, decent human being? Because she's so beautiful? Open your eyes, George! You're not helping her by letting her get away with this kind of behavior. Lake has serious problems. We're talking about a girl who's so insecure she can't bear to see her old roommate get a lousy walk-on! How can you love a girl like that?"

"Whatever Lake wants," George said, looking Sid straight in the eye, "I will do for her. I love her. You're my good friend, Sid, but don't push me into making any decisions I'd rather not make." He smiled hopefully. "We can all be friends, can't we? Come on, Sid. For me."

"I'll always be your friend," Sid said in a low voice. "It's late. I think I'd better be geting home. Right after I thank our charming hostess for a lovely evening." He walked toward the kitchen.

Lake was drinking a glass of water.

"I suppose you heard every word."

She said nothing.

"So you can relax, Lake. Apparently there's nothing I can do to hurt you."

She uncapped a small vial and took a pill, washing it down with a sip of water. "For my nerves," she explained coolly. "You know what shitty nerves I have, Sid."

He brushed past her.

"I think Sid's a little jealous of you." George smiled as Lake joined him on the couch.

"He'll get over it," she said briefly. "Will you stay tonight?" Harry had to be with Chris that night. Lake had begged and she'd pleaded, but he had insisted Chris needed him that night. Lake was damned if she was going to be alone. "I want you to stay, George." She kissed his ear, tonguing the lobe gently.

"I'll do anything you want me to do," George said hoarsely. "I love you."

15

LAKE WAS TAKING advantage of a lengthy break between scenes at *The Girl Upstairs* to put her feet up and relax in her dressing room. The phone rang (rank not only had its privileges, rank also had a private line in the dressing room), and she reached for it lazily.

"Hello, beautiful."

The sound of George's familiar voice annoyed her. Old faithful. She winced at that thought, realizing she wouldn't want him even if he did lead her a merry chase. Poor man. She forced warmth into her voice. "Hi, George. How's everything going?"

"Excellent. You should send your little friend a thank-you note."

"My little friend?"

"Karen."

Her pulse began to speed up. Was Karen in LA? "What do you mean?"

"I just saw Harry Townsend's screen test."

She feigned nonchalance, easy on the phone. "Oh?"

"I think we have our leading man." He was exultant. "The guy was terrific. As soon as I saw him, I remembered. He'd been in my office a few years ago, but he wasn't ready then. He was just outgrowing juvenile lead—you know, the awkward age for an actor. I always meant to call him, but I never got around to it. Your friend did me a big favor. You should invite her out to LA; we'll show her the sights."

"I'll do that, George." She hesitated a moment, unsure of how far to push him. "So you really liked this guy? You think he's our man?"

"Unless there's a serious lack of chemistry between the two of you, we're in business. I don't think there will be a problem, and I'm a pretty good judge of human nature. He seems like a nice guy, very down to earth. Just got married—"

Lake bit back an "I know." Chris Hargreave was opening a boutique. Apparently she knew a lot of people in the fashion world, since the wedding announcement had rated a paragraph in *WWD.* Frantically Lake had tried to contact Harry. She'd reached him once in the past two months, only to receive a terse "I can't talk now. I'll call you when I can—I still love you" for all her trouble. She clung to that "I still love you" like a drowning woman. Other than that she did what she had to, holding things together as best she could. Lake knew all her weaknesses, but it was easy, so damn easy to get pills, to get drink, to get blow, to get men. Work was the best place to hide, but Silky was a joke. She could play the ditsy blonde in her sleep, undulating and ooohing to get a laugh. You needed to be high to walk through that and keep your sanity. I need this movie, she thought anxiously, and I need it to be perfect.

"Earth to Eastman, Earth to Eastman." George was laughing. "Are you still there, lady?"

"Sorry, woolgathering," she apologized. "Did I miss something?"

"Well, I just told you that Harry's wife is having a party to celebrate the opening of her boutique. Might be good publicity to have the both of you there. What do you think?"

She considered carefully. If she said no (which she dearly wanted to), he might think something was up. On the other hand, if she attended, George would see them together, her and Harry. And so would Harry's wife. Either way she was surely screwed. "Oh, I don't care," she said with studied indifference. "Whatever you decide, George, that'll be fine with me."

"I can't pass up publicity like that. We'll dazzle them for a few minutes," he said brightly.

She tried to match his tone. "Fine with me. Sounds like fun."

"Hey, maybe I'll drop by the set this afternoon. Drive you home after work, buy a starving girl a lobster dinner."

"Sounds very enticing, but you know I get nervous when you watch me work. Besides, if we go out for dinner, I won't get a chance to look at next week's script."

"But I'll miss you," George wheedled.

"I'll miss you, too." She would, at night, but right now the night seemed light-years away. "You'll call me? Just before I go to sleep so I'll have sweet dreams."

"Maybe I'll do more than call," he said suggestively.

"Miss Eastman?" A voice rang out outside her door. "We need you on the set."

"Oh, George, I've got to go. I'll talk to you later." She hung up before he could start making kissing noises into the phone.

"Miss Eastman." The voice was getting querulous. "We *need* you."

'Just a minute." Preparation, she thought, reaching for her little vial of coke, every actor needs preparation. She checked her nose in the mirror, then opened the door.

It was Harry, wearing a huge grin, carrying a single white rose. "Flowers, Miss Eastman," he drawled.

"It's lovely," she said coolly. "Did you save it from the bride's bouquet?" She tried to shut the door, but he was faster and stronger.

Her nerves sang. She wanted to fight him, to get him down on the floor and savage him with her teeth."You could have called me," she panted, trying to force him away from the door. "At first I thought you were away on location. You see, I don't read *Women's Wear Daily* on a regular basis. It was lying around my hairdresser's. That's how I found out about the little wife. She looks old, Harry. She really does."

He shook her sharply. "Don't ever say anything about Chris. You don't know her."

"I do," she whispered."She's got you, and I don't."

His arms tightened around her. "Only for now. Play your cards right, and you could be stuck with me for life." His grin faded a little. "Besides, I'm not the only one with entanglements."

"Oh, George."

" 'Oh, George' could fuck up both our careers royally if he had reason to."

She twisted around in his arms to look into his face. "Is your career that important to you?"

He laughed, "You bet. Just as important as your career is to you. You should know better than to play little saint with me. We both have a lot of mercenary in us. That's why we get along so well."

"I can't stand you." She kissed him hungrily. "I can't stand anybody having so much control over me. Can I see you tonight?"

"Maybe. Chris is real busy with her boutique, and my looney sister is in town keeping her company. I might be able to slip away. Either way I'll try to call. How's that?"

"Not good enough."

"That's all I can offer you right now." His hands tangled in her long, silky hair. "I do love you," he murmured against her ear, "and we'll be together as soon as it's possible."

She pulled away. "I'm not very patient, Harry. For my own good reasons I'm not very patient. I don't love George, but I need him to keep the nightmares away. And he's always available. People like George and Chris have a way of becoming habits—they're too easy, too forgiving, too loving. If you wait too long, neither one of us will ever be able to get away."

"You're so melodramatic," he chided her gently. "I've given this a lot of thought, and as long as we don't blow our cool here, everything is going to work out just fine. We'll be able to walk away into the sunset with our sanity and our careers intact."

She smiled faintly. "George called just before you came. He was very impressed with your screen test. He told me to write Karen a thank-you note for bringing the wonderful Harry Townsend to his attention. I thought that was pretty funny."

He seemed perplexed. "Why is it funny?"

"Karen had nothing to do with it."

"Not exactly true, Lake." Harry gave her a wry look. "I may be a former country bumpkin, but even I know there have been a few too many coincidences concerning you and me. Out of all the actors in this town, you give me a call. Why? What have we got in common besides an old buddy in New York? I figure Karen wrote you about me, and it piqued your curiosity. I don't care how it happened. Maybe *I* should write her a thank-you note."

Her face was sharp. "You still love her."

"Oh, sure," he said easily, "I'll always love her in a way, and I think she feels the same. I'll never do anything about it; it wouldn't be right. I just hope she's happy with Matt. Now don't look so threatened. Karen's a part of my past, like my high school buddies, people like that. There's room for them in my heart, and for you, too."

"No," she whispered petulantly against his shoulder.

He laughed. "I can't believe a girl like you is jealous of little Karen Singer."

She stared at him. "I can't believe you're such a fool sometimes. There will come a day in the not too distant future when all of a sudden Karen will look a lot different in your eyes. Not just yours; everyone will see it. All of a sudden she'll be beautiful and witty and all those good things. And I'll be last year's blonde. That's all I am, Harry. So don't blame me for the way I feel about Karen."

"You're more than just a beautiful blonde to me." Harry chuckled. "You're a paranoid, too."

Again she pulled away from his encircling arms. "What am I really?" she asked him, eyes sober. "Do you know?"

"I think," he said slowly, "a lot of you is hurt and sad. And part of you is a screaming bitch trying to keep anybody from getting at the hurt part of you. Then again, just because you're paranoid doesn't mean they're not out to get you. It's a carnivorous business. I don't blame you for being a little crazy. I don't blame you for anything."

"And you love me."

"That I do—the good and the bad equally."

"And I love you." She put her hands on either side of his face and kissed him lightly on the mouth, a preamble. "Can you stay and watch the taping a little?"

"A little."

"I've still got some time before they call me for the next setup . . ." She let her words trail off as she began to throw cushions off the couch.

Harry tried to look offended. "You think I'm that easy."

"I know so." She giggled. "I hate these stupid little cushions. Here, give me a hand."

"I'll do better than that." He covered the distance between them swiftly, his hand stroking her crotch through the thin denim of her jeans, his mouth sealing hers warmly. She reached for him blindly. They fell onto the couch, a tangle of arms and legs and eager mouths.

"Miss Eastman? Five minutes."

"Shit!" Lake muttered under her breath. "That's Pam, one of our goddamn production assistants. Let's be quiet; maybe she'll go away."

Pam continued to knock timidly. "Uh, Lake? I don't mean to rush you, but they can't start without you."

"I'll be there in a minute," Lake called. "I want to fix my mascara. Okay, Pam? You can go away now, secure in the knowledge that you have done your duty. P.A.'s all over the world look up to you as a source of inspiration."

"I can wait for you if you like." Pam's hopeful voice filtered through the door.

"Go away, Pam, or I may never come out."

Pam went away.

"Damn it."Lake brushed her hair furiously. "That girl's got the world's worst timing."

"She's just doing her job."

"I know." Lake reached for her little vial, handed it to Harry. He hesitated a moment before using the coke. Lake began to laugh. "Oh, Harry, you're such a reluctant sinner."

"Don't want to mess up my pretty face. Enough of this stuff and your nose slides off your face and winds up in the gutter. Besides, I'm an old-fashioned guy. I believe in liquor."

Lake smiled at him, eyes glittering. A dare. How low can you go? "I tried heroin once. When I first came out to California and couldn't decide whether I wanted to die or just disappear. I met some real interesting people in the same situation, and that's where I got the stuff. They cooked it up for me and everything. Do you know why people do heroin, Harry? Because it feels wonderful. It takes you to heaven. Nothing can touch you there. Nothing can hurt you. Oh, I wouldn't do it again," she said casually. "I really think that would be the end of me. I'm not a strong person. I'd want to stay there forever, and then I'd die. I don't want to die yet. I want to stick around and be with you." She gave him a slow smile. "I'm a pretty crazy lady, huh?"

"Sure are," Harry agreed. "But I think I've got you figured out."

"No, you don't," Lake said agreeably. "That's why you love me."

She was lying in bed reading when the phone rang. "Hello?" She fumbled for the receiver, putting the book down on the floor.

"Hi. It's your sweet-dreams man."

"Hi, George." She smiled to herself. Harry was going to come over later tonight. She'd have sweet dreams all right. She was grinning like a milk-fed tabby.

"Well, you're sounding pretty chipper. You don't need me to cheer you up."

"You sound like you need some cheering up. Is something wrong?"

"Wrong? No, nothing's wrong." He sighed heavily. "I'm worried about the script; it's got problems."

"You'll fix it, George. You always do."

He sighed again. "Maybe I won't be able to. Maybe I'm losing my touch."

Her antennae went up. Something told her to go slow. "Something's bothering you, pal, I can tell. Spill it."

He was reluctant to speak. "Someone . . . someone told me

there was a man in your dressing room this afternoon. And he was there for a while. Someone said they heard you talking to this man."

Pam, Lake thought. Pam had been George's little spy, keeping an eye on things in his absence. Well, she'd see to it that Pam was soon looking for another job. "Someone?" She mocked his intonation. "I didn't know you felt the need to spy on me, George. I'm a little offended. Think a minute. What do I have in my dressing room? A couch, a little refrigerator, a little *TV*—"

"Oh, Jesus, that was the TV? It was only the TV?"

"I like to watch the soaps, George. Is that all right with you?"

"Oh, honey, I'm so sorry. I know I'm driving you nuts. You forgive me?"

She felt a wash of pity for him. "Sure, I forgive you. Let's just forget the whole thing." She'd learned her lesson, though. They'd have to be very careful, she and Harry. George was a fool for her, but he wasn't a fool in general. "So, is there anything else on your mind?"

She almost heard him mentally back down. "I don't know, I'm really upset about this script. I *know* something's wrong here, but I just can't put my finger on it."

"Probably needs another rewrite."

"Easier said than done. The guy who wrote this is no Shakespeare."

"Hire another writer. You've got lots of them."

"Dime a dozen," he said irritably. "My lady, you're a charmer, but you have no understanding of this business."

"Stop worrying." She laughed. "You'll make it come out just fine." She lowered her voice. "And you mean an awful lot to me. Does that help?"

"Always. Are you sure you don't want me to come over tonight?"

"No, I'm a big girl. Besides, I've got to study my script. Good night, George."

"Good night."

She hung up the phone, stretching luxuriously in bed. The sheets were perfumed, the heat of her body intensifying the scent, bringing out the lower, muskier notes. Not a minute after she had put the receiver back in its cradle, the phone rang again.

'Hello?"

"Hi," Harry said in a low voice. "I'm sorry, things just aren't working out. Can't make it tonight. I'll call you as soon as I can. I love you." He hung up.

She sat up very straight in bed, blinking in the darkness. After a while she got up and began to dress.

"So?" Sid said brightly when George had hung up the phone. "You feel better now? Did she put your mind at ease? Can I pack up my backgammon board and go home now?"

George looked at him blankly. "Oh, yeah, sure. I feel better now. Thanks for coming over and baby-sitting me, Sid. You're a real pal."

"Yes, you certainly *do* seem considerably perked up. What the hell's the matter with you? You asked her, and she told you what was going on. What more do you want?"

"It's not that. It's the script," George insisted. "Fucker doesn't work. It *should* work, it reads fine, but it doesn't work. I can feel it."

"That's what's bothering you."

"That's it."

"You're a fucking liar, my friend."

George grinned weakly. "Well, the script's bothering me, *too.*" He laced his fingers behind his head, mouth drawn into a serious line. "I can't explain it, Sid. There's never anything to call her on, but I have the feeling there is someone else, maybe a lot of someone elses. That she's holding on to me like a security blanket."

"I'm sure that's not so," Sid forced himself to say.

"I just wish I could shake that feeling." He picked up the dice and began to toy with them, flipping them from hand to hand. "I feel like my presence in her life is optional."

"C'mon, George," Sid burst out, "this isn't like you. Is any lover worth this kind of aggravation? There are a lot of nice ladies out there. For a straight guy who's not into S and M, it's a seller's market."

"I don't know if I can manage without her," George said in a small voice. "If she left me for somebody else, I really think I'd lose it completely."

"That's not love," Sid said tartly, "that's high school." He started packing up."You'll do what pleases you despite my sage advice. Just be careful, wear your rubbers—you know the whole speech. I'm bushed; I'm going home. Take two Valium and call me in the morning." He stopped for a minute. "Oh, God, listen to me, I'm babbling. Definitely time for little Sid to hit the sack."

"You can sleep here if you're too tired to drive home," George offered.

"Oh, no," Sid said quickly. "I think I'd better go home."

She drove fast, but she drove well, and she knew where she was going. She was following the trucks. Sometimes she almost felt like she knew their routes, where they liked to eat, where they would stop for a beer. But she could never find these places in the daytime.

This particular truck pulled into a roadside diner. Two men got out, but they did not enter the diner. Instead they walked to a plain, boxy clapboard structure behind the diner. Live country music filtered through the boards—whining guitars, thumping bass, and a female singer with an adenoid problem. She and her adenoids were trying real hard to sound like Tammy Wynette. The clientele didn't seem to have any problems with that or her rendition of "Your Cheatin' Heart." The song selection made Lake smile.

Inside the roadhouse men were drinking and talking and playing cards, trading stories. Lake saw a flock of brightly painted girls, pros by the looks of them, sitting near the card players, smiling at whoever smiled at them.

Lake went to the bar and got a beer. She saw a young trucker negotiating with one of the whores. He wasn't extraordinary-looking in any way, but he wasn't dirty and he didn't look mean. He had a nice body, which meant he probably hadn't been a trucker very long. Most truckers seemed to have spindly little legs and big bellies hanging over their fancy belt buckles. She felt sorry for the young trucker, sorry he was going to look like that.

The whore waved him away, laughing. "I don't take no charity cases. No money, no nookie." He tried to grab her breast playfully, and she slapped him down, sashaying over to a more profitable part of the room.

Woeful, the young trucker rejoined his buddies at the bar. He looked up, catching sight of Lake. "Oh, hey," he called out excitedly, "I seen you in the movies."

"Television," she corrected, smiling into his eyes, a frank invitation. "Why don't you buy me a beer, and I'll tell you all about my wicked life."

He motioned to the bartender. "So what do you think, Miss Movie Star?" the trucker kidded her. "Can I get an autograph?"

She put her foot up on his barstool. "Maybe you'll get more than that."

His buddies hooted derisively. She didn't care. She knew what she was doing. Confidence flowed through her, stronger than any drug. Drugs were temporary, and she had to be careful with them if she didn't want to hurt her looks. The only thing that calmed her was her nocturnal adventures. She didn't care. She knew what she was, and if it was bad, it was better than nothing at all.

16

AFTER AN ALL-NIGHT discussion that several times threatened to become an argument, it was Jackie, Harry's twin sister, who came up with a name for the boutique. "Carnelian," she announced happily at breakfast. "Carnelian is a stone that heals anger. Oh, it's beautiful—all red and brown, real pretty." Jackie then said that she had sensed a lot of anger in the general population of Los Angeles ever since she got off the plane. (Chris personally didn't think anybody *ever* got angry in L.A. because it was bad for their skin.) Jackie had arbitrarily decided to leave her husband and her boys. Out of the blue she had called Harry from the airport, told him the news, and asked if she could stay with him for a while. Harry had tried to explain to Chris that his sister probably wanted a little glamour in her life, and all "Dorothy" jokes aside, the move from Kansas to the Pacific version of Oz, coupled with a divorce, was enough to make anybody a little eccentric. Chris had tried to explain to Harry that Jackie had made it to major weird, and these living arrangements were strictly temporary. She was not crazy about the idea of sharing her home with a self-proclaimed holistic, card-reading, recently divorced Kansas housewife. But she grudgingly admitted that she liked "Carnelian." It had a nice ring to it, and the meaning was pleasant. Besides, a little esoteric hoo-hah never hurt business.

For the opening-night party Chris found a beautiful carnelian necklace, its smooth reddish-rust stones joined together in a vaguely Egyptian design. The gown she chose was a strapless sheath of champagne-colored silk. It looked fabulous, Harry assured her many times, as she modeled it for him.

Jackie had proved a little harder to outfit. Her own taste ran to rococo excess, gowns hung with more festoons and draperies than the curtains at Radio City Music Hall. Ruffles enough to keep an army of Victorians happy. Jackie herself was not exactly prime raw material. Twins she and Harry most assuredly were. Their voices echoed the same notes. However, while Harry was a good-looking man, the same features that seemed so much at home on his face didn't seem to work for Jackie. Strangely enough, while Chris could see where Jackie had probably been a nice-looking teenager, adulthood had not done well by her at all. She had not taken good care of herself and would let her nail polish chip, her lipstick rub onto her teeth—things like that. Her smile was filled with desperate good will, and she was so starstruck that on the ride home from the airport, she had begged Harry to take her past some movie stars' homes. Grinning, he had said she was going to stay at one. "I meant a *real* star," she'd answered. Finally Chris had compromised. She had shut her eyes and let Jackie pick out her own beribboned monstrosity. Chris would just make her wear a sign saying "This dress not purchased at Carnelian." The next day after the shopping spree, Jackie made breakfast in bed for Chris and Harry. She had obviously copied the menu out of a magazine, painstakingly arranging a colorful small bouquet in a tiny cobalt blue vase. There was also a lovely thank-you note.

Marshmallow that she was, Chris melted."She's a real space cadet, but she's quite sweet under all that garbage." Harry also suspected Chris rather enjoyed having a poverty case (concerning fashion sense) to play fairy godmother to. He began to feel happy his sister was there.

Jackie's goofy influence began to infect all of them. Harry started reading their horoscopes out loud at breakfast. Chris arranged for a small velvet-covered table to be set up in the boutique. She found some beautiful crystals and geodes and displayed them there, for her customers' delight and fascination. "I think this is going to work," she said nervously to anyone who would listen. "This is going to work, or I am going to kill myself."

"You're not going to do any such thing," Jackie said firmly, dealing out tarot cards. "I'd know if you were. It'd be in the cards."

"Jackie," Harry said softly, "you're turning into a first-class loon." But he was having a good time. It was nice to have Jackie around, nutty as she was; she was still his twin, and he loved her. It was nice to have Chris fluttering around preparing for her opening, flustered but happy and so proud of herself. It was a real pleasure to be in the company of women, their smells and warmth, even the panty hose that seemed to be everywhere. Idly Harry wondered if the harem would ever come back into vogue. He would have liked to slip Lake in there somewhere, but as it was, he made an effort not to think about her too much. When he was away from her, he could do that. It was only when she was maddeningly near that he could hardly keep himself from reaching for her. He kept his time filled and his thoughts on a narrow track. He began to find himself looking forward to the party.

On the evening of the big event, as Harry was dressing and Chris was having a small nervous breakdown, Jackie timidly knocked on their door.

"What does she want now?" Chris muttered under her breath. "I haven't got time to fix her bra strap or whatever's broken now. Come in!" she called.

Jackie closed the door behind her. "Is this okay?" she asked shyly. Instead of her Frederick's of Hollywood extravaganza, she was wearing a quiet-looking dress. It was nondescript and did nothing for her figure, but the dark rose color was nice, and the beading at the neckline and sleeves was quality work. Chris knew Jackie had spent more on that dress than she usually spent on a season's wardrobe. "I thought this would be more appropriate for your party."

"Yes, it's fine," Chris said softly, touched by the gesture. "But—I hope you'll forgive my saying so—that green glass pendant doesn't exactly go."

Jackie set her jaw. "That's my lucky charm, and I'm not taking it off for nothing. Your friends won't think more or less of me just 'cause I'm clashing a little." She exited.

Chris burst out laughing. "Oh, I give up. I'm just going to enjoy her and stop trying to make her over. She'll change me before I change her."

"Bite your tongue," Harry said. "Just keep her away from the real important people."

Except for the fact that Jackie kept up a nonstop stream of conversation on the ride, they reached the boutique without any mishaps. Chris had done a wonderful job. In keeping with the metaphysical theme, she had engaged a string quartet. When they took a break, a harpist, silver glitter spray in her long hair, took over. Models glided over the silvery gray carpet showing off the stock, their heads nodding on their slender necks like the fresh flowers that were everywhere, perfuming the air with a heady scent. The caterers had even tucked flowers around the trays of salmon and into the ice buckets cradling champagne. Every light had a pink gel, softening the atmosphere to a rosy, flattering glow. In the dressing rooms this was a particularly strategic move. Chris was not catering to the punk-rock twelve-to-eighteen set. Her clients were older and monied, and took their rosy glows wherever they could get them. Carnelian was going to suit them just fine.

"This is really something," Jackie marveled. "I never thought I'd be meeting famous people like I see on the TV all the time." She energetically pumped the hand of a man who was actually a chef on a morning magazine show. He was grinning broadly, enjoying Jackie's hero-worship.

Harry wanted to crawl under a rock and die, especially when Jackie offered to read his palm for free.

"Relax," Chris whispered. "Everybody's getting a big kick out of her. She's a novelty."

"Sure." Harry winced. "Like the two-headed snake at a sideshow."

"Not like that at all." Chris gave him a quick kiss. "Here, hold on to this." She plucked a crystal from the display table and put it in his hand. "That's gonna do wonders for you." She zipped off to mingle, politicking with charm and energy, working her way through the crowd. Idly Harry popped a strawberry into his mouth, checking out the female guests, most of whom would make it into anybody's top ten of ladies to be stranded on a desert island with. He picked another fat strawberry, tossed it into the air, and missed his mouth completely. In shock he watched Lake Eastman arriving on the arm of George Nichols. He'd been very sure she'd want to miss this little do.

"She's done a wonderful job," Lake admitted grudgingly. The party appeared to be in full swing, people laughing and talking, having themselves a fine time. Lake wore a sarong-style blue sequined mini-dress, so tight that the only parts of her that could breathe were her kneecaps. It was much flashier than her usual style, but she felt the need to dazzle. And George had insisted. For the sake of publicity. Her hair was wild and full. She probably looked like a floozy, but heads were turning, which was the desired effect.

Her eyes raked the crowd, searching.

"There's your leading man," George whispered in her ear, waving to Harry. "I've got a little surprise for both of you."

Oh, goody, Lake thought faintly. All she needed now was an introduction to the little woman, and she could die happy.

George escorted her over to Harry. "Look after my lady," he commanded, "and don't budge, either one of you." He checked his watch, then dashed out the door.

"What the hell's going on?" Harry asked mildly. "I'm not too crazy about this."

"Wait," Lake cautioned. "I have a feeling it could get worse."

It did. Chris came over. "Hello, Lake." She extended her hand graciously. "It's a pleasure to meet you at last. I've heard so much about you."

"The place looks beautiful." Lake shook her hand.

"Well, I hope you'll come browse someday."

"I'm sure I will."

"You'll excuse me." Smiling, Chris disappeared into the crowd.

George was back, waving at them frantically from the door. There was a woman with him, but her slight body was all but hidden behind George. Harry's practiced eye told him something about her was special. He nudged Lake. "You were right," he whispered, moving toward George.

Right about what? Lake wondered, threading her way after him. Harry was hugging the woman. Her back, toward Lake, was narrow, almost like a child's. Her outfit was unusual but appealing, a variation of Lord Fauntleroy's gear. Fawn-colored trousers, a soft dark jacket cut to show off a small waist, white lace at the cuffs.

George was beaming, his face positively moony. "Look who I've brought to California for a visit, Lake."

"Hello, Lake," Karen said shyly. "It's been a long time."

Harry's expression was similar to George's. "You got beautiful, Kar. Lake said you would.'

Karen looked at Lake. "Did you? Did you really?"

Lake stared at her for a long time. "No," she said finally. There was no apology in her voice or in the gentle sway of her sequined back as she walked away.

Harry tried to cover up the embarrassed silence created by Lake's rudeness. "So, where's Matt?" he said hurriedly. "How come he isn't with you?"

"He should be here any minute. He's been out here a week already," Karen answered, still looking a little dazed at the brevity of her reunion. "Did I write you about the movie Matt and a couple of the people at *Hurdy-Gurdy* put together?"

"A little," Harry admitted.

"Nothing special. A real low-budget comedy. I wrote it;

everybody mortgaged their homes, hit up their parents. Well, they're going to release it this month, and a couple of people out here think it's kind of good. So Matt's been out, taking a lot of lunches. George arranged for me to come out."

George was looking pretty upset. "I'm sorry, Karen. I had no idea this would happen."

"What happened?" Matt appeared at George's shoulder.

"Nothing," Karen said, taking his arm. "Isn't this place beautiful? Let's take a look around. Harry, I can't wait to meet Chris. Just looking at the way she decorated this place, I know we're going to get along."

Lake was over at the champagne, catching up with some of the other guests. A grinning woman practically leaped in front of her, catching one of her hands.

"You're Silky," she squealed. "I can't believe I'm actually standing here talking to Silky Shaugnessy. Oh, God, you're practically my favorite, and here I am, talking to you like anybody." She held on to Lake's hand and continued to prattle away happily.

"Please let go of me," Lake said firmly, but the woman seemed oblivious to her words. Finally Lake just yanked her hand free.

The woman's jaw hung open. She blinked in a dumb agony of shame. "I'm terribly sorry." She came to herself with an effort, wearing her dignity like a shabby coat. "I didn't mean . . . I never mean to do things like that. . . ."

"Jackie?" Harry was making his way through the crowd, alarm plain on his face. With an effort he got his host's smile back on. "Lake Eastman, I'd like you to meet my sister, Jackie Haber. Jackie's a little overwhelmed by all this."

"So am I sometimes," Lake said pleasantly. "Don't worry about it, Ms. Haber."

"Oh, I'm going back to my maiden name," Jackie said seriously. "I'm getting divorced. I don't plan to go back to Kansas."

"And your little dog, too?" Lake couldn't help herself. "I'm sorry, Jackie. That's uh . . . that's quite a necklace."

Harry drifted off in the general direction of the dressing rooms. Lake kept track of him from the corner of her eye.

"It's my lucky charm," Jackie was explaining, "but I don't think it goes with my dress too well." She frowned.

"Then it'll be your lucky charm for the outfits it goes with, and you'll find another charm for everything else." Lake patted her arm. A quick look around convinced her that neither George nor Chris could observe her. "Would you excuse me?" She smiled at Jackie, then fairly ran to the dressing room and slipped in unnoticed.

He was waiting for her. Harry pulled her into one of the cubicles, pushing the door shut. Outside in the narrow hall people were walking back and forth, talking and laughing. A few people were even trying on clothes. Without a word Harry kissed her shoulder. She pulled his head down to her breast, the blue sequined dress peeling back obligingly. Her breasts slipped free to meet his mouth. She'd only had one glass of champagne, but she'd eaten very little all day, and she felt suddenly light-headed. She almost lost her balance. He steadied her, then slipped his hand under her short dress, caressing first her thighs then the demanding little triangle throbbing beneath her damp panties. She pushed against his searching fingers, frantically reaching for his belt. Which was when the door, the door that Harry had pushed shut in his haste but hadn't locked, that very same door swung open.

Matt had been passing by, and he was now the sole spectator of a very interesting still life. Lake and Harry had frozen to the spot. Matt just stood there, goggling slightly.

Very precisely, eyes averted, Matt reached out and shut the door. They heard him walking away, laughing softly.

"He won't tell," Harry said with even less confidence than he felt. "I know Matt, and he won't tell."

"He hates my guts," Lake put in, pulling her sarong up. "Especially after how charming I was to Karen."

"We're fucked," Harry moaned.

"A very unfortunate choice of words."

"We're still fucked." He checked her clothes for signs of disarray; she checked his. "All right. This is the plan. We deny everything."

She smiled wryly. "That's my boy. Hang in there. If Mr. Singer wants to play tough, I've got a few tricks of my own."

He kissed the top of her head. "I think *I'm* supposed to make the macho noises. You first or me?"

"You."

Checking the hall first he left the dressing room and merged into the general traffic.

"There you are!" Laughing gaily, Chris linked her arm with Harry's. "Where've you been?"

"Looking for you, pretty lady."

Her body brushed against him. He felt a hard lump in his pocket. "I've got a rock in my pocket," he observed.

"Is that your way of saying you're glad to see me?"

"Not exactly." He felt in his pocket and pulled out the crystal Chris had given him to hold earlier.

"Oh, that's what it was." Chris laughed. "Well, did it bring you luck?" she asked in all innocence.

Harry gave her the rock back. "You keep it."

Matt and Karen were coming over. Harry held his breath.

"Thanks for having us," Karen said politely. "It's a lovely party, but I'm still on New York time. I've got to get some sleep."

"I hope we get to see you again soon." Chris and Karen cheek-kissed. Matt smiled in a friendly way at Harry, but it read plainly: *I've got your number, Townsend. Always did and always will.* They said good night and left.

"I think you were right about him," Chris said decisively. "He is very cold. But she's darling. Loved the outfit."

"Love you," Harry said, filled with relief at his escape. The relief began to ebb, and he started to think he was a pretty smart dude after all. Smart and lucky.

"Love you, too." Chris put her arms around him. In the background Lake was leaving the party alone. "I think I've got the nicest fella in the whole world."

Suddenly he didn't feel so smart.

Lake drove fast.

A guy in a BMW pulled alongside her and hollered, "Hello, beautiful. You believe in love at first sight?"

She gave him the finger.

"Hey, baby," he quoted the Big Bopper, "you know what I like!"

He fell behind, swallowed up in the rearview as she accelerated away. Almost an hour later she figured it was time to make a pit stop. The car needed gas, she needed a rest room, and her eyeballs were slowly succumbing to highway hypnosis.

The next ramp spun her out onto a small stretch of road boasting a gas station (which sold milk and eggs in addition to gas and oil), a diner, a Dunkin' Donuts, and a Burger King. A small sign announced: "Welcome to Rosedale." It was hard to read because some dissatisfied citizen had spray-painted "Rosedale sucks" over the original message.

She pulled into the gas station. After the attendant had had his fill of staring at her sequined sarong, he filled up the car, checked her oil, and washed her windshield. He even offered to throw in a free alignment and a lube job (heh-heh), but she gave him a quick smile and escaped to the ladies' room. On her way back she ducked into the station and found an old denim jacket. "Can I borrow this?" she asked the attendant.

He nodded, dazed. "You can have anything you want, sweet thing!" he thought to yell after her as she peeled out of the gas station.

Even a small town like Rosedale had what she was looking for. She found it at the next intersection, its neon sign proclaiming "Schlitz" in bright letters. The name of the bar was spelled out in smaller letters. "Nobody's Inn." Lot of comedians in Rosedale.

It wasn't bad inside, not bad at all. The bar felt a little greasy under her elbows, but the bartender more than made up for that. Nice. Real nice.

Above his head a TV flickered softly, an old movie Lake couldn't identify. She sat at the bar looking around. There were a few tables covered with the ubiquitous red and white checked oilcloth. A couple of kids occupied one; at another a young waitress was working on a hamburger deluxe plate. She was not terribly attractive, and these were most likely her best years.

"Evening." The bartender greeted Lake. "What can I do for you?"

"Scotch rocks."

He did a double take. "Hey, you're—"

"Nope." She shook her head. "I just look like her. Happens all the time. I'm Lisa. Lisa with an 's.' As in Scotch rocks?"

"Got you." He turned away to get her drink.

"Does this place ever liven up?"

"Give it about an hour. We get a late crowd." He gave her her drink, took her twenty, and went over to the register. Lake decided right then and there that she liked him, in that moment when his back was to her as he hunkered over the register. He was broad-shouldered but not especially tall or heavy. His shirt had a way of hanging straight from those big shoulders that she found particularly endearing.

He returned with her change, fanning the bills out in front of her. His smile showed deep dimples.

The waitress got up, carrying her plate toward the kitchen. "You want anything?" she yelled over to the bartender.

"Nope, I'm fine."

She gave him a smile. "I've always thought so." She was much prettier when she smiled. As if her exit had been a cue, people began to trickle in, some filling up the bar, others taking up tables. Most of them looked blue collar. There must be a factory or a plant around here, Lake reasoned. This must be the late shift.

There was another Scotch sitting by Lake's elbow. The bartender pointed to a man three barstools away. He looked normal. A little over blow-dried but normal.

She picked up the drink and saluted him, remarking to the bartender in a low voice, "If he starts to get weird on me, will you rescue me?"

"Oh, why don't you pass on him, Lisa? I think you can do better."

"I'm not looking to." The name jarred her a little. She'd have to remember to keep her lies straight.

"Hi. I'm Glen." He sat down next to her, carting his drink along.

"Lisa."

"Anyone ever tell you that you look like—"

"Uh-huh, all the time." She didn't care for his suit much; it looked like that Haitian cotton that was so popular for couches. Still, he was okay. A lot of women were looking at her enviously. Glen was probably Nobody's Inn's idea of the Catch of the Day.

"I'm a lawyer."

But, Glen, your suit looks like a couch. She started to giggle. "Sorry, funny thought."

"Hey, I like a good joke. Care to share it?" He was smiling, white teeth in a tanned face.

"Nooo, it wasn't that funny. So you're a lawyer. Must be very interesting."

"Oh, sure. You learn a lot about people." He nodded wisely. "Like you, for instance. I could have sworn you're an actress or a model."

"So's everybody else in L.A."

"But not in fair Rosedale. What brings you to good old Rosedale, anyway?"

"Need a change of scene." Her glass was empty. She waggled it at him, and he signaled the bartender. *Good for you, Glen.* "How 'bout you?"

He was debating whether he should even attempt to match her drink for drink.

"Hmm? Oh, sure, everybody needs a change of scene. Me, I see to it that I get away to Vail at least once a year. You ever been to Vail?"

"No." She had already made up her mind: she would go home with him if nothing better showed up.

"That's too bad. Vail's fantastic."

"Uh-huh." She stared at him over the rim of her fresh drink.

The glass cut his face in half; his jaw misaligned with eyes and nose by a scant quarter inch. It looked very funny when he talked.

The juke was going loudly, some anonymous rock tune with a stripper's backbeat. BOOM-BA-DA-BOOM. Glen asked her to do the Hustle. She said she thought she was. They laughed. He dragged her out onto the dance floor, and they swayed together. She was drunk enough to think she was dancing just fine, but she was just hanging on to Glen's couch-suit, drifting in whatever direction possessed him.

The waitress went over to the bartender. "You'll think I'm horrible—"

"You? Never."

"I just love watching them cut up like that. I love seeing the pretty ones make fools of themselves. Pretty shitty, huh?"

He shrugged. "Just human. You're still the prettiest girl in the place, if you ask me."

Her smile lit up her almost-plain features, bones seeming to shift imperceptively to more harmonious lines. He made her *feel* pretty. "Just for that, pal, you've won yourself a wild night." She squeezed past him, giving his ass an affectionate pat.

Over Glen's shoulder Lake watched, a hot, cutting pain in her chest as if a piece of broken glass was lodged there. Glen was kissing her ear sloppily, trying to figure out how to tactfully work around to her mouth. His lips puckered around her neck, little centipede feet.

She pushed him away unsteadily. "Sorry Glen, but this isn't going to work. I have an uncontrollable urge to sit on your suit—"

"That's okay with me." He laughed.

"And I think I should go home now." She went back to the bar, left a staggering tip, and navigated woozily to the parking lot.

"Keys," she muttered, digging through her bag with numb fingers. They had to be in there somewhere.

"Come on, babe." Glen. He had followed her.

"Get lost, Glen. I cannot date a man whose wardrobe comes from K-Mart shop-at-home service." She laughed. Glen was still standing there, and he wasn't smiling. "Leave me alone. Understand?"

"You don't mean that. Not really." He backed her up against the car, pressing his groin against her body. "The way you came on to me in there, I know you're really hot for what I got."

"Not for long." She reached down and yanked. Hard.

Glen screamed and doubled over. "Oh, Jesus," he yelped over

and over again. "Oh, Jesus!" He wound down to a soft, wounded mutter. "All you had to do was say no," he told her, all injured pride. "Cockteasing cunt!" Still doubled over he waddled back to his car and gunned it, gravel spitting from his tires.

"Your suit *still* looks like a couch!" she screamed back, eating a little more dust than she usually liked in the process. It turned out she had forgotten to lock the car in the first place, so she sat inside to search for her keys.

"Keys," she said, this time a little mournfully, "where the fuck are you?"

"Wake up. Come on now."

Someone was shaking her. Not rough, nice, really. Someone whose body held a pleasant smell, rather like thyme. "Thyme is on my side," Lake's mind sang idiotically. She had a headache.

She opened her eyes and groaned. "Mr. Bartender, do you know what's worse than waking up hung over?"

He nodded. "Waking up still drunk."

"Uhhh, killer headache."

"Look, you really shouldn't drive yourself home—"

"Pete!" The waitress was waiting on the stoop, shivering in a light jacket. Apprehension carved her face sharply. He trotted back to the stoop, where they conferred briefly. You didn't have to be a lipreader to figure out the gist of their conversation.

—What's going on?

—Had a little too much. I'll drive her home, leave my car here. Pick me up tomorrow?

—Sure.I love you.

Love you, too.

He got into Lake's car, searched through her bag for exactly eight seconds, found her keys, and started the car up. They got on the main road. "Where do you live?"

She bit her lip and looked anxious.

His eyes flicked over at her. "You got a problem?"

"Sort of."

"Your old man waiting up for you?"

She nodded miserably. It was *so* easy. All you had to do was let somebody else start the machinery of a lie for you. Then, as long as you kept it simple, you were safe.

He was thinking, trying to put the scene together in his head. Jealous boyfriend or husband waiting up, sitting in an armchair, pretending to watch the late show, just waiting for the little woman to come home so he could pop her one in the chops. "What do you want to do? You got to face him sooner or later."

"Later would be better, when I've had time to think. Could I . . . could I stay at your place tonight?" She saw the hesitation in his eyes. "Come on. Help me out. You can't tell me you haven't. . . screwed up a little in your life."

"Oh, I've screwed up plenty," he said evenly. "I just hoped the majority of my screw-ups were behind me. I have a lady. I'd like to play it straight with her, and that might be a little difficult with a beautiful stranger sleeping on my very accessible couch."

"Well." She smiled. "I'll respect your privacy if you respect mine."

He smiled back. "Oh, hell, why not? I haven't had a good cold shower in a long time."

The house was small, barely more than a cabin. But it had a brick fireplace in good working order, a separate kitchen, and the bedroom, which he had insisted she take. The couch was comfortable enough for him, and warm enough when he built a fire. He had built the house, he told her proudly, from a kit. Except for the electrical stuff, he had built the whole damn thing, and he said he thought that was pretty good for an ex-hippy, college-dropout kind of guy. He showed her around, pointing out his small treasures.

Over the bed there was a framed print that he drew her attention to. She moved closer to see it better. "Jesus! What the hell is that?"

"That's something, isn't it?" he agreed. "Would you believe that's actually an illustration from a children's book?"

"It's horrifying.'

"Yeah, it's pretty unnerving, but it's a beautiful piece of artwork. If I had the book this illustration was cut from I'd have something worth a nice bit of change. As it is, I don't think it's worth much. Just the intrinsic value of the art." The print showed a man cautiously entering a bedroom, holding a lighted candle before him. He looked like he was expecting the worst. Behind the door he held open so timidly lurked a second man, in face and form exactly like the first. From his expression it was plain to see his intent was far from friendly. "You ever hear of the doppelganger?"

"No. Sounds like a new breed of hunting dog."

He smiled. "Not exactly. It's a German myth," he explained. "I'm not sure I have it all straight. Everybody has a double, an evil doppelganger. According to the story the doppelganger must take his look-alike's place in the real world in order to have a life of his own."

"Like the changeling child," she whispered.

"Kind of," he agreed. "The Germans had this decidedly morbid streak when it came to children's stories."

A sick feeling of foreboding washed over her, making her feel weak-kneed. "I wouldn't want that hanging over my bed." She laughed faintly.

"Oh, I don't know. It's sort of compelling in its own strange way. The strongest emotions are the primitive ones. Strong and beautiful." He gave her pajamas, a robe, and a towel. "Bathroom's down the hall. Can't miss it. You may have to jiggle the toilet, or it'll run all night."

"I won't forget. Pete?"

"Yes, ma'am."

"You've been seeing your lady for a long time?"

"A few months." He sat on the edge of the bed looking at her. He had good lines in his face, not pretty but strong-looking. Thirties. His hair had an unruly curl to it that looked boyish. The body went with the face, strong but not showy.

"Ah." Lake smiled. "True love."

"Maybe. I sure would like to stick around long enough to find out."

"You're a real romantic, Pete."

"Trying to be. Good night."

She heard him go into the living room. There were sounds of fussing as he messed around, setting up his blankets, adjusting the fire. Then there was only the quiet of his peaceful sleep. Lake lay in bed staring up at the ceiling. The blackness of the room abated, the shape of things creeping into murky relief. For an eternity she played little games with herself: did the bureau look like a sleeping giant hunched in the darkness or a dragon-child playing marbles? Either an hour or six days passed by like that. In the living room Pete was sleeping like a baby. Lake envied him. She remembered what a mystery sleep had been to her as a child. She had asked her mother if people breathed while they slept. Maybe you were supposed to hold your breath; she wasn't sure. Her mother had laughed. Of course you breathed; everybody did. Sleep was a natural thing. Anyone could do it.

It was the idea of that picture hanging over her head that was keeping her awake. Oh, be reasonable, she chided herself. That wasn't the only thing that was keeping her awake.

She slipped the pajamas off and padded naked into the living room. The fire had died down to glowing coals, but they gave off heat, low light, and a soft crackle from time to time. Pete was curled up on the couch, a blanket thrown over his large frame. She knelt by the side of the couch, slipping her hand under the blanket. He was naked. Why would he have done that if he wasn't expecting her?

She ran her hand down the length of his body, feeling him wake to her touch, blood surging through muscle. You sing like a wire, she thought with satisfaction. He moved softly under the blanket, making room for her. His eyes were still closed; she wondered if he thought he was dreaming. The blanket fluttered like a slow-breaking wave as she eased under it, next to his warm skin. He turned again, and she scooted under him, his hardness pressing against her soft belly. His eyes opened slowly, sleep fleeing, realization seeping into his brain. He knew exactly what was going on. All he had to do was say no, tell her to get out of his bed and back into her own. Tell her how much his lady meant to him, how he loved her, how he would never find the Holy Grail unless he remained chaste and pure.

She stretched beneath him, all silken hide and tawny hair. His resolve shattered. He lowered himself onto her, wrapping his arms around her. His breath whistled softly in her ear, quickening with a raspy urgency as her legs locked around his hips.

"Landing gear." She laughed throatily, catching his earlobe between her teeth. In return he held her even closer, pushing into her as slowly as his mounting passion would allow. She urged him on, thrusting her hips against him. Again he lost himself, pulsing to her rhythm, his long shaft glistening with her wetness.

She was insane, he thought. Once, she pulled him into her so deeply, fingers sinking into his back, that he felt they might be joined that way forever. Once, she arched away from his frantic pumping, keeping herself a maddening fraction of an inch out of his reach. She made him groan with pain for wanting her, then teased the tip of his cock with her warmth, her nearness, before escaping again. His big arms trapped her, large hands pillowing her head, muscular forearms clothed with her streaming hair. He kissed her long and deep, relishing the way she yielded her soft mouth to him. But she would not slow her pace, closing her legs ever so slightly to exert an unbearably exquisite pressure on him. He came, shuddering, the sweat that slicked his body dripping down to mingle with hers. He heard laughter in his ear. It sounded triumphant.

He fell asleep trying to erase the sound of that victorious laugh.

When he woke in the morning, she was already up and starting to dress. In the cold light of morning, she was still the most beautiful woman he had ever seen, and he had never wanted anybody gone more than he wanted her out of his house.

"See?" she told him. "Nobody stays pure. Nobody."

He looked at her. "There's something you may want to keep in the back of your mind. I don't know whether you're an evil angel or just pretending to be. But after a while"—he smiled bleakly—"the distinction fades."

Her laughter was light and false. "Just think. Now you can tell all your friends you fucked a television star."

When the sound and smell of her was no longer in his house, he ripped the sheets off the couch and stuffed them in the garbage. He showered and dressed, feeling like everything was going to go wrong from now on. He would break up with his girl, his house would burn down, Rosedale would get hit by an earthquake. All because he had let that woman into his home and she had been too beautiful to resist.

Not surprisingly, Harry couldn't sleep after the party. Chris was cutting some major Zs next to him, but he was wide awake. After tossing and turning a while, he called Matt, not really giving a shit if he woke him or not, and arranged to meet at the hotel. He left a note for Chris—"Couldn't sleep. Went for a drive"—and pulled the car out of the driveway as quietly as he could.

Matt was waiting in the hotel bar with a pot of coffee and one cup. Matt didn't drink coffee and had a soda for himself. "Karen's asleep," he said in his abrupt way. "She doesn't know anything about this, and I don't intend to tell her, in case you were curious."

"Thanks." Harry poured himself a cup of coffee. It was so bitter it made his nose curl.

"So." Matt was smiling a little to himself. "When did you first have occasion to be fucked by the lovely Ms. Eastman?"

Harry laughed in spite of the situation. "You've got a way of putting things. This has been going on for a few months. Look, I've got a feeling George Nichols is going to give me the lead in a film; I can't have this blow up in my face. I've got to know what you intend to do."

"Not a damn thing. It's your funeral. You're entitled to plan it any way you like."

He took a deep breath. "I thought it was just going to be

fantasy time. I didn't know we were going to fall in love. You're the lucky one, Matt. You're the smart one. God, Karen got so beautiful. You must be taking good care of her."

"Don't even look at her funny, Harry," Matt said quietly, "or I'll do more than tell on you." His face was completely serious.

"I wouldn't," Harry said. "I wouldn't fuck up her life like that."

They were quiet for a moment.

"What are you going to do?" Matt asked him.

"Coast. Try not to hurt Chris. I really do care for her, and God knows she's been good to me."

"Going to break it off with Lake?"

"No," Harry said quietly, "I don't intend to do that." He sipped his coffee, grimacing at the bitter taste.

Matt shook his head. "Lake was the only thing Karen and I ever fought over. Some people have bad luck. Lake's a carrier. I was so damn happy when Lake took off for California. I figured that was the end of it. But just when Karen was about to give up on her, a little gift or a Christmas card would come, and we'd be back to square one. I think Lake tried to let go of her; she just wasn't able to. And Karen couldn't break it off, because, well . . . I suppose you don't get over Lake so fast. The only way to be safe is to stay away for good."

"I'm not staying away," Harry said.

"She's a death sentence, Harry."

"I love her," he said.

At eleven o'clock Matt nudged a still sleeping Karen to a groggy semblance of wakefulness. "Wake up already; you've got work to do."

"No, I don't. I'm on vacation." She grabbed a pillow and pulled it over her head. "Go away. I don't love you anymore. I've never loved you."

"I have coffee for you."

Karen sat up. "I still don't love you, but there's hope." Gratefully she accepted the cup. "Were you up earlier?"

"Nope."

"Oh, I thought you were. Must have dreamed it."

Matt frowned. "I had to go downstairs to pick this up from the front desk." He waved a large manila envelope at her. "It's for you."

Karen opened it slowly. It was a script with a note clipped

onto the cover. The letterhead announced proudly that it was from the Nichols Agency.

Karen-

I really enjoyed reading those samples of your work you sent me, and I must say I'm quite impressed. Why don't you take a look at the enclosed script and give me some feedback.

-G-

She put down her coffee and wriggled into a torn sweatshirt and jeans. "What am I supposed to do with this?"

Matt scanned the note. "You're supposed to feed back. It says so right here."

Reading as she walked, Karen miraculously navigated herself and her coffee out to the terrace without any spills or toe-stubbing.

"Karen?"

She looked up. For a moment Matt saw one perfect frame of film, the way the sun back-lit her hair and scooped out the dish of her cheekbones. The mild expression of curiosity, mouth softly open. God, he loved her.

"What, Matt?" she asked impatiently.

"You're beautiful."

She grimaced. "Who wouldn't be in this lovely ensemble? You're lucky to have me, boy."

"I know it. Are you going to read that whole thing now?"

"Yep."

"Mind if I turn on the TV?"

"Nope." She settled herself on the balcony, absorbed in the script. The TV played softly. Sunday morning programming tended to be a little more laid back than the usual daytime fare. Someone knocked on the door.

"I'll get it," Matt called out. He opened the door. "Hello, George."

The agent muttered a greeting. "Could I speak to Karen?"

"Please, come in," Karen called out. "Can't very well have a conversation in the doorway. I'm afraid I haven't had a chance to read the script yet."

"No, I didn't come for that. Lake is in Angelwood."

Karen looked at him uncomprehendingly.

"It's sort of a health spa," George explained.

"It's where the rich go to dry out," Matt put in.

George did his best to ignore Matt. "She showed up this morning in a terrible state, agitated to the point of hysteria. I calmed her down and she agreed to spend a few days at Angelwood. Hopefully, she'll be back at work mid-week. We won't lose too much time." He took Karen's hand. "She wants to see you. She feels terrible about the way she treated you last night; she wants to apologize; it would really help her. I can drive you over," he looked at her hopefully, "if you're willing to see her."

"Why the hell should she?" Matt demanded angrily. "After that lovely greeting last night—"

"Matt, please. The least I can do is hear her out." Karen turned back to George. "Just give me a minute to change." She pulled something out of the closet and went into the bathroom. In her absence, Matt did not say a word.

The silence got to George. "Lake is very lucky to have such a loyal friend. We should all have friends like that."

"Lake is a lunatic," Matt observed. "This isn't her first time at the nut farm, is it?"

"No."

"I thought I remembered reading something about that in one of the tabloids," he smiled slightly, "an unimpeachable source. George, I'm not trying to give you a hard time, I just don't want Karen hurt."

George shrugged helplessly. "The way I see it, this is between them. I'm just a messenger boy."

"And you need Lake back at work as quickly as possible."

"It's a little more than that," George said stiffly.

"Ready." Karen came out of the bathroom, still brushing her hair. She wore a plain white shirt, collar turned up, the ubiquitous jeans, and a soft-looking gray-green jacket. "Let's go." Even George's practiced eye could detect nothing more than mascara, blush, and a slick of clear lip gloss. Maybe even Vaseline. She looked like one of the horsey set who just leaped out of bed in the morning with every hair in place. Not a drop-dead stunner like Lake, George decided, but a very classy looking girl. Cool and intelligent. Funny, but from Lake's description he just hadn't been expecting such a beauty.

As they drove to Angelwood, George replayed his last conversation with Lake; the tears, the pleading, *please, please, tell her anything, just make Karen come.*

"Talk to *me*," he had begged, "why can't you tell *me*?"

But she had insisted, and, as he had told Matt, George was only a messenger boy.

They turned into the long driveway.

"It's beautiful," Karen murmured.

"Angelwood used to be a family estate. It's over a hundred years old. The family went broke, some enterprising soul came in, bought up the place, refurbished it, and turned it into a retreat for tired minds and bodies. People come here for a lot of reasons. Get in shape for a new film, recover from a messy divorce, lots of reasons."

The big white house looked like an elegant, slightly Victorian hotel. Karen recognized some of the people sitting in big wicker chairs on the porch, some dressed in bathrobes, some in sweatsuits, a few in street clothes.

"There doesn't seem to be any staff around."

"They don't wear uniforms," George told her. "Everyone's more comfortable that way."

"But the doctors wear white coats, don't they?"

"Yes, they wear white coats."

"No matter how it's dressed up, this is still a place for drunks and junkies." Karen shook her head. "What is she doing here? She's beautiful, rich and famous . . . didn't that make her happy?"

George smiled sadly. "Only at first."

Lake was not on the porch. They checked at the desk and were sent around back to the pool.

"Maybe you should handle this alone," a nervous George said. "I'll wait for you in the dining room. I could use a cup of coffee anyway."

A man Karen knew, from one of her favorite TV shows of a few years back, was swimming laps, barely breaking the water with expert strokes. He wasn't wearing his hairpiece and he'd put on a few pounds. Since his series had been cancelled he hadn't done much work. Sunning at the edge of the water, a woman, second-generation famous, raised herself to stare at Karen. Her eyes looked tired and hurt.

I've seen these people in the movies, Karen thought.

"Stop gaping and come sit with me," Lake said. She too was curled up in a chaise, wearing sunglasses, a black maillot, and a layer of rich-smelling tanning lotion. "I can't believe you came."

"I'm a little surprised myself," Karen said, her tone a little formal. She wanted Lake to know she was more than a little pissed off, but she sat down with her old friend anyway. "You really hurt me."

"I know. I'm sorry." She took off the sunglasses, revealing

eyes that were bloodshot and puffy. She grimaced at Karen's expression. "Seems the old bod won't put up with my rampages anymore, not like it did when I was twenty. Do you want to know something, Karen? Everything you ever heard about this business is absolutely true. At first it's so much fun you can't believe it's really happening to you. Somewhere along the way, you stop being a person. You're a commodity. Specially someone like me. I've never been anything more than a face and a body. Ball players have longer careers than people like me."

"Oh, is that why you were so shitty to me?"

"I'm trying to explain. Karen, you've changed, I don't think you know how much. Last night at the party, everybody was playing the game, but you just seem above it somehow. Every good-looking girl anywhere near our age had her tits half hanging out of her dress, mingling like crazy, trying to make a few nice connections, just working that party. You're in a little corner, talking with Harry's weird sister, covered up to your neck, not making any effort whatsoever and everybody is asking 'Who is that girl?' And hating you a little because you don't play the game like the rest of us have to. You're above it. You always were. I need them to look at me, Karen. The day they stop, I'll lose everything I have. I was so jealous I couldn't see straight. I couldn't help but wonder—maybe you were writing me all those years because you wanted me to help your career."

Karen started to laugh. "Absolutely. If I was doing better than you, don't you think I'd help you out?"

"I'm sure you would. I'm just not that secure."

Karen shrugged. "I can accept that. That wasn't the only reason why I kept writing. You disappeared for two years. I thought you were lying dead somewhere. I even went to see your mother. God, Lake, no wonder you're screwed up. She's completely inadequate."

"She can't help the way she is," Lake said faintly.

"I'm sure that didn't make your life any easier. I just wanted to know that you were all right. The other part, well, that was just human nature. Since I've had some success as a writer, you'd be amazed how many 'old friends' have crawled out of the woodwork asking me to help them out. It's kind of funny. Like I know anything or anyone, for that matter."

"You still want to be an actress?"

Karen was silent for a moment. "I think I've *had* my acting career. I've wrestled with agents; I've gone on the road and slept five grubby actors to a room, and considered myself lucky to clear twenty dollars a show. I've sung in bars so dirty I wouldn't dare use their bathroom, and that's not the worst of it. Nobody listens. If I'm so damn wonderful, how come I couldn't make them listen? I finally got it through my head that I am not destined to have an acting career, at least not yet. So, I scribble, and they pay me nice and treat me nice and that's just fine with me."

"But you still want it."

"On my terms," Karen said firmly. "I won't be treated like that anymore."

"Then you'll make it. It won't be overnight, my love, but you won't owe anybody anything. If you were really smart, you'd be happy with what you've got. Because you really do have it all. You're intelligent, you're beautiful and you've got a man who loves you."

"So *that's* why you wanted to see me, to give me this little bit of career advice."

"No, it's just hard to say . . ." she put the sunglasses back on and took them off again. "Face to face, right? I promised myself I'd go through with this." Her mouth trembled. "Remember when you first moved in with me? You said eventually I'd have to talk to somebody about my nightmares, my problems. Well, I never have. Not the doctors here, certainly not George, no one. You're the only person I can talk to, Karen." She took a deep breath. "You've met my mother, so maybe you understand that in my whole life I've never had anyone I can trust, anyone I can turn to. I don't know why it had to be that way, but . . . for whatever reason, it simply is. So she couldn't help me, couldn't stop things, no one could, not that I blame her, or hate her," her breath came quicker now, "she's still my mother, I love her. All the secrets in my family, God! If you knew—"

Alarmed, Karen stroked her arm, "Lake please, slow down. It's okay. I'm here."

"I never told anyone, not even George. My God, he'd be repulsed, and to the shrinks it's just another story. You were so right. Karen, I have to tell someone and you're the only person I can trust. I thought if I never spoke about it, I'd forget, but I never could. Even when I'm drunk or high, I remember it. Not all, but enough. God, I'm so scared!" Her fingers closed around Karen's with surprising force. "Like something awful is going to happen to me if I say it out loud." Her whole body was shaking. "He raped me."

"Who did?" Karen asked in a comforting voice, but Lake was lost in her memory.

Someone's Here.

Her heart fluttered in her chest. She was small, even for five. Pulling the covers up, she tried to make herself smaller and disappear altogether, feeling a deep and instinctual fear of the person hiding in the corner. Yet she could neither run away nor call out for help.

Because you're asleep, silly, she told herself. It's a dream and it goes away when you wake up.

The nursery light went on, the one that shot out streaks of lightning if you squinted real hard, only it was much dimmer than usual, barely bright enough to light up the corner. Someone was there. It was a lady, all coated with sparkles, or crystals, like Lot's wife in the Storybook Bible. The little girl smiled in greeting but the lady couldn't respond. She was just a statue, although her eyes looked just like a real person's. The little girl wondered if it was lonely being a statue. Probably. She squinted to make lightning flash from the ceiling lamp but the light was fading.

The little girl's leg itched. She snuck a hand under the covers to scratch and froze instead. Someone was touching her. Under the covers. A hand was wrapped firmly around her ankle.

It's just a dream she whispered.

The statue could barely be seen now, faintly glimmering in her corner, but her eyes were filled with tears. And the hands were very much there, big strong hands under the covers, moving up the length of her small body. Her nightgown was being pulled up over her head, pinning her arms. Tears of shame streamed down her face. She tried to scream but no sound came out. Peering around the upended hem of her nightgown, her eyes silently implored the statue. Help me.

The hands were touching her down there. She begged the statue to make it stop. Maybe it wasn't real, maybe it was a lady playing statue, like the little girl had with her mother on the big lawn in front of the house. Either way, statue or lady, it couldn't or wouldn't help her, and with the nightgown once again firmly held over her face, she no longer believed the statue was there at all anymore. Only the hands were there, hurting her terribly, because they were so big, much too big for such a little girl.

Wake up, she begged herself, wake up and make it go away now!

Her eyes opened. Then, her tears began to fall in earnest, tears of despair and fear. No one was coming to help her, not ever. She was little, they were big, and anytime they wanted they could come in and get her. Anytime at all.

Downstairs, the statue did needlepoint and wept.

"I was little, I think five, around five years old, and he came into my room to tuck me in."

"Oh, my God." A sick knot of apprehension tightened in Karen's stomach. She could picture the child, beautiful beyond words, playing quietly in her room, waiting to be tucked in, waiting . . .

"—my father came in and he hurt me." Her voice became high and soft, like a child's. "I kept thinking, what have I done? What bad thing have I done for him to do this to me? And then I realized, it was just me. *I* was the bad thing. I'm all messed up inside, I can't have children, everything's all messed up in there. Because I was so little and everything . . . it just broke. Children aren't strong," she said in a patient, pedantic tone, "they break easily. You understand?"

Karen nodded, tears silently streaming from her eyes.

"Sometimes I would look at you and get so angry. If he hadn't hurt me, I could have been like you, have a lot of friends, I could have been *good.* But I can't be good now. I can't help myself. Just like my mother. Both defective." She seemed to come back to herself. "You can't tell anybody, Karen, not even Matt. I'd be so ashamed. I'd rather have people think I'm a bitch than feel them pity me."

"Lake, you have nothing to be ashamed of, it wasn't your fault."

"Promise you won't tell."

"You have to tell your doctor here. How else can you get well?"

Lake shook her head violently. "Promise."

"I promise," Karen said reluctantly.

Lake's relief was as obvious as her earlier panic had been. She smiled, touching Karen's tear-stained face. "After all we've been through, it's a miracle you can cry for me. You're the only one, Kar, the only one who really gives a damn about me."

"That's not true, Lake," Karen protested, "What about George?"

"I'm just glad you're here." She sighed contentedly. "I really think I can do it this time. I think if I try very hard, everything will be all right. You're staying for a while, aren't you?"

"Our plans are sort of up in the air."

"That means you can stay."

"As long as you want me to."

The man Karen used to watch on TV rose dripping from the pool to drape a towel around his neck. He waved at Lake. "Hello! Nice seeing you again. How're you doing?"

"Fine," Lake replied, "I'm going home on Tuesday. You won't see me here again," she announced jubilantly.

"Well, that's just fine. I wish you all the best, I really do." His hard eyes spoke differently: *you'll be back, we all come back.*

17

LIKE THE CHARACTER in the children's story, George was curious. He was a common-sense man, and he did not believe that Karen's sole purpose in life was to act as Lake's nursemaid. He kept waiting for the demands to begin, but they never did.

Sid had laughed at him. "You're jealous, jealous of the little girlfriend. George, relax. You should be happy. Lake's never felt better."

Which was absolutely true. She was on time for work, and she knew her lines. Karen always went with her, sitting on the set in her own chair with her name on the back in script, scribbling in the ever-present notebook. She didn't hand out 8 x 10 glossies of herself; she didn't introduce herself to the director. In short, there was nothing George could point to to prove that Karen was using her friendship with Lake to further her own career. Of course, just being around Lake assured her a certain amount of publicity. The fan magazines were having a lot of fun—wasn't it wonderful that Lake Eastman, big star that she was, hadn't forgotten her friends? It made wonderful copy, and as they were both quite photogenic, the photographers were having a good time as well. Again George knew he should be happy; Lake's image had never been particularly sterling, and this was doing wonders for it. Still, George felt uneasy about Karen, as if she was hiding something from him. Within him was the fear that, Svengali-like, she had a great power over Lake, the power to turn his lady away from him permanently. Because, after all, the fact that Lake was with him at all was the cosmic joke of all time. Oh, he was a sharp guy when it came to wheeling-dealing, but deep in his heart he was still the geek of the eighth grade. The kid any other kid could feel superior to. Maybe that was why Karen made him so uneasy. She would look at him with those almost Oriental green-amber eyes and see right through to who he had been. He wondered if she and Lake talked about him.

Finally he arranged to take both "his girls" out to lunch. The reservation was at Ma Maison, which he thought would impress Karen.

Both women were beautifully turned out. Lake wore silk, a beige tank top with a matching straight skirt. The color gave the illusion of nudity. Throughout the meal, other patrons stole admiring glances at her. More quietly attired, Karen was also getting her share of appreciative looks. She wore a bulky sweater of loden green, knee-high matching boots over tight jeans and an ivory lace scarf around her neck.

"I feel like an ancient Inca god." She smiled, spearing a flower with her fork. They were scattered liberally throughout her salad.

Lake tried one. "Doesn't taste like much, does it?" She frowned.

"No," Karen agreed, "but they look nice." She smiled at George, trying to include him. He did his best to smile back, but she just made him uncomfortable.

Lake announced she had to go to the ladies' room. George panicked slightly; he'd have to make intelligent conversation with Karen for a while.

"So!" he said brightly. "I saw you guys were on one of our local magazine shows last night."

"Yes, when Lake took me to Disneyland. Their people helped set it up. We had a lot of fun. I can't believe you never went there together."

"Well, it's not the first place you think of for a date," he bristled. "Uh, you watched the show?"

"Oh, sure." She played with her salad. "I like to watch myself on television. I don't think I'm particularly videogenic—"

You are, George thought silently. You know you are.

"But I always get a kick out of seeing myself on TV."

"You're very well adjusted."

"I'm afraid so. No interesting neuroses. I don't even bite my nails anymore." She fell silent, hoping he didn't think she was making a disparaging remark about Lake's aberrant nature.

A few people were looking over at her, trying to figure out if she was one of George Nichols's new discoveries. George noticed, and it made him a little angry. "I suppose you've gotten a lot of acting offers since your newfound notoriety."

"Not really." Karen shrugged, "A few horror films, exploitation things. Mostly they want to see if I can get Lake to talk to them, or they want me to write an exposé thing, an outsider's view of Hollywood, what the real Lake Eastman is like."

"And you won't do anything like that."

"No." She looked directly at him. "I would never do anything like that."

He leaned closer. "Doesn't it piss you off, Karen? You can't be satisfied playing second banana."

"You piss me off, George," she said, a little angrily, "right now. You're the last person who should accuse me of trying to make a buck off Lake. I can pay for my own lunch, thanks." She started rummaging in her bag.

"Sit down!" George hissed, taking hold of her arm. "This isn't New York. You won't find a cab waiting outside. Look, I'm sorry. I'm a little over-protective." His eye was on Lake, returning to the table. "Please, there's no reason we can't just forget the last five minutes."

"Everything okay?" Lake asked, reclaiming her seat.

"Just fine," Karen said. Her look told George quite clearly that bailing him out was a major effort on her part and he'd better appreciate it.

After lunch George and Lake dropped Karen off at her hotel. Lake went up with her and returned with a manila envelope.

"Here." She handed him the envelope. "Karen gave this to me. It's the rewrite you asked her to do. I don't know why she didn't give it to you herself."

He frowned. "Because we're not getting along that well. This wasn't such a good idea. I'll just return—"

"You asked Karen to fix the script. Before you say anything else, why don't you just read the damn thing? Okay?" She put her hands on either side of his face. "You can be a real jerk sometimes, George, but you don't make mistakes about the business. So read the stupid thing, if only as a favor to me."

He turned his head to kiss the palm of her hand. "I can never resist you. Okay, you want me to read it, you got it."

Lake instructed the driver to take a leisurely lap around the city.

"Now?" George asked incredulously.

"Right now." Lake linked her arm through his and leaned against his shoulder. "So I can watch you." She snuggled against him. "It won't be so tough, will it?"

He grunted, already turning pages. He knew the story pretty well, so it was easy to see what changes Karen had made. It wasn't so much that she had rearranged the plot, but he felt her deft hand in the characters, particularly Lake's. Silky had been tailor-made for Lake. The character's natural ebullience blended with Lake's cooler personality. Anyone else would have made Silky cloyingly sweet. Lake had balanced the character against her own style, and it had worked like a charm. In the original screenplay, Victoria had been a master spy, sort of a female James Bond. It hadn't quite sat right with George, but he was never sure exactly why. Now he knew. Lake would have played Victoria too cool; the character would never have been likable.

Karen had made Victoria an amateur, an art student who becomes involved with a master spy (Harry's character, with a few changes thrown in). She even suggested changing the title to *Maiden Voyage,* as a good part of the story took place on a freighter.

The villain had been changed from a wheelchair-bound maniac to a charming young man who had some of the best lines in the screenplay. All the dialogue was sharpened, and, George realized three-quarters of the way through, the whole film had been transformed from a rather serious thriller to a lighter, more comedic adventure story, the kind of thing audiences would want to see over and over again.

He closed the script. "It's brilliant," he said quietly. "Especially the villain. You know who I could see playing him?"

"Who?"

"John Allison."

"John Allison?" Lake laughed. "The spiritual brother of Gidget?"

"Even Gidget grew up, and it so happens John Allison is shopping for a serious change of image. No one can hang around the beach forever, and anyway, they're not beach movies, per se."

"Oh, youth exploitation films." Lake waved her hand vaguely. "Big difference."

"Albie Weiss got John Allison a part in a Broadway drama. I understand he's getting good reviews. One of these days he's going to leave Weiss. I'd sure like to be around then. I think he's got a lot of ability."

"Why don't you send him a copy of the script?" Lake started to grin. "And then, after he's had ample time to read it, you can send a gorgeous emissary or two to twist his muscle-bound arm."

She leaned on his shoulder. "I haven't been back to New York in ages."

"Lake, I can do my own dealing."

"Oh, please. No way will Allison take a second lead; all I'm asking for is a little vacation for me and Karen, back on our old stomping grounds. We won't screw up any deals because there isn't going to be any deal. You know it as well as I do."

"Not necessarily. Actors have been known to do strange things. Still"—he returned her smile—"I don't see what I'd stand to lose by sending my favorite person to the theater."

She hugged him frantically. "Thank you, thank you! You won't regret this, George. We're going to have such a good time, I'll be all psyched to start the film when we get back. You're the best!"

"Okay, okay." He chuckled. "And don't worry if you can't get to the famous Mr. Allison. It's a vacation."

"I'll get to him," Lake promised.

"That's what I'm afraid of." He disappeared under a barrage of kisses and hugs.

Later that afternoon George had Matt come into his office to sign a contract as the director of a project tentatively called *Maiden Voyage.* He was the first person to be admitted to George's office who had said absolutely nothing about the airplanes. Not "How interesting," or "How unusual," or "How Freudian." Nothing whatsoever. George knew he was taking a big risk. The low-budget film Matt and his *Hurdy-Gurdy* pals had put together was going to be released in a matter of days. If it went as big as it was expected to, every producer in town would be clamoring for the young director. George was jumping the gun, but if the picture stunk, he'd be stuck with an inexperienced director with an ironclad contract in his young claw. Thin ice, but George trusted his instincts. He didn't know much about Matt, who was the original closed-mouth individual, but he did know that Matt was a brilliant director, seemingly impervious to all of Hollywood's fabled charms: fame, drugs, eager starlets. His passion seemed to be only for his work and his wife. George knew he needed a good director for *Maiden Voyage.* He liked what little he'd seen of Matt's cinematic style, and he liked the fact that Matt wasn't exactly likely to be tempted by Lake. Too many directors had wound up wrapped around her little finger. It was October now, George figured. If John Allison was a particularly slow reader, he'd give him to December and send the girls to New York for the holiday season. They'd do as much pre-production as humanly possible and start shooting in April, when *The Girl Upstairs* went on hiatus. So far, so good.

Matt looked up from the contracts. "What about the rider I asked for?"

"Matt, that's a very strange item," George fenced.

"I don't think it's so strange. I don't think I've asked you for anything out of the ordinary."

"Not everybody asks for a part for his wife."

Matt took off his glasses. Since a scratched cornea a few years ago, he had given up the contacts for good. "It's a very small part; total screen time, maybe five minutes. I don't see what the big deal is. It's done all the time. People constantly give small roles away like gifts. It's not worth fighting over."

"No, it isn't." George considered. April was a long time away. Plenty of time to renege. He signed the rider. "There you are. Well, this shoot is going to be like old-home week for you. All your old friends are together again."

Matt shrugged. "I wouldn't say we were all that friendly. Harry I knew because I cast him in a student film. Lake was my wife's roommate. I wouldn't say we were particularly close one way or the other. All we had in common was Karen."

"Karen's quite a girl."

"Yes, she is." Matt smiled, the first real smile George had ever seen on him. "If you were a smart guy, you'd sign her up, put her in her own movie."

George felt weary. "One thing at a time, Matt, one thing at a time."

18

IT WAS FREEZING, a typical December day in New York, so after a marathon shopping festival they decided to go to the Palm Court in the Plaza for tea.

"God, I missed this town so much," Lake said as she poured milk into her tea. "Feels good to be back."

Karen wrinkled her nose. "I wish we could go see some other show. This one sounds horrible."

"Come on, now," Lake teased her. "Aren't you excited at the prospect of meeting the extremely attractive John Allison?"

"No. I can't stand people like that."

"Like what? You've never met him before."

"You know what I mean. Guys who think they're God's gift to women."

Lake sighed. "Fine, hang the guy without a trial. *I'll* do all the talking tonight. You just enjoy the show. Fair enough? Here, try one of these little sandwiches; they're fabulous." Lake was digging in with gusto when a well-meaning fan clattered up to the table. A younger woman, obviously a mortified daughter, trailed in her wake, protesting in a low voice.

"You're Silky!" the older lady exclaimed. "We watch you all the time. I almost feel like you're one of the family."

"I'm glad you like the show. That's what we're there for."

The older lady nodded. "I feel I can tell you, dear, you shouldn't wear such revealing outfits. You're a pretty girl; you don't have to cheapen yourself like that."

The daughter was quietly dying.

"Thank you for telling me," Lake said in all seriousness. "It's good to know these things."

"You're welcome." The lady beamed. "You're a very nice girl." She held out an autograph book, pen clipped to the spine. "Would you mind?"

"Not at all." Quickly she scrawled "Best Wishes, Lake Eastman" and handed the book back. Stoically the daughter stared at her own shoes, devoutly wishing to be someplace else—the Belgian Congo, up the Amazon without a paddle, *anywhere*.

The lady hesitated, book in hand, staring at Karen. Karen smiled pleasantly. The lady smiled back. "Are you somebody?" she asked.

Karen waited a beat. "You mean, you don't recognize me? Well, I guess people don't recognize me without the wig. That'll teach me to go without it. You were right." She nudged a mystified Lake. "She said nobody would recognize me. We even made a little bet," she remarked conversationally to the lady. "There you go." She dug a dollar bill out of her purse and handed it to Lake. "A wager's a wager."

"Oh, my, now I recognize you. I'm so sorry." The flustered lady handed over the book. "Would you?"

"Good Luck in all you undertake," Karen wrote. "Love, Dolly Parton."

The lady was too embarrassed to even peek at her book until she got to the door. She looked back at Karen, confusion plain in her face. "You don't think she actually *is* . . ." she questioned her daughter.

They heard the daughter laughing all the way to Fifth Avenue.

Lake stared at Karen in amazement. "I didn't know you had that in you. I am in shock."

Karen looked terribly innocent. "All she had to do was say no, she didn't recognize me. I didn't exactly wrestle the book out of her hands."

"You're incredible." Lake chuckled. "At first I thought you were just going to freak out, or at least get righteously indignant. A lot of people would have. You've really got it together."

Karen gave her a strange look. "Never make the mistake of thinking that people who can handle life feel things less than people who can't."

"Meaning what?" Lake pressed her.

"Skip it." Karen sipped her tea. "Unimportant." They both let it go.

Lake rummaged through the packages at her feet, seizing one. "This is for you. Oh, don't open it now. Wait till we get back to the hotel."

Karen poked at the box curiously, trying to pry up one of the corners. "What is it?"

"It's for tonight, and if you're going to break the box before we get back, *I'll* carry it, thank you very much." She started to shrug into her coat. "You're going to dazzle that little jerk."

"Dazzling is your department," Karen answered firmly. "I do not dazzle. Boy, I am really not looking forward to this evening. I'm out of my league."

"John Allison will adore you." Lake started gathering up her packages, trying to figure out which bag should be delegated to which arm.

Karen shrugged, suggesting a nonchalance she hardly felt. She knew John Allison all right; there was a John Allison in every high school, every college, every office. The guy who could do no wrong, who could be a total bastard and sport a smile that could bamboozle Mother Teresa. The guy all the girls were in love with and nobody got. Except the girl who got voted Best Body in the yearbook, and that relationship only lasted until the cute English exchange student caught his eye. Yeah, Karen knew John Allison, and guys like that always made her feel like an invisible girl.

"It's okay," she said half to herself. "I can take it for one evening."

"What are you talking about?" Lake laughed at her. "You're muttering to yourself like a bag lady. Come on, let's get a cab. I want to rest up a little before the show."

John Allison had not done much of anything in high school except smoke pot and get into trouble. School was boring; everything was a total waste; he was going to live and die in Highland, New York, the small upstate town he'd spent his whole life in. He was the youngest of six, and by the time he came around, his folks were worn out. They'd seen every trick a kid could pull, and they weren't in the mood to witness any new variations. They were also pretty broke from putting five other not-terribly-bright kids through various stages of schooling: guitar lessons, religious instruction, college. They told Johnny in no uncertain terms that if he had any intention of making something of himself, he was bloody well on his own concerning tuition or anything of that nature. Johnny got a job in a gas station and figured that that was it for the sum total of the life and times of John Allison. Born too late and into the wrong family. He dealt a little pot—nothing big time, just enough to keep him in Adidas and Saturday night movies with a date. His hair was long and greasy, and as soon as he could grow a beard, he did. On the few occasions he went into the city, most good citizens steered clean around him. He was a young tough, and he was trouble. In his senior year the yearbook staff voted him "Most Likely to Wind Up in Prison."

At nineteen Johnny was still pumping gas, still a small-time dealer. One of his old high school buddies, a real head, talked Johnny into coming with him to the city. Some soap opera was having an open call—what the hell, they weren't lepers; they should go read for the part. What the hell, Johnny agreed; it was a way of making one day different from the rest.

The two boys walked in, their long hair uncombed, wearing fatigue jackets and jeans. The soap people were not looking for Marlon Brando. They wanted a young, sweet, slightly tough guy, not a kid who looked like a menace to society. Albie Weiss, a personal manager of one of the boys reading, was watching the auditions. He had a lot of friends in the business, and his opinion stood for a lot. He watched Allison closely.

"Thank you," someone said to Johnny. "We'll let you know."

Johnny's face fell almost comically. "Ah, I sucked," he said honestly, handing the script back. "This is my first time doing this; I don't *know* how you do this. I'm sorry. I fucked up."

"There'll be other times," the monitor, a young but not especially attractive girl, said softly.

Johnny smiled at her.

She melted. A woman impervious to actor bullshit had virtually turned into a puddle right in front of Albie's eyes. The manager had seen all he needed to see. He stopped Allison and his friend out in the hallway.

"Hey you," he called, puffing as his pudgy little body protested the run he was forcing it into. "Young man, do you want to be an actor?"

Johnny and his friend looked at each other.

"You." Albie pointed at Johnny. "Do you want to be an actor?" he repeated.

"Sure," Johnny said with a laugh. "Beats the hell out of pumping gas upstate."

Albie came up to them, still panting a little. "Good. I'll need you to stay in the city for the next few days. You can stay at my apartment."

"Hey, wait a minute," Johnny said slowly. "What is this? You got eyes for me, mister?"

"I am a personal manager." Albie drew himself up proudly. "And I think you have what it takes. Here, my card."

The boys studied it. "Engraved," the friend said approvingly. "This guy must have bucks."

"Do you want to be an actor?" Albie asked for the third time. "Because if you do, I can help you."

Johnny pocketed the card. "Lemme think on it," he told Albie, offering his piercingly sweet smile. "No good to make a hasty decision, right?"

"No." Albie felt his mind fog up. This was his golden boy, this was the one that would do it for him. He'd never been more certain of anything in his entire life.

The boys went back upstate.

"You're crazy," the friend told Johnny. "You should have grabbed that old fart and taken him for what he's worth, which is plenty."

"I gotta think on it," Johnny said serenely, "and that's what I'm gonna do."

That night he told his mother and father he was moving out, going to live in the city, make something of himself. He was going to be an actor. Briefly he told them about Albie Weiss.

His father was a little drunk. He was not a bad man, but he was tired, and his life seemed sometimes like one long, nasty joke. He had written poetry when he was young, and Johnny was the one child who had inherited his dreams. Big dreams, the father thought with a laugh; they'd gotten him far.

"Turning into a faggot on me?" the father bellowed.

Johnny's mother started clearing the table. "Leave him alone," she muttered. "You're always picking on him." She took the dishes into the kitchen and stayed there, even though she could still hear them yelling. It was better than watching them fight.

When the kids were little, John Senior (they called him Big John) had taken the strap to them to make them mind. When they got bigger, he hit them with his hand. None of the other kids made him as mad as Johnny did, because he loved Johnny the most. Johnny was the only kid who wouldn't hit back. He was strong; at five foot ten he could probably kill his father, but he would never strike the old man. In his own way Johnny had developed his personal code of ethics, and he adhered to it.

She heard Big John slapping the kid around. The sound made her sick. "I won't stand for it," she said between clenched teeth, the words sounding strangled. "I can't take it anymore." She went out to the living room. "You stop it!" she screamed.

"Stay out of it," Big John warned. "Come on," he taunted his son, "come on, hit me, you little faggot. See what I raised? A little girl, a pretty little girl. Hey, sweetheart, what's your name? Mary? Susan?"

"Leave me alone," Johnny said. "I just want to get my things and go." He brushed past the old man and started up the stairs. Bellowing insanely, his father grabbed his arm and pulled him backward. Johnny was off balance. He snagged the railing of the banister and hung on. His father was still a strong man, and Johnny had to let go. He slipped and came crashing down, his father still holding on to his arm. The angle was too awkward; they all heard the snap.

For a moment they were all still. Johnny got up slowly, amazed at how bad he could feel so quickly. "Get away from me," he told his father, inching his way to the door. "I'm never coming back here, not as long as I live." He walked out the door, not sure at all what the hell he would do next. He didn't even have busfare.

"Johnny, Johnny!" His mother was running after him crying. "Here, it's all I got." She pressed some money into his hand. "He's not a bad man. It was an accident, Johnny, you know it was," she cried.

"I hate that bastard."

"You don't; it's not in you, Johnny," his mother said. "You got the sweetest nature out of the bunch. You just never got a break, that's all. You'll forgive him—it's the way you are, it's the way God made you."

"I'll never forgive him," Johnny said.

By the time his bus pulled into the Port Authority, his arm was throbbing and he felt pretty rank. With his good arm he fished Albie's card out of his pocket. His mother had given him a little more than fifty dollars. A few cabs passed him by, put off by his scruffy appearance, but he finally got one to take him to Albie's address, a brownstone in the east sixties.

The housekeeper was scared to let him in. "What's the problem, Esther?" Albie came up beside her, hearing a commotion.

Johnny was leaning against the door. If he'd been an animal, someone would have put him out of his misery. "Mr. Weiss, I thought it over," he said. "If you want to help me, that's okay with me." Then he fainted dead away, right on Albie's doorstep.

The first thing Albie did was call a doctor, who set Johnny's arm and assured Albie that none of the bruises on his face signified any kind of permanent damage.

"Who did this to you?" he asked Johnny when he woke up the next morning.

"My old man." He caught Albie's expression of horror. "Don't look that way. It was an accident. My old man's a bull; he doesn't know his own strength." He yawned hugely. "So when do we start this actor bullshit?"

Albie laughed. "Right now."

Albie thought Johnny should have a full day of rest, so he arranged for a hairstylist to come in. A haircut and a close shave later, it turned out Albie's instincts about Johnny were right on the money. His dark, almost black hair contrasted beautifully with his light gray eyes. Like summer fog those eyes were. He was still a tough guy, but there was a vulnerable sweetness that shone through, charming everyone he met.

Under a different name and carefully coached by Albie, Johnny went back and auditioned for the soap people. They ate him up, plaster cast and all. Here at last was the genuine article, not some dickless actor playing dress-up. They wanted to sign him immediately.

They all went to lunch, some ritzy French place, and nobody seemed to care that Johnny was just a dumb kid from upstate New York. Albie took care of everything, seeing to it that Johnny signed nothing before a lawyer had a chance to look it over. Johnny got blissfully drunk on the vintage wine and fell asleep in the limo on the ride home. He had to be carried upstairs, where Albie put him to bed.

Albie's wife was in the living room crocheting. "You like him." She'd been with Albie a long time. In college there'd been an incident, an experiment on Albie's part. She did not think of it often, but it did come to mind every now and then.

"He's a good kid." Albie shrugged. "He's going to do very well on the soap; they're lucky to have him."

Albie's wife put down her crocheting. "Albie, don't get too involved with this boy. They all get crazy when they get a little fame. He'll cut you off when he gets too big."

Albie smiled, remembering Johnny's valiant struggle to conceal the fact that he was slightly drunk from the soap people, who knew and didn't really care. How Albie and Johnny had laughed in the car! "You think they knew?" Johnny asked, giggling. He said he wasn't used to much besides beer. Then he slept on Albie's shoulder.

"No," Albie said thoughtfully, "he's not like the others. This boy is different."

After six months on the soap, Johnny was famous and on his way to Hollywood to make his first movie. After the initial meeting with the producers and various studio people, they went to a party in Johnny's honor. He was offered coke, every beautiful woman in the room, anything and everything he could possibly want. He wanted it all.

At around seven o'clock the next morning, Albie went into one of the bedrooms, pulled Johnny off one of the other guests, and threw him into a car. They went back to the hotel. Albie didn't know what Johnny had taken and was scared he would stop breathing in his sleep. He sat up in a chair pulled next to Johnny's bed, eventually falling asleep.

When he woke, he found Johnny out by the pool, tossing a football around with one of the bellboys.

"Are you all right?" Albie asked.

Johnny shook his head. "It's too fast, Albie. I can't handle this shit. I'm scared."

Albie put his arm around Johnny's shoulder. "You'll learn how to handle it. I'll show you." And Albie taught him the cardinal rules: Always be straight for work. Partying is fine in moderation. Find a steady girl and don't mess with whores; herpes is no joke. Never, never, never, never do anything that'll hurt your looks, because the business is all looks.

Johnny was a decent guy, but he was no saint. He followed Albie's counsel, but every now and then he would have to run wild, be on his own, do crazy things. It had all come too quickly, and while he was always together when it came to work, the dangerous side of life fascinated him. He was pretty careful not to let any of it get the better of him, but the cutting loose was important to him, too. He figured he was smarter than the hordes of young actors and rock stars who had come before him and burned out or shot themselves down with too many drugs. He was learning to be smart, and he figured he could have everything, as long as he was careful.

John Allison, twenty-five years old, rich, famous, good-looking, and enjoying his Broadway debut, was peeking out at the house like any kid at the high school talent show. Albie came up alongside him. "Is that the girl?"

"What girl?"

"The one you got a house seat for."

"Just a girl, Albie. Nothing strange there."

"She's not your usual type," Albie said. "This one's got small breasts, and she looks rather bright."

Johnny grinned. "I want to be stimulated intellectually." He looked through the curtain. So that was the writer everybody was making such a fuss over. Skinny little girl.

Albie was also looking. "Well, you have a good time. At least she looks clean." He patted his protégé's shoulder. "I'm going out front. Break a leg."

Albie went out to the orchestra seats filled with wealthy visiting Europeans, industry people, and the just plain rich. *A Little War* was a pretty standard tale of marital infidelity, but it was also the season's hot ticket. Some came to see a highly lauded British import by a renowned young playwright. Both the husband and the unfaithful wife were being played by two veterans of the English theater, so some people came because it wasn't often you got to see actors of such caliber. Most people came because they wanted to see a movie star fall on his face on Broadway. Johnny had worked very hard, and his reviews had been glowing. For four months his nose had been to the grindstone, and he was angling for a brief vacation. Albie knew he needed to cut loose for a while.

In the orchestra section Albie picked out Johnny's girl, sitting quietly in her seat, reading her *Playbill.* She was wearing a yellow silk dress of an Oriental design, a high collar wrapped around her slim neck. She looked like something out of an old movie. After a moment she was joined by a woman Albie recognized as either Lake Eastman or a darn good copy. Albie knew he was in trouble. Nichols had probably sent her with a purseful of contracts, trying to woo Johnny away from Weiss permanently. Albie didn't feel that confident. He knew Johnny was itching to try his wings on more serious projects. Albie didn't feel you should argue with success. He had relented on the Broadway show, even though nobody ever got rich doing Broadway. So . . . Lake Eastman in a house seat, provided by Johnny. Maybe there was a little romance going on there. Lake was his type, flashy and dangerous. The girl in the Oriental silk was probably a New York buddy, glad to get a free theater ticket and a chance to dress up. The two girls chattered happily. Unknowingly Karen turned toward Albie, giving him his first good look at her. Really a beautiful girl, Albie thought, warming to her, but not in the way anybody seemed to appreciate these days. A quiet beauty, with a hint of steel underneath. Those Chinese eyes, like Gene Tierney. The oriental dress accentuated the feeling of foreignness. A pity, Albie thought with a sigh; nobody seemed to go for the subtle kind anymore.

The play began. The audience was fairly restless, coughing and shifting around in their seats until John Allison's entrance. God, he's good, Karen thought with a shock. He commanded the stage with as much presence as the seasoned professionals he was working with. After she had adjusted to the shock of hearing a British accent coming out of his mouth, she realized how much Allison had matured past the teen-idol image. He was going to do great things.

The play ended on a very depressing note, the wife leaving her husband for her young lover, only to find that her lover has replaced her with a young, beautiful blonde. The wife walks out, and that was the curtain.

"Boy, is that depressing," Karen whispered to Lake. "I can just see that sort of thing happening to me."

"Stop it," Lake whispered back. "We're going to have fun tonight. You look beautiful."

Karen smiled. "It is a pretty dress. Thank you so much for the lovely present."

"Well, you can't go out on the town with John Allison dressed in rags," Lake teased.

"I'm going home." Karen felt suddenly panicky. John Allison would know immediately that she was a total jerk. She wished she were home with Matt.

Lake grabbed her arm. "No, you don't, my girl. I am no diplomat. I need you in there. Besides, you can't spend your whole life like a hermit, hunched over your typewriter. Come on, we're going backstage."

He was waiting for them, leaning against his dressing room door, still very up from the show. "Hi, hi, you're Lake, I watch your show, you're very funny." He shook her hand, his energy practically contagious. "And this is the writer. Karen, right?" He pumped her hand up and down, showing the two women into his dressing room. He had a little radio on, piping staticky rock and roll into the room.

"Johnny, did you have a chance to look at the script?" Lake asked, the cool professional to the hilt.

"I don't want to talk about business right away." Johnny reached into the fruit basket near his mirror. "Apple?"

"Yes, thanks." That was Karen. He tossed one to her. Lake declined.

Looking into the mirror, Johnny started to remove his stage makeup. "I've been a good boy for the longest time. I am going *out* tonight. If you ladies want to join me, that's fine. Then we'll talk business."

Lake leaned forward so that the neckline of her dress gaped alarmingly. "That sounds fine with me. Where do you want to go?"

Johnny eyed her speculatively. "You up for Phantom's?"

Her face lit up. "I've always wanted to go there. Do you have a member's card?"

"Sure do. I belong to all the best places; been kicked out of most of them. But I go to Phantom's for the music. Best jazz in the city."

"Sounds good to me."

Johnny turned to Karen. "What about you, silent Sam? Phantom's sound good to you?" If she was a writer, she was probably pretty smart, Johnny figured. He wondered if she thought he was stupid or uneducated. In his meteoric rise to stardom, Johnny hadn't exactly taken time out to read *Moby Dick.* He was sensitive to the fact that people might think he was dumb.

Karen chewed her apple thoughtfully. "I like jazz," she said, doubtful that most people went to Phantom's for the fine music.

"Bite." Johnny took the apple from her, took a bite, and handed it back. He looked into Karen's eyes. "I won't let anybody bother you there."

She bristled. "I can look after myself."

"I bet you can," he said innocently. "You know who your friend reminds me of?" he said to Lake. "Bunny rabbit."

"Bunny rabbit?"

"Yeah. Little guy on Captain Kangaroo, always managed to trick the Captain out of his carrots, trick the Captain and send all these Ping-Pong balls bouncing down on his head. You gotta remember the Ping-Pong balls."

"Sure," Lake said, not sure at all, "bunny rabbit."

He turned suddenly to Karen. "You don't like me, do you? I can feel it."

Looking into those strange gray eyes, she believed he did. "You irritate me, Mr. Allison. You're very lazy and completely inconsiderate. You were wonderful tonight, but I've screened all your films, and you sleepwalk through half of them. How could we possibly know you wouldn't do that on our film?"

"You wouldn't let me, bunny rabbit," Johnny said unconcernedly. "So you thought I was good. 'Wonderful,' if I may quote."

"Yes, you were good," Karen said, vexed.

"Wonderful."

"Yes, wonderful, I said wonderful," she repeated. Damn John Allison. Guys like that really burned her up.

He took the apple from her hand. "I read your script. I'd say wonderful. Yeah, I'd definitely say wonderful. You're good."

"Thank you." She was looking down at her shoes. For a moment her eyes flashed up, almost defiantly, catching his. The electricity was like a live thing, a separate entity that had walked in on its own power, an uninvited guest that could not be ignored.

Sparks are flying around here, Lake thought in amazement. They were arguing, John Allison and Karen, about some meaningless thing or other, but all Lake could see was the excitement on their faces. They were arguing about movies.

"You know what your problem is?" Johnny was telling her. "You're a snob. You're prejudiced against good-looking men. I bet somebody has to look like a real charity case to make it in your book."

"That makes absolutely no sense," Karen yelled back at him.

Lake was definitely beginning to feel left out. "Are we going or not?"

"Going," Johnny said, putting on his coat. "Coming, bunny rabbit?" They continued arguing out onto the street. Johnny stopped only when he saw someone he knew, likewise trying to get out of the December chill. "Hey, there's a friend of mine." He pointed at a man across the street. "Well, not a close friend, but he's good for a party. Hey, Foxy!" he called out loudly.

Karen and Lake looked at each other. It couldn't be.

He was crossing the street to them, each step revealing the truth. It was Daniel Fox.

"Hey, Foxy," Johnny repeated happily, "meet my new pals. This is Karen Singer and Lake Eastman."

"Hello, Lake," Daniel Fox said, smiling into her eyes. "And Karen. You've grown up lovely. What a pleasant surprise." He looked sleek and prosperous.

Karen turned and walked away.

"Hey, what's wrong?" Johnny trailed after her. "I don't understand what's going on."

"He's a terrible man," she said in a low voice.

"He's a little crazy," Johnny admitted, "but that's not enough to keep anybody off my guest list."

"He used to see Lake. He tried to rape her; he tried to kill her."

"I'm sorry, I didn't know. Jesus, I never would have called

him over." He looked so genuinely contrite that Karen didn't doubt him at all. She smiled wearily.

"I'm sure you wouldn't have, but the damage is done. Lake is very high-strung; I just hope this isn't going to upset her all night."

Lake was running toward them, one hand holding her coat closed. "It's all right," she told Karen. "I'm going to go with him for a cup of coffee. Please, Karen, don't get upset. I can't spend the rest of my life being afraid of this man. Let me get it over with once and for all." She kissed Karen's cheek. "I'll be okay."

"I think you're crazy."

"Certifiable," Lake agreed, already running away, across the street to Daniel. "Hey, Johnny," she yelled back, "don't keep her out all night."

Anxiously Karen watched Lake and Daniel walk off together.

"Hey," Johnny said gently, "don't worry about your friend. She's a big girl. She can take care of herself."

Karen shook her head. "No, not really. I don't know why she's doing this."

"Maybe she still has a thing for him," Johnny offered, starting to feel the chill settle into his bones. He wanted to get off the street in a hurry.

"I don't think so."

Johnny sighed. "Maybe she wants to make sure she's over him." A cab pulled over. "Come on, let's go."

Karen hesitated. If she was any kind of friend, she'd go look after Lake, take care of her.

"Come on, bunny rabbit." Johnny was holding open the cab door, grinning at her. Acting like she was the only person he wanted to be with that night.

Tonight is my night, Karen thought decisively. She stepped into the cab.

Daniel took Lake's arm as they crossed Broadway. The traffic was fierce and they were going against the light, so she allowed it. He dropped it when they reached the other side. She looked at him, thinking how little he had changed.

"You look fine," she said to him. "Better than you deserve."

Daniel threw back his head and roared. A few people looked up at his hearty laugh. "You're sounding very puritanical these days. I should never have abandoned you to the tender mercies of that little hausfrau."

"You hardly abandoned me, and Karen's not a hausfrau."

"Of course she is. That's the way you like her." He smiled mirthlessly. "Salt of the earth. Not like us." He stopped in front of a bar popular with actors. "Here okay?"

I don't have to be here, Lake thought slowly. I can turn and go right now, and he won't stop me. He has no power over me; that's dead and buried. He's nothing to me.

"Fine," she said tonelessly, sweeping past him into the bar. It was a pretty nice place—dark wood, long bar, tables covered with white butcher paper for patrons to practice their artistic talents. A juice glass holding crayons sat on each table. A waiter, obviously an out-of-work actor, presented them with a limited après-theater menu, took their drink order, and left. Minutes later martinis materialized. Daniel sipped his, his eyes on her.

He still excited her, she had to admit that, partly because of the danger. Here, she thought, is my death. Oh, he was bad for her, he scared her, but he made her feel alive and gave her a strange sense of belonging, of being less alone. And there were other things, things she didn't dare whisper to herself. Things too painful to be examined. Ever.

He was smiling, as if he could read her mind. "Tell me about Hollywood." He touched the glass in front of him with delicate fingers. "Are you having fun?"

She lifted her chin, staring down at him. "Aren't you curious why I'm here with you now?"

"You're here because you want to be."

"That's right, Daniel. Because I had to prove to myself that whatever I felt for you was dead. It doesn't work anymore. Not the scare tactics, not the bogeyman tricks, none of it. I'm in love with somebody, Daniel, and he's the only man on my mind."

"Yes, I know." His smile grew at her shocked expression. "Don't ever play poker, my love. You haven't got the face for it. Do you think it was just coincidence that I happened to be outside that very theater?"

"I didn't think about it at all."

His eyes moved over her. "Any time I want to, I can find out where you are, who you see, what you're up to. It isn't very difficult. You live a fishbowl existence. Anyone can pick up a paper and know what you had for dinner last night. I know about your charming little boyfriend. And his wife. I know about all the little boyfriends. You miss me, Lake. You need me."

She laughed scornfully at him. "You've always been the master at self-delusion. I'm in love, Daniel, and it's the real thing. I pity you because you'll never know that kind of happiness."

"Yes, he's a nice, decent man, but if you could have him, Lake, if you could get him away from his wife, you'd toss him aside like yesterday's newspaper. You don't want what you can get, my love, and you don't want what's good for you. In your heart you know he doesn't really understand you, not the way I do. I'm the only one who knows all your secrets. You'll see. You'll tire of him as soon as he's yours."

All I have to do is get up and walk away, she thought numbly. He won't stop me, not with all these people around. But she sat, fingers frozen on the stem of her untasted drink. "You're wrong."

"I'm never wrong about you. We're cut from the same cloth, you and I. Cold as ashes inside, but the world clamors for our attention, our love, because of our gifts. Our emotions are mimicry, the result of years of careful observation. How normal people live, how they feel. We're not like that. It's all pretense. The only time I feel anything real is when I'm with you."

He bolted forward, catching her hand so suddenly that she was frightened. "We belong together, Lake. *I am you.*"

"Stop it!" she snapped, her voice a harsh whisper. "I feel sorry for you because you are truly sick. Maybe I've shared that sickness in the past, but my life is different now. I have good friends who look after me, I have a man who loves me, and you better believe it's real, you bastard. My career is doing well, and if I'm not as sane as I'd like to be, I will get there."

"Lake," he said in that soft, dead voice, "did you ever consider that when you get rid of the sickness, there may be nothing left?"

She started to shake. Only by giving her body precise, step-by-step instructions was she able to get her coat on, rise from her seat, and leave.

Midnight.

He was lost. Horribly, terribly lost in the most frightening city on earth, New York. Miles was a teacher from Fresno, California. Right now he was a lost teacher from Fresno, California. His buddies had wanted to pick up whores near the Lincoln Tunnel. Miles was smarter and had a lot more respect for sexually transmitted diseases.

He was freezing. Fresno was never like this. He picked out a bar that looked a little less threatening than its neighbors and walked in, hoping for drinkable beer and somebody who could give him intelligible directions back to his hotel.

There was a blonde at the bar. He couldn't see her face, but when he sat down next to her, she turned to check him out. Not a casual glance, either.

"Oh, my God," Miles said, aghast, "you're Lake Eastman, you really are. I can't believe this. My buddies—shit, I wish they were here to see this."

She was just looking at him, her face an impassive mask. "I went back to my hotel," she said in a singsong voice, "but he'd been there before me and broken *everything*. Well, all of *my* things."

"He?" Miles asked, confused.

"The bogeyman, the doppelganger." She was watching him so closely, she was making him nervous. "I'm scared to go back. What if he's hiding in the closet?" She finished her drink and put the empty glass inside the bar rail for the bartender to refill. While she was waiting for her fresh drink, she reached inside her handbag and pulled out a vial of pills. Miles knew what Valium looked like.

"I'm sure he's not hiding in the closet," he said reassuringly. "Burglars don't usually hang around."

Her big eyes looked doubtful. "But I'm scared. Will you take me back to my hotel? Just stay with me until my friend comes home."

"Well, I don't want your friend to get the wrong idea . . ."

"My girlfriend," she explained with exaggerated care. The fresh drink came, and Miles paid for it. "You could stay with me, you could do anything you like with me. Please, I'm scared."

Miles knew he had a first-class lunatic on his hands, but God, she was beautiful! Besides, stars always traveled with an entourage; he'd see her to her hotel, her hairdresser or her astrologer would look after her, and Miles would get, at the very least, a limo ride home.

"Okay," he said, "I'll take you home."

The cab driver had not liked the idea of going up to Harlem at night, but his reluctance had vanished when Johnny waved a hundred dollar bill under the man's nose. In the back seat of the cab, Johnny tried to explain what Phantom's was like. "You ever been to Bourbon Street?"

"In New Orleans? No." Karen was watching the familiar terrain give way to scenes from the six o'clock news. Her confidence was slipping away just as quickly.

"Bourbon Street is a very nonjudgmental kind of place. Whatever you want, you can get it there. Very free and easy. That's what Phantom's is like. It's a little wild, but there's no place like it."

"Except Bourbon Street," Karen said.

"I think Phantom's has an edge on Bourbon Street." The cab pulled over to the curb. "This is it."

"This is what?" Karen looked around upon alighting from the cab. The street was deserted, storefronts hidden behind metal gates. Johnny instructed the cabbie to wait, peeling another bill off a sizable roll and giving it to the man.

He walked over to a door that looked like it was a delivery entrance, a solid metal affair. "Phantom's" was spray-painted on the door in bold purple graffiti. Through the door Karen could faintly hear music. She felt it rather than heard it; the bass was practically making the sidewalk thump. In answer to Johnny's knock the door opened. Standing behind it was the largest black man Karen had ever seen.

"Hello, Johnny boy," he said. "Welcome back. The Phantom-man himself will be real pleased to see you." He ignored Karen, and she got the distinct feeling that she was not the only woman John Allison had ever squired around the club.

They followed the giant down a narrow spiral staircase. Karen had trouble navigating the steps in her heels and adjusting to the almost total darkness at the same time. She felt Johnny's arm go around her waist. "Okay?" he asked.

"Yes," she whispered.

For one brief moment he thought he should kiss her. She was a funny girl—serious at the wrong times, too honest, too open, too everything. But he felt drawn to her, and he knew she was attracted to him. In the darkness he ran his hand over her hair. She moved her head slightly, and he felt the satin of her cheek against his hand. I shouldn't have brought her here, he thought suddenly; she wasn't the kind of girl you took to Phantom's. Then he remembered that he really didn't know her at all, and it was *she* who wanted something from him, so she could damn well dance to his tune. One thing his sudden success had taught him was that when you were famous, everybody wanted something, and it was up to you to see they paid for what they got.

The staircase came down in one corner of a large room, just off the huge dance floor. Another corner was dominated by a gleaming black bar, purple and pink neon announcing "Phantom's" in blowsy script. Directly across, on a small podium, a five-piece band played smoky rhythm and blues. Patrons danced in front of the band, their feet slurring over the floor, weaving intricate patterns. Everyone was beautiful.

"Oh, my God," Karen said, her vocabulary exhausted. "Wow." Smoke rolled across the floor, curling around the legs of dancing patrons, creeping over the elegant shoes of resting owners sitting at small tables and chatting above the din. High overhead a trapeze act was doing its thing, oblivious to the crowd below and the excellent R&B. There were unearthly statues of naked women, except they weren't statues at all, they were real women, powdered white, standing placidly on pedestals. From time to time someone would come over and offer the statue-women smoke or pills or drink or whatever they wanted. Against the fourth wall, beneath another purple and pink logo, sat a stark white baby grand. At the keyboard was the strangest looking creature Karen had ever seen anywhere.

He was an albino Negro. A white black man. Karen stared. Behind those dark glasses she felt he was staring right back.

"The Phantom-man himself," Johnny whispered in her ear. "C'mon, I'll introduce you." They navigated their way across the dance floor. "Karen," Johnny said proudly, "meet the original, the one and only Phantom, Ernest Rich."

The albino held out his hand. "A pleasure." His grip was frail, and Karen was afraid to squeeze hard. "John, I'm glad your taste in women has improved. You brought us a class act tonight." His lips curved into a big smile. "Welcome to Phantom's, miss," he intoned grandly. "Don't take nothing here too serious, and have yourselves a good time."

"We will," Johnny promised.

The albino reached forward and put a little paper bundle in Johnny's pocket. Karen could have sworn he was winking behind those dark shades. "Birthday present," he said. "Enjoy. We got a little show tonight. Maybe you and your lady want to stick around."

"I don't know." Johnny shot a sidelong glance at Karen. "Me and the lady are still getting acquainted."

The dark glasses turned toward Karen. "You don't do nothing you don't want to do, unless you're susceptible to his brand of bullshit. Then you got my sympathy."

Karen smiled. "I won't do nothing I don't want to do, that's a promise." They staked out a table, and a waiter (who looked like a waitress, but Karen had her doubts) brought them drinks. Johnny tapped his pocket. "You want some blow?" he asked her in a friendly way.

"No. I wish you wouldn't either."

He shrugged. "You do what you want. I'm going to have a good time."

The trapeze act executed a particularly difficult move to applause. A beautiful woman came over and asked Johnny to dance. He got up, and they moved onto the dance floor. The woman's hand moved lightly over his thigh, circling. To hell with you, Karen thought. She was going to do a little exploring on her own.

A few people were starting to drift off the dance floor down a hallway streaked with tubes of purple neon. Karen joined them. "Where are we going?" she whispered to anyone who would answer.

"Show time," came the reply. The mood was one of hectic anticipation, and it was contagious. The hallway splintered off into rooms divided further into small cubicles. Karen looked into one of the cubicle rooms. Around one partition she saw two naked legs twining around each other, the foot of one affectionately rubbing the calf of the other. Obviously the legs belonged to different owners. She veered back into the general flow of traffic in the hallway. They came to what looked like a miniature theater, complete with stage appointed with velvet curtains and plush seats, all of a deep royal purple.

Karen sank into a seat, filled with misgivings. Damned if she was going back into the main room to be ignored by a snotty brat. The theater went completely black, and the curtains parted.

A pretty girl came out and began dancing. She wasn't really a trained dancer, but she had a glorious body and moved nicely. The light, gauzy dress she wore swirled around her plump hips and strong legs. Her bare feet were pink and chubby. Beneath the bright makeup and false eyelashes, her face was doll-like and sweet. She looked like a big, pretty doll moving her full woman's body across the stage. It was curiously mesmerizing. After a moment a male performer, identity hidden by hood and cape, stepped onto the stage. The woman recoiled, slipping to her knees in a dumb show of terror and repulsion. The hooded figure teased the cape off one muscular brown shoulder.

The woman put her hand up to her full red mouth, mimicking a swoon. Her other hand plucked at her gauzy dress. Two other men came out from the wings. They wore business suits complete with ties and white button-down shirts. The only discordant notes were the masks they wore of almost clear, soft plastic fashioned like handsome, human, female faces, only terribly blank and sinister. Karen knew that the plastic would feel toad-belly damp if touched. The business suits lined up, one on either side of the girl. They held her fast. The masked and hooded man came forward and made the doll-girl rub her face in his crotch. Suddenly he spun to face the audience, glaring balefully from the hood's eyeholes. In one fast movement the cape was shrugged free of the upper body and pulled tight against the hips, hiding everything below the waist.

It was a woman. Her breasts jutted around a leather harness cutting across her chest, showing her muscles in sharp relief. Under the cape she began to move, swaying like a snake charmer. She turned to the stricken girl, who began to sway to the same pulse. The men tightened their hold on her. One pulled at the long golden hair. It came off in his hand. Beneath the wig the girl was shorn like a convict. The men (if that *was* what they were) began to pull at the thin dress, stripping away not only the dress, but layers of artful padding. A boy was revealed; not a doll-woman, a beautiful boy with soft, marshmallowy skin. His doe eyes looked up blankly.

Disdainfully the harnessed woman dropped the cape, showing her lean, hard body. Leather straps around her hips held a huge flesh-colored phallus. She bore down on the boy, much to the delight of the crowd. Whether his screams were real or just another part of the act, Karen never found out. She ran from the room, horrified at what she had seen, and she didn't stop running until she was outside.

"Hey, wait a second!" Johnny was running after her. "You can't stand around without your coat. Jesus! It's December!"

Karen was crying, ashamed at what she'd sat through, ashamed she was too unsophisticated to regard the "show" as entertainment.

"Oh, Jesus," he said faintly, still holding her coat, feeling like a jerk. His first thought was that she was cramping his style. He wanted to get laid, he wanted to get high, he just wanted to have some fun, goddamn it. But he hadn't been having such a good time that night, even with a pretty lady groping him on the dance floor. The Phantom had a stable of very attractive and able-bodied hookers, and right at that moment Johnny could think of one he wanted more than this little idiot crying without her coat on a Harlem street corner.

"Here, put your coat on." She was still sniffling away, so he draped her coat over her shoulders. "I'm really sorry, Karen. I didn't mean to upset you. I knew I shouldn't have brought you here."

"No, you shouldn't," Karen sobbed. "That was completely insensitive. Are you always this charming?"

He glared at her. "Well, the hell with you, lady. You think just because you're a hotshot writer, you can treat me like some jerk-ass from the boonies. Well, I haven't done too badly for myself, and I've had enough of your attitude!"

"My attitude!" Karen shrieked. "You are the most insufferable little bastard I've ever meet! *My* attitude! I don't believe you—"

Suddenly they were kissing, arms around each other, bodies pressed together. Her coat slipped off her shoulders unheeded and fell to the pavement. They broke, but he kept his arms around her. Johnny's history with women was pretty one-note; he dealt with whores mostly, because at least he knew where he stood with them, and whores were unlikely to slap a paternity suit on him. He knew some wild ladies in the business, hangers-on hoping for a crumb or two, and before that there were the bad girls in his hometown, all two of them. He had never spent time with anybody like Karen, and he was beginning to think he could like it. She didn't reek of perfume, and her body felt so frail in his arms. He felt as if he could pick her up and carry her off if he had a mind to. Which he did. Yes, he definitely did.

"I'm married," she said unhappily.

"I know."

"So what do we do now?"

"We go get something to eat," he said promptly, summoning the cab. They rattled away, downtown. They talked about their hometowns and held hands. "My friends would laugh if they saw me holding hands like a teenager," he told her.

"Do you really care what they think?" she asked.

"No. I don't feel very close to a lot of people," he admitted. "There are so many bloodsuckers in this business, you can't tell the decent people on the rare occasions they're passing through."

She smiled. "I know what you mean."

He moved closer, and though she felt it was wrong, it was disloyal, she rested her head on his shoulder and was very happy.

The cab stopped. "Okay, we're here." They got out of the cab. "You'll like this place," Johnny promised.

She did like it. It was called the Pink Tea Cup, and at three in the morning it was hopping. People were eating fried chicken and collard greens, there was sweet-potato pie, and everyone seemed to be coolly together. Black waitresses glided around dealing out plates of food while good rock and roll jumped on the juke. Karen liked the Pink Tea Cup fine.

Johnny was explaining his situation to her, restlessly pushing the hair off his forehead. "I love Albie, and I'm grateful to him. I know I'd still be pumping gas upstate if it wasn't for him. I just can't play teenagers for the rest of my life, and I don't think Albie understands that. But I can't just cut him off, which is what I think Nichols will do if I sign with him."

"Probably," Karen agreed. "But he's dead set on getting you for this project. Let him know you're interested but still play hard to get. He'll work something out."

"Albie won't go for it." Johnny shook his head. He reached for a biscuit and smeared butter on it. "He's not going to want to share the wealth. The guy practically discovered me. He made my career what it is."

"Which is not enough."

"I want to be a serious actor," he said earnestly. "I want people to think of me when they cast the good films. I think you're going to write good films."

"I'm going to try." She hesitated. "I'm not sure how honest to be with you."

"Very honest," he prompted.

"Okay, here goes. I don't know how much good George will do you. He's very wrapped up in Lake right now, so that's all he's thinking about. Personally I don't see you playing the villain, but the hero is already cast. If you do sign with George, he'll probably put you into vehicles that are similar to what you've been doing. No, the only way to deal with George is to come in with a project of your own, something definite so he can't push you into things you don't want to do. You have to be strong with George, or he'll railroad you. Have you optioned any properties?"

"No. Albie usually reads the scripts that are sent to me."

"Well, you start reading them."

"I hate to read," he said moodily.

"Tough." She laughed. "Start with something easy. *Treasure Island.*"

"*That* one I read. Liked it." He took a piece of bacon from her plate. "You write something for me."

"I might," she said slowly. "Stranger things have happened. I guess I could find a good story for you." She leaned forward, speaking wistfully. "I wish they still liked Westerns; I'd love to write one. You'd make a good cowboy."

"My old man would have a good laugh at that." He signaled the waitress for the check. "He used to work on a dairy farm, and he told us in no uncertain terms that there was nothing romantic connected to working anywhere near cows. Hated those damn cows. Wouldn't drink milk. Still doesn't." He paid the check, leaving another hundred dollar bill as a tip.

Karen's eyes widened. "Johnny, that's a lot of money."

"I liked the waitress. Didn't you like her?"

"I loved her, but I didn't know you were planning to put her through college."

He flashed another grin. "See that? They pay me a lot of money just to do that." He held the door for her, and they squeezed their way outside. "I waited a few tables in my time, and I used to dream that somebody would leave me a tip like that."

Karen said nothing. If success had come overnight for her, she probably wouldn't have known the value of a dollar, either. But eventually she'd learn. Maybe it wasn't that good to have somebody looking after you all the time. You never learned how to do for yourself.

It was cold, but the wind had died down, and that kept the bitterness out of the air. Johnny dashed into the liquor store and bought some Scotch, then he went into a coffee shop and took out a cup of coffee for Karen. Carefully she tore a triangle out of the plastic lid. They walked all the way to Washington Square Park. Their faithful cabby, his meter still ticking away, trawled after them. What did he care? He was on the payroll for the evening.

They found a bench and sat. "Tell me about your husband," he asked her. Seeing her reluctance, he pushed a bit. "Oh, come on. We're probably not going to see each other ever again. You can tell me anything."

"You won't do the movie?"

"No. I'm not ready to leave Albie. I'm an ignorant bastard. I can't read a contract, I don't know anything—"

"You don't like to read—"

"You don't forget anything, do you, bunny rabbit?"

"No, I don't." She smiled at him. "I'm freezing." She held out her coffee cup, and he poured a little Scotch into it.

"I knew I'd corrupt you." He leered.

"I knew it, too."

"So . . . tell me about your husband."

"He's a brilliant director." She sipped the coffee, grimacing. "This is truly god-awful."

"He poured a little more Scotch in. "Kill the taste. So he's brilliant. Is he a good guy?"

"Well, sure. He doesn't drink or take drugs or run around with other women. He doesn't beat me."

Johnny was getting a little fed up hearing about this paragon of virtue. "What *does* he do?"

"He directs," Karen said patiently. "Matt's passion is his work."

"Oh?" He took her hand. "Not you? 'Cause if he's under fifty, it should be. Or else somebody's getting cheated, and it sounds like it's you, bunny rabbit."

She buried her face in her hands. She'd been carting around her own petty secret for so long, sometimes she could forget how much it hurt.

"Holy shit, this is the second time I've made you cry tonight. And we just met." He searched his pockets for a handkerchief. "Can you imagine if we really knew each other? Here, use my sleeve."

She looked at him doubtfully.

"Go on, I have four sisters. My sleeves have been cried on before." He watched her, concerned. "Better? I'm sorry. I didn't know things were that rough."

"It's not rough," Karen insisted. "It's just not the way I thought it would be."

He kissed her gently. "Is that how you thought it would be?" She nodded. "Yeah, me, too. I like you. I want to see you again."

"You can't."

"People cheat, Karen. They do it every day, and nobody seems to grow little horns. They go on like they always do."

She shook her head. "I can't see you, Johnny. I don't give a damn what other people do. I've always lived by my own rules, nobody else's." She smiled, almost laughing to herself. "This is a little hard for me to absorb. I was a real nerd in high school."

"I was a doper."

"We wouldn't have gotten together then, either."

"Maybe we would have," he said quietly. "Your hands are freezing." He took them and slipped them inside his shirt, against his warm skin. She could feel his heart beating against her hand. His mouth descended on hers. She leaned against him weakly. Sweet, wayward boy. Maybe she should have met him first. Maybe, maybe—you could go mad from all those maybes. She closed her eyes and thought of nothing but the moment.

He told her things he had never told anyone, not even Albie. The fear that it would all vanish: the fame, the money, everything.

He supported his family, all the brothers and sisters; he sent his nieces and nephews to private school. What would happen to them if he screwed up? Then his dad would have the last laugh. He'd have it engraved on Johnny's tombstone: "Here lies a fuck-up." She listened intently, helping him find the words he needed, being quiet when he needed her to be quiet. For the first time in his life, he felt like he was with somebody who cared about him for himself. Not the money. Not the influence. He wasn't about to let her go so easily. "Stay with me tonight."

Her hands moved through his hair. "You know I can't," she said sadly. "Just kiss me good-bye."

He looked into her eyes for a long moment. "I'm not making this up," he told her seriously, "and I'm not drunk, either. I'll feel the same way tomorrow and the day after that. One of these days you just won't want to go on with the brilliant husband, and I'll be there. I'll always be there for you. So you see, I can't kiss you good-bye, because it's not good-bye."

She leaned into him and softly kissed his closed eyes. "It is for me. But just for the record, no, I don't think this is going to go away, either." She got into the cab.

"I'm going to walk around for a while," he said, closing the cab door after her.

"Don't." She grabbed his sleeve. "Go straight home now, promise me?"

He gave her the Boy Scout sign. "Promise."

The cab pulled away.

John Allison hailed another and headed back to Phantom's. He just didn't feel like lying awake all night thinking of her.

As soon as Karen unlocked the door, an unmistakable odor assailed her. She flicked on the light.

The hotel suite looked like a very selective cyclone had hit it. Lake's half of the room had been razed. Her clothing had been tossed out of the dresser and hung from the drawers like festoons. The closets had been emptied out onto the floor, the contents piled in heaps. The puke was in the bathroom, spattering the toilet bowl and floor tiles.

There was a man in the bedroom, sitting in a chair pulled alongside Lake's bed. Karen screamed.

"Please don't do that," Miles begged. "I can explain. Please sit down. Karen? You are Karen, aren't you?"

She sat down, feeling numb and sick. "Yes. What the hell happened? Who are you?"

"The place was like this when I came in. She said—I met her in a bar—she told me someone had broken in to her place. I thought she meant like a burglar."

Karen looked around. "Does it look to you like a burglar did this?" The room was carefully divided. Absolutely nothing of Karen's had been touched. She went over to Lake, hunched under the covers. Only her hair, lank and sweaty, showed. "Lake?" She shook her gently.

"Go 'way," Lake moaned.

"Who did this? Did you let Daniel in?"

Lake pulled the covers up over her head.

"She got sick," Miles explained. "I think she took some pills. It's just as well she threw up."

"Super," Karen agreed dryly. "It was like this when you came in?"

"Yes, I didn't touch anything." Miles got up and put on his jacket. "You'll look after her now," he said hopefully. "I just didn't think she should be left alone, but you're here, so I guess I can go."

"Yes, I'm here."

Miles went to the door. "I never thought of myself as a naive guy," he said, "but it never occurred to me that she was really nothing like the person I saw on television."

Karen started to clean the bathroom. She believed people should tend to their own messes. "You can go, mister. I'll look after her."

He nodded. "You know, she said the bogeyman came and did this. She scared the shit out of me." He closed the door behind him.

The smell of puke was overwhelming. Karen felt as if she was going to bring up whatever was left in her stomach. She decided to take a break from the bathroom and started to get the closets back in order, scooping up a big handful of clothes. Something sticky touched her arm.

It was semen.

Repulsed, she dropped the clothes. The tears came even though she fought them. That's three times, she thought. Three times she had shed tears in one day. Everything came in threes. Three men in her life. Harry, Matt, and—was Johnny in her life or not? "I wish I'd said yes," she whispered. "I wish I was with him now." Picking her way carefully, she rolled up the soiled garments and stuffed them into a plastic bag the hotel had provided for dirty laundry. Next she went to the phone to call the police.

"Don't." Lake, looking like she'd accompanied Dante on his guided tour of Hell, was standing next to her. "He'll come back if you tell on him."

"Who? Who will come back?"

Lake shrugged her shoulders tiredly. "I don't know. A disgruntled fan, some crazy. You know how angry they get if you let them down." She took the phone from Karen's hand. "If you love me, you won't call."

"Was it Daniel?"

"No."

A growing horror seized her. "Lake, did you do this?"

Lake shook her head, a slow tear coursing down her cheek. "No," she whispered. "Do you really think I'm that far gone?" She sank into a chair and cried quietly.

"Stop that," Karen said, worn to the bone. It was too late for histrionics. "I know you didn't do it; I'm just too tired to think straight. Lake"—she stroked her damp hair—"no matter how totally nuts you get, I doubt that at any point in your career you will be able to produce what I found on your clothes. Don't cry, please don't cry."

Lake took her hand. Her smile was sad and gentle. "I'm so sorry, Kar. We'll clean up together." She picked up the plastic bag and moved it next to the door. "I don't want them anymore. I'll buy new things tomorrow."

Karen shrugged. "Suit yourself." She went into the bathroom and worked methodically, wadding up toilet paper and dropping it on top of the vomit, then transferring the whole mess to the toilet to be flushed away. At that moment she would have killed for a pair of rubber gloves.

Lake drifted over to her. "What happened tonight? Was he terrible?"

"No," Karen said shortly. "He wasn't terrible."

"Was he . . . nice?"

Karen threw some more toilet paper onto the floor. "Lake, he asked me to spend the night with him. I wish I had."

"Then you should have," Lake said. "There's no forever to life; there's only separate little moments, some good, some bad. The rest is just remembering. That's all there is to it."

"God, I hope not." She started working on the toilet. The water running in the sink gave off a high, annoying whine. "Why don't you go to bed? This is really a one-person job."

Lake nodded, but she kept standing there in the bathroom doorway.

"What?" Karen was in no mood for company. "Lake, I'm tired, it's very late, and I've had a bad day. If there's something on your mind, I'd just as soon you came out with it. *Now.*"

"I was just thinking how it was in the beginning, when we were sharing a place. It's not like that anymore, is it?"

"Everything changes," Karen said sourly.

"I just need to know that you still care for me, that you won't leave me."

Karen softened. "I'll be here as long as you want me to."

"But it's not the same."

"No, it's not the same." She gave the bowl a final swipe. "And it never will be."

Lake was crying again, soundless tears shining on her face. "I just need to know that everything will be all right."

"Oh, honey." Karen gave her a reassuring hug. "Everything will be just fine."

At Phantom's night lasted a very long time.

In addition to the usual services—the shows, the cubicle rooms, the everyday assortment of willing freaks—Phantom's had a nice selection of working ladies who specialized in the out-of-the-ordinary. They could handle rough trade without a whimper. They were a tough and funny breed, and they had no pity, for their own lives or anybody else's. Most of them were decent-looking, although Phantom's had a few real hags, if that was your pleasure. Rumor had it Phantom's would find you a one-legged ambidextrous dwarf with platinum blonde hair, but you'd have to phone ahead.

Generally a client would select a girl from a book of 8 × 10s. Obviously if you booked early, you could get exactly what you wanted. Otherwise it was catch as catch can. It was a particularly busy night. A good-looking man in a three-piece suit was waiting for a girl. He had a membership card, but nobody remembered him from previous occasions. The girls didn't have long memories for anyone but steady customers. This man had specifically requested a blonde.

Two girls were available that night, a slim black who styled herself after Catwoman (a lot of mature men had these comic-book fixations, she insisted) and a bleached blonde called Candy. She had a very pretty face but was a little heavy, particularly around the hips and ass. Candy went to nursing school part time. When she graduated, she intended to quit whoring and be a private nurse, hopefully to a sweet old guy who was both incredibly rich and terminally ill. If he was really sweet, she wouldn't mind if he lingered a few years. It would be nice, like having a daddy look after you like he should. Candy's dreams were not complicated or devious because Candy herself was not. She loved to read romance novels, and she honestly believed some people's lives were like the stories; it all had to do with whether you had luck or not. Candy had no luck. She knew it, but she tried to keep that knowledge from ruining her days. She dyed her hair blonde because she thought it might be good for business, and it was. But she still had no luck, and she didn't try to kid herself about it. That rich old guy had better come along soon, she told herself.

Catwoman was drinking orange juice because she had one of those lingering, sniffly colds. "He wants a blonde," she sniffled to Candy. "Girl, that sure ain't me."

"How's he look?" Candy asked a little warily. She just wasn't in the mood for any gymnastics. Anyway, when you had no luck, you had to be extra careful.

"Okay," Catwoman answered. "Too normal for this joint. He's a member, so he's got to have plenty of cash. Bet he's good for a big tip."

"This hasn't been my best night." Candy ran her fingers along the thin gold chain suspending a heart-shaped locket around her neck. It wasn't real gold, not for three dollars, but Candy thought it looked pretty decent for a Woolworth's purchase. As soon as some nice man came into her life on a permanent basis, she would put his picture in the locket. For the moment, it was empty.

"I sure could use a good tip. You think this guy has bucks, huh?"

Charmaine, their all-around general manager/madam and swing-shift lady, chuckled deeply. "He's a regular Prince Charming, Candy girl. Maybe if you're real nice, he'll take you away from all this. Now move your butt."

"Okay, I'm going." She straightened her pale blue corselette. "He want anything special?"

"Call him 'Daddy.' "

"My kind of man." Candy grinned. She grabbed a hand towel and headed down the hall.

He was waiting in the room. Catwoman had been right; he was nice-looking, real classy, and his thick hair had a deep wave. Natural, Candy guessed. So what if he wanted to pretend he was screwing his daughter? Better he should go to a pro than actually put it to the poor kid. Candy's own dad had put it to her when she was a little kid, and she strongly felt this had influenced the path her life had taken. No luck to that at all, and it was damned near impossible to turn out right after your own trusted dad had fucked you over.

"Give me a kiss," he said gruffly.

"I'm sorry, Daddy, I was just going to. I forgot." She pecked him on the cheek, climbing into his lap. "Is that better?"

"You know perfectly well it's past your bedtime." He pushed her away. "Go get ready for bed."

"Yes, Daddy." Obediently she unlaced the pale blue corset and wriggled out. It was slow going over her Silly Putty hips, but she managed. He watched impassively as she stepped out of her high-heeled mules.

"Get in bed."

She slipped under the covers. She hoped to God he didn't want to spank her; she hated getting spanked. Some of these guys really hurt. Instead he came over and lay on his side next to her, his weight balanced on his hip and elbow. He stroked her hair with gentle hands.

She closed her eyes. It felt *so* good. Maybe this was the whole stunt; she'd had guys who got off like that. That would be nice for a change; she wouldn't have to work at all.

"Would you like to hear a story?" he asked her, still being very loving and kind.

"Yes, Daddy."

"Once upon a time there was a beautiful little girl with long blonde hair and big blue eyes. She was so beautiful that even the fairies were jealous. Their own children were not so perfect as this little girl. Her parents did their best to hide her away so no one could do her harm, but they were so proud of her that they couldn't help but show her off to everyone."

His voice was lulling her. The fog creeps in on little cat feet . . . she thought errantly. Sandburg—she remembered that from school. The sleep creeps in on little cat tootsies . . . She couldn't have opened her eyes if she'd wanted to. God, it had been so long since somebody was just plain nice to her.

"One night the fairies kidnapped the little girl, and in her place they left a changeling child. And the changeling was evil and foul and ruined everything it touched. It brought bad luck to the entire household. The mother and father wanted their own sweet child back, but what could they do? The fairies' magic was strong, and they were very frightened. No, lie still, that's best to do . . . They could only get their child back if they could get rid of the changeling; then the enchantment would be ended. So very late one night the father went up to the changeling child's room. He had to be very quiet." The man took off his jacket and laid it carefully down. There was a knife in his pocket, not a large one but sharp. "All he wanted was his own little girl back, not the monster sleeping in her crib, the monster who poisons—"

Her eyes snapped open in alarm. This was no sweet daddy come to take care of her, this was death with a scythe in one hand and a load of lollipops to beguile her in the other. She tried to get off the bed, but he was strong, as strong as the delusions eating wormlike through his brain, and there was no way she could escape. It was a small knife, but it did the job well, as he knew it would. All told, she never even got off one good scream, and if she had, who would have noticed it in the vaults of Phantom's?

Fastidiously he removed the rest of his clothing and fucked the dead body. Then he wiped himself off as best he could with the hand towel and dressed. He pulled the sheet up to her neck and tucked her in. She looked fine. He never cut up the faces; that would have been horrible. Finally he unfastened the gold chain from around her neck and put it in his pocket.

As usual he had worn a dark suit. There was blood on it, of course. Not lots but some. In the strobe-lit darkness of Phantom's, he could walk to the front door without anyone noticing something was amiss.

He sat for a while, talking to the body. She was a good little girl, he thought fondly; she never talked back.

"What?" George yelled into the phone. "Are you sure you got that message right?"

"Positive," the answering service said. "John Allison called you not five minutes ago, and he left this number." She read it to him. "Mr. Nichols, he was not exactly sober as a judge, if you catch my drift."

"Thank you." He hung up, then dialed the number she had given him.

"Phantom's," a voice informed him.

He asked for Allison and waited while the actor came to the phone. "Hey, nickels and dimes." Johnny laughed. "I'm gonna do your movie. How's that sound?"

"Sounds great." I guess the girls did an ace job, George

thought, surprised. "Only you can't cut Albie out; you gotta work a deal with him. Okay?"

"Ah, Johnny, maybe you want to talk about this in the morning. I can call you back—"

"Hey," Johnny said sharply, "I *know* I'm drunk, but I'm not gonna change my mind on you. Send me the papers. I'm doing this for bunny rabbit, understand?"

George didn't understand, and he didn't care. The papers wouldn't get there until way past the cold light of morning, plenty of time for Allison to sober up and make an intelligent decision. George decided to send the contracts; he had nothing to lose. "Okay, Johnny. I'm looking forward to talking with you in person."

Johnny hung up chortling. Game plan in action. He had a charmed life; he could get anything he wanted. They'd be seeing each other every day, and when the sterling priceless husband ignored her once too often, he'd be there. And he'd be good to her. He knew how to treat a lady.

He staggered back to the bar and told the bartender he knew how to treat a lady.

The bartender agreed with him but wouldn't serve him another drink. "You are shit-faced," the bartender told him, "and I am going to call you a cab."

Someone came over, a waitress or a working girl or somebody looking vaguely female, and said it had just started snowing and the street looked beautiful.

Johnny smiled. The first snow falling on the evening he had met her—that was perfect. And why not? His life was perfect. He was rich and pretty, and those old days pumping gas were a bad dream. "Yeah, I think I'll go home. I can't fuck around no more; I'm in love."

The bartender laughed. "That's real nice, Johnny. I hope it lasts." He pulled a phone out from under the bar and started dialing a cab company. He liked Allison. He tipped big, he was not an obnoxious drunk, and the girls in the back said he never beat up on them, and that was all the bartender cared about. He'd seen it plenty, and the one thing he would not tolerate was a man who'd beat up on a woman.

"No, that's okay," Johnny was saying. "I see a friend of mine. I'll get a ride with him." He dug a crumpled pile of bills out of his pocket and dropped them onto the bar. "Are we cool?"

"Very cool."

"Okay, I'm going home. Hey, Foxy," he called to a man who was quietly crossing to the door. "Wait up for me; I need a ride home."

He floundered out the door, nearly killing himself on the spiral staircase.

"Hey, Foxy. Hey, Dan-my-man," he called down the deserted street, "wait up!" He blundered right up to the man, the man in the dark suit, catching hold of a sleeve to steady himself. His hand came away dyed inky dark and smelling of supermarket meat.

"You're not Foxy," he said unsteadily, backing away, "are you?" This man was no one he knew.

Johnny screamed. In Phantom's they heard only R&B music, live from the very best, and the clink of ice in tall glasses held by graceful fingers. On the street some people closed their windows. The drunks and junkies were always screaming about something, and it did no good to listen to their cries.

The dark-suited man was on him. Instinctively Johnny threw his hands up to protect his eyes. The little knife flashed along his arm. Ignoring the pain, Johnny tried to get his hands around the man's neck, cut off his air. He was unbelievably strong. He brushed Johnny's hands away. The knife came down into his chest. Johnny's strength leaked away steadily. Vainly he reached for the knife. The point bit deeply into his hand, but he held on in a dim kind of triumph. The man didn't need the knife. He lashed out with his fists and feet, and he kept going even after Johnny had lapsed into unconsciousness.

Even though he was afraid someone would see him, he couldn't stop himself from reaching into Johnny's pocket and pulling out his wallet. It was a difficult choice, but he finally selected a card which identified John Allison as a member of the Actors' Equity Association.

Candy's date replaced the wallet and went down into the subway. He was the only white man on the train, which would have made some ill at ease, but he was also crazy, and that was something to be respected. Nobody bothered him.

Catwoman found Candy an hour later. The bartender called the cops, and then he called the Phantom-man, who had gone home a few hours earlier. Feeling sick to his stomach, disgusted with the whole human race, the bartender covered poor Candy up with a sheet. Fuck the cops if he was destroying precious evidence. Then he cleared the place. After they'd all gone, he walked outside. Right then he needed to see a little snow falling peacefully on Harlem.

Something moaned near the garbage against the wall. "Oh, shit, oh, fuck," he said over and over again. "Who did this to you, man? Who did this?" He tried to move Johnny off the cold pavement.

"Don't!" Johnny cried out. "There's something broken inside."

The bartender didn't know what to do. He sat down next to Johnny and put his arm around him awkwardly. "Take it easy. The cops are coming." He felt sure that whoever had offed Candy was responsible.

The cops were taking their goddamn time, the bartender thought. He saw one of the waitresses coming out of Phantom's and sent her in to call an ambulance. She moved her butt *fast.* He could have kissed her. "Take it easy," he repeated.

"You saved my life." Johnny was freezing to death, and nothing hurt at that particular moment. He dearly wanted to go to sleep, but he had the strange feeling that if he did, there would be no waking. "I don't know your name."

"Sam Tyler." Tyler did not think he had saved Johnny's life, because he knew Johnny was going to die. He had seen death, and this was it, up close and personal. Damn shame, damn shame, Tyler thought, a nice kid like that—a little wild, but he never hurt nobody.

"Hey, Tyler," Johnny said, his voice a bare whisper, "I'm gonna be fine. I'm in love."

"Yes, I believe you are," Tyler said.

Albie was talking to the doctor. He listened patiently as he explained. There was internal damage. There were broken bones. These things were present in abundance. What there was not was a whole lot of hope. Still, he was fighting.

Albie listened. "What about his face?"

The doctor stared.

"Come on, doctor. You know he's an actor. His face is his fortune."

"There is some facial damage," the doctor said dryly. "But reconstructive surgery is very highly advanced . . ." His words trailed off.

"Can you make him look the same?"

"No, I don't think so."

Albie lowered his face into his hands. Big sobs shook his body. "Oh, my boy, my beautiful boy, gone forever."

The doctor left him crying in the lounge.

The next morning, bright and early, Karen and Lake were in a cab headed for the airport. Neither one of them had had much sleep, and they were both touchy as hell and not exactly talking to each other. When they arrived at the airport uneventfully, Karen checked their luggage and Lake asked blearily, "Have you got a quarter? I want to watch some television." Karen dug through her purse. "Here. I'm going into the bookstore." She darted away.

Lake fed the change into the machine, easing herself into the molded plastic seat. Her backbone protested. She scooted down a little lower. The news came on. She was just about to turn the channel when the reporter said a woman had been killed and the actor John Allison had been severely beaten at the famed private sex club Phantom's. He was in critical condition.

Lake went into the bookstore. She found Karen reading the latest edition of the morning paper. There was a copy of *Treasure Island* in her hand.

"I'm going to take a later flight," she told Lake. "You go ahead. George will be waiting for you."

"I'm going with you."

Miraculously they hit no traffic going back, and their cab deposited them in front of the hospital in short order. Lake waited downstairs in the car.

Apparently he had been calling for her, so they let Karen in. She really wasn't prepared for all the tubes and the machines humming away, and the worst was the blood steadily dripping through a tube into his arm. A bandage covered almost the entire left side of his face.

She sat there listening to him breathe until she could convince herself that he wasn't going to stop suddenly. She took his uninjured hand in hers and kissed it, trying not to disturb the IV.

His eyes rolled open, and she could have cried.

"See?" he said confidently. "I told you it wasn't good-bye."

"You were right."

"You'll see me again."

"Yes," she lied.

"Karen?" His face suddenly twisted with anguish. "I didn't go home like you said. I'm sorry."

"That's okay," she said soothingly. "Look, I brought you a present." She held up the copy of *Treasure Island* so he could see it.

"I like that one." He sounded sleepy. "Thanks."

"Finish that, and I'll send you *Moby Dick.*"

"I love you," he said, "and you love me." He fell asleep.

"Yes, I do love you." She kissed him and left quietly, leaving the book on his nightstand.

At the nurses' station there was a huge black man, a giant, holding a bouquet of flowers. It was the most grotesque bouquet Karen had ever seen, with huge sprays of gladiolas sticking out in all directions. He looked familiar to her, and her mind remembered. The bartender at Phantom's.

He was coming toward her beaming. That's her, Tyler thought exultantly, that's her! He had seen terrible things in his life, but he had a wife he thought the world of and two children he would walk through fire for, and they had kept him from getting sour on the world and hating all the people in it. But every now and then you needed a little extra shine in the darkness. Now Tyler felt he could go home and tell his wife and kids that he had saved somebody's life, because he believed he had actually done it.

He pulled a daisy free from his monstrous bouquet. "Miss?" He smiled at her. "This is for you."

In California George was watching the morning news, shaking his head. Still frowning, he buzzed his secretary. "Did you send out those contracts to John Allison?"

"Not yet. I was just about to."

"Don't bother. I don't think he'll be working for a while."

19

March 1978

WITH THE FILMING of *Maiden Voyage* to commence in less than a month, George was naturally quite concerned with Lake's behavior. She seemed fine. There was no drinking, no disappearing acts, no drugs. Twice a week she ran on the beach with Karen. George would watch them from his window, sand flying up from their feet. He felt sure they were talking about him, and that made him very unhappy. Since they'd come back from New York, Karen and Lake had been thick as thieves. They had secrets they shared. George felt keenly that he had been replaced in Lake's affections. Yet she was with him every night, even though she insisted on schlepping back to her apartment when morning came. She got a new place, also on the beach, and she would call Karen the night before they were to run, telling her where they would meet.

For the first time in a long time, George began to hope that Lake would marry him. He knew she needed him, and he loved her enough for both of them.

Lake came in from her run.

"Are you staying with me today?" He looked at his watch. "That was a hell of a long run."

"We didn't run all the time. We stopped to get a soda." She looked at him hard for a moment, studying him. He felt like withering under the scrutiny. What the hell did that little bitch say about me today? he wondered. "We have to talk, George."

"Ready, willing, and able, my lady." He forced a cheeriness he did not feel into his voice.

"You're a wonderful man, better than I deserve, but—"

He felt sick. He'd heard this speech many times before, and

he knew how it went. "You know what I think?" he said quickly. "I think this John Allison thing has really upset you. It's perfectly understandable. You need a little vacation. Maybe you could sneak away just for a week before we start shooting. How about Hawaii? You could take Karen if you wanted. Or what about Paris? Anywhere you want to go."

"George, it isn't working. I tried, I honestly tried, but I just don't love you, and needing you isn't enough. You deserve better." She went to the closet and removed the few clothes she kept there. She took a small overnight case from the bottom of the closet and started packing.

"I don't want better. I'm happy."

"No, you're not. You're insecure. Half the time you're trying to please me, and the other half you're making deals. That's no kind of life." She laughed shortly. "Actually I'm doing you a favor. There's a nice lady out there, waiting for you, George, but you won't look for her until I get out of your life."

He tried unsuccessfully to wrestle the bag out of her hand. "What have I done wrong?" he begged her. "Talk to me. I'll fix it; I'll make it better."

"George, don't," she whispered. "I can't bear to see what I've done to you. It's become painfully evident to me that the only thing worth a damn in this life is love. It's the only thing that comes close to being perfect, *if we let it be.* I can't make myself love you just because you've been good to me. It just isn't there. I'm sorry. I won't lie to you anymore, or to myself. I want to live an honest life. I want to start fresh."

"Is there somebody else?"

She hesitated. "No." There was no reason to involve Harry in all this. Not with his career on the line.

"Fucking liar." Bitterness tainted his voice. "All this shit just because you've got some pretty boy waiting in the wings? What's the matter? All of a sudden old Georgie's not good-looking enough to sleep with anymore?"

She ignored his outburst, moving purposefully toward the door.

"Wait!" He caught her arm. "I'm sorry I lost my temper. Let's just talk this thing out. That's what mature people do when they have problems. They don't walk out on each other."

"Please move away from the door."

He sank down onto the bed, putting his hands up to his face. Harsh sobs shook him.

"Please don't." Gently she pulled his hands away. "I never meant to hurt you, but every day I put this off, it was just giving you false hope. We never had a chance. It was all self-delusion, on my part as well as yours."

"You never gave us a chance." Fully aware of how pathetic he looked, he gripped her hand. "You were always holding back."

"I'm sorry. I really am."

"The fuck you are!" he roared. "What did your little bitch girlfriend say about me? What poison has she been feeding you?"

"Karen never said one word against you. Don't use her. This is between you and me."

"Lake?" His voice was a choked whisper. "You'll come back, and you better pray I'm in a mood to take you back."

She went downstairs, his voice screaming after her. "Nobody understands you the way I do, Lake! I've had it! If you walk out that door—"

He heard the door slam behind her.

Some time before, Lake had bought a piece of land high in the hills. The land was very isolated and not to everyone's taste. At first she thought of it solely as an investment. The realization that she wanted her own home, built to her own design, didn't manifest itself until later. She was going to start building after the movie was finished. After one of their morning runs, Lake had driven Karen up to the site.

Karen had been properly horrified. "This is ax-murder country," she stated emphatically. "This is where Norman Bates goes jogging." Lake loved her land, and nothing Karen could say ("If you broke your leg, it would take them weeks to find you.") would sway her. She had no intention of letting her nerves get the better of her. A house was an extension of one's self. Karen's house was small and cluttered with books and good paintings and lots of plants. Lake wanted her house to be far away from other people.

Now she drove up to the site, winding her way carefully around hairpin turns. She had called Harry and told him she was cutting herself free. She wanted to see him that night, but as for the rest of it, well, she wouldn't pressure him. He'd have to do what he felt was right.

He said he could meet her.

The night magnified every sound. She had almost talked herself into getting a little jumpy when he pulled up.

"Harry?" She could see him better now, as he walked into the circle of light provided by her headlights.

"You expecting anybody else?"

She took his hands and wrapped them around her waist. It was an unusual gesture for her, vulnerable and touching. "I told him."

Harry kissed her. A magic circle, forehead, eyes, tip of the nose. "How'd he take it?"

"Pretty bad. I'm just glad it's over. For the first time in my life, I feel like an honest woman."

"I can't ask Chris for a divorce right now," Harry said tersely. "George would have me kicked off the picture, I know it. Damn, I feel like a prize shit."

"Don't you dare." She kissed him. "You're absolutely right about that. Besides, I don't want George to think I'm leaving him for you. That's adding insult to injury. No, we'll wait a while. I can be patient." Her lips moved over him again. "But not about everything . . ."

"You don't have to ask me twice." Harry nuzzled her neck. "Do you want to take my car or yours?"

"Yours." Her hands moved over him busily. He didn't need the urging.

"Motel?"

"Fine."

They drove to a motel called the Lucky Armadillo. They'd been there before, partly because the name provoked major hysterics, mostly because it was way, way off the beaten path.

They undressed hurriedly. She watched him.

"Voyeur." He grinned at her. "Your turn."

She pulled her sweater over her head and stumbled out of her jeans. No underwear hampered her progress. "Ta-dah. Move over." She scooted into bed. The sheets were freezing. "Brrr. Warm me."

"I'll try, lady." He moved on top of her, his tongue darting into her mouth. Her legs opened eagerly, knees poking at the sheet. "Hey, take it easy." He laughed. "We've got time."

"Do we?" she asked in a small voice. "John Allison thought he had plenty of time. That really spooked me."

Sighing, Harry rolled over onto his back. "Lake, the guy hung out in very strange places. His number was up, that was all."

"You read what they said in the papers. That bartender said he heard Johnny call that man Foxy. That's what he called Daniel when he saw him outside the theater. What if it was Daniel Fox?"

"Then Daniel Fox would be in jail," Harry reasoned. "Lake,

what happened to Allison has nothing to do with you or me. It's sad, but it happens. It was just some crazy off the street." He slipped his arm under Lake's neck as a makeshift pillow.

"That night he came to my hotel room. He trashed the place."

"Fox?" Harry shored himself up on one elbow, staring at her in disbelief. "Are you sure?"

"Yes."

"Did you see him?"

"No, but I'm sure just the same."

"Jesus, Lake. Why didn't you call the cops?"

"Because," she whispered, "I just wanted him to be gone. If I called the cops, it would go on, like before. Maybe he'll leave me alone if I just leave him alone. I don't think he'll bother me anymore."

"Doesn't make sense." Harry raked his hand through his hair. "Something here doesn't make sense."

She gave him a strange smile. "You can't reason with a sane man's mind and expect any of this to make sense."

"Lake, I really think you should tell the police what you told me."

"No." She reached down and stroked his cock. "Now forget all this and make love to me."

"This is serious—"

"No more talk." She pushed him down and climbed on top, impaling herself. She was a little dry, but after she moved up and down a few times on his shaft, it felt like her insides were molten wax. She fondled his testicles with gentle fingers. "Still want to talk?" she teased.

He took his mouth off her breast just long enough to mumble, "We'll talk later." She pulled a long moan out of him when she rose off him. "Baby, don't," he groaned. "Come back. We miss you."

"Wait," she promised. Her long hair trailed silkily over his stomach. Her tongue explored his navel, traveling downward, hands massaging his groin. He started to shake as her lips closed around his inflamed organ. His hands reached for her, but she was intent on his pleasure. Her tongue flicked around his shaft so softly, and then she would give him a small taste of her teeth. He arched madly; his body was on fire. She sucked at him furiously. "Oh, God," Harry moaned. He grabbed her and pulled her up to him, driving his tongue into her mouth. Barely able to control himself he got on top of her, sliding into her easily. They were both wet, from sweat and their own juices. He tried to go slow, thrusting with long strokes that drove her mad, but neither of them could wait another second.

Arms wrapped around her tightly, he drove home a hundred times, until they were both shuddering, laughing, crying, giggling weakly, stomachs fluttering.

They stayed together, glued together, until he began to shrivel inside her. "Oh, don't go," she said, with mock reluctance.

"Give me an hour." He looked over her shoulder at his watch. "Shit. I've got to be getting back."

"I know," she said quietly.

"I'd better take a shower. You gonna take one?"

She looked at him, the sheet pulled down around her waist, her smile secret and knowing. "No. I like the way I smell."

He went over and kissed her one more time before he stepped into the shower.

"Do you think he'll tell?" she yelled to him when she heard the water go off. She had dressed, and her jeans felt decidedly squishy.

"Who'll tell?" Harry asked, stepping from the bathroom. He frowned. "Shouldn't have got my hair wet. How the hell am I going to explain a wet head at this hour?"

"Flash flood?"

"Cute, real cute, lady-of-the-lake." He ruffled his hair wildly with a towel.

"Do you think Matt will tell?" she repeated patiently.

"Nope." He inspected his hair in the mirror. "Goddamn-it-to-hell. This will never do."

"I thought Chris was away in Europe."

"She is. But I think she's got my sister keeping an eye on me. Don't worry about Matt. He's a decent guy."

"He hates me."

"No, he doesn't," Harry said, buttoning his shirt. "He minds his own business. That's the kind of guy Matt is."

"You think he told Karen?"

"Did you get a lecture from her?"

"Only on the evils of hard liquor and controlled substances."

"Then he hasn't told her." He zipped up his pants.

Lake was motionless on the bed. "I was just thinking how nice it'll be when we can sleep together all night."

He sat next to her. "That'll be wonderful."

"Seems so far away, I don't believe it'll ever happen sometimes."

"It'll happen," he promised. "We're going to get married." Thinking of weddings made him think about families. "Lake, how come you never tell me anything about your family?"

"Nothing to tell. I think your hair's dry. It looks dry, anyway."

"Darlin', I don't understand you." He stroked the back of her hand. "I believe you love me, but you don't trust me."

"All because I don't want to talk about my boring childhood," she scoffed. "Mommy's an airhead, and Daddy's wrapped up in business. There, satisfied?"

Angrily he scooped the car keys off the table. "You drive me crazy sometimes, you know that? You tell Karen, I bet. You tell her everything."

"I don't tell anyone."

He watched as she rummaged through her purse. She tucked a pill into her mouth, swallowing it dry. She winked at him. "Keeps the bad dreams away."

"Be careful with that shit," he warned her.

"I can handle it. I know my limitations."

He doubted it, but Harry wasn't one to preach. He liked the occasional chemical vacation, but he was more afraid of blowing what had taken him years to scrape together. He didn't think Lake was afraid of that.

He dropped her off at her apartment, feeling only the smallest qualms as he watched her run up the walk and disappear into the house.

She was a big girl, he thought as he made for home. And he was a big boy, and to a certain extent they took care of themselves—so much for "Darling, let me share your inner being." Well, when you grew up, you left a certain amount of illusion behind. He knew he loved Lake, and he was willing to accept that nothing in life was exactly the way he had imagined it.

There were lights on at the house. For a moment Harry wondered if Chris was home early from her continental shopping trip. How was he going to explain coming home so late? If he was lucky, she would have gone to bed already.

As soon as he cracked the door, he smelled incense. "Jackie," he groaned.

His sister was sitting in the "office," as Chris jokingly referred to a small corner of the living room she had given Jackie for her readings. Jackie did "readings" now, mostly for unemployed actors, but she was moving up to hairdressers and budding restauranteurs and lots of students, curious about their grades.

Jackie had discovered Laura Ashley, and she now looked like a refugee from *Little House on the Prairie.* Her ruffles and homespun annoyed the shit out of Harry. At the present moment a young woman was sitting with Jackie. Both of them looked pretty intense.

"I don't know about this agent," Jackie said, looking distressed.

"Oh, no," the young woman groaned. "Do you know how long it took me to get *him?*"

"Well." Jackie shook her head sadly. "I just don't know. He doesn't really believe in you. You need somebody to get behind you a hundred percent."

The woman nodded, confirming the diagnosis. "Yeah, it's not like you're telling me something I don't know. Shit. What the hell am I going to do?"

"Things are going to happen for you," Jackie promised. "I can see it. Your difficulty lies in keeping yourself well, body and spirit, until then. That's all you have to do. There is success in your future; it's your destiny. You have to be patient. All right? That'll be forty dollars." She collected the money and showed the young woman to the door.

"It was an emergency." Jackie plopped into a chair, looking defiantly at her brother.

"The first thing you got to do," Harry told her, "is extinguish that essence of bordello."

"Chris likes my incense."

"Chris lets you get away with murder because she doesn't know you as well as I do. This is my house, and I take exception to it smelling like an invitation to a horny Arab. Off that fucking incense, Jackie."

She did. "What's wrong with you, brother? We used to get along so well. What happened?"

You became a geek, Jackie. You turned my home into a carnival sideshow. He gestured to her "office." "Why do you need to clutter up my house with this shit? Looks like a goddamn storefront fortune teller has squatter's rights here."

"These things are all important to me," Jackie said with dignity. "They bring good fortune to this house."

He laughed at her. "How they gonna do that, Jackie? They're just roots and rocks and bits of junk."

She put out the incense. "Don't make fun of me, Harry. You never used to."

"Well, you're a little strange these days. You never used to do this kind of stuff. I was always the wild one. You did the right thing. You got married, you settled down, you had two wonderful kids—"

"I hated my life!" she screamed at him. "Every day like the one before it. God, I hated *him,* and I hated the boys a lot of the time. You're not the only one in the family who's special, Harry." She held up the deck of tarot cards. "I can do this. This is my gift. I tell people what they want to hear, and they go away happy. And they pay me, Harry, they pay me good. So don't you dare tell me how to run my life. At least I never stepped out on my husband when I was married."

"I think," Harry said slowly, "you should get a new place to live. We're not kids anymore. We don't owe—"

"I wish we were kids," she cried. "We were good when we were kids. We were friends, and we're not anymore. How can people change so much? You got to slow down, Harry; you got to think about what you're doing."

"I want you out of my house." He turned away from her and walked upstairs.

"Hello?" Lake reached for her phone.

"Where were you?" George screamed. He sounded drunk. "I've been calling for hours. Who were you fucking? Did you show him a good time?"

She hung up, knowing it would do no good to try to reason with him. She'd call him tomorrow and try to make amends. The phone rang again. She eyed it suspiciously.

"Were you in the shower?" Karen asked. "It took you forever to pick up."

"No, I was reading something scintillating. Couldn't put it down. Are we running tomorrow?"

"Sure. Shall I meet you at George's or your place?"

"My place. Oh, Kar, I had a big fight with George, and I feel rotten. Will you come and spend the night with me? I'm scared to fall asleep."

"I'm awfully tired, Lake. You can come over here if you like, but I'm really exhausted. Drink some warm milk."

Lake grimaced at the thought. "I hate warm milk. I'll take half a Valium; that'll put me out."

"I'll come over."

"No, you're tired. I'll be fine; I won't take anything, I promise.

Jesus, Karen, are you jockeying for Mother Teresa's job? I'll see you tomorrow, bright and early."

"Okay, sweet dreams."

"You, too." She hung up, went into the bathroom, and took a tranquilizer. Well, it wasn't a Valium; she hadn't lied about that. These were Percodan. They were heavy-duty pain pills, and praise the Lord, they *worked.* She took another one and stumbled back to bed. Her stomach was pretty empty, and all she could think about was a couple of hours of unconsciousness. Deep, dreamless darkness.

The phone rang again. She let it go, not yet asleep, just drifting aimlessly, feeling pleasantly warm and safe. She liked the downers better than coke. Coke made you jittery and irritable when you came down. And drinking was fine for killing the dreams, but they had to come out sometime, and they would play themselves out before your waking, horrified eyes.

The phone stopped.

Slowly she turned her head to look at the instrument. "Harry?" She had the strangest feeling that that had been him. Maybe he had something important to tell her. She should have picked up the phone. The one call she'd missed had been the only one she wanted to hear. She stared at the phone, willing it to ring again. *C'mon, Harry, dial that number one more time. You can do it, boy . . .*

After a moment the phone began to ring.

Lake smiled. Now that was the power of love. She picked up the receiver. "I knew it was you," she whispered.

"Hello, my sweet girl."

"Harry, I can't sleep. I don't know what to do."

"I'll tell you a story, and then you'll go to sleep." His voice was softly hushed, thrilling with love.

"Yes, that would be nice." She pulled the covers up to her chin, feeling like a very small, very loved child.

"Once upon a time there was a beautiful little girl—"

She felt the tranquilizers stealing through her body, making her feel thick and sludgy.

"With long blonde hair and big blue eyes."

"No more story," Lake said thickly. "Sleepy."

"But you have to hear the rest of the story. You have to be a good little girl and hear the whole thing. Isn't that right?"

"Who is this? You're not Harry."

"No, I'm not." The voice was sepulchral, mesmerizing. "You know who it is. We belong together. Forever, you and I."

"Who are you?" she whispered.

She actually heard the voice smile. It sent a chill through her. "Doppelganger," the voice said.

"Daniel!" she screamed. "Daniel, is that you? Why are you doing this to me?"

"Because I love you," the voice said serenely.

"Lake?" Karen let herself into Lake's apartment. "Very bright, leaving the door open. Ready to run? Got your sweats on?" She went into the kitchen, smelling coffee.

The machine was on automatic pilot. For some reason the sight of the machine calmly spewing forth coffee all by itself filled Karen with a vague feeling of dread. Something was terribly wrong.

She began to check the house, starting with the small bathroom. It was empty—a mess but empty. Well, that was normal. Lake's usual state of housekeeping was total chaos. Lake was nowhere to be found. Not in her bedroom, not in the living room or the cluttered second bedroom. The door was jammed on the master bathroom. Karen set her shoulder against the door and pushed steadily, trying not to panic. The door creeped open. Lake's nerveless hand flopped through, blood from her wrist puddling on the hallway carpet.

Karen couldn't get the door to open any farther—Lake's body was blocking it. Reaching through, she shoved Lake's body clear and yanked the door open completely. She had cut both wrists, and the fingertips on her right hand were slashed as well, but she was still semi-conscious. She probably held the blade in that hand, Karen guessed. Blood was everywhere. In Lake's hair. On the mirror. Splashed on the walls. In the delicate whorls of Lake's ear.

"Oh, Jesus!" Karen shrieked, running to the phone. She dialed the emergency number before she realized there was no dial tone. Someone had pulled the wire from the jack. Adrenaline washed through her. Karen wrapped Lake's wrists up, first in a shower cap filled with ice, then in about six towels. Somehow she managed to drag her to her feet and wrestle her into the car. She was terrified that if Lake lost consciousness, she would never wake up. Karen pulled into the hospital driveway with the radio blasting, the windows rolled up, and the air conditioning on arctic stimulation.

The first person she thought to call was Matt, and he promised he would get in touch with George.

By the time both men got there, Karen had already spoken

to a doctor. "She's going to be all right. It looked a lot worse than it was."

George looked terrible. "Thank God for that. Did you see her?"

"Not yet. I'm afraid all we can do for the moment is wait around."

George went off in search of a doctor or a nurse who could apprise him of Lake's condition in more scientific terms.

Mildly surprised, Karen watched Harry running down the hallway toward them. She turned to Matt. "Why did you call Harry?"

Harry went directly to Matt. "Is she all right?"

He nodded.

Harry sank into a seat. There was no mistaking the emotion in his face or what it meant. Karen caught his eye.

She knew.

He looked at her sharply, then nodded his head, a barely perceptible up-and-down movement.

She walked down the hall to the vending machines. Harry followed her.

"Karen, I'd like to explain—"

"Got any change?"

He gave her some coins. "The first time I met her—"

"What happened to 'be true to your school'?"

"You don't understand. It wasn't like that—"

"How dare you peddle your morality to me?" she hissed. "I believed in you; I looked up to you."

"I never asked for that. I love her."

"How could you do this to Chris?"

"I don't know," he said miserably. "Karen, you don't know what's it like to want somebody so bad it's practically eating you alive. You are not the kind of person who allows herself to be ruled by passion."

"Damn you, am I made of stone? I feel, Harry, I need, and Matt is not the answer I thought he would be. But I have learned to control myself and to think of other people, no matter how it hurts me. I don't care how you look at it, what you have done is *wrong.*"

The doctor came over to them. "Are you Ms. Singer?"

"Yes."

"Ms. Eastman would like to see you. Just for a minute or two."

She looked very small and lost in the hospital bed against the white mass of pillows and blankets. Lake smiled. "Poor you," she said to Karen. "You must be sick to death of hospitals." She held out her hand. "I'm so sorry."

"Why?" Karen asked.

"I hurt," Lake said softly, "and I wanted out of the pain for a while."

"Something must have happened."

"He called me." Lake turned her face away. "It was the doppelganger."

"The what? Oh, honey, there's no such thing. That's just a story." Karen tried to reason with her.

"He won't find me here," Lake said confidently. "I have to talk to George now. You think he still cares for me? I need him."

"He'll always love you."

Lake rubbed her face sleepily against the pillow. "Will you tell him to come in?"

"Yes."

"Karen?" Her smile was peaceful. "Tell Harry I love him."

Chris came home from her European trip that morning. She was in the kitchen drinking coffee, looking a little bilious, when Harry came back from the hospital and told her what had happened.

"God, that's horrible," she sympathized, pouring Harry a cup of coffee. "What's going to happen to the movie?"

"I have no idea," he answered honestly. "It wasn't exactly a priority on anybody's mind. I guess George will have to cast somebody else."

"What about Karen? I think she's adorable."

"Well, we know the director likes her. How'd the trip go?"

Chris made a face. "Between air sickness and jet lag, it wasn't the best jaunt I've ever had. I made some good purchases, though."

"Is that all you're having for breakfast—coffee? Chris, that stuff will eat holes in your stomach lining. Let me make you some toast or something."

"I'd sick it up for sure. Thanks, anyway." She smiled sheepishly. "Look, I have something to tell you, and it's a little difficult. I'm pregnant." She laughed. "I'm as surprised as you are. My periods have been pretty irregular lately, but when they stopped altogether . . . Harry, did you hear me? We're going to have a baby."

"A baby?" Harry seemed to be having trouble processing the information. "You and me?"

"No, me and the counter boy at Del Taco. Of course you and me, idiot."

He was still staring at her with the most antic expression on his face.

"A baby," she said with exaggerated slowness, as if she were talking to a mental case, "as in little person? You know, your looks, my brains? Harry? Are you with me on this?" She pushed her cup away. "Do you want this child? Because if you don't . . . well, maybe we shouldn't be together. I want this baby, Harry. I love it already."

He put his hand on her stomach. A part of me, he thought in wonder. When I die, there will be a part of me walking the earth, living and breathing. "I think I feel it moving around in there."

"Oh, honey." She pealed laughter. "It's much too early for that. That's my stomach growling."

"How do you feel?"

"Like I have to go to the bathroom constantly. I'm tired, I'm irritable, touchy as hell, periodically depressed, very sentimental —which is all pretty good for the first trimester." Tears came into her eyes without warning. "See? You do want her, don't you? I just know it's going to be a girl."

Harry considered. Chris had just handed him his way out. She'd give him a divorce rather than consent to an abortion. He'd be free, and it would be Chris who had asked for the divorce, not him. He wouldn't have to feel guilty about anything except abandoning his child. Would it hate him when it grew up? No, Chris was above that; she was a decent woman. The kid wouldn't know him, that's all. He'd be the weekend daddy, buying expensive presents to make up for all the times he couldn't be around: first smiles, first steps, first dates. He'd be the stranger in the kid's life; how many times could you take your kid to the zoo?

"I want the baby." He went around the table and put his arms around her in a big bear hug. "Yeah, I want to be a daddy. Full time."

She looked up at him anxiously. "Sure?"

"Positive." He caressed her belly. "She's in there right now?"

"Right now. Harry, you have any weird diseases in your family?"

"Just Jackie," he said absently.

"Speaking of which, she's upstairs packing. Did you two have a row or something?"

"Something," he admitted.

"Well, I wish you'd go up and talk to her. She shouldn't leave angry; family's important."

Harry sighed. "Chris, she said some rank things to me. I don't see why I have to take that when she's a guest in my home."

"She's not a guest; she's *family*. When I first found out about the baby, she was the only one I told. I just didn't know how you'd feel about it. She really set my mind at ease. She helped me remember all the good things that made me fall in love with you in the first place. I may not see eye to eye with Jackie on most things, but I trust her, and I know how much she cares about you."

"Oh," Harry said, feeling like the prize at a turkey shoot. "I think I'll go talk to her." He went upstairs to Jackie's room.

She was packing, flinging things angrily into her suitcase. "Keep your shirt on," she told Harry as he came in. "I'll be gone as soon as I got all my stuff together. I don't want to have to come back and bother you just because I forgot something."

"Jackie, stop that for a minute and sit down."

"Oh, no," she said, fuming. "You said out, and out I go."

He picked up her suitcase and upended it, dumping the contents out onto the floor. "Now, are you going to sit down and talk to me like a human being?"

"That was nasty, Harry."

"Sit."

Glaring, she sat.

"Chris told you about the baby."

She nodded. "Harry, I don't care how you run your life. I know it's none of my business, but—"

"I know. You were right."

"I was?" She stared at him. "But I haven't done so good with my own life. I've tried, but I could never make a go of it as a housewife and a mother. Oh, I love the boys, but they were never enough. I knew you'd want the baby. You love kids. I sure don't, but you do. You'll be a good daddy."

He smiled. "You think so?"

"I know so."

"Auntie Jackie." He grinned at her. "Auntie Jackie, I owe you a big apology. Please stay here. After all, we need a built-in babysitter. Maybe you could have the boys come out and visit. Please stay."

"I'm sorry, too, Harry," she whispered, looking down at her hands. "I'd like to stay."

He kissed her cheek. "Jackie, now that we've made up, can I ask you a question?"

"Sure."

"You can't really tell the future, can you?"

She winked at him. "Fooled you, too?"

"I just wanted to make sure you hadn't lost it completely." He gave her a cagey look. "This town has a way of doing that to you. You start believing your own publicity."

"We're a lot alike," Jackie said. "I could never stand going along just like everybody else, but Mommy and Daddy told me that as a girl, I was expected to marry and have kids, and I wanted so bad to do the right thing and please them. It was too soon. They just should have let me run wild a little, and then I could have settled down and it wouldn't have felt like a prison sentence. I'm just doing now what I should have done then. The cards and all that, they're just my specialty act. I don't hurt anybody, and I have fun. But many's the time I wish I could look into the future and see what will be. I wish I could see that everything will be all right for you."

"It will," he said uncertainly.

"You can't give her up, this other lady, can you?"

He shook his head.

"Harry, what are you going to do?"

His grin was sickly. "I don't know."

"You realize we have a serious problem," George said.

They were in his office—George, Matt, Karen, and Sid. Sid was there primarily as moral support. Also, George knew Matt and Karen would stick together on just about anything. He wanted somebody there who was on his side. "We're shooting in a month, and the doctor said there was no way Lake would be able to return to work by then."

"I assumed you were going to recast," Matt said. "There's plenty of time for that, and you represent a lot of good actresses."

"I'm not going to give somebody else their big break because of what happened to Lake!" George yelled.

"Take it easy," Sid said quietly. "We all understand your feelings, George. You've got every right to be upset. Let's just calm down a moment and try to get a handle on our options. Matt? Any ideas?"

He shrugged. "If you don't want to recast, you can do one of two things. We can push the starting date back to some unknown time when Lake will be able to come back to work. Or you can write out the female role completely—make it an adventure film without a romance. Either way you're going to hurt the film. Push it back, we have financial trouble. Lose the romance, alienate fifty-one percent of the audience."

"Shit," George said softly.

Sid sat up suddenly. He looked electrified. "I've got a terrific idea. You wouldn't have to lose any money on this. Let Karen play Lake's part."

Matt smiled at the agent. "You've already got her under contract, George. It's a perfect solution."

"No." George addressed himself directly to Karen. "You're an unknown; so's Harry. Why would anybody come to see the film? Besides, you're a writer, not an actress. You'll be busy doing rewrites."

"You're wrong," Matt told him strongly. "You're a whiz at publicity; you'll find some way to get people into the theater. Karen's a wonderful actress. For God's sake, she's read lines with half the people you've auditioned here; you *know* she's good. And she's worked with Harry before."

"No."

Matt turned in shock. "Karen, what the hell are you saying?"

"Yes, what are you saying?" George mimicked nastily. "This is your big chance, Karen. Don't you want it?"

"You know I want it." She glared at him. "You know I want it more than anything in the world. I just don't want it like this. And most of all, George, I don't want to look back at some point down the road and find that I owe you for *anything.* If it's meant to be, it'll happen in its own good time, and not because my friend is unable to go on." She took Matt's hand. "It would be wrong," she said simply.

"Well," Sid sighed, "that brings us back to square one."

"I can rewrite the script," Karen said, "reduce the female role. She'll be a love interest. We can keep the romance, but she won't be the lead and won't be carrying a great deal of the plot. It'll be Harry's film essentially. You'll have to recast, but you can use one of the models you represent who's been getting a little notoriety. People will come in—they'll be curious just to hear her talk. George, that sound all right to you?"

He nodded his head slowly. "I've got Harry signed to a multiple-picture deal. If he takes off after this film, I'll have him sewn up for a couple of years. Yeah, I could live with that. Karen, when could you give me a rewrite?"

"As soon as you give me back my contract."

Matt stared at her. "What are you doing?" he said under his breath.

"You have no intention of doing anything for me as an actress, and I don't think you'll let me write anything except star vehicles for Lake. Lake doesn't use me," Karen said in a fury, "but you have. You've tried to turn me into her little puppy so I would resent her, but it didn't work. You don't own me. I want my contract back, and then you'll get your rewrite."

"It better be brilliant," George told her with a smile. "I'll send you my copy of your contract in the mail. You can rip it up or burn it, anything your little heart desires. You'll never make it on your own, Karen. I'm the best agent in this town. You just cut your own throat."

"I'd rather be a failure on my own terms," she said.

"Okay," Sid cut in. "Is everybody happy, more or less?"

Matt nodded his grudging consent.

"Then I suggest everyone goes to their respective homes and gets some rest," Sid went on. "It has not been one of our better days."

George put on his jacket, shrugging his shoulders to ease some of the tension. "It's a damn shame about what happened to John Allison. We could have done a buddy picture, and then we wouldn't need a female lead at all. I could have had another *Butch Cassidy and the Sundance Kid,*" he mused.

"What do you mean?" Sid asked. "Allison wasn't going to do a picture with you."

"Yes, he was. He called here that night I sent the girls to the show. Told me to send the contracts right over." He smiled. "I guess he was pretty taken with Lake."

Karen's expression was unreadable as Matt turned to her. "Is that what happened?"

"Sure," she said. "What else?"

He was a detective. Not a Sam Spade detective. He was real, and not by any stretch of the imagination was he a romantic figure. A big spare tire hung over his belt. He bought his clothes wherever they were cheapest, not caring if the patterns clashed. He was an independent. No big security firm for him.

Mostly he did divorce work. He got the kind of people who didn't have a lot of money but did have a burning wish for vengeance. There were a few clients who paid the big money, kept his phone from being turned off and the landlord from driving him nuts. You didn't get the big money for nothing. Usually the big money people wanted him to do something just slightly outside the law. He took the money, did what they wanted, and covered his tracks thoroughly. He had a lot of strange clients, but the one who made him wish he'd stuck to the straight and narrow was Daniel Fox. Crrrrazy like a Fox. Which he undoubtedly was. But he kept it under control, so the detective had nothing to hang his suspicions on. It made him think he was getting old, when a guy like Fox could give him the creeps. He had a nightmare that one day Fox would come to him with a bloody bundle to dispose of, and it would not be a human lying wrapped in that bloody cloth. It would be some misbegotten *something* that should never have been allowed to walk the earth in the first place.

He went to his office on Saturdays to pick up the mail. This particular weekend he came in very late, flicking on the light carelessly. There was somebody in his office.

"Jesus." He sank into his chair. "You almost gave me a heart attack. What are you doing here, Fox?" For a moment he thought he was losing it. Fox was holding something in his lap, and in the light it looked like the soiled baggage of the detective's nightmare. But it was only a fat manila envelope.

"Fox?" The writer wasn't answering. He was unshaven and unkempt. The light in his eyes was hectic, like the glaze a high fever inspires.

Daniel turned his head slowly. "Could you trace a phone call? If somebody came into your home and used your phone to call somebody else? Could you trace that?"

"I don't think so."

"Neither do I. But there's a call on my phone bill that I don't remember making, so obviously somebody else made that call. Wouldn't you think that would be it?"

"Well, yeah. Unless you made the call and forgot about it. Happens all the time."

He stared at the detective for a very long time.

"Everybody forgets things. Am I right?"

He tapped the envelope with his forefinger. "I've had this a long time, not with any plan to use it. But he's gone too far, to come into my house, use my phone, make me think I'm going crazy. He *was* there, I know it."

"Yeah, sure." The detective wished Fox would go away. Far, far away.

"When I was in jail I met a lot of interesting people. One of the men I played cards with was a danger junkie. Anything for a thrill. I don't remember what he was in for. I do remember he wasn't very good at cards. Evey time he had a good hand it was written all over his face. One day, we were cutting for high card and I bet him a very unusual bet. The loser would have to commit a crime for the winner when he got out. You can guess who won. I think he was relieved that all I had in mind was a simple burglary. First he went to Karl's house. Even though we've never met I feel we're on a first-name basis. My thrill-seeking friend stole the envelope, I had copies made, very good copies, then my friend put the copies back and I kept the originals. Karl never knew the difference. A word of advice; if you ever go in for a little murder, don't keep any souvenirs. Police love that sort of thing." Fox got to his feet. He held out the manila envelope.

"What do you want me to do with this?"

"Mail it." He smiled at the detective mirthlessly. "Oh, not now. It's to be delivered in the event of my death. You will be informed when that occurs."

He got up and walked into the night.

The detective looked at the envelope. It was addressed to a Karen Singer in L.A.

April '78

Dear Karen,

Well, you must have started working on the film by now—hope all goes well. Sorry for all the self-pity last letter. Guess I was feeling pretty forlorn after George reneged on the deal and Albie cut me off financially. I really thought he cared about me, bunny rabbit. It was a real shocker when I found out he'd put a casting notice in the trades. And the body barely cold, as they say, ha-ha.

I am feeling pretty good, all things considered, although I am going to be a lefty now. The doctor tells me the nerve damage in my right hand is permanent. Ah, what the hell, lefties are interesting people, right?

I know what you must have read in the paper, and I just want to straighten it out. I swear, Karen, it wasn't Fox. *It sure as hell looked like him, but when I got closer, it was more like the ghost of Foxy. The way he disappeared when the cops went to look for him, it really does look suspicious, but I didn't lie. It wasn't him. I just wanted you to know. I told that detective about my Equity card disappearing but he seems to think I misplaced it. It's obvious he doesn't know actors.*

Well, I know you are real busy, so I'll let you go. You know, when this first happened to me, I cursed you, Karen. If only you'd come home with me, this never would have happened. Well, I have been through the fire, and I have had time to think. I should have gone home that night like you told me to. That was the one night, my sweet lady, I should have been true.

John

Part 3

20

September 1980

ANGELO'S was a bar in Hell's Kitchen owned by a Greek who felt people found Italian names more appetizing when it came to eating and drinking establishments. Like lots of New York bars, Angelo's dealt mostly in beer, bar Scotch, and the odd hamburger, always of the same grayish hue. They had an okay juke and a wide-screen TV suspended over the front door. The TV was supposedly to entice the sports fans, but like as not, it played soaps and game shows during the day. In the evening, if there was no sporting event to take precedence, the bartender and the waitresses would watch what they wanted. Angelo's didn't hop til way after prime time.

So the TV would play, and the help would eat their dinners, grab a free beer, and catch up on *Dallas.* The Greek owner would sit at a corner table, scowling at the sight of his help hanging around doing nothing on his time while they waited for the evening rush. He liked the waitress, a short girl with a truly awe-inspiring chest that defied logic and gravity with mutual ease. She would not sleep with him, however, which only added to the Greek's irritation.

The short girl scooted past the Greek's table, smiling pleasantly but keeping well out of pinching distance.

"Katie," the owner called in a caressing tone, "you come here a minute. Please."

Still smiling, she sat on the chair he pulled out for her. Wary as she was, keeping Spiros on simmer had made her job easier and far more lucrative. No sense in screwing up a good thing. "Sure, Spiros. You need something?"

"You do me a favor, you keep an eye on Louie for me. Make sure he's not robbing me. I trust you, you look out for me." He patted her shoulder, thinking lower.

"Oh, Louie's not gonna rob you, Spiros. He's a good guy."

"You watch him anyway. For me, huh?" He took her hand, pressing a folded bill into it.

A twenty, she knew it almost instinctively. She could stretch a twenty a long, long way. "Okay, sure. I'll watch him." She started to get up, transferring the bill to the pocket of her jeans.

"Stay. Have a cup of coffee with me."

She sat down, wishing she'd been born with a rich father and a smaller chest.

Spiros beamed at her. "Maybe we go out this weekend—piano bar, nice restaurant, anything you like. You ever been to Atlantic City?" He practically licked his lips. "We could stay overnight. Beautiful hotels there, like you never saw in your life."

Oh, shit, Katie thought. She took his money, sooner or later there would have to be a payback. There always was. Well, she'd worry about it later, as long as she had a choice. "Yeah, maybe. Sounds nice. Not this weekend, though. I gotta help out my mom. She's sick, and I promised to shop for her."

"You're a nice girl, Katie, a good girl," Spiros said.

Katie got up to get Spiros a fresh cup of coffee. Eight o'clock and still light out. She looked down the street, watching for Louie. He had come to work at Angelo's about two months ago. He was quiet and kept to himself, which was probably why Spiros didn't trust him. Katie liked Louie.

She poured coffee for Spiros and started wiping down the tables. The chimes over the door clashed atonally. Louie must have come in. Katie looked up from her work. "Hi, Louie." She turned back and winked at Spiros. "Relax," she whispered. "I'm on the job."

Louie went behind the bar and started setting up. He walked slowly because he was a gimp, moving awkardly to accommodate his weak left leg. He had a full, dark beard that looked soft rather than wiry and a scar on his left temple that notched his eyebrow and ran up into his hairline. The hair grew pure white along the scar's path. It made him look older than Katie thought he was. She told him she thought the scar was sexy, and he grinned at her. He had a sweet smile, and his eyes were young and open. He was no pushover, though. Some guy had been hassling Katie one night, and Louie had chucked him out pretty quick, thank you very much. He was skinny as a junkie, except for his arms, which were knotted with thick muscles, like a wheelchair man. Despite Spiros's reservations, Louie was tops as a bartender. People loved to tell him their troubles. They figured a guy like Louie understood.

Katie thought about him a lot. She wondered where he lived, how he managed, if anyone looked out for him. She thought he was on his own like she was. He was a good-looking man once you got used to that weird white streak. Katie didn't mind the gimp, either. She'd rather take a gimp than a fuck-around or a bastard. Louie was a sweet guy. If he had asked her out, she would have said yes. He never did, so maybe he wasn't all alone in the world after all.

But Katie thought he was. He had the look.

She went around behind the bar and helped Louie pack ice around the beer bottles.

"Hello, Miss Kitty." He smiled at her. He called her that, like the saloon lady from *Gunsmoke.* "How are you doing?"

"Pretty good," she said, shaking her hands to get the circulation going. The ice made them feel like they were burning. "I started that book you loaned me. I don't understand one word of it."

"Give it time," he advised her. Louie was a voracious reader, another thing about him Katie really respected. Oh, hell, she had a case for the gimp. She really, really liked him.

"Look," she whispered, "I just want to let you know—Spiros asked me to keep an eye on you. It's not that he doesn't trust you, he just doesn't trust *anybody.*"

"Thanks, no problem. He giving you a hard time?" He waved a hello to Spiros, who scowled in return. He knew Katie liked Louie.

"I'm making out okay." Boastfully she displayed her twenty.

"Shouldn't take his money, Miss Kitty. That old shit's gonna expect something back one of these fine days." He got out a tip glass and stuffed in a dollar bill, just to get things going.

"I can handle Spiros." She squirted herself a Coke from the soda gun. "You worried about me?" she asked hopefully.

"You? Never. You want a lime for that?"

"Yeah, thanks." She consoled herself with the knowledge that he remembered she liked lime in her Coke. "Louie?"

"Yeah?"

She took a deep breath. Now or never. "Louie, you busy Saturday night? 'Cause if you're not, maybe we could go to a movie or something."

He looked at her in mild surprise. "I'm sorry, Katie, I can't. I'm busy."

She felt herself turning red. "Well . . . what about Sunday?"

He gave her that beautiful smile. "Sunday's fine. I guess we got a date."

"Yeah, I guess we do." She smiled back, feeling for once like more than a walking ad for Maidenform.

A few customers started to trickle in, mostly regulars. A lady reporter who always seemed to carry the weight of the world on her shoulders. She would routinely get drunk on Jack Daniels and Coke and then proceed to pick up strange men. Katie thought it a miracle nobody had cut her throat yet. The reporter had hit on Louie once, taking his polite refusal in stride. Another regular was a hawk-faced pimp, who wore his long black hair skinned back in a ponytail. He was always accompanied by at least one beautiful woman, whom he euphemistically called his "daughter." His escort that particular evening was an exotic. Her black hair was cut short, with heavy bangs masking her forehead. Her nose was straight, and her lips were full, stained a bright red. Malachy's daughters were not known for their subtlety. She was dressed, costumelike, in a short white toga, with a hammered necklace and slave bracelets of gold-tone metal. The pleated material of her dress was pressed flat by the considerable weight of her heavy breasts. She wanted a draft beer with an ice cube in it.

Another regular came in, a big black man who drank boilermakers and looked like he could rip the place apart but never caused anybody a lick of trouble. He was an electrician.

The juke was talking to itself. Two young guys came in, sat at a table, and started perusing menus. Katie went over with her order pad.

Malachy pulled at his long ponytail. "Louie, where's my Irish coffee?"

The daughter grimaced. "In this heat? Have something else, Daddy."

Malachy threw his hands up helplessly. "How can I resist such a sweet child? Louie, something that will not offend my girl's aesthetic sensibilities."

"I know just the thing." Louie made him a sombrero with a splash of soda to cut the sweetness.

"Perfect," Malachy declared.

His girl pouted. "I want a taste."

"Well, don't cry, sweetheart. Here you are." Malachy slid the glass over to her.

She fit her sensuous lips on the edge of the glass and slid her tongue into the drink, making little sighing sounds. Her body swayed slightly. A calculated show but effective. One of the young guys was on his way to the men's room. He stopped, mesmerized, watching. He sighed heavily and continued on his way.

Katie trotted back to the bar to hand in her drink order. "Cheap thrills," she scoffed, leaning across the bar to grab the soda gun. When she leaned, the tops of her breasts were visible through the V-neck she was wearing. All the gentlemen at the bar permitted themselves a chaste peek at her perfection. Piqued, the daughter sat back frowning. "Like I said"—Katie's grin was triumphant—"cheap thrills." She brushed against Louie on her way to pick up a Lite beer.

"Come on, girl," he admonished her gently. "I'm trying to concentrate on my job here."

The two young guys at the table asked if they could move over to the bar; that's where all the action seemed to be. Katie said that would be fine. She wouldn't have to work as hard, she'd still get her tip, and she could hang around the bar all night and be around Louie, which was fine with her. She ordered two hamburgers for the guys, fries well done.

Spiros turned up the juke a little. He was scowling a little less now. People were drinking. They were spending money. His place was cooking, and that was what he liked to see. The reporter moved to the stool next to the black man drinking boilermakers. She asked him if he wanted to try Jack Daniels and Coke. He said no. She asked him if he wanted to try something else. He said he'd think on it.

Malachy listened in. "Think over here," he offered. "My daughter's taken a liking to you."

"How much for the pleasure of your daughter's company?" Louie asked.

"Hundred fifty."

"For the whole night?"

Malachy laughed. "Does it take you all night? Hundred fifty for one time." He stroked the girl's hair. "She's worth it. Hundred fifty, and you won't limp anymore."

Louie roared laughter. "You kidding? That limp gives me character. Drives the ladies crazy."

The daughter was still looking at him with her secret smile. "Does it take you all night, Louie?"

"Would that it did," he said reluctantly.

The black and the reporter left together. She was weaving a little.

"That was fast," Louie observed.

"Tough news day." Katie brought him a burger. "Eat that. You're much too skinny." She went back to the kitchen to forage around.

Malachy handed Louie his card.

Louie stared. "Malachy, I didn't think people in your line *had* business cards."

"Why not?" the Irishman said, unconcerned. "I'm a businessman like anyone else. Call me in case you change your mind. My girl likes you; she'd treat you right. No rough trade, of course, Louie. I won't stand for that."

"I'm no tough guy," the bartender said. "I used to be, but I learned my lesson."

"Eat that burger," Katie said sternly. She had a platter of French fries and a piece of chocolate cake. "I'll mind the bar so you can eat your dinner. Spiros said it's okay. Go on, eat."

Louie checked his customers. Everyone had fresh drinks, and they all looked happy enough. He bit into the burger while Katie watched him approvingly. She got him a beer. "Here, live it up."

"Thanks."

She couldn't help herself; something about him seemed to call out to her. She reached out and touched the white streak in his hair.

He pulled away slightly, like a delinquent kid who fears he is going to get smacked anytime somebody lays a hand on him.

"I'm sorry," she said quietly. "Let me get you some ketchup for those fries."

"Katie, you don't understand."

"You're wrong there." She cleaned the ketchup bottle with a bar towel. "I understand pretty good. A girl like me . . . look, I've had a lot of conversations with guys, but I can't remember one of them looking me in the eye. You get gun-shy. A guy asks me for the time, and I'm practically ready to call the cops. I just don't want nobody to hurt me no more. I understand real good, Louie. If you need time, well, I can understand that good, too." She smiled acidly at Malachy's daughter. "Better than some." She went back to her movie magazine. "Oh, I wish I was one of *them.*" There was real longing in her voice. "I'd give anything just to be friends with these people."

"They're no better than anybody else," Louie said tartly. "Most of them are worse."

"How would you know?" Katie laughed.

He smiled at her. "Used to be an actor."

"Would I know who you were?"

"I don't think so."

"Were you any good?" she teased.

"Nope," he said regretfully. "I'm a much better bartender."

"New York's full of lousy actors," Katie said placatingly. "How many good bartenders are there?"

"Not enough," one of the guys called out. "Can I get a beer?"

"I'll handle it," Katie said, fishing a bottle of Lite out of the ice.

While she was occupied, Louie debated reading a letter he had received that morning. He hadn't had time to get around to it earlier, but he didn't want Katie to see.

She was back. "What do you want to do Sunday? Movies okay? I love the movies."

"Movies are fine."

"Well, *Maiden Voyage* was just re-released. God, that Harry Townsend is such a hunk. Or we could see Lake Eastman's new movie, although that's a little hot for a first date. I can't believe that movie only got an R; I heard it was triple-X all the way."

"Whatever you want to see is fine with me."

"Louie," she said hesitantly, "you don't have a girlfriend, do you?"

He thought about the letter in his pocket. "No." I have a pen pal. It wasn't quite the same thing. He put down his burger half-eaten. The evening rush was starting, and he had to work.

It was four o'clock in the morning. Katie lived on Tenth Avenue, and Louie insisted on walking her home. She knew his leg had to be killing him after a long shift, and she was touched by his gallantry. She chattered on about the movies and other things that interested her, until they came to her door.

"Do you want to come up?"

"I'm pretty beat," Louie said. "I'll see you Sunday."

"Sunday." She nodded. She wanted to kiss him, but she was scared he'd pull away again. Sans kiss she dashed up the stairs.

In a few minutes he was at his own door, letting himself into the decaying vestibule. His mailbox read 'R. Louie Stevenson,' and it was truly amazing that nobody seemed to get it. He could have called himself John Allison, which had been fine for almost twenty-seven years, except that he didn't feel like that person anymore.

Oh, he missed Johnny boy. He certainly missed Johnny boy's

money, and he missed the business, which surprised him. He didn't miss the drugs, because in the hospital there had been pain medication and then there had been the slow, painful process of being weaned off it. It was either that or realize that he'd been turned into a junkie and go to Union Square Park to hang out with the rest of the boys. He didn't miss having a different woman every night. But he missed Albie's affection and support. And he missed living in a clean place with no roaches and having somebody else see to it that there was enough milk for coffee in the morning and clean sheets on the bed.

He missed the proper use of his leg and a right hand that was like other people's. He missed walking down the street and feeling on top of the world instead of scared. He missed feeling safe and whole, but most of all he missed *her.*

He took the letter out of his pocket and stretched out on his bed.

Dear Johnny,

I will not be writing you anymore after this. I—

He folded the letter back up and stuffed it into the envelope. *No.* He'd had enough. If it was a contest, Job could have the crown and title; he'd settle for first runner-up.

He unfolded the letter, smoothing it out carefully.

Dear Johnny,

I will not be writing you anymore after this. I always felt so guilty about our letters, because it was really a love affair on paper. We can't ever be together, and it's time you got on with your life. Please forgive me for letting this go on as long as I have; I was being selfish.

Your letters have meant everything to me; I lived for them. I'm sorry about a lot of things. Mostly I'm sorry I didn't meet you first, but I didn't, *and there's nothing I can do about that.*

It's time to pick up the pieces, Johnny, and get on with it.

This much was typed. There was no signature. At the bottom Karen had scrawled hurriedly:

I love you. Please don't ever believe different.

He folded the letter up and put it with the others, the ones he had saved for the past few years. She was right; he knew that. He'd been expecting it. You couldn't have a relationship on paper, and she couldn't have a relationship with him anyplace else.

The problem was, he was never going to love anyone else, and he didn't think she would, either.

21

HARRY TOWNSEND was a big star.

Maiden Voyage had turned out a lot better than anyone had dreamed. There'd been problems—daily rewrites, a smoke machine that went haywire and held up production for a full day—but work had pushed forward steadily. Matt had learned a lot since his NYU days, and Harry had begun to feel confident they would break even. His work was good; he felt the film would be a solid credit.

They decided to sneak the film in a small suburb of L.A. Karen, Matt, Harry, Chris, and Sid piled into a car and drove out to the movie house. They all wore dark glasses and porkpie hats. Karen had joked that they looked like a Blues Brothers convention.

From the moment the film started, the audience was with it all the way. They laughed in all the right places, they cheered the hero, they booed the villain, and they applauded as the final credits rolled.

"Now for the acid test," Karen whispered, heading for the ladies' room. A few minutes later she met them out in the parking lot. "The word in the ladies' room is that Harry Townsend is a hunk."

Harry looked at her in shock. "They liked me?"

"Honey." Chris took his arm gently. "They loved you."

It was the finest moment of his life. No matter how many other successes followed on the heels of that first, sitting through that sneak, listening to the audience loving him, was always the best.

Harry was thinking about that moment as he drove to Ranger's. Ranger's was a small club popular with industry people. The general public didn't seem to know about Ranger's. It was plain, inside and out, and it didn't look very inviting. But it was a place to let down your hair, to be left alone to your thoughts. And Ranger's had very good music. James Galway, visiting with some friends, had played his flute there. When she was feeling well, Lake would get up. Her voice was nothing much, but people were always interested in seeing her. Linda Ronstadt had overcome her legendary shyness and warbled "I Never Will Marry." Nobody, but nobody ever asked for an autograph at Ranger's, and that was another one of the club's charms.

He parked his car and went inside. Karen was waiting, reading a script. She looked up. "Hello, Harry." She closed the script and slipped it into her briefcase.

The waitress came over, wearing a New York Rangers jersey. "Hello, Mr. Townsend. What can I get for you?"

"Just some coffee, thanks." It was eleven o'clock in the morning. Karen and Harry had taken to meeting at Ranger's when they had to talk about things they didn't want other people to know about. Which was Lake.

He waited for the coffee to come before he spoke. "You picked her up today?"

"Yes."

"How did she seem?"

"She seemed fine," Karen sighed tiredly. "Lake always seems fine when she goes away for a while. It doesn't seem to matter whether it's a nut farm or a health spa. She's fine as long as somebody looks after her constantly. I just like picking her up from the spas better. The shrinks always try to analyze me: Tell me, Mzzz. Zinger." She put on a phony Viennese accent. "How do you really feel about your friend'zzz prrroblemz?"

Harry smiled briefly. "But she seemed okay?"

"Yes. She asked me why you couldn't come get her."

"I called her yesterday; I said I'd see her tonight. She said she understood." He sipped his coffee.

Karen shrugged. "Maybe she forgot. Harry, why didn't you stop her from doing that awful film?"

"You know how she felt about not being able to do *Maiden Voyage*. George rushed her into doing that movie with that French director so the audience wouldn't forget about her and so the industry wouldn't think she was incapable of working. Okay, so it wasn't exactly art."

"It was pornographic."

"It was controversial," Harry argued. "Maybe the critics hated it, but the public came out in droves to see it."

"They came to see Silky Shaugnessy take her clothes off."

"Who cares!" His voice rose. "She's box office, and that's damned important in this business. *You* be the artist; see how far it gets you." He fell silent.

"Not very far, I guess." While Lake had been off doing her "controversial" film, Karen had gone to New York and done an Off-Broadway musical. The show had been brilliant, all the performances sparkling, and the reviews would have packed them in if they'd ever gone to press. The opening of the show had coincided with a newspaper strike. The musical had languished, and died three days before the papers came back. Karen had returned to L.A. in a very subdued mood. She'd had great hopes for that show. It was very hard for her to get work in L.A. because George had quietly had her blacklisted, and he was a very powerful man. Sid had done his best to get George to let up, but it was no use. Harry hadn't even tried very hard. He had a three-picture deal with George, and he didn't want to invoke the man's wrath and upset his own house of cards.

Harry found himself going to every new film with a growing sense of dread. Every time he turned around, there was some new leading man the papers were trumpeting about. A "young" Harry Townsend, they would say. Before he had made it, Harry reflected, his life had been relatively simple. Now that he had actually achieved that elusive goal he'd pursued for so long, there were a hundred things to worry about. He had to take care of himself—keep the body hard, the eyes clear, the face relatively unlined. He had to make sure that he wasn't allowing himself to be overexposed—nothing bred contempt like too many magazine covers—and he had to make sure that he was kept in the public eye just enough. Recognizable but not accessible. He had to choose the right scripts, do the correct talk shows, appear at the correct functions, and pray the public's love affair with him didn't just blow over because somebody else came along.

"I'm sorry, Karen. I feel like a tightrope walker these days. I thought this was going to be a lot more fun than it is."

"Baloney. You're having fun." She grinned. "You're just scared to admit it."

"The most important thing is still my friends. Like you, kiddo."

Her smile faded. "Sometimes I don't feel like your friend, Harry. I feel like your go-between. You can't go on this way; you know it. Sooner or later push will come to shove and you're going to have to choose."

"I'll take later." He leaned in a little, lowering his voice, even though they were practically alone. "I don't want to divorce Chris and let my little girl grow up without a daddy."

"Then stop seeing Lake."

Harry's face was set in a hard line. "I can't. Is my relationship with Lake unimportant compared to yours because it's not chaste?"

"No, Harry. But my relationship with Lake doesn't encompass my cheating on my husband." Her anger flared, and he could actually see her fighting to control it. "We *are* friends, but this thing hangs between us. I wish I had never found out. I feel like an accomplice."

"You're not."

"Would Chris think so?" She looked at him guiltily. "Even if you and Lake can go on this way, I'm not sure I can. I'm sorry, I don't think I should help you out like this anymore."

"It's easy for you, Kar, isn't it?" he cut in. "Everything worked out just fine. Well, if you were in love with somebody other than your husband, you'd be just like everybody else. It wouldn't be in a neat little package anymore. You'd spend your whole day scheming; how can I see him? How can I arrange to be with him this time? You'd see—you'd act just like the immoral lot of us out here in the real world. You've been lucky, so you can act high and mighty with me. You better believe you'd be different if you were in love with somebody else."

"I suppose you're right, Harry," she said tonelessly. "I'd better go. I promised Chris I'd stop by for a visit this afternoon. You and Lake have a nice evening."

He paid for the coffee and followed her to the parking lot. "Karen, don't be mad at me. I've come to a decision. I just didn't want you in this any deeper than you already are."

She studied his face closely. "You're going to leave Chris."

He nodded.

"Oh, Harry," she burst out, "how can I make you see what a terrible mistake you're making?"

His voice was cold. "Don't even try." He turned away and got into his car.

Chris looked up from the table, where she was trying to deal with a wriggling two-year-old. "Oh, hi," she said to Karen, seeing her at the screen door. "Come on in. Just trying to get the princess to eat."

"No mas!" Roseanne yelped, flopping out of her chair. She trotted out the door and into the yard to play.

"I've got to start hiring people who speak English," Chris groaned. "I can't deal with a bilingual kid. Coffee?"

"Thanks. Roseanne gets prettier every day."

"She does, doesn't she?" Chris beamed. "Don't get me started; I'll drag out the family album and bore you to tears. I must have something around here to go with the coffee. I'm constantly dieting, but I'm sure I could scare up a cookie . . ."

"Don't bother. How's the store doing?"

"Oh, Jackie practically runs the place, although I still do all the buying. I don't like being away from the kid." As if to give weight to her words, she went over to the screen door to check on Roseanne. She shook her head in wonder. "It doesn't matter how many you have, every child is a small miracle. You know, I didn't become a businesswoman until my first marriage broke up. The kids were grown; I honestly couldn't figure out what to do with myself. The last thing I expected was to be successful. Then Harry came along, and here I am, back to square one and loving it even more than the first time." She laughed self-consciously. "Must sound pretty silly to a real businesswoman like you. I envy you, Karen, I really do."

Karen smiled. "There's a pro and con to everyone's life. I don't have a cute little person throwing her arms around my neck and saying 'I love you, Mommy.' "

Chris sipped her coffee. "That's the nicest feeling in the world, Karen. Don't wait too long to have a child. Take my word for it, I'm a little too old for this particular gig." She pushed her cup away. "Lake got out today, didn't she? How is she?"

"She's just fine." Karen sipped incautiously and scalded her tongue. She was never sure just how much Chris suspected.

"Poor girl. She never seems to get well completely."

"Well, Lake is very high-strung. She just needs vacations periodically."

"Checking yourself into a rest home every six months is not a vacation. I feel sorry for her, I really do."

"Mommy!" Roseanne shot through the door, clutching a fistful of dirt. "Look!" She thrust her grimy fist at her mother, displaying a pale worm burrowing among her small fingers. "Auntie Karen, look!"

"Oh, you remember my name now, fickle-pickle." Karen hoisted the child onto her lap.

"Don't," Chris protested, "she's filthy."

"I love dirt," Karen said blithely. "Mud's better, but dirt will do in a pinch. Roseanna-banana, Mr. Worm has to go back outside."

Roseanne gave the classic response. "Why?"

"Because he has work to do."

"Why?"

"Because he's got to make little holes in the ground so the rain can reach all the flowers down where the roots are."

"It's not raining," Roseanne informed her.

"There you have me, Roseanne," Karen admitted.

"Out." She squirmed out of Karen's lap and ran outside.

"You're good with her," Chris said. "You and Matt should have a baby. I think your urge to look after people is a terrifically strong, totally misguided maternal instinct."

Karen laughed. "Spoken like a devoted mother. I'm just not ready."

Chris was slowly turning her wedding band around, her face soft and thoughtful. "How did she look?"

"Lake?" Now it was Karen's turn to squirm, wishing she was outside in the dirt. "She looked beautiful, the way she always does."

"Do you really think she'll be all right?"

"Well, sure."

"You know, Harry really feels for that girl. I think he feels guilty because she couldn't do *Voyage,* and he feels it would have made her a big star. At least she wouldn't have had to take her clothes off. God, that was a horrible film she did. I do feel sorry for her myself." She nodded slowly, the wedding band slipping on and off her finger. "I've never seen anybody who's so truly self-destructive and yet terrified of really going down the tubes. Such an unhappy person. You know that special glass they put on the limos, so you can look out but nobody can see in? She lives in a little cubicle made of that special glass. She can see everybody on the outside, but nothing can reach her, not light, not warmth. Oh, I do feel sorry for her." Chris put her hand up to her mouth. "I'm sorry. I know how close you are with Lake. I didn't mean to insult her."

"No, you're very perceptive."

"But tactless as all get-out." Chris was complacent. "Let's face it, it's easy to feel like the wise woman of the village when you've got everything you've ever wanted. Give me time, I'll learn to keep my valuable opinions to myself. It's just . . . oh, there's something about Lake that makes you want to make it all better. Like I would for Roseanne. You know, kiss the hurt and make it go away. I always felt she was holding me at arm's distance, but I did want to be friends."

And wouldn't Harry just love that? Karen thought.

"Well, I'm not going to lose any sleep over that." Her smile was open and genuine. "I look at my life, and I can't believe how good God's been to me. I keep waiting for somebody to pull the rug out from under my feet. You know?"

Karen said she knew.

"When my first husband said he wanted out, I thought I'd lose my mind. You don't. You go on, and maybe you find somebody else to love. Usually you don't find somebody else. I think you only get one chance at the kind of love you read about in books. So you go on alone and try not to get too sour. Harry really saved me. I love him more than my own life."

"That's the way it should be," Karen said numbly. Keeper of the sacred secrets was starting to look like a lousy job. "Chris?"

Chris went over by the door, watching her daughter play. "Hmmm?"

Karen was silent.

"Yes?" Chris turned to look at her. "Did you say something?"

Karen lost her nerve. Let Harry destroy his wife's fool's paradise; Karen would stay out of it. "Nothing."

Chris was beaming again, awash in love for her little girl. "Come see this." She waved Karen over to the door. "She's so cute when she's playing."

Karen stammered something about having to leave.

"I didn't expect you." Lake was digging in her yard. She'd had a landscaper set up a little garden for her.

"I told you I'd be by tonight."

"It's four o'clock in the afternoon, Harry." She got up and went inside her house.

"I'm going to ask Chris for a divorce," he called after her. "Did you hear me? I said I'm going to ask Chris for a divorce. My God, that's the first time I've said it out loud."

"Are you sure about this?" She sank onto the couch.

He felt like laughing. "I thought you'd be happy. Isn't this what you want?"

"I want *you.* What I don't want is for you to resent me for breaking up your marriage and taking you away from your child."

"It's not you," he said wearily, "it's me. I'm not in love with Chris. I've stayed with her because I was so damn sure she'd fall apart without me. Well, she won't. She's a strong lady. Besides, Carnelian is going great guns; she and Jackie are buddies. As for Roseanne, it was going to hurt her no matter when it happened. This way she'll have plenty of time to get used to the idea. Kids are very adaptable."

He took Lake's hand and rubbed it against his jaw. "I love you. Only you. And I want to be with you always."

I'm home free, Lake thought joyfully. At long last everything will be okay. And it wasn't the lying everything-will-be-okay that cocaine whispered in your ear so insidiously. This was for real. Gratefully she crept into his arms and made herself a little nest there. "That's all I've ever wanted. To take care of you and me and do nothing else. I'll get fat and lazy."

He rubbed her slender hip. "I'd like you fat. I can just imagine you with a big belly and six chins. I'll eat you up."

Her big eyes regarded him steadily. "It's really going to happen? You're really going to be with me forever?"

"Forever," he agreed. "Lake? Tell me what it was like in the hospital."

"It's not exactly a hospital. It's just where everybody goes when they get tired or scared, or they can't handle whatever they've been shooting up or snorting."

He stroked her hair gently. "What was it like?"

"It's like a hotel, except they don't give you knives to cut your food with and you have to go talk to the doctor every day."

"Were the doctors nice?"

"They're all right." She shrugged. "I never could tell them anything important. I have secrets that I could never tell anyone, especially the doctors." She looked at Harry suspiciously. "Why do you want to know?"

"Because I'm curious. You always get better when you go away. I want to know what they did to make you feel better so I can take care of you."

"You take care of me better than the doctors." She kissed him quickly. "I'm okay now, Harry. Now that things are different between us, I'll be just fine."

He had to admit he had never seen her looking more beautiful than she did at that moment. Her eyes were clear, the blue even darker than he remembered. Her face was relaxed, mouth ever so slightly open. She looked as if a bad thing had never happened to her, as if her life had been easy and full of happiness.

But he knew different. He knew the truth of her life was full of dark demons that haunted her relentlessly, forcing her to shut them out any way she could—drugs, drinking, hard nights with any man she could find to take the taste of nightmares out of her brain. He knew these things, and he was not revolted. What bothered him was the fact that she kept the source of her pain a secret from him. He loved her. He wanted to know everything. No matter how horrifying it was, he would not turn away from her in disgust.

She seemed to know what he was thinking. "Don't try to figure me out, Harry. I am the only way I can be." She unbuttoned his shirt, pulling it free from his jeans. Her lips pressed against his bare chest.

"One day you'll tell me everything."

She pulled away. "No," she said quietly, and something in her voice told him never to bring it up again.

By ten o'clock that evening Ranger's was hopping. The piano player danced his fingers over the keys, people chattered, deals were being made. Karen was back, sitting at a table with Sid. Matt was busy that night, editing a new film, and Karen felt that if she stayed home alone, she'd scream.

"Sing something for me," Sid suggested. "I missed your show, and I just realized now that I've never heard you sing. Go on. There's nobody here but sixty of the most important people in the business." He gave her a little push. "Go on, dear one. You have absolutely nothing to lose but the respect of your peers."

"Sid, I'm really not in the mood."

"I asked you to sing, not have sex with me."

"Sorry, not tonight—for either one."

Sid got up and went over to the piano player. The musician nodded, grinning. Before Sid had returned to his seat, the piano player had introduced Karen and started a round of applause going for her.

"Thanks a lot," Karen said under her breath. "I'm not dressed for this, I'm totally unprepared—"

"You look fine. That's extremely important if you're planning to fall on your face. Go on, darling, everybody's waiting."

Reluctantly she walked up to the piano player, and they conferred. He played the intro to "Cry Me a River."

Sid sat back and listened. Her voice was very good, soft and husky with a sweet, hollow resonance that made him want to cry. All around the room people were listening attentively. She'll get a break from this, Sid thought confidently, no matter how much muscle George tries to exert. He leaned back and enjoyed her singing, eyes closed.

Suddenly he realized she'd lost the audience. They were restless; he could hear them turning around in their seats, shifting. He opened his eyes and swiveled around.

Lake Eastman was standing in the doorway dressed in her usual drop dead style, a gold mesh halter and tight black pants. Harry Townsend stood at her side. She was trying in vain not to draw attention to herself, but it was no use. People were talking openly. Lake was back from the nut farm, and didn't she look good for somebody who was slowly cracking up? Maybe being looney tunes was good for the complexion. The chatter became louder.

Karen stopped singing. "Ladies and gentlemen," she said into the microphone, "please help me welcome my good friend Lake Eastman back into our midst. Lake, we missed you."

Embarrassed, Lake came up to the microphone. She started to sing "My Heart Belongs to Daddy." Her voice sounded tinny and flat, but she threw the song out to Harry, making a little scene out of it. The crowd seemed to love it. Most of them knew about Lake's affair, but they had never seen her be so open about it.

As Karen returned to her seat, she caught Harry looking at her with thinly disguised sympathy. "Don't you dare pity me," she snapped at him.

He threw his hands in the air helplessly and went over to the bar. Lake finished her song to hearty applause and joined Karen and Sid.

"Lake, can I bring you a club soda?" asked Sid.

"Thank you." She smiled at him gratefully, watching him go off to the bar. "Sid's a good person, but I'll always feel uncomfortable around him. Karen, I'm sorry about that—"

"Forget it. It wasn't your fault."

Lake smiled brightly. "Harry's going to get a divorce."

"I can't be happy about that, but I am happy for you." Karen squeezed Lake's hand. "You really do look wonderful."

"Thank you. Kar—" Her eyes flickered for a moment. "I'm going to do another movie. No—" She laughed, seeing Karen's expression. "Not like my last one. I know how you felt about that. I've got a reputation as a troublemaker, Karen. I had to do something that was guaranteed to do well at the box office or nobody would touch me with a ten-foot pole. Well now they're all dying to talk to me, crazy as a bedbug or not, because I'm a moneymaker. Kar, I want to do something good. I want you to write me a script."

"George won't produce anything I write; he hates me."

"You could submit it under a different name."

"Eventually he'd find out, and you can imagine the problems then."

"Maybe somebody else could produce it. Maybe I will." Lake smiled. "Don't look so incredulous. I was a rich girl before I ever set foot in this business. I've got the money to do it if I want to. Write me a story, Karen. Write me a story about a pretty little girl whom everybody loves and nobody knows. Give it a happy ending. I live for them. Will you write that story for me?"

"All right," Karen said slowly. She had the feeling she was getting in way over her head, but something about Lake's words had started her thinking. She could almost feel the story happening in her mind, curling around the edges like a piece of paper when a match is touched to it. "Yes, I'll write it."

"Good." She started toying with a paper napkin, ripping it slowly into long strips. "Are you still writing to Johnny?"

"No."

"Why?"

Karen looked at her for a long time. "I don't know, Lake. You figure it out and tell me. Things just haven't worked out for me as smoothly as they have for you."

"You're making a big mistake, Kar," Lake said in her low voice. "You don't love Matt; maybe you never have."

"Maybe not," Karen said, "but he loves me, and I will not do to him what Harry's going to do to Chris."

"You're wrong," Lake argued. "You'll pay for your morality by spending the rest of your life with a man you don't love."

Karen's eyes began to fill with tears. "I understand what you're saying, and the truth in it sits in my heart like a stone. But if I did what you think I should do, it would taint my love for a very sweet man, and I would never be happy with him. Eventually the guilt would destroy anything we could have had together. I can't do it, Lake. We're very different, you and I."

"I know," Lake said quietly. "I didn't mean to make you feel bad. And I sure as hell didn't mean to ruin your song."

Karen collected herself, wiping her eyes on one of the paper napkin strips. "That's okay. You know when the cowboy says to the gunslinger, 'This town isn't big enough for the two of us'? Well, I get the funny feeling we can't both be successful actresses at the same time. Either you've got to be coming up and I'm going down or the other way around. I just don't think this town can take both of us at the same time."

"It's not that. George is making it difficult for you." Lake rubbed her big-knuckled hand. "I could talk to him; I could get him to lay off."

"If you want to." Karen couldn't disguise the longing in her voice.

She still wants it, Lake thought. She still wants it as badly as she ever did. Lake wasn't going to speak to George. She wanted to, for Karen's sake, but she did believe, as Karen did, that as Karen's star rose, her own would surely plummet. "It will happen for you," Lake said soothingly. "And when you finally make it to the top, you'll stay there for a long, long time." She attempted a light laugh. "And you won't have to do the shoddy things I have."

Sid came back with the sodas. Harry was still at the bar, having run into an acquaintance. "How's the reunion going?"

"Just fine!" Lake's voice was slightly brittle, a warning note, Sid thought. Karen's mascara looked like it had been through the wringer. Sid wondered how just fine things actually were. Lake excused herself. "I'd better rescue Harry. Kar, you won't forget about my story?"

"No, I won't."

Lake went over to the bar. She hung on Harry's arm, laughing at something he said. They looked very happy.

"Are you all right?" Sid asked Karen.

She nodded, looking like she wanted to cry.

"Why don't you call Matt? Maybe he's through editing by now."

"No, he'll work all night." She hid her face in her hands. "God help me, Sid, I see them together, and all I can think is that it shouldn't be working out. He's married, and I was taught infidelity is wrong. I believed it. I have been a good and faithful wife, Sid, and I am *alone.* I am alone a lot of the time, and I don't feel Matt loves me as much as he loves his work. I have lived by the rules, and my life is empty. Lake does everything I was taught is wrong, and she's got it all—an acting career and the man she loves. How can it be that way?"

"Because, my dear," Sid said softly, "life is strange, life is wonderful, but it is rarely just. You've got a right to be upset right now, but when you come to yourself, you'll realize you don't envy Lake. Not really."

"You're wrong, I do," she said very seriously.

"No, you don't," he chided, offering her his handkerchief. "You'll go on just as you have been. You'll do your best, and you'll live by your own rules. You'll forgive when you can and try not to take your own disappointments too hard. You're a good person, Karen, and I believe that counts for something in this world. I depend on it."

Karen blew her nose. "I do, too."

They wound up closing up the place. Karen and Sid talked for hours. They were both hoarse when the bartender came over and said it was last call, could he get the swingers two more sodas?

Karen went over to the piano player to thank him.

"I wish you'd gotten to finish your tune," he said regretfully. "You sing sweet as an angel. You got style like they had when I was starting out. When I started out, women wore silk stockings. That tells you how far back I go."

"You must have seen a lot of changes."

"I have." He nodded his gray head. "I have seen more than I care to. I played just about every kind of place there is. In the thirties I played the Cotton Club in Harlem. They wouldn't let my momma come in and hear me play. Five years ago I played Phantom's, just a few blocks away, and I saw a black woman dancing with a white man. Everybody smiling at them. Never thought I'd see that. Phantom's was a good place. My good friend Ernest Rich was the proprietor of that establishment. Tomorrow I am going back to New York to bury my friend Ernest."

"I'm so sorry," Karen said respectfully. "Stroke?"

"Somebody killed my friend," he mourned, his fingers stroking the keys in a minor vein. "Who'd want to kill a poor old blind man?"

22

NOT MANY PEOPLE attended the funeral service and burial of the Phantom-man, née Ernest Rich. Murder has a way of making people feel edgy. A lot of working girls were there, some the Phantom had employed, some he had not. And there were a few plainclothes detectives. It *was* a murder after all, and kooks had a habit of coming around to admire their handiwork. It was an interesting-looking assembly: the representatives of the finest in jazz, even a black professor from Cornell, whom, it was whispered, was the only living relative of the Phantom-man. There was even a young, pretty black woman who was making a name for herself in rock and roll, looking demure without her customary leather.

The weather had taken a quick, nasty turn. The sunshine of the previous day had given way to gray, windy gusts. Although it wasn't really cold, people had dug out their heavy raincoats. Bleakly they stood around, commenting that summer was at long last gone for good. Latecomers began to struggle toward the burial site, among them a young man with startlingly beautiful eyes and a white streak in his hair.

The plainclothes man in the car turned to the detective sitting next to him. "Is that the guy?"

"Yes."

"Are you sure, Brooks?"

"Positive."

Some wept. Almost all were angry and scared. The Phantom, though he professionally catered to the vices of man, had, in his personal life, been a decent man. He did not judge, and he did not condemn. He had kept his own counsel, he had stayed out of people's way, and he had minded his own business. According to all the laws of city life, Ernest Rich should have died in his bed some ten years or so in the future.

People began to drift away. They were anxious to return to the world of the living. The whores were the last to leave. And the man with the white streak in his hair. He stayed to the end, supporting himself with a cane.

"Johnny?" A big lady with a hard set to her mouth and tears in her eyes tentatively approached him. "Is that you? Jeez, I thought I recognized you."

"Hello, Charmaine. I'm glad to see you. Just wish it was under happier circumstances."

"Don't we all." She dabbed at her eyes. "God, it's so awful sad. That man was so decent to us. They always take the good ones. You got time to have a drink with me? I don't feel like going home while I'm still so upset."

Gallantly he offered her his arm. "I'd be honored to have a drink with a good-looking broad like you."

"You're still the same old Johnny." She linked her arm through his. "Always knew the right thing to say."

They walked until they found a little bar just far enough away from the cemetery so they didn't have to think about it.

Charmaine had a Bloody Mary, because it was still pretty early, and Johnny had a beer. She looped her raincoat over the back of her chair, revealing a worn black V-neck sweater and a black straight skirt that was a little too tight and a little too short. It wrinkled slightly over her belly.

She smiled at Johnny, covering a lull. "You got so thin. I wish I had that problem." It was very evident they didn't have a whole lot to say to each other. Mostly, whenever Charmaine had seen Johnny, he'd been on his way to get laid or coming back from having been laid. It didn't make for easy conversation. What could she say? "You doing okay?"

"Fine."

"You still acting?"

"No, I'm sort of taking a little time off. I got a bartending job."

"Yeah?" She looked interested. "They know they got a celebrity working for them?"

"I'm not much of a celebrity anymore. Don't look so sad, Charmaine. It is what it is." He wasn't drinking much of the beer, just letting it get flat in front of him. "Charmaine, do you think the cops have any leads on this? Anything at all?"

"They wouldn't say shit to us. What are we but a bunch of dumb whores? Personally I think they got nothing. Why would they still be picking up people if they knew anything? Who would want to kill poor Ernie? He was such a sweet guy—didn't owe a cent, never said a bad word about anybody. It's just like Candy, they never found that guy, either."

"Nobody got a good look at him, Catwoman, any of the other girls?"

"Christ, Johnny. All I remember is he wore a nice suit and he looked all right. Who looks at faces? He even had a membership card, but it turned out to be a phony. If Catwoman remembers more than I do, she's keeping it to herself. So that leaves Candy, and she's not talking."

Suddenly he didn't want to talk about the Phantom-man anymore. "What are you going to do, Charmaine?"

She sniffled. "Oh, I got a friend in Vegas. She says business is good. Besides, I'd sure as hell prefer Vegas to Atlantic City. They got dry heat in Nevada. I'm not going to hang around here. What about you?"

"I've got no plans. I guess I'll just keep on doing what I've been doing."

She gave him a long, searching look. "You think about it a lot? You think about that night you got hurt?" She took his right hand, the bad one, in hers.

"I try not to, but it has a nasty habit of creeping in there," he admitted. "It doesn't matter what I'm doing. Sometimes I'm at work, and everything is going along fine. Then I start remembering, and I get so . . ."

"Scared," she supplied.

"Yeah, so scared I don't think I can breath. The worst is when I dream. I see myself like I was before, and everything's fine."

She smiled. "That sounds nice."

"But then I wake up." His face was bitter. "I can't run, I can't do shit with my right hand, I lost most of the sight in my left eye. I owe a lot of money to doctors, and just about every friend I had in the world has turned away from me."

"You're still alive," she said stonily "and that's something, take my word for it. You'll get over what you're feeling, unless you need to be scared more than you need to get on with your life. Don't let anybody out there kid you. When somebody hurts you—I'm not talking heartache bullshit, I mean *hurts* you, with their hands or a knife—it really breaks your spirit. I know, Johnny.

I've had my share. You'll be okay, and you'll get over this, because the alternative sucks and you've always been a pretty smart guy." She patted his shoulder reassuringly. "I know you'll be okay."

For some absurd reason he felt like crying. For his own sweet body, which would never be the same, for the Phantom-man, who'd been good to the working girls, for Sam Tyler, the bartender who had saved his life. He'd sworn he was going to keep in touch with the man, but his resolve had vanished when he'd gotten out of the hospital. Tyler had moved himself and his family back to Louisiana, where he was from. "Charmaine," he said with a quirky smile, "life's a tragedy." Then he winked at her.

She winked back. "I'm not going to waste my time worrying about you. You're gonna be fine. How come you never asked for me? Huh? I don't mean to brag, but an old girl like me puts those young broads to shame. They just don't know how to move it nice. You should have tried me one night."

"I fucked up." They both started laughing. "You take care of yourself, Charmaine. I hear Vegas can be pretty tough."

"Nah, I worked Pittsburgh. I thought the weather alone would kill me. And there's no theater. I like you artsy-fartsy types." She shrugged into her coat; he helped her. "Be well, Johnny. You were a little shit sometimes, but you were always nice to the girls." She gave him a big hug then clacked away on her spike heels.

The waitress came around and asked him if he wanted another beer. He decided against it and ordered a coffee. She brought it quickly and stood there, staring at him while he poured milk into his cup. "Yes?" he asked mildly.

"Oh." She flushed. She was pretty, not yet twenty. "You look sorta familiar, but I can't quite place it. Sorry for staring." She went back to the bar, hoping for a profitable lunch crowd. She hated working so close to a cemetery and was thinking about finding another job. Yawning, she went into the kitchen to flirt with the cook.

"Mr. Allison? Do you remember me?"

Johnny looked up. He nodded slowly. "Oh, yes. Detective Brooks, right?"

"That's very good. Most people wouldn't remember a name for two years. May I join you?"

"Detective Brooks, please don't take this personally, but the last time I saw you, I told you I never wanted to see your charming face again. I meant it."

Brooks sat down. "It'll just take a minute." He was a stocky black of about forty, high cheekbones hinting at some Indian blood a few generations back in his family. He was a smart man, a little too proud, but he'd paid a lot of heavyweight dues, and the pride had helped him keep it together. It bothered the hell out of him when he could not conclude an investigation to his liking. He had been the investigating officer in the stabbing death of a whore named Candy. There'd been one reliable eyewitness: John Allison. The two whores, Charmaine and Catwoman, swore all their clients looked alike. Sure enough, they had picked different men out of a police lineup, one of them a homicide detective.

The only thing the two whores agreed upon was that Candy had been wearing a cheap little necklace the night she was killed, a heart-shaped locket, which had not been found on her body. No doubt Candy's locket and John Allison's Equity card had gone home with the killer. This only served to irritate the detective further. Somewhere out there the evidence he needed to put away a murderer was hiding. Without the evidence, Brooks had nothing but two flighty whores and Allison. Brooks hoped Allison was capable of identifying the man. But Allison, for his own reasons, had not, and Brooks, having no other clues, had looked him up periodically until Allison had disappeared on him. On a wild hunch Brooks had gambled that the former actor would turn up at the funeral.

The waitress came by and brought Brooks a menu. Johnny took the menu out of his hand and gave it back to the girl. "No, no, he isn't staying."

"Just coffee," Brooks said.

"Am I under any legal obligation to talk to you?" Johnny wanted to know.

"No. I'm not here on official business."

"Then why are you here?"

Brooks took a memo pad out of his pocket and started doodling. His coffee came. He thanked the girl and waited until she was out of earshot. "I just want to talk to you, to have a little talk with you about human nature. Mr. Allison, you have any idea how a psychopath functions?"

"I hear they doodle on memo pads a lot, Detective Brooks."

"Well, we got all these shrinks and experts to tell us how they function, and it comes down to this—none of those college birds knows jack shit about anything. Lunatics follow their own patterns, and sometimes it takes a while to figure out what that pattern is." He kept on doodling, drawing a big open eye. "Fox is my man.

I can feel it, but I can't prove it. Everything fits. He had a history. Did you know about Mr. Fox's interesting history?"

"I think you told me."

"He assaulted his girlfriend. Locked her up in a closet. She made out a complaint; he jumped her in her own apartment, tried to rape her. Luckily her roommate came home early from a date and called the cops. The roommate held him at knifepoint until the cops arrived. Off Fox goes to jail, where he is a model prisoner. He gets out early for good behavior and turns his prison experience into an Off-Broadway play, which I understand did pretty good. Did you see that play, Mr. Allison?"

"No," he said sullenly. "Fox wasn't the one. I told you that two years ago, and I'm telling you now. I've talked to shrinks; I've done my own reading up. It is highly unlikely that a man who victimizes women would suddenly do a complete turnaround and attack a man."

"Ah," Brooks said softly, "but you were a witness, Mr. Allison. That's why he had to kill you." He tucked the memo pad back inside the suit jacket. "I made a mistake. I didn't check Fox's prior record myself; I had somebody do it for me. So I never knew the names of the girlfriend or her roommate. I remedied that. The girlfriend was Lake Eastman. You must have heard of her.

"The roommate got married. Her name is Karen Singer. Do you remember a man named Sam Tyler? Used to be a bartender at Phantom's. He positively identified Karen Singer as the woman who was with you the night you were attacked."

"I told you nobody was with me."

"Could be you lied, Mr. Allison."

"No," he struggled, knowing how harebrained this was going to sound. "We were there together earlier. Then I took Mrs. Singer home and I went back."

"Why didn't you tell me about the woman sooner?"

"Because she had nothing to do with what happened to me."

"She might have seen something."

"She didn't."

"You sound very sure," Brooks told him. "You better pray the killer is as sure as you are. There's nothing to stop him from paying her a little visit, is there?"

"It's been two years," Johnny argued. "Why should this guy even be around two years later?"

"Who do you think killed Ernest Rich, Mr. Allison?"

"I have no idea."

"Do you think it could be the same man who tried to kill you?"

"I have no idea." He got up clumsily, reaching for his cane. "It's been good seeing you again, Detective Brooks. Don't be a stranger."

"I know it was Fox," the detective repeated. "All you have to do is give me a statement. I can guarantee you protection, John, if I have to look after you myself. All you have to do is say it was him."

"I told you." Johnny's voice rose dangerously. "It wasn't Fox."

"You said it looked like him."

"Maybe he has a twin brother." His fingertips brushed the cane. It fell with a loud clatter.

Brooks bent and retrieved it. "He's an only child. I checked." He held out the cane.

Johnny looked at him helplessly. "What I told you was the truth. The man who attacked me was not Fox. I thought it was at first; that's why I followed him outside. It was not Daniel Fox. The man who attacked me was somebody I had never seen before. You've hounded me for two years. Please, believe what I've told you is the truth."

"You said you weren't sure it was Fox," Brooks went on inexorably.

"Yes, I remember saying that after an all-night session with your charming self."

"Are you sure it wasn't?"

He started to laugh softly. "You're a pip, detective."

"I think Fox paid you not to identify him."

Johnny walked out the door and kept going. He just wanted to go home.

Katie was crying. "I thought you'd be surprised," she sobbed. "I just wanted to make you ha-ha-happy!" Her words dissolved into a long, drawn-out wail.

I'm not in the mood for this, Johnny thought, searching his apartment for a Kleenex. His little discussion with Brooks had really shot his nerves. He'd been sure someone was following him home. By the time he'd convinced himself that such a thing was highly unlikely, he had discovered Katie in his locked apartment, happily making herself at home.

He ripped off a yard or two of toilet paper and handed that

to her. "You shouldn't have let yourself in, Katie. You scared the shit out of me. I thought you were a burglar." She was still howling. "Jesus, Katie, you know I had to go to a funeral this morning. I was freaked. I'm sorry I yelled at you. I didn't mean it."

Katie sniffled. "Yeah . . . well, let's just forget about the whole thing. Right?" She blew her nose and smiled at him sunnily. "I got us a nice dinner cooking. Roast beef with the little potatoes that cook in the pan. When was the last time you had a real roast beef dinner like that?"

That table was set with a rainbow of paper goods, bright purple paper plates clashing merrily with a lime green paper tablecloth. Katie had obviously gone to a great deal of trouble to create a festive mood, but it didn't seem particularly cheery. It all looked so sad that he wanted to cry. "Katie, you shouldn't have done this."

"Why not?"

"You shouldn't have spent all this money—"

"What money?" She shrugged. "Spiros gave me a little bonus; I smiled at the creep or something. Now don't give me a speech, Louie. Why shouldn't I take advantage of Spiros? The roast has got another twenty minutes. Why don't you shower, relax a little. You look like you could use it. By the time you finish drying your hair, I'll have supper on the table."

He went into the bedroom, pulling his shirt over his head and tossing it into a corner. He stretched out on his bed in his T-shirt and jeans. In the kitchen Katie was humming as she worked. She sounded very happy.

I let this thing go too far, he thought with a pang. But R. Louie was a lonely guy, and he needed her. Correction: he needed somebody, and somebody was far away and very married. R. Louie had had hard times, and he just wanted somebody to look after him.

He felt very sleepy. In the moment just before he fell asleep, he had a brief flash of pure clarity of thought. He felt he knew the one thing that Brooks had overlooked in his investigation. He felt he knew, with a grave and beautiful certainty, who the killer was. Then he fell asleep and forgot about the whole thing.

"Louie? Dinner's ready." Katie stood at the foot of the bed watching him sleep. "Hey, sleeping beauty." She shook him gently. He groaned and flipped over onto his back.

Katie felt she was in a unique situation. She stroked his hair, feeling how thick and soft it was. She explored his crippled hand, noting the ragged, dead white scar in the center of his palm. Someday she'd ask him about that. She traced the scar that notched his brow. Even in his sleep he jerked away from her. "Poor Louie." Gently, so as not to wake him, she stretched out alongside him, prying her shoes off and letting them drop to the floor. She aimed well; they hit the rug and barely clunked. "What are you dreaming about?" she whispered. "Are you dreaming of me?" By inching over she was able to rest her head on his shoulder. After that first Sunday at the movies, they'd gone out a few times. Always friendly, always a good time. He had never kissed her, except for a brotherly peck. Fear of rejection had kept her from pushing it further. Besides, Louie was a gimp; maybe he had other problems she didn't even *want* to know about. Right now, lying next to him, she was feeling bold. She was in his house, and her dinner was cooking in his oven. She knew where he kept his pots and pans. In some countries that meant a couple was engaged.

She wondered if he could kiss in his sleep. Eyes closed, she pressed her lips against his. He wasn't terribly responsive. She slipped her hand under his T-shirt and stroked his chest. Her hand moved downward. Through his jeans she could feel his erection. She rubbed gently, and this time you better believe he was responsive. Nothing wrong with him there. That's more like it, she thought smugly. No matter who you were dealing with, men were men, and sex was the constant whether it was Spiros or sweet Louie.

She pushed herself closer, throwing her leg across his hip, feeling her own need now. "Oh," she whispered against his ear, "I love you, Louie, I really do."

His eyes opened, and they were so full of love that she thought she would die of happiness, just break apart into a zillion little glass shards. Then the last bit of sleep wore off, and he was staring at her like he'd never seen her before. Like she was some stranger he'd just caught with her hand down his pants. Katie had had a crush on a boy once, a boy who worked part time in a home for girls. One day she'd heard him laughing with his friends, saying how the older girls in the home were so horny, they'd grab your privates if you stood still for more than a minute. Katie had cringed because she knew exactly how those girls had felt. She understood the hunger, the need to be loved so badly that you'd do anything, any base, low, stupid thing just so somebody would want you.

Anything at all.

He didn't move. He just lay there blinking at her.

In for a penny . . . She tried to kiss him again. This time he pulled away. "Katie, I think we should talk."

She turned away in anguish, but he put his hand on her shoulder and kept it there until she could look at him again.

"So? Let's talk." She smiled, but her voice was thick with tears.

"I let this go too far. I like you, Katie, I care about you a lot, but I don't think it's the way you want me to care about you."

"You're trying to say you don't love me. Is that it?"

He lowered his head. "Yes. I'm real sorry."

"Don't you think I know that?" Her tears fell. "I don't hope for much, Louie, just somebody who's kind. I know I pushed it, but you didn't seem to mind. I figured you were lonely enough to want somebody like me. Somebody who's nobody."

"You're not nobody."

She laughed bitterly. "Then what is it you don't like, Louie? Spiros thinks I'm okay. Maybe you don't want me, but he sure does. Maybe I'll just go to Spiros."

"Don't go to Spiros just to spite me. Katie, you have to be right with yourself before you can really love anyone else."

"That's a lie," she said deliberately, with such conviction that his little homily sounded as trite as it was. "Some people just come into the world as strays. Just like some people are born mean. I can't help what I am. I'm sorry if it's not good enough for you."

"That's not it, Katie."

She started to laugh. It built to a full bellow. "Tell me you got somebody else, Louie. Oh, that is rich. Dumped by a gimp. Even the cripples don't want me. Well, fuck you, Louie. I don't need you, either." She stormed to the door.

He didn't hear her go out. "Katie?" He limped to the door. She was quietly crying, leaning against the jamb. "We could still be friends, Katie, if you want to be. I could use a friend."

She gathered up what was left of her dignity. "Go to hell."

The roast beef burned, and he threw it out, along with all the paper stuff. It looked as if someone had thrown a birthday party and nobody had decided to show. Belatedly it occurred to him that he should have asked Katie how she'd gotten into his apartment. A quick examination proved his worst fears correct; anybody with a credit card and an IQ of six could gain admittance with a minimum of effort. Suddenly he had an uncontrollable desire to leave New York, just bolt like a frightened rabbit. Frequently of late he'd begun to feel that he was being followed, that nothing had resolved itself, and that the events of the past two years would be coming to a head very soon.

A new lock tomorrow morning at the latest, he swore.

He found a matchbook, ripped out the matches, and wedged the cover into the door, then locked it. If anyone came in while Johnny was out, the matchbook would fall unnoticed to the hallway floor. Not as good as a burglar alarm, but Johnny would know to sleep elsewhere that night.

He moved onto the street, plying his cane rhythmically. He realized he was very hungry and stopped in a McDonald's for a hamburger. It barely took the edge off his hunger. He kept walking, not sure where he was going until he got there. And then he laughed, shaking his head in gentle amusement, wondering what unanswered question had prompted him to show up at this particular address.

Much to the doorman's chagrin he walked up to the desk and asked him to buzz Albie Weiss.

"Who is it?" An unfamiliar young voice rang tinnily through the intercom. "Oh. Send him right up."

Albie had left the brownstone over a year before, and Mrs. Weiss had sent Johnny Albie's new address. He knocked, composing a little speech. *Hi, Albie. Sure has been a long time, hasn't it?* He checked out his reflection in the shiny doorknob, trying to neaten his hair.

The boy who opened the door was so beautiful he was unreal. His white-blond hair curled around his oval face. His soft, full mouth was coral kissed with rose. He was the Marilyn Monroe of boydom. He was also approximately fifteen. "Hi," he said breathlessly, "I'm Gideon. Like the Bible? Actually I've been Gideon for about a year now. I thought it would be so literary. People could call me Giddy for short. But of course nobody does. It's just too affected. Mostly they just call me Gideon. Or Goldie. Like Goldie Hawn?" He chewed on his full lower lip. "I'm babbling. Sorry. I'm just so tha-rilled to be meeting you at long last. Come in, come in!" He led Johnny into the apartment. Ertes prints were strongly in evidence, along with some lovely silk flower arrangements. Johnny suppressed a smile. *All a place needs is a woman's touch.*

Gideon curled up on the white leather sofa, eyeing him curiously. "I love the streak. Do you do anything to it, or does it just grow like that?"

"Just grows like that."

"Fabulous." He vaulted off the couch lightly. His pink feet

were bare. Johnny envied his freedom of movement. "Where are my manners? Would you like some coffee? Or a drink? Albie's got all sorts of fabulous things."

"Where is Albie?"

"At Zabar's. Albie's an absolute foodie. Why don't you have some coffee? I was going to put some on anyway, and it'll take forever for Albie to cab it crosstown. Please?" He smiled engagingly. "I just adore cooking for people. The domestic type, that's me."

"Coffee would be fine."

"Fabulous." Bare feet slip-slapped to the kitchen. "Keep me company? I hate to be alone when I cook." Again the magic smile, head tipped to one side, outstretched hand extended. Johnny lumbered to his feet and hobbled after the boy.

Gideon put water up to boil and started rummaging around in the refrigerator. "I'm too short to model, although Albie says I can do print work. I wouldn't mind doing movies, though. You did movies, didn't you? Are they fun? Do you like apple pie? We've got this *incredible* green apple and sour cream pie." He brought out half a pie, a box of crackers, three kinds of cheese, a small jar of caviar, some pâté, and a jar of cornichons, tiny sour gherkins. "The hostess with the mostess, don't you know," he remarked brightly, getting a tray and assembling their repast with much artistry. "I was always very curious about you."

"Why?"

"Weeelll." Gideon smiled secretively. "Albie simply doesn't stop talking about you. He adored you."

"Albie?"

"Who else, silly? He loved you so desperately, but you didn't love him back."

Johnny was mystified. "It never occurred to me that Albie was that way."

"You had to know. How could you not?"

Because I was too wrapped up in myself in those days to notice anything, Johnny admitted to himself.

The water boiled. Gideon poured it into a carafe with a plunger top. "Krups. Absolutely the best coffee, but it doesn't keep it warm very long. Nothing's perfect." Except me, Gideon's sweet smile seemed to imply. "See, I really love Albie, and I think I make him pretty happy, but sometimes I just know he's thinking about you. There's nothing I can do with him then. Well, I was just so curious about you." He pushed the plunger contraption, trapping the coffee grounds at the bottom. "I just wanted to know what the attraction was. He said I was prettier than you. Of course, now I understand." Slip-slap, his bare feet went back to the living room. Carrying his tray, Gideon looked like a slightly perverse angel. "Everybody wants what they can't have. Don't you think that's true?" He poured coffee, handing Johnny a cup.

"I don't know."

Gideon inspected his pink feet. "Does it hurt terribly? Your leg?"

"Sometimes. When it feels like pins and needles. No, I guess it doesn't really hurt anymore."

"But it did."

"Oh, yes. Hurt like hell."

The boy digested this information. "I've never been hurt in my whole life. It's a pity; I think suffering makes people stronger. Kind of noble. You're *terribly* noble. It practically shines from you. I know a couple of boys who'd simply die for you."

Johnny said he was very flattered but not interested.

"I know that," Gideon said. "Otherwise you'd be here with Albie and I'd be selling my ass on the street." He cut himself a piece of pie. "I'm not an idiot, you know. I genuinely love Albie, and if we broke up I'd be truly devastated. But I'd find a way, I'd manage; people do. I don't get real attached. It's not in me. I bet you get very attached. Are you in love with anybody right now?" The sound of a key in the lock distracted him. "Albie!" he squealed, racing to the door. Albie carried a big Zabar's bag in one hand and a few smaller packages in the other. Gideon swarmed all over him. "Did you bring me a little something? I've been terribly good."

Smiling, Albie handed him a small package. "You're always my good boy." He bent and kissed the precious lips, seeing for the first time his visitor waiting patiently in the living room.

Gideon was ripping into the package. It was a cashmere scarf in a soft coral. "Oh, perfect!" Gideon moaned, rubbing the scarf against his velvet cheek.

"Sweetheart," Albie said to Gideon, "would you mind if I spoke to Johnny alone?"

"I'd go to the movies if I had any pocket money." Gideon pouted.

Albie gave him enough money for all his pockets, and Gideon took off. Albie hung up his coat and sat down across from Johnny. "So." He looked down at his hands. "You all right?"

"I'm fine," Johnny assured him.

"I never expected to see you here."

"I'm kind of surprised myself." Johnny laughed. "I didn't plan to come here. I just started walking, and before I knew it, here I was."

"You talked to Gideon?"

"Oh, yeah. He's a sweet kid, a very interesting person." Johnny laughed self-consciously. He should never have come. "When did you move out of the brownstone?"

"Shortly after your accident."

"Albie, I never knew . . ."

"Why should you have?" A soft struggle went on behind his eyes. "I didn't know myself. I'm not one of the good-looking boys on Christopher Street. I thought I just enjoyed the company of other men. Companionship. There was one boy I cared about a good deal in college, but I outgrew that. I thought I had, anyway. Then I found you, Johnny." He smiled sadly. "And it was like a trap-door was opened, letting out all my feelings. I loved you, but I knew you would never understand that love. So I was always a little careful around you. And a little frightened that if I showed you too much, you would turn away from me in disgust and fear. Still, I loved you, and love makes idiots of us all, a little bit. I dreamed of the day when I would tell you how I felt. Part of that dream was your accepting me as I am." He touched the glass carafe. "This coffee is cold." He got up and carried it into the kitchen. He sat down again and picked up where he'd left off. "We delude ourselves, especially when it comes to the things we want. I refused to realize how hopeless my love for you was, until the night you got hurt. It wasn't my name you called out in your pain. It wasn't me you wanted. Not until that moment did I see how things really were. I had to turn my back on you to go on with my life."

"I needed you, Albie," Johnny said quietly, without accusation. "I really needed a friend, and I didn't understand why you didn't want anything to do with me anymore. I thought it was because I was crippled."

A shadow flickered across Albie's face. "No, that wasn't it."

Johnny didn't believe him. He thought of the beautiful boy who had taken his place. "Albie, I looked up to you. I trusted your judgment. I still do. I'm thinking of going back to acting. It's the only thing I really want to do with my life. I just wanted to ask your opinion about it. You think I have a shot?"

"Johnny, you can do anything you set your mind to."

He touched the white streak in his hair. "Gideon liked it."

"It's distinctive," Albie agreed. "Will the limp get any better?"

Tentatively he reached out and traced the thin line notching Johnny's eyebrow. "My poor boy," Albie murmured. His heavy hand rested on Johnny's forehead.

Embarrassed, Johnny pulled away. "I'm okay, Albie, honestly I am. I think I'm starting to get over it. Takes time." He got up clumsily. "Guess I should be going. You take care, Albie."

"You too, Johnny. Johnny?" Albie was reaching into his pocket. For a moment Johnny thought he was going to pull out another cashmere scarf. "You need any money?"

Johnny hesitated.

"Here, take it. It's the least I can do." He patted Johnny's shoulder. "Hey, maybe I'll give you a hand getting your career started. Like old times, hmmm?" In his smile was the ghost of hope, grinning slavishly. Oh, yes, Johnny thought, we always want what we can't have, and I'm no different from him.

"That's okay, Albie. It's time I did for myself. Thanks, anyway." But he did accept the money. He went into a phone booth on the street to count it. It was a hundred fifty dollars, and he knew exactly how he wanted to spend it.

"Louie, Louie." Malachy's daughter smiled, taking his money. "I knew you were gonna come see me sooner or later. My daddy told me so." She wore a tight white sweater and a black mid-length skirt slit all the way up to show the tops of her gartered legs.

"Can you do something special for me?"

She was wary. "No rough stuff."

"No rough stuff. I'll pay you extra."

"Then it's okay with me." She shrugged. "What is it you want me to do?"

"Take the jewelry off."

She removed her slave bracelets and chunky earrings.

"Uh . . . what kind of underwear do you have on?"

Coyly she showed him. Black satin with lace trim. "Like what you see?"

"Do you have any plain white ones? Pastels are okay, but nothing wilder than that. And if you have a plain white bathrobe, something simple, put that on."

"That all?" she asked sarcastically.

"One more thing. No talking. Not a word from you. That's it. That's everything."

She looked amused. "Louie, my daddy never figured you for

a kink. Hey, takes all kinds, right? Don't bother me none. I'll change my little panties, and then we can take the vow of silence."

While she splashed in the bathroom, he inspected the room. Tacky but surprisingly clean. He went through a chest of drawers until he found a gauzy shocking pink scarf, which he draped over the lamp. The old diffused lighting trick. When he turned off the overhead, the effect was quite pleasant. Positively atmospheric, Gideon would have said.

She came out looking something less than demure in an aqua satin robe. He supposed it was the plainest thing she had. She shucked the robe and tossed it over a chair. The panties were white, the kind sold in Woolworth's, which was just what he wanted. She lay down next to him.

"It is all right if I kiss you?" he asked. "Just nod."

Yes, it's all right, she nodded.

His lips pressed against her gently. His breath was sweet, and she couldn't believe how clean he was. To her that meant a hell of a lot. An easy job for a change, she thought, lying back. He worked the panties down, caressing her. His mouth moved to her breasts. When she reached for him, he took her hand and pushed it down. "No, let me do it." His lips crawled over her neck. She found herself responding, urging him with the steady motion of her hips to penetrate her. He moved against her, then inside her, his arms pillowing her head. His weight was slight; she felt comfortable underneath him. She felt his breath quicken as her fingernails trailed over his back. He came, his head turned away from her.

Sighing, he settled down next to her.

She shook him. "Hey, sweetheart, you can't take a nap here. Come on, get your clothes on."

"Sorry." He roused himself and started dressing.

"Hey."

He looked up mildly.

"I'd lose that beard if I were you. You'd be better-looking without it."

He rubbed his jaw sleepily. "Thanks. I'll think about it."

She handed him his jacket. "You must miss her a lot, your little girlfriend with the white panties. She gone for good? I mean, is she dead or something?"

"Or something," he admitted.

"Maybe she'll come back one of these days."

"I don't think so," Johnny said. "For the first time I really don't think so. Well . . . good night."

"Night." Malachy's daughter put on her robe, pulled the cover on the bed straight, inspected her dark-polished nails, and hoped the rest of her evening would be this easy.

The matchbook was lying on the floor.

Taken out of context there was nothing horrifying about a matchbook cover lying with all the other assorted trash that collects on an average floor in a New York City tenement building. This one, however, told Johnny that he had had a visitor who hadn't bothered to call first.

It could have been Katie.

He doubted that very much. After their parting words that afternoon, he really didn't expect to be seeing her again.

It could have been the wind.

Impossible.

Somebody had broken into his home. For all he knew he was still in there, waiting for him to come home. Waiting to finish a job that was botched two years ago.

He pushed the door. It swung open effortlessly. He started to laugh.

Everything looked fine; everything *was* fine. He had just forgotten to lock the damn door. He must have been pretty upset about Katie or thinking about Albie subconsciously. Whatever the reason, he had just forgotten to lock the door.

Still laughing at himself, he flipped on the television, letting its sound and light dispel any bogeyman that might be lurking in a dark corner. He went into the bathroom to wash up.

His blood froze.

Written in the mirror in some dark fluid that could easily have been blood, was

ANYTIME I WANT YOU

He left without bothering to turn the television off.

There was no one for him to turn to. The only number he had to call was Malachy's. The Irishman told him to come over right away and make sure he wasn't followed.

"Is it you?" Malachy inquired sharply, peering out through his chained door.

"Yes. For God's sake, let me in."

Malachy unchained the door and ushered him in quickly.

Malachy's apartment was decorated in early harem, except for his books, which covered nearly an entire wall and were almost exclusively poetry. Two girls were sitting in one big chair watching television. Their legs were bare. They turned to stare disinterestedly at Johnny before returning to the program on TV.

Malachy and Johnny sat in the kitchen with two pussycats, one black, the other an orange tiger.

"So," Malachy said, pouring Irish whiskey for them. "Your name's not Louie, is it then?"

"No, it's John. I'm John Allison."

"So you are, and I never recognized you," Malachy said in wonder. "You don't think some burglar came in and scrawled on your bathroom mirror?"

"Maybe if it was 'Fuck You' or some other sentiment along those lines. No, that wasn't any burglar. It was the man who crippled me."

"Why would he be after you now?"

"I don't know." Johnny sipped the whiskey, grateful for the warmth it spread through his body. "Everybody thinks I can identify him, but *I can't.* The cops think he paid me off."

Malachy raised an eyebrow. "Maybe it was the cops trying to shake you up so you'd come to them for protection. They're figuring to get a statement from you any way they can."

"Cops wouldn't do that."

"They've been known to do many unusual and interesting things. You might consider that."

"I'm not crazy about Detective Brooks, but I think he is one cop who plays it straight."

"Detective Brooks?" Malachy grimaced.

Johnny grinned at his expression. "Would I be correct in assuming you have met the gentleman?"

"I have. You're right. It's not Brooks's style. Louie—sorry, John—you should think about leaving this city for a short while."

"Maybe a long while. I just don't know where to go. I changed my name, I went underground, and he still found me. How do I know he won't find me no matter where I go?"

"You don't, John. Unless they catch him or he comes to some misfortune of his own devising. It could happen. People who live violently bring violence upon themselves."

"I can't count on that. Malachy, I'm going to get out of town. There are these services; people pay you to drive their cars cross-country. I can't afford to pay, but I can sure as hell drive. I just need someplace to spend the night. Malachy, can I stay here? I won't bother your girls; you have my word on that."

"I trust you." The pimp frowned. "But I've got to look after my daughters. What if your friend finds you here? I've taken enough of a risk letting you come here at all. I'm sorry, I cannot let you stay. You have to go now."

Johnny stared at him in disbelief. "Malachy, it's just for the night."

"No." There was steel in his voice. "I can't allow it. I have to look after my own."

Johnny sat up abruptly. "Damn you, you can't just turn me out onto the street!"

"I can," Malachy said calmly. He held open his greasy suit jacket so Johnny could see the revolver tucked into his belt. "You see now that I can, don't you, boy?"

"Yes, I see," Johnny said bitterly.

He wound up sleeping in the Port Authority Bus Terminal. The good citizens gave him a wide berth, figuring he was a drunk or a junkie. About three o'clock in the morning, one of the other temporary residents tried to wrestle his shoes away. Johnny gave him a solid kick. A cop came by and threatened to take them in if they didn't stop disturbing the peace.

Johnny started to laugh. "It's got to get better, 'cause sleeping in a bus terminal is about as *low* as I go."

A woman walked by quickly, dragging a small child. "All the lunatics talk to themselves," she muttered.

The child looked back, curious to see a real honest-to-gosh lunatic.

"Hi," Johnny said and winked.

The child smiled and winked back before it was whisked along by its mother.

23

KAREN WAS TRYING to put the pieces together.

She found it hard to think without scribbling notes on a sheet of paper, so she was scribbling away, trying to get 2 plus 2 to equal 4.

"Think," she told herself sternly. "You're supposed to be an intelligent woman. People actually think you know what you're talking about." She looked at what she had written on her pad.

1. Daniel Fox
    lock in closet
    rape attempt

And why had Lake been attracted to such a sick man to begin with? Karen reasoned that it had to do with Lake's own sad history of abuse. She must have done her best to bury that incident after it had happened. Maybe she didn't even remember it at all. But somewhere had been the memory of a crazy man she had once trusted and loved. So Daniel Fox had simply been the abusive father returned to her life.

2. Phantom's

She closed her eyes, pushing her fingertips gently against her temples. *Think.* What had that girl's name been?

"Candy," she wrote.

Candy murdered.
John Allison witness? Attacked and left for dead.

Equity card stolen for some unknown reason.

And on that same night something had happened to Lake. The hotel room had been decimated, but only Lake's possessions. About three months later Lake had tried to kill herself.

"Lake suicide attempt," Karen wrote dutifully. She thought again of the phone being pulled clean out of the wall.

Who had called?

Beneath that she wrote:

Phantom-man murdered.

"Okay," she muttered. "Now what do all these incidents have in common? Absolutely nothing."

Fox could have done it. Karen had been a witness when he had tried to rape Lake. He could have messed up their hotel room, carefully avoiding Karen's side of the room, then jumped in an uptown-bound cab, killed that poor hooker, knifed Johnny and left him to die. Then a few months later Fox flies out to L.A., visits Lake, does or says something to get her upset. When Lake tries to call for help, Fox pulls the phone from the wall. Or . . . Fox himself calls, and *Lake* was the one who pulled the phone from the wall in her anguish.

Maybe.

What bothered Karen was the fact that motivation was not clear. Daniel Fox's possessiveness would certainly explain the rape attempt, the hotel room, even Lake's suicide attempt. It did nothing for the things that had happened at Phantom's. And Johnny had said *it was not Fox.* But he had called to the man, the bartender had sworn, and he had called him Foxy, plain as day. None of it made sense.

Karen got out another sheet of paper and tried again.

"Lake," she wrote in big letters and then stopped dead. What happened to the developing psyche in the case of child abuse? How could you ever be well? Lake had accepted Daniel with open arms; a sane woman would not have. But Lake was not exactly sane. Her perceptions had been warped by her childhood experiences, so she had loved Daniel Fox. Like the first man in her life, he, too, had shown her violence and hurt her. After that Lake had disappeared. Almost as though she had been trying *not to be Lake,* frightened to cling to her past, terrified of moving into the future. But all the elements of her past life had resurfaced. Karen and Matt had moved to California; Lake had put herself into another self-destructive relationship. No, no, Karen chided herself. Lots of women saw married men; you couldn't necessarily call it self-destructive.

But Lake could have been angry. She constantly told Karen she was jealous of her. Lake could have been angry that John Allison had preferred Karen to her. The seeds planted by that initial abuse could have been nurtured into full flower by her experiences with Daniel Fox. Lake lived on the edge. Maybe she had stepped over. Daintily she could have dabbled her feet in the waters of madness, and finding them to her liking, she could have decided to take the plunge.

Lake could easily have messed up the hotel room. No one had seen it, and she herself knew what things were hers and which were Karen's. It was easier to trash her own goods, get that man she'd picked up to soil them, and pin it on Mr. X than to ruin Karen's. Blame would have come to rest squarely on her shoulders then. After Karen was asleep, Lake could have gone up to Phantom's. Or she could have sent someone. She could have sent Daniel. He would do anything for her. Maybe Karen had the whole thing turned around. Johnny hadn't been the witness, *Candy* had. And so she'd been killed.

The phone call Lake had received three months later? Two choices. It could have been Daniel, pressing her to see him again, since he'd been her faithful henchman. Or it could have been Ernest Rich, the Phantom-man, telling her he'd figured the whole thing out and he was on to her.

She had waited patiently, playing the part of deranged innocent, and then she had killed him or had him killed.

It could have been Lake, Karen puzzled, all the time.

But she knew Lake, and she couldn't believe that, and she'd learned the hard way to trust her instincts.

"John Allison," she wrote. Then she wrote her own name and drew a circle slowly around both of them. She did this without thinking, faithfully turning to her intuition for guidance.

"Witnesses," she wrote in large letters.

Johnny had seen the killer. Fox and yet not Fox, how could that be?

And what had she seen? What information had she pushed out of her mind to deal with more pressing matters?

Then she remembered. She practically wept with joy. "Oh, thank you, thank you," she whispered. She ripped up her doodling papers and locked them into her desk drawer. Then she walked into the living room, where Matt was relaxing, a rare event.

"I'm going to New York for a while," she told him, "to research this new script I'm working on."

"You told me you had a serviceable rough draft."

"I didn't like the ending."

"Well," Matt said logically, "can't you rewrite the ending here?"

"No," she said, "I have to go back."

Lake and Harry were having an argument.

They had just made love, and Harry had the sneaking suspicion that Lake had been extra loving in bed just to get a little leverage for the coming fight.

"You didn't tell Chris yet," she said accusingly. "Harry, it's been almost two months. Now it's rolling around to the holidays, and God forbid you upset Chris around the holidays. Maybe she'll burn the turkey!"

"Lake, don't start," Harry warned. "I told you I would tell her; you have to be patient."

"I have been!" she stormed. "For many a year I have been patient. *You* brought the whole thing up—you said you'd tell her. When, Harry? That's all I want to know. When?"

"When *I* say so, that's when."

"Maybe I should tell Chris, get it over with. Would you like that?" she taunted.

He grabbed her arm at an awkward angle, holding it steadily, letting her own exertions hurt her. "Don't even say it, Lake. I'll tell Chris in my own way in my own time. I have to think about my daughter."

Big tears welled up in her eyes. "Who is it you love, Harry? Which one of us?"

He closed his eyes in pain. "I love you, Lake, but Chris is my wife, and I have to consider her feelings."

"You can't have us both," she said quietly. "Just remember that." She got up and started to pace. Clad only in his shirt, the tail exaggerating her round bottom, she was so beautiful he couldn't believe he'd been in her bed, those satin thighs wrapped around him like a new and improved seat belt just a short while ago. He couldn't believe that warm, passionate woman was giving him such a hard time now. "I love you, Lake, but you have to trust me about this. Please."

"How can I compete against the mother of your child?"

He put his arms around her and held her close. "It's not a contest. I love you. Hear me? I love you, lady-of-the-lake."

"I wish I could have your baby," Lake said softly. "I can't have children. Did I tell you that?"

"I believe you mentioned it." He rocked her gently. "We'll adopt."

She laughed. "Oh, I can just see the social worker coming to visit. Harry and looney Lake, just regular folks sitting around, shooting up dope." She giggled. "It just strikes me funny."

The phone rang. Lake disentangled herself to answer it.

"Hi, Kar, what's up? How's my story coming along? I loved the rough draft . . ." She listened for a moment. "New York? When?" She rose to her feet, hooking her fingers around the phone cord. "I just don't understand why . . . Oh, I'll be fine; you do what you have to do. Take care of yourself. I'll see you when you get back." She hung up, mystified. "Karen's going to New York."

"Business?" Harry asked.

"I don't know; she wouldn't say."

Harry started to grin. "Didn't you say she had a big crush on some guy in New York? I bet she's going to see him."

"You don't know Karen the way I do." Lake shook her head. "She's never going to see him again. She won't let herself."

"Uh-uh," Harry said. "Maybe *you* don't know Karen as well as you think you do."

It was a solid week before Lake could arrange a lunch with Matt. At first she thought he was ducking her. Harry convinced her the boy wonder was just busy. Finally they got their schedules together, and after an exhaustive restaurant search (Matt hated Los Angeles trendy, and Lake refused to dine Hollywood fast-food; he even refused Ranger's, that old standby) met at a totally nondescript place called Mooney's. The waitress advised them not to order anything more creative than a grilled cheese and bacon. Lake risked a cheese omelet and a club soda. Matt had a bacon cheeseburger and a Coke.

"You'll never change," Lake said. "No matter how much money you have, you'll always prefer places like this. Poor Karen, does she ever get a decent meal?"

"On rare occasions." Matt was trying to be pleasant, if only for Karen's sake. Still, there was a limit to his charm. He was an abrupt person, and he made no secret of the fact that he did not trust Lake any farther than he could clean and jerk her. They sat there, looking uncomfortable, smiling insincerely at each other.

"How's Karen?" Lake said politely. "Enjoying New York?"

"She's having a good time. I insisted that Sid go along with her. I hated to think of Karen wandering around that filthy city by herself."

"She used to *live* there," Lake said pointedly.

"Once you move away, you lose the knack of street survival. Look, at least with Sid, wherever she goes, her makeup will be perfect." He sighed. "Lake, what was it you wanted to see me about?"

The waitress plunked down their plates, giving Lake a moment to gather her thoughts. "You know Karen is writing a script for me."

"Yes, I read the rough draft."

"It's wonderful, isn't it?" Lake said excitedly. "It's just what I need for my career to get a little respect."

"What about the script?"

"I want you to direct it."

Matt started to laugh, shaking his head. "In the first place, we're talking about a project that doesn't even exist yet. In the second place, why on earth would I want to work with a star who has a history of holding up shooting with her antics and has become so indisposed because of her emotional problems that she had to leave a picture completely?"

She kept her eyes on her plate. "*Maiden Voyage* didn't turn out so badly, did it, Matt? And if it wasn't for me, Karen would never have been given the opportunity to write a screenplay at all."

"That was George's idea, my love, not yours."

"He would have tossed that script out the window if I'd asked him," she pointed out.

"Oh, yes," Matt said sarcastically, "you've just done wonders for Karen's career. I really must thank you someday." It was rare that he lost his temper, but Lake could do it every time. "I've spent years trying to tell Karen to stay away from you, but she would never believe me."

"Don't make her choose between us, Matt. You may not like the way it falls out."

He looked at her evenly. "I'm not someone you want to get angry, Lake. Think about it." He tossed some money on the table and walked toward the door.

"I own the script," she called after him softly. "Karen signed it over to me. A present."

He walked back to the table purposefully. "Well, Karen couldn't really do that. She doesn't have a very good sense of the legalities involved. You see, anything she writes belongs to Singer Productions. Even before she writes it. So she gave you something that wasn't hers to give." He patted her shoulder. "Have a nice day."

He was pulling out of the parking lot just as Lake discovered that one of the mysterious little doohickeys that made her car go had given up the ghost. Her extremely expensive car was sputtering like a twelve-year-old Chevy.

Matt was backing up, coming back to see what the problem was. She gunned the motor again only to hear a choking gasp. Shit.

"Come on." He leaned over and opened the door. "I'll give you a lift."

She shook her head obstinately.

"I can't just leave you here. Karen would never forgive me." His fingers drummed against the dashboard impatiently. "Hop in."

"No, I'll phone someone to come and get me."

"Who? Your best friend's in New York, George is in conference, and—" *Your lover has to spend some time with his wife and kid, doesn't he?* "Just get in the car," he finished.

"Well, at least he didn't say it," she muttered under her breath as she climbed into the car. "Can you take me home?"

"Anywhere you want to go."

"Home."

"Home it is." They drove in silence. "The script is yours." He said it with a certain amount of anger, but she heard the words clearly.

"Matt? You did say what I thought you said?"

"If Karen wants you to have it, it's yours. Oh, hell, I read the damn thing. It's perfect for you. The leading lady is schizoid."

Her eyes met his briefly. "What is it with the two of us, Matt? Seems like we can't have a simple conversation without bringing out the heavy artillery. I dimly remember the three of us being friends. You used to bring me all those horrible hangover cures from every bartender and witch doctor in the Village. What happened to us?"

"You know what happened," Matt said. "We both fell for the same girl because in one way we are very much alike, my old friend. We are cold, distant people, so we need somebody like Karen. But it doesn't change us; we're still the same. So there's always a little anger, a little guilt, and the need to hold on tighter. Sometimes I think, if I was really a nice guy, I'd let her go, let her find somebody who can love her the way it should be. I really feel there is a prototype love, and all the variations are just expressions of sickness. That's you and me, pal."

"I care about her."

"I know you do." He turned off the freeway. "But your love brings her nothing; it just takes."

She let it go, hard as it was. "Will you direct? You're the best, Matt. That's why I want you."

"No." It wasn't a no that could be argued with. "I wish you the greatest success on the picture, but you'll have to do it without me. I think that's best." He pulled into her driveway. "Here you are. Door-to-door service."

She tried to sound jaunty. "Thanks for the lift. Matt?"

He turned to her, looking for a moment very much like the boy who'd taken his girl and her roomie to the movies some years ago. "I love her, Matt," she said in a low voice. "It may not always look like it, but I do."

"So do I," he said. "But I don't think either one of us is very good for her."

"Then let her go," Lake said.

"I can't."

"Neither can I."

24

THREE TIMES Karen attempted to contact Karl Eastman. She wasted a day sitting in the reception area of his Manhattan office. The next day, not anxious to repeat the performance, she called and gave a false name, well-schooled by countless detective shows. The receptionist politely informed her that Mr. Eastman was away. She volunteered no other information and Karen began to get the sneaking suspicion that Karl *had* been there the day she'd spent keeping his couch warm, peeking through the door and seeing someone he did not wish to speak to.

Frustrated, she hung up the phone, marched back to the office, and attempted to run right past the receptionist. The receptionist was determined to earn her pay. Additionally, she was no dainty flower. She literally dragged Karen back to the reception desk.

"I have to see Mr. Eastman," Karen maintained stubbornly.

"I told you he's not in. I told you that yesterday."

"The security guard downstairs said he saw Mr. Eastman in the elevator this morning."

"Fine. I'll call the guard and the two of you can discuss it on your way out." She reached for the phone.

"No! Wait. Just tell me when Mr. Eastman will be back."

The receptionist sighed. "He didn't say. Why don't you go away like a nice girl?"

"He *is* here, isn't he?"

She folded her arms resolutely.

"Look, I'll go away quietly, if you just answer that one little question. For my own sanity. He *is* here."

The receptionist didn't say a word but her eyes darted towards the hall behind her desk, leading to the executives' offices.

Again, Karen tried to outrun her, only to be bodily hauled back to the starting block.

"If you don't leave *right now,*" the receptionist warned, "I'll be forced to call the police."

"All right, I'll go." Quickly, she scribbled a note. "Will you give this message to Mr. Eastman?"

"He's not here right now—"

"Whenever she *does* show up," Karen amended, secretly wishing the receptionist a fatal and immediate union with a large truck. "Could you do that?"

The receptionist scanned the note.

Mr. Eastman—

Tried to reach you 3X. I know about the envelope under your desk. Now will you talk to me? I will call again this afternoon, DON'T duck me.

Karen Singer

Karl Eastman was not in his office all afternoon. When Karen went by the building around five, the security man told her that he hadn't seen Eastman all day and had clearly been mistaken earlier that day.

Rena Wheaton had done well for herself. She had a nice office, not on Park Avenue, but she had the whole ground floor-through of a pretty brownstone in an up-and-coming neighborhood. Her office was appointed modestly, but each piece had been chosen with care. The waiting room felt warm and comforting. Karen was very appreciative, because she was nervous as hell and needed all the comforting that was available.

A receptionist showed her into Rena's office. They shook hands gravely. "Are you ready to go?" Karen asked.

Rena shook her head. "I don't know why I'm doing this. Are you sure about this?"

"Yes. Look, if anything goes wrong, I'll take the blame. You and your mother won't be involved at all."

"You bet you will," Rena said strongly. "Damned if I can figure out why I'm doing this. You won't tell me what you need from the house?"

"You're better off not knowing."

"You're starting to sound like one of your screenplays."

"Rena, you can back out now if you want to. I know you have your reputation to think of. I'll find some other way to do what I have to do."

"That's what scares me," Rena muttered darkly. "If what you've told me is true, I can't turn my back on you, no matter how crazy your little scheme sounds."

"Let's go." Karen smiled. "I've got a limo waiting."

An hour and a half later the car pulled into the long driveway of the Eastman home. "Not this way," Rena called out. "You have to go around to the service entrance. Otherwise we have to get past Amanda the wonder horse." She turned to Karen. "Old Karl is away on business—Europe, I think—and Mrs. Eastman is away God knows where—probably getting shock treatments. But that doesn't mean you have the run of the place. There's a security guard in the house at all times when Karl's away. He's a paranoid if I ever saw one." On Rena's instructions the limo pulled off onto a lane that curled around the back of the house. The road looked naked compared to the landscaped main drive. Rena gave her a tight smile. "Welcome to the downstairs part of *Upstairs, Downstairs.* It's a whole other world."

The service drive led directly to the kitchen, where Mrs. Wheaton was eagerly awaiting her daughter's weekly visit. She was a round woman, a series of circles and globes. A little round face with big open eyes belied a sharp mind. Mrs. Wheaton was nobody's fool. Circumstance had put her where she was, and inertia had kept her there. For her child she had always had greater ambitions.

"How are you, baby?" Mother and daughter embraced warmly.

"Fine, mom," Rena said cheerfully. "Lots of crazy white people out there. I'm making lots of money. Mom, this is my friend Karen. She's just in from California, so I figured you wouldn't mind if I brought her along."

"No, no, that's fine," Mrs. Wheaton said, smiling at Karen. "You look familiar to me. Rena ever have you over to the house?"

"Right," Rena interjected quickly. She went over to the stove, a complicated affair that looked as if it belonged in a hotel kitchen. She put up a kettle of water and got some cups.

"I got coconut macaroons," Mrs. Wheaton called out. "I know how you like 'em."

"I don't like them; *you* do."

"Excuse me," Karen cut in, her nerves starting to get the best of her. "Could you tell me where the bathroom is?"

Mrs. Wheaton gave her directions. "Nothing like a long car ride to get your plumbing in an uproar," she said sagely.

"That and three cups of coffee," Karen agreed. She left the two women chattering in the kitchen and made her way cautiously toward the stairs.

The house was quiet. She couldn't help but contrast it in her mind with her family's home in Chicago, where somebody was always screaming about something. TVs would be squawking, a radio blaring, her mother on the phone with a Mah-Jongg buddy discussing the game, her father engaged in his many home repair schemes that never quite turned out. There would have been plenty of noise in her house—the sounds of people arguing, fighting with each other, caring about each other. *Life.* This house had no life in it, and it frightened Karen a little. The older she got, the more she realized how viable the idea of fate was. Life ran the people, not the other way around.

She heard only the distant hum of a vacuum cleaner being operated by one of the housekeeping staff. It didn't even *smell* like people in the Eastman house, just furniture wax and lemon oil.

She walked through the empty hallway and up the stair without incident. A security guard was flirting with a pretty Colombian maid. They spoke musically in their own language. Karen plastered herself into a tiny alcove and waited.

"I don't hear working up there!" thundered from down the hall.

That voice Karen recognized as the dread Amanda. Shit. Why couldn't this be her day off?

The maid went back to her vacuum cleaner, the guard to his patrol. Amanda came out from the room she'd been working in to make sure she'd successfully squelched that little romance. In her arms she carried a load of dirty linen. She stuck her head in the door and spoke sharply to the Colombian girl, then tromped down the stairs. Casually the guard moseyed down the hall and checked to see that the ogre had surely departed. Then he made a beeline for the Colombian maid.

Thank God for young love, Karen thought, running lightly to the door of Karl Eastman's study. As her hand closed around the doorknob, a rush of excitement washed over her. I am doing it, she marveled. I am finally going to learn the truth.

The door was locked.

"You idiot!" she berated herself in an angry whisper. "Of course it's locked. What the hell did you expect?"

"Miss?"

She spun around.

It was the security guard. "Can I help you?"

She tried to look relieved. "I'll say. Can you tell me where the bathroom is?"

"Sure can." He chuckled. "Right over here." He opened the door directly across from the study.

"Thank you." She went inside and ran the faucet in case he was listening. On her way back downstairs she peeked into the room where the Colombian girl was working. She and the security guard were kissing.

Better not let Amanda catch you, she thought, heading back to the kitchen.

Rena looked up anxiously. "Everything okay?"

Karen shook her head no. She smiled quickly as Mrs. Wheaton turned around. "Just fine," she said.

Mrs. Wheaton smiled. "I'll make you some tea."

"Would you excuse me again?" Karen stammered, rushing from the room.

Mrs. Wheaton looked at her daughter sharply. "Is your friend having some kind of problem?" she inquired.

The upstairs Colombian maid stared in amazement as Karen pressed one of her cards into the maid's hand. The hotel phone number was scribbled on the back. "Do you want to make a thousand dollars?" she hissed.

The maid continued to stare, frozen with shock.

"Do you understand me? Yes or no. For God's sake nod your head."

The girl nodded her head. Yes. Her face broke into a smile. "T'ousand dollar?"

"Yes, that's right. I need the key to Mr. Eastman's study. I'll come back at midnight. All you have to do is leave the kitchen door unlocked and leave the key there for me. Here's a hundred dollars; it's all I have on me. I'll bring the rest tonight. Okay?"

She nodded again.

"Good." Stealthily she ran back down the stairs and rejoined Rena and her mother.

". . . and tomorrow we'll go to the theater. How's that sound, Mom?"

"Fine." Mrs. Wheaton turned to Karen. "You should see your

doctor about that bladder problem, sweetheart. That's nothing to fool with."

"No, ma'am. I'll have it checked out," Karen said respectfully.

Rena looked at Karen almost pleadingly. Karen gave her a slow nod yes. There was no reason for her to be involved further.

It was pointless to go back to the city and then drive out again, so Karen gave Rena the car to go back to her office. Besides, Karen would have to figure out how to get on the grounds again without breaching security. It made much more sense to stay put and wait out the evening. The gardener had the shed open. He was covering up the rose bushes for the coming winter, trudging back and forth from the shed to get burlap. She waited until his back was turned, slipped inside, and hid, praying he wouldn't lock her in for the night. She set the alarm on her wristwatch for five minutes to twelve, then settled down to get what little sleep she could in such cramped quarters. Surprisingly enough she drifted off quickly.

The tiny buzz of her wrist alarm sounded disembodied. It took Karen a while to remember where she was and what could possibly be ringing next to her ear. The shed door wouldn't give at first; she began to panic. After a moment she saw what the problem was—the gardener had parked a bag of soil against the door. She felt the weight give as she pushed harder. Grunting, she put her shoulder to the door and shoved it open, just wide enough for her to slip through. The shed had been very dark, so she didn't have to get accustomed to the nighttime gloom.

The path from the shed to the house looked pretty clear, but Karen didn't feel like taking any chances. She had found an old jacket in the shed, probably the gardener's, and put it on over her clothes. It was a little fragrant from being parked near the manure, but maybe it would fool a suspicious guard, if she happened to run into one.

She ran to the kitchen door. Locked. "Goddamn it!" Karen felt like screaming. She rattled the doorknob. The maid was waiting inside, and she took her sweet time coming to Karen's aid. She looked like she'd changed her mind about the whole thing. Regardless of any second thoughts she was entertaining, she held out the key. But when Karen reached for it, she pulled her hand away.

"Money." She smiled.

"I didn't have time to get the money," Karen explained, "but I can write you a check. It's good; I give you my word."

She slipped the key back into her apron pocket, shaking her head emphatically.

"Look, I haven't got time to bargain," Karen whispered angrily. "I don't know what I can give you to—"

The maid pointed to Karen's necklace, a slim white-gold chain with a pear-shaped diamond pendant. It was worth considerably more than a thousand dollars.

"You give me," the maid said. "If the check is good, I send back to you."

Sighing, Karen handed over the necklace and another card, this one with her California address. "Just so you send it back to the right address."

The maid took the card. "I send back," she repeated. "I swear on the Blessed Mother."

Karen didn't believe her for one minute, but she was stuck. She took the key and started upstairs.

The study looked the same as it had the first time she'd seen it so many years ago, when she'd come across Amanda giving Rena a hard time. The huge desk, walls of bookshelves. A print of a lion attacking a white horse. She shivered. The expression on the doomed animal's face was one of complete, abject fear. Karen wouldn't want anything like that near *her* desk.

She bent next to the desk and pulled the drawer out, cautiously supporting it so it wouldn't bang noisily to the floor. Carpeting would only muffle so much; she knew she'd have to be very careful. It was there, right where she remembered, taped to the underside of the drawer. She ripped the envelope free. The temptation to peek inside was strong, but Karen didn't dare stay any longer than necessary. She stuffed the envelope in her handbag and quickly put the drawer back. Her hands were shaking now. Get out now, her mind sang shrilly. She got up off her knees and made a last check around to make sure she hadn't left something behind to incriminate herself. The drawer the envelope had been taped to had been empty. On impulse she opened another drawer. It, too, was empty.

The whole desk was. Had something spooked Karl, prompting him to clear out?

She looked at the bookshelves. All classics, leather-bound, gold-stamped. Either Karl wasn't into modern fiction and diet books, or a decorator had merely stocked the shelves with books by the yard, picking out what she thought was appropriate for an executive's study.

It doesn't make sense, Karen thought. Any room held a hundred clues to the personality of the inhabitant. Who the hell was Karl Eastman, anyway?

She found her eyes drawn magnetically back to the print of the lion's kill, and this time she was very frightened, for no reason she could put into words. It was the kind of fear a good ghost story will provoke in a six-year-old. Irrational and encompassing.

She thought she heard voices in the hallway and flicked off the light, trying to fit herself into a good hiding place.

—I saw a light in the old boy's study. You want to take it or should I?

—I'll take it.

The door opened, and a powerful light shone in.

Under the desk Karen held her breath.

The light swung away. "Nothing."

The second man in the hall grunted a reply, and soon his heavy tread moved down the stairs. The study door was closed; the flashlight was snapped off.

Karen climbed out of her hiding place. She stifled a shriek, shoving her hands against her mouth.

"Hello," the security guard said pleasantly from his post at the door. He reached over to turn on the overhead light. He was holding something out to her. "Go on, take it."

It was the check she had given the maid.

"The necklace is enough." He smiled at her. "Consider it a wedding present."

Riding back to the city in a cab called by the ever-helpful security guard, Karen felt like a prize fool. Then she thought of the envelope in her purse, and she smiled. It didn't matter what it had cost her; she had accomplished what she had set out to do. Suddenly she recognized the neighborhood they were rattling through. The sign flashed past: Angelo's.

"Stop here," she told the cabbie. "I've changed my mind."

It was a real dive, with a big TV over the door and aspirations of dark-wood and stained-glass pub gentility. In one corner a big man was punishing a squealing video game. A short blonde with most of her weight up front eyed Karen suspiciously. She was sitting at a table with an older man. His hand was draped around her shoulder possessively, sausage fingers dangling above her breast.

There was nobody else to ask, so Karen addressed the blonde. "Excuse me," she said timidly. "Is there . . . does Louie work here?" The blonde was silent, measuring her. "Is this his night off?"

"He doesn't work here anymore." She brushed past Karen to squirt herself a Coke from the soda gun, adding a shot of rum. The high-heeled sandals on her little feet almost made them seem like tiny hooves. "Nice clothes." She examined Karen from head to toe. "You're somebody, aren't you?"

"Did he say where he was going?"

"No," the blonde said, "he didn't say. He didn't say nothing." She went halfway through the rum and Coke, then topped it off again, watching the Coke grow pale under the influence. The man at the table called to her sharply, and she trotted back to him on her little hooves. Under the table his hand curled around her thigh. The blonde stared at Karen defiantly, holding up her wounded life like a trophy.

I am this way because of you, her dull eyes seemed to say.

Without another word Karen left. She walked west to Tenth Avenue, aware that the neighborhood was getting funkier the farther she went. Her breath came faster. The letter, she should never have sent that letter. It was a mistake, she would have to tell him. She loved him, and she could never let him go. She just wanted to see him, that was all. See him and know that he was all right.

She found the building and went through the unlocked outer door into the vestibule. Checking the mailboxes brought on a fresh attack of anxiety. No R. Louie. Maybe someone had scratched his name out. She pushed all the buzzers, hoping someone would admit her, but they were all either not at home or too cagey to fall for such an old dodge.

An old black man was charging angrily down the stairs. Through the locked door she heard his screaming, mercifully dimmed.

"You get away from here. Waking decent folks at such an hour! Get! I got me a gun, then you'll get!"

She ran. The walk back to Ninth Avenue seemed unbearably long. He had gone, of that she was certain. She had written the words, and once they had been written, they had become real. She walked with her head down, not concentrating on her surroundings, which was a big mistake.

"Hey, hey." A man jumped out in front of her from a side alley. He was dirty, white, probably a junkie. One hand snagged the strap of her handbag, the other held a knife. "Gimme," he said with a nervous grin.

"There's no money in there," she said quickly. "Just personal things. Here, take this." She pulled her watch off and offered it to the mugger. "It's worth a lot of money."

He touched the knife to her throat. "You gimme the purse."

"The watch is worth a lot more money," she said, trying to sound calm.

Too fast for her to see, the knife flashed down on her hand. She yelped, letting go of the handbag. It fell to the pavement. He pounced on it.

"No!" She grabbed the strap and held on, eyes tightly shut.

He started to laugh. "I'll take the fuckin' watch." Then he ran down the street.

Karen examined her injury. He had cut the back of her hand, not deeply, but it hurt more than she would have thought possible for such an insignificant wound. She ducked into the lobby of the nearest building and opened her purse. The prize was still safe. She could wait no longer. With shaking fingers she opened it.

The envelope was filled with cut up newspaper.

"No," Karen moaned. Thanks to her little love note to Karl, he'd had plenty of time to switch envelopes. She'd almost gotten herself killed trying to protect a handful of worthless newspaper.

Outside she found a trash basket and dumped the envelope in. The blood from her hand pattered like rain onto the newspaper.

She had no money left, so she started to walk crosstown, very slowly.

Sid jumped off the bed when she came in. "My God, what happened to you?"

"I got mugged." She went into the bathroom and tended to her hand.

He followed her. "You said you were going shopping and that you'd be home to have dinner with me."

"I hope you didn't wait," she said grimly.

"Karen, what the hell happened?"

She turned to him suddenly. "Sid, don't ask me." Her voice was sharp, and her panic was very close to the surface. "It's better if you don't know anything about it."

He shook his head. "What are you getting yourself into?"

"I'm working on the script," she said slowly, "and I'm having a little logic problem. Would you help me?" She took a towel and wrapped it around her hand. "Let's say you knew someone had committed a crime, but you couldn't prove it. What would you do?"

Sid looked at her, puzzled. "Nothing. I mean there's nothing you could do, is there?"

She nodded. "That's right. That's the part that's got me stuck. *Something* has to be done, am I right? If only to keep the story moving alone. So what do you do?"

"I don't know." He looked at her for a long time. "This isn't a story, is it? What were you up to all day today? Karen, you've *got* to tell me."

She went to the window and looked out, half expecting to see what she saw. He was out there, just standing in front of the hotel, loitering, much to the doorman's chagrin. Just a man, nobody she recognized, just hanging around. Her heart froze as he lifted his eyes, zeroing in on her window. Then he walked away.

Oh, it had to be her imagination. She was spooked, and she'd been jumping at shadows for weeks.

"Karen?" Sid was looking at her with a mixture of concern and fear. "What is it we're talking about? Tell me."

She closed her eyes, feeling very alone. "It's just a story, Sid, that's all. Just something I made up."

On the same evening, at about the same time Karen was getting her hand slashed to save a bunch of torn newspaper, Lake was answering her phone.

"Hello?"

It was Harry. "Sorry," he said in a low voice, "I can't make it tonight. Roseanne has a little fever. Chris is real worried."

Lake's teeth came together, making a sharp little click. "But I was counting on you," she said in a low voice. She didn't want George to hear. He was over, trying to convince her to return for another season of *The Girl Upstairs,* which she hated dearly at this point.

"I'm sorry," Harry said, and then he hung up.

George sat quietly, an elaborately unlistening look on his face. "I could stay if you want me to, if you don't want to be alone tonight. I wouldn't . . . make any demands on you. I just want to be here if you need somebody." Then he recognized the expression he'd seen her wearing so often of late. She pitied him, old faithful, standing by, hoping for her lover to cancel out so he could catch a crumb or two of affection. Well, if pity was all she could offer, he'd take it and be grateful.

"George, that really isn't necessary."

His smile sickened and died. "I know a lot more than you think I do."

"Meaning what?"

"I just want you to be happy," he maintained stubbornly. "I can make you happy, I'll take care of you, I'll be there for you. In time you'll know that. There may be somebody else in your life right now, somebody you think you care for more than you care for me, but we both know that isn't going to last. You need someone constantly. You need me, Lake."

"I'm tired," she said carefully. "You must be, too. Let's just call it a night. We can discuss the resurrection of *TGU* tomorrow, if you like." A hundred times she had tried to be honest, to tell him that she could never love him the way he wanted. Then she would relent and take him back, negating the power of her words. She always meant to do right, but he continued to offer her his heart, his soul, his passion. She took when she could not help herself and cursed herself in private. Too damn hard to let go of his doglike devotion. He made it hard by being so vulnerable.

She saw him out to his car. "I will never understand why you had to build a home out here in the boonies," he grumbled, getting in.

"I like it out here."

"Gives me the creeps."

"Gives me the creeps, too." She laughed. "But I like it. Drive safe."

He caught her hand. "Are you sure you don't want me to stay? I know you don't like to be alone at night."

She steeled herself. "I'll be fine. Go on."

Five minutes after he'd gone, she sat listening to the airplanes overhead, carrying people . . . where? To visit, to do business, to kill other people, to drop the bomb. The sounds of airplanes terrified her.

Twenty minutes after George left, Lake was in her car, the radio on so she couldn't hear the planes.

"Matt, let me in." She pounded on the door. "It's Lake. Let me in!"

He came to the door, bleary-eyed, dressed in his now-ancient NYU sweats. The little torch emblem had almost completely faded away. He was obviously pissed off. "This better be good, Lake."

"It's business." She brushed past him and went into the living room.

He followed her. "You usually do business at this hour?"

"You know me, Matt, spontaneous as hell." She curled her legs up under her. "You remember our last meeting?"

"Vaguely. I'm still not going to direct your film without some assurance that you're not going to flip out and jeopardize the entire picture."

"What if I backed the film with my own money, and only my money? I've got that kind of money, Matt, you know I have."

"You'd cut George out, just like that?" He sat down slowly.

She ignored his question. "I'd give you your entire salary up front. I'll give you points if that's what you want. Whatever you require."

"Complete artistic control?"

She hesitated for only a second. "Yes. Will you do the film?"

"I'm thinking."

"Of course I want Harry for the male lead."

"I bet you do."

"You have any problem with that?" she asked stiffly.

"No. Harry's a fine actor; he's never given me any trouble. I still have to think about it, Lake."

"There's something else. The character is a singer. You know damn well I can't sing for shit. I want Karen to dub my voice. With screen credit, of course." She leaned forward, lightly touching his arm. "It could make her, Matt; she sings like an angel. The record companies would be dying for her, and George doesn't have any influence over those people."

"I still have to think it over."

She played her last card. "What if I promised you that after this film is completed, I would get out of your lives forever?"

He laughed. "Can I have that in writing?"

"If necessary."

"Are you serious?" He stared at her. "You'd promise never to see Karen again?"

"Yes."

"Never to call her?"

"Yes."

"Never to write?"

"Not so much as a postcard," she said coolly.

"You really want this film that bad?" He shook his head in wonder.

"Yes, I do. Now." She took a deep breath. "Will you direct my film?"

"Lake, I can't make any decisions in the middle of the night. I'll give you my answer in the morning." Sighing, he went into the kitchen. "Do you want coffee? I can make instant."

"No, thanks."

He came out carrying a glass of milk and settled himself on the couch. Lake hadn't moved. "Yes?" he said. "Something else I can do for you?"

She gave a nervous little laugh. "I know this is going to sound a little odd, but . . . can I sleep here tonight? *Here.*" She patted the couch. "I'm too tired to drive home."

"Too tired, huh?"

"Yes."

"Lake, you're going to have to get over these night frights. You're a big girl now."

"Please," she whispered, "just let me stay here tonight."

"I can't very well throw my wife's best friend out on her ear. You can stay in Karen's office. The couch there pulls out. Come on, I'll get you settled in." He gave her a grudging smile. "You won't have any nightmares in there unless you're allergic to typewriter ribbons."

"Thank you," she said quietly. "I know you don't want me here."

"Well, that makes two of us. Relax. I suppose I can stand you for one night." He handed her a sheet, a pillow, and a blanket and wished her a pleasant night.

"Aren't you going to give me a good-night kiss?" she teased, feeling secure again.

He turned abruptly and left.

"Miserable man," Lake grumbled, making up her bed. She had to be very careful because Karen had open books and loose papers scattered all over the place.

"Lake?"

She looked up.

Matt lobbed a small silvery object at her. "Catch."

It was a Hershey's kiss. She started to laugh.

"Sweet dreams," he said to her.

Although she had originally felt too keyed up to sleep, her eyelids started to droop as soon as she pulled the blanket up to her waist. The little room felt like Karen. It smelled of her perfume; her cup, the ancient "Gorgeous Brunette," was sitting on her desk. Lake almost felt as if they were roommates again and Karen was sleeping in the room next to hers, breathing evenly, waking to croak a demand for Pepsi.

Her head sank deeper into the plush pillow. She slept, blissfully dreamless.

"Hey, wake up." Matt was shaking her. "It's eleven o'clock, sleeping beauty. If you're waiting for another kiss, forget it. I'm out of chocolate."

Groaning, she pulled herself to a sitting position. "Wha . . . ?" A big smile bloomed on her face. "God, I slept *wonderfully.*"

"I'm thrilled. Are you cognizant?"

"Dipping into the thesaurus a little early, aren't we?" She felt pretty good. Actually, she felt damn good. "What is it?"

"I have an idea."

"Stop the presses." She almost giggled. A good night's sleep was pure gold. Oh, how she loved to sleep! "Sorry. Please go ahead."

"How important is this movie to you?"

"Don't joke."

He held up his hand. "Wait a second. I'm willing to do the film under one additional condition. No way can I trust you to look after yourself for the duration. I'm going to give you a baby-sitter—two of them, as a matter of fact."

She grimaced. "No more spas. If I have to look at another leotard, I'll puke."

"No, you're going to live here with us. I couldn't figure out a better way to keep an eye on you."

She pealed laughter. "Live here? Oh, that's going to do wonders for *our* relationship, my dear Matthew."

"Look," he said angrily, "that's the deal. Take it or leave it."

"Why the change of heart?"

He hesitated a second. "It's a good script. Oh, hell, I think it may be the best thing Karen's ever written. How could I trust that to anybody else? And . . . I may not have a lot of respect for your acting ability, but this part has your name on it. The critics will eat every word they ever said about you."

Her eyes shone. "I know. It's the script I've always waited for."

"So we are going to make a movie. The best movie to come out of this town in years."

"Oh, yes." She had never felt so close to Matt. He really understood her.

He patted her arm. "And when the movie's finished, we won't ever have to see each other again." Whistling, he got up, leaving her with the smile still frozen on her face.

25

"YOU KNOW WHAT'S WRONG with California?" Karen mourned. "The coming of spring means absolutely nothing. Here it is April again, and there's nothing to get excited about. April looks just like December out here."

"Look," Lake said sourly, "I am not going to do any more situps unless I have your full, undivided attention."

"Baby."

"Absolutely. I thought I was going to be a houseguest. Little did I know I was entering boot camp."

"You told Matt you'd do whatever he felt was necessary. Come on," Karen coaxed, grabbing Lake's ankles securely, "five more. Just in case I decide to write in a nude scene."

"Don't you dare!" Lake threatened darkly.

Karen made her do ten.

"Arghhhh!" Lake screamed, pulling herself into a little ball. "My stomach muscles are cramping. I'm dying. Tell Matt to get another actress; I'll be dead. It's all over."

"Does that mean you don't want lunch?" Karen asked coyly.

"Can you bring it out here? It's such a beautiful day."

"It's always a beautiful day," Karen grumbled. "Wait here; we can eat by the pool."

Karen ran into the house, returning shortly with two cold plates of boiled shrimp and salad. Under her arm was tucked a bottle of white wine.

"Breaking training, are we?" Lake inquired innocently.

"I told Matt that if he pushed you too hard, we'd have you jumping ship altogether. You've been very good. I don't think one glass of Ernest and Julio's best is going to kill you. Shit, I forgot the glasses."

"No matter." Serenely Lake swigged from the bottle and passed it to Karen. "We're also going to have to eat with our fingers because you forgot the silverware." She leaned back on her elbow. "It feels so good to be here."

Karen smiled. "Does it?"

"Yes, it sort of feels like the beginning, you know, when we shared a place. I feel like everything is still ahead of me. Kar, I've been thinking—"

"Dangerous habit."

"Oh, we are cute today. I've been thinking, after this film I may just disappear for a while, start fresh at something else."

"Nuclear physics?" Karen said archly.

"You're laughing at me."

"Oh, honey, you just come up with these statements out of the clear blue. Just get through one thing at a time. Finish the movie, then worry about what you're going to do next."

"Maybe I'll disappear," Lake repeated, rolling over onto her back, crushing the soft grass beneath her. She waved her hands slowly back and forth, watching the patterns they weaved through the air. "I prefer to grow old and lose my looks in total anonymity."

"They won't let you. Somehow they'll find you, and your picture will be on the cover of the *Enquirer:* 'Star Found, Lives on Cat Food.'"

"Beast." Lake punched her in the arm. "Kar, if I ask you something, will you tell me the truth?"

"Maybe."

"Come on, promise."

"No." Karen laughed. "I know you too well."

"Promise," Lake wheedled.

"All right."

"Did you go to New York to see John Allison?"

Karen let her breath out in a long, low whistle. "You waited a long time to ask that, didn't you? No, Lake, I am sorry to disappoint you, but I did not go to New York to see him. I tried to, once I was there, but that was not why I went in the first place."

"Why did you go?" She squinted into the blue sky, enjoying the sun on her face. "Kar? Still with me? Why'd you go?"

"The truth?"

"I made you promise, didn't I?"

"I went to see your father."

All of a sudden Lake seemed to be perfectly still, her body frozen, the way small animals go when caught in a headlight's glare.

"You said you wanted the truth," Karen said uncomfortably. "Lake, he's still trying to control your life, and I think he's done some terrible things. I could never get any proof, but I know—"

"You don't know anything!" Lake shrilled. "Who the hell do you think you are to go messing around in my life? Who appointed you my personal savior?"

"You did," Karen said quietly.

"Damn you and your safe little life," Lake went on, anger seething in her voice. "What do you know about the things that have happened to me? Leave it alone. What happened between me and my father is ancient history. It is *over.* All you are doing with your misguided intentions is stirring up a lot of feelings that are better left alone. Let it go, Karen. This has nothing to do with you."

Karen started to pile up their now-empty plates. "I better put these in the sink," she muttered.

Lake grabbed her arm. "Things haven't gone the way you would have liked them, have they, Kar? It's easy to make my father your catch-all bogeyman for your little disappointments. And just think what a terrific script it'll all make when you unravel the mystery of my life all by yourself! What a wonderful girl you are! Well, you don't know shit about anything, my girl. He isn't a madman; he isn't even an especially interesting person. And he is not evil incarnate. Life isn't that simple. If it was, you'd be happy with Matt and getting fucked once a year."

Karen hit her. She pulled back at the last minute so it wasn't very hard, but there was anger behind it, the kind of anger Karen hadn't even known she possessed. She sat down on the lawn and started to cry, quiet tears slipping down her cheeks.

"Shit," Lake said softly. "I always go too far. Kar, I'm sorry . . . "

"Leave me alone. Please." She got up and walked to the far side of the pool. The dishes lay unattended, stacked neatly. Lake picked them up and walked with them into the kitchen.

"Anybody home?"

She looked up, startled. "Harry, is that you? What are you doing here?" She went to the door and let him in.

He kissed her. "I just wanted to talk."

"I told you last time, we've nothing to say to each other unless you and Chris have a little talk."

He sat down at the kitchen table. "Lake, sit with me."

"You didn't tell her," Lake sighed. "You'll never tell her."

"This film is important to both of us. I don't want to have a lot of personal problems hindering my concentration. I swear to you, I'll talk to Chris as soon as we wrap. How long is that? We start filming the end of May. Even with problems and delays, what are we talking about? A few months? August, maybe September. Is that long to wait?"

"I no longer believe you. You've given me this little speech too many times, Harry. I can't depend on you." She laughed bitterly. "Do you know Matt made me sign a paper swearing I wouldn't see Karen once the movie was finished shooting? That I would stay out of their lives forever. That's what I had to do to get him to direct this film. Well, this movie will be over one fine day, and I will have nothing. Matt will have this little piece of paper to keep me away from my friend, and where will you be, Harry? I can tell you that. You'll be with your wife." Her anger ebbed. "I'm tired. Tired of these little scenes. If you can't leave her, tell me. Just let me know, Harry, that's all I ask."

In answer he took a little box out of his pocket. "Take it." He pushed it across the table toward her. "Go on, it's for you."

She opened the box.

"That was my mother's. My father couldn't afford a ring, so my grandmother gave him hers to give to my mother. It's pretty old. When my father passed on, my mom gave it to me. She told me to give it to the woman I love."

Harry stood beside her and slipped the ring onto her finger. "Someday, very soon, I am going to make you my wife. You are the only woman I love. If I lost you, I would die. Please, Lake, please give me time."

She turned to him and hid her face against his neck. "Don't make it a long time."

"I won't."

"Just tell me it's all going to happen. Just the way I dream it will be."

"It'll put your dreams to shame."

She smiled. "Oh, you don't know my dreams."

He pulled away from her gently. "I have to go."

"I know," she sighed.

"We'll be together all during the shooting. Chris won't think it strange if I stay in town after a long, hard day. We'll be together a lot. I love you."

"I love you, too."

He started toward the door. "Hey, there's a florist's truck in the driveway. You got a secret admirer?" he teased.

"Just you."

The delivery man rapped on the door, a long florist's box tucked under his arm. "Thank you." Lake signed for the delivery and tipped the man. "Oh, how lovely," she said in a low voice. "White roses. Must have cost a small fortune." She read the card. "Oh, shit, these are for Karen. I hope she isn't pissed I opened them."

"From Matt?"

Lake waved the card. "No signature, just two theater tickets. Probably some starving playwright trying to get Matt and Karen to produce his show, something like that. They get a lot of this sort of thing."

Harry kissed her forehead. "I'll see you soon."

She smiled wanly. "Is that a promise?"

He crossed his heart. "Promise." Then he ran out to his car.

Lake picked up the flowers and carried them out to the pool. Karen was still sitting. She kept a few paperbacks in the pool shed, and one was balanced on her lap. "These are for you. Sorry I opened them."

Mystified, Karen fished the card out of the box and read. "Oh." Her face reflected annoyance. "Another one of them."

"Maybe you should go. You could use a chance to dress up. A date. That's what you and Matt need to spice things up."

"Of course you are the expert on my marriage," Karen said coolly.

"I suppose I had that coming. Karen, you know I'm sorry. I'm always sorry about *something* when it comes to you. I shouldn't have said half the things I said. I never *mean* to hurt you; it just sort of happens."

"Well," Karen said, still miffed but willing to be wooed, "I should have minded my own business. I'm sorry, too."

"Are you going to go to the play tonight?"

"I don't know. I'm supposed to be taking care of you."

"Hire me a baby-sitter. Or better still, maybe I'll look after myself for one night. I think I can handle that. You should go out, Kar. It'll be fun. I'll pick out something a little risqué for you to wear. Go on, you'll enjoy it." She brushed the soft rose petals against Karen's cheek. "I'm so sorry, baby, I didn't mean to hurt you."

"The truth always hurts."

"Yes, it does," Lake agreed.

"Aha," Matt said as they settled into the worn plush seats of the playhouse, "I sense Lake's influence in the wardrobe department."

"Do I look okay?" Karen asked anxiously. She was wearing a white silk blouse and a red straight skirt. Red anything made her feel a little conspicuous.

"You look great," Matt reasssured her. "Whenever Lake helps you get dressed, you look like something Bogie would go for in a big way. That's all I meant." He began to study the program.

"No, you don't." Playfully Karen pulled the program out of his hands. "Talk to me."

"You look beautiful."

"Thank you very much."

"Now can I read my program?"

She stood up, put both programs on her seat, and sat on them, smiling sweetly all the while. "Come on now, we can have an intelligent conversation. We've done it before."

The house lights flickered. "During intermission we'll talk," Matt whispered. "We'll dissect the first act."

The curtain rose. All Karen knew about the play was from a brief synopsis; a college professor reminiscing about the summer he spent in his youth, working for a carnival. In particular the play dealt with the narrator's friendship with a mentalist, the protagonist, a self-professed phony.

"Nightmare Alley," Matt whispered.

She didn't hear him. After the professor's rambling monologue, a change of lighting signified a flashback to his carnival days, and the mentalist came onstage. It was John Allison.

Undeniably he had changed. He commanded the stage in a way he had never been able to before. He moved with a barely detectable limp, but it added to the character. The audience practically held its collective breath every time he set foot on the stage. The odd white streak in his hair gleamed in the light. His performance was confident and exciting.

"He's good," Matt said to Karen, setting off a chain reaction of shushing. "I suppose he sent the tickets."

"Yes," Karen whispered back. She stared up at the stage, unblinking. She wondered if he knew she was there.

At the end of the show, Karen put her hand on Matt's arm. "Well, that was an interesting evening. Let's go."

"Why are you in such a hurry? We have to go backstage and thank him for the tickets. The play sucked, but he was excellent. I'd like to tell him that."

"Write him a letter."

Matt laughed. "That's your department. Come on, Karen, it'll be painless. I thought you liked the guy."

"I met the man once almost three years ago. That's hardly the basis for a lasting relationship." She almost laughed at her own words.

Matt had his way. He rapped on the door of a closet labeled the men's dressing room. "Hey, Johnny, your fan club is here. You got guests."

He came out, still rubbing the greasepaint from his face, good-natured gibes from his fellow actors following him out of the dressing room.

"John." Matt held out his hand. "Very good performance. Pleasure to meet you."

"Thank you."

Karen offered her hand, not daring to look up. Silly to think that if she looked at him, Matt would know everything she was feeling. But it was a look that had given away Harry. Karen would never have known if it hadn't been for that one look. "Very good performance," she parroted softly. At last she permitted herself to look up.

I still feel the same, his eyes said.

So do I, she answered silently. "Matt and I have to be getting back," she said slowly. "It was good to see you again."

"You can stay and chat," Matt said, glancing at his watch. "I'm sure John will get you a cab. No reason both of us have to go home and baby-sit." He kissed her proprietarily on the cheek. "I'll see you at home. Have a nice visit."

He was gone before she could protest.

"You look fine," she said hollowly, not trusting her voice.

He took her hands, placing them on either side of his face. He tapped her right hand. "That's the plastic part. Feel the difference?"

She wasn't sure what he meant. Her hand moved up, tracing the scar that ridged his brow. "My God," she said softly, almost too softly for him to hear. Her body trembled. For a crazy moment he felt she was lifting a whole freightload of bitterness and anger from his shoulders.

"I'm not going to lose you again," he said.

Lake heard a car in the driveway. "Back so soon?" she murmured, running to the door. "Guess the play was a bust." She peered through the door. She recognized the car, but it wasn't Matt's.

"Oh, shit," she said under her breath. "George?" She walked toward the car warily. "What do you want?" She had successfully dodged him for quite some time, but this moment was inevitable. "George?"

She got scared when he got out of the car, because it was the first time she had ever seen George drunk. Not just a little high, but falling-down, mean drunk. Instinctively she began to back toward the house.

"Why?" he croaked, leaning against his car. "I think you owe me an explanation. Why'd you cut me out of your life?"

"I'm sorry." She couldn't think of anything else to say.

He laughed. "No, you're not. You really don't give a shit about any of us, never did. I made you up. I made you up to be as good as you are beautiful. You're not beautiful. You're nothing." He lunged forward, practically falling on her.

"Get off me." She pushed him away. "I tried to tell you, George. I tried to make it easy on you. This is as much your doing as it is mine."

"A cold-hearted bitch and a fool." He pointed his finger at her, shaking with silent laughter. "Funny thing is, I'd still take you back. Once a fool, huh? If you would say one little word, I'd take you back. Say something to me, Lake, talk to me." His laughter turned to sobs. "Say one little word." She turned away. He caught her arm and held her. Drunk or sober, he was a lot stronger than she was. "Tell me you still love me. Tell me how much you need me to keep your career going."

"I never said I loved you."

"You said you needed me. You made me hope." He pulled her closer. "You gave me just enough to keep me hanging on. That's what you do to all of us. Just enough so we don't starve, but it's never enough to satisfy." His lips brushed against her hair. The smell of him made her sick with fear. "Prince Hal will never leave his wife and kid for you. You scare him, Lake. He knows how heartless you really are." He caressed her back, his hand settling heavily on her waist. His smile was crafty. "You didn't think I knew, did you? See? You don't know everything about me." He moved to kiss her.

Lake punched him in the stomach. The result was immediate and gratifying. He doubled over and started puking in the bushes. She ran inside the house and dialed the phone quickly. George was very quiet out there. The retching had stopped along with all other sounds of life.

She ventured outside. He was just sitting, propped up against the tires of his car, crying, mouth working helplessly.

"I called Sid to come get you. George? You understand me?"

He turned to glare at her, hate plain in his eyes. "Look what you've done to me," he cried, tears puddling in the hollow of his throat. "Everything you touch turns to ashes. My beautiful angel. You're the Angel of Death."

She went into the house and would not come out until she heard Sid's car pull up.

He came to the door and rapped. "Lake? I've got George in my car. Are you all right?"

She opened the door. "Yes, I'm fine."

"You don't look fine."

"He called me the Angel of Death." She smiled wanly.

Sid grimaced. "Well, we all wax poetic when we're in our cups. Thanks for calling me instead of the cops."

"Thanks for coming. I never thought there was any love lost between us."

Sid cocked his head to one side. "I thought that's exactly what there was. Are you sure you're okay? I can drop George off, put him to bed, and come stay with you."

"No." She took a deep breath. "I'm not going under just yet."

They were sitting in the empty theater. Johnny was telling Karen the events that had led up to his rather hasty departure from New York. She had already told him about her brief career as a breaking-and-entering artist.

"Do you think the guy who tried to mug me was him?"

"Him?" Johnny said wearily. "Who is this guy? That's what I want to know. The mysterious Mr. X. I don't know, Karen, I just don't know. I just want to stay clear of it." He touched the back of her hand. A tiny scar curled the skin like a hair. "We both have our scars."

"I went to Angelo's. I looked for you everywhere I knew to look," she said quietly.

He felt like kicking himself. Right about the time she had been looking for him, he had been with Malachy's daughter. That was two. Three strikes and you're out!

"He's a nice guy, your husband."

"Oh yes, he's a very nice guy."

He watched her face carefully. "Tell me you love him, and I swear I'll never bother you again."

"I'm married to him."

"That's not the right answer."

"I don't know what the right answer is anymore," she cried out. "Matt is my friend. I do care for him. It's not perfect, but nothing is. I'm grown up now; I've put aside my dreams, and this is what life is. I don't need perfect."

"I do. I want friendship, trust, passion—the whole ball of wax. The only thing in life that comes *close* to perfect is love. You bet I want it. And so do you."

"So what happens?" she said in her quiet voice. "I can't have an affair with you. It would change what I feel for you, what I feel for myself. I can ask my husband for a divorce, but I won't leave him if he doesn't agree to it. Where does that leave us? We can be friends."

"Sure, we can have lunch." He gave her a bitter smile. "All those letters were lies."

"They weren't," she whispered. "You're the only man I'll ever love."

"For the longest time you were the only thing that kept me going. Everything I did was to get me back here with you. Well, here we are. You're going to have to make a decision. I love you, Kar, but if you can't make up your mind, I will go on without you. We both deserve a little sane happiness. I won't wait around for you forever, and I won't torture myself, wondering if you'll come around."

She moved into his arms; the touch of her lips against his was ephemeral. "You were right," she murmured, "we won't be friends. We won't see each other again."

He saw the blaze of her red skirt as she walked out of the empty theater.

Matt drove up to the house with the feeling that something was terribly wrong. "Lake?" The place smelled like a distillery.

"In the kitchen."

He followed a trail of broken glass. Lake was on her hands and knees, mopping up the kitchen floor. "Step carefully. There's broken glass everywhere."

He stepped carefully. "What the hell happened?"

"George, came over." She grimaced. "It got pretty hairy. I had to call Sid to come get him."

"I take it he shook you up."

"He shook me up all right. Knowing how well I deal with

stress, I decided to remove all sources of temptation. Luckily you guys don't keep a well-stocked bar. I managed to break everything in a quarter of an hour."

Incredulous, Matt shook his head. "You could have just thrown it all out."

"No, I couldn't," Lake said serenely. "You'd find me scrounging in the trash cans at four in the morning."

"That bad?"

"You hurt, you want out. George just struck a sore spot. I also went through the medicine cabinets." She pointed to a paper bag on the counter. "I flushed it down the toilet, but I saved the vials and bottles in case you needed them."

He peeked inside. "Aspirin? You threw out aspirin?"

"Better safe than sorry."

"You threw out all of Karen's vitamins."

"She never takes them." Broken glass clunked into the garbage.

"I kind of thought she was into the zinc."

"Merely a fad," Lake said. "How was the play?"

"Strange. Okay."

"Which one?"

"Both. Play wasn't worth much; some good performances."

"Where's Karen?"

"She knew one of the actors. I left them to catch up on old times." He went to the fridge and poured himself a glass of milk. "You want?"

"I'd rather have coffee."

"Fix it yourself."

"Charming as always," she muttered, putting the kettle up. "When is Karen going in to record my song?"

"Probably next week. You're welcome to come to the studio if you want to."

"No. If I see her recording the song, it'll be harder to pretend that it's my voice. I'm really looking forward to that. I've always wished I could sing like her. I always envied certain things Karen had." She held up her large-knuckled hands. "Wish I could turn in these gunboats for hers. Karen has beautiful hands."

"Yes, she has," he said slowly.

"And I always wanted someone like you."

"I thought you'd found your man of the hour."

"He's not mine. I rent him."

"Your choice." He backed away from her, uncomfortable with her revelations.

"Take it easy, Matt. I just wish my life had been a little more like Karen's. The two of you are so perfect. Such good friends. I love Harry, I really do, but we'll never be like that. Neither one of us has that depth of emotion. I know you would do anything for Karen, no matter what it cost you." The water boiled, and she set about making a cup of instant.

"Lake, remember when you went to New York with Karen? My God, that must be nearly three years ago."

"Just about," Lake agreed. "Sure I remember it. What do you want to know?"

He thought about what it was he wanted to know. "Nothing. Just couldn't remember whether you guys had a good time or not."

"As I remember, it wasn't one of the all-time nonstop parties. No, I don't think it was the best. Why?"

"Go to sleep," he said abruptly. "You need your rest. I'll finish up in here. All it needs is a good airing out." After she'd gone, he opened up some windows, relishing the kiss of cool air breezing through the kitchen.

He was waiting for his wife to come home, wondering if he was going to tell her that he was pretty sure she was in love with another man.

She came in about an hour later. "Matt? I thought you'd be asleep by now. Lord, what smells in here?"

"Lake broke something."

"She okay?"

"She's fine. She's asleep."

"Is something wrong?"

"Sit with me for a minute." He pushed out a chair.

"I'm awfully tired, Matt."

"Just a minute. Please." He took her hand. "Maybe I don't tell you enough, but I love you, Kar. Always will. You're the only thing that makes me bearable. Without you I'd be a pretty sad specimen. Maybe in the beginning I was everything you needed, but people grow. They change. There isn't anything I wouldn't do for you, but I can't read your mind. You have to let me know. There's no need for you to go to anyone else but me. Please, Karen, tell me the truth. What's going on in your mind?"

She squeezed his hand. "Nothing's changed, Matt. I love you." She got up. "I'm beat. I think I'll go up to bed."

"Karen?"

She turned around slowly.

"Is there something between you and John Allison?" Fear was

plain on his face. He didn't want to lose her. Ever. "You can tell me the truth."

For the first time in all the years they had been married, she deliberately lied to him. "Of course not," she assured him. "Good night."

About six o'clock in the morning, he went up to Lake's room and shook her awake. "Here, take this," he said roughly, thrusting a paper at her.

"What the hell is this?" she said sleepily.

"A bad idea, that's what that is."

It was the paper Matt had made her sign, promising to stay out of Karen's life when the movie was done.

She stared at him. "Why?"

"Because I just realized it doesn't matter." He turned and left.

26

ROSEANNE was not being a good little girl. "Can we go now?" she asked loudly, tugging at her mother's skirt.

"Not yet, sweetie," Chris said. "I have to talk to Aunt Jackie. Why don't you go play with Kelly? You like her."

"No, I don't."

"Don't give Mommy a hard time," Chris said sweetly. "Mommy is having a bad day. Kelly!"

A smiling blonde saleslady came and took the restless child away with a promise of cookies.

Jackie saw her sister-in-law coming and steeled herself. Of late Chris had been more than a little irritable. Jackie had assumed it was because Harry was in the thick of filming and he just wasn't around much. After so many years Jackie knew how to handle Chris's tirades. She blew up frequently, but it was all smoke and little fire. "Hi, Chris. How's everything?" she said innocently.

"We've got to talk, Jackie."

"Fine. It's almost one o'clock, we can get some lunch."

"I don't like your telling fortunes in the store." Chris set her mouth in a thin line. "This is a boutique, not a sideshow."

"I've been doing it for years, Chris. I thought people liked it—you know, something that set your place apart from all the others."

"Well, maybe I don't like being so different!" She lowered her voice as a few patrons looked over curiously. "You take too many liberties, Jackie. Not just here. You can believe whatever metaphysical bullshit you want to, but don't fill my daughter's head with such things."

"I've never done anything to hurt Roseanne," Jackie said testily. "You want to back off, Chris? You're angry and upset, and you're taking it out on me. I love you like you're my own sister, but I won't let you use me to take out your frustrations."

"I tell my daughter there's nothing to fear in the dark, and you tell her the world is filled with ghosts. It's got to stop."

"Children believe in ghosts," Jackie said quietly. "Tell them they don't exist, and kids know you don't understand the things that scare them. I understand all right. There's plenty to fear in the dark. Chris, tell me what's got you so scared."

Chris stared at her sister-in-law. "What the hell are you talking about? I'm scared my business is going into the toilet, that's what I'm scared of!" Without warning she buried her face in her hands. Her shoulders jerked up and down. Her voice came out in a strangled whisper. "I just wish that damn movie was over and done with, that's what I wish."

Jackie patted her shoulder. "It will be. They must be about halfway through with it by now, don't you think? Harry said it's going to be a good movie."

"Who cares?" Chris said tiredly. "All I know is I miss him. When he's home, he's exhausted, so I can't talk to him. Most of the time he stays in a hotel near the set, so I can't have him then, either. So I snap at anybody and everybody." She smiled apologetically at Jackie. "And I hate myself for doing that."

"It'll be over soon," Jackie said soothingly, "and everything will be just fine, you'll see."

Chris smiled uncertainly. "You're right. Well, let me collect my child and be off. Hold down the fort." She took in Jackie's little corner table, complete with tarot cards and other magic paraphernalia. "Maybe I should let you tell my fortune."

"Why, Chris." Jackie leaned forward, her voice a confidential whisper. "You know that stuff's just a bunch of garbage." She winked. "Go buy your kid an ice cream."

Chris waved good-bye. In the car she buckled the squirming three-year-old into the passenger seat.

"Radio," Roseanne announced.

"Just a minute." Chris turned it on and selected a soft-rock station.

Roseanne smiled. "Kenny."

"That's right, Kenny Rogers." She couldn't help but smile back. "Want some ice cream?"

"Uh-huh. Is Daddy coming home tonight?"

"I don't know." She threw the car in gear and pulled out

without looking. Miraculously no cars were coming. After a quick stop for milk and butter and the promised ice cream for Roseanne, Chris got them home. She unbuckled Roseanne. "Go in the house. I'm going to get the mail."

"Okay," Roseanne sang.

Chris watched the small figure trudge up the walk and disappear into the house. A fierce, protective feeling washed over her, animalistic in its strength. She knew she could easily kill anyone who tried to hurt her child. Protecting herself seemed much harder.

She touched the mailbox, trying to divine its contents by psychometry. Too bad Jackie was a phony; this would have been a good time to have a genuine psychic in the house. Probably junk mail. Or maybe it was a letter. In a light green, very small, delicate envelope. The kind a woman would use. But a real lady would have monogrammed stationery.

The envelopes had begun showing up just before shooting had started on the new film. *Angel of a Brighter Day* it was called. Chris thought it was pretty but too long. That was what Chris thought when she did think about things other than the little green envelopes that came two or three times a week. One more month, and the movie would be done. She wasn't altogether sure she could take four more weeks of little green envelopes.

She touched the mailbox again with tentative fingers. She didn't think it was in there today. She opened the mailbox.

Pale green colored the interior. It took her a bit, but she finally managed to get the envelope open. Today it simply read: "Your husband is in love with another woman."

The letters were cut out of magazines, so Chris didn't think she was dealing with somebody sane and normal. Chris didn't know who she was dealing with, and if they would just go away and leave her alone, she would have liked to forget about the whole mess. She stuffed the note in her pocket. Her hands were clammy. One more month. Four more weeks. Then she'd laugh at this. They would both laugh, she and Harry.

Inside the phone was ringing. She raced to catch it. "Hello?"

"Hi, Chris. It looks like we're going to run late again."

"So you won't be home tonight," she said slowly. In her pocket paper crinkled.

"If I could, I would; you know that. Kiss the baby for me."

She hung up, went upstairs, and stashed the note in her jewelry box with the others.

They were all clowning around, telling each other ridiculous puns, getting silly and weak with laughter.

"So," Karen said, giggling, coming to the end of a very long, drawn-out story, "the bank manager says to the teller, "it's a knick-knack, Patty Mack, give the frog a loan." She dissolved into laughter.

"That's terrible," Lake giggled. She, Harry, and Karen were hanging around between setups, wasting a little time. "Anybody got another one?"

"That's it for me," Karen said. "Hey." Her eyes danced. "Let's cornrow Harry's hair."

"Oh, no, you don't." Lake got into the act and he had to fight off both of them. The two women collapsed into a corner, weak with laughter.

"You guys think you're pretty cute, huh?"

"Yes, we do," Lake said modestly. "Admit it, we are cute."

"Damn cute," Karen put in.

"You know how I feel about you two." Harry grinned. "The great tragedy of my life is that I couldn't invent a cosmic blender. I'd put you in there, and *voilà,* the perfect woman."

"Perfect?"

"Oh, yes." Harry smiled, eyes closed. "I'd have this wonderful, sweet, nurturing, wild, unpredictable, absolutely gorgeous female."

"With two-tone hair." Karen smirked. "Wait, I've got one. Adam and Eve are in the Garden of Eden, you know, just hanging out, and Eve says—"

"You really think we'd be perfect?" Lake was intrigued by the idea.

"It's the old housewife-whore syndrome," Karen said.

"Oh, thanks a lot. I guess I know which contribution is mine."

"It's not that," Harry argued. "You guys are symbiotic. Together you are perfect."

"I wish they'd get on with it," Lake sighed. "I'm getting tired of sitting around. My energy is dissipating."

"Just listen to me a second. It's Karen's voice singing, right? But if you ask anybody who goes to see this film, it's Lake singing. Okay, the credits go by. They read, if they read credits, that somebody else is singing—Karen Singer. So who's really singing? Both of you."

Karen patted his head. "You're starting to sound like your sister. Weird. I'm going to see if they need me. If not, I'm going to go home, swim a few laps. See you guys." She waved a cheerful good-bye.

"I'm free tonight," Harry leered at Lake.

She leered back.

An assistant director knocked on the dressing room door. "Ms. Eastman, they're ready for you."

"About time," she grumbled. "Harry, are you going to watch?"

"Want me to?"

"Please."

"You got it." They walked onto the set together.

Matt came over to speak to Lake as her makeup and hair were being touched up.

"I want to do a run-through first, Lake, so you can take it easy. Just listen to the playback, lip-sync, do whatever feels comfortable for you. Harry, are you here for moral support?"

"Yes."

"Fine, just pick a clear spot and don't move a muscle. Just a run-through, everybody!" But when he got back to his place, Matt said to the cameraman, "Let's roll very quietly. I want to catch her before she starts acting."

"Playback!" someone yelped.

Music flooded the set. The intro flowed through Lake's body. Her neck trembled like a flower in the wind, head tipped to one side like a tender stalk. She opened her mouth and a voice as sweet and perfect as her face issued forth. Karen's voice, vibrating inside Lake's lips and buzzing sweetly on her tongue. Her teeth hummed with the sound. She could actually *feel* the phrasing of the song, what emotional choice Karen had made for each word. She felt the music inside herself, and she was filled completely.

The last notes faded away. The set was quiet.

An assistant director standing next to Matt whispered under his breath, "Fuck, that's *strange.*"

Lake was bewildered. "Is everything okay?"

"Did we get it?" Matt quietly asked the cameraman. The cameraman gave him the okay sign.

"Was it good?" Lake called out, beginning to feel anxious.

Harry spoke up. "It was perfect."

"Do you ever think about dying?" Lake asked Harry later that night.

"Hell, no." He laughed, spooning peanut butter from the jar, trying not to glob any on his bare chest. "Jesus, it's cold in here."

"The cleaning girl must have reset the thermostat."

"Get another cleaning girl."

She pulled the blanket up over his ribs. "You never answered me."

"Yes, I did. I said, 'Hell, no.' That's a quote."

"I think about it," Lake said pensively. "You know how they say if you see yourself die in a dream, you'll really die?"

"That's not so, Lake. I read that in a magazine."

"Oh, I know." She nodded. "I die in my dreams all the time, but here I am, still kicking. I think such crazy things, Harry. I dream I die a little bit at a time. I just disappear. First my legs, then the hips, up and up, until everything is gone. Like I never existed. Lately I've been thinking I won't disappear completely. I'll trick them. I'll hide all the good parts of myself someplace safe; I'll hide them in Karen, and a part of me will always be alive." She withered a little under his unreadable expression. "Don't look at me that way. Like I'm crazy. I'm not. Everybody has secret thoughts."

"Sure they do," Harry said evenly.

"But you don't."

"I'm an unimaginative guy."

"But you still love me?"

He kissed her neck. "That I do. I'm going to ask Chris for a divorce the night we wrap."

"I'm glad," Lake said decisively. "You'll keep the secret thoughts away, won't you, Harry?"

He took her in his arms. "I'll try."

They were both tired. It was silly to attempt to make love when they were both exhausted, but Matt insisted. He was trying to be nice to her, Karen realized. But it had been so long since they had even attempted intercourse; better to sleep through the night curled up together like a brother and sister in the enchanted wood than to try to act like a husband and wife.

She lay under him and tried to behave in an encouraging fashion. It was over quickly. He rolled off and stretched out alongside her.

"Did you have fun?" he asked in the darkness.

"Well, sure." She got out of bed and went over to the window, pulling the hair away from her face.

"It looks pretty that way."

"What?"

"Your hair looks pretty back like that. I always like it when you put your hair up."

"I'm scared, Matt. I'm scared we're not going to make it."

He set his mouth. "We'll make it if you want to, Kar," he said grimly. "It's up to you."

27

JACKIE STOOD, transfixed. "My God!" Her eyes widened. "You cut your hair!" She took Karen's hand and pulled her into the September sunlight pouring through the large window. "Carnelian" was reflected backward onto the gray carpet. "Well, aren't you brave."

"Not that brave. I practically cried in the hairdresser's," Karen admitted.

"Why'd you do it?"

"Oh, I don't know, I suppose I needed a change. Kind of nice to find out I have ears."

"We got some real nice earrings in," Jackie offered. "I bet you could use those."

"I'll take a look," Karen promised. "But what I really need is a terrific dress for the wrap party tonight. Now that I've finally gotten used to my new haircut, I realize I don't have any clothes that go with it."

"We'll find you something." Jackie started sifting through a rack of dresses. "So they finished the movie."

"Just about. Lake's done. I think they're picking up a few of Harry's close-ups today, just for insurance."

Jackie's hands rested on a bright purple dress. She smiled at Karen. "You'd look truly for shit in this color, wouldn't you?"

"Absolutely."

Jackie's smile grew. "Just pulling your leg. We'll find you just the right dress." She lowered her voice. "Have you spoken to Chris lately?"

"Well, no. I've been pretty busy, what with rewrites, things like that. Why? Something up with her?"

"Keep it down," Jackie said. "She's in the back room. Yeah, something's up with her, only she's keeping it to herself, and I'm starting to get pretty worried. Maybe she'll talk to you." She held up a dress. "How about this?"

They both shook their heads no.

"Don't worry," Jackie insisted, "that dress is in here, I just know it."

"Well, hello." Looking tired and drawn, Chris came from the back room carrying a stack of boxes. "What brings the original blue jean lady to Carnelian?" She set the boxes down and got her first good look at Karen's hair. "I like it," she said slowly. "Nope, change that. I *love* it. Really brings out those big hazel eyes. Did you just come by to visit, or can I relieve you of some of your money?"

"Both." Karen tried to smile. In truth she was appalled. Chris looked haunted, and by a hyperactive ghost. She had lost weight, and something in her face looked slack. Karen explained her wardrobe problem.

"Go in the dressing room," Chris said. "I'll bring you in a few to get started. Want some coffee?"

"Only if you'll have a cup with me. For the past few months all anybody's ever said to me is 'I need this rewrite tomorrow.' I'm starved for a little conversation."

Karen had just pulled her sweater over her head when Chris reappeared, two cups balanced in one hand, four dresses in the other. Karen took the dresses from her and hung them up. "Please, sit, relax," she told Chris.

"All right. What do you want to talk about?"

"Anything but this movie."

"Fine." Chris smiled tightly. "But try this on. Straight from Paris. *Vogue* hasn't even seen it yet."

Karen squirmed into the dress quickly. She took one look at herself in the mirror. "I look like a total fool," she said succinctly.

"Nooo," Chris hedged. "Let's just say you're not the *Vogue* type. Try this one."

"You really think I can wear this color?"

"Oh, sure, if you wear a very pink blush. Blue-pink."

"Blue-pink," Karen muttered, struggling into the dress.

Chris sipped her coffee. "I don't think a blusher could save that dress."

"Me, neither."

"Karen," Chris said slowly, "Harry didn't . . . " She sighed, dragging the words out with a visible effort. "That is . . . oh, shit. When you were working on the movie, did you ever see him with someone?"

"Someone?" Karen repeated stupidly.

"A woman." She grabbed Karen's hand as she was trying to poke it through a sleeve. "I know I can trust you. You'd tell me if something was going on? Wouldn't you?"

"Sure I would, Chris," Karen replied guiltily.

Chris started to cry. "I'm sorry, this is so embarrassing. If you knew what I've been going through these past three months . . . " She dug into her pocket and pulled out a pale green envelope.

Karen read it. "You've been getting these for three months?"

Chris nodded. "Since the movie started, maybe a little before."

"Have you been to police?"

"No."

"You've got to, Chris. They handle this sort of thing."

She spoke bitterly. "I didn't want the cops to know I thought my husband was sleeping around. Can you beat that? I was too scared to ask Harry about it, in case it was true." She bit her lip. "He's been so preoccupied lately that those notes . . . well, maybe somebody *does* know something I don't."

"That's ridiculous," Karen said hotly. "Chris, this is just a sick mind getting its kicks, harassing some innocent person. He probably picked your name out of the phone book."

"Why, Karen." Chris measured her words. "You know we're unlisted."

"Probably picked your mailbox at random. There are a lot of sick people in this town." Karen was shaking with anger. She couldn't believe Lake had done such a horrible thing. But, of course, she wasn't responsible; that was the standard excuse.

"I couldn't stand to lose Harry," Chris was saying. "I'd really go crazy. You *would* tell me if anything was wrong, wouldn't you, Karen?"

"Of course I would," she soothed, feeling like a heel. "Don't worry about a thing, Chris." She shrunk from the frightened woman's cloying touch. "Honest. Everything's fine."

Finally Chris seemed to relax. "I think you'll like this dress. It's one of a kind, an antique." She held up a high-waisted ivory velvet dress, its round neck trimmed in seed pearls.

Karen held her breath. "Yes, that's gorgeous."

"A gift." Chris held it out. "Go on, take it. I bought it years ago in London; it's not even my size. It was just so beautiful I had to have it."

"Thank you."

"Besides, you need the proper accessories for a dress like that. I'm *still* going to make a fortune off you. Get dressed. I'll meet you over at the jewelry counter."

Chris left the dressing room area, noting with some surprise that Lake Eastman was browsing around the belts and handbags. She'd never seen Lake in the shop before and knew the blonde shopped elsewhere. "Hello, are you together?"

Lake looked around. "Excuse me?"

"No, I meant Karen. She's in the dressing room."

"Just a coincidence." Lake smiled. After tonight she'd have Harry all to herself. She couldn't help but gloat a little. She held out a leather belt. "I'll take this. What have you got in lingerie?"

"Something for that special someone?"

She practically laughed out loud. "Someone very special."

Chris took some lace-trimmed teddies out of a case and put them on the counter for Lake's examination. "Jackie?" she called. "Would you take care of Ms. Eastman? I promised I'd show Karen that pearl choker."

"This is lovely," Lake purred, fingering the lace trim on a bikini panty.

"Hello, Lake," Karen said pointedly. "What are you doing here?"

"Shopping," Lake sang blithely. She held up the panties. "Think that special someone will appreciate these?"

Karen said something under her breath.

"I can't hear you."

"I said I think you're a cunt." She turned to Chris. "Look, I've really got to run. Just wrap up whatever you think goes with the dress. I trust your taste. Here's my charge card."

"What's wrong with you?" Lake whispered.

"Wrong with me?" Karen snapped. "That's a good one, Lake." She signed the charge slip hurriedly and walked out to her car.

Lake ran down the street after her. "Karen, wait! I was just having a little fun with Chris. I know it was bitchy, but I was just so excited, Harry's going to ask her for a divorce tonight."

"Why'd you have to do it? That's all I want to know." Karen turned on her furiously. "And don't you dare tell me you couldn't help yourself. I've heard that excuse just once too often to buy it anymore."

"Do what?" Lake was mystified. "I don't know what you're talking about."

"Oh, don't play innocent. The notes, Lake, the nasty little notes you've been sending Chris for the past three months. Why, Lake? In case Harry changed his mind?"

"What notes? Karen, I swear I don't know what you're talking about." Lake grabbed at her sleeve. "Karen, please! Don't run away from me. Tell me what's going on! We're friends—"

"Not anymore." Karen gunned the motor and drove away.

Sid was doing a new face. Some wish-upon-a-starlet, as he called them, a producer's favorite, an agent's bedside companion. She was fair and buxom as a Gibson girl, but the camera liked bone structure and abhorred jowls. Sid was doing his best, but after three quarters of an hour, he was more than willing to give up show biz and try real estate. So when the phone rang, it was a more than welcome diversion.

"George! You must be a mind reader. I could use a friendly voice right about now."

"Could you use dinner tonight?" George asked.

"Who am I to turn down a free meal? We *are* talking free, aren't we, dearie?" He picked up a shade of blush and discarded it, frowning.

"We're talking home cooked." George laughed. "Considering how you've looked after me these past couple of months, it's the least I could do for you. How's eight?"

"Terribly sophisticated and eminently satisfactory. Shall I bring some wine?"

"Just bring yourself. See you at eight." He hung up.

The starlet laughed at Sid's expression. "Who was that? Your boyfriend?"

"No, just a friend."

"I'll just bet."

Sid smiled, arming himself with brush and powder. "Now, let's coax those cheekbones out of hiding, shall we?"

The end of a film always signaled a period of introspection for Matt. Not depression—he knew himself well, and he was not a man given to depression. He was a man in control of his life and his emotions. But from time to time he wondered at the apparent ease with which success had come to him. The brass ring had always hovered close at hand. There would have to be a payback; he believed it firmly.

"You are very tired," he told himself, stabling his car in the garage, searching for his house keys. Karen's car was gone, and she'd left a note for him on the kitchen table.

Out riding. Back at five—will kiss the horsie for you.
Love,
Karen

He smiled. He'd gotten her a horse on her last birthday, and he was always happy when she seemed to enjoy his gifts.

Five o'clock was at least an hour away. Being introspective, he was thinking about things he did not normally think about. He got a soda out of the fridge, said an introspective hello to the once-a-week cleaning lady, then went upstairs to the bedroom.

My wife, he thought in amazement, opening drawers, touching her clothes—everything soft and fragrant. Everything smelled like her. A miracle that she belonged to him. After the film was edited, they'd be able to spend more time together.

He opened her nightstand. Karen was meticulous about her work, but her closets and drawers looked as if the cyclone that had transported Dorothy to Oz had hit her bedroom first. In her nightstand was a paperback novel, a frowsy ball of silk scarves, all knotted and wrinkled, one slipper, a narrow leather belt, Isotoner gloves still in the box, and a box of stationery with two rubber bands around it. Idly he pulled the rubber bands off and opened the box. It was full of letters.

Karen wasn't all that sentimental. She hated clutter and threw out everything from old birthday cards to family newsletters. These were something else, something she couldn't bring herself to part with. Love letters.

You are always a trespasser when you read somebody else's letters. An emotional voyeur. Matt, a man of carefully controlled emotions, read the letters he should have written to his wife. He never burned that way; it wasn't a part of him.

They were beautiful letters. The voice behind them was sweet and true. He was probably a good man.

Of course, Matt reasoned. What other kind of man would Karen be in love with?

He put the letters back and closed the box. Funny she hadn't hidden them in a safer place. Maybe she wanted him to find out. Maybe she had just assumed he would never go through her things. And he never would have if there hadn't been a seed of doubt deep inside, germinating. He took the box and went out to his car.

Although he'd only been there once, he remembered how to get to the little theater. The stage manager was only too happy to tell the big Hollywood director where to find one of the actors. His directions took Matt to a small development, one of those already furnished places that featured lime green shag carpeting.

He found the right apartment but hesitated before he knocked, hearing the man, the *lover,* inside. It sounded like he was on the phone.

" . . . take it easy," Matt could hear plainly through the door. "Your parents are *never* going to like him. They're not going to change after all these years. You just have to take a hard line with them. You love him, he loves you; that's enough. We're a little old to need Mommy and Daddy's approval, right? Okay, call me later. I'm here if you need to talk."

A dog woofed softly. Not a "hey, somebody's breaking in" woof; more like "I smell somebody in the hall, boss. How do you want to handle this?"

Matt rang the doorbell. The dog started earning his keep, barking up a storm.

Johnny came to the door wearing an old sweatshirt turned fleecy-side-out and a surprised expression. For a moment it was clear he didn't know who Matt was.

"Yes?" he said pleasantly. Then he remembered.

"Can I come in for a minute?"

Johnny hesitated. The way his luck was running lately, this little tête-à-tête would wind up in tomorrow's *Enquirer:* "Jealous Husband Shoots Actor and Dog. Dog Survives." "Sure, come on in."

The dog, a shepherd mix of advanced years, sniffed Matt's sleeve curiously.

"He's not mine," Johnny explained. "I'm watching him for a friend. He's a good dog." He rubbed the dog's chest, uncertain of what to do.

"He looks like a good dog," Matt pitched in. He had no idea what to do, either. He patted the dog's head. The dog was practically fainting with joy at all the unaccustomed attention.

"Can I get you some coffee?"

Matt didn't drink coffee. "That would be fine."

The apartment was very small, but it had a separate kitchen and bedroom, and it was very neat. The omnipresent lime green shag carpeting was as intrusive as always, but there was a good art print on one wall, a framed poster on another. Johnny went into the little kitchen and started fiddling around with a Melita.

Matt watched him. He must have really done a good job on stage, because the limp was very pronounced now. He put the box of stationery on the table.

Johnny came back with the coffee. "You want sugar or milk?"

Matt pushed the box toward him. "Open it. Go on."

Puzzled, Johnny complied. "She kept my letters," he said with quiet pride. He looked up at Matt. "What is it you want from me?"

Good question, Matt thought to himself. I wanted you to be a child molester, an ax murderer, anything but a nice guy who dispenses advice to the lovelorn via Ma Bell, dog-sits in his spare time, and has paid enough dues to keep the nice-guy union solvent for the next decade. "I don't know what I want. I'm sorry if I bothered you."

"We never slept together."

Matt started to laugh. "Well, that certainly makes a whole lot of difference. I'm not going to give her a divorce, you know. And she'll never leave without my blessing."

"Then give it," Johnny said quietly. "If you love her enough, let her go."

"No," Matt said.

Eight p.m.

Karen was in the shower when he got back. Karen's showers could go for a half-an-hour easily. He stretched out on the bed, listening to the water run, listening to Karen sing as the water pelted her. She would sing the most idiotic things in the shower: selections from *The Rocky Horror Picture Show;* Jeanette MacDonald-Nelson Eddy duets, both parts.

I'm losing her. The water stopped. She would be toweling off, rubbing her body briskly.

Correction, you've lost her.

She came out of the bathroom wrapped in a towel and smiling. "Hi. Sorry I'm running so late. I hung out at the stable longer than I should have."

"I just got in myself."

"Oh, where were you?" She went over to the dresser to her underwear. Water glistened on her back.

"I went to see a friend of yours."

"Oh? Who?"

He held up the stationery box. Her back was to him as she fished a pair of pantyhose out of a dresser drawer. "I asked you who—" She sat on the bed next to him and took the box away. "You had no right to go through my things," she said lamely.

"Then you should have hidden them better."

"Nothing happened. I didn't—"

He closed his eyes in pain. "I know you didn't." He handed her the box. "Put that away someplace safe. We don't ever have to talk about it again."

"Matt?"

"It's over," he said firmly. He took the box from her and put it on the highest shelf in her closet, the one she couldn't reach without a stepladder. "It's over," he repeated and sounded satisfied.

"You look beautiful!" Lake came over to greet them, temporarily relinquishing her proprietary hold on Harry's arm. She kissed Karen's cheek, aware that Karen pulled back slightly.

"You're drunk," she whispered to Lake.

"It's a party!" Lake crossed her eyes and stuck out her tongue. "Karen's mad at me," she told Harry and Matt, "and I don't even know why." She attached herself to Matt. "Let's mingle," she said coyly. "Harry will look after Karen for us." She dragged Matt off, leaving Harry and Karen staring at each other awkwardly.

"Something going on between you two?" he asked. "Lake was very upset."

"Nothing important." Karen shrugged. She didn't want to get into it at that moment.

He looked down at his feet. "I'm going to tell Chris tonight."

"Are you sure? About Lake?"

"Yes." He smiled. "No, maybe."

She rose on tiptoe and hugged him. "I wish you the best, Harry, I really do."

He laughed. "You mean I have your blessings?"

"Well, let's just say I wish you the best."

His fingers touched the little seed pearls decorating the scoop neck of her dress. "You used to have a V-neck sweater this color."

"I can't believe you remember my wardrobe from ten years ago."

"You'd be surprised at what I remember. Look at you now, kiddo. Rich and successful. I always knew you were going to make it."

"You *never* did." Karen stared at him in amazement. "If you had honestly believed that for one second, you wouldn't have left me behind when you came to California. You've always gone for pick of the litter when it came to women, Harry. That's why you're leaving Chris for Lake. She fits your image—beautiful, young, famous. You're going to find you miss your wife a lot more than you planned to."

He gave her a strange smile. "All the wives stick together. Well, I can't blame you for feeling threatened. If Matt ever found somebody else, you'd be in Chris's shoes."

"You might be, too, someday."

He walked away from her, shaking his head.

"Matt?" Anxiously she combed the crowd, looking for him.

"Here I am." He appeared at her side. "What's the matter?"

"I'm having a shitty time at this party. Let's go home."

"We'll go home in an hour, how's that?"

"I'd rather go home *now.*"

Matt looked at her curiously. "Are you and Lake on the outs?"

"Oh, you know I hate it when she's drunk."

"She's just a little buzzed. Must be something else," he said shrewdly. "Come on, I know you better than that."

Karen hesitated. "Lake has been sending anonymous notes to Chris. You know, there-is-another-woman type notes. I guess she wanted to twist Harry's arm a little."

"Doesn't sound like Lake at all." Matt frowned. "To do that you need somebody who's been on simmer for a long time. Lake goes directly to boil."

"And when did you become an expert in psychology?"

He smiled. "I bow to my resident authority on Lake Eastman's frazzled psyche. I've got to talk to a few people, thank them for a job well done—you know the routine."

"Unfortunately," Karen groaned.

"One hour," he promised.

Loud rock music was playing. Couples were dancing, pausing to dip into the caterer's trays of dainties, sampling each other's pet drugs before returning to their dizzying gyrations. Karen was bored, and she was starting to get a headache. She amused herself by picking strawberries out of a mountain of beautifully displayed fresh fruit.

A man came over and started foraging next to her.

"Hi," Karen said, "I don't remember you. You'll have to forgive me."

"No, I'm a guest of one of the sound guys. Karen Singer, right?" He shook her hand. "I heard some of the music for the film. Outstanding."

"Glad you think so."

"You sing beautifully. I'd like you to have my card."

"Oh?" Karen was wary. Gingerly she accepted the card. "Michael Chernick," it read, "President, Red Hot Records."

"Thank you, Michael."

"Please, give me a call when you have some free time. I've got some tunes I think would be dynamite with your sound."

"Thanks." She slipped the card into her bag only because he was watching. It was hardly an original pickup line. Michael Chernick, President, wandered away.

Matt found her. "Dance with me." He smiled, holding out his hand to his wife. Obligingly the loud rock music segued into a loud rock ballad. "I think I can manage this tempo."

They moved onto the dance floor, adopting the shambling gait of the other couples. "I hear they're going to give out awards later," Matt shouted in her ear. "Strictly on the QT, the word is you're a shoo-in for a Major Rewrite memorial award. Then again you are the only nominee in that category."

"Flatterer," she told him. Matt trod firmly on her foot. "Klutz."

"That's more like it." He pulled her closer. "I love you, Kar."

"Uh-oh. Every time you say that, I get the sneaking suspicion you're going to ask me to do another rewrite."

"Not tonight."

Lake's bright laughter rode the crest of the music. She and Harry danced over. Lake had switched to red wine. Karen eyed the dark liquid with a certain foreboding. She pushed against Matt, trying to get him to dance farther away.

"Still mad at me?" Lake pouted. "For once in my life I am innocent. Am I not innocent, Harry?"

He mumbled something and tried to steer her away.

"I want to talk to my friend," she said insistently, pulling back. They twirled, careening into another couple. Lake's hand dipped, and the wine sloshed over, splashing onto Karen's neck, dripping bloodily down the front of her one-of-a-kind dress.

"Oh!" Lake put her hand up to her mouth. "I'm so sorry. It was an accident."

The wine felt clammy against Karen's skin. Everything would be stained.

"I'm sorry," Lake repeated. Clumsily she began to brush at the stain with her hands. The second she touched her, Karen exploded.

"Get away from me!" she screamed.

Lake sobered immediately. "I said I was sorry. I'll replace the dress. You should get out of that wet thing; it'll probably stain right through to your skin." Again she moved to help.

"Don't touch me," Karen warned. "Don't ever come near me again." She walked out.

Lake started to run after her.

"Don't." Harry grabbed her arm. "Give her time to cool off. You can call her tomorrow."

Relief flooded her face. "I'll do that," Lake said. "Karen won't stay mad at me. She never has before. I'll call her tomorrow."

Harry whispered something in her ear.

She pealed laughter. "That's exactly what I was thinking. Let's go home."

George sputtered with helpless laughter. "Where the hell did you get that sharp little outfit?"

Sid turned around gracefully. "What's the matter? You act as if you'd never seen a hot pink tuxedo before."

"Where the hell did you get that?"

"Wardrobe department at the studio. Will I clash with dinner?"

"I don't think so. Let me give you a drink." George dashed into the kitchen. "You want wine or something stronger?"

"What are you drinking?" Sid called. Whatever it was, George had had a head start of considerable proportions.

"Jack Daniels."

"You're kidding."

"No, I'm not."

"I'll stick to white wine." Sid settled himself into a chair, frowning. "Now I'm clashing with your furniture. This suit was a stupid idea. Well, it was worth it to hear you laughing again, my friend. For a while I was worried about you." The phone rang. "Want me to get that?"

George was crashing around in the kitchen. "What?" he yelled over the din.

"Never mind." Sid reached for the receiver. The voice at the other end uttered a terse message, then hung up. "Now that was the strangest wrong number I ever heard," Sid said as George reappeared, bearing drinks.

"What do you mean?" George asked.

"Didn't give his name, didn't ask who I was, just said 'They left together'—gave it a perfectly awful dramatic reading—and hung up."

George grinned sloppily. "Yeah, that really is a weird wrong number. Only in California, land of fruits and nuts. Uh, sorry about the fruits—it's just an expression."

"I've heard it before."

George just stood there, head bobbing slightly. He seemed to be trying to make a very important decision about something.

"George, is something wrong?"

"No." George snapped to himself. "I just forgot something. Would you excuse me a sec? Keep an eye on dinner; if anything burns, just throw it in the sink." He went into the bedroom, locking the door. Gulping his drink, he reached for the phone, dialing a number he had committed to memory.

His throat burned. He couldn't believe he was actually doing this. The decision had been toyed with for a long time, but George hadn't really believed he would actually go this far.

"Hello?" She sounded frightened.

All I have to do is hang up, he told himself, and everything will be just as it was. All I have to do . . . "Mrs. Townsend?" he whispered, "they'll be together tonight. All night."

"Who is this?"

"They'll be at her place. I think you know where Lake Eastman lives, don't you?"

"I don't believe you."

"Then where is your husband, Mrs. Townsend?"

She was silent.

"Why don't you go over there and see for yourself?" Carefully he replaced the receiver on its cradle.

Sid rapped on the door. "Unless you're a fan of well done, dinner is served." There was no answer. He rapped again. "George, are you okay?"

Smiling, George came out of the bedroom. "Couldn't be better. Let's eat."

"Who was that on the phone?" Jackie asked. She was trying to learn a new stitch in her knitting, and she was completely tangled up in yarn. She'd heard Chris on the phone, but Jackie had been so preoccupied with her wool that she hadn't heard any of her sister-in-law's conversation.

Roseanne sat on the floor playing with the yarn, which wasn't helping Jackie much.

"No one," Chris said abruptly. "Wrong number."

"That was a pretty long conversation for a wrong number."

Chris shrugged. "Was it?" She yawned elaborately, pretending to concentrate on the program on the TV. "How's the knitting coming along?"

"Well, don't count on seeing it before next spring."

Chris looked at her watch surreptitiously. If he wasn't home by two a.m., maybe she'd take a little ride.

One a.m.

"Absolutely, I remember that girl." Sid nodded emphatically. "She was deadly."

"She was a total pig," George reminisced. "But the first time is always a little disgusting, a little bit of a letdown. I always figured that's what put you off women. Just got grossed out the first time out of the gate." He topped off his glass.

"Hey, take it easy on that, George."

George waved his objections aside. "So, tell me, was the first time really so bad? With a girl, I mean."

"It was all right. Just nothing to write home about."

"Could you function?"

He laughed. "I thought of Clark Gable."

"Clark Gable?"

"A classic never goes out of style." Sid smiled. "It was fine. Clark, me, and the little lady got along just fine. It just wasn't what I wanted."

"What about the first time with a guy?"

"That was no great shakes, either."

"You remember your first big romance?"

Sid eyed him suspiciously. "Are you interviewing me for *People* magazine?"

"Just curious."

"Sure I remember my first big romance," Sid said slowly.

"Did I know him?"

"No, it was before we met. He was such a good person. Not flashy, not flamboyant—just a very good, quiet man."

"What happened? I mean, did you just outgrow the relationship? Did he find somebody else?"

"No," Sid said tiredly. "He was driving home from work one night, and someone was coming in the other direction. This other man . . . his headlights just shorted out. Just like that, no reason, it just happened. There was a head-on collision. They were both killed."

"Must have been his time to go."

"I guess." His voice was bitter. "There are a lot of things I just don't understand, and that's top of my list. I've loved others since, but I can't say it's been the same."

"Then you still miss him."

"Oh, yes."

"Then how is it you don't understand how I feel about Lake?" he asked with drunken cunning. "It's the same thing."

Sid winced. "No it isn't, George. Your love for her almost destroyed you. Thank God it's over now."

"Maybe not," George said, enunciating with a drunk's exaggerated care.

"I heard Harry's going to leave the wife and kid for Lake. Pretty reliable source, too."

"He'll only leave her if it's easy. I know that guy like I know myself. He'll bail out as soon as it gets messy." His leer resembled a Halloween pumpkin face. "And it's going to get messy."

Sid got a sick feeling in the pit of his stomach. "What do you mean?"

"Sid, you understand. You know that a person falls in love only once in his lifetime. Everyone else is a substitute, more or less. But that first one, either you get them or you don't. And if you don't, you spend the rest of your life trying to get that feeling back. You don't just get over it because it's the intelligent thing to do. You think about her, and the pain is as sharp as if it happened yesterday." His voice softened. "I would have done anything for that girl. I would have killed for her."

Panic supplanted the sick feeling. Sid tried to laugh, but it stuck in his throat. "You're kidding me, George. You couldn't hurt a fly."

"I'd do anything to get her back. You know that, Sid."

"You . . . you haven't done anything to Harry, have you?"

George laughed humorlessly. "I could. He's not under contract to me anymore." His smile widened at Sid's horrified expression. "Relax. There's a real problem with violence. If they catch you, they put you away for a long time. A good lawyer can get you off on a multitude of charges, but murder? That's a real crapshoot, particularly if the accused had a good motive. Love or money. Those are your basic good motives. No, I haven't done anything to Harry. Haven't harmed a hair on his precious little head. Satisfied?" He patted Sid's hand. "I didn't have to do anything to Harry. Lake's going to come back to me; she always does when everything falls apart. Be happy for me, Sid."

Sid was staring at him, horrified. "What have you done,

George?" His mind played back the earlier part of the evening—the strange wrong number, George's subsequent disappearance into his bedroom. He'd been phoning, Sid was almost positive. "Who did you call?"

"Call?"

"After the wrong number. You went into the bedroom and made a phone call. Who did you call?"

"Should that be whom? No," George mused drunkenly, "whom never sounds right, even when it is. I guess you just have to use it with confidence. Who or whom did I call? I called an understanding woman. She knows just how I feel, because . . . " His mouth stretched into a rubbery grin. "Her husband is fucking my lady. I felt she had a right to know."

"Oh, my God," Sid mumbled. "How could you do such a thing to that poor woman?"

"She must be on her way over there," George said placidly. "I figured she'd think about it for a while, but eventually she'd have to go and see for herself."

Sid got up and stumbled to the door in shock. He gunned his car, hoping he could remember where Chris lived to tell her she'd been the victim of a cruel, twisted mind.

I thought I knew him, he repeated to himself, over and over. I thought I loved him. In a way he had never considered, Lake had taken George away from him forever. His foot pressed harder on the accelerator.

Bright lights reflecting in his rearview almost blinded him. A cop. Oh, Jesus, that was all he needed. Obediently Sid pulled over.

The cop shone a flashlight in the window. "License and registration, please."

Sid fumbled for a while, then handed them over. He glanced hurriedly at his watch. Almost two o'clock. "Officer, I'm terribly worried about a friend of mine. I was just driving over to see how she is."

"That's no excuse for speeding. Would you get out of the car, please?" He grinned broadly at Sid's attire. "Oh, I like the little toy suit."

Sid knew better than to start an argument. "Please, I'm really very worried about this friend. Could you possibly call? Mrs. Chris Townsend. Just to see if she's all right." He scrawled her number on the back of a scrap of paper.

"You can make the call yourself later. Right now I'd like you to take a breathalyzer test."

"Please, call *now.* Can't you radio in, have somebody call her *now?* I think something terrible is going to happen."

Something in his face convinced the cop. He accepted the paper and tramped back to his black-and-white. After five unbearably long minutes he was back. "Busy. She can't be in too much trouble if she's yapping on the phone, can she?"

"Send a car out there," Sid begged. "Please, officer, a phone can be out of order, the lines can be down temporarily—"

"This is a very interesting little dodge you have cooked up. I think you're going to take a little test."

Sid practically cried. That feeling of impending disaster would not go away. He felt terrible. If he had known that Jackie liked to take the phone off the hook at night so no one would wake the baby, he would have felt worse.

Chris sat in her car and laughed. Two-time loser, she thought. It sounded like a song. A song that was getting too much airplay and was starting to grate on the nerves.

She had waited until one-thirty, worrying over her decision like a terrier would worry a bedroom slipper. To go or not to go . . . that was the question.

To trust or not to trust.

Somewhere along the line she had stopped trusting. At some point between the first husband, who had left for someone younger, and the younger husband, who had left for someone prettier, she had come to realize that her place in the world was precarious. She did not trust her life to remain pleasant. Goddamn it, she trusted the voice on the phone. Evil was a very tangible force, much more so than good.

Her hands were clammy against the steering wheel as she drove, practically crawling over the winding hillside roads. It wouldn't do to wrap herself around a telephone pole before she even got there, now would it?

He won't be there, she told herself, making up a little tune. He won't be there, he won't be there, tra-la! She would drive home and find Harry snuggling with a sleepy Roseanne on the couch. They'd be waiting up for her. At first he would be angry with her—how could she doubt him? But soon after they would be laughing together, whispering like any pair of lovers. Home safe. Olly-olly-oxen free.

I'll be home again soon, she told herself, getting out of the car. And everything will be all right. Her feet trod over the grass. She didn't see his car, which encouraged her greatly.

She was right in front of the house.

The curtains weren't drawn in the big bay window that looked in on the living room. She could see some movement within. She peeked through the window.

A fire burned merrily in the fireplace, soundless through the glass. She imagined its crackling and popping. In front of the fire a man and a woman writhed in mute passion. They were both very, very beautiful, but they looked as graceless as any other pair of rutting animals. Their breath would be harsh and unlovely; flesh would slap against flesh with a damp sound.

Numb, Chris watched her husband make love to another woman. Her little tune, "He won't be there," turned into that cloying old song, number one on her hit parade, by popular request, "Two-time loser."

So she sat in the car and laughed. Because laughing was always better than crying. And she was done crying. There were no tears left in her. In fact there was not a great deal of any emotion left in her. She got back into her car and drove home carefully. She swiveled around and checked to see that the garage door was closed. Then she turned on the motor.

A few hours later Roseanne woke up. "Mommy?" she called, slipping from her bed. "Mommy?"

She started downstairs.

28

THE NURSE POINTED to the man in the waiting room. "The husband," she whispered to the doctor. "I think it's so horrible. The little girl going down and getting into the car with her mother. It's fine for them to screw around and do whatever they want, but when the children become involved, that's where I draw the line."

The doctor walked away from her without saying a word. "Mr. Townsend?"

The man looked up hopefully. He'd spent the night in hell; whether he deserved it or not was a moot point. "Is there any change?"

"I'm sorry, your daughter is still in a coma. We can't tell if there's any permanent brain damage; I'm afraid we just have to wait and see. It's very lucky your sister happened to find them when she did."

"Lucky." He rubbed his hands absently. "What about my wife?"

"I'm sorry, Mr. Townsend. Her EEG is completely flat. We have her on respirators and other life-support systems. But . . . " He hesitated, broaching a particularly difficult area. "Mr. Townsend, were you aware that your wife had a donor card? That she wished to donate her organs for transplant in the event of her death?"

"No, I didn't know." He looked at the doctor dully. "What of it? Chris isn't dead. If she's breathing, she's still alive."

"Yes, well . . ." The doctor's voice trailed off. "I just felt you should know."

"Can I see Chris?"

"Yes, of course." He walked Harry over to Chris's room. "Stay as long as you like." He closed the door, leaving them alone.

Chris was lying there, her chest going up and down, mimicking normal sleep. He knew it was the respirator, but it was easy to fool himself. He closed his eyes and tried to imagine the doctors cutting her up, taking bits and pieces out of her body so other bodies could keep running. No, he couldn't agree to that. She was still alive. Heart pumped, blood flowed. That was life.

A nurse came in and checked the machines.

"She's still in there," he told her.

She was plainly startled. "That's right," she said after a while. "She's still there."

"What would happen if you turned off the machines?"

"She can't breath for herself," the nurse said gently.

After ten more minutes he went down the hall to Roseanne's room, but he could not bring himself to go in.

Jackie found him there.

"I couldn't go in," he explained to her, then started to cry.

She held him. "That's okay, that's okay," she said soothingly. "She's a tough little girl, she'll be okay. Let's go home."

"Thank God you found them, Jackie."

"Come on." She sounded as if she were coaxing a balky child. "We'll go home now."

She drove. They did not speak much, and they did not discuss what had happened at all. Jackie didn't pull into the garage. Inside they drank coffee in silence. After a while she got up and poured him a stiff drink. "Roseanne will be okay," she said again, there being nothing else to say.

"I've been thinking," Harry said. "What was it that made you wake up and go down to the garage?"

"I don't know. Probably just heard the car running."

"Maybe you've got the gift, Jackie."

She gave him a wry smile. "I don't think so."

"What happened?" He shook his head slowly. "All I ever wanted was to be in the movies. I wanted to be a movie star. How the hell did all this happen? Is it just this place? Is it really as bad as everybody says?"

"I don't think a place can ever be bad," Jackie said slowly. "It's just . . . here they've got the best of everything—the most beautiful clothes, the finest food, the prettiest people—but it's not the way it really is. It's the same here as anyplace else. You can make the same mistakes here as anyplace else, only you don't feel like you're going to have to pay for it."

Harsh sobs shook his body. "I loved Chris. I never knew how much."

"I know."

"Hell of a time to find out."

The phone rang. Jackie moved to get it.

"Let it ring," Harry said. "We both know who it is."

It rang twenty-seven times.

"I'm glad you called me."

"It was simply parasitic," Sid said apologetically. "I could have called a limo to take me to the airport—"

"Don't be silly, Sid." Karen kept her eyes on the cardboard coffee cup. "Any excuse to get away from the house."

"Lake still calling you?"

She nodded. "Every hour on the hour. Harry won't talk to her; she's going out of her mind. Poor Harry. His little girl's been in a coma for almost a week, and he can't bring himself to terminate Chris. 'Terminate.' " She laughed hollowly. "That sounds nice and sterile. The last time we spoke . . . Sid, he can't accept the fact that she's *dead.* As long as the machines are going, he can make himself believe she's alive. It's so sad." She started to uncurl the lip of her cardboard cup. "How long do you think you're going to be away?"

"Until I get tired of England. The countryside should be lovely this time of year. And I hear Nottingham is *trés* gay."

"Nottingham. Robin Hood and his Merry Men?"

"I rest my case."

She smiled weakly. "I don't want you to go, Sid. You're the only normal person I know."

"Darling, I am a middle-aged black homosexual makeup artist. If that is your idea of normal, your life is in sad shape."

"My life is in sad shape." A tear fell on the terminal floor. "Sid, I try so hard to do the right thing."

He tugged a strand of hair. "Don't try so hard. Karen, life is hard and miserable and too damned short. You're not happy with Matt, are you?"

She looked at him in alarm.

"Oh, there aren't any rumors going around. It's just something I've felt for a long time. There's a lot of affection between you two, but I never felt that you loved him, not the way it should be. Is there someone else you're thinking of?"

"Just thinking," she swore. "Nothing else."

"Then go to the man you love. Whether you stay or go, Matt

will be hurt, and if you try to spare him the pain, something else will give and your house of cards will come down on you just the same. You can't make life less tragic by being a good little girl, Kar. You'll follow all the rules, and you'll be miserable. Do what you want to do; trust yourself a little more. You'll do the right thing."

"You make it sound so easy."

"No, dear one." He smiled. "What it is is *simple.* Easy is a whole other story." The announcement for his flight came over the PA. "Here's for good-bye," he said in his lilting voice, kissing her cheek. "Take care of yourself."

"Tell me *how,"* she begged.

"Write me care of the American Express office in London," he called as he ran to the gate. "That's where I usually pick up my mail when I don't know where I'm going to be."

A smiling woman gave him a seat assignment. "That's the last window seat I have," she told him. "You must be lucky."

He touched the brim of his hat jauntily. "Always." Sid picked up his shoulder bag and went on into the plane. More smiling people greeted him, telling him how happy they were he had decided to fly with them. He smiled back. He stowed his bag under his seat, busied himself with adjusting his seat belt, felt a momentary pang of "I am leaving" poignancy. He did not expect to see George again. Even if he did, it would never feel the same. He pulled the airline magazine out of the pocket of the seat in front of him and began to read.

I am *old,* he thought suddenly. Too old to cruise the bars. Nothing worse than an old gay. He was rich enough to buy somebody nice, but he was sappy enough to still hope for Mr. Right to fandango into his life.

"You've got a case, Sid Fraser," he grumbled to himself.

A man who embodied the word "rugged" claimed the seat next to Sid. He wore a leather jacket, denim jeans that were distressed to the point of tears, and a moss green plaid shirt. He bumped Sid's arm, murmuring an apology.

"That's quite all right," Sid said gallantly.

The man looked at him briefly; they smiled. "That's a great hat," he said.

"Thank you." Idiotic as it was, Sid's pulse began to perk up. Part of him started to ask questions. Was the Marlboro man gay? Would he possibly be interested in a long-term relationship with a witty, charming black man in his prime? Would he . . .

I still believe, Sid marveled. After everything I have seen and done, and had done to me, I still believe in the almighty power of love. And that it will one day find me. I believe we are all worthy of love and it is attainable in this life.

I still hope.

The thought comforted him immensely.

Karen had to fight rush-hour traffic, so it was early evening by the time she got home from the airport. Lake was waiting for her, sitting in front of the house.

She got up and ran over to the car before Karen had a chance to get out. "Where is he?" she demanded.

"Which he?" Karen said wearily. "Sid's on a plane bound for England, if that's who you mean. Lake, please, I'm awfully tired. I've apologized six times already. I'm sorry I thought you wrote those notes; it never occurred to me that George would pull a stunt like that. I'm sorry, I'm sorry. Now please, just leave me alone."

Lake ignored her. "Where is Harry? He won't see me, won't even come to the phone. I've got to see him . . . " She took a deep breath. "Jackie told me he was coming over here to talk to you."

"I've only just come home myself."

"Why won't you tell me!" she shrieked, grabbing Karen's shoulder in a crushing grip.

"I'd tell you if I knew."

Lake's hands shifted to her neck. "I don't know about that," she said evenly. "Maybe you wouldn't. Maybe you still blame me for what happened."

"Lake, let go. You're hurting me!" She swung clear and stood back a few paces. "I don't know where Harry is. Probably at the hospital with his wife and child."

Wild-eyed, Lake got into her car and screeched away.

Karen rubbed her sore neck. She stared at her hand in amazement. Blood. Lake's nails had actually drawn blood, her grip had been that frenzied. She went into the house and examined her neck in the hall mirror. Barely a scratch on her collarbone, but it stung, and something about it scared the shit out of her. First the wine-soaked dress, the dark stain mimicking blood. Then the actual drawing. What was going to round out the final trilogy?

A piece of paper rattled beneath her feet.

A letter had been thrust under the door.

She opened it and began to read. "Oh, my God," she cried, sinking to her knees. "You bastard, how could you do it?"

Harry was signing papers. "That's it? That's everything?"

The doctor nodded. "You've made a very courageous decision, Mr. Townsend. We can save a lot of lives thanks to you and your wife."

"I want to be with her for a little while before they . . . stop the machines."

"Of course."

They were alone. Chris's chest went up and down in feigned sleep, wakeful death.

"I'm sorry," Harry told her. He was buzzed from prescription Valium and guilt. "Doesn't change a damn thing, but I am sorry. I never meant to hurt you." He laughed shortly. "I never meant to hurt anybody. For what it's worth, I loved you. Only you." The only answer was the whoosh of the respirator.

Creeping around the edges of the Valium fog was a terrible fear, which Harry could not seem to push out of the way. He took another pill, swallowing it dry. If the fog lifted, he would never do what he had come there to do.

Better. He drew a deep breath.

He locked the door, and, sitting on the edge of his wife's bed, blew his brains out with a gun he had brought with him for precisely that purpose.

At almost the exact moment Harry Townsend was squeezing the trigger, Karen Singer called the hospital to say she had received what she believed was a suicide note from Harry Townsend and would they please look after him if he arrived at the hospital?

Six hours later Roseanne Townsend came out of her coma. She was coherent and did not appear to have any problems that time would not heal. She asked for some green Jello, which was promptly brought to her. Her aunt stayed with her and drove the nurses insane by insisting she sleep in the child's room. They evicted the aunt and discovered the woman camped out outside the door. A cot was brought in, and Aunt Jackie slept in her niece's room through the night. No ghosts got either one of them.

At three in the morning John Allison's apartment was being broken into. He knew this because he was home at the time. He lay awake in bed, listening with consternation to the sounds of someone insistently ringing the doorbell. He grabbed the baseball bat he kept under his bed, but who the hell would come calling at this hour?

The dog jumped onto the bed and cowered. "Fuck you, dog," Johnny whispered unsympathetically. "If I go down, you go with me."

The dog growled softly, jumped off the bed, and walked stiff-legged into the living room. He barked at the doorbell once, then crawled back to the bedroom and hid under the bed.

Hanging on to the Louisville Slugger, he limped to the door, sheet bunched around his waist, "Johnny, it's me. Please let me in."

He opened the door. "You almost got batted into oblivion, do you know that?"

Karen's hair was different, shorter, he noted. If anything it made her look even more vulnerable. He ached to hold her.

"Can I talk to you?" she asked.

"Sure." He couldn't squelch the yawn. "But I'm going back to bed. Can you talk to me there?"

She hesitated—"Yes"—and trailed him into the bedroom, perched on the edge of the bed. "A friend of mine killed himself today. He left me a note." She started to cry. "Please hold me."

He held her and let her cry herself out. She seemed to liquefy in his arms, leaving only little bird bones and silken hair. Do you love me as much as I love you? He wondered if that could be possible. She turned her face toward him. "You were the only person I wanted to see."

He kissed her softly. "Do you want to stay?"

"Yes, I want to."

"But you won't."

"No."

"Karen," he sighed. "What am I going to do with you?"

"Love me."

"You won't let me."

She smiled faintly. "Love me in a spiritual way."

"Oh, grow up."

They both laughed.

"I'm sorry about your friend." He stroked her hair with his good hand. "Is there anything I can do?"

"No." She pulled away from him, sniffling a little, drying her eyes on a corner of his sheet. "I'm okay now."

"Sure?"

"Yes."

He brushed the hair out of her eyes. "This is probably a rotten time to bring this up, but you remember what we said the last time we saw each other?"

She nodded slowly.

"I can't spend my life hanging around on the off chance that you might need me for a little moral support. You can't have me chastely, and still remain faithful to your husband. You can't have us both. I live on the earth, Kar. I need more than poetry and pretty words. I need you here with me all the time. If I can't have that with you, I'll find it with somebody else. Stay here tonight."

"Or?"

"Or get out now."

Without another word she left.

The dog whined reproachfully as he leaped onto the bed. "I know," Johnny sighed, scratching the dog's ear. "I didn't think she'd go, either."

29

IT HAD TO BE the sixth time during November that the blonde had showed up at the precinct house to lodge a complaint. By now the detective (his name really was Bill Smith, much to the smirking amusement of hotel clerks) knew what to expect when he saw her coming.

She was a good-looking blonde, but her recreational drugs and drinking were taking their toll. The skin around her eyes was puffy; her mouth hung slack. He hadn't gotten the chance to look at her arms, but he was pretty sure he'd find tracks if he did. When he gave her coffee, she ladled sugar in like any other junkie. He'd never seen anybody so hell-bent on slow destruction, but Bill Smith had lived in Beverly Hills all his life, and he knew he had not seen everything.

"She's trying to kill me," the blonde said in her slow way. "What are you going to do about it?"

"You want some coffee?" Bill Smith asked.

She thought about it a good long time. "Yeah. Okay."

He brought her the coffee and a handful of sugar packets. "So what did she do this time?"

The blonde leaned closer. "She bought a gun. I saw it. I've been watching her, you know. She wanted me to see the gun so I'd be scared." She laughed throatily. "I'm not scared. I don't care if she kills me; I just want you to catch her." She sipped her coffee. "Because you didn't catch her the first time. You never catch any of them. I keep telling you where to look, but you just don't catch 'em."

"Uh-huh." He was casual; he'd heard it before.

"She killed Harry Townsend." The blonde was starting to nod

out. "I don't know how, but she did it. Because I loved him. You should do something about that. You should be investigating. Are you?"

"Oh, yes."

"Good." Her eyes narrowed shrewdly. "You call me when you bring her in. I want to be there. So . . ." She licked her dry lips. "I'm going now."

"Why don't you wait a little while; I'll take you home," Smith offered. Something about her got to him. He wanted to help her.

"No." She waved her hand lazily. "Here." Laboriously she scrawled her number on his memo pad. "My private line. So you can reach me when you bring her in." Her smile was almost coy. "You don't remember me, do you?"

He said he didn't.

"I was Silky Shaugnessy. The Girl Upstairs? I have a movie coming out soon. Editing. Takes a long time. *Angel of a Brighter Day.* That's me. I'm the Angel."

He said he was looking forward to seeing her movie.

"Me, too. But she's going to kill me before then," she said wisely. "Maybe Christmas."

"We'll catch her long before then," he soothed. "Thanksgiving is still a week away."

Her shoulders slumped. "You won't catch her." She yawned suddenly in his face. "I'm going home to sleep."

After she'd gone, Smith turned to one of his fellow detectives, a sage by the name of Delgado. Delgado was a master of useless information.

"Hey, Delgado," Smith called. "You remember, oh, about two months ago, an actor died, Harry Townsend?"

Delgado nodded. "He was no Olivier."

"Picky, picky," Smith chided. "You remember the circumstances?"

"Suicide, wasn't it?" He paused, mentally flipping magazine pages. "Yeah. There was what they call a family tragedy, and the guy killed himself." Delgado had only gotten in minutes before. "Was your blonde here tonight?"

Smith grimaced. "She's not my blonde."

"Well, you give a lot of credence to what she says." Delgado went over to the coffee urn. "She's just a junkie, Bill."

"I'm just curious. Can't a guy be curious?"

"Sure a guy can be curious," Delgado said equivocally. He liked Smith, but he thought he had about ten percent more asshole in his personality than was good for a cop.

Smith got up and sauntered over to one of the switchboard girls, who was relaxing on her break.

"Marie?"

She looked up at him and smiled. "Hi, Bill. You off duty now?"

"No, I just wanted to ask you something?"

Marie looked very interested. "You can ask me anything you want."

"You remember an actor called Harry Townsend?"

She was obviously disappointed. "That's it? That's what you wanted to ask me?"

He nodded.

"Well, sure I remember him. I must have seen *Maiden Voyage* six times. He was a real hunk. I cried when he killed himself. What a loss, good-looking guy like that."

"Why would a guy like that kill himself?"

She laughed. "What are you so interested for? I didn't even think you liked the movies. I thought you only liked public television, Billy." She twisted her foot coyly. "Now I love the movies. That's my favorite kind of date, going to the movies."

"So what happened with this guy?"

Marie sighed. Some men were just thick. "His wife died. I don't remember what happened exactly; I think it was a car accident. No, wait . . ." She frowned. "It was something like that. Anyway, the funeral was *wild* because his mistress showed up, and there was like a knock-down drag-out fistfight." Her eyes glowed. "It was in all my magazines. *Un*believable. That guy was a pistol. The ladies were still fighting over him while they were nailing the lid on."

He had made no provisions, assuming death was far in the dim future, so Jackie had made all the funeral arrangements, hoping she was doing what would have pleased him. Roseanne was still in the hospital. It was a small gathering, a few friends, a few business associates. Jackie's ex-husband and her two children flew in from Kansas. The boys were quiet and well-behaved, and addressed their father as "sir." Between Jackie and her former family Karen sensed not exactly tension, but a sense of regret. She'd been away from home a long time.

Just as the service was beginning at the graveside, a limo pulled up and Lake spilled out, sobbing.

"I don't want her here," Jackie said in a low voice. "Karen, please . . ."

"You can't send her away," Karen protested.

"She's the reason all of this happened," Jackie said dully. "Either you tell her to go, or I'll get the security people to do it."

Reluctantly Karen went over. "I'm sorry, Lake. You can't stay. Jackie . . . well, she'd rather you didn't."

"I have as much right to be here as anybody else." Her eyes blazed. "Get out of my way."

"I'm sorry," Karen said firmly. "You'll have to go."

Lake tried to push past her.

"No." Karen held her fast.

Furious, Lake pulled free. "This is what you always wanted, isn't it?" she whispered. "The sanctity of marriage protected and the harlot ostracized. Maybe it wasn't George who sent those notes; maybe it was you."

"Go home, Lake. You can pay your respects later."

Suddenly Lake stopped struggling. She wept quietly. "Please, Karen. Let me stay. Let me have this one thing."

"I can't," Karen said miserably. "I *am* sorry, but you'll have to go." She watched as Lake got back into her car and drove away.

About a week later Karen became aware that Lake was following her everywhere she went.

Bill Smith had to work on Thanksgiving, which, secretly, he considered a blessing. His family held Thanksgiving so holy that he was always relieved when he had a legitimate excuse to miss the annual gathering of relatives. His one concession to the holiday was a turkey sandwich for lunch.

His blonde came back on Thanksgiving Day. She had a hell of a shiner.

"What happened to you?"

She shrugged. "I can't remember. I wanted to see how you were coming along with my case."

"Well, it's a little difficult," he said vaguely. "We don't have anything concrete to work with—"

"Daniel Fox," she said suddenly. "You check up on him." She smiled wryly. "Old boyfriend. He has a record in New York. They're working together, you know. Daniel and Karen, together again for the first time." She laughed inappropriately. "I don't think I'd mind being dead; it's getting dead that bothers me. It *hurts.* It takes a very long time to be over and done with."

"Look," he said slowly, "why don't you stay here, take a little nap. You seem tired. I'll drive you home."

Her head drooped. "That would be nice."

He took her to one of the interview rooms and got her settled with a blanket. She was pretty bruised all over; he could easily believe someone had worked her over. Trouble was, it could have been anybody—a pusher, a creep she had picked up for the night.

"Bill," she said quietly. "That's your name, isn't it?"

"Yes."

"I went to see my old friend yesterday, Bill."

He almost smiled. "The one who's trying to kill you?"

"I hurt." She turned her face away from him. "I used to be able to control things, but now they're controlling me. So I went over there yesterday to see what I could see," she said in a drowsy sing-song. "And do you know what I saw?"

"What?"

She smiled. "I saw me."

Matt was in the thick of the editing process, so it was not unusual that his workday extended far into the night. He would stumble home exhausted, grab a few hours sleep, and stumble back to the editing room. Generally he would try to speak to Karen on the phone twice a day, but it was not uncommon for a week to go by before he got a chance to see her. Finally he decided to take off a little early one day. Maybe they'd go out to dinner, get a chance to talk a bit.

There was a note waiting for him, tacked to the refrigerator with a magnet.

Gone to barn. How's the editing coming along?

Love,
Karen

Light laughter sounded from upstairs.

"Karen?" he called out, running up the stairs to the bedroom.

"Do I look like Karen?" Lake was lying on their bed, shoes kicked off, seeming very much at ease. "I have a key, you know. Karen never asked for it back, trusting soul that she is. I can come and go as I please."

Matt hadn't seen Lake for a while, not since the wrap party and her brief appearance at the funeral. In that short time she seemed to have gone to hell and returned shell-shocked. Whatever madness she had been quietly nurturing all those years had sprung loose. He wondered if it was Harry's death alone that had destroyed her.

"You went to see him, I know." Her laugh was strange. "The boyfriend, the other man. I've always known about him. She told me things she could never tell you."

"Lake, what the hell are you doing in my house? Do you know I could have you thrown out of here for breaking and entering?"

She held out the phone. "Go on, call the cops. Only Karen wouldn't like it if you did that, and you're on thin ice as it is. John Allison—that's his name. You went to check out the competition. Verrry thin ice, my friend. You don't really think she went to the stable tonight? Or all those other nights?" She slipped off the bed and walked up to him. Her pallor contrasted oddly with her seductive smile. "You can't blame her, Matt. All the time everyone thought you were the virtuous husband, resisting those enticing young starlets for the sake of fidelity. Everyone thinking you were such a good man. Sid Fraser was more your style. No, I don't blame Karen. I just feel sorry for you."

"I want you out of this house."

"Can't even get mad decently," she murmured. Rising on her toes she kissed him on the mouth. "It should have been you and me, Matt. We deserve each other."

He grabbed her wrists and pushed her hands away from his neck. "Get out."

"I'm sorry. You're going to have to try harder than that." Her hand fumbled at his crotch.

"Leave me alone!" He knocked her back against the wall. They were both stunned.

"Go on," she said quietly. "Finish it."

He picked up her shoes and gave them to her. "You stay. I'll go."

She started to laugh. "In that case there's no reason to stick around." She struggled into her shoes. "See you around, Matthew, my love."

He knew better than to believe anything she had said, but he still found himself in his car, fifteen minutes later, on his way to John Allison's apartment.

In answer to his insistent knock, the door was opened by a very pretty, very young girl, who said, "I can't believe this is really you. You're a major somebody."

"Excuse me, do I have the right apartment? I thought John Allison lived here."

"This is it. He's on the road with a show. I'm subletting."

"How long has he been gone?"

"Oh, gee, since September. Were you going to audition him for something?"

"No." Matt smiled wanly. "We're friends."

"Yeah?" She flexed a little, posing in the doorway. "I'm an actress."

"Did John say when he was coming back?"

"I don't think he is. Things just didn't work out here like he hoped they would. I played Viola in *Twelfth Night,*" she put in. "I got *incredible* reviews. Would you like to see them? I could make some coffee . . ."

"I don't drink coffee," he said pointedly.

"Never ever?" she asked, coy as anything.

"Never ever."

"Well." She shrugged. "Can't blame me for trying. It's not every day a famous director comes to my door. One day I might be in one of your movies. Who knows?"

Matt knew. "Never can tell." He echoed her sentiment. "Thank you for your help."

"Anytime," she yelled after him.

Matt got to the stable around nine o'clock. The lights were on around the outdoor ring, and he could see Karen cantering around the ring, her face intent. She didn't see him.

A few jumps were set up. The little mare took them neatly, legs tucked. Karen's face wore an expression halfway between exhilaration and determination. He wondered what she thought as they sailed over the jumps.

"Good girl." She patted the mare's neck as they walked around the ring cooling off. "How long have you been there?" she called to Matt.

"Not long."

"I've got to cool her off for a couple of minutes."

"That's okay. I'll hang out."

"How's the editing going?"

"Fine," he called back. "It's going to be a pretty good flick. Of course, people are going to come just to see Harry Townsend's last performance, but I don't care. Any way I can get them into the theater."

She smiled. "That's my boy."

She does love me, he marveled. How can that not be enough? But he knew it wasn't. For nearly nine years he had watched her growing and changing from an insecure, awkward girl to a self-assured woman. A beautiful woman. People stopped to look at her as she passed down the street. In the land of leggy California blondes, she was a rarity. Matt would have liked to take some of the credit for her metamorphosis, but it had nothing to do with him. People changed when they were good and ready. Either they were sick and tired of hauling around their old insecurities like so much baggage, or the desire for change was stronger than the fear of the unknown. Or it was simply right and natural for them to change, like fawns losing their yearling spots.

She had changed, and she needed more than he could give. He could hold on to her through guilt and fear, and after a while she would begin to hate him as surely as any slave hates his master. "I love you," he whispered under his breath. "I always will."

She put the little mare into her stall and started to brush her. "Isn't she good?" Karen said happily. "Just pops right over those jumps like a pro. Makes me look like I know what I'm doing, which is a total lie, but as long as nobody else picks up on it—"

"Karen?"

She looked at him.

"I want a divorce."

Her eyes began to tear slightly, but she nodded slowly.

"I'll pack up my things tomorrow."

"Not tomorrow," she said quickly. "Tomorrow's Thanksgiving. Nobody should have to leave home on Thanksgiving."

Since it was only the two of them, she cooked a chicken. Neither of them particularly liked turkey, anyway. Conversation was steered carefully away from the separation, but eventually their talk of movies dried up and they fell silent.

Karen took his hand. "Will we always be friends?"

He didn't think so. He thought they'd drift apart like every other divorced couple. One day he'd pass her on the street and not be able to remember her favorite color or what side of the bed she'd preferred. "Sure, Kar."

"I know other people don't, but we won't be like them. We'll be different."

He smiled. "I hope so."

"And we'll still work together."

"That I can promise you. Do you know how you want to go about this thing?"

"I guess we call lawyers and they do . . . lawyer things." She waved her hands vaguely. "Does that sound about right?"

"About."

"And I suppose you take your records and I take mine, and we do that with everything." She shivered. "It doesn't matter how amiable a divorce is, it's still horrible. I hate to think of you out there all alone."

He felt something that was kin to spite. "You won't be alone, will you, Kar?"

She got up and started to put away the leftovers, which was quite a job, as neither of them had been terribly hungry.

He came into the kitchen. "I didn't mean that."

"It's all right if you did," she said quietly. "I just don't want to argue today."

He put his arms around her. "This should have worked. I love you, you love me. We're not like everyone else in this town. We're both quiet, hard-working; we never cheated on each other. It should have worked."

"Sometimes it doesn't," she said.

"Come on, I'll take you home." Smith gently shook his blonde awake.

"Mmmm." She stirred sleepily. "Time to go?"

"Time to go."

Her directions led him up into the mountains, to an isolated area that Bill Smith, the cop, did not feel particularly good about. She was quiet on the trip, and he had to ask her whether to turn right or left. He idled in the driveway, waiting for her to get out.

"We're here." He tapped her shoulder.

In a flash she was all over him, her silky hair falling over his face, her mouth pressed frantically against his. "Stay with me," she whispered huskily. "I can't be alone tonight." Her hand slipped inside his shirt. "I know you want to be with me."

He *did* want to be with her, in her bed. But for one night only. And he had the strangest feeling that if he went with her one night, she'd own him forever and make him do terrible things. He was afraid of her.

She pulled away. "At least come in for some coffee or a drink."

"Okay," he said after a brief struggle with his emotions.

Much to his surprise the house was Spartan neat.

"Cleaning lady," she explained, going about the coffee with slow, graceful motions. "Cleaning girl, really. She's younger than I am."

"You have a nice house."

"Thank you."

He held up a paperweight he found on a table. "Very unusual. Pink snow?"

She smiled. "Mars is nice this time of year."

"I'll take your word for it."

She put the coffee down in the living room. "Come here."

He went. She was sitting on the couch, one leg up, no panties. "You like me, don't you Bill?"

Like a demented adolescent he couldn't stop himself from looking up her skirt. She held out her arms. "Closer."

"I have to be getting back," he mumbled, dry-mouthed.

"No, you don't. You're off duty. Come here, Bill."

He moved closer, sitting on the couch. She took his hand and guided it up her skirt. "I'd do anything you want me to, anything at all. Nothing shocks me." She was warm and wet. As she rubbed his hand against herself, he felt himself getting aroused. "All you have to do is say you'll stay. It's just for one night, Bill, and then you can go back to the land of the living."

He pulled away, suddenly spooked. For a brief second he had believed that someone was lurking behind the couch. A trick of the light, her own sepulchral charm getting to him—he didn't care. He wanted out. "I'm sorry. I really have to go."

She released his hand. "Bill, you've disappointed me. I thought you wanted to help me."

"I do." He backed toward the door. "I'm going to go back to the precinct, investigate your case."

"Yes, you'd better go." She was smiling at him. "You'd better run, Bill. There are things in this house that could eat you up alive if they catch you. And they're awfully fast, Bill, faster than I thought they were. *RUN!*" she screamed, and he pelted out the door.

Detective Brooks was having a bad day. Not only had the Macy's Thanksgiving Day Parade provided its annual traffic snarl, but life in general was not working out the way he had planned.

He had been so close to nabbing Daniel Fox. It had taken time, but he had finally located the man. If Fox made one wrong step, if the man so much as jaywalked, Brooks would find him, bring him in, and have a little chat with him.

On Thanksgiving Day Brooks got a call. The caller did not identify himself. "You wanted him, Brooks," the caller said, "you can have him." He gave the name of a downtown hospital.

Daniel Fox was barely alive. He lay in the hospital bed broken, tubes running in and out of his body. Stubborn or not, he was going to die very soon.

"Who did this?" Brooks asked him. "Come on, Fox. You and I are old friends at this point. You can tell me." Inside he was berating himself. All along Allison had been telling the truth. It hadn't been Fox, just somebody who bore a slight resemblance to the man. Brooks had been wrong from the very beginning.

Daniel Fox's eyes rolled open.

"Who did it?" Brooks asked again. "He can't hurt you where you're going."

It sounded like Fox was laughing, but his expression was one of terror. "He can," he whispered.

He died a few minutes later.

Pissed off as hell, Brooks went back to his desk and tried to rethink the situation. Just as he was getting ready to leave for the day, his phone rang. "Brooks," he snapped.

"Detective Brooks," a youngish voice said. "I'm Detective Smith with the LAPD. I was wondering if you had any information on a Daniel Fox. It seems—"

"Somebody put you up to this?" Brooks asked suspiciously.

"No. Why would anybody put me up to this? I'm calling on police business."

"Okay, Smith. Daniel Fox expired today at three oh—"

"Expired? He's dead?"

"You *have* heard the word before, haven't you, Smith?"

There was a long silence on the other end. "Thank you very much for the information, Detective Brooks."

Delgado was casually listening in. "So what did you get?"

"Fox is dead," Smith said in a bewildered tone.

"So that's the end of that."

"Guess so," Smith said, unconvinced. "Jesus, Phil. I had this all worked out. I was so positive the old boyfriend was harassing her. I even thought he was lurking around her house this evening, scaring the shit out of her."

"Scaring the shit out of you." Delgado laughed. "Well, there goes your theory."

"No Fox," Smith agreed sadly. "All that leaves is the old friend, Karen Singer."

"That leaves nothing," Delgado corrected. "You got a paranoid junkie, and that's all you got."

"Phil," Smith sighed. "I got some famous last words for you, and I quote: 'Just because you're paranoid doesn't mean they're *not* out to get you.' "

Delgado yawned. "I'll remember that."

30

"IT'S RARE that you do interviews," the young reporter said. "Why is that?"

Karen took a deep breath. She didn't like doing this, but in the month's time since Matt and she had decided to separate, the rumors had been flying merrily. If any story had to circulate, Karen wanted it to be the truth. "I guess I just have a terrible fear of being misquoted."

The interviewer smiled. "I'll do my best to put your fears at rest. Are you willing to talk about your divorce?"

"Only to say that I have nothing but the highest regard for Matt as a friend and as a director."

"What about off the record?"

"The same. It's the truth." Karen smiled.

Karen Singer was a very nice lady. Everybody said so. The interviewer didn't buy it for one second. "I understand you're having some trouble with your old friend Lake Eastman."

Karen stiffened. "Lake is having a very difficult time accepting Harry Townsend's death. I guess you know they were pretty close."

"Whether she's having a difficult time or not is no excuse for the way she's been harassing you, don't you think, Karen? I mean, she's practically dogging your footsteps; she follows you just about everywhere you go. You must be ready to strangle her."

Karen looked down at her folded hands. "I don't talk about my friends behind their backs."

There was a considerable commotion at the entrance of the restaurant. The interviewer craned her neck. "Well, Karen, it looks like you won't have to. Lake is here."

"My friend is sitting right over there," Lake said grandly, waving aside the three waiters who were trying to convince her to have lunch someplace else. "I will have lunch with my dear, dear friend." She nearly upended a dessert cart in a headlong stumble that landed her at Karen's table.

"Well, here we are!" Lake sang.

"Don't, Lake," Karen said under her breath. "Please don't do this. Not here."

The interviewer flipped to a clean sheet in her memo pad. Things were just starting to get interesting.

"I know you." Lake poked the interviewer in the chest. "You work for a magazine."

"Yes, I sure do."

Lake leaned in. "Would you like to interview me?"

"I'm sure we can set something up in the near future—"

"How 'bout now? I've got some very interesting things to tell you."

"Lake, you're not well. We should go home." Karen caught a waiter's eye. "Bring her some coffee, please."

"Please, thank you," Lake mimicked angrily. "She's so polite. So damned *nice*. Don't you think she's a real sweetheart, Miss Reporter? I bet you'd like to know what she's really like underneath all those phony manners." The waiter came by with the coffee. "Take that away," Lake snapped. "I don't want it." She almost knocked the cup out of the poor man's hand. "Aren't you curious why everybody's favorite couple is splitting up?"

Karen rose from her seat. "You can carry on any way you want. I don't have to stick around and watch."

"Sit down!" Lake grabbed her wrist and twisted it savagely. She wouldn't let go. "You'll go when I tell you to." She smiled triumphantly at the reporter. "He was sleeping with me," she announced. "Her saintly husband. It was going on for years. You were the only one who didn't know, my dear friend." She laughed, high and dangerous, leering at the reporter. "How's that for a story?"

The reporter looked at Karen. "Do you want to deny or confirm that?"

Moving very fast, Karen knocked Lake to the ground. Her small, fine hands locked around Lake's throat and pressed.

It took two waiters to pull her off.

Clumsily Lake got to her feet. She laughed hoarsely. "Don't try running away. I won't let up on you. Not ever."

Karen was shaking with rage. "Leave me alone," she whispered, eyes blazing, "or I swear, Lake, I'll kill you." She stalked back to the table to get her purse.

The reporter looked up. "Let me see if I got this straight. 'Leave me alone, or I'll kill you.' Is that right?" She smiled. "I wouldn't want to misquote you."

About ten o'clock that evening Karen was doing her best to relax. Jackie had come over, and they had played rummy for a while. "How's Roseanne?"

Jackie shrugged. "I guess as well as can be expected. Our mother's looking after her for a while. If nothing else, I suppose she'll fatten her up."

"You going home for Christmas?"

"Uh-huh." Jackie nodded. "Tomorrow night. I sure hate leaving you alone, especially after what happened today."

Karen made a face. "Everybody knows about it? What am I saying? There was a reporter not two feet away."

"Maybe you should go away for a while."

"Until people forget how she humiliated me in public? That could take a long time. Besides, I'm not going to let her chase me away."

"Maybe you should," Jackie advised. "Take a vacation until the whole thing blows over."

"No," Karen said stubbornly. "There's no place I want to go, anyway."

The doorbell rang. "Sit," Karen said. "I'll get it."

She didn't recognize the man at the door, but he seemed to know her. "You're Karen Singer." He nodded to himself. "Well, I found you at last, and believe me it wasn't easy." He was a rough-looking man.

Instinctively Karen stepped back. "Who are you?"

He ignored her question. "Here." He held out a greasy manila envelope. "This is for you. Don't ask me what's inside, 'cause what ain't my business ain't my business. Go on, take it."

She accepted it gingerly. He started to walk away. "Hey, wait a second!" she yelled after him. "I don't even know who this is from!"

He stopped. "It's from Daniel Fox. Kind of a last request, you might say."

"What do you mean?"

"I mean Foxy wasn't so Foxy. He's dead."

Karen shut the door and ripped into the envelope. Several smaller, letter-sized envelopes fell out onto the floor.

Jackie picked one up. "There's a date written on the outside. What is all this stuff?"

"I don't know." Karen opened another envelope and spilled its contents onto her hand. It was a heart-shaped gold locket.

One envelope held a college I.D. card. One a passport. Another an immigrant's green card. Another envelope held a five-dollar bill on which had been scribbled "Happy Birthday, Tracy!" One had an A. & P. check-cashing card.

Another held an Equity card. There was a bloody thumbprint in the upper right-hand corner.

Only a single envelope was sealed. In it was a statement written by Daniel Fox, swearing that the manila envelope had been found in Karl Eastman's study.

Hurriedly, Karen stuffed everything back in the larger envelope and thrust it into Jackie's hands. "Listen to me carefully. I have to go over to Lake's—"

Jackie's eyes almost bugged out. "Are you crazy?"

"Just do what I tell you to do. If I'm not back in three hours, call the police."

"I'm going with you."

"No, you're not. Don't even try it." Karen opened a dresser drawer. Jackie was shocked to see her take out a gun and slip it into her purse.

"And what's that for?"

"Do what I tell you," Karen repeated. "My life may depend on it."

At 1:05 a.m. an anonymous woman phoned the police and told them to get over to 1124 Knight Street.

Smith looked up in alarm. "That's her address."

"Your blonde?" Delgado inquired. "Let's go."

"Next time I trust my gut instinct," Smith said angrily.

The Medical Examiner was on the scene when they got there. The house was a mess. There was a Christmas tree, as yet undecorated, tipped over in one corner. Bloody handprints on the wall behind it dripped to the floor. They found the corpse in the kitchen. The ME told them to step carefully; the blood had made the floor quite slippery.

A hand had been severed. They found it in the refrigerator, the pads of the fingertips neatly sliced off. The remaining hand had been similarly treated. Her face was beaten beyond recognition, all the teeth knocked out, the jaw caved in. Smith said he thought he recognized her necklace, and a ring that was on the hand found in the refrigerator. He didn't need those things; he could tell from the shape of the body. It was his girl.

Delgado came into the kitchen. He had a gun encased in a plastic bag. "A twenty-two."

The ME shook his head. "She was beaten to death. The mutilation was done after she was already dead."

"I should have known something like this was going to happen," Smith said bitterly. "She trusted me to look out for her."

"There's a woman sitting out back," Delgado said quietly.

"What?"

"She's all right; she's not going anywhere. She just won't come through the house." Delgado and Smith walked to the back of the house.

"You took your time getting here," she said.

"Miss," Delgado said gently, "would you like to tell us who you are?"

"Karen Singer."

He held up the plastic bag. "Is this yours?"

"Yes, I think so."

"Ms. Singer, you are under arrest . . . You have the right to remain silent. You have—"

She cut off Detective Smith. "That isn't Lake."

He read her the rest of her rights, and then they took her in.

"You requested to speak to me?" Delgado lit a cigarette. "I'm sorry. I should have asked you first."

"It's all right with me," Karen said. "I just didn't want to talk to Detective Smith."

"Why not?"

"Because"—Karen smiled wryly—"I'm sure he's a nice guy, but I get the feeling he's a jerk."

It's that extra ten percent, Delgado thought.

She let out her breath in a long, slow stream. "Can I have a cigarette?"

"Of course." He offered her the pack.

She selected one with exaggerated delicacy. "I don't smoke, but sometimes I envy people who do. Gives you something to do with your hands." She played with the cigarette.

"Doesn't look natural on you."

She put it down. "I'm very tired, Detective Delgado. I just want to tell you Lake's story, everything she told me last night. It's the last thing I can do for her."

"Take your time," he assured her.

"Do you know what people do to cope when terrible things happen to them?" she said slowly.

He shrugged. "Many things. They deny. They get depressed—"

"They forget. They block the incident completely from the conscious mind. But the sleeping mind remembers, and it tries to find a path back to sanity in any way it can. Dreams aren't always dreams, Detective Delgado. Sometimes it's the mind replaying a horrible incident, trying to make sense of it all. My friend Lake had terrible nightmares, but she only had them when she spent the night alone. What would you think of something like that?"

"I would think she didn't like to be alone."

She nodded. "That's why I was such a good roommate. I wasn't a wild girl; I was home every night. So there were no bad dreams. When she left for California, she disappeared for a while, living quietly, rooming with a girl who was like me in her nocturnal habits. Nobody knew where Lake was except me. Eventually George Nichols found her, and then there was no hiding."

"Hiding from what?" Delgado asked.

Her smile was quirky. "Her father. I told you, detective, dreams aren't always dreams. Lake *said* she had had a nightmare, but in reality, there was never any dream at all; she just couldn't handle what was happening to her. Everytime she was alone, he would come to her."

"*Her father?*" he whispered.

"Yes. He would come to her and rape her, every night she was alone. It had been going on since she was a very small child. He bought her silence by preying on her childhood fears. He had told her—oh, God!—when she was little, he told her she was some evil double left in place of his real daughter. Maybe he told her he was going to send her back, get his 'real' child once and for all. I don't know about that. All I know is that he always found her. She was his property, and if anybody got in his way, he killed them."

"Fox."

"Daniel knew. I guess he loved Lake in his own way. He sent me the information, the *evidence.*" She licked her lips. "I'm awfully dry. Can I get some water?"

"Of course." He got her a paper cupful and set it at her elbow. "What exactly happened last night?"

"A man came and gave me an envelope. He said it was from Daniel. I don't know how Daniel got it but he did. I took one look, and I knew I had to get Lake away from him. I don't know what I thought I was going to do—hide her somewhere . . . She saw my face, and she knew why I had come." Her words came faster now, her eyes fastened on the cup of water. "But she wouldn't come with me. She said it was too late for her and that he was coming to get me. She said he was coming and I had to hide right away."

"What happened to the envelope?"

"I gave it to a friend for safekeeping. She should be here any minute." She gulped water.

"Okay. What happened then?"

"There's a crawlspace above the ceiling. Lake showed it to me and helped me hide there. She said in the morning, when he left, we could get away, but for now I'd have to be quiet." She began to weep quietly. "I heard him come in. I heard him kill her. The way she cried out . . . But I was too frightened to come down. I heard everything, but I never saw his face. Some witness, huh?" She wiped her nose on her sleeve.

"By the time I got down from the crawlspace, he was gone. I took out the gun; I was that scared he was still there. When I saw . . . the room,—you know—I just dropped the gun and ran outside. I couldn't see her like that."

"Her? But you said it wasn't Lake?"

"It didn't look like her; it didn't look like anybody anymore. What time is it?"

He looked at his watch. "Two o'clock in the afternoon. You got plans?"

"No. Just curious. This is the first time I've been up all night in a long time."

"Wish I could say the same. Ms. Singer, do you think Lake Eastman was killed last night, or was it someone else, mutilated to obscure her identity?"

"I'm not sure," she said honestly. "I don't want to believe it was Lake, but I think it had to be."

The phone rang. Delgado answered. It was the desk sergeant and he sounded very excited. "Delgado, some weird lady walked in here, handed me an envelope she said had something to do with Lake Eastman. That's your case, right?"

"Right, me and Smith."

"I got Smith right here. You wouldn't believe what's in this envelope. This fuck kept *souvenirs,* little mementos of everyone he offed. ID cards, stuff like that, everything dated. He couldn't have made it easier for us if he tried. We got NYPD on the phone and they've already got a few matches. Plus we got an Actors' Equity card issued to John Allison with a beautiful thumbprint in the corner in blood. This guy Brooks in N.Y. was real happy to hear about that. A *thumbprint,* Delgado. All we got to do is identify the print, pick up another print, even a partial at Knight Street, and we're in business."

"Call Brooks back. See if he can find Karl Eastman's fingerprints on file anywhere."

"Is he our boy?"

"He's our boy." He hung up the phone and turned to Karen. "Looks like your friend made it."

"So now you have the proof that it was Karl."

"We just don't have Karl. Yet."

Something stuck in his mind. "I think we can release you now," Delgado said in measured tones. "But I think we'll have a uniform hanging around your house, just for today."

"Why?"

"You said Lake told you her father was looking for you."

"Why would he do that"—she was perplexed—"unless he knew I was there?"

"Maybe it has nothing to do with that."

"I don't understand."

"Well," Delgado said slowly, "you said Lake's father told her she was a bad child, sent as a replacement for his good child. Maybe he thinks you're the good child."

Matt was waiting for her. "Everything's okay. It's all over," he said soothingly, holding her.

"Thank you for being there." She pulled away from him. "I'm all right. Got to learn to get along by myself sooner or later."

"We're still friends, Kar," he said, "as long as you want to be."

She took a deep breath. "Sorry. I've had a bad day." She began to laugh softly. "I just want to go home, take a hot bath. Matt, this is what you call lousy timing. If I'd known I was going to have a crisis in the near future, I would have pushed the divorce back a few months."

He smiled. "You want me to stay with you?"

"No." She shook her head. "I don't think that's very fair to you. I'll be okay. Just expect a panic call at two a.m."

"I'll still be editing. You know where to reach me." He took her arm. "The least I can do is give you a ride home."

The bright sunlight outside startled her. Although sunshine was perfectly normal at three o'clock in the afternoon, Karen had expected pitch blackness. When she was a child, nighttime had seemed to last forever, especially after an indulgent babysitter had allowed her to stay up late and watch the Saturday Night Creature Feature. Well, what she'd been through made the Creature Feature look like an afternoon at the zoo, and the daylight seemed like a lie to lull her into a false sense of security. In her heart she knew it was still dark and that night was a long way from over.

She blinked, adjusting her eyes. The fluorescent lights inside the police station had been light enough to work by, but the sunlight was glaringly bright by comparison. "Matt? Where's the car?"

"Right over there." He pointed.

At the curb was an old, beat-up Mustang convertible, its owner leaning against the car door.

"Johnny!" Karen called out and ran to him.

There was nothing for Matt to do but stand and watch. After a while, he started to walk away.

Karen disentangled herself from Johnny's arms. "Please wait for me," she whispered to him.

"Sure," he smiled, "I'm getting very good at it."

She caught up with Matt. "Matt, I'm so sorry. I never meant for things to turn out this way."

He shook his head. "How did you think things were going to turn out, Karen? Like an old movie where everybody gets just what they want? You're always trying to make life come out as neatly as one of your stories. We're all supposed to walk away smiling. My God, Karen, I loved you. You were my life."

"I never felt it." Tears came to her eyes. "Oh, I felt affection, but never passion."

"It was the best I could do, Kar. It was all I could do."

"I'm sorry," she said again, not knowing what else to do. She put her arms around him and they embraced awkwardly. "We'll be friends, Matt, you'll see, we'll all be friends, you'll like Johnny—"

Gently, he pushed her arms away, smiling sadly. "There you go again," he said. "Goodbye, Karen." He kissed her on the cheek. "I'll always love you. But your friend can go fuck himself."

She watched him get in his car and drive away. Johnny was getting a little anxious.

"I thought I was going to lose you again."

"Oh, no," she snuggled into his arms, "nothing's going to keep us apart anymore."

Detectives Smith and Delgado went down to the morgue. The ME had still not been able to positively identify the body found at 1124 Knight Street because of the extent of the mutilation.

Bill Smith looked at the body for a long time. "That's her. I knew this woman pretty well. Take my word for it, that's her."

"Are you family?" the ME asked.

"No," Smith admitted.

"Then I'm afraid your word is not enough."

Detective Delgado looked at his friend closely. "Bill, are you sure?"

"Yes."

"I believe you," Delgado said. "That is Lake Eastman."

"God rest her soul," Smith said.

"God rest her soul," the two men echoed.

31

"IS HE STILL out there?" Karen asked, toweling off her hair.

Johnny peered out the window. "Yep."

"What's he doing?"

"Same as before. Just sitting in his car."

"You'd think they'd let them read a magazine or something," Karen said, annoyed.

Johnny laughed. "I don't think you're supposed to do that when you're on a stakeout."

"It's not a stakeout."

"Police protection, then."

"Well, I don't need any protection," she said tartly. "I wish they'd send that poor man home."

"After tonight they probably will."

She looked out the window, still frowning. "Poor man." Her Chinese eyes regarded Johnny gravely. "Did I tell you I'm very glad you're here?"

"Not yet."

"I am. Very, very." She sat next to him. "Give me your hand."

He held out his good hand.

"Not that one. The other."

Very hesitantly he put his crippled hand in hers. Out of all his injuries that was the one he hated most. Nothing could be done about it, and time only made it worse. The fingers were gnarled and useless. It was ugly, and he hated it.

Tenderly she kissed his hand. "I love you," she murmured, "just the way you are now. I think that was a question in your mind."

He nodded his head, not trusting himself to look her in the eyes. Somehow, eyes closed, emotions awry, he managed to find her mouth, soft and yielding against his. Somehow, after endless liquid kisses on the couch, they managed to find the guest bedroom and slide under the cool, fresh sheets, touching each other with the delight of people who have been deprived of such pursuits for a long, long time. Her body was a joy to him; her small, firm breasts, her tiny waist and beautiful hips. And inside she was as complicated as a seashell, and as delicate. He was gentle, as gentle as he could be, sensing her inexperience, but soon she was urging him with her teeth and tongue, and the undulations of those beautiful lyre-shaped hips, to thrust deeper and harder. He reached down and stroked the downy skin along the inside of her thigh. She gasped in pleasure, opening even more to him, moving with him instinctively. Suddenly he felt her tense, her little cries turning into a soft sigh. Her body danced under him. He felt like he'd just won the Indy 500.

He smiled into her eyes. He kissed the tip of her nose. "I love you."

"I love you, too. When can we do this again?"

"In about an hour."

"Will you wake me?"

He couldn't help but grin. "I promise."

"Good." She turned on her side, one arm and leg thrown over his body, and was soon quickly asleep.

"Karen?" He shook her gently. "Hey, the guys are supposed to fall asleep." He yawned. "Hey, bunny rabbit." His eyes closed of their own accord, and he joined her.

He got up in the middle of the night and went to the bathroom. He peed and flushed, then realized he was unbelievably thirsty. Karen was still sleeping, and it looked like she was out for the duration. After what she'd been through, sleep was exactly what she needed. Remembering the cop outside he pulled on his jeans and went downstairs.

"Remember me?" an amused voice said.

Johnny's mouth went suddenly dry. "My God," he managed to say. He cast his eyes toward the door.

"He's dead," Karl Eastman said. "Police usually have guns, so I had to kill him. I took the gun, but I don't care for them as a rule. *You* know that." He smiled pleasantly. "She's a heavy sleeper. I know a lot about her, more than you do. And I know a lot about you. But then we're old friends. You don't want me to hurt you again, do you?"

"No," Johnny croaked.

"Because there's no need to. Some of them had to be killed. The Phantom . . . he was smart; he was putting it all together. Fox." He stood up, reaching into his pocket with one hand. The other held a gun. The policeman's gun, Johnny assumed. "Turn around, please."

Johnny stood frozen to the spot. In one brief moment he understood it all. He was going to die. His own personal executioner had followed him, lovingly cataloging his life, waiting for the one moment of total happiness. This man was going to kill him.

"Karen, wake up!" he screamed. Karl was very fast. In seconds he was on Johnny. The gun came down quickly, the butt connecting with Johnny's head. He went down and stayed there.

Karen was on the stairs.

"I've been waiting for you," Karl whispered.

She was trapped. She could not go down and get past Karl. If she went back the way she had come, he would follow her and she would again be cornered.

"Come." He held out his arms to her.

She couldn't take her eyes off his face. It was Daniel Fox at fifty, Daniel Fox crazier than she'd ever seen him. Karen wanted to laugh. What perfect sense it all made. Lake had found a man who physically resembled the first man, the only man in her life, her father.

Her eyes slid toward Johnny. It was impossible to tell how badly he was hurt.

Karl was walking to her, arms still outstretched. "Come to me."

She turned and fled back up the stairs. He caught up with her on the landing. "I see they turned you against me," he said sadly, gripping her arm. "They even cut off your beautiful hair. No matter." Inside his jacket he had a blonde wig. "Put it on. I want you to." He let go of her arm. "That's a good girl."

She slipped the wig over her hair.

"That's my girl," he murmured. As soon as she had the wig on, he seized her arm again. "Now we have to find you something to wear." He led her to the bedroom and started rummaging in the dresser. Karen felt his grip weaken as he became preoccupied with the clothes. She wrenched her arm free and ran for the phone. There was no dial tone.

He made no move to stop her; he merely regarded her as though she were acting in a particularly idiotic fashion. "I took care of that. I didn't think we'd want to be disturbed." He threw a white cotton nightgown at her. "Put that on. Go on, be a good little girl. It's very late. You should be in bed." He sighed tiredly. "Take off the robe. Take it off!" His voice became sharp. "I haven't come all this way so you could give me a hard time."

An inspiration came to her. "Daddy," she said softly.

"Yes, what do you want?"

"What happened to the other?"

He stared at her. "The changeling? You don't have to worry, she's gone forever. She's dead. Finally," he said dully, "she's gone. It's time we put you to bed." He turned down the covers. "Now hop in."

"You killed Lake."

He stared at her in surprise. "You are Lake. No more trouble, young lady, *in bed.*"

She took the nightgown and balled it up, tossing it to the far corner of the room. "No," she said playfully, "I don't want to go to bed."

He went to retrieve the gown. As soon as he turned his back, she darted into the hallway, but at that point she realized how foolish her plan was. She couldn't go downstairs and take that madman past Johnny. There was only one place to go. Quickly she ran into the bathroom, locked the door, jerked open the window, and clambered outside. Her fingers scrabbled madly for purchase. With an effort she hauled herself onto the roof.

"Help!" she shrieked. "Help me!" Now it *was* black outside; the never-ending night had descended at last. No one would hear her; no one would come to her rescue.

Karl was on the roof now, glaring at her reproachfully. "I thought you'd be happy to see me again. All you want to do is run away. I won't have that, Lake. If you're going to be bad, you have to be punished. You know that as well as I do."

"I'm not Lake," she sobbed. "Mr. Eastman, you need help. We'll go down; I'll call somebody. They'll see you get the help you need."

"Come here, Lake." The sharp little knife was in his hand. "You've been very bad." She saw it glimmer in the night air as it flew toward her.

Wake up. His subconscious mind was trying to wake him, but the conscious mind wasn't buying it.

One eye rolled open. He couldn't hear anything, but he wasn't sure there was nothing to hear. Johnny got up slowly.

"Help me!" came clearly from the roof. He'd never make it. His equilibrium was shot from the blow to his head, and as an added attraction he was seeing double. He staggered out to the police car. The cop was dead and his gun was gone. He remembered reading somewhere that a lot of cops liked to carry extra weapons as a sort of security blanket. He felt the dead man's pockets gingerly. Nothing. But strapped to one ankle was a small handgun. He took that and as a second thought tipped the body forward against the steering wheel so that a resounding blast issued from the horn. There, he thought with satisfaction. Let the toney neighbors call the cops about that.

Now all he had to do was figure out how to get up on the roof.

"See what you're making me do?" he said reproachfully as he handcuffed her. After she had screamed, he had choked her almost to the point of fainting. She felt dizzy and sick, and the knowledge that he could kill her at any time he chose, with nothing other than his bare hands, all but paralyzed her.

Easier to die than fight, she realized. Much easier. Dully she regarded the handcuffs in front of her. Courtesy of the cop he had killed, no doubt. Karl pulled her up to a standing position. "Come, we're going."

"Going where?"

"Someplace where they won't find us."

"No," she moaned. On the street she heard a car horn. What the hell was going on? "Somebody'll come."

"They won't come up here." Karl smiled. Over his shoulder Karen could just see Johnny on the street, coming back toward the house. "And if they do, I'll kill them." He took the gun out of his waistband.

Anger flared in her suddenly. If she was going to die, she wanted to take this madman with her. She swung her handcuffed hands, knocking the gun away, throwing her body after it. She felt the metal against her stomach, but in a second he was on her, his hand sliding under her.

"No!" she screamed, but he easily pushed her away, reaching for the gun.

"Get away from her!" Johnny had made his way onto the roof and was holding the dead policeman's gun on Karl.

Karl looked up, smiling wolfishly. "Now where did you get that? From the dead officer in the car? Strapped to his ankle, wasn't it? I took the clip out. I'm afraid there are no bullets in that gun."

"You forgot," Johnny said calmly, "the one left in the chamber." He pulled the trigger.

It was not a particularly good shot, but it was acceptable under the circumstances. The bullet hit Karl in the right hand, where it caused him a great deal of pain and ruined his concentration. He sank to his knees, and Karen seized the opportunity to throw her handcuffed hands around his neck and yank with all her strength.

Then they heard the most beautiful sound in the world—Detective Delgado on the bullhorn, assuring Karl Eastman that he was surrounded by L.A.'s finest.

Delgado was the first on the roof. Between him and Johnny they managed to persuade Karen to loosen her hold on Eastman. An ambulance came, and he was taken away.

Delgado took Johnny and Karen to the hospital in his own unit. Karen had only a few cuts, and Johnny's vision had cleared, so Delgado wasn't particularly worried about either one of them.

He turned on the radio. Some DJ was playing "Little Saint Nick," the Beach Boys' Christmas tune. He glanced at his watch. It was well after midnight. He looked in the rear-view mirror until his eyes caught Karen's. "Merry Christmas," he told her.

She smiled, dog tired. "Merry Christmas."

Johnny squeezed her hand. "Merry Christmas."

She closed her eyes and slept.

Epilogue

At long last, Matt felt happy with Angel of a Brighter Day. *He had cut the film the way he wanted. Lake's will had provided for that, and he had been very grateful to her poor soul. The movie was wonderful. It was also the Flying Dutchman of filmland, populated with ghosts. Surefire box office, he thought sourly. But, dammit, it was good. One scene in particular called to him poignantly. Lake singing in Karen's voice. It wasn't just Matt and his involvement with both women; anyone who saw the scene became mesmerized. He was happy with the film.*

The divorce had just become final. April again. What a lousy time to get divorced, when most people are falling in love. Johnny and Karen had a pretty home in San Francisco, and they would be married as soon as possible. Chernick from the record company had steadfastly tracked her down, waited for the controversy to blow over, and then dragged Karen into a recording studio to cut an album. He knew Karen was going to make it. Music had always been her language.

He missed Karen terribly, so he had thrown himself into the work, and now that was done. The movie was done. At three in the morning Matt was just replaying portions of the film to assure himself that it was as good as he thought it was. He was all alone in the editing house. Everyone else had gone home to their families.

He heard her come in. Even before he turned to see her, even before he heard her voice, he knew who it would be. He always knew he'd see her again.

"Hello, Lake."

"Hello, Matt." She looked terrible. She was skin and bones, dark smudges circling her eyes, blonde hair lank and dirty. A filthy

odor came off her body, like she'd been sleeping in the street, doing whatever she had to do to keep herself in the drugs that were her life. "You don't seem terribly surprised to see me."

"Karen never believed you were dead. It took us a long time to convince her, but we finally did."

"It was the cleaning girl," Lake said tonelessly. "I owed her money, so she came that night to collect and he found her. I just ran away, and it made him angry." She dug around in her huge sacklike bag. "Here, I want you to have this." She dropped a scrap of paper in front of him. It was the contract he had made her sign saying she would never see Karen again. She smiled. It was a scary thing to see. "In case I change my mind. And this . . ." She handed him a heavy glass object. "It's the only thing I have that's really mine, and I want you to have it. You always understood me, Matt. You were smart enough to run in the other direction. It should have been you and me, always should have been." She licked her dry, cracked lips. "Karen made a terrible mistake; she didn't kill the bastard. He'll get out, and he'll find me."

"He's going to be in jail for a long, long time."

"Oh, you don't know him," Lake said in a singsong voice. "He'll get out. They'll close their eyes for a second, and he'll escape. He can flow through a keyhole like a vampire. I know; he's shown me his black magic. No, I'll never get away from him unless I die, and I suppose that's coming soon enough." She shivered. "I do feel it coming, and no one will come bury me, because I'm already buried." She laughed. "I just wanted to see an old face."

He picked up the heavy glass object. A paperweight, with a little winter scene inside, only the snow was pink.

Her smile chilled him. "An interesting dilemma," she said tiredly, "I wanted to write his name on the wall, but what if I had to leave before the writing was on the wall, so to speak? If I began to write his name, 'Karl,' and had to stop, they would think I meant Karen. So I thought I would write 'Daddy,' but then they would think it was Daniel. So I wrote nothing."

"Lake, let me call someone. You need help."

That terrible smile reappeared. "Everyone thinks I'm dead, Matt. That's what I wanted. You see, after my father left, I came back and I fixed it so no one would be able to identify that poor girl. I did that. Not him. If Karen knew I was still alive, she would never stop looking for me. You're not going to tell her you saw me, are you?"

Ashamed, he turned away from her. "No."

"I'm a Christian," she said suddenly. "I know you're not, but will you say a prayer for me?"

"Yes," he whispered. "Lake? The movie . . . it's wonderful. You were wonderful in it."

"Yes?" she said disinterestedly. "I'm glad. Good-bye, Matt. You won't see me again."

"Wait, the least I can do . . ." He fumbled in his pockets and found some money, which she took with the same indifference.

"Pray for me," she said again. "Pray he dies in jail."

He never saw her again.

San Francisco
January 1985

Dear Matt,

We are all well, and I hope you are the same. I'm sorry I haven't written in so long—no excuse as usual. Johnny is fine and sends his best. Last night I was actually the guest of honor at a retrospective of my work. God, I feel so old! Anyway, they showed some of the oldies but goodies, Maiden Voyage *and of course* Angel of a Brighter Day. *I guess that one will always be special; it was the only serious piece I feel I ever did, the only thing I ever won an award for. But it did make me blue, and I couldn't help but think of that terrible time.*

I know this is just brooding, but I still feel it hard to believe that Lake is gone. Sometimes, I'm walking down the street, and I see a tall blonde, and I think, oh, that must be her, she's come to see me at last. And I think how surprised she'd be to see that I have a two-year-old son. But she is gone, and that's that. It's just, I know *I would feel it in my heart if she were dead, and I don't. That's it.*

Please Matt, I know you feel uncomfortable, but you really should come out and spend a few days with us. The house is huge, and I'd like you to get to know Mark. He really is a sweet kid, if I say so myself. I'll write again soon, I promise. Take care of yourself. By the way, if you heard anything of Lake, you'd tell me, wouldn't you?

Love always,
Karen